NGC 2000.0

NGC 2000.0

The Complete New General Catalogue
and Index Catalogues of Nebulae
and Star Clusters by J. L. E. Dreyer

Edited by

Roger W. Sinnott
Sky Publishing Corporation

1988

Sky Publishing Corporation
Cambridge, Massachusetts

&

Cambridge University Press
Cambridge   London   New York
New Rochelle   Melbourne   Sydney

Published by Sky Publishing Corporation
49 Bay State Road, Cambridge, Massachusetts 02138
and by the Press Syndicate of the University of Cambridge
The Pitt Building, Trumpington Street, Cambridge CB2 1RP
32 East 57th Street, New York, New York 10022
296 Beaconsfield Parade, Middle Park, Melbourne 3206, Australia

First published 1988

Printed in the United States of America
by Murray Printing Company
Westford, Massachusetts

Library of Congress Cataloging-in-Publication Data

Dreyer, J. L. E. (John Louis Emil), 1852-1926.
NGC 2000.0.

Originally published as: A new general catalogue of nebulae and clusters of stars. 1888.
Centennial edition, corrected and updated, combining in one listing the objects in the original work (NGC) and two later installments known as the Index catalogue (IC), which appeared in 1895 and 1908.
Includes index.
1. Stars — Clusters — Catalogs. 2. Nebulae — Catalogs. I. Sinnott, Roger W. II. Dreyer, J. L. E. (John Louis Emil), 1852-1926. New general catalogue of nebulae and clusters of stars. III. Title.

QB853.D74 1988   523.8'908   88-29962
ISBN 0-933346-51-4
ISBN 0-521-37813-3 (Cambridge Univ. Press)

PREFACE

In astronomy today, those nonstellar objects that are nearest, brightest, and most readily studied still bear the simple four-digit catalogue numbers assigned by J. L. E. Dreyer of Armagh Observatory a century ago. His famous *New General Catalogue of Nebulae and Clusters of Stars* (NGC), listing 7,840 objects, first appeared in 1888. Seven years later another 1,529 objects were added in an *Index Catalogue* (IC). By the time Dreyer's *Second Index Catalogue* appeared in 1908, the number of IC objects had grown to 5,386.

Dreyer's compilation was the last great effort with the stated aim of including every nonstellar object discovered by astronomers up to that time. Soon after 1908, the concept of "discovery" lost its meaning as powerful photographic telescopes began finding ever more galaxies and nebulae with ease. Astronomers working in narrow fields of study have continued to compile specialized catalogues of fainter objects, of course. But the best known wonders of the sky are still widely identified in the literature by their NGC and IC numbers.

In 1953 the Royal Astronomical Society reprinted the NGC and IC in a single volume, using the Replika process. Then in 1973 the University of Arizona's *Revised New General Catalogue* (RNGC) appeared, omitting the IC objects but including modern brightnesses, descriptions, and types for most of those in the NGC itself. However, neither work gives positions with respect to a standard modern reference frame (equinox 1950.0 or 2000.0), so their use today is awkward at best.

NGC 2000.0 meets the need of a modern reference frame, and it also incorporates the more than 700 errata compiled by Dreyer in his lifetime. These corrections appear not to have been used by many subsequent astronomers, so that quite a few typographical errors committed a hundred years ago still find their way into modern atlases and catalogues. Furthermore, Brent A. Archinal (U. S. Naval Observatory), Harold G. Corwin, Jr. (University of Texas at Austin), and Brian Skiff (Lowell Observatory) have gathered their own extensive lists of newfound errors in the NGC, IC, and RNGC. They kindly shared these with the *NGC 2000.0* project.

Our work to update the NGC started with the machine-readable version of the RNGC, for which we thank William G. Tifft and Jack

Preface

W. Sulentic. Other key sources were the same magnetic tapes from the Centre de Données Stellaires at Strasbourg and the NASA Goddard Space Flight Center's Astronomical Data Center that were used for *Sky Catalogue 2000.0*, Vol. 2. In no sense does *NGC 2000.0* supersede or replace that work, which gives much more detailed information about specific objects. But it contains less than 3,500 of the best-studied NGC and IC objects, while *NGC 2000.0* has all 13,226 of them. This is the first update of Dreyer's complete work attempted in 80 years.

During the early stages of this project, Leonard E. Silverman keyboarded the positions and Dreyer descriptions of all 5,386 IC objects on our office computer system – a massive undertaking that he accomplished with exceptional accuracy. Alan Hirshfeld gave valuable recommendations on the source tapes that would be most useful, and Dennis di Cicco helped unravel several longstanding NGC puzzles. Richard Tresch Fienberg introduced me to the wonders of the TₑX typesetting system. Gene Campbell and the staff of the Smithsonian Astrophysical Observatory Computation Facility lent their expertise and solved a critical tape-format problem. The project's overall manager, William E. Shawcross, handled many of the production details as well.

To all of these people, hearty thanks! They have helped make *NGC 2000.0* what I believe it can be, a valuable aid to amateur and professional astronomers engaged in photographic and visual sky patrols, comet hunting, and leisure observing.

Roger W. Sinnott
September, 1988

CONTENTS

INTRODUCTION

DISCOVERIES of new nebulae and star clusters were coming at a fast and furious pace over a century ago, when in 1874 a young graduate of Copenhagen University arrived at Parsonstown, Ireland. Johann Louis Emil Dreyer, 22 years old, was about to join a long line of distinguished assistants at Lord Rosse's observatory on the grounds of Birr Castle. For the next four years he had the privilege of observing with what was then the world's largest telescope – Rosse's 72-inch speculum-metal reflector.

The chief reference then in use by observers of nonstellar objects was John Herschel's monumental "General Catalogue of Nebulae," or G. C., which had been published in 1864 as part of the *Philosophical Transactions* of the Royal Society of London. The G. C. was based largely on Herschel's own pioneering observations and those of his illustrious father, William. It contained a total of 5,079 nonstellar objects.

Meanwhile, H. L. d'Arrest, Albert Marth, and other European astronomers were publishing lists of still newer discoveries and refining the positions of those already known. To help with the work at Birr, Dreyer compiled a list of all known corrections to the G. C. and also of the more recent finds; this was published in 1878. But the situation was quickly getting further out of hand as Ormond Stone and colleagues tallied 476 new nebulae with the Leander McCormick 26-inch refractor at Charlottesville, Virginia. Comet hunter Lewis Swift, using the 16-inch refractor at Warner Observatory in Rochester, New York, was even more prolific. From Paris Observatory, G. Bigourdan contributed about 100 new nebulae.

By 1886 Dreyer, now the director of Armagh Observatory, proposed to the Royal Astronomical Society that it was time for yet another supplement to the G. C. Instead the society suggested that Dreyer himself undertake the task of merging all the prior catalogues and all of the new discoveries, as he later wrote, "into a new General Catalogue."

So began Dreyer's great enterprise of just a century ago – the comprehensive work that is responsible for the NGC and IC designations sprinkled throughout the modern astronomical literature. All told there are 13,226 of these celestial objects, mostly nonstellar. What

Introduction

information there is about them has been gathered, updated, and presented here in *NGC 2000.0*.

MODERN DATA

The left-hand columns of *NGC 2000.0* give data that are in full harmony with modern astronomical practice. Their content is summarized in the explanation of the column headings that faces page 1. For example, all positions are given with respect to the equinox 2000.0, whereas those of the original NGC and IC were for 1860.0. Not only has precession in 140 years caused significant changes in both the right ascensions and declinations of all objects, but it has to some extent disrupted their original strict ordering by right ascension. Today the 2000.0 coordinates are much more convenient for setting a telescope, and they also match the reference frame of two major star atlases that have recently been published, *Sky Atlas 2000.0* and *Uranometria 2000.0*.

Immediately to the right of the position is a single letter, in italics, identifying our source of the modern data for each object. These codes are explained on page xxiii. Then comes the constellation in which it lies. Nowadays there can be no dispute about the constellation, but there certainly would have been in Dreyer's time for many of the borderline cases. Precise boundaries were not worked out until the 1920's by the Belgian astronomer Eugène Delporte and subsequently approved by the International Astronomical Union. Table I gives the number of NGC and IC objects within each of the 88 constellations now recognized, and it also lists their standard three-letter abbreviations.

It is perhaps surprising that Sagittarius and Scorpius, so famous for their showcase nebulae and star clusters, are fairly run-of-the-mill in the overall count of deep-sky objects they contain. A somewhat different picture emerges when we take each constellation's sky area into account, as tabulated in *Sky & Telescope* for June, 1983, page 521. Coma Berenices, Dorado, and Canes Venatici are found to be the three richest constellations, each averaging more than one NGC or IC object per square degree. Octans is the most sparsely populated constellation by density of objects. Several others in the far southern skies, along with Auriga in the north, are not far behind.

When available, the angular sizes of NGC and IC objects are listed in arc minutes. The largest catalogue entry is IC 1318 in Cygnus, 240′ or a full 4° across. Even larger would have been the Large and Small Magellanic Clouds (LMC and SMC), except that they are regarded as assemblies of many smaller nebulae and clusters. For any oval

Introduction

TABLE I. NGC AND IC OBJECTS BY CONSTELLATION.

Abbrev.	Name	Count	Abbrev.	Name	Count
And	Andromeda	199	Lac	Lacerta	38
Ant	Antlia	92	Leo	Leo	828
Aps	Apus	28	Lep	Lepus	62
Aql	Aquila	49	Lib	Libra	76
Aqr	Aquarius	267	LMi	Leo Minor	111
Ara	Ara	25	Lup	Lupus	29
Ari	Aries	147	Lyn	Lynx	135
Aur	Auriga	39	Lyr	Lyra	39
Boo	Bootes	493	Men	Mensa	86
Cae	Caelum	22	Mic	Microscopium	27
Cam	Camelopardalis	74	Mon	Monoceros	67
Cap	Capricornus	57	Mus	Musca	9
Car	Carina	54	Nor	Norma	16
Cas	Cassiopeia	58	Oct	Octans	14
Cen	Centaurus	198	Oph	Ophiuchus	64
Cep	Cepheus	47	Ori	Orion	95
Cet	Cetus	648	Pav	Pavo	280
Cha	Chamaeleon	7	Peg	Pegasus	433
Cir	Circinus	5	Per	Perseus	155
CMa	Canis Major	46	Phe	Phoenix	61
CMi	Canis Minor	25	Pic	Pictor	21
Cnc	Cancer	337	PsA	Piscis Austrinus	55
Col	Columba	25	Psc	Pisces	473
Com	Coma Berenices	983	Pup	Puppis	64
CrA	Corona Australis	8	Pyx	Pyxis	13
CrB	Corona Borealis	54	Ret	Reticulum	36
Crt	Crater	119	Scl	Sculptor	96
Cru	Crux	8	Sco	Scorpius	66
Crv	Corvus	51	Sct	Scutum	15
CVn	Canes Venatici	492	Ser	Serpens	147
Cyg	Cygnus	90	Sex	Sextans	103
Del	Delphinus	29	Sge	Sagitta	8
Dor	Dorado	335	Sgr	Sagittarius	128
Dra	Draco	355	Tau	Taurus	90
Equ	Equuleus	15	Tel	Telescopium	115
Eri	Eridanus	436	TrA	Triangulum Australe	10
For	Fornax	110	Tri	Triangulum	120
Gem	Gemini	114	Tuc	Tucana	122
Gru	Grus	78	UMa	Ursa Major	510
Her	Hercules	311	UMi	Ursa Minor	56
Hor	Horologium	93	Vel	Vela	41
Hya	Hydra	369	Vir	Virgo	1181
Hyi	Hydrus	13	Vol	Volans	10
Ind	Indus	89	Vul	Vulpecula	27

Introduction

or elongated object, the tabulated size always refers to the greatest dimension. Keep in mind that many diffuse objects appear much smaller visually than they do on well-exposed photographs.

For galaxies with a source code of s, v, t, or c, the sizes listed here have a specific technical meaning. They are on the so-called D_{25} system, or else they have been converted to that system by an approximate procedure. A brief discussion of this method of defining size appears in *Sky Catalogue 2000.0*, Vol. 2, page xxxii. Sizes given for other galaxies, and for other types of objects, are not as homogeneous.

The brightnesses of objects are visual (yellow) magnitudes wherever possible, in keeping with the spirit of the original NGC. After all, most of the Dreyer descriptions came from observers peering into eyepieces. In a great many cases, however, only a photoelectric **B** (blue) magnitude, or else one determined photographically in blue light, is to be found in the literature. Noting the lack of homogeneity in the methods used, the RNGC compilers converted photographic values to half-magnitude steps. For present purposes it seemed best to truncate the RNGC values to make whole magnitudes (so that 11.5 and 11.0 become 11). Higher-precision blue magnitudes have been rounded off instead of simply truncated. All blue magnitudes are identified by the letter "p" to avoid confusion with visual magnitudes.

DREYER'S DESCRIPTIONS

The abbreviated descriptions in the main catalogue are remarkable for their information content, as explained in Table II on page xiv. This shorthand notation was not invented by Dreyer. Quite a similar system had been used in the earlier catalogues of John Herschel. We can picture him at the eyepiece of his $18\frac{3}{4}$-inch speculum-metal reflector, calling the words out in the darkness to an assistant who took notes by lamplight during one of his famous "sweeps."

Later observers continued the same abbreviations, even the pioneer photographers who were responsible for many of the IC objects (especially those numbered after 1529). Remember that they are purely *descriptive* comments, not intended as interpretions or theoretical conclusions. To each user of a large amateur reflector, the visual description by skilled astronomers of the last century is perhaps closer to the mark than what appears on a photograph taken at one of the world's large observatories.

Today the terms "globular cluster" and "planetary nebula" have technical meanings that distinguish them from open clusters and diffuse nebulae, respectively. Modern photography has also helped clar-

Introduction

ify what many of the objects really are, and sometimes the verdict is quite different from the early visual impression. Thus the galaxy NGC 628 (M74) and the open cluster NGC 2136 are both described as globular clusters (the symbol ⊕) by Dreyer.

Even for the clear misidentifications, I felt it was important not to change or "modernize" the Dreyer descriptions. They retain value if taken for what they are: pure visual impressions, for the most part, made without the benefit of knowing the object's true nature. Any experienced observer is aware that certain galaxies may indeed resemble an unresolved globular cluster.

In an eyepiece field, position angles are measured eastward (counterclockwise) from north. The galaxy in this view is extended npp and sff, toward position angle 113°. The diagram, executed by Steven Simpson, has south up to match the inverted view with an astronomical telescope in the Northern Hemisphere.

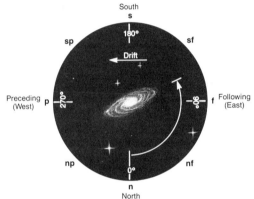

Directions on the sky use "preceding" for west and "following" for east. To see what this is all about, turn off a telescope's clock-drive (if it has one) and let the stars and nebulae drift through the field. Given the confusing way an optical system inverts and sometimes reverses the field of view, these terms are altogether more natural at the eyepiece than "east" and "west."

Quite often the notes speak of groups. The "1st of 4" is the first member of a group of four nebulae to drift across the field. Thus it is the westernmost one, preceding all the rest. By scanning the other notes on the same page it is usually easy to spot others in the group; they will have nearly the same declination.

By analogy with the cardinal points of a compass, Dreyer often combines terms. Thus "nf" is north-following (northeast), "ssp" is south-south-preceding (south-southwest), and so on. More accurate astronomical directions are expressed by *position angle,* as defined in the illustration above. John Herschel used this method to describe how the components of a double star were oriented on the sky. The position angles scattered throughout Dreyer's notes help to describe

TABLE II. ABBREVIATIONS USED IN THE DESCRIPTIONS.

ab	about	N	nucleus, or to a nucleus
alm	almost	p	preceding (westward)
am	among	pf	preceding-following
att	attached	p	pretty (*adv.*, before F, B, L, S)
b	brighter	pg	pretty gradually
bet	between	pm	pretty much
biN	binuclear	ps	pretty suddenly
bn	brightest to n side	plan	planetary nebula (same as ◯)
bs	brightest to s side	prob	probably
bp	brightest to p side	P	poor (sparse) in stars
bf	brightest to f side	r	resolvable (mottled,
B	bright		*not* resolved)
c	considerably	rr	partially resolved,
chev	chevelure		some stars seen
co	coarse, coarsely	rrr	well resolved, clearly
com	cometic (cometary form)		consisting of stars
comp	companion	R	round
conn	connected	RR	exactly round
cont	in contact	Ri	rich in stars
C	compressed	s	suddenly (abruptly)
Cl	cluster	s	south
d	diameter	sf	south following
def	defined	sp	south preceding
dif	diffused	sc	scattered
diffic	difficult	sev	several
dist	distance, or distant	st	stars (*pl.*)
D	double	stell	stellar, pointlike
e	extremely, excessively	susp	suspected
ee	most extremely	S	small in angular size
er	easily resolvable	S*	small (faint) star
exc	excentric	trap	trapezium
E	extended	triN	trinuclear
f	following (eastward)	v	very
F	faint	vv	*very*
g	gradually	var	variable
gr	group	*	a single star
i	irregular	*10	a star of 10th magnitude
iF	irregular figure	*7-8	star of mag. 7 or 8
inv	involved, involving	‡	double star (same as D*)
l	little (*adv.*); long (*adj.*)	*****	triple star
L	large	!	remarkable
m	much	!!	very much so
m	magnitude	!!!	a magnificent or otherwise
M	middle, or in the middle		interesting object
n	north	△	triangle, forms a tri-
neb	nebula		angle with
nebs	nebulous	⊕	globular cluster of stars
neby	nebulosity	◯	planetary nebula
nf	north following	⊙	annular or ring nebula
np	north preceding	st 9...	stars of 9th magnitude
ns	north-south		and fainter
nr	near	st 9...13	stars of mag. 9 to 13

Introduction

not only the locations of adjacent stars but also the direction toward which a nebula is elongated. When the greatest diameter runs "nfsp," closer examination could refine this to, say, "mE 51°" (moderately extended toward position angle 51°). No modern catalogue or star atlas informs us so richly as to the orientations of deep-sky objects.

The modern ear is apt to be confused by certain aspects of 19th-century usage. Dreyer means angular size, of course, when he describes a nebula as "vS" (very small) or "pL" (pretty large). But astronomers in Dreyer's day also commonly called a faint star a *small* one, and a bright star *large*. An "eS∗" is the same as an "eF∗" – extremely faint star. Both methods of describing a star's brightness occur interchangeably in Dreyer's notes.

Also, if you ask a modern English-speaking person whether "considerably bright" is brighter than just plain "bright," the reply will probably differ from the ranking Dreyer intended. A similar system ranks objects by their relative angular size. In the introduction to his work Dreyer explains the order he meant (derived from John Herschel) as follows:

Brightness		*Size*	
eF	excessively faint	eS	excessively small
vF	very faint	vS	very small
F	faint	S	small
cF	considerably faint	cS	considerably small
pF	pretty faint	pS	pretty small
pB	pretty bright	pL	pretty large
cB	considerably bright	cL	considerably large
B	bright	L	large
vB	very bright	vL	very large
eB	excessively bright	eL	excessively large

A similar progression is used for the *Form* of an object: R (round), vlE (very little extended), E, cE, pmE (pretty much extended), mE, vmE, and eE.

We should not, of course, imagine that 10 or more shades of brightness, size, and shape are accurately distinguished in Dreyer's notes (as he'd have been the first to admit). Sky clarity, aperture, magnification, experience of the astronomer, and so on inject enormous uncertainty into these capsule summaries of how an object looks through a telescope. But Dreyer excercised prudence in compiling his notes. "I have always changed M. Stephan's *eeF* into *eF,* and his *eF* into *vF,* as ... other observers have always [called the same nebulae] somewhat brighter ...," he wrote. Later, when introducing the second installment of the IC with its numerous photographic entries, he warned:

A very marked peculiarity of photographic records of nebulae is the general ten-

Introduction

dency of observers to overestimate the brightness, even to the extent of two or three degrees of brightness. This fact must always be borne in mind by observers using even very powerful telescopes, but it did not seem feasible to allow for it in this catalogue, as the objects observed both visually and photographically are hardly yet numerous enough.

Early visual magnitudes, as quoted by Dreyer in the notes, are not the same as those we use today. The Greek astronomer Ptolemy ranked the naked-eye stars into magnitude classes from 1 (brightest) to 6 (faintest), and 19th-century astronomers extrapolated these magnitudes mentally to the dimmer telescopic objects. It is important to remember that Dreyer's notes do not contain magnitude *measurements* in any sense. A "*8-9" is a star estimated to be of magnitude 8 or 9; a cluster with "st 11...15" seems to contain stars from 11th to as faint as 15th magnitude.

Some observers on occasion gave magnitudes as faint as 19 or 20. These clearly need to be adjusted downward to perhaps 15 or 16 to match the magnitudes measured today. Lesser adjustments are called for as we get brighter. A "*9" is likely to be of magnitude 8 on the modern photoelectric V scale, but no definite conversion procedure can be applied. Dreyer's magnitudes are chiefly useful today for the way they rank stars visually by brightness.

The third Earl of Rosse and his assistants, using the 6-foot reflector, had noticed before 1850 that certain nebulae had a spiral structure. Dreyer's notes frequently say as much. But we should remember that the term "galaxy," which comes from the Greek word for milk, referred in the 19th century only to the Milky Way. It was not until the Shapley-Curtis debate of 1920 and Edwin Hubble's discovery, a few years later, of Cepheid variable stars in the Andromeda nebula NGC 224 (M31) and a few others that astronomers came to recognize the many spiral nebulae as true external galaxies of stars, like our Milky Way system.

When Dreyer includes "r" in the notes for what is now known to be an external galaxy ("Gx" in the Type column), it does not mean that the observers thought they could resolve its individual stars. Dreyer stressed that "resolvable" did not mean "resolved," only that the object seemed mottled or gave signs of being composed of stars. Of course, there are a few examples of galaxies called "rr" where we know the observer was deceived. No 19th-century telescope could show the individual stars of an external galaxy.

Here are some other subtleties to be wary of. A superscript "s," as in 5^s or $2^s.9$, means seconds of time; an "s" detached from a number means south. A single star is always "*"; more than one

Introduction

is "st." Also, "pf" means in the preceding-following (east-west) direction, while "pF" is pretty faint. A "Cl" is an open cluster, and some of them are also "cL," considerably large.

Yet by far the most cryptic part of a description, at first glance, is the group of concatenated letters giving a nebula's "degree and rate of condensation," as John Herschel put it. A simple example is "gbM," which means gradually brighter in the middle. Many objects are "psbM," or pretty suddenly brighter in the middle. But then we come upon NGC 4725, which is "vsvmbMeBN," or very suddenly very much brighter in the middle to an extremely bright nucleus. With practice even such a mishmash of upper- and lowercase letters is easy to decipher, even though the "plaintext" version is more than seven times as long as the encryption!

Often in his own errata Dreyer corrected or revised a description. Thus, for example, NGC 3313 originally had a "∗15 n 3″," but in the errata section of the second IC installment Dreyer quoted a remark by H. A. Howe of Chamberlin Observatory, Denver, Colorado: "The ∗ is south of the nebula." Our description has been altered accordingly (page 93). Further corrections are found in Brent Archinal's erratum list, code *A*. The "3 st 10" near NGC 2101 were originally said to lie "sf" the nebula; they are actually "sp" according to Harold Corwin. Both Archinal and Brian Skiff (code *F*) acknowledge Corwin as the chief source of their errata of all varieties. Steve Gottlieb, Malcolm Thomson, and Jeffrey Corder did an important part of the sleuthing, as well.

Apart from corrections of this nature, Dreyer's descriptions are reproduced much as he wrote them. An exception occurs in cross references, where he favored the old Herschel designations. As he explained:

It was with much regret that I found it necessary to introduce new [NGC] numbers, and it is greatly to be hoped that these will be *quoted* as little as possible, but that the old nebulae, as hitherto, will be chiefly mentioned by their *h* number, or failing such by their *H* class and number.

But the Herschel numbers have fallen completely out of fashion today. So while Dreyer's description of NGC 4357 went

F, pS, gbM (? = II 743),

in *NGC 2000.0*, near the top of page 127, it is rewritten

F, pS, gbM; = 4381?

because William Herschel's II 743 is the same as NGC 4381. The authors of the RNGC performed the same substitution in their work.

Introduction

The familiar Messier (M) numbers of some of the brightest nebulae and clusters are also added. These are the 103 objects described by the Parisian comet hunter Charles Messier in the *Connaissance des Temps* in 1784 and 1787, along with some others he is thought to have seen, bringing the total count to 110. Their corresponding NGC numbers are listed in Table III, except for a few that are not in the NGC at all. These omissions include M45 (the Pleiades) and the M24 star cloud in Sagittarius. M40 is nothing more than a double star, and M102 is an accidental reobservation of M101. Modern astronomers do not agree entirely on the identities of some Messier objects; our table matches that in *Sky Catalogue 2000.0*, Vol. 2.

The column arrangement of *NGC 2000.0* did not leave enough room to include the popular names of objects. Many of these are found in Table IV (page xx).

EDITING PHILOSOPHY

Time and again during the preparation of *NGC 2000.0*, our expert consultants voiced a common plea: Stick to the objects originally listed by Dreyer! Many astronomers over the years have tinkered with the NGC and IC designations, with conflicting and confusing results.

For example, it has been common to append capital letters to a Dreyer number when referring to specific features of a complex object. NGC 4496 in Virgo, called "binuclear" by Dreyer, is actually a close pair galaxies (possibly colliding); today the components are often named NGC 4496A and B. This is understandable, but a parallel practice assigns letters to entirely separate field galaxies, sometimes not very near the one Dreyer described. Thus NGC 3846A is the recent name of a galaxy in Ursa Major fully $\frac{2}{3}°$ south of NGC 3846 itself and not even mentioned in Dreyer's description. All extraneous additions and distinctions of this sort have been omitted from *NGC 2000.0*.

More problematic are the instances when a Dreyer object cannot be found at the place he gave, and some astronomer has reassigned the number to a different object in the general vicinity. It may not match Dreyer's description at all; it might even be too faint for the telescopes of his time, as is true of many objects on the *Sky Atlas* photographic plates of the National Geographic Society – Palomar Observatory Sky Survey. A concerted effort was made to avoid these reassignments in *NGC 2000.0* and to relocate the original objects.

The question of the "missing" Dreyer objects is knotty indeed. Was some error committed in recording the coordinates? Was the

TABLE III. NGC NUMBERS FOR THE MESSIER CATALOGUE.

M1	1952	M23	6494	M45	—	M67	2682	M89	4552
M2	7089	M24	—	M46	2437	M68	4590	M90	4569
M3	5272	M25	IC 4725	M47	2422	M69	6637	M91	4548
M4	6121	M26	6694	M48	2548	M70	6681	M92	6341
M5	5904	M27	6853	M49	4472	M71	6838	M93	2447
M6	6405	M28	6626	M50	2323	M72	6981	M94	4736
M7	6475	M29	6913	M51	5194-5	M73	6994	M95	3351
M8	6523	M30	7099	M52	7654	M74	628	M96	3368
M9	6333	M31	224	M53	5024	M75	6864	M97	3587
M10	6254	M32	221	M54	6715	M76	650-1	M98	4192
M11	6705	M33	598	M55	6809	M77	1068	M99	4254
M12	6218	M34	1039	M56	6779	M78	2068	M100	4321
M13	6205	M35	2168	M57	6720	M79	1904	M101	5457
M14	6402	M36	1960	M58	4579	M80	6093	M102	—
M15	7078	M37	2099	M59	4621	M81	3031	M103	581
M16	6611	M38	1912	M60	4649	M82	3034	M104	4594
M17	6618	M39	7092	M61	4303	M83	5236	M105	3379
M18	6613	M40	—	M62	6266	M84	4374	M106	4258
M19	6273	M41	2287	M63	5055	M85	4382	M107	6171
M20	6514	M42	1976	M64	4826	M86	4406	M108	3556
M21	6531	M43	1982	M65	3623	M87	4486	M109	3992
M22	6656	M44	2632	M66	3627	M88	4501	M110	205

original observer mistaken? Each discoverer surely believed in the find, but a star that looked nebulous on one occasion could later prove (when viewed with better skies or a more powerful telescope) to be nothing more than a triple, double, or even single star. Clarifications of this sort are still being made today.

An intriguing example is NGC 7088 in Aquarius. Soon after the English amateur Joseph Baxendell first reported this nebula in the fall of 1880, doubts seem to have arisen as to its reality. Dreyer reassured readers in the Notes section of the NGC:

A very large and very diffused nebulosity north of the cluster M2. I have seen it without difficulty in the Armagh 10-inch Refractor. It seems to extend about 35' northwards from the parallel of the * 10' nf M2, and to be about 45' or more in length (Mr. B gives 52' by 75').

Yet NGC 7088 has not been definitely seen again. The early astrophographers failed to record it, and it was dubbed "Baxendell's unphotographable nebula." Such a term made sense with emulsions that only responded to deep-blue and ultraviolet light, but even a modern red-light plate of the M2 region taken with the Palomar 48-inch Schmidt camera fails to show any trace of Baxendell's object.

Introduction

TABLE IV. COMMON NAMES OF NGC OBJECTS.

47 Tucanae. NGC 104.
γ Cassiopeiae nebula. IC 59, 63.
γ Cygni nebula. IC 1318.
η Carinae nebula. NGC 3372.
κ Crucis cluster. (See Jewel Box.)
λ Centauri nebula. IC 2944, 48.
ρ Ophiuchi nebula. IC 4604.
ω Centauri. NGC 5139.
Antennae. NGC 4038-9.
Barnard's galaxy. NGC 6822.
Baxendell's unphotographable
  nebula. NGC 7088.
Bear Paw galaxy. NGC 2537.
Beehive cluster. (See Praesepe.)
Black-eye galaxy. NGC 4826.
Blinking planetary. NGC 6826.
Blue planetary. NGC 3918.
Blue Snowball. NGC 7662.
Bode's nebulae. NGC 3031, 34.
Box. NGC 4169, 73-5.
Box nebula. NGC 6309.
Bubble nebula. NGC 7635.
Bug nebula. NGC 6302.
Butterfly cluster. NGC 6405.
Butterfly nebula. IC 2220.
California nebula. NGC 1499.
Christmas Tree cluster. NGC 2264.
Cocoon nebula. IC 5146.
Cone nebula. NGC 2264.
Copeland's Septet. NGC 3745-6,
  48, 50-1, 53-4.
Crab nebula. NGC 1952.
Crescent nebula. NGC 6888.
Double cluster. NGC 869 and 884.
Dumbbell nebula. NGC 6853.
Eagle nebula. NGC 6611 (but
  sometimes IC 2177).
Eight-burst planetary. NGC 3132.
Eskimo nebula. NGC 2392.
The Eyes. NGC 4435, 38.
Filamentary nebula. NGC 6960
  (part of the Veil nebula).
Flaming Star nebula. IC 405.
Ghost of Jupiter. NGC 3242.
Great Cluster in Hercules. NGC 6205.
Great Neb. in Andromeda. NGC 224.
Great Nebula in Orion. NGC 1976.

Helix galaxy. NGC 2685.
Helix nebula. NGC 7293.
Hind's variable nebula. NGC 1555.
Horsehead nebula. Dark nebula in
  IC 434.
Hourglass nebula. Brightest part
  of NGC 6523.
Hubble's variable neb. NGC 2261.
Jewel Box. NGC 4755.
Lace-work nebula. (= Filamentary.)
Lagoon nebula. NGC 6523.
Little Dumbbell. NGC 650-1.
Little Gem. NGC 6445.
Maia nebula. NGC 1432.
Merope nebula. NGC 1435.
The Mice. NGC 4676.
Network nebula. NGC 6992, 95
  (part of the Veil nebula).
North America nebula. NGC 7000.
Omega nebula. NGC 6618.
Owl nebula. NGC 3587.
Papillon. IC 708.
Pelican nebula. IC 5067, 70.
Pin-wheel nebula. NGC 4254.
Polarissima Australis. NGC 2573.
Polarissima Borealis. NGC 3172.
Praesepe. NGC 2632.
Ring nebula in Lyra. NGC 6720.
Rosette nebula. NGC 2237-9, 46.
Saturn nebula. NGC 7009.
Sculptor galaxy. NGC 253.
Siamese Twins. NGC 4567-8.
Sombrero galaxy. NGC 4594.
Southern Pleiades. IC 2602 (θ Car).
Spindle galaxy. NGC 3115.
Star Queen nebula. IC 4703.
Stephan's Quintet. NGC 7317-20.
Struve's Lost nebula. NGC 1554.
Sunflower galaxy. NGC 5055.
Tarantula nebula. NGC 2070.
Toby Jug nebula. IC 2220.
Triangulum galaxy. NGC 598.
Trifid nebula. NGC 6514.
Veil nebula. NGC 6960, 92, 95.
Whirlpool galaxy. NGC 5194-5.
Wild Duck cluster. NGC 6705.
Witch Head nebula. IC 2118.

Introduction

Is NGC 7088 nonexistent, then? While a true *nebula* may not lie at its location, other possibilities are worth exploring. Did a chance arrangement of faint stars fool both Baxendell and Dreyer into believing they perceived a large nebula? Declaring that an NGC object does not exist, just because it doesn't show on a Palomar print, can be a mistake. A number of sparse clusters and asterisms (like NGC 1523, 2408, 2609, and 3446) were classed nonexistent in the RNGC because they blended with the crowded background stars on such photographs. Yet they are perfectly real in the sky.

As mentioned earlier, many objects accidentally found their way into the NGC and IC twice, and even three times, under different numbers. Dreyer faced a huge task avoiding such duplicate entries, for many of the discoverers were reporting things at the extreme limits of visual detection. "It was frequently a matter of some difficulty," he wrote, "to decide about the identity of objects announced independently by several observers, differing little as regards place, but often much as to description."

Nevertheless, a modern telescope user often benefits by having two independent descriptions of the same object. When an identity seems certain, I have tried to find out which of the positions is more nearly correct and make them agree so that the entries fall close to each other in the catalogue's listing by right ascension. It would be pedantic to keep an obviously wrong place, such as the 1^h typographical error that Dreyer himself later discovered for NGC 3760, causing it to be listed as a different object from 3301. But other proposed identities are by no means certain; it makes good sense to leave many of these discordant positions alone until matters can be straightened out.

Dreyer's first big list of NGC corrections appeared with the 1895 installment of the IC. And here is where the concept of "nonexistent" NGC objects got its start. Among his many revisions to the places and descriptions, Dreyer had this to say of NGC 3531: "to be struck out, is = 3526." He also advised deleting seven others, but he never addressed the problem of what to do with the vacancies that such a procedure would leave in the catalogue.

In recent years, the roster of NGC objects deemed not to exist has mushroomed. Fully 799 items in the RNGC are assigned type code 7, "nonexistent" – a staggering 10 percent of the original count. But the RNGC's New Description column explains a sizable fraction of these as single, double, or triple stars, nebulous knots that are parts of large galaxies having their own separate NGC number, or else duplicate entries. Many of these explanations are from Dorothy Carlson's paper, "Some Corrections to Dreyer's Catalogues of Nebulae

Introduction

and Clusters," *Astrophysical Journal*, **91**, 350-359, 1940. By including the codes ∗, D∗, ∗*∗ , Ast, and Kt in *NGC 2000.0*, the number of RNGC type 7's (denoted "—" here) has been reduced to 463.

The IC posed an even greater problem as *NGC 2000.0* was being planned. Here was a catalogue largely bypassed by professional astronomers as they pushed forward their photographic surveys in the early 20th century, assigning new designations to objects in their special fields of interest. In compiling the *Master List of Nonstellar Optical Astronomical Objects* (MOL), Robert S. Dixon and George Sonneborn sought out all available references to IC objects *per se*. Of the 5,386 entries in Dreyer's two installments, they could find only 1,031 of them mentioned in the astronomical literature since 1908.

Yet the rest of the IC objects, for the most part, certainly do exist. It's just that no one has recently matched them individually against other tabulations, looked for them on photographs, or sought them out in the sky. In quite a few cases a work like the *Morphological Catalogue of Galaxies* (MCG) lists a single galaxy, and not more than one, very near the IC position as given by Dreyer. By cautious comparisons of this sort, using the magnetic-tape version of the MOL, I could tentatively identify 1,614 additional IC objects with known galaxies. In no case did this do violence to an IC position from Dreyer, changing it generally less than 2′.

Another 1,025 IC objects have come from magnetic-tape versions of the catalogues of Gerard de Vaucouleurs and Brent Tully, and also from *Sky Catalogue 2000.0*, Vol. 2, and Harold Corwin's *Southern Galaxy Catalogue*. Because the identities in these works are explicit I gave them more weight. In the end, *NGC 2000.0* has modern identities for 3,201 (59 percent) of the IC objects. The rest are essentially unchanged, except for precession, from Dreyer's works of 1895 and 1908.

To call an object "nonexistent" is ambiguous at best, and this practice has been avoided in *NGC 2000.0*. If it cannot be found at the place given, perhaps the place is wrong. If it is the same as another object, so be it. And if merely a star, double star, or asterism, then the Type column of the catalogue calls it that. When no modern explanation can be found for an entry in Dreyer's lists, the message is clear: we have detective work to do!

REFERENCES

This list covers all the sources that have directly contributed to the entries in *NGC 2000.0*. At left is the code letter given in the main tabulation just after each object's coordinates. These references have been used to correct or update modern data only (type, position, magnitude, and size), and not the original Dreyer descriptions. Uppercase letters denote special NGC and IC errata lists, which have usually been accorded more weight than the source catalogues themselves. In parentheses after each citation is the number of times it has been used to update NGC entries (first number) and those in the IC (second number).

A Archinal, Brent A. Version 4.0 of an unpublished list of errata to the RNGC, dated March 19, 1987. (110, 0)

a Arp, H., "Atlas of Peculiar Galaxies," *Astrophysical Journal Supplement Series,* **14**, 1, 1966. (1, 2)

c Corwin, Harold G., Jr., A. de Vaucouleurs, and G. de Vaucouleurs, *Southern Galaxy Catalogue.* Austin, Texas: University of Texas Monographs in Astronomy No. 4, 1985. (152, 564)

d Dreyer, J. L. E., *New General Catalogue of Nebulae and Clusters of Stars (1888), Index Catalogue (1895), Second Index Catalogue (1908).* London: Royal Astronomical Society, 1953. (28, 2157)

D Dreyer, J. L. E., *ibid.* Errata on pages 237, 281-283, and 366-378. (158, 28)

F Skiff, Brian, private communication of February 27, 1988. (93, 36)

h Holmberg, E., "A Study of Double and Multiple Galaxies," *Lund Annals,* **6**, 1937. (13, 2)

k Karachentsev, I. D., "A Catalogue of Isolated Pairs of Galaxies in the Northern Hemisphere"; also, Karachentseva, V. E., "A Catalog of Isolated Galaxies." *Astrofiz. Issled. Izv. Spetz. Astrofiz.,* **7**, 3, 1972, and **8**, 3, 1973. (0, 4)

m Vorontsov-Velyaminov, B. A., and V. P. Arhipova, *Morphological Catalog of Galaxies,* Parts I-V. Moscow: Moscow State University, 1962-74. (9, 679)

n Reinmuth, K., "Photographische Positionsbestimmung von

References

Nebelflecken," *Veroff. der Sternwarte zu Heidelberg,*
several papers, 1916-40. (0, 4)

o   Alter, G., B. Balázs, and J. Ruprecht, *Catalogue of Star
Clusters and Associations,* 2nd edition. Budapest: Akadémiai
Kiadó, 1970. (5, 0)

r   Sulentic, Jack W., and William G. Tifft, *The Revised
New General Catalogue of Nonstellar Astronomical Objects*
(RNGC). Tucson, Arizona: University of Arizona Press, 1973.
(4016, 0)

s   Hirshfeld, Alan, and Roger W. Sinnott, eds., *Sky Catalogue
2000.0,* Vol. 2, Cambridge, Massachusetts: Sky Publishing
Corp. and Cambridge University Press, 1985. (3098, 238)

t   Tully, R. B., *Nearby Galaxies Catalog.* New York: Cambridge
University Press, 1988. A preliminary version on magnetic
tape (1981) was used here. (23, 17)

u   Nilson, P. N., *Uppsala General Catalogue of Galaxies.*
Uppsala: Uppsala Astronomical Observatory, 1973. (15, 543)

v   de Vaucouleurs, G., A. de Vaucouleurs, and H. G. Corwin, Jr.,
Second Reference Catalogue of Bright Galaxies. Austin,
Texas: University of Texas Press, 1976. (118, 206)

x   Dixon, R. S., and George Sonneborn, *A Master List of
Nonstellar Optical Astronomical Objects* (MOL). Columbus, Ohio:
Ohio State University Press, 1980. It should be noted that most
of the information for codes *a, h, k, m, n, o, u* and
z was extracted from the magnetic-tape version of this
catalogue. The *x* code refers to IC objects identified
in a literature search by these authors. (0, 526)

z   Zwicky, F., E. Herzog, and P. Wild, *Catalogue of Galaxies
and Clusters of Galaxies,* Vol. I. Pasadena, Calif.: California
Institute of Technology, 1961. Also, successive volumes
through 1968. (1, 380)

NGC 2000.0

COLUMN HEADINGS

NGC – The object's number in J. L. E. Dreyer's *New General Catalogue of Nebulae and Clusters of Stars* (NGC) or *Index Catalogue* (IC). An "I" follows all numbers from the latter source.

Type – The object's classification according to modern astronomy. Abbreviations are as follows:

Gx	Galaxy external to our own Milky Way.
OC	Open cluster.
Gb	Globular cluster, usually in our own galaxy.
Nb	Bright nebula, shining by emission or reflection.
Pl	Planetary nebula.
C+N	Cluster associated with nebulosity.
Ast	Asterism or group of a few stars.
Kt	Knot or nebulous region in an external galaxy.
***	Triple star.
D*	Double star.
*	Only a single star.
?	May not exist, or of uncertain type.
[blank]	Unverified at the place given, or type unknown.
−	An object called nonexistent in the RNGC.
PD	Photographic plate defect.

α_{2000} and δ_{2000} – Right ascension and declination, referred to the 2000.0 equinox. After the position is a code letter for the source of modern data about the object (see page xxiii).

Const. – Constellation in which the object lies.

Size – Angular size in arc minutes, measured along the greatest diameter. The symbol "<" means "smaller than."

Mag. – Total visual (yellow) magnitude, except that when "*p*" is appended the value is a rounded photographic (blue) magnitude.

Description – The coded appearance as given by Dreyer, or as corrected by him. No attempt has been made to modernize these characterizations by skilled telescopists of the 19th century. For an NGC object, it is always a *visual* impression; the IC descriptions are often based on the photographic appearance. A full list of abbreviations appears in Table II. Messier (M) designations and proposed identifications with other NGC or IC objects are sometimes appended.

NGC	Type	α_{2000}	δ_{2000}	Const.	Size	Mag.	Description
		h　m	o　　′		′		
5370 I	Gx	0 00.1	+ 32 45 m	And	0.7	15p	pB, S, R, stell N
5371 I		0 00.2	+ 32 49 d	And			F, vS, *15 att
7801	−	0 00.4	+ 50 42 r	Cas			Cl, pRi, pC, st 9...
5372 I	Gx	0 00.4	+ 32 47 m	And	0.7	15p	F, vS, R N
5373 I	Gx	0 00.4	+ 32 47 m	And	0.7	15p	pB, S, R, stell N
7802	Gx	0 01.1	+ 6 13 r	Psc		14p	vF, S, R, psbM
5374 I		0 01.1	+ 4 30 d	Psc			F, S, E ns, gbM, r
5375 I	Gx	0 01.1	+ 4 31 m	Psc	0.9	14p	cF, E ns, gbMN, r
7804		0 01.3	+ 7 45 D	Psc			only a F D*, not nebs
7803	Gx	0 01.4	+ 13 06 r	Peg		14p	pF, pS, R, F* np vnr
7805	Gx	0 01.4	+ 31 26 s	Peg	1.4	14p	eF, S, R, sbM, stellar, sp of 2
5376 I	Gx	0 01.4	+ 34 32 u	And	2.1	15p	F, S, E ns, gbM
7806	Gx	0 01.5	+ 31 27 s	Peg	1.3	14p	eF, S, R, stellar, nf of 2
1526 I	Gx	0 01.6	+ 11 21 z	Peg		15p	F, S, bMSN
5377 I	Gx	0 02.1	+ 16 36 u	Peg	1.3	16p	vF, S, R, dif
7809	Gx	0 02.2	+ 2 56 r	Psc		15p	eF, vS
7810	Gx	0 02.4	+ 12 57 r	Peg		14p	pF, stellar, 2 st np in line
1527 I		0 02.4	+ 4 07 d	Psc			F, R, r, vF* sf
7811	Gx	0 02.5	+ 3 20 r	Psc		15p	vF, S, R, stellar
5378 I		0 02.6	+ 16 37 d	Peg			F, pS, E ns, *15 inv
5379 I		0 02.7	+ 16 35 d	Peg			F, S, lE pf, lbM, *17 close p
5380 I		0 02.7	− 66 11 d	Tuc			vlE
7812	Gx	0 02.9	− 34 15 r	Scl			vF, S, R, am st
7813	Gx	0 03.2	− 11 59 d	Cet		15p	eF, vS, E 160°, *8.5 p 49^s, 2 st 9 n 8′
5381 I	Gx	0 03.2	+ 15 58 v	Peg	1.5		pF, S, lE spnf, bM, *13 nr
7814	Gx	0 03.3	+ 16 09 s	Peg	6.3	10.5	cB, cL, E, vgbM
7815	−	0 03.4	+ 20 41 r	Peg			F, S, lE, 7817 nf
5382 I		0 03.4	− 65 11 d	Tuc			alm R, lbM
7808	Gx	0 03.5	− 10 45 r	Cet		14p	eF, vS, R, stell N, *8.5 sp 3′
7822	Nb	0 03.6	+ 68 37 s	Cep	60		! eeF, eeL
7816	Gx	0 03.8	+ 7 28 s	Psc	1.9	14p	vF, pL, R, gbM
5383 I		0 03.8	+ 16 00 d	Peg			F, S, R, bM
7817	Gx	0 04.0	+ 20 45 s	Peg	3.7	12p	pF, cL, mE 45°±, lbM
7818	Gx	0 04.2	+ 7 21 r	Psc		15p	eeF, pS, v diffic, sf 7816
5384 I	Gx	0 04.2	− 11 58 m	Cet	0.8	15p	eF, vS, E 160°; = 7813?
7819	Gx	0 04.4	+ 31 29 s	Peg	2.0	14p	eF, L
7820	Gx	0 04.6	+ 5 11 r	Psc		14p	pF, vS, vsmbM, *14 sp
7823	Gx	0 04.8	− 62 04 c	Tuc	1.4		F, S, R, gbM
1528 I		0 05.1	− 3 07 d	Psc			no description
7824	Gx	0 05.2	+ 6 54 r	Psc		14p	pF, S, R, *10 np
7825	Gx	0 05.2	+ 5 12 r	Psc		15p	vF, S, gbM
7826	−	0 05.2	− 20 44 r	Cet			Cl, vP, vlC
1529 I		0 05.2	− 11 30 d	Cet			F, S, R, biN, r
7821	Gx	0 05.3	− 16 29 r	Cet		14p	vF, pS, iF, glbM
7827	Gx	0 05.5	+ 5 13 r	Psc		14p	vF, S, R, *12-13 nf
7830	*	0 06.2	+ 8 22 A	Psc			eF, neb* 13m
7828	Gx	0 06.4	− 13 24 v	Cet			eF, S, E 130°, sbMN, *15 sf
7829	Gx	0 06.4	− 13 24 v	Cet			only a *13 at 100°, 20″ from 7828
5385 I		0 06.4	− 0 04 d	Psc			eF (not verified)
7833	−	0 06.5	+ 27 38 r	Peg			Cl, vS, vF, 2′.5, nebs?
5386 I		0 06.5	− 3 43 z	Psc			pB, pS, mE ; = 7832
7832	Gx	0 06.6	− 3 42 r	Psc		13p	vF, vS, R, vgpsmbM, 2 st 9 sf; = IC 5386
7834	Gx	0 06.7	+ 8 21 r	Psc		15p	eeF, vS
7835	Gx	0 06.8	+ 8 25 r	Psc		15p	eF, S, R
7837	Gx	0 06.9	+ 8 20 r	Psc		16p	eF, p of Dneb

NGC	Type	α_{2000}	δ_{2000}		Const.	Size	Mag.	Description
		h m	o ′			′		
7838	Gx	0 07.0	+ 8 20	r	Psc		15p	eF, f of Dneb
7839	D∗	0 07.0	+27 38	A	Peg			vF, pS, dif, r
7840	Gx	0 07.1	+ 8 33	A	Psc			eF, S
1	Gx	0 07.3	+27 43	s	Peg	1.9	13p	F, S, R, bet ∗11 and ∗14
2	Gx	0 07.3	+27 41	s	Peg	1.4	15p	vF, S, s of 1
3	Gx	0 07.3	+ 8 17	r	Psc		14p	F, vS, R, alm stell
7831	Gx	0 07.3	+32 35	r	And		14p	eF, vS, mE, vF∗ vnr
1530 I	Gx	0 07.3	+32 37	v	And	1.8		vF, S, iF, bM
4	Gx	0 07.4	+ 8 22	A	Psc			eF
5	Gx	0 07.8	+35 21	r	And		14p	vF, vS, N = ∗13, 14
7836	Gx	0 08.0	+33 04	v	And	1.2		eF, vS, R, bet 2 st
6	−	0 08.3	+32 30	r	And			eF, vS, cE; = 7831?
7	Gx	0 08.4	− 29 55	v	Scl	2.5		eF, cL, mE, vgvlbM
1 I	D∗	0 08.4	+27 43	x	Peg			D∗, 13 & 13, one nebs
10	Gx	0 08.6	− 33 52	v	Scl	2.7		F, cL, vlE, glbM
11	Gx	0 08.7	+37 26	r	And		14p	vF, vS, vlE, 2 vF st inv
12	Gx	0 08.7	+ 4 37	s	Psc	1.9	15p	eF, pL, vglbM
8	D∗	0 08.8	+23 50	A	Peg			vF, N in n end
13	Gx	0 08.8	+33 26	s	And	2.7	14p	vF, vS, S st + neb
14	Gx	0 08.8	+15 49	s	Peg	3.0	12p	vF, pS, R, glbM
9	Gx	0 08.9	+23 49	s	Peg	1.5	15p	F, R, ∗9, 10 sf
15	Gx	0 09.1	+21 36	r	Peg		15p	vF, vS, R, bM
16	Gx	0 09.1	+27 44	s	Peg	2.1	12.0	pB, S, R, bM
18	D∗	0 09.4	+27 43	r	Peg			F, vS, iR, mbM, 16 p 19ˢ
19	−	0 09.4	+32 50	r	And			eeF, lE, 3 vF st around
20	Gx	0 09.5	+33 19	s	And	2.0	15p	F, ∗10 att
1531 I	Gx	0 09.6	− 32 17	c	Scl	1.9		vF, vS, R, D∗ n
22	Gx	0 09.8	+27 50	r	Peg		15p	vF, pS, R, lbM, r
23	Gx	0 09.9	+25 55	s	Peg	2.3	12.0	3 S st + neb
24	Gx	0 09.9	− 24 58	s	Scl	5.5	11.5	vF, cL, mE, gbM
25	Gx	0 09.9	− 57 03	r	Phe			vF, S, R
1532 I	Gx	0 09.9	− 64 22	c	Tuc	1.6		2′ l, mE, bM
28	Gx	0 10.3	− 57 01	r	Phe			eF, p of 2
26	Gx	0 10.4	+25 50	s	Peg	2.2	14p	vF, pL, R, 2 F st n
27	Gx	0 10.5	+29 00	r	And		14p	eF, vS, E, B∗ nr
31	Gx	0 10.5	− 57 00	r	Phe			eeF, S, R, f of 2
1533 I		0 10.6	− 7 25	d	Cet			eeF, vS, R, v diffic; ∗7.5 n, ∗9 s
21	Gx	0 10.7	+32 59	s	And	1.4	14p	eF, S, lE
29	Gx	0 10.8	+33 21	s	And	1.8	14p	pB, pL, E 0°
30	D∗	0 10.8	+21 57	r	Peg			neb ∗13
32	Ast	0 10.9	+18 47	r	Peg			F
33	D∗	0 10.9	+ 3 40	F	Psc			eF, vS, or neb st
17		0 11.0	− 12 06	D	Cet			vF, eS, iR, D∗ 2′ p; = 34
2 I	Gx	0 11.0	− 12 49	x	Cet			F, S, bM
34	Gx	0 11.1	− 12 06	r	Cet		13p	pF, S, R, 2 st nr
35	Gx	0 11.2	− 12 00	r	Cet		14p	eeF, pS, R
37	Gx	0 11.3	− 56 58	r	Phe			eF, S, R
36	Gx	0 11.4	+ 6 23	s	Psc	2.4	15p	vF, pS, iF
38	Gx	0 11.9	− 5 36	r	Psc		13p	F, S, R, mbM
3 I	Gx	0 12.1	− 0 25	x	Psc			F, vS, iF, r
39	Gx	0 12.3	+31 03	r	And		14p	vF, pS, R
41	Gx	0 12.8	+22 02	r	Peg		14p	pF, S, lE, gbM
42	Gx	0 12.9	+22 06	r	Peg		15p	F, vS, stell
40	Pl	0 13.0	+72 32	s	Cep	0.6	11p	F, vS, R, vsmbM, ∗12 sp
43	Gx	0 13.0	+30 54	r	And		14p	eF, ∗12 np 45″

NGC	Type	α_{2000}	δ_{2000}	Const.	Size	Mag.	Description
		h m	° ′		′		
44	–	0 13.1	+ 31 17 r	And			eF, vS
4 I	Gx	0 13.4	+ 17 29 x	Peg			vF, vS, R
1534 I		0 13.8	+ 48 09 d	And			pF, vS, diffic, *10 nr nf
48	Gx	0 14.0	+ 48 14 s	And	1.7	15p	eeF, pL, R, v diffic
1535 I		0 14.0	+ 48 09 d	And			vF, S, 48 nf 6′
45	Gx	0 14.1	− 23 11 A	Cet	8.1	10.4	eF, L, vgvlbM, *9 cont s
46	*	0 14.1	+ 5 59 r	Psc			nebula
1536 I	Gx	0 14.2	+ 48 08 m	And	0.7	15p	F, S, R
49	Gx	0 14.3	+ 48 14 r	And		15p	eeF, S, R, 2nd of 3
47	Gx	0 14.5	− 7 11 r	Cet		13p	vF, vS
58		0 14.5	− 7 10 D	Cet			vF, pS, R; = 47
51	Gx	0 14.6	+ 48 15 s	And	1.8	15p	pF, pS, R, bM
52	Gx	0 14.6	+ 18 33 r	Peg		14p	vF, S, E
50	Gx	0 14.7	− 7 20 v	Cet			vF
53	Gx	0 14.7	− 60 20 c	Tuc	2.1		eF, S, R, bM
55	Gx	0 14.9	− 39 11 s	Scl	32.4	8p	vB, vL, vmE, triN
54	Gx	0 15.1	− 7 08 r	Cet		14p	vF, pS, R, 50 sp
56	–	0 15.4	+ 12 26 r	Psc			eF, eL, diff
57	Gx	0 15.4	+ 17 18 r	Psc		13p	F, S, R, sbM
59	Gx	0 15.5	− 21 27 r	Cet		13p	vF, pS, iR, gbM
60	Gx	0 16.0	− 0 18 r	Psc		15p	eF, vS, R, lbM
1537 I		0 16.0	− 39 19 d	Phe			eeF, vL, vmE; 55 np
61	Gx	0 16.5	− 6 14 r	Psc		15p	vF, S, iR, psvlbM
62	Gx	0 17.1	− 13 28 r	Cet		14p	F, vS, R, glbM
5 I	Gx	0 17.4	− 9 33 m	Cet	0.8	14p	F, neb *13
64	Gx	0 17.5	− 6 51 r	Cet		14p	eeF, vS, R, v diffic
63	Gx	0 17.7	+ 11 27 s	Psc	1.9	13p	pF, S, R, sbM
1538 I	?	0 18.0	+ 30 04 x	And			eF
67	Gx	0 18.2	+ 30 04 s	And	0.4	16p	eF, vS, R
68	Gx	0 18.3	+ 30 04 s	And	1.5	13.0	eF, L, 3 or 4 st + neb
69	Gx	0 18.3	+ 30 02 v	And	0.4	14.8	eF, vS, R
70	Gx	0 18.4	+ 30 05 s	And	1.7	15p	eF, vS, R, bet 2 F st
71	Gx	0 18.4	+ 30 04 s	And	1.8	13.0	eF, vS, R
1539 I		0 18.4	+ 30 06 x	And			eF, bet 2 st 13; = 70
72	Gx	0 18.5	+ 30 02 s	And	1.4	13.4	eF, vS, R
73	Gx	0 18.8	− 15 21 r	Cet		13p	vF, S, R, eF D* close f
74	Gx	0 18.9	+ 30 03 r	And		16p	eF, S, E, last of 6
6 I	Gx	0 19.0	− 3 16 m	Psc	0.5	14p	F, vS, R, mbM = *14
65	Gx	0 19.1	− 22 54 r	Cet		15p	eF, vS, R, gbM, p of 2
7 I		0 19.1	+ 10 33 d	Psc			F, vS, R, *12.5 close
8 I	Gx	0 19.1	− 3 13 m	Psc	0.7	15p	vF, vS, irr E, lbM
66	Gx	0 19.2	− 22 57 r	Cet		14p	eF, pS, E 225°, *9 n 1′, f of 2
75	Gx	0 19.5	+ 6 25 r	Psc		15p	vF, vS, R
76	Gx	0 19.6	+ 29 56 r	And		14p	vF, S, bM
9 I	Gx	0 19.7	− 14 07 m	Cet	0.4	15p	vF, pL, R
1540 I		0 19.8	+ 23 43 d	And			F, S, iF
77		0 20.0	− 22 31 D	Cet			eF, vS, iF (*?), *9 p 3′
1541 I	Gx	0 20.0	+ 22 01 z	And		15p	F, S, R, lbM, r
12 I	Gx	0 20.3	− 2 39 m	Psc	0.7	16p	pF, S, E ns
78	Gx	0 20.4	+ 0 49 r	Psc		14p	vF, S, R
10 I	Gx	0 20.4	+ 59 18 s	Cas	5.1	10.3	F* inv in eF, vL neb
13 I	Gx	0 20.4	+ 7 42 u	Psc	1.6	15p	vF, pL, E ns, dif
11 I		0 20.5	+ 56 36 d	Cas			vF, L, triple * on np corner
1542 I	Gx	0 20.6	+ 22 37 m	And	0.7	15p	F, dif, gbM
1543 I	Gx	0 20.9	+ 21 53 u	And	0.8	14p	F, S, R, gbMN

NGC	Type	α_{2000}	δ_{2000}	Const.	Size	Mag.	Description
		h m	o ′		′		
79	Gx	0 21.0	+ 22 34 r	And		15p	vF, S, vlbM
80	Gx	0 21.2	+ 22 21 s	And	2.5	12.1	F, S, R, psbM
81	Gx	0 21.2	+ 22 22 r	And			eeF, sp 83
87	Gx	0 21.2	− 48 38 r	Phe			eF, S, R, gbM, 1st of 4
88	Gx	0 21.3	− 48 39 r	Phe			eF, vS, R, 2nd of 4
89	Gx	0 21.3	− 48 41 r	Phe			vF, S, R, gbM, 3rd of 4
1544 I		0 21.3	+ 23 02 d	And			F, S, R, vlbM
1545 I		0 21.3	+ 21 59 d	And			F, vS, R, dif, vFN
82	Gx	0 21.4	+ 22 26 u	And	1.3	14p	eF, stellar
83	Gx	0 21.4	+ 22 26 s	And	1.6	12.6	E, biN, 3 B st nr
85	Gx	0 21.4	+ 22 30 r	And		15p	eeF, cL, R
84	Gx	0 21.5	+ 22 36 r	And		17p	eF, st & neb
86	Gx	0 21.5	+ 22 33 r	And		15p	eF, vS, lbM
92	Gx	0 21.5	− 48 38 r	Phe			F, S, R, gbM, 4th of 4
1546 I		0 21.5	+ 22 30 d	And			vF, S, v diffic
1547 I	?	0 21.6	+ 22 31 x	And			eF.pS, sbM *
91	Gx	0 21.8	+ 22 25 s	And	2.5	15p	vF, vS, *13 sp
90	*	0 21.9	+ 22 25 r	And			vF, lE
1548 I	Gx	0 21.9	+ 22 01 z	And		16p	F, vS, R, stell
93	Gx	0 22.0	+ 22 25 r	And		14p	vF, vS
94	Gx	0 22.2	+ 22 28 r	And		15p	eF, vS
95	Gx	0 22.2	+ 10 30 s	Psc	1.9	12.6	F, pL, R, gbM
96	Gx	0 22.3	+ 22 33 r	And		17p	vF, S, vlbM
97	Gx	0 22.4	+ 29 44 r	And		13p	F, vS, R, gbM
14 I		0 22.6	+ 10 29 d	Psc			susp neb
98	Gx	0 22.8	− 45 16 c	Phe	1.8		vF, pS, R, bM, r
1549 I		0 23.2	+ 6 59 d	Psc			eF, D* f 46ˢ
101	Gx	0 23.9	− 32 34 r	Scl		13p	pB, pL, lE, *14 f
99	Gx	0 24.0	+ 15 47 s	Psc	1.7	14p	vF, pL, R, gbM
100	Gx	0 24.0	+ 16 29 v	Psc	5.8		vF, pS, mE, 2′ long
104	Gb	0 24.1	− 72 05 s	Tuc	30.9	4.0	⊕ !! vB, vL, vmCM
102	Gx	0 24.4	− 13 57 r	Cet		14p	eF, vS, R
1550 I	Gx	0 24.4	+ 38 12 m	And	0.6	15p	R, stell, vFN
106	Gx	0 24.7	− 5 10 D	Psc			pF, vS, R, lbM
103	OC	0 25.3	+ 61 21 s	Cas	5	9.8	Cl, pS, pC, st 11...18
105	Gx	0 25.3	+ 12 53 s	Psc	1.2	13.2	vF, S, R, vlbM
107	Gx	0 25.6	− 8 17 F	Cet			F, pL, *7 sf 5′
108	Gx	0 25.9	+ 29 13 r	And		13p	pF, pL, R, pslbM
109	Gx	0 26.2	+ 21 49 r	And		15p	vF, S, 3 st nr
111	−	0 26.7	− 2 38 r	Cet			vF, S, R, lbM, *8.5 p 36ˢ, n 2′; = 113?
112	Gx	0 26.7	+ 31 43 r	And		14p	eF, vS, R
115	Gx	0 26.8	− 33 41 r	Scl			vF, pL, lE, D* 2′ np
121	Gb	0 26.8	− 71 32 s	Tuc	1.5	10.6	pB, pS, lE, vgbM
113	Gx	0 27.0	− 2 30 r	Cet		13p	vF, S, sbM
114	Gx	0 27.1	− 1 47 r	Cet		15p	vF, S* in centre, p of 2
119	Gx	0 27.1	− 56 59 r	Phe			pB, S, R, mbM
116	Gx	0 27.2	− 7 42 r	Cet		14p	vF
117	Gx	0 27.2	+ 1 19 r	Cet		15p	F, vS
118	Gx	0 27.3	− 1 47 r	Cet		15p	vF, S* in centre, f of 2
110	OC	0 27.4	+ 71 23 r	Cas			Cl, pR, lC, st 9...12
120	Gx	0 27.5	− 1 31 s	Cet	1.8	15p	nebulous *
1551 I	Gx	0 27.6	+ 8 53 u	Psc	2.7	15p	F, vS, R, r
122	?	0 27.7	− 1 38 F	Cet			1st of 2 vF neb 4′-5′ np of *8.5
123	?	0 27.8	− 1 36 F	Cet			2nd of 2 vF neb 4′-5′ np of *8.5
124	Gx	0 27.9	− 1 49 s	Cet	1.6	14p	vF, L, dif, 2 F st np

NGC	Type	α_{2000}	δ_{2000}	Const.	Size	Mag.	Description
		h m	° ′		′		
16 I	Gx	0 27.9	− 13 05 m	Cet	0.5	15p	pB, R, bM
15 I		0 28.0	− 0 04 d	Cet			vF, vS, iF, sbM
17 I	Gx	0 28.5	+ 2 39 z	Cet		15p	pB, vS, R, stellar
20 I	Gx	0 28.5	− 13 00 m	Cet	0.6	14p	pB, R
18 I	Gx	0 28.6	− 11 34 m	Cet	0.6	15p	pF, S, iF, gbM
19 I	Gx	0 28.7	− 11 38 m	Cet	0.6	15p	R, S, stellar = 14m
125	Gx	0 28.8	+ 2 50 s	Psc	2.0	12.3	vF, S, bM, D∗ sp
126	Gx	0 29.1	+ 2 49 s	Psc	1.4	16p	vF, S, lE
127	Gx	0 29.2	+ 2 52 s	Psc	1.0	14.0	vF, vS, R, p 128
128	Gx	0 29.2	+ 2 51 s	Psc	3.4	11.6	pB, pS, lE 2°, bM
21 I	Gx	0 29.2	− 0 10 m	Cet	0.4	14p	pB, vs, iF
130	Gx	0 29.3	+ 2 52 v	Psc	0.9	14.3	vF, vS, R, f 128
131	Gx	0 29.6	− 33 16 s	Scl	2.1		F, pL, pmE, vgbM, p of 2
22 I	Gx	0 29.6	− 9 03 m	Cet	0.6	15p	F, S, lbM, r
1552 I	Gx	0 29.6	+ 21 29 u	Psc	1.1	15p	F, pL, dif
129	OC	0 29.9	+ 60 14 s	Cas	21	6.5	Cl, vL, pR, lC, st 9...13
132	Gx	0 30.2	+ 2 06 s	Cet	2.0	14p	pF, cL, R, vglbM, R
134	Gx	0 30.4	− 33 15 s	Scl	8.1	10.1	vB, L, vmE 47°, psbM, f of 2, ∗10 np 45″
23 I		0 30.9	− 12 44 d	Cet			pB, S, R, bM
138	Gx	0 31.0	+ 5 10 r	Psc		15p	F, eS, sbM
139	Gx	0 31.0	+ 5 05 r	Psc		15p	eF, S
137	Gx	0 31.1	+ 10 11 r	Psc		14p	F, iF, lbM
133	OC	0 31.2	+ 63 22 s	Cas	7	9p	Cl, pL, st 10..., D∗ inv
24 I	OC	0 31.2	+ 30 51 z	And			S, Cl, 30″-40′, nebs?
25 I	Gx	0 31.2	− 0 24 m	Cet	0.8	15p	F, vS, irrR, vlbM, r
140	Gx	0 31.3	+ 30 47 r	And		14p	vF, S, R, gbM
142	Gx	0 31.3	− 22 37 r	Cet		14p	eF, S, lE, 1st of 3 and faintest
141	Gx	0 31.4	+ 5 11 r	Psc		15p	vF, vS, iR
143	Gx	0 31.4	− 22 34 r	Cet		15p	eF, S, mE, 2nd of 3
144	Gx	0 31.4	− 22 39 r	Cet		14p	eF, pS, R, 3rd of 3 and brightest
136	OC	0 31.5	+ 61 32 s	Cas	1		⊕, vF, S, eC
145	Gx	0 31.7	− 5 09 s	Cet	1.8	12.8	F, pL, vlE, vgbM, ∗8-9 f 5′
135		0 31.8	− 13 22 D	Cet			vF, vS, R
26 I		0 31.8	− 13 20 F	Cet			F, S, R, gbM; = 135
1553 I	Gx	0 32.7	− 25 35 m	Scl	1.0	14p	vF, vmE 10°
152	Gb	0 32.8	− 73 09 r	Tuc		12p	vF, L, R, vglbM
146	OC	0 33.1	+ 63 18 s	Cas	7	9.1	Cl, pL, lC, st 11-12, D∗
27 I		0 33.1	− 13 22 d	Cet			F, vS, lE pf, bM
28 I		0 33.1	− 13 27 d	Cet			vF, dif, vlbM
1554 I	Gx	0 33.1	− 32 16 c	Scl	1.6		vF, vS, eE 170°, sbM
147	Gx	0 33.2	+ 48 30 s	Cas	12.9	9.3	vF, vL, iR, gsmbM ∗11
149	Gx	0 33.7	+ 30 43 r	And		15p	vF, vS, R, gbM ∗14, ∗12 sp
151	Gx	0 34.0	− 9 42 s	Cet	3.7	11.5	pF, pL, lE 90°, vglbM
153		0 34.0	− 9 42 D	Cet			pF, pS, R, ∗ nr nf; = 151
154	Gx	0 34.1	− 12 39 r	Cet		14p	eF, vS, R
29 I	Gx	0 34.2	− 2 11 m	Cet	0.6	15p	vF, S, R, lbM
148	Gx	0 34.3	− 31 47 s	Scl	2.4	12.1	vB, S, lE 90°, smbM ∗11
150	Gx	0 34.3	− 27 48 s	Scl	4.2	11.1	pF, pS, R
30 I	Gx	0 34.3	− 2 05 m	Cet	0.4	15p	vF, S, R, lbM
31 I	Gx	0 34.4	+ 12 17 u	Psc	1.4	15p	F, E pf, dif
156	D∗	0 34.6	− 8 21 F	Cet			vS, np 157
159	Gx	0 34.6	− 55 47 r	Phe			vF, pS, R, glbM, 3 st f
1555 I	Gx	0 34.6	− 30 01 c	Scl	1.5		eeF, S, R, 2 st p in line
155	Gx	0 34.7	− 10 46 r	Cet		13p	pF, S, R
157	Gx	0 34.8	− 8 24 s	Cet	4.3	10.4	pB, L, E, bet 2 cB st

NGC	Type	α_{2000}	δ_{2000}	Const.	Size	Mag.	Description
		h m	° ′		′		
158	D∗?	0 34.9	− 8 19 F	Cet			vS, nf 157
32 I	Gx	0 35.0	− 2 08 m	Cet	0.4	15p	vF, vS, R, lbM
33 I	Gx	0 35.1	− 2 08 m	Cet	0.5	15p	vF vS, R, lbM
1556 I	?	0 35.1	− 9 34 x	Cet			eeF, pS, R, v diffic
167	Gx	0 35.3	− 23 22 r	Cet		13p	vF, pS, iR
161	Gx	0 35.5	− 2 50 r	Cet		15p	eF, eS, R, nearly bet 2 st; = IC 1557
1557 I	Gx	0 35.5	− 2 51 m	Cet	0.6	16p	eF, vS, 2 vF st close; nr 161
34 I	Gx	0 35.6	+ 9 08 u	Psc	3.4	14p	vF, pS, lE
166	Gx	0 35.8	− 13 37 r	Cet		15p	eF, S, lE, ∗11 np
176	OC	0 35.8	− 73 11 r	Tuc		12p	eF, S, vlE, r, ∗8 nr
1558 I	Gx	0 35.8	− 25 22 c	Scl	3.4		E 160°, ∗ n, perhaps spir
163	Gx	0 36.0	− 10 07 s	Cet	1.4	12.8	vF, vS
160	Gx	0 36.1	+ 23 57 s	And	3.2	12.4	vF, vS, stell, ∗8, 17°, 4′
162	Gx	0 36.1	+ 23 58 r	And			eF, stellar, 160 sp
164	Gx	0 36.5	+ 2 45 r	Psc		16p	eF
165	Gx	0 36.5	− 10 06 s	Cet	1.6	13.2	F, L, st in centre, f of 2
168	Gx	0 36.7	− 22 36 r	Cet		14p	eF, S, E 30°, ∗10 nf 3′
170	Gx	0 36.7	+ 1 51 r	Cet		15p	F, S, R
169	Gx	0 36.9	+ 23 59 s	And	3.0	13p	F, pL, D or biN, ∗6 nf 4′
174	Gx	0 36.9	− 29 29 r	Scl		14p	eF, S, vlE, am B st
1559 I	Gx	0 36.9	+ 23 59 v	And	0.9		vF, 0′.5 ssf 169
173	Gx	0 37.2	+ 1 56 s	Cet	3.5	15p	vF, S, R, vgbM, ∗11 sp 80″
172	Gx	0 37.3	− 22 36 v	Cet	2.6		eF, S, E, ∗13 close sp
171		0 37.4	− 19 56 F	Cet			vF, pL, lE, 2 pB st sf; = 175
175	Gx	0 37.4	− 19 56 s	Cet	2.6	12.1	pB, pL, E, gbM, R
177	Gx	0 37.5	− 22 34 r	Cet		13p	eF, S, E 175°
35 I	Gx	0 37.7	+ 10 21 u	Psc	1.3	15p	vF, S, dif, ∗9.5 nf
1560 I		0 37.7	+ 2 40 d	Cet			eF; = 164?
179	Gx	0 37.8	− 17 53 r	Cet		14p	eF, eS, R, B∗ np
36 I		0 37.8	− 15 26 d	Cet			F, vS, R, dif
180	Gx	0 38.0	+ 8 38 s	Psc	2.6	14p	vF, pL, iR, ∗ np inv
181	Gx	0 38.2	+ 29 28 r	And		15p	eF, eS, irr, vF∗ att
182	Gx	0 38.2	+ 2 44 s	Psc	2.3	12.6	vF, S, iR, vgbM
183	Gx	0 38.3	+ 29 30 r	And		14p	pF, vS, R, gbM
184	Gx	0 38.5	+ 29 26 r	And		15p	eF, eS
186	Gx	0 38.5	+ 3 09 r	Psc		15p	F, S, R, lbM
37 I	Gx	0 38.5	− 15 23 m	Cet	0.7	15p	eF, vS, R, dif
1561 I	Gx	0 38.5	− 24 20 m	Cet	1.3	14p	E 105°, ∗ n
38 I	Gx	0 38.6	− 15 26 m	Cet	0.6	14p	F, S, R
1562 I	Gx	0 38.6	− 24 17 c	Cet	2.1		S, R, psbM
190	Gx	0 38.9	+ 7 02 s	Psc	1.0	14p	vF, S, lE, sev st nr sp
185	Gx	0 39.0	+ 48 20 s	Cas	11.5	9.2	pB, vL, iR, vgmbM, r
191	Gx	0 39.0	− 9 00 s	Cet	1.5	12p	pB, pL, iE 0°
1563 I	Gx	0 39.0	− 9 01 v	Cet	0.6		eF, stellar, 0′.6 sf 191
178	Gx	0 39.1	− 14 10 s	Cet	2.0	12.6	F, S, mE 0°, bM; = IC 39
209	Gx	0 39.1	− 18 38 r	Cet		14p	vF, vS, R, bM
39 I		0 39.1	− 14 10 x	Cet			pB, pl, E ns, gbM; = 178
1564 I		0 39.2	+ 5 58 d	Psc			eF
192	Gx	0 39.3	+ 0 51 s	Cet	2.3	14p	F, pS, pmE, bM
193	Gx	0 39.3	+ 3 20 s	Psc	1.7	12.3	F, L, p of 2, ∗15 close sp
194	Gx	0 39.3	+ 3 02 s	Psc	1.9	12.1	pB, S, R, vgbM
196	Gx	0 39.3	+ 0 54 r	Cet		14p	F, pS, R, psmbM
197	Gx	0 39.4	+ 0 53 r	Cet		15p	eF, s of 196
198	Gx	0 39.4	+ 2 48 s	Psc	1.3	12.8	F, S, vgbM
1565 I	Gx	0 39.4	+ 6 43 v	Psc	1.7		F, S, R, gbM

NGC	Type	α_{2000}	δ_{2000}	Const.	Size	Mag.	Description
		h m	° ′		′		
1566 I	Gx	0 39.4	+ 6 48 m	Psc	0.6	15p	F, S, R, gbM, r
40 I	Gx	0 39.5	+ 2 26 u	Cet	1.2	15p	F, S, R, gbMN = 13.5
187	Gx	0 39.6	− 14 41 r	Cet		13p	F, S, mE 150°, bM
189	OC	0 39.6	+ 61 04 s	Cas	4	8.8	Cl, pL, R, st 11...15
195	Gx	0 39.6	− 9 12 v	Cet	1.3		F
199	Gx	0 39.6	+ 3 07 r	Psc		15p	F, vS, *8 p 27ˢ, 45″ s
200	Gx	0 39.6	+ 2 53 s	Psc	2.0	14p	pB, S, vgbM
1567 I		0 39.6	+ 6 37 d	Psc			neb *
201	Gx	0 39.7	+ 0 51 s	Cet	2.2	15p	vF, cL, E, vglbM
202	Gx	0 39.7	+ 3 31 r	Psc		15p	eF, vS, ibM
203	Gx	0 39.7	+ 3 26 r	Psc		15p	F, R, *9 sp 8′
41 I		0 39.7	− 14 10 d	Cet			vF, S, dif
204	Gx	0 39.8	+ 3 17 r	Psc		14p	F, pS, R, vgbM, f of 2
1568 I	Gx	0 39.9	+ 6 50 m	Psc	0.8	15p	F, S, R, gbM, r
207		0 40.0	− 14 18 d	Cet			vF, S, lE, stellar
212	Gx	0 40.1	− 56 10 r	Phe			vF, S, R, p of 2
205	Gx	0 40.4	+ 41 41 s	And	17.4	8.0	vB, vL, mE 165°, vgvmbM; = M110
208	Gx	0 40.4	+ 2 44 r	Psc		15p	pF
1569 I	Gx	0 40.4	+ 6 42 m	Psc	0.2	15p	vF, vS, R, gbM
220	OC	0 40.5	− 73 24 r	Tuc		11p	F, iR, vgbM, 1st of several
206	C+N	0 40.6	+ 40 44 r	And			vF, vL, mE 0°
210	Gx	0 40.6	− 13 52 s	Cet	5.4	10.9	B, pS, psbM, r, *11 p 2′
222	OC	0 40.6	− 73 24 r	Tuc		11p	vF, R, 2nd of several
1570 I		0 40.6	+ 6 45 d	Psc			vF, vS, R, vFN
1571 I	Gx	0 40.7	− 0 19 u	Cet	1.3	15p	F, pS, R, dif
215	Gx	0 40.8	− 56 13 c	Phe	1.2		F, S, R, am st, f of 2
211	*	0 41.0	+ 3 26 F	Psc			eF, S, mbMN
231	OC	0 41.0	− 73 22 r	Tuc		12p	i train of st and neb
42 I	Gx	0 41.1	− 15 26 m	Cet	0.6	15p	S, irr, v dif
213	Gx	0 41.2	+ 16 28 r	Psc		15p	F, S, bet 2 S st
1572 I		0 41.2	+ 16 16 d	Psc			eF, stell, 213 nr
216	Gx	0 41.4	− 21 03 s	Cet	1.8	13.3	eF, vS, lE
214	Gx	0 41.5	+ 25 30 s	And	2.1	12.2	pF, pS, gvlbM, r
217	Gx	0 41.5	− 10 02 v	Cet	3.3		F, S, lE 90°, glbM
218	Gx	0 41.8	+ 36 21 r	And		15p	eF, vS, R, gbM
44 I	Gx	0 42.2	+ 0 51 m	Cet	0.5	14p	eF, S, R, bet 2 st
1573 I		0 42.2	− 23 32 d	Cet			eF, eS, mE 60°
219	Gx	0 42.3	+ 0 54 r	Cet		15p	F, S, R, *11 sp 1′
230	Gx	0 42.4	− 23 38 r	Cet		15p	eF, eS, R, bMN
43 I	Gx	0 42.4	+ 29 38 v	And	2.1		vF, S, mbM
227	Gx	0 42.6	− 1 32 s	Cet	2.1	13p	F, pL, lbM
221	Gx	0 42.7	+ 40 52 s	And	7.6	8.2	! vvB, L, R, psmbMN; = M32
223	Gx	0 42.7	+ 0 51 r	Cet		14p	vF, pS, R; = IC 44
224	Gx	0 42.7	+ 41 16 s	And	178	3.5	!!! eeB, eL, vmE (Andromeda); = M31
232	Gx	0 42.7	− 23 34 r	Cet		14p	eF, S, R, bMN
45 I		0 42.7	+ 29 40 d	And			susp neb
226	Gx	0 42.8	+ 32 34 r	And		14p	eF, S, R, *13 s 20″
228	Gx	0 42.8	+ 23 30 r	And		15p	eF, S, R, fainter of 2
235	Gx	0 42.8	− 23 33 r	Cet		14p	eF, S, R, bMN
47 I	?	0 42.9	− 13 45 x	Cet			eF, eS, R, stellar
229	Gx	0 43.0	+ 23 29 r	And		14p	vF, S, R, smaller of 2
46 I	Gx	0 43.0	+ 27 15 z	And		15p	pB, S, R, bM
1574 I	Gx	0 43.1	− 22 15 c	Cet	2.5		vF, vmE 0°, gbM
225	OC	0 43.4	+ 61 47 s	Cas	12	7.0	Cl, L, lC, st 9...10
233	Gx	0 43.4	+ 30 35 r	And		14p	F, vS, R, lbM

NGC	Type	α_{2000}	δ_{2000}		Const.	Size	Mag.	Description
		h m	° ′			′		
234	Gx	0 43.4	+ 14 20	r	Psc		13p	F, pS, ilE, bM
238	Gx	0 43.4	− 50 11	c	Phe	1.9		ef, pL, R, gvlbM
241	−	0 43.4	− 73 26	r	Tuc			vF, R; = 242?
236	Gx	0 43.5	+ 2 56	r	Psc		14p	vF, pL
237	Gx	0 43.5	− 0 07	s	Cet	1.8	14p	vF, pS, lE, lbM
242	OC	0 43.6	− 73 27	r	Tuc		12p	vF, S, biN
48 I		0 43.6	− 7 53	d	Cet			pF, S (var brightness?)
1575 I		0 43.6	− 4 09	d	Cet			eF, S, R, *10 s
188	OC	0 44.	+ 85 20	s	Cep	14	8.1	Cl, vL, R, 150-200 st 10...18
49 I	Gx	0 44.0	+ 1 51	v	Cet	1.9		eeF, pS, R, e diffic
1576 I	Gx	0 44.2	− 25 06	m	Scl	0.6	15p	vF, vS, cE 135°, bet 2 st
1578 I	Gx	0 44.5	− 25 04	m	Scl	0.6	14p	vF, vS, vmE
239		0 44.6	− 3 47	D	Cet			pF, pS, E 20°, bMN, *8 f 20ˢ
1577 I		0 44.6	− 8 08	d	Cet			pB, S, R, gbM stell N
240	Gx	0 45.1	+ 6 08	r	Psc		15p	vF, S, R, * nr s
248	Nb	0 45.4	− 73 23	r	Tuc			F, S, E or biN, vglbM
249	Nb	0 45.4	− 73 05	r	Tuc			F, pL, vlE, r
1579 I	Gx	0 45.6	− 26 34	m	Scl	0.8	15p	eF, eS, cE 15°, gbM
244	Gx	0 45.8	− 15 36	s	Cet	1.3	13.3	vF, S, iR, r, *10 s 5′
243	Gx	0 45.9	+ 29 56	r	And		14p	F, vS, R, gbM, *10 p
256	C+N	0 45.9	− 73 30	r	Tuc		12p	F, S, R, gbM, *9 nf 40″
245	Gx	0 46.1	− 1 44	s	Cet	1.4	13p	F, pS, iF, er
1581 I		0 46.1	− 25 54	d	Scl			eF, eS, E 45°, gbM
50 I	Gx	0 46.2	− 9 30	m	Cet	0.6	14p	F, = neb *13
1580 I		0 46.3	+ 29 55	d	And			vF, v stell
1582 I	Gx	0 46.3	− 24 18	m	Cet	1.2	15p	eF, eS, E 45°, sbM *
51 I	Gx	0 46.4	− 13 26	m	Cet	1.0	13p	pB, S, bM, r
261	Nb	0 46.5	− 73 07	r	Tuc			F, pL, R, gbM *13
246	Pl	0 47.0	− 11 53	s	Cet	3.8	8p	vF, L, 4 st in dif neb
247	Gx	0 47.1	− 20 46	s	Cet	20.0	8.9	F, eL, vmE 172°
1583 I		0 47.2	+ 23 05	d	And			F, vS, R, stell N
250	Gx	0 47.3	+ 7 55	r	Psc		15p	eF, vS, R, am 3 st
1585 I		0 47.3	+ 23 03	d	And			F, vS, R, stell N
1584 I	Gx	0 47.4	+ 27 49	u	And	1.8	15p	eF, L, dif, r
254	Gx	0 47.5	− 31 25	s	Scl	2.1	11.8	vB, pS, lE, smbM, *8 nf 5′
253	Gx	0 47.6	− 25 17	s	Scl	25.1	7.1	!! vvB, vvL, vmE 54°, gbM
265	Gb	0 47.6	− 73 29	r	Tuc		12p	F, pS, R
251	Gx	0 47.8	+ 19 34	r	Psc		14p	vF, S, R, lbM, * inv, 2 vS st f
255	Gx	0 47.8	− 11 28	s	Cet	3.1	11.8	F, pS, R, gbM
1586 I	Gx	0 47.9	+ 22 22	v	And			F, vS, R, gbM, r
252	Gx	0 48.0	+ 27 38	s	And	1.8	13p	pB, S, R, pmbM, r, ⁂ p
267	C+N	0 48.0	− 73 17	r	Tuc			Cl, F, pL, st vS
257	Gx	0 48.1	+ 8 19	s	Psc	2.1	14p	pL, lE, gbM, r
259	Gx	0 48.1	− 2 47	v	Cet	3.2		F, S, E 135°, lbM
258	Gx	0 48.2	+ 27 38	r	And		15p	eF, S, vF st close
264	Gx	0 48.3	− 38 14	c	Scl	0.9		F, S, R, vsvmbM *13
52 I	Gx	0 48.4	+ 4 06	u	Psc	1.2	15p	vF, vS, R, gvlbM
269	Gb	0 48.5	− 73 32	r	Tuc		12p	vF, S, R
260	Gx	0 48.6	+ 27 42	s	And	1.0	14p	eF, pS, lE
262	Gx	0 48.8	+ 31 57	s	And	1.4	15p	eF, vS, R, v diffic
1587 I	Gx	0 48.8	− 23 34	m	Cet	0.8	15p	eF, eS, alm R
263	Gx	0 48.9	− 13 06	r	Cet		14p	eF, vS, lE 30°
266	Gx	0 49.8	+ 32 16	s	Psc	3.2	13p	pB, pS, lE, psbM, r, *8 sf 4′
268	Gx	0 50.2	− 5 12	s	Cet	1.7	13p	vF, pS, ilE, r
53 I		0 50.5	+ 10 37	d	Psc			eeF, pS, R, others susp

NGC	Type	α_{2000}	δ_{2000}	Const.	Size	Mag.	Description
		h m	° ′		′		
270	Gx	0 50.7	− 8 39 r	Cet		13p	pF, vS, iR, pgbM
271	Gx	0 50.8	− 1 53 s	Cet	2.5	13p	pF, S, lE, psbM, *8 f 5ˢ
273	Gx	0 50.8	− 6 53 s	Cet	2.6	13p	vF, vS
54 I	D*	0 50.8	− 2 17 F	Cet			neb or S Cl, 2′, bM
274	Gx	0 51.0	− 7 03 s	Cet	1.7	13p	pB, pS, smbM, np of 2
1588 I		0 51.0	− 23 33 d	Cet			vF, vS, cE 155°
275	Gx	0 51.1	− 7 04 s	Cet	1.5	12.5	vF, S, R, sf of 2
290	OC	0 51.3	− 73 09 r	Tuc		12p	eF
272	OC	0 51.4	+ 35 50 r	And			Cl, L, lC
277	Gx	0 51.5	− 8 35 r	Cet		13p	F, pS, *11 np
56 I	Gx	0 51.5	− 12 51 v	Cet	1.3		vF, S, lbM
1589 I		0 51.5	− 34 28 d	Scl			eF, eS, R, like Dneb
55 I	Gx	0 51.7	+ 7 43 m	Psc	0.5	14p	F, vS, dif, *13 close
276	Gx	0 52.1	− 22 41 r	Cet		14p	eF, pS, E 265°, *8 nf is a close D*
278	Gx	0 52.1	+ 47 33 s	Cas	2.2	10.9	cB, pL, R, 2 st 10 nr
294	Nb	0 52.1	− 73 21 r	Tuc			vF, pL, R, vglbM, r
1591 I	Gx	0 52.1	− 22 41 c	Cet	1.3		vF, vS, cE 95°, bM; = 276
279	Gx	0 52.3	− 2 12 s	Cet	1.8	14p	vF, S, iR, bM, stellar
280	Gx	0 52.5	+ 24 20 r	And		14p	eF, S, R, *15 f 30″
289	Gx	0 52.7	− 31 12 s	Scl	3.7	12p	vB, L, pmE, gbM, *11 np
281	C+N	0 52.8	+ 56 37 s	Cas	35	7p	F, vL, dif, S triple * on np edge
282	Gx	0 52.8	+ 30 37 r	Psc		14p	F, S, R, lbM
288	Gb	0 52.8	− 26 35 s	Scl	13.8	8.1	⊕, B, L, lE, st 12...16
292	Gx	0 52.8	− 72 50 r	Tuc			Cl, F, eeL, R, st 12...18
1590 I	OC	0 53.1	+ 56 35 x	Cas			Cl, vL, st sc; 281 f
283	Gx	0 53.3	− 13 11 r	Cet		14p	eF, S, R, 1st of 4
1592 I	Gx	0 53.5	+ 5 46 u	Psc	1.1	15p	eF, S, bet *12 and *13
1597 I	Gx	0 53.5	− 58 07 c	Tuc	1.4		eF, eS, cE 165°, cbM
284	Gx	0 53.6	− 13 09 r	Cet		15p	eF, S, R, 2nd of 4
286	Gx	0 53.6	− 13 06 r	Cet		14p	eF, S, R, 4th of 4
287	Gx	0 53.6	+ 32 29 r	Psc		15p	eF, S, R; RA 1ᵐ greater?
291	Gx	0 53.6	− 8 45 r	Cet		14p	vF, vS, lE, alm stellar
285	Gx	0 53.7	− 13 10 r	Cet			eF, S, R, 3rd of 4
1594 I	Gx	0 53.7	− 47 39 c	Phe	1.2		eF, eS, cE 130°, stell N
1595 I	Gx	0 53.8	− 45 11 c	Phe	1.2		eF, S, mE 10°, stell N
299	C+N	0 54.0	− 72 10 r	Tuc		11p	pB, vS, R, gvlbR, r
293	Gx	0 54.3	− 7 14 r	Cet		14p	vF, S
1599 I	Gx	0 54.5	− 23 29 m	Cet	0.8	15p	vF, vS, cE 100°
1593 I		0 54.7	+ 32 30 d	Psc			eF, semi-stellar
1596 I	Gx	0 54.7	+ 21 31 u	Psc	2.5	15p	F, S, E pf, gbM
1598 I	Gx	0 54.7	+ 5 46 u	Psc	1.3	15p	neb *11; *9 p 10ˢ, 4′.5 n
303	Gx	0 54.8	− 16 40 r	Cet			eF, vS
57 I	Gx	0 54.8	+ 11 50 u	Psc	1.1	16p	F, vS, R, vlbM, F* close
300	Gx	0 54.9	− 37 41 s	Scl	20.0	9p	pB, vL, vmiE, vgpmbM
306	C+N	0 54.9	− 72 13 r	Tuc		12p	F, vS
297	D*?	0 55.0	− 7 21 F	Cet			eF
298	Gx	0 55.0	− 7 21 r	Cet		13p	pF
1600 I	Gx	0 55.0	− 23 31 m	Cet	0.7	15p	vF, vS, cE 95°
58 I	Gx	0 55.1	− 13 41 m	Cet	0.6	15p	F, vS, R, r
295	Gx	0 55.2	+ 31 31 r	Psc		13p	F, S, R, * 10″ n, 296 nf
296	Gx	0 55.4	+ 31 40 r	Psc		15p	F, lE, *10 nf 2′
1601 I		0 55.6	− 24 09 d	Cet			vF, vS, lE 105°
1602 I	Gx	0 55.9	− 9 59 m	Cet	0.7	14p	vF, S, nr 309
305	Ast	0 56.0	+ 12 06 A	Psc			Cl, S, sc st
304	Gx	0 56.1	+ 24 07 r	And		14p	pF, S, R, svlbM

NGC	Type	α_{2000}	δ_{2000}	Const.	Size	Mag.	Description
		h m	° ′		′		
60 I	Gx	0 56.1	− 13 23 m	Cet	0.6	15p	F, vS, R, SN
330	OC	0 56.2	− 72 29 s	Tuc	2	9.6	⊕, vB, S, lE, st 13...15
301	Gx	0 56.3	− 10 40 F	Cet			eF, S, iR, gbM, *8 p 30ˢ
312	Gx	0 56.3	− 52 47 c	Phe	1.8		F, S, R, *12 f
302	*	0 56.4	− 10 39 F	Cet			eF, vS
308	*	0 56.4	− 1 47 A	Cet			vF, eS, 1′ sf 307
307	Gx	0 56.6	− 1 46 r	Cet		14p	pF, S, E
309	Gx	0 56.7	− 9 55 s	Cet	3.1	11.8	pB, pL, *12-13 n
323	Gx	0 56.7	− 52 59 c	Phe	1.3		pF, S, R, bM, p of 2
59 I	Nb	0 56.7	+ 61 04 s	Cas	10		pF, eL! (nf γ Cas)
310	*	0 56.9	− 1 46 A	Cet			stellar
314	Gx	0 56.9	− 31 58 c	Scl	1.2		eF, vS, R, pB* f 2′
319	Gx	0 57.0	− 43 50 c	Phe	1.1		eF, vS, R, lbM
328	Gx	0 57.0	− 52 55 c	Phe	2.8		vF, lE, vgbM, f of 2
1603 I	Gx	0 57.0	− 45 25 c	Phe	1.3		eF, eS, cE 115°, cbM
61 I	Gx	0 57.1	+ 7 31 u	Psc	1.5	15p	pF, vS, R, vlbM
322	Gx	0 57.2	− 43 44 c	Phe	1.3		vF, vS, R, lbM, 3 st p
321	Gx	0 57.4	− 5 02 v	Cet			eF, vS
311	Gx	0 57.6	+ 30 16 r	Psc		14p	pF, vS, R, gbM
317	Gx	0 57.6	+ 43 47 r	And		15p	eeF, pS, lE, D* close f
1605 I	Gx	0 57.6	− 48 54 c	Phe	1.6		vF, eS, R
339	Gb	0 57.7	− 74 29 s	Tuc	2.2	11.9	F, L, R, vgbM
313	Gx	0 57.8	+ 30 21 u	Psc	3.6	12p	vF, eS, 1′ np 315
315	Gx	0 57.8	+ 30 21 s	Psc	3.2	13p	pB, pL, R, gbM, *9 nf 3′
316	Gx	0 57.8	+ 30 21 u	Psc	3.6	12p	vF, eS, stellar, 1′ f 315
325	Gx	0 57.9	− 5 08 r	Cet		16p	vF, vS
327	Gx	0 57.9	− 5 08 s	Cet	1.9	13p	F, S, E
329	Gx	0 58.0	− 5 04 s	Cet	1.9	13p	F, E
1604 I		0 58.0	− 16 15 d	Cet			pF, vS, *7.5 np, F* nr sp (= 333?)
318	Gx	0 58.1	+ 30 25 r	Psc		15p	vF, vS, R, bM
326	Gx	0 58.4	+ 26 52 s	Psc	1.5	13.2	F, lE, *9-10 sf
1606 I		0 58.4	− 12 11 d	Cet			eF, pS, nearly bet *7 p and *9 nf
324	Gx	0 58.6	− 40 30 r	Phe			(?), F, S, stellar
331	?	0 58.6	− 2 43 F	Cet			eF, vS, R, lbM, *12 nf 3′
62 I	Gx	0 58.7	+ 11 49 u	Psc	1.0	15p	vF, pL, dif
320	Gx	0 58.8	− 20 50 r	Cet		15p	vF, pS, E 160°, *10 n
332	Gx	0 58.8	+ 7 06 r	Psc		15p	vF, S, R, sev st nr S
333	Gx	0 58.8	− 16 29 r	Cet		16p	no description
334	Gx	0 58.8	− 35 08 r	Scl			vF, S, R, glbM, 2 st 11 s
336	Gx	0 58.8	− 18 46 r	Cet		12p	vF, vS, R, sbM
1607 I	Gx	0 58.9	+ 0 36 u	Cet	1.1	14p	vF, pS, R, lbM
346	C+N	0 59.1	− 72 11 s	Tuc	14	10.3	B, L, viF, mbM D*, r
335	Gx	0 59.3	− 18 14 c	Cet	1.2		vF, pS, E, bM
64 I	Gx	0 59.4	+ 27 03 u	Psc	1.3	16p	F, S, R, gmbM
1608 I	Gx	0 59.4	− 34 20 c	Scl	1.7		pB, pS, R; 2 st nf, 2 np
63 I	Nb	0 59.5	+ 60 49 s	Cas	10		pF, eL! conn with np one
1611 I		0 59.7	− 72 21 d	Tuc			vF, bM
337	Gx	0 59.8	− 7 35 s	Cet	2.8	11.6	pF, L, E, glbM, *10 f 21ˢ
1609 I	Gx	0 59.8	− 40 20 c	Phe	1.4		vF, vS, R
1612 I		1 00.0	− 72 23 d	Tuc			eF, vS
67 I		1 00.3	− 6 55 d	Cet			vF, suspected
68 I		1 00.4	− 6 57 d	Cet			vF, suspected
66 I	Gx	1 00.5	+ 30 48 u	Psc	1.1	15p	vF, vS, irr
338	Gx	1 00.6	+ 30 39 r	Psc		14p	vF, vS, iF, bM
340	Gx	1 00.6	− 6 53 r	Cet		14p	vF, S, E

NGC	Type	α_{2000}	δ_{2000}	Const.	Size	Mag.	Description
		h m	° ′		′		
341	Gx	1 00.8	− 9 11 r	Cet		13p	F, pL, R, lbM, r
342	Gx	1 00.8	− 6 47 r	Cet		14p	vF, vS
343	*	1 00.8	− 23 14 r	Cet			eF, vS, iR, sbMN (*?)
348	Gx	1 00.9	− 53 15 c	Phe	1.1		eF, S, R
65 I	Gx	1 00.9	+ 47 41 s	And	4.3	13p	eF, pL, mE, B st f & s
70 I		1 01.1	+ 0 03 d	Cet			vF, vS, lbM
71 I		1 01.3	− 6 47 d	Cet			vF, suspected
345	Gx	1 01.4	− 6 54 r	Cet		13p	vF, vS, gbM
347	Gx	1 01.4	− 6 49 r	Cet		14p	vF, vS
69 I	Gx	1 01.4	+ 31 03 z	Psc		15p	F, iF, lbM
72 I		1 01.5	− 6 46 d	Cet			neb; *7 sf 2′
344	Gx	1 01.6	− 23 16 c	Cet	0.9		eF, vS, iR, sbMN (*?)
1610 I	Gx	1 01.7	− 15 34 m	Cet	1.2	14p	pF, pS, R, *10 np
349	Gx	1 01.9	− 6 49 r	Cet		13p	vF, vS
350	Gx	1 02.0	− 6 49 r	Cet		15p	eF
351	Gx	1 02.1	− 1 55 r	Cet		14p	eF, pS, np of 2
352	Gx	1 02.1	− 4 15 s	Cet	2.7	13p	pF, S, iE, *8 f 97^s
361	Gb	1 02.2	− 71 33 s	Tuc	1.5	11.8	vvF, pL, vlE, vgbM
353	Gx	1 02.6	− 1 56 r	Cet		14p	eF, pS, R, sf of 2
360	Gx	1 02.9	− 65 37 c	Tuc	3.3		eF, vmE 145°, vlbM
355	Gx	1 03.2	− 6 20 r	Cet		15p	eF, vS
362	Gb	1 03.2	− 70 51 s	Tuc	12.9	6.6	⊕, vB, vL, vC, vmbM st 13-14
354	Gx	1 03.3	+ 22 20 s	Psc	0.9	14p	vF, vS, R, vS* inv, *14 close p
356	Gx	1 03.3	− 7 00 r	Cet		13p	vF, S, iR
371	OC	1 03.3	− 72 05 s	Tuc	8		Cl, F, L, R, pC, st 14...16
357	Gx	1 03.4	− 6 20 s	Cet	2.6	11.8	F, S, iR, sbM, *14 nf 20″
376		1 03.9	− 72 49 D	Tuc			only a D*, pos 270°, dist 10″
365	Gx	1 04.1	− 35 07 v	Scl			F, S, R, glbM
1615 I	Gx	1 04.1	− 51 08 c	Phe	1.2		eF, S, cE 140°, cbM
1617 I	Gx	1 04.3	− 51 02 c	Phe	1.5		eF, S, cE 130°, cbM
359	Gx	1 04.4	− 0 45 r	Cet		15p	eF, vS
368	Gx	1 04.4	− 43 16 r	Phe			eF, vS, *7-8 sp 3′
364	Gx	1 04.6	− 0 51 r	Cet		14p	vF, vS
1613 I	Gx	1 04.8	+ 2 07 s	Cet	12.0	9.3	F, eeL
367	?	1 04.9	− 12 09 F	Cet			eF, pS, E 175°, bn, 3 st 12 np
73 I	Gx	1 04.9	+ 4 46 z	Psc		15p	vF, pL, dif
1616 I	Gx	1 04.9	− 27 26 c	Scl	1.7		eF, pS, 3 st in line nr
369	Gx	1 05.1	− 17 45 c	Cet	1.3		vF, vS, R, gbM
1614 I		1 05.1	+ 33 13 d	Psc			vF, S, E 120°, vlbM, *15 nr
358	Ast	1 05.2	+ 62 02 r	Cas			Cl, vlRi
395		1 05.3	− 72 00 D	Tuc			group of about 10 st, no neb
1624 I		1 05.3	− 72 02 d	Tuc			vF, S, R
74 I	Gx	1 05.9	+ 4 05 z	Psc		15p	vF, S, stellar
1618 I	Gx	1 06.0	+ 32 25 u	Psc	1.2	16p	vF, S
363	Gx	1 06.1	− 16 34 r	Cet		15p	eF, eS, R
1626 I		1 06.1	− 73 17 d	Tuc			vF, cS, R
378	Gx	1 06.2	− 30 11 r	Scl		14p	vF, S, R, gbM
377	*·*	1 06.3	− 20 03 F	Cet			vF, vS, mE, sbMN
366	OC	1 06.4	+ 62 14 s	Cas	3		Cl, S
1621 I		1 06.4	− 46 43 d	Phe			eF, eS, mE 0°, cbM
370	−	1 06.6	+ 32 25 r	Psc			vF, *13 s 15″, dif
372	*·*	1 06.7	+ 32 26 r	Psc			stellar, mbM, r
373	Gx	1 07.0	+ 32 18 r	Psc			vF, vS
374	Gx	1 07.1	+ 32 46 r	Psc		14p	F, S, bet 2 st 15
375	Gx	1 07.1	+ 32 21 s	Psc	1.3	16p	vF, vS

NGC	Type	α_{2000}	δ_{2000}	Const.	Size	Mag.	Description
		h m	o ′		′		
1620 I	Gx	1 07.1	+ 13 58 u	Psc	1.2	14p	F, pS, dif
75 I	Gx	1 07.2	+ 10 51 u	Psc	1.6	15p	vF, vS, dif, vlbM
379	Gx	1 07.3	+ 32 31 s	Psc	1.8	12.6	pF, S, R, bM
380	Gx	1 07.3	+ 32 29 s	Psc	1.6	12.5	pF, S, R, sbM
382	Gx	1 07.4	+ 32 24 s	Psc	0.4	14p	vF, S, R, sp of D neb
383	Gx	1 07.4	+ 32 25 s	Psc	2.3	11.9	pF, pL, R, gbM, nf of D neb
384	Gx	1 07.4	+ 32 18 s	Psc	1.1	13.0	pF, pS, sp of 2
385	Gx	1 07.4	+ 32 19 s	Psc	1.5	12.9	pF, pS, R, nf of 2
406	Gx	1 07.4	− 69 53 s	Tuc	3.8	12p	F, vL, vglbM, bN with eE wisps 165°
1619 I	Gx	1 07.4	+ 33 04 z	Psc		15p	F, S, R, gbMFN, bet 2 st 13
386	Gx	1 07.5	+ 32 22 v	Psc	0.9	14.1	cF, S, R
387	Gx	1 07.5	+ 32 23 r	Psc			vF, S, R
391	Gx	1 07.5	+ 0 56 r	Cet		14p	F, S, r
1622 I		1 07.5	− 17 30 d	Cet			vF, S, R, sp of 2
1623 I		1 07.7	− 17 28 d	Cet			B, cS, lE, nf of 2
1625 I	Gx	1 07.7	− 46 54 c	Phe	2.1		eF, vS, R, susp
388	Gx	1 07.8	+ 32 19 v	Psc	0.8	14.3	vF, S, R
411		1 07.9	− 71 46 D	Tuc			cB, S, R, stellar
396	Gx	1 08.0	+ 4 32 A	Psc			eF, S, lE
390	Gx	1 08.1	+ 32 27 r	Psc			vF, vS, stellar
416	Gb	1 08.1	− 72 21 s	Tuc	1.1	11.0	F, pS, R, gbM
76 I	Gx	1 08.2	− 4 32 m	Cet	0.7	15p	F, vS, R, lbM
1627 I	Gx	1 08.2	− 46 06 c	Phe	2.5		cF, S, eE 135°, vmbM
381	OC	1 08.3	+ 61 35 s	Cas	6	9p	Cl, pC
405	D*	1 08.3	− 46 40 r	Phe			eS, stellar, = *7
419	Gb	1 08.3	− 72 53 s	Tuc	2.6	10.0	pB, pL, R, gbM
1630 I	Gx	1 08.3	− 46 45 c	Phe	1.7		eF, eS, E 60°, susp
392	Gx	1 08.4	+ 33 07 r	Psc		14p	F, vS, R, mbM, bet 2 st
394	Gx	1 08.4	+ 33 08 r	Psc		15p	F, S, 50″ nf 392
389	Gx	1 08.5	+ 39 42 r	And		15p	eF, eS, R, * nr
397	Gx	1 08.5	+ 33 06 r	Psc		15p	eF, S, R, vF* p
393	Gx	1 08.6	+ 39 40 r	And		13p	F, vS, vlE, gbM, 4 S st nr
77 I	Gx	1 08.7	− 15 25 x	Cet			vF, S, irr, bM
398	Gx	1 08.8	+ 32 30 r	Psc		15p	vF, vS, stellar
78 I	Gx	1 08.8	− 15 51 x	Cet			F, S, lbM, r
79 I	Gx	1 08.8	− 15 57 v	Cet	0.7		R, S, bM N = 14m
1628 I	Gx	1 08.8	− 28 35 c	Scl	1.4		cB, pS, R, 3 st 8 nr
1631 I	Gx	1 08.8	− 46 29 c	Phe	1.3		eF, S, R, susp
422		1 08.9	− 71 46 D	Tuc			only 3 eF st, close, in SMC
80 I	Gx	1 08.9	− 15 24 x	Cet			vF, S, R, gbM
399	Gx	1 09.0	+ 32 37 r	Psc		14p	vF, S, R
400	−	1 09.0	+ 32 44 r	Psc			eF, vS, 403 f
401	−	1 09.1	+ 32 46 r	Psc			eF, stellar, 403 f
82 I	Gx	1 09.1	− 16 00 x	Cet			F, S, gbM
402	−	1 09.2	+ 32 49 r	Psc			eF, vS, R, 403 s 3′
403	Gx	1 09.2	+ 32 45 s	Psc	2.1	13p	vF, pS, cE, *11 s 85″
81 I		1 09.2	− 1 41 D	Cet			eF, S, lE, * 1′ sff
1644 I		1 09.2	− 73 12 d	Tuc			◯ , stell
1641 I		1 09.3	− 71 46 x	Tuc			eF, eS, R; = 422
404	Gx	1 09.4	+ 35 43 s	And	4.4	10.1	pB, cL, R, gbM, β And sf
1629 I	Gx	1 09.4	+ 2 34 z	Cet		16p	F, vS, R, stell
409	Gx	1 09.5	− 35 48 c	Scl	1.5		eF, S, R, vS* nr
413	Gx	1 09.5	− 2 50 r	Cet		16p	eF, pS, vlE
1633 I	Gx	1 09.9	− 45 56 c	Phe	3.0		vF, S, R, vF* f
415	Gx	1 10.2	− 35 29 r	Scl			vF, S, R, glbM

NGC	Type	α_{2000}	δ_{2000}	Const.	Size	Mag.	Description
		h m	° ′		′		
412	−	1 10.3	− 20 01 *r*	Cet			vF, eS, R, sbMN (neb?)
83 I	Gx	1 10.5	+ 1 41 *m*	Cet	0.5	15*p*	F, S, dif, lbM
407	Gx	1 10.6	+ 33 07 *s*	Psc	2.0	14*p*	vF, vS, sp of 2
418	Gx	1 10.6	− 30 13 *s*	Scl	2.3	13*p*	F, pL, R, vglbM, p of 2
1632 I		1 10.7	+ 17 41 *d*	Psc			vF, vS, dif, *15 v close
408	Gx	1 10.9	+ 33 06 *A*	Psc			vF, vS, 410 f 8ˢ
410	Gx	1 11.0	+ 33 09 *s*	Psc	2.6	13*p*	pB, pL, nf of 2
1637 I	Gx	1 11.0	− 30 26 *c*	Scl	1.8		eF, S, R, susp
417	Gx	1 11.1	− 18 10 *r*	Cet		15*p*	eF, eS, R
1634 I		1 11.1	+ 17 39 *d*	Psc			F, S, R, gbM, r
1635 I		1 11.1	+ 17 39 *d*	Psc			F, S, R, gbM, r
414	Gx	1 11.3	+ 33 06 *r*	Psc		14*p*	vF, S, iR, mbM, 410 np
423	Gx	1 11.4	− 29 13 *r*	Scl		14*p*	eF, S, E, glbM, f of 2
424	Gx	1 11.5	− 38 05 *c*	Scl	2.1		vF, S, R, glbM
84 I	Gx	1 11.5	+ 1 39 *z*	Cet		15*p*	pB, S, iF, bM
1636 I		1 11.6	+ 33 21 *d*	Psc			F, vS, gbMN
432	Gx	1 11.8	− 61 32 *c*	Tuc	1.5		F, S, R, gbM, *12 f
85 I		1 11.8	− 0 28 *d*	Cet			eF, close to *8
1639 I	Gx	1 11.8	− 0 39 *s*	Cet	0.8	14*p*	vS, R, stell
1649 I	Gx	1 11.8	− 55 51 *c*	Phe	1.6		eF, cS, E 140°, cbM
1640 I	Gx	1 11.9	− 0 37 *z*	Cet		15*p*	vS, R, bMN
1655 I	OC	1 11.9	− 71 20 *z*	Tuc			Cl, C, eF, vS
420	Gx	1 12.1	+ 32 06 *r*	Psc		13*p*	F, pS, R, bM
421	−	1 12.1	+ 32 09 *r*	Psc			eF, vS
434	Gx	1 12.2	− 58 15 *s*	Tuc	1.9	13*p*	B, S, R, psbM
1643 I	Gx	1 12.2	− 0 24 *z*	Cet		15*p*	F, S, R, gbM
1638 I	Gx	1 12.3	+ 33 21 *m*	Psc	0.4	15*p*	F, vS, R, gbMN, r
1650 I	Gx	1 12.3	− 50 24 *c*	Phe	1.5		cF, S, mE 55°, cbM
1642 I		1 12.4	+ 15 45 *d*	Psc			F, S, R, lbMN
427	Gx	1 12.4	− 32 03 *r*	Scl		15*p*	3 vS st with neby (?)
1645 I		1 12.5	+ 15 44 *d*	Psc			F, S, R, dif
1660 I		1 12.6	− 71 45 *d*	Tuc			eF, vS, R, stell N or F* in M
1662 I	OC	1 12.6	− 73 27 *z*	Tuc			vF, eS; vS Cl?
1646 I	Gx	1 12.7	+ 15 41 *m*	Psc	0.5	15*p*	vF, pS, dif
426	Gx	1 12.9	− 0 17 *r*	Cet		14*p*	vF, vS, R
428	Gx	1 12.9	+ 0 59 *s*	Cet	4.1	11.4	F, L, R, bM, er
440	Gx	1 12.9	− 58 17 *s*	Tuc	1.0		F, vS, R
425	Gx	1 13.0	+ 38 48 *r*	And		13*p*	vF, vS, R, lbM, *11 att
429	Gx	1 13.0	− 0 20 *r*	Cet		14*p*	vF, vS
430	Gx	1 13.1	− 0 15 *r*	Cet		13*p*	F, vS, R, vsbM *
1647 I	Gx	1 13.2	+ 38 53 *z*	And		15*p*	vF, S, R, diffic
438	Gx	1 13.4	− 37 56 *r*	Scl			pF, S, R, glbM
86 I	Gx	1 13.5	− 16 14 *z*	Cet			F, sbM
1651 I		1 13.5	+ 2 06 *d*	Cet			*13 with neb, chiefly nnf
1648 I		1 13.7	+ 33 13 *d*	Psc			F, vS, R, N, r
439	Gx	1 13.8	− 31 45 *s*	Scl		13*p*	pB, S, R, gbM
435	Gx	1 14.0	+ 2 04 *r*	Cet		15*p*	eF, S, E
441	Gx	1 14.0	− 31 47 *r*	Scl		14*p*	pF, S, R, gbM
1657 I	Gx	1 14.1	− 32 39 *c*	Scl	2.1		eF, S, vmE
1663 I		1 14.1	− 32 39 *c*	Scl			eF, mE 350°; = IC 1657
431	Gx	1 14.2	+ 33 44 *r*	And		14*p*	F, S, vsbM
87 I	Gx	1 14.3	+ 0 46 *z*	Cet		15*p*	F, pS, R, dif
1664 I	?	1 14.3	− 69 48 *z*	Tuc			2 F st inv in eeF neb
437	Gx	1 14.4	+ 5 56 *r*	Psc		14*p*	pF, vS, R, F* np
454	Gx	1 14.4	− 55 24 *c*	Phe	1.9		vF, S, R, bM

NGC	Type	α_{2000}	δ_{2000}	Const.	Size	Mag.	Description
		h m	° ′		′		
456	Nb	1 14.4	− 73 17 s	Tuc	15		pF, pL, iR, r, 1st of sev
88 I		1 14.5	+ 0 48 d	Cet			pF, S, R, vlbM
442	Gx	1 14.6	− 1 01 s	Cet	1.2	15p	vF, S, R, B∗ sf
460	C+N	1 14.8	− 72 18 r	Tuc			F, pL, iR, gbM, r, 2nd of sev
445	Gx	1 14.9	+ 1 56 r	Cet		15p	vF, vS
446	Gx	1 14.9	+ 4 11 r	Psc		15p	F, vS, stellar; = IC 89
458		1 14.9	− 71 33 D	Tuc			prob Cl, eS, close, no neb
1652 I	Gx	1 15.0	+ 31 58 u	Psc	1.4	14p	F, S, E ns, ∗12 v close
443	Gx	1 15.1	+ 33 23 r	Psc		14p	F, S, R, ∗15 p 8ˢon parallel
1653 I	Gx	1 15.1	+ 33 23 s	Psc	1.1	13.5	F, vS, R, gbMN, r
1654 I	Gx	1 15.2	+ 30 12 u	Psc	1.6	14p	F, S, lE, gblM, r
433	OC	1 15.3	+ 60 08 s	Cas	3		Cl, S, lC
448	Gx	1 15.3	− 1 37 r	Cet		13p	pB, vS, lE
450	Gx	1 15.5	− 0 52 s	Cet	3.2	12.1	vF, L
465	OC	1 15.5	− 73 20 D	Tuc			many st, no neb, perhaps Cl
436	OC	1 15.6	+ 58 49 s	Cas	6	8.8	Cl, S, iF, pC
447	Gx	1 15.6	+ 33 04 v	Psc	2.6	14.0	F, pL, bM, ∗11 nf
1656 I		1 15.6	+ 33 05 x	Psc			neb, S∗ close sf, ∗9 sf 3′; = 447
1658 I		1 15.8	+ 31 05 x	Psc			vF, pS, E, N, r; = 444
444	Gx	1 15.9	+ 31 05 r	Psc		14p	vF, mE 135°, lbM; = IC 1658
455	Gx	1 16.0	+ 5 11 r	Psc		14p	F, vS, alm stell
449	Gx	1 16.1	+ 33 05 v	Psc	0.7	14.3	vF, vS, R, vlbM, vF st inv
89 I	Gx	1 16.1	+ 4 18 v	Psc	2.3		F, S, iF, N = 13m; 462 f; = 446?
1659 I	Gx	1 16.1	+ 30 21 u	Psc	1.6	15p	F, S, R, N, r
451	Gx	1 16.2	+ 33 04 r	Psc		15p	vF, vS, R, vlbM; = IC 1661
1661 I		1 16.2	+ 33 05 x	Psc			eF, S, R; = 451
452	Gx	1 16.3	+ 31 02 r	Psc		14p	vF, E, ∗9 np, S∗ nf, vnr
453	∗∗∗	1 16.3	+ 33 05 A	Psc			vF, vS, R, vF st inv
90 I	Gx	1 16.5	− 7 58 m	Cet	0.5	14p	B, vS, sbMN
466	Gx	1 17.2	− 58 55 c	Tuc	2.1		vF, pS, R, gbM
461	Gx	1 17.3	− 33 50 c	Scl	1.2		pB, R, glbM
1667 I		1 17.6	− 17 07 d	Cet			eF, pS, R
1665 I		1 17.7	+ 34 42 d	And			F, vS, R, like 2 or 3 F st in neb
459	Gx	1 18.0	+ 17 33 r	Psc		15p	eF
462	Gx	1 18.1	+ 4 14 r	Psc			eF, vS, stellar
1666 I		1 18.5	+ 32 28 d	Psc			F, pS, dif, ∗13 att
91 I		1 18.7	+ 2 33 d	Cet			F, S, r, N = 14m
1668 I	Gx	1 18.8	+ 33 11 z	Psc		16p	eF, vS, R, vFN
463	Gx	1 18.9	+ 16 19 r	Psc		15p	eF, vS, R, lbM
464	Gx	1 19.0	+ 34 58 r	And			S
93 I	Gx	1 19.0	− 17 04 m	Cet	1.2	14p	vF, pS, lE, ∗8 f 14ˢ, 1′ n
1674 I		1 19.0	− 50 39 d	Phe			eF, eS, bM, 2 spir wisps
457	OC	1 19.1	+ 58 20 s	Cas	13	6.4	Cl, B, L, pRi, st 7, 8, 10
467	Gx	1 19.2	+ 3 18 s	Psc	2.4	11.9	pB, pL, R, gbM
1670 I		1 19.2	− 16 51 d	Cet			vF, pS, lE, 2 st nr nf
95 I		1 19.3	− 12 34 d	Cet			F, vS, dif, vlbM
469	Gx	1 19.4	+ 14 53 r	Psc		15p	eF, S, R
484	Gx	1 19.6	− 58 31 c	Tuc	2.2		vB, S, lE, psmbM
1671 I		1 19.6	− 17 06 d	Cet			eF, vS, R, ∗7 nf 47ˢ
470	Gx	1 19.7	+ 3 25 s	Psc	3.0	11.9	pB, L, iR
468	Gx	1 19.8	+ 32 47 r	Psc		15p	vF, eS, stellar
471	Gx	1 19.9	+ 14 47 r	Psc		14p	neb ∗12
473	Gx	1 19.9	+ 16 33 s	Psc	2.2	13p	eF, S
92 I	Gx	1 19.9	+ 32 46 m	Psc	0.7	15p	eeF (different from 468?)
475	Gx	1 20.0	+ 14 51 r	Psc			eF, S

NGC	Type	α_{2000}	δ_{2000}	Const.	Size	Mag.	Description
		h　m	°　′		′		
97 I		1 20.0	+ 14 51 d	Psc			stellar = 13.5m
474	Gx	1 20.1	+ 3 25 s	Psc	7.9	11.1	pB, S, smbM, f of 2
94 I		1 20.1	+ 32 42 d	Psc			neb *13
1669 I	Gx	1 20.1	+ 33 12 z	Psc		16p	vF, S, dif
476	Gx	1 20.2	+ 16 01 r	Psc		15p	eF, vS, stellar
478	Gx	1 20.2	− 22 22 r	Cet		15p	eF, eS, R, sbMN
482	Gx	1 20.3	− 40 57 r	Phe			eF, lE
96 I		1 20.3	+ 29 40 d	Psc			pB, pS, vmbMN = 12m
472	Gx	1 20.5	+ 32 43 r	Psc		14p	eF, vS, *9-10 p 14^s, v diff
1672 I	Gx	1 20.7	+ 29 42 u	Psc	1.8	14p	pB, S, R, gbMN, r
1673 I		1 20.8	+ 33 01 d	Psc			F, R, stell N
480		1 20.9	− 9 52 F	Cet			eF, vS, R (neb?); = 481?
481	Gx	1 21.0	− 9 12 r	Cet		14p	vF, vS, R, F* np
98 I	Gx	1 21.0	− 12 37 m	Cet	0.6	15p	vF, vS, iF, bM
1675 I	Gx	1 21.0	+ 34 16 u	And	0.8	14p	F, S
1676 I	Gx	1 21.0	+ 30 16 z	Psc		16p	F, vS, stell N
1678 I	Gx	1 21.0	+ 5 34 z	Psc		15p	F, vS, R, stell
1677 I	Gx	1 21.2	+ 33 14 m	Psc	0.9	15p	F, pS, R, bMN
477	Gx	1 21.3	+ 40 29 r	And		14p	vF, pS, vlE, vglbM
479	Gx	1 21.3	+ 3 52 r	Psc		15p	eF, S, R
485	Gx	1 21.4	+ 7 01 s	Psc	1.9	14p	cF, pL, R, *8 sp 3′.5
491	Gx	1 21.4	− 34 03 s	Scl	1.5	13p	B, S, vlE, bM, vS* nr
1681 I	Gx	1 21.4	+ 0 05 z	Cet		15p	F, S, R, gbM, r
487	Gx	1 21.8	− 16 21 r	Cet		14p	eF, vS, R
488	Gx	1 21.8	+ 5 15 s	Psc	5.2	10.3	pB, L, R, svmbM, *8 f 10′
489	Gx	1 21.8	+ 9 12 r	Psc		13p	pB, S, E
1679 I	Gx	1 21.8	+ 33 28 m	Psc	0.5	15p	F, S, iF, vlbM, dif
1680 I	Gx	1 21.9	+ 33 18 m	Psc	0.6	15p	F, vS, bMN
483	Gx	1 22.0	+ 33 32 r	Psc		14p	vF, vS
486	Gx	1 22.1	+ 5 24 r	Psc		15p	eF, eS, stell, 5′ n of 488
490	Gx	1 22.1	+ 5 22 r	Psc		15p	vF, vS, R, 8′ nf 488
492	Gx	1 22.2	+ 5 25 r	Psc		15p	eF, vS, R
493	Gx	1 22.2	+ 0 57 s	Cet	3.8	12.5	vF, L, mE 60°, lbM
1682 I		1 22.2	+ 33 13 d	Psc			F, vS, R, stell
497	Gx	1 22.4	− 0 53 s	Cet	2.4	14p	eF, pS, R, vlbM, r
99 I	Gx	1 22.5	− 12 57 m	Cet	0.5	15p	vF, S, lbM
1683 I	Gx	1 22.6	+ 34 27 u	And	1.7	14p	F, S, E ns, gbM, r
500	Gx	1 22.7	+ 5 24 r	Psc		15p	vF, vS, mbM, *11 nf 1′
502	Gx	1 22.8	+ 9 03 r	Psc		14p	cB, S, R, bMN
495	Gx	1 22.9	+ 33 28 s	Psc	1.5	13.2	vF, S, 1st of 3
505	Gx	1 22.9	+ 9 28 r	Psc		15p	vF, vS, stellar
100 I		1 22.9	− 4 39 d	Cet			F, vS, R, N = 12.5m
1684 I		1 22.9	+ 33 23 d	Psc			F, S, R, dif
494	Gx	1 23.0	+ 33 11 r	Psc		14p	vF, pL, E, 3 F st s
1685 I	Gx	1 23.0	+ 33 11 m	Psc	1.9	13p	F, S, R, vlbM, dif
499	Gx	1 23.2	+ 33 28 s	Psc	2.0	12.0	pB, pL, R, 3rd of 3; = IC 1686
1686 I		1 23.2	+ 33 26 z	Psc			pB, pS, lE pf, gbMN; = 499
496	Gx	1 23.3	+ 33 33 r	Psc		14p	vF, vS, 2nd of 3
498	Gx	1 23.3	+ 33 30 r	Psc		16p	eeF, np 499
501	Gx	1 23.4	+ 33 27 r	Psc		15p	vF, S
509	Gx	1 23.4	+ 9 26 s	Psc	1.7	15p	vF, S, E
1687 I	Gx	1 23.4	+ 33 17 m	Psc	0.4	16p	F, vS, R, bMN
1688 I		1 23.4	+ 33 04 d	Psc			F, vS, R, bMN
503	Gx	1 23.5	+ 33 21 r	Psc		15p	eF, eS, D* 4′ sp
504	Gx	1 23.5	+ 33 13 r	Psc		14p	vF, S

NGC	Type	α_{2000}	δ_{2000}	Const.	Size	Mag.	Description
		h m	o ′		′		
511	Gx	1 23.5	+ 11 17 r	Psc		15p	eF, vS, S∗ inv, S∗ att
506	−	1 23.6	+ 33 14 r	Psc			vF, vS, sp 507; = 504?
507	Gx	1 23.7	+ 33 15 s	Psc	4.3	11.2	vF, pL, R, bM, s of 2
508	Gx	1 23.7	+ 33 17 s	Psc	1.6	12.8	vF, S, n of 2
510	Gx	1 23.7	+ 33 26 r	Psc			vF, vS, lE
513	Gx	1 23.8	+ 33 49 r	And		13p	F, S, stellar
1689 I	Gx	1 23.8	+ 33 04 m	Psc	0.7	15p	F, vS, R, gbMN, ∗14 close
1690 I	Gx	1 23.8	+ 33 10 z	Psc		15p	F, vS, R, stell
526	Gx	1 23.9	− 35 03 r	Scl			F, S, E, p of 2
512	Gx	1 24.0	+ 33 55 r	And		14p	vF, vS
527	Gx	1 24.0	− 35 06 r	Scl			F, S, lE, bM, f of 2
1693 I	Gx	1 24.0	− 1 39 z	Cet			eF, vS, possibly F∗
514	Gx	1 24.1	+ 12 55 s	Psc	3.5	11.9	F, L, lE, vglbM, ∗̣ f
516	Gx	1 24.1	+ 9 33 s	Psc	1.6	14p	eF, S, v diffic, 524 f 41ˢ
101 I	Gx	1 24.1	+ 9 56 u	Psc	1.6	15p	vF, pL, E, dif
518	Gx	1 24.3	+ 9 20 s	Psc	1.9	14p	F, vS, R
102 I	Gx	1 24.4	+ 9 54 u	Psc	1.0	16p	eF, S, dif
519	Gx	1 24.5	− 1 38 v	Cet			eeF, vS, R, v diffic
1691 I		1 24.5	+ 33 23 d	Psc			pF, vS, R, dif
515	Gx	1 24.6	+ 33 29 r	Psc		14p	pF, vS, R, np of 2
520	Gx	1 24.6	+ 3 48 s	Psc	4.8	11.2	F, cL, E 137°
521	Gx	1 24.6	+ 1 44 s	Cet	3.4	13p	F, pL, R, gbM
534	Gx	1 24.6	− 38 07 r	Scl			eeF, S, R, vgbM, 1st of 4
103 I	Gx	1 24.6	+ 2 02 u	Cet	1.4	15p	F, vS, R
104 I	D∗	1 24.6	− 1 27 z	Cet			stellar 13m
1692 I	Gx	1 24.6	+ 33 15 z	Psc		16p	F, vS, R, gbM, r
517	Gx	1 24.7	+ 33 27 r	Psc		13p	pF, R, stellar, sf of 2
530	Gx	1 24.7	− 1 35 A	Cet	1.9	14p	eF, S, mE, F∗ sf; = IC 106
105 I	Gx	1 24.7	+ 2 05 z	Cet		16p	F, eS, R, lbM
106 I		1 24.7	− 1 35 z	Cet			vF, S, dif, lbM; = 530
108 I	Gx	1 24.7	− 12 38 m	Cet	0.8	15p	F, pL, E ns
522	Gx	1 24.8	+ 10 00 s	Psc	2.8	14p	eF, pL, iF; Cl + neb?
524	Gx	1 24.8	+ 9 32 s	Psc	3.2	10.6	vB, pL, mbM, 4 S st nr
525	Gx	1 24.8	+ 9 42 r	Psc		14p	vF, vS, ∗11-12 p 5ˢ
1694 I	Gx	1 24.8	+ 1 36 z	Cet		15p	vF, S, mbM
1696 I	Gx	1 24.9	− 1 37 v	Cet	1.4		eF, eS, 530 np
1708 I		1 24.9	− 71 11 d	Hyi			vF, vS, R, ∗9 sf 4′
1695 I		1 25.0	+ 8 44 d	Psc			eF, pS, R, ∗10 att p
544	Gx	1 25.1	− 38 05 r	Scl			eeF, S, R, vgbM, 2nd of 4
546	Gx	1 25.1	− 38 03 r	Scl			eeF, S, R, vgbM, 3rd of 4
1697 I	Gx	1 25.1	+ 0 27 z	Cet		15p	F, vS, R, gbM
107 I	Gx	1 25.2	+ 14 53 u	Psc	1.2	15p	vF, vS, R, ∗ close p
109 I	Gx	1 25.2	+ 2 04 u	Cet	1.3	15p	pB, vS, R
523	Gx	1 25.3	+ 34 02 s	And	3.1	14p	Dneb, vF, vS, pos 90°, dist 30″
532	Gx	1 25.3	+ 9 16 s	Psc	2.8	14p	vF, pL, E 30°, bM
539	Gx	1 25.3	− 18 09 s	Cet	1.8	14p	vF, vS, R
538	Gx	1 25.4	− 1 33 s	Cet	1.3	15p	eF, S, mE, F∗ n
1698 I		1 25.4	+ 14 51 d	Psc			pB, S, iF, bMN
1699 I		1 25.4	+ 14 57 d	Psc			vF, vS, R, gbM
528	Gx	1 25.5	+ 33 41 r	And		13p	F, pL, R, lbM
533	Gx	1 25.5	+ 1 46 s	Cet	3.7	13p	pB, pL, R, gbM
535	Gx	1 25.5	− 1 25 s	Cet	1.3	15p	vF, vS, 1st of 3
549	Gx	1 25.5	− 38 16 c	Scl	2.0		eeF, S, R, vgbM, 4th of 4
1700 I		1 25.5	+ 14 52 d	Psc			pB, S, R, gbMN
529	Gx	1 25.7	+ 34 44 r	And		13p	pB, vS, sbM, p of 2

NGC	Type	α_{2000}	δ_{2000}	Const.	Size	Mag.	Description
		h m	° ′		′		
541	Gx	1 25.7	− 1 23 s	Cet	2.7	12.0	F, S, R, bM
543	Gx	1 25.8	− 1 18 s	Cet	0.7	13.3	eF, eS
1701 I	Gx	1 25.8	+ 18 11 u	Psc	1.6	15p	F, S, dif, N 13m
110 I		1 25.9	+ 33 30 d	Psc			vF
1702 I	Gx	1 25.9	+ 16 36 u	Psc	1.5	14p	eeF, pS, lE, v diffic, bet 2 st ns
545	Gx	1 26.0	− 1 20 s	Cet	3.0	14p	stellar, p of Dneb
547	Gx	1 26.0	− 1 21 s	Cet	1.7	12.3	stellar, f of Dneb
548	Gx	1 26.0	− 1 14 v	Cet	1.5		eF, eS
111 I		1 26.0	+ 33 29 d	Psc			*13 with neb
112 I	Gx	1 26.0	+ 11 27 u	Psc	0.9	14p	F, S, dif, E pf
531	Gx	1 26.3	+ 34 45 r	And		15p	F, S, R
537	−	1 26.3	+ 34 05 r	And			stellar; = 523?
114 I	Gx	1 26.3	+ 9 56 u	Psc	1.6	16p	eF, vS, R
536	Gx	1 26.4	+ 34 43 s	And	3.7	13p	pB, pL, gbM, f of 2
113 I		1 26.4	+ 19 12 d	Psc			vF, 3′ nf of *5
1703 I	Gx	1 26.4	− 1 38 v	Cet	2.3		eF, S, dif
542	Gx	1 26.5	+ 34 41 r	And		15p	eF, diffic
557	Gx	1 26.5	− 1 38 F	Cet		15p	eF, S, R, *10 nf; = IC 1703
550	Gx	1 26.7	+ 2 01 s	Cet	1.7	14p	F, S, E 90°, bM, r
1705 I		1 26.7	− 3 30 d	Cet			neb *12, FD* nf 2′
116 I		1 26.8	− 4 59 d	Cet			F, S, R, lbM
567	Gx	1 26.9	− 10 15 r	Cet		14p	eF, vS, R
115 I	Gx	1 26.9	+ 19 13 v	Psc	0.6	14.2	vF, *6 3′.5 npp
1704 I		1 26.9	+ 14 43 d	Psc			pB, pS, dif, iF, gvlbM
540	Gx	1 27.1	− 20 02 c	Cet	1.4		vF, vS, R, sbMN
563	Gx	1 27.1	− 18 38 r	Cet		14p	vF, pS, lE, bMN, sev F st nr
554	Gx	1 27.2	− 22 43 r	Cet		15p	eF, vS, E, 1st of 3, *11 f
555	Gx	1 27.2	− 22 45 r	Cet		15p	eF, S, iR, 2nd of 3
556		1 27.2	− 22 42 D	Cet			eF, vS, R, 3rd of 3
1706 I	Gx	1 27.2	+ 14 47 v	Psc	1.4		F, S, dif, vlbM
558	Gx	1 27.3	− 1 58 v	Cet	0.7		eF, S, E, *10 p; = IC 117
560	Gx	1 27.4	− 1 55 s	Cet	2.3	12.9	vF, vS, iE, p of 2
117 I	*	1 27.4	− 1 52 z	Cet			pF, S, dif, 560 sf
551	Gx	1 27.6	+ 37 11 r	And		13p	vF, S, E, vglbM, *13 nr
118 I		1 27.6	− 5 00 d	Cet			vF, vS, R, lbM
552	−	1 27.8	+ 33 28 r	Psc			vS, stellar, p of 2; RA?
553	−	1 27.8	+ 33 28 r	Psc			vS, stellar, f of 2; RA?
564	Gx	1 27.8	− 1 53 s	Cet	1.8	12.5	vF, vS, iF, f of 2
568	Gx	1 27.9	− 35 43 r	Scl			vF, S, R
119 I	Gx	1 27.9	− 2 03 v	Cet	1.6		F, E pf, dif, 564 n
1709 I	Gx	1 27.9	− 35 43 c	Scl	2.7		eF, pS, R, v diffic; = 568
561	Gx	1 28.2	+ 34 19 r	And		14p	eF, pL, R
565	Gx	1 28.2	− 1 18 s	Cet	1.6	15p	S, E (biN?)
120 I	Gx	1 28.2	− 1 55 v	Cet			F, S, dif
122 I		1 28.2	− 14 50 d	Cet			pB, S, bM
562	Gx	1 28.4	+ 48 23 s	And	1.5	15p	eF, pS, R, D* nr s
121 I	Gx	1 28.4	+ 2 31 u	Cet	1.2	14p	F, S, R, gbM
572	Gx	1 28.6	− 39 18 r	Scl			eF, S, att to S*, B* nr
123 I	Gx	1 28.8	+ 2 27 m	Cet	0.4	15p	F, S, R, sbM
1707 I		1 28.8	+ 33 36 d	Psc			eF, dif, *13.3 close
576	Gx	1 28.9	− 51 36 c	Phe	1.2		F, S, R, bM, am st 11
566	Gx	1 29.0	+ 32 21 r	Psc		14p	vF, S, R
570	Gx	1 29.0	− 0 57 s	Cet	2.5	14p	vF, pL, R, mbMN
574	Gx	1 29.0	− 35 35 r	Scl			vS, D* pos 225°inv
569	Gx	1 29.1	+ 11 09 r	Psc		14p	eF, vS, R

NGC	Type	α_{2000}	δ_{2000}	Const.	Size	Mag.	Description
		h m	° ′		′		
124 I	*	1 29.2	− 1 56 x	Cet			vF, vS, dif
125 I	Gx	1 29.3	− 13 18 m	Cet	0.4	15p	vF, vS, R, lbM
559	OC	1 29.5	+ 63 18 s	Cas	4	9.5	Cl, B, pL, pRi
602	C+N	1 29.6	− 73 33 r	Hyi			B, S, R, psbM*, r
583	Gx	1 29.7	− 18 19 r	Cet		15p	eF, S, R
126 I	Gx	1 29.8	− 1 59 x	Cet		16p	eF, stellar, 557 f
127 I	Gx	1 29.8	− 6 59 v	Cet	2.1		F, pS, dif, *11.5 close
571	Gx	1 29.9	+ 32 31 r	Psc		15p	vF, pS, *13-14 sp
578	Gx	1 30.5	− 22 40 s	Cet	4.8	10.9	B, L, pmE, gpmbM
577	Gx	1 30.7	− 1 59 r	Cet		14p	F
580		1 30.7	− 2 00 D	Cet			pF, pS, R; = 577
575	Gx	1 30.8	+ 21 26 r	Psc		14p	eF, pL, iR; = IC 1710
1710 I		1 30.8	+ 21 26 x	Psc			F, pL, dif, *13.5 att; = 575
573	Gx	1 30.9	+ 41 16 r	And		13p	vF, vS, R, gbM
1711 I	Gx	1 30.9	+ 17 11 u	Psc	2.7	15p	F, pL, E 260°, gbM
584	Gx	1 31.3	− 6 52 s	Cet	3.8	10.4	vB, pL, R, mbM, p of 2; = IC 1712
128 I	Gx	1 31.3	− 12 38 m	Cet	0.8	14p	F, R, S, N
1712 I		1 31.4	− 6 52 x	Cet			no descr; = 584
130 I		1 31.5	− 15 35 d	Cet			vF, S, dif
586	Gx	1 31.6	− 6 54 s	Cet	1.6	13.2	vF, vS, R
129 I	Gx	1 31.6	− 12 41 m	Cet	1.0	14p	F, pL, R, dif
579	Gx	1 31.7	+ 33 38 r	Tri		13p	vF, pL, gbM
585	Gx	1 31.7	− 0 55 r	Cet		14p	vF, S, R, bM
582	Gx	1 31.9	+ 33 30 r	Tri		13p	vF, pL, pmE, *12 p
597	Gx	1 32.2	− 33 29 r	Scl			F, S, R, bM
593	Gx	1 32.3	− 12 21 r	Cet		14p	vS Cl, lE, nebulous
587	Gx	1 32.5	+ 35 22 r	Tri		13p	vvF, S, S Cl?
1717 I		1 32.5	− 67 32 d	Hyi			eF, eS, mE 25°, stell N
589	Gx	1 32.6	− 12 02 r	Cet		14p	vF, S, R, gbMN, *10 sp 2′
588	Kt	1 32.7	+ 30 40 r	Tri			F, p of 2
1713 I	Gx	1 32.7	+ 35 20 m	Tri	2.2	13p	*13, nebs ?
599	Gx	1 32.8	− 12 11 r	Cet		13p	F, S, iF, er
141 I	Gx	1 32.8	− 14 49 m	Cet	1.0	14p	pB, S, R, N 11.5 excentr
596	Gx	1 32.9	− 7 02 s	Cet	3.5	10.9	pB, R, bM, R, *6 f 12′
1714 I		1 32.9	− 13 30 d	Cet			eeF, S, lE, v dif, *8 n
594	Gx	1 33.0	− 16 32 r	Cet		14p	F, pS, E, glbM
138 I	Gx	1 33.0	− 0 42 u	Cet	1.4	15p	no description
600	Gx	1 33.1	− 7 19 s	Cet	3.5	12.4	eeF
581	OC	1 33.2	+ 60 42 s	Cas	6	7.4	Cl, pL, B, R, Ri, st 10...11; = M103
592	Kt	1 33.2	+ 30 39 r	Tri			F, pL, f of 2
131 I	Nb	1 33.2	+ 30 45 x	Tri			vF, close to *13.5
135 I	Nb	1 33.2	+ 30 28 x	Tri			vF
136 I	Nb	1 33.2	+ 30 30 x	Tri			eF, diffic, *10 np 3′
601	−	1 33.3	− 12 12 r	Cet			vF, vS, R, 4′ sf 599
132 I	Nb	1 33.3	+ 30 57 x	Tri			vF, D* (13, 13) close
133 I	Nb	1 33.3	+ 30 53 x	Tri			vF, S, vlb south, dif
134 I	*	1 33.4	+ 30 53 x	Tri			vF, susp, *9 n 3′
591	Gx	1 33.5	+ 35 41 r	And		14p	eF, pS, R, lbM, B* sf
595	Kt	1 33.5	+ 30 42 r	Tri			vF, S, R, inv in M33
1716 I	*	1 33.5	− 12 19 F	Cet			eF, r, neb?
590	Gx	1 33.6	+ 44 56 r	And		14p	F, vS, rr?
137 I	Nb	1 33.6	+ 30 31 x	Tri			vF, pL, dif
1715 I	Gx	1 33.6	+ 12 34 u	Psc	0.8	14p	F, S, R, N, r
139 I	*	1 33.7	+ 30 28 x	Tri			vF, v dif, vlbM
140 I	*	1 33.7	+ 30 29 x	Tri			vF, dif

NGC	Type	α_{2000}	δ_{2000}	Const.	Size	Mag.	Description
		h m	° ′		′		
598	Gx	1 33.9	+ 30 39 s	Tri	62	5.7	! eB, eL, R, vgbMN; = M33
617	Gx	1 33.9	− 9 47 r	Cet		15p	eF, S, lE
142 I	Nb	1 33.9	+ 30 45 x	Tri			vF, stellar, or ∗13 inv
612	Gx	1 34.0	− 36 30 s	Scl		13.2	F, vS, R, ∗12 p
143 I	Nb	1 34.1	+ 30 47 x	Tri			vF, S, dif, ∗13 f 0′.6
607		1 34.3	− 7 25 D	Cet			∗11, ∗14 close s
610	−	1 34.3	− 20 09 r	Cet			eF, vS, R, vgbM, ∗10 p 2′
611	−	1 34.3	− 20 08 r	Cet			eF, vS (F∗?), 30″ nf 610
613	Gx	1 34.3	− 29 25 s	Scl	5.8	10.0	vB, vL, vmE 118°, sbM, ∗10 nf
603	∗*∗	1 34.4	+ 30 11 A	Tri			only an eF∗?
604	Kt	1 34.5	+ 30 48 r	Tri			B, vS, R, vvlbM
619	Gx	1 34.8	− 36 28 r	Scl			eeF, vS, R, p of 2
606	Gx	1 34.9	+ 21 26 r	Psc		14p	eF, pS, R, vlbM, r?
623	Gx	1 35.0	− 36 29 r	Scl			F, S, R, f of 2
605	Gx	1 35.1	+ 41 16 r	And		14p	vF, vS, R, bM
615	Gx	1 35.1	− 7 20 s	Cet	4.0	11.5	pB, pL, ilE, gbM, r, ∗8 np 10′
625	Gx	1 35.1	− 41 26 s	Phe	3.0	12p	B, L, mE, gpmbM
643	Gb	1 35.1	− 75 33 A	Hyi		13p	vF, pS, R, vglbM
626	Gx	1 35.2	− 39 08 r	Scl			pF, S, R, bM
608	Gx	1 35.4	+ 33 41 r	Tri		14p	vF, psbM, stellar
630	Gx	1 35.6	− 39 21 r	Scl			pF, S, R, bM
624	Gx	1 35.7	− 10 00 r	Cet		14p	eF, S, am vS st
614	Gx	1 35.8	+ 33 42 r	Tri		14p	pF, psbM, stellar
616	D∗	1 36.0	+ 33 46 r	Tri			neb D∗, ∗8 np
622	Gx	1 36.0	+ 0 40 s	Cet	2.0	14p	eF, pL, dif
618		1 36.3	+ 33 24 D	Tri			nonexistent
633	Gx	1 36.4	− 37 18 r	Scl			pB, S, R, gbM, ⁎ np
621	Gx	1 36.7	+ 35 32 r	Tri		14p	vF, eS, R, bMN
628	Gx	1 36.7	+ 15 47 s	Psc	10.2	9.2	⊕, F, vL, R, vg, psmbM, rr; = M74
631	Gx	1 36.8	+ 5 51 r	Psc		15p	vF, S, gbM
620	Gx	1 37.0	+ 42 20 r	And		14p	eF, vS, R, lbM
627		1 37.1	+ 33 35 D	Tri			nonexistent
609	OC	1 37.2	+ 64 33 s	Cas	3	11.0	Cl, S, pRi, st 14...
632	Gx	1 37.3	+ 5 53 r	Psc		13p	pB, S, R, psbM
646	Gx	1 37.4	− 64 55 s	Hyi			vF, iR, vglbM
1719 I	Gx	1 37.6	− 33 55 c	Scl	2.1		vF, S, R, cF, ∗ nr nf
144 I	Gx	1 37.7	− 13 19 m	Cet	0.6	15p	eF, eS, stellar
634	Gx	1 38.2	+ 35 23 r	Tri		14p	eF, eS, sev F st inv
635	−	1 38.3	− 19 56 r	Cet			eF, vS, R
1718 I		1 38.4	+ 33 21 d	Tri			F, pS, pR, ∗13.5 att
641	Gx	1 38.7	− 42 31 r	Phe			F, S, R, gpmbM, p of 2
648	Gx	1 38.7	− 17 50 r	Cet		14p	vF, vS, vlE, sbMN
145 I	Gx	1 38.7	+ 0 44 m	Cet	0.6	15p	F, S, dif
146 I	Gx	1 38.7	− 17 50 c	Cet	1.4		F, vS, R, lbM; = 648
639	Gx	1 38.9	− 29 55 r	Scl		15p	vF, vS, p of 2
644	Gx	1 38.9	− 42 35 r	Phe			F, S, vlE, glbM, f of 2
642	Gx	1 39.0	− 29 54 r	Scl		14p	vF, pS, R, gbM, ∗ f nr, f of 2
636	Gx	1 39.1	− 7 31 s	Cet	2.3	11.3	pB, vS, R, mbM, r
640	Gx	1 39.3	− 9 23 r	Cet		15p	eF, S, lE 170°, lbMN, ∗10 s 4′
638	Gx	1 39.6	+ 7 14 r	Psc		14p	vF, pS, R
647	Gx	1 39.8	− 9 13 r	Cet		14p	eF, pS, lE 160°, bMN, ∗8 f 16ˢ
649	Gx	1 40.0	− 9 14 r	Cet		15p	eF, S, E 0°, bM D∗?
147 I	Gx	1 40.0	− 14 52 m	Cet	0.8	14p	F, vS, R, vF∗ close
645	Gx	1 40.2	+ 5 44 r	Psc		14p	F, pL, mE
629	−	1 40.3	+ 72 53 r	Cas			iF, 3 st + neb

NGC	Type	α_{2000}	δ_{2000}	Const.	Size	Mag.	Description
		h m	° ′		′		
1720 I	Gx	1 40.4	− 28 55 c	Scl	1.3		eF, eS, R, B, * p
652	Gx	1 40.7	+ 7 59 r	Psc		14p	eeF, pS, R, v diffic
1721 I	Gx	1 41.4	+ 8 30 u	Psc	1.2	14p	pB, pS, E pf, gbM, r
2573	Gx	1 42.	− 89 20 c	Oct	3.6	13.5	F, S, R, glbM, Polarissima Australis
655	Gx	1 42.0	− 13 04 r	Cet		14p	eF, eS, gbMN
658	Gx	1 42.2	+ 12 35 s	Psc	3.2	14p	pF, pS, mE, mbM
650	Pl	1 42.3	+ 51 34 s	Per	4.8	12p	vB, p of Dneb; = M76
651	Pl	1 42.3	+ 51 35 d	Per		12p	vB, f of Dneb; = M76
653	Gx	1 42.4	+ 35 39 r	And		14p	vF, pL, mE, lbM, sev st inv
656	Gx	1 42.4	+ 26 09 r	Psc		13p	F, vS, R, r?
148 I		1 42.4	+ 13 39 d	Psc			eeF, pS, v diffic, 660 sf
149 I	Gx	1 42.4	− 16 18 m	Cet	1.0	14p	F, pS, E pf, lbM
637	OC	1 42.9	+ 64 00 s	Cas	4	8.2	Cl, pS, B & vF st
660	Gx	1 43.0	+ 13 38 s	Psc	9.1	10.8	pB, pL, E, bM, r
150 I	Gx	1 43.0	+ 4 12 u	Psc	1.0	15p	F, S, R, dif, *10.5 near, 664 f
1722 I	Gx	1 43.0	− 34 11 c	Scl	1.8		F, S, cE 45°
1723 I	Gx	1 43.2	+ 8 53 v	Psc	3.5		F, pL, E 200°, glbM
1724 I	Gx	1 43.2	− 34 15 c	Scl	1.6		F, S, cE 175°
657	OC	1 43.7	+ 55 53 r	Cas			Cl, pRi, st 12
664	Gx	1 43.8	+ 4 14 s	Psc	1.8	14p	vF, S, R
151 I		1 44.0	+ 13 12 d	Psc			eF, pS, np of 2
654	OC	1 44.1	+ 61 53 s	Cas	5	6.5	Cl, iF, Ri, one *6-7, st 11...14
152 I		1 44.1	+ 13 02 d	Psc			eF, S, R, vF* close, sf of 2
659	OC	1 44.2	+ 60 42 s	Cas	5	7.9	Cl, lRi, st B
661	Gx	1 44.2	+ 28 42 s	Tri	2.2	13p	F, S, R, bM, r
662	Gx	1 44.5	+ 37 41 s	And	1.0	14.3	F, S, R, mbM
153 I		1 44.6	+ 12 38 d	Psc			eF, pS, R, sp of 2
665	Gx	1 44.8	+ 10 26 r	Psc		13p	F, S, lE, bM, r
667	Gx	1 45.1	− 22 56 r	Cet			eF, S, R, *10 np 100″
1725 I		1 45.2	+ 21 47 d	Psc			F, S, pR, dif
154 I	Gx	1 45.3	+ 10 39 u	Psc	1.3	15p	F, vS, lbM, *11.5 sp
1726 I	Gx	1 45.3	+ 4 37 z	Psc		15p	F, vS, gbM, *13.5 close
156 I	Gx	1 45.5	+ 10 33 u	Psc	1.8	15p	pB, S, R, mbMN = *12
157 I		1 45.7	+ 12 52 d	Psc			eeF, S, R, D* p, nf of 2
158 I		1 45.9	− 6 56 d	Cet			vF, vS, R, mbM
663	OC	1 46.0	+ 61 15 s	Cas	16	7.1	Cl, B, L, eRi, st pL
666	Gx	1 46.0	+ 34 23 r	Tri		13p	vF* in eF, eS neby
668	Gx	1 46.3	+ 36 27 s	And	2.3	14p	pF, pS, R, gbM
160 I	Gx	1 46.4	− 13 15 m	Cet	0.8	14p	F, stellar, 13m
159 I	Gx	1 46.5	− 8 39 m	Cet	0.6	16p	pB, S, R, mbM
671	Gx	1 46.9	+ 13 06 r	Ari		14p	eF, pS, R, bet D* & *
669	Gx	1 47.2	+ 35 33 s	Tri	3.4	13p	pF, pL, mE, gbM
670	Gx	1 47.4	+ 27 53 s	Tri	2.5	12.1	F, S, lE
155 I		1 47.5	+ 59 47 d	Cas			vF, eL, dif
1727 I	Gx	1 47.5	+ 27 20 s	Tri	6.2	11.6	F, L, st inv, 672 nf
1728 I	Gx	1 47.7	− 33 36 c	For	1.4		F, S, E 160°, mbM
685	Gx	1 47.8	− 52 47 s	Eri	4.1	12p	F, vL, R, vgvlbM
690	Gx	1 47.8	− 16 43 r	Cet		14p	vF, vS, R, lbM
672	Gx	1 47.9	+ 27 26 s	Tri	6.6	10.8	F, pL, mE 80°
1729 I	Gx	1 47.9	− 26 53 c	For	1.9		pB, eS, alm stell, rr?
673	Gx	1 48.4	+ 11 32 s	Ari	2.4	13p	pF, pL, E, lbM, *11 nf 3′
692	Gx	1 48.7	− 48 39 c	Phe	2.4		B, S, R, gbM
161 I		1 48.7	+ 10 22 d	Psc			eeF, vS, R
162 I	Gx	1 48.9	+ 10 31 u	Psc	1.9	15p	eeF, S, lE
675	Gx	1 49.0	+ 13 02 r	Ari		15p	vF, S, R, lbM, sp of 2

NGC	Type	α_{2000}	δ_{2000}	Const.	Size	Mag.	Description
		h m	° ′		′		
676	Gx	1 49.0	+ 5 54 s	Psc	4.3	11p	vF, E 161°, sbM *9
682	Gx	1 49.0	− 14 59 r	Cet		13p	cF, S, R, gvlbM
686	Gx	1 49.0	− 23 48 r	For		13p	vF, vS, R, gbM, er, 2 st nr
677	Gx	1 49.1	+ 13 02 r	Ari		14p	eeF, S, R, nf of 2
164 I		1 49.1	− 3 55 D	Cet			pF, S, R, bet 2 st (S Cl?)
674	−	1 49.2	+ 22 20 r	Ari			pB, vmE, *14 f 8ˢ; = 697?
681	Gx	1 49.2	− 10 26 s	Cet	2.8	11.8	pF, cL, R, glbM, S* p 90″
163 I	Gx	1 49.3	+ 20 42 t	Ari	1.8	14p	F, pS, R, bM
1734 I	Gx	1 49.3	− 32 45 c	For	1.5		vF, pS, lE 100°, bM
678	Gx	1 49.4	+ 22 00 s	Ari	5.0	13p	pB, S, iR, mbM, p of 2
696	Gx	1 49.4	− 34 55 r	For			F, S, R
683	Gx	1 49.6	+ 11 41 r	Ari		15p	eF, 2 st 14 p 90″
698	Gx	1 49.6	− 34 50 r	For			eF, S
679	Gx	1 49.7	+ 35 47 s	And	2.3	12.4	F, stellar
680	Gx	1 49.8	+ 21 58 s	Ari	2.9	13p	pB, S, iR, mbM, f of 2
689	Gx	1 49.9	− 27 28 r	For		15p	vF, pL, R, gbM
1730 I	Gx	1 50.0	+ 21 58 m	Ari	0.6	15p	F, S, R, gbM
684	Gx	1 50.2	+ 27 39 s	Tri	3.9	13p	F, vlE, *13 f 100″; = IC 165
165 I	?	1 50.2	+ 27 38 z	Tri			eF, S, lE, vF* close f; = 684
1731 I	Gx	1 50.2	+ 27 12 v	Tri	1.7		F, E npsf, bM, prob spir
1739 I		1 50.4	− 34 03 d	For			cF, cS, R, mbM
693	Gx	1 50.5	+ 6 09 s	Psc	2.7	14p	pF, S, E 90°, vglbM, *10 nf
168 I		1 50.5	− 8 32 d	Cet			vF, stellar, *10 f 4′ (707 f 1ᵐ)
687	Gx	1 50.6	+ 36 21 r	And		13p	vF, stellar
699	Gx	1 50.6	− 12 03 r	Cet		14p	eF, pS, E 105°, bnp, curved
169 I		1 50.6	− 12 41 d	Cet			F, S, E pf, bM, r
691	Gx	1 50.7	+ 21 46 s	Ari	3.5	12p	F, cL, vglbM
1733 I		1 50.7	+ 33 06 d	Tri			F, vS, pR, r
688	Gx	1 50.8	+ 35 16 r	Tri		13p	vF, vS, r?
1732 I	Gx	1 50.8	+ 35 55 u	And	1.7	15p	vF, pS, mbM; eF st inv?
1735 I		1 50.9	+ 33 06 d	Tri			vF, vS, R
1736 I	Gx	1 50.9	+ 18 18 u	Ari	1.4	15p	F, pS, E 210°, glbM
694	Gx	1 51.0	+ 22 00 s	Ari	0.8	14p	F, S, R, bet 2 st 15
701	Gx	1 51.1	− 9 42 s	Cet	2.5	12.2	F, pL, E, vgvlbM, r
167 I	Gx	1 51.1	+ 21 55 v	Ari	3.0		eF, *10.5 n 4′
1738 I	Gx	1 51.1	− 9 47 v	Cet	1.2		eF, vS, 701 p
695	Gx	1 51.2	+ 22 35 s	Ari	0.7	14p	vS, stellar
707	Gx	1 51.2	− 8 30 r	Cet		14p	vF, F* in centre
697	Gx	1 51.3	+ 22 21 s	Ari	4.7	13p	F, cL, E, mbM
702	Gx	1 51.3	− 4 03 s	Cet	1.5	14p	eF, vlE 0°, *13 s 90″
1740 I		1 51.3	− 29 57 d	For			pB, eS, lE, like D*
1737 I		1 51.7	+ 36 15 d	And			eF, 3 or 4 vF st in neb
706	Gx	1 51.8	+ 6 18 s	Psc	2.2	13p	F, S, bM, *13 n 1′
1741 I	Gx	1 51.9	− 16 47 m	Cet	0.7	14p	eF, eS; = 690?
170 I		1 52.0	− 8 32 d	Cet			F, vS, R, stellar
700	Gx	1 52.2	+ 36 04 r	And		15p	eF, vS, R, sp 703
711	Gx	1 52.5	+ 17 30 r	Ari		14p	vF* in vF, vS neby
166 I	OC	1 52.5	+ 61 50 s	Cas	5	11.7	S Cl, nebulous?
725	Gx	1 52.6	− 16 31 r	Cet		14p	vF, vS, R
704	Gx	1 52.7	+ 36 06 r	And		14p	vF, vS, R, 2nd of 4
703	Gx	1 52.8	+ 36 09 s	And	1.5	15p	vF, vS, R, 1st of 4
705	Gx	1 52.8	+ 36 08 r	And		14p	vF, vS, R, 3rd of 4
708	Gx	1 52.8	+ 36 10 s	And	3.3	15p	F, pL, bM, 4th of 4
709	Gx	1 52.9	+ 36 13 r	And		15p	vF, pS, bet 2 st, group sp
716	Gx	1 52.9	+ 12 32 A	Ari			eF, S, R, B* f

NGC	Type	α_{2000}	δ_{2000}	Const.	Size	Mag.	Description
		h m	o ′		′		
1743 I	Gx	1 52.9	+ 12 43 v	Ari	2.1		vF, pS, lbM, dif; = 716?
710	Gx	1 53.0	+ 36 02 r	And		14p	vF, pS, 2 st s
720	Gx	1 53.0	− 13 44 s	Cet	4.4	10.2	cB, pL, lE, psmbM
1745 I		1 53.0	− 16 40 d	Cet			eF, eS
712	Gx	1 53.2	+ 36 48 r	And		14p	vF, R, am pB st
715		1 53.2	− 12 50 D	Cet			eF, S, gbMN
718	Gx	1 53.2	+ 4 12 s	Psc	2.8	11.7	pB, S, iR, psmbM
1742 I	Gx	1 53.2	+ 22 43 m	Ari	0.7	15p	F, S, lE pf, glbM
714	Gx	1 53.6	+ 36 12 r	And		14p	F, vS, R, 2 st 13 p and np
1744 I	Gx	1 53.6	+ 19 50 u	Ari	1.4	15p	F, S, R, glbM
719	Gx	1 53.7	+ 19 49 r	Ari		14p	eF, R, vF∗ f
727	Gx	1 53.7	− 35 52 r	For			F, S, R, bM
724	−	1 53.8	− 23 52 r	For			vF, pL, R, gbM, S∗ ssp; = 723
723	Gx	1 53.9	− 23 46 r	Cet		13p	pF, vS, R, vgbM
717	Gx	1 54.0	+ 36 13 r	And		14p	vF, pS, ∗15 sf 1′
729	D∗	1 54.0	− 35 49 A	For			eeF, S, R
745	Gx	1 54.2	− 56 41 c	Eri	1.5		pB, S, R, gbM
1746 I	Gx	1 54.3	+ 4 48 v	Psc	1.9		F, S, pR, gbM
754	Gx	1 54.4	− 56 46 c	Eri	0.7		vF, S, R, bM
756	Gx	1 54.5	− 16 43 r	Cet		15p	F, vS, R, bMN
721	Gx	1 54.8	+ 39 23 s	And	2.0	13.4	eF, pL
722	Gx	1 54.8	+ 20 41 r	Ari		14p	vF, vS, R, β Ari n
734	Gx	1 54.8	− 17 03 r	Cet			vF, vS, R, bMN, ∗11 p 11ˢ
731	Gx	1 54.9	− 9 01 s	Cet	1.7	13p	eF, stellar
172 I	Nb	1 54.9	+ 0 49 x	Cet	0.1		pB, S, R, bM
713	Gx	1 55.1	− 9 05 r	Cet		15p	eF, pS, E 90°, glbMN, ∗14 np
728	∗∗∗	1 55.1	+ 4 12 r	Psc			suspected neb
171 I	Gx	1 55.2	+ 35 17 u	Tri	2.5	14p	pB, pS, cE, ∗ nf
730	∗	1 55.3	+ 5 37 r	Psc			vF, very stellar
726	Gx	1 55.6	− 10 49 r	Cet		14p	vF, pL, iR, ∗9 3′ f
749	Gx	1 55.6	− 29 57 r	For		14p	pB, S, E, bM
758	Gx	1 56.0	− 3 06 r	Cet			vF, vS
173 I	Gx	1 56.0	+ 1 17 v	Cet	1.2		F, pS, R, lbM
1748 I	Gx	1 56.1	+ 17 39 u	Ari	1.2	15p	vF
747	−	1 56.2	− 9 28 r	Cet			eF, pS, lE 180°
1749 I	Gx	1 56.2	+ 6 45 u	Psc	1.2	15p	F, S, E ns, biN, r
174 I	Gx	1 56.3	+ 3 46 u	Psc	1.7	15p	neb ∗13
175 I	Nb	1 56.3	+ 1 20 x	Cet	0.2		vF, dif, diffic
733	Gx	1 56.4	+ 33 04 r	Tri			vF, 2′ p 736
741	Gx	1 56.4	+ 5 38 s	Psc	3.2	11.3	pF, S, R, p of 2, pos 102°
748	Gx	1 56.4	− 4 28 v	Cet	2.9		pF, ∗9 np
755	Gx	1 56.4	− 9 04 v	Cet	4.0		vF, pS, vlE
757	−	1 56.4	− 8 55 r	Cet			F, S, gbMN; = 755?
1750 I	Gx	1 56.4	+ 4 05 u	Psc	1.1	15p	vF, vS, pR, N
1751 I		1 56.4	+ 5 38 x	Psc			pB, pS, R, ∗9 np; = 741
732	Gx	1 56.5	+ 36 48 r	And		15p	vF∗ in vF, vS, R neby
742	Gx	1 56.5	+ 5 38 s	Psc	0.2	15p	vF, vS, R, sbM, f of 2
735	Gx	1 56.6	+ 34 11 s	Tri	2.0	14p	eeF, stellar
736	Gx	1 56.7	+ 33 03 s	Tri	2.0	12.2	pB, R, bM
737		1 56.7	+ 33 03 D	Tri			only a faint star
796	C+N	1 56.7	− 74 13 r	Hyi			eF, vS, R, ∗ np 25″
738	Gx	1 56.9	+ 33 03 r	Tri		15p	neb, 75″ nf 736
740	Gx	1 56.9	+ 33 01 s	Tri	1.7	15p	F, L, cE
176 I	Gx	1 56.9	− 2 01 u	Cet	2.4	15p	pB, S
1754 I	Gx	1 56.9	+ 4 02 u	Psc	1.1	15p	F, S, gbM

NGC	Type	α_{2000}	δ_{2000}	Const.	Size	Mag.	Description
		h m	° ′		′		
1758 I		1 56.9	− 16 32 d	Cet			F, eS, sbM *11
739	Gx	1 57.0	+ 33 14 r	Tri		15p	cF, vS, R, in △ of st
1756 I		1 57.0	− 0 28 d	Cet			vF, E npsf, *13 close sf
762	Gx	1 57.1	− 5 26 r	Cet		13p	vF, S, lE, vglbM
177 I		1 57.1	− 0 09 d	Cet			F, vS, R, dif
1757 I		1 57.1	− 0 29 d	Cet			ef, vS, R
764	D*	1 57.2	− 16 02 F	Cet			ef, vS, iR, gbM
1755 I	Gx	1 57.2	+ 14 34 u	Ari	1.6	15p	F, S, dif
1752 I		1 57.3	+ 28 37 d	Tri			F, vS, *14.5 att
1753 I		1 57.3	+ 28 36 d	Tri			F, vS, dif, 14.5 close
763	−	1 57.4	− 8 59 r	Cet			vF, pL, E 65°, gbMN
750	Gx	1 57.5	+ 33 13 s	Tri	1.6	12.2	cB, pL, R, D with 751 at 25″, pos 173°
1760 I		1 57.5	− 32 00 d	For			ef, pS, R, (decl 1° farther s?)
751	Gx	1 57.6	+ 33 12 s	Tri	1.3	12.5	pF, eS, R, bM, Dneb with 750
1747 I	Pl	1 57.6	+ 63 20 s	Cas	0.2	14p	◯, stell
753	Gx	1 57.7	+ 35 55 s	And	2.9	12.4	pB, pL, R, gmbM
752	OC	1 57.8	+ 37 41 s	And	50	5.7	Cl, vvL, Ri, st L & sc
759	Gx	1 57.8	+ 36 20 s	And	2.1	14p	Cl, vS, R
760	D*	1 57.8	+ 33 21 r	Tri			vF, R, 761 nf
761	Gx	1 57.8	+ 33 23 s	Tri	1.6	15p	pF, cL, 4 F st nr
782	Gx	1 57.8	− 57 46 s	Eri	2.1	13p	pB, pL, lE, *12 att
1762 I	Gx	1 57.8	− 33 14 c	For	1.7		eeF, pS, R, *7 nf
746	Gx	1 57.9	+ 44 56 s	And	1.9	13p	vF, pS, lE, sev st nr
1759 I	Gx	1 57.9	− 32 59 c	For	1.8		pB, vS, R, bM, *10 close sp
744	OC	1 58.4	+ 55 29 s	Per	11	7.9	Cl, pL, pRi, iF, st 11...13
775	Gx	1 58.5	− 26 18 r	For		14p	pF, S, R, glbM
743	OC	1 58.7	+ 60 11 s	Cas	5		Cl, not Ri, D* (h 1098)
766	Gx	1 58.7	+ 8 20 r	Psc		14p	vF, S, R, *11 at 2′, pos 75°
768	Gx	1 58.7	+ 0 31 r	Cet		14p	ef, pS, R, *8 f 30ˢ
765	Gx	1 58.8	+ 24 53 r	Ari		14p	vF, vS
1763 I		1 58.8	− 27 47 d	For			eeF, S, R, *8 ssf
767	Gx	1 58.9	− 9 35 r	Cet		14p	ef, pS, E 160°
178 I		1 58.9	+ 36 37 d	And			pF, N = 13m
1761 I	Gx	1 58.9	+ 0 34 z	Cet		15p	vF, vS, R, gbMN
773	Gx	1 59.0	− 11 31 r	Cet		14p	cF, pL, E 0°, glbM
802	Gx	1 59.1	− 67 52 c	Hyi	0.7		eeF, vS, R, *13 p 100″
770	Gx	1 59.2	+ 18 57 s	Ari	1.3	14p	vF, S, R, sp 772
772	Gx	1 59.3	+ 19 01 s	Ari	7.1	10.3	B, cL, R, gbM, r
774	Gx	1 59.4	+ 14 01 r	Ari		14p	vF, stellar
769	Gx	1 59.5	+ 30 54 r	Tri		13p	vF, vS, iR, bM, F* att
183 I	Gx	1 59.6	− 5 22 m	Cet	1.0	15p	F, vS, R, lbM
779	Gx	1 59.7	− 5 58 s	Cet	4.1	11.0	cB, L, mE 162°, mbM
795	Gx	1 59.8	− 55 49 c	Eri	1.5		pF, S, R, 2 st 11 nr
182 I	Gx	1 59.8	+ 7 25 u	Psc	2.0	15p	F, pL, biN
776	Gx	1 59.9	+ 23 38 r	Ari		13p	F, pL
184 I	Gx	1 59.9	− 6 50 m	Cet	1.0	14p	ef, vS
180 I	Gx	2 00.0	+ 23 37 z	Ari		15p	vF, eS, R, stellar, sf 776
181 I	Gx	2 00.0	+ 23 40 z	Ari		16p	ef, eS, stellar
1767 I		2 00.0	− 11 07 d	Cet			ef, pS, bet 2 st 10.5, 2 st n
781	Gx	2 00.1	+ 12 38 r	Ari		14p	ef, stellar
185 I	Gx	2 00.1	− 1 31 m	Cet	0.5	16p	ef, vS, dif
777	Gx	2 00.2	+ 31 26 s	Tri	3.0	12p	pB, pL, R, glbM
179 I		2 00.2	+ 38 02 D	And			pB, S, lE, *9.5 nf
778	Gx	2 00.3	+ 31 17 r	Tri		14p	ef, vS, R, lbM
186 I	Gx	2 00.4	− 1 33 z	Cet		15p	F, double, dist 15″

NGC	Type	α_{2000}	δ_{2000}	Const.	Size	Mag.	Description
		h m	° ′		′		
1764 I	Gx	2 00.4	+ 24 34 u	Ari	1.7	14p	F, vS, R, lbM
780	Gx	2 00.5	+ 28 13 r	Tri		14p	vF, vS, E, 3 st p
1765 I		2 00.6	+ 31 51 x	Tri			S* att p; = 783
1768 I	Gx	2 00.8	− 25 02 c	For	1.9		eeF, pS, R, 3 st 9 sf, v diffic
1769 I		2 00.9	− 31 55 d	For			eF, eS, mE 80°
787	Gx	2 01.0	− 9 00 r	Cet		13p	vF, S
783	Gx	2 01.1	+ 31 52 s	Tri	1.8	13p	eF, S, iR, vF st att; = IC 1765
788	Gx	2 01.1	− 6 49 s	Cet	1.8	12.3	pF, pS, R, bM
1766 I		2 01.2	+ 31 47 x	Tri			no descr; = 785
784	Gx	2 01.3	+ 28 50 s	Tri	6.2	11.8	vF, L, E (double?)
786	Gx	2 01.5	+ 15 38 r	Ari		14p	eF, vS
790	Gx	2 01.5	− 5 23 r	Cet		13p	cF, cS, R, bM
813	Gx	2 01.6	− 68 26 c	Hyi	1.3		pF, S, R, gbM
791	Gx	2 01.7	+ 8 29 r	Psc		15p	vF, S, *14 f 3′
785	Gx	2 01.8	+ 31 49 r	Tri		14p	eF, eS, vF* att; = IC 1766
187 I		2 01.9	+ 26 28 d	Tri			eeF, R
189 I	Gx	2 01.9	+ 23 33 m	Ari	0.7	15p	vF, vS, R, *13.5 close
188 I		2 02.0	+ 27 02 d	Tri			eeF, vS, R
190 I	Gx	2 02.1	+ 23 32 m	Ari	0.3	15p	F, vS, R, mbM
1770 I		2 02.2	+ 9 59 d	Psc			F, vS, R, stell
792	Gx	2 02.3	+ 15 42 r	Ari		14p	eF, S, R, *11 75°
799	Gx	2 02.3	− 0 06 r	Cet		14p	eeF, pS, n of 2
800	Gx	2 02.3	− 0 08 r	Cet		14p	eeF, S, R, s of 2
1771 I		2 02.3	+ 9 58 d	Psc			F, vS, R, stell
789	Gx	2 02.5	+ 32 04 r	Tri		14p	vF, S, lE
794	Gx	2 02.5	+ 18 22 r	Ari		14p	vF, cS, stellar; = IC 191
191 I		2 02.5	+ 18 22 x	Ari			pB, pL, lE; = 794
192 I	Gx	2 02.5	+ 16 01 u	Ari	1.1	15p	F, L, R, lbM
1772 I	Gx	2 02.6	+ 7 44 m	Psc	0.6	15p	F, S, slbM, *8.5 166″ n
193 I		2 02.7	+ 11 05 d	Ari			eF, pS, lE, B* sf, F* f
793	−	2 02.9	+ 32 00 r	Tri			vvF, bet 2 st, sf 789
814	Gx	2 02.9	− 14 38 A	Cet		16p	eF, S, R, gbM
815	Gx	2 02.9	− 14 42 A	Cet		16p	eF, vS, R, gbM
194 I	Gx	2 03.1	+ 2 36 u	Cet	1.7	15p	vF, vS, R, *9.5 f 15^s
771	−	2 03.4	+ 72 25 s	Cas		4.0	suspected neb* (50 Cas)
797	Gx	2 03.4	+ 38 07 r	And		13p	vF, S, iR, sbM, * nr
798	Gx	2 03.4	+ 32 04 r	Tri		14p	eF, vS
806	Gx	2 03.6	− 9 56 r	Cet		14p	eeF, S, R, v diffic, pB* n
801	Gx	2 03.7	+ 38 15 r	And		13p	eF, pS, iR, D* close f
195 I	Gx	2 03.7	+ 14 42 u	Ari	1.5	14p	eeF, S, R, F* s
803	Gx	2 03.8	+ 16 02 s	Ari	3.3	12.4	vF, S, iR, glbM, *10 p 3^s.5
804	Gx	2 03.9	+ 30 49 r	Tri		14p	eeF, vS, R, lbM
196 I	Gx	2 03.9	+ 14 43 a	Ari			pF, pS, R, 3 st nr
1774 I	Gx	2 03.9	+ 15 18 u	Ari	2.1	15p	vF, dif
808	Gx	2 04.0	− 23 19 v	Cet	1.6		vF, pS, vlE
1773 I	Gx	2 04.0	+ 30 49 u	Tri	1.4	15p	vF, vS, gbM, r
197 I	Gx	2 04.1	+ 2 47 u	Psc	1.0	14p	pB, S, E 225°gbM
805	Gx	2 04.4	+ 28 48 r	Tri		14p	eF, eS, R, 2 st 14 p
809	Gx	2 04.4	− 8 43 r	Cet		14p	vF, S, R
811	Gx	2 04.7	− 10 06 r	Cet		14p	eF, eS, R (neb?), *10 s 1′
807	Gx	2 04.8	+ 28 59 r	Tri		14p	vF, vS, iR, bet 2 st n & sp
1776 I	Gx	2 05.2	+ 6 06 u	Psc	2.3	14p	F, pL, iR, dif
810	Gx	2 05.3	+ 13 14 r	Ari		15p	vF, vS, R, bM
1775 I	Gx	2 05.3	+ 13 31 m	Ari	0.6	15p	F, S, dif, *13.5 nr
198 I	Gx	2 06.1	+ 9 17 v	Psc	1.4		pB, pS, R, bM

NGC	Type	α_{2000}	δ_{2000}	Const.	Size	Mag.	Description
		h m	o ′		′		
1777 I	Gx	2 06.1	+ 15 12 z	Ari		16p	F, eS, R, stell
199 I	Gx	2 06.3	+ 9 13 u	Psc	1.6	15p	F, S, R, bM
1778 I		2 06.3	+ 9 13 d	Psc			F, S, R, gbMN
1779 I	Gx	2 06.5	+ 3 41 z	Cet		15p	F, S, R, *14 nr
822	Gx	2 06.6	− 41 09 r	Phe			cF, vS, R, sbM, r
812	Gx	2 06.8	+ 44 34 s	And	3.2	13p	eF, pL, E 45°, bM
824	Gx	2 06.8	− 36 28 r	For			F, S, R, vsvmbM *13
1781 I	Gx	2 06.9	− 0 31 z	Cet		15p	F, vS, R, N
1780 I	Gx	2 07.0	+ 14 44 m	Ari	0.6	15p	F, S, dif, sev st 9-10 nr
823	Gx	2 07.3	− 25 27 r	For		14p	vF, vF D* inv
201 I		2 07.3	+ 9 06 d	Cet			vF, S, dif
1782 I	Gx	2 07.3	− 25 27 c	For	2.2		vF, D* in neb; = 823
200 I		2 07.4	+ 31 10 d	Tri			pB, pL, R, bM
204 I		2 07.4	− 1 23 d	Cet			no description
205 I	Gx	2 07.4	− 2 06 u	Cet	1.1	15p	pB, vS, irr R
202 I	Gx	2 07.5	+ 9 10 u	Cet	1.6	15p	vF, vS, dif
203 I		2 07.5	+ 9 07 d	Cet			vF, vS, R, *10 sf
206 I		2 07.5	− 7 02 d	Cet			pF, S, irr R
207 I		2 07.7	− 6 59 d	Cet			pF, S, irr R
816	Gx	2 08.0	+ 29 15 r	Tri		15p	vF, vS, iF
817		2 08.4	+ 17 12 D	Ari		14p	eF, vS, R, 2 st nr
820	Gx	2 08.4	+ 14 20 r	Ari		13p	F, vS, R, bM
821	Gx	2 08.4	+ 11 00 s	Ari	3.5	10.8	pB, vS, vlE, svmbM, *10 np 1′
208 I	Gx	2 08.4	+ 6 23 m	Cet	1.5	13p	vF, pL, dif
819	Gx	2 08.5	+ 29 14 r	Tri		14p	pF, vS, R, *13 n
825	Gx	2 08.5	+ 6 19 r	Cet		14p	F, S, mE
818	Gx	2 08.7	+ 38 47 s	And	3.2	13p	pB, cL, lE, mbM
829	Gx	2 08.7	− 7 47 v	Cet	1.4		F, S, *11 s, 1st of 3
827	Gx	2 08.8	+ 7 58 r	Cet		14p	vF, S, E, bM, am st
852	Gx	2 08.9	− 56 44 r	Eri			pF, pS, R, glbM, r
830	Gx	2 09.0	− 7 46 r	Cet		14p	pF, vS, R, 2nd of 3
209 I	Gx	2 09.0	− 7 04 h	Cet	0.8	13p	pB, S, dif
833	Gx	2 09.3	− 10 08 s	Cet	1.9	12.7	F, S, R, 1st of 4
826	Gx	2 09.4	+ 30 44 r	Tri		15p	eF, S, R, lbM
835	Gx	2 09.4	− 10 08 s	Cet	1.4	12.2	F, S, R, 2nd of 4
210 I		2 09.4	− 9 40 d	Cet			no description
831	Gx	2 09.5	+ 6 06 r	Cet		15p	vF, pS
838	Gx	2 09.6	− 10 09 s	Cet	1.7	12.8	vF, vS, R, 3rd of 4
839	Gx	2 09.7	− 10 11 s	Cet	1.8	13.0	vF, pS, R, 4th of 4
842	Gx	2 09.8	− 7 45 v	Cet	2.0		vF, vS, R, psbM, 3rd of 3
832	Gx	2 10.1	+ 35 32 r	Tri			F, vS, *9-10 sp
1783 I	Gx	2 10.1	− 32 56 s	For		13p	pF, vS, mE ns, F* p
828	Gx	2 10.2	+ 39 12 s	And	3.2	13p	pB, S, iR, D* f 15ˢ
840	Gx	2 10.2	+ 7 50 s	Cet	2.5	15p	eF, vS
844	Gx	2 10.2	+ 6 03 r	Cet		15p	F, S
849	Gx	2 10.2	− 22 19 r	Cet			eF, vS, R (neb?)
848	Gx	2 10.3	− 10 19 s	Cet	1.9	13.1	eeF, pL, v diffic, * nf
837	Gx	2 10.4	− 22 26 r	Cet		15p	eF, pS, mE 0°, *10 n 1′
836	Gx	2 10.5	− 22 04 r	Cet		14p	eF, S, R, gbMN
834	Gx	2 11.0	+ 37 40 r	And		13p	vF, S, lE
843	*·*	2 11.1	+ 32 06 r	Tri			⊕, F, S, R
211 I	Gx	2 11.1	+ 3 52 v	Cet	2.5		F, pS, R, bM, 851 sf
850	Gx	2 11.2	− 1 30 r	Cet		14p	eF, eS, iF
851	Gx	2 11.2	+ 3 47 s	Cet	1.5	15p	eF, pS, R, v diffic
841	Gx	2 11.3	+ 37 30 s	And	2.0	13p	pB, vS, mbMN = *13-14

NGC	Type	α_{2000}	δ_{2000}	Const.	Size	Mag.	Description
		h m	° ′		′		
854	Gx	2 11.6	− 35 51 r	For			cF, pS, lE 0°, gbM
853	Gx	2 11.8	− 9 18 r	Cet		13p	F, S, E
846	Gx	2 12.2	+ 44 34 r	And		13p	eF, vS, R, gbM
847	Gx	2 12.2	+ 44 34 D	And			vF, pL, R; = 846
845	Gx	2 12.3	+ 37 29 r	And		14p	vF, iF, stellar
858	Gx	2 12.5	− 22 27 s	Cet	1.6	13p	eF, pL, R
857	Gx	2 12.6	− 31 57 r	For		13p	cB, S, E, psmbM
862	Gx	2 13.0	− 42 04 r	Phe			F, vS, svmbM
856	Gx	2 13.6	− 0 44 r	Cet		14p	eF, S, lE, F∗ close f
212 I	Gx	2 13.6	+ 16 36 z	Ari		16p	F, vS, R, stellar
859		2 13.9	− 0 44 F	Cet			pF, pS, R, lbM; = 856
855	Gx	2 14.0	+ 27 53 r	Tri		13p	F, S, lE 90°, bM
213 I	Gx	2 14.0	+ 16 28 z	Ari		15p	F, S, gbM, ∗13.5 close
214 I	Gx	2 14.0	+ 5 11 u	Cet	0.9	14p	pB, S, gbM, r
215 I	Gx	2 14.2	− 6 47 m	Cet	1.0	15p	pB, E pf
863	Gx	2 14.6	− 0 46 s	Cet	1.4	14p	vF, R, bM, stellar
866		2 14.6	− 0 46 F	Cet			pF, pS, R, lbM; = 863
885		2 14.6	− 0 46 F	Cet			vF, pS, R, lbM; = 863
860	Gx	2 15.1	+ 30 47 r	Tri		15p	∗13 in F neb
872	Gx	2 15.4	− 17 48 r	Cet		14p	vF, pS, mE 0°, gvlbM, sev F st inv
864	Gx	2 15.5	+ 6 00 s	Cet	4.6	11.0	eF, cL, R, gbM, ∗12 sf att
861	Gx	2 15.8	+ 35 55 r	Tri		15p	vF, S, D∗ att sp
216 I	Gx	2 15.8	− 2 01 z	Cet		16p	vF, eS, R, lbM
1788 I	Gx	2 15.8	− 31 12 s	For	2.5	12.4	pF, pS, R, 2 st nf
867		2 15.9	+ 1 03 F	Cet			eF, vS, R, bM; = 875
868	Gx	2 16.0	− 0 44 r	Cet		15p	eF, pS, R
1786 I	Gx	2 16.0	+ 5 09 z	Cet		15p	vF, vS, R, N
865	Gx	2 16.1	+ 28 36 r	Tri		14p	eF, eS, iR
874		2 16.1	− 23 11 D	Cet			no neby; = D∗?
217 I		2 16.2	− 11 56 d	Cet			F, pL, E ns
1784 I	Gx	2 16.2	+ 32 39 s	Tri	1.6	13.2	F, L, E pf, gbM
1787 I		2 16.2	− 11 57 d	Cet			eF, vmE, bet 2 st pf, ∗8 nf
1785 I		2 16.4	+ 32 39 d	Tri			F, S, R, stell
873	Gx	2 16.6	− 11 20 r	Cet		13p	F, pL, R, vglbM
879	Gx	2 16.8	− 8 58 r	Cet			eF, pS, iR, bM
875	Gx	2 17.1	+ 1 14 r	Cet		14p	vF, vS
218 I	Gx	2 17.1	+ 1 18 m	Cet	0.7	15p	vF, S, dif, ∗13.5 close, 875 sf
870	Gx	2 17.2	+ 14 33 r	Ari		16p	eF, stellar, 2 vF st sp, s of 871
871	Gx	2 17.2	+ 14 33 s	Ari	1.3	13.5	vF, vS, E, ∗10 sf 5′
888	Gx	2 17.5	− 59 52 c	Hor	1.3		eF, S, R, 2 or 3 vF st nr
1790 I		2 17.6	+ 12 30 d	Ari			F, S, dif
1791 I	Gx	2 17.7	+ 12 29 u	Ari	1.2	15p	S, R, like neb ∗11
878	Gx	2 17.8	− 23 22 r	Cet		15p	eF, vS, R
876	Gx	2 17.9	+ 14 31 v	Ari	2.1		eF, S, R, 107″ sp 877
877	Gx	2 18.0	+ 14 33 s	Ari	2.3	11.8	pF, pL, lE, pgbM, ∗12 sf 1′, ∗9 166°, 285″
1789 I		2 18.2	+ 32 24 d	Tri			F, S, iF, ?
880	Gx	2 18.4	− 4 11 F	Cet			eF, vS, R, sbMN
219 I		2 18.6	− 6 55 d	Cet			pB, S, stellar
881	Gx	2 18.7	− 6 35 s	Cet	2.9		F, pS, E, bM, 2 or 3 st nr
869	OC	2 19.0	+ 57 09 s	Per	30	4p	! Cl, vvL, vRi, st 7...14
883	Gx	2 19.0	− 6 45 r	Cet		13p	pF, pS, vlE, bM, D∗ nr
1792 I	Gx	2 19.0	+ 34 29 u	Tri	1.7	15p	F, S, pR, gbM, r
889	Gx	2 19.1	− 41 45 r	Phe			vF, vS, R, bM, ∗7 sf
220 I		2 19.2	− 12 47 d	Cet			vF, dif, vlbM
887	Gx	2 19.6	− 16 04 r	Cet		13p	F, S, iR, pgbM

NGC	Type	α_{2000}	δ_{2000}	Const.	Size	Mag.	Description
		h m	° ′		′		
882	Gx	2 19.7	+ 15 49 r	Ari		15p	eF, R, gbM, *16 nr
893	Gx	2 20.0	− 41 23 r	Phe			pF, pS, R, lbM, *8 f 4′
892	Gx	2 20.7	− 23 07 r	Cet			eF, eS, E?, neb?
897	Gx	2 21.1	− 33 42 r	For			pB, S, R, psbM, *10 f 35″
1794 I	Nb	2 21.5	+ 15 46 x	Ari			F, vS, dif, r
894	−	2 21.6	− 5 30 r	Cet			vF, E, bM, Dneb with 895, conn
895	Gx	2 21.6	− 5 31 s	Cet	3.6	11.8	F, vL, iR, gbM, Dneb with 894, conn
1793 I	Gx	2 21.6	+ 32 34 u	Tri	1.8	15p	F, S, E 200°, glbM
899	Gx	2 21.9	− 20 48 s	Cet	1.9	13p	pB, S, gbM, r, D* p
890	Gx	2 22.0	+ 33 16 s	Tri	2.9	12p	B, S, R, bM, 3 F st sp
223 I	Gx	2 22.0	− 20 45 c	Cet	1.4		vF, S, dif, vF stell N
884	OC	2 22.4	+ 57 07 s	Per	30	4p	! Cl, vL, vRi, ruby * M
902	Gx	2 22.4	− 16 40 r	Cet		14p	eF, vS, R
891	Gx	2 22.6	+ 42 21 s	And	13.5	10.0	! B, vL, vmE 22°
905	Gx	2 22.6	− 8 43 r	Cet			eF, eS, R, *?
221 I	Gx	2 22.7	+ 28 16 u	Tri	2.2	14p	F, pL, R
222 I	Gx	2 22.7	+ 11 38 m	Ari	0.6	14p	F, S, irr, N, excentr
1796 I	Gx	2 22.8	− 41 22 c	Phe	1.5		vF, vS, R
907	Gx	2 23.0	− 20 43 s	Cet	1.9	13p	F, S, E 90°, gbM
908	Gx	2 23.1	− 21 14 s	Cet	5.5	10.2	cB, vL, E
898	Gx	2 23.3	+ 41 57 s	And	2.1	14p	eF, vS, lE
886	−	2 23.5	+ 63 47 r	Cas			Cl, L, lC, sc, st 9...13
900	Gx	2 23.5	+ 26 31 r	Ari		15p	vF, vS, stellar
901	−	2 23.6	+ 26 34 r	Ari			eF, vS; = 900?
903	Gx	2 23.8	+ 27 22 r	Ari			eF, eS, R
904	Gx	2 24.0	+ 27 21 r	Ari		15p	vF, vS, R, lbM
224 I	Gx	2 24.7	− 12 34 m	Cet	0.5	14p	F, S, irr R, lbM
896	Nb	2 24.8	+ 61 54 s	Cas	27		eF, pL, iF
922	Gx	2 25.1	− 24 47 s	For	1.9	12.2	cF, pL, R, gpmbM
906	Gx	2 25.2	+ 42 06 s	And	2.0	14p	eF, iE
909	Gx	2 25.4	+ 42 03 r	And		14p	vF, vS, vS* inv
910	Gx	2 25.4	+ 41 50 s	And	2.3	15p	vF, pS, stellar
1797 I	Gx	2 25.5	+ 20 24 u	Ari	1.2	15p	F, vS, iF, dif
915	Gx	2 25.7	+ 27 14 r	Ari		15p	eF, vS, stellar
916	Gx	2 25.7	+ 27 15 r	Ari		15p	eF
911	Gx	2 25.8	+ 41 59 r	And		14p	eF, vS, R, bM
912	Gx	2 25.8	+ 41 47 r	And		15p	F, vS, R, bM
913	Gx	2 25.8	+ 41 48 r	And			eF, vS, lbM
918	Gx	2 25.9	+ 18 30 s	Ari	3.4	13p	pF, L, R, *10 sf 3′
914	Gx	2 26.1	+ 42 09 r	And		14p	eF, pL, dif
917	−	2 26.1	+ 32 14 r	Tri			vF, S, R, 4 st nr (vS Cl?)
926	Gx	2 26.1	− 0 20 s	Cet	2.5	14p	vF, pS
919	Gx	2 26.2	+ 27 13 r	Ari		15p	eF
1798 I		2 26.3	+ 13 27 d	Ari			vF, vS, sbM *15
939	Gx	2 26.4	− 44 26 r	Eri			vvF, S, R, gvlbM
225 I	Gx	2 26.5	+ 1 09 u	Cet	1.8	15p	F, S, R, vlbM, *14 nf 2′
1795 I	Nb	2 26.5	+ 62 04 x	Cas	20		patch of neby
921	Gx	2 26.6	− 15 50 r	Cet		14p	eF, S, R, gbM
927	Gx	2 26.6	+ 12 09 s	Ari	1.4	15p	F, S, bM
944	Gx	2 26.7	− 14 30 r	Cet		14p	eF, S, mE 0°, sbM; = IC 228
228 I	Gx	2 26.7	− 14 31 m	Cet	0.8	14p	vS, R, gbM
924	Gx	2 26.8	+ 20 30 r	Ari		14p	eF, vS, iR
925	Gx	2 27.3	+ 33 35 s	Tri	9.8	10.0	cF, cL, E, vgbM, 2 st 13 np
929	Gx	2 27.3	− 12 05 r	Cet		15p	eF, S, E 170°, *8.5 n 4′
229 I		2 27.4	− 23 49 d	Cet			neb, 10m

NGC	Type	α_{2000}	δ_{2000}	Const.	Size	Mag.	Description
		h m	° ′		′		
923	Gx	2 27.6	+ 41 59 r	And		14p	vF, S, R, gsbM
934	Gx	2 27.6	− 0 14 r	Cet		14p	vF, eS, ◯ ?
936	Gx	2 27.6	− 1 09 s	Cet	5.2	10.1	vB, vL, R, mbMN, p of 2
928	Gx	2 27.7	+ 27 14 r	Ari		14p	eF, vS, stellar
226 I	Gx	2 27.7	+ 28 11 u	Tri	2.3	16p	pF, S, R, bM, 2 F st n
920	Gx	2 27.8	+ 45 58 r	And		15p	eF, eS, R, 1 or 2eF st nr
930	Gx	2 27.9	+ 20 20 r	Ari		13p	eF, S, iR, vgbM, 932 sf 1′
932	Gx	2 27.9	+ 20 19 u	Ari	1.9	14p	F, S, lE, 3 st inv
227 I	Gx	2 28.0	+ 28 10 u	Tri	2.3	15p	F, pS, R, lbM
935	Gx	2 28.2	+ 19 36 r	Ari		14p	pB, pS, R, * f 6ˢ
1801 I		2 28.2	+ 19 35 d	Ari			F, S, glbM, dif
931	Gx	2 28.3	+ 31 19 r	Tri		14p	F, pL, iR
938	Gx	2 28.5	+ 20 17 r	Ari		14p	pB, S, R, lbM, *11 sf
941	Gx	2 28.5	− 1 09 s	Cet	2.8	12.4	vF, cL, R, f of 2
947	Gx	2 28.5	− 19 04 s	Cet	2.6	12p	pB, E, gbM
945	Gx	2 28.6	− 10 32 s	Cet	2.5	12p	vF, L, iR, glbM
1800 I	OC	2 28.6	+ 31 24 x	Tri			eF, S; eS Cl?
1799 I	Gx	2 28.7	+ 45 58 u	And	1.3	15p	vF, S, lbM, *13 p 0′.5
1802 I		2 28.7	+ 23 07 d	Ari			*11 np 1′
948	Gx	2 28.8	− 10 31 s	Cet	1.4	14p	vF, S, R
951	Gx	2 28.8	− 22 20 r	Cet		15p	eF, S, E 0°, D*?
230 I		2 28.8	− 10 50 d	Cet			eF, S, *9.4 np 9′
954	Gx	2 28.9	− 41 25 v	Eri			vF, pL, lE, gbM, *8 sf 3′
933	Gx	2 29.2	+ 45 56 r	And		15p	eF, eS, R, B* nf
942	Gx	2 29.2	− 10 50 s	Cet		14p	vF, R, Dneb with 943, F Nucl
943	Gx	2 29.2	− 10 50 v	Cet			vF, R, Dneb with 942, F Nucl
950	Gx	2 29.2	− 11 01 r	Cet		14p	eF, S, gbM
1803 I		2 29.3	+ 23 09 d	Ari			stell N
940	Gx	2 29.4	+ 31 39 r	Tri		13p	F, S, R, bM
1804 I		2 29.4	+ 23 10 d	Ari			no descr
1810 I	Gx	2 29.4	− 43 04 c	Eri	1.4		vF, R, stell N
937	Gx	2 29.5	+ 42 16 r	And		15p	vF* slightly nebulous
1812 I	Gx	2 29.5	− 42 49 c	Eri	2.1		vF, bM
1806 I		2 29.6	+ 22 57 d	Ari			F, vS, R, bMN
231 I	Gx	2 30.0	+ 1 10 u	Cet	1.1	15p	F, vS, R, stellar
1807 I	Gx	2 30.4	+ 22 57 z	Ari		16p	F, vS, R, lbM
963	Gx	2 30.5	− 4 14 F	Cet			eF, S, R, gbM, r; = IC 1808
1808 I	Gx	2 30.5	− 4 14 m	Cet	0.6	14p	F, vS, R, gbM, r
955	Gx	2 30.6	− 1 07 s	Cet	3.0	12.0	pB, S, E, psbM
1811 I	Gx	2 30.6	− 34 16 c	For	1.9		eeF, S, R, 2 st p, np of 2 (sic)
946	Gx	2 30.7	+ 42 15 r	And		14p	F, S, R, glbM
958	Gx	2 30.7	− 2 57 s	Cet	2.8	12.2	pF, ilE, bM
949	Gx	2 30.8	+ 37 08 s	Tri	2.8	11.9	cB, L, E, vgbM
1813 I	Gx	2 30.8	− 34 13 c	For	1.6		eF, eS, R, F* n, 2 st np, sf of 2 (sic)
964	Gx	2 31.1	− 36 01 r	For			pB, pS, mE 215°
1814 I	Gx	2 31.1	− 36 02 c	For	2.1		pB, pS, mE; = 964
953	Gx	2 31.2	+ 29 36 r	Tri		14p	pF, S, R, mbM
961	−	2 31.2	− 6 54 r	Cet			eF, pS, E 230°, *10 att
232 I	Gx	2 31.2	+ 1 15 u	Cet	1.7	14p	vF, S, R, (= IC 231?)
952	−	2 31.3	+ 34 45 r	Tri			vF, vS, R, bM
979	Gx	2 31.5	− 44 31 r	Eri			F, S, R, bet 2 st in par
960	Gx	2 31.6	− 9 17 r	Cet		14p	eF, vS, R, neb?, *9 sp
233 I	Gx	2 31.6	+ 2 49 z	Cet		15p	pF, S, R, lbM, vF* s 1′
1809 I	Gx	2 31.6	+ 22 55 u	Ari	1.2	15p	pB, pL, E 135°, gbM
234 I	Gx	2 31.7	− 0 08 z	Cet		15p	F, S, dif, r

NGC	Type	α_{2000}	δ_{2000}	Const.	Size	Mag.	Description
		h m	o '		'		
966	Gx	2 31.8	− 19 53 r	Cet		14p	eF, R, *9.5 sp 1'
1816 I	Gx	2 31.9	− 36 40 c	For	1.9		vF, S, R, 2 st nr p
967	Gx	2 32.2	− 17 13 r	Cet		14p	F, S, iR, gbM
959	Gx	2 32.3	+ 35 30 s	Tri	2.2	13p	eF, pL, lE, lbM
956	OC	2 32.4	+ 44 39 s	And	8	9p	Cl, pRi, st 9...15
965	Gx	2 32.5	− 18 39 r	Cet		14p	vF, S, gbM
1805 I	C+N	2 32.7	+ 61 27 s	Cas	60	6.5	Cl, co, eL neby extends f
962	Gx	2 32.8	+ 28 05 r	Ari		14p	eF, S, gbMN
235 I	Gx	2 32.8	+ 20 39 v	Ari	0.5	14.7	F, S, dif
981	Gx	2 32.9	− 10 57 r	Cet		14p	eF, S, gbM
236 I		2 32.9	− 0 08 d	Cet			F, S, dif, vlbM
977	Gx	2 33.0	− 10 44 r	Cet		13p	eF, pS, R, vlbM, am sc st
975	Gx	2 33.2	+ 9 37 r	Cet		14p	vF, cE
237 I	Gx	2 33.5	+ 1 08 m	Cet	0.5	15p	F, S, R, *9.5 p
957	OC	2 33.6	+ 57 32 s	Per	11	7.6	Cl, pL, pRi, st 13...15
986	Gx	2 33.6	− 39 02 s	For	3.7	11.0	pB, L, pmE, sbM, biN
989	Gx	2 33.8	− 16 30 r	Cet		15p	F, vS, R, bMN
1817 I		2 33.8	+ 11 12 d	Ari			F, pL, E pf, dif
976	Gx	2 34.0	+ 20 59 s	Ari	1.7	12.4	vF, vS, 4 F st nr
968	Gx	2 34.1	+ 34 30 r	Tri		14p	pF, pS, R, bM
969	Gx	2 34.1	+ 32 58 r	Tri		13p	S, R, psbM, 1st of 5
1818 I		2 34.1	− 11 02 d	Cet			vF, eS, R, prob neb*
970	Gx	2 34.2	+ 33 00 r	Tri		15p	vF, vS, R, 2nd of 5
971	Gx	2 34.2	+ 32 59 r	Tri			vF, vS, R, 3rd of 5
972	Gx	2 34.2	+ 29 19 s	Ari	3.6	11.3	pB, cL, lE, gmbM, 3 st s
973	Gx	2 34.3	+ 32 31 r	Tri		13p	eeF, S, mE, pB* nr sp
1815 I	Gx	2 34.3	+ 32 26 u	Tri	2.0	14p	F, S, R, gbMN
974	Gx	2 34.4	+ 32 59 r	Tri		14p	vF, R, bM, 4th of 5
985	Gx	2 34.6	− 8 47 s	Cet	1.3	13.5	vF, vS, R, bMN
984	Gx	2 34.7	+ 23 26 r	Ari		14p	vF, eS, R, bM
978	Gx	2 34.8	+ 32 52 r	Tri		14p	pB, R, 5th of 5
983	−	2 35.0	+ 31 31 r	Tri			eF, vS, R, bM
238 I	Gx	2 35.3	+ 12 49 u	Ari	1.8	14p	vF, vS, R, mbM
982	Gx	2 35.4	+ 40 57 r	And		14p	F, S, nf of 2
988	Gx	2 35.4	− 9 21 s	Cet	4.7	11p	neb *7.5
980	Gx	2 35.5	+ 40 54 r	And		13p	vF, pS, sp of 2
991	Gx	2 35.5	− 7 09 s	Cet	2.7	12p	vF, cL, iF, vlbM
1819 I	Gx	2 35.7	+ 4 03 z	Cet		15p	F, vS, R
1822 I		2 35.7	− 8 34 d	Cet			*13.5 slightly nebs
1820 I	Gx	2 35.8	+ 6 03 z	Cet		15p	F, vS, R, bMN
1025	Gx	2 36.3	− 54 52 c	Hor	1.2		eF, S, R, p of 2
990	Gx	2 36.4	+ 11 39 r	Ari		14p	F, S, R, psbM
1821 I	Gx	2 36.4	+ 13 46 z	Ari		15p	pF, S, gbM, dif
239 I	Gx	2 36.5	+ 38 58 s	And	4.6	11.2	vF spiral, F stellar N
1031	Gx	2 36.6	− 54 52 c	Hor	2.2		F, S, R, gbM, *11 s 2'
993	Gx	2 36.7	+ 2 03 u	Cet	1.1	15p	eF, vS
994		2 36.7	+ 2 03 F	Cet			eeF, pS, R, vF*; = 993
987	Gx	2 36.8	+ 33 19 r	Tri		13p	F, S, vlE, bM, r, 2 st 14 np
992	Gx	2 37.2	+ 21 06 D	Ari		13p	pF, pS, mE, * s
997	Gx	2 37.2	+ 7 18 r	Cet		14p	F, S
998	Gx	2 37.2	+ 7 26 r	Cet		15p	vF
1006		2 37.4	− 11 02 F	Cet			eeF, pS, R, lbM; = 1010
1010	Gx	2 37.5	− 11 02 r	Cet		14p	eF, S, R
1004	Gx	2 37.6	+ 1 57 r	Cet		14p	pF, vS, R, vmbM, *11 p 2^s
1011	Gx	2 37.6	− 11 01 r	Cet		15p	eF, S, R, lbM

NGC	Type	α_{2000}	δ_{2000}	Const.	Size	Mag.	Description
		h m	o ′		′		
1007	Gx	2 37.8	+ 2 08 r	Cet		15p	eF, stellar
1013	Gx	2 37.8	− 11 31 r	Cet		14p	eeF, vS, R, bet 2 dist D st
1014	−	2 37.8	− 9 32 r	Cet			eF, eS, iR, p of 2
1017	Gx	2 37.8	− 11 01 r	Cet		14p	eeF, vS, R, v diffic
1008	Gx	2 37.9	+ 2 04 r	Cet		15p	vF, eS, stellar
241 I	Gx	2 37.9	+ 2 20 u	Cet	1.2	14p	vF, pS, R, stell N
1018	Gx	2 38.0	− 9 34 r	Cet		15p	eF, vS, E 180°, f of 2
1037	Gx	2 38.0	− 1 51 r	Cet		14p	eeF, vS, mE, v diffic
1015	Gx	2 38.1	− 1 19 s	Cet	3.5	12p	vF, S
1034	Gx	2 38.2	− 15 49 r	Cet		14p	vF, vS, lE, lbM, 2 st 11-12 p 20ˢ
1009 ′	Gx	2 38.3	+ 2 18 r	Cet		15p	eeF, pS, R, *9 sf
1016	Gx	2 38.3	+ 2 08 s	Cet	2.8	13p	F, S, R, psbM
1019	Gx	2 38.4	+ 1 55 s	Cet	1.2	15p	vF, S, lE
995	Gx	2 38.5	+ 41 32 r	And		15p	vF, vS
1022	Gx	2 38.5	− 6 40 s	Cet	2.5	11.4	cB, pL, R, mbM, *11 nf 2′
242 I	Gx	2 38.5	− 6 55 m	Cet	0.9	15p	eF, eS, vF* close
243 I	Gx	2 38.5	− 6 55 m	Cet	0.9	15p	vF, vS, R, bM
1823 I	Gx	2 38.6	+ 32 04 u	Tri	2.3	15p	F, S, iF, dif
996	Gx	2 38.7	+ 41 39 r	And		14p	vF, vS
1020	Gx	2 38.7	+ 2 13 r	Cet		15p	eF, vS
999	Gx	2 38.8	+ 41 40 r	And		14p	eF
1021	Gx	2 38.8	+ 2 12 r	Cet		15p	eF, S
1000	Gx	2 38.9	+ 41 27 r	And		15p	vvF, pS, dif
1002	Gx	2 38.9	+ 34 37 r	Tri		14p	vF, vS, iR, bMN
245 I	Gx	2 38.9	− 14 18 m	Cet	0.7	14p	pB, S, R, lbM
1825 I	Gx	2 38.9	+ 9 06 u	Cet	1.4	15p	F, S, R, gbMN
240 I		2 39.1	+ 41 44 d	Per			vF, pS
1826 I	Gx	2 39.1	− 27 27 c	For	1.7		pB, cS, R, *8 nr p; = IC 1830
1830 I	Gx	2 39.1	− 27 27 s	For	1.8	12.8	vF, S, susp, eF* 1′.5 sp
1001	Gx	2 39.2	+ 41 40 r	Per		14p	vF, vS
1024	Gx	2 39.2	+ 10 51 s	Ari	4.7	14p	pF, S, lE, bM, *11 nf 1′
1003	Gx	2 39.3	+ 40 52 s	Per	5.4	11.5	pF, L, E 90°±, mbM, r
1012	Gx	2 39.3	+ 30 09 s	Ari	2.9	13p	F, pS, iR, bM, st inv
1026	Gx	2 39.3	+ 6 32 r	Cet		14p	pF, S, R, psbM
1032	Gx	2 39.4	+ 1 06 s	Cet	3.6	13p	pB, S, vlE, bM, 3 st trap
244 I	Gx	2 39.4	+ 2 43 m	Cet	0.6	15p	vF, vS, dif
1005	Gx	2 39.5	+ 41 29 r	Per		14p	vF, vS
1028	Gx	2 39.5	+ 10 50 r	Ari		15p	eF
1029	Gx	2 39.5	+ 10 47 r	Ari		14p	F, S, mE
1035	Gx	2 39.5	− 8 08 s	Cet	2.2	13p	pF, L, mE, r, *17 att sf
1049	Gb	2 39.7	− 34 17 r	For			pB, S, R, stellar
1827 I	Gx	2 39.7	+ 1 33 u	Cet	1.2	14p	F, S, fan-shape, *13.5 close s
1030	Gx	2 39.9	+ 18 01 r	Ari		14p	vF, iE
1033	Gx	2 40.1	− 8 48 r	Cet		14p	eF, pL, iE 190°, sbMN
1038	Gx	2 40.1	+ 1 30 r	Cet		14p	eF, pS, R, lbM
247 I	Gx	2 40.1	− 11 44 m	Cet	1.2	14p	pB, S, R
1041	Gx	2 40.3	− 5 28 r	Cet		14p	pF, pS, iR, bM
1023	Gx	2 40.4	+ 39 04 s	Per	8.7	9.5	vB, vL, vmE, vvmbM
1042	Gx	2 40.4	− 8 26 s	Cet	4.7	10.9	eeF, L, R, np of 2
1045	Gx	2 40.4	− 11 18 r	Cet		13p	F, S, R, bM
1828 I	Gx	2 40.4	+ 19 18 u	Ari	1.6	13p	F, S, iF, gbMN
1036	Gx	2 40.5	+ 19 18 s	Ari	2.0	13p	F, S, R, lbM
1047	Gx	2 40.5	− 8 09 s	Cet	1.5	15p	eeF, pS, R, v diffic
246 I		2 40.5	+ 2 29 D	Cet			eef, vF, R, 2 eF st nr
1048	Gx	2 40.6	− 8 33 s	Cet	1.3	14p	eeF, pS, R, sf of 2

NGC	Type	α_{2000}	δ_{2000}	Const.	Size	Mag.	Description
		h m	° ′		′		
1043	Gx	2 40.7	+ 1 20 r	Cet		15p	eeF, S, R, v diffic
1829 I		2 40.7	+19 19 d	Ari			vF, vS, dif, r
250 I	Gx	2 40.9	−13 19 m	Cet	0.8	15p	vF, pS, iF
1044	Gx	2 41.1	+ 8 44 s	Cet	0.6	13.2	vF, vS, p of 2, *10 p
1051	Gx	2 41.1	− 6 56 t	Cet	1.9		eF, lE npsf, * att np; = IC 249
1052	Gx	2 41.1	− 8 15 s	Cet	2.9	10.6	B, pL, R, mbM *12
249 I	Gx	2 41.1	− 6 56 t	Cet	1.9		pB, vS, R, dif, 1051 f
1046	Gx	2 41.2	+ 8 43 v	Cet			eF, vS, f of 2
251 I	Gx	2 41.2	−14 58 m	Cet	0.4	15p	F, S, lbM
1824 I	OC	2 41.3	+61 37 x	Cas			Cl, st F, perhaps F neby p extends to it
248 I	Gx	2 41.4	+17 48 u	Ari	1.3	14p	vF
1833 I	Gx	2 41.6	−28 10 c	For	1.6		eeF, S, R, 3 D st nf
252 I		2 41.7	−14 51 d	Cet			F, S, bM
1055	Gx	2 41.8	+ 0 26 s	Cet	7.6	10.6	pF, cL, iE 80°, bM, *11 n 1′
1832 I	Gx	2 41.9	+19 02 m	Ari	0.4	15p	F, iF or lE ns, bMN
1039	OC	2 42.0	+42 47 s	Per	35	5.2	Cl, B, vL, lC, sc st 9; = M34
1065	Gx	2 42.1	−15 06 r	Cet		14p	eeF, pS, * nr s, *7.5 p; = IC 254
253 I	Gx	2 42.1	−15 03 m	Cet	0.3	14p	pB, iF, bM
254 I	Gx	2 42.1	−15 05 m	Cet	0.5	14p	vF, eS, R, 1065 close
1040	−	2 42.2	+41 30 r	Per			F, S, bM; = 1053?
1054	Gx	2 42.2	+18 12 r	Ari		14p	vF, vS, lE
1063	Gx	2 42.2	− 5 34 v	Cet	1.6		vF, pS, iR, r?
1064	Gx	2 42.2	− 9 22 r	Cet		14p	eF, S, R
1050	Gx	2 42.5	+34 46 r	Per		13p	F, S, *18 inv n
1059	D*	2 42.6	+18 01 D	Ari			nonexistent
1027	OC	2 42.7	+61 33 s	Cas	20	6.7	Cl, L, sc st, one 10m
1068	Gx	2 42.7	− 0 01 s	Cet	6.9	8.8	vB, pL, iR, sbMrrN; = M77
1069	Gx	2 42.8	− 8 18 r	Cet		14p	eeF, pS, R, *8.5 nr f
1834 I		2 42.8	+ 3 07 d	Cet			F, pS, pR, glbM
1056	Gx	2 42.9	+28 33 r	Ari		13p	F, S, R, psbM
1057	Gx	2 43.0	+32 29 r	Tri		15p	vF, double
1071	Gx	2 43.0	− 8 46 r	Cet		15p	eF, vS, E 0°, bet 2 st
1053	Gx	2 43.2	+41 30 r	Per		14p	vF, vS, lE, 3 or 4 st in line nr
1060	Gx	2 43.2	+32 24 r	Tri		13p	F, pL, R, lbM, *7.5 f 46ˢ, 3′ s
1061	Gx	2 43.2	+32 27 r	Tri		15p	vF, S, R, bM
1070	Gx	2 43.3	+ 4 58 r	Cet		13p	pF, S, iR, gbM
1836 I	Gx	2 43.3	+ 3 06 m	Cet		15p	F, S, R, vlbM
1058	Gx	2 43.5	+37 21 s	Per	3.0	11.5	pF, cL, R, glbM
1072	Gx	2 43.5	+ 0 18 s	Cet	1.7	14p	eF, vS, R, sev vF st inv
1837 I		2 43.5	+ 0 07 x	Cet			F, vS, R, gbM, r; = 1072
1062	Gx	2 43.7	+32 30 r	Tri		15p	eeF
1073	Gx	2 43.7	+ 1 23 s	Cet	4.9	11.0	vF, L, lbM, er
1074	Gx	2 43.7	−16 18 r	Cet		14p	eF, vS, R
1075	Gx	2 43.7	−16 11 r	Cet		15p	vF, vS, bMN
1076	Gx	2 43.7	−14 45 r	Cet		13p	vF, pS, R, B* f 22ˢ
1079	Gx	2 43.7	−29 00 s	For	3.1	11.4	B, pL, pmE, sbM
1066	Gx	2 43.8	+32 27 r	Tri		15p	vF, pL, R, lbM, s of 2
1067	Gx	2 43.8	+32 31 s	Tri	1.3	15p	eF, S, n of 2
1096	Gx	2 43.8	−59 55 c	Hor	2.3		F, pS, R, glbM
1835 I		2 43.8	+14 53 d	Ari			F, S, R, dif
1840 I	Gx	2 43.8	−15 42 m	Cet	0.6	15p	vF, vS, mbM, 1C81 nf
1831 I		2 44.1	+63 36 d	Cas			vF, eeL
1078	Gx	2 44.2	− 9 26 r	Cet		15p	eF, eS, R; = 1064?
1838 I	Gx	2 44.7	+19 27 m	Ari	0.6	16p	F, vS, R, sbM *14
1839 I	Gx	2 44.8	+15 15 u	Ari	1.1	15p	vF, S, R, dif

NGC	Type	α_{2000}	δ_{2000}		Const.	Size	Mag.	Description
		h m	o '			'		
1098	Gx	2 44.9	− 17 38	D	Eri		14p	F, vS, R, bMN, 1st of 3
1845 I		2 44.9	− 27 57	d	For			eeF, S, R, D ∗ np
1080	Gx	2 45.2	− 4 43	v	Cet	1.4		vF, pS, iR
1081	Gx	2 45.2	− 15 35	r	Eri		13p	eF, pS, R
1099	Gx	2 45.3	− 17 43	D	Eri		13p	F, pS, lE, bMN, 2nd of 3
1091		2 45.4	− 17 33	D	Eri			vF, vS, R, sbMN
1842 I	Gx	2 45.4	+ 11 28	z	Ari		16p	F, vS, R, glbM
1843 I	Gx	2 45.4	+ 2 53	u	Cet	1.7	14p	F, pL, E pf, dif
1100	Gx	2 45.6	− 17 41	D	Eri		13p	F, vS, lE, bMN, 3rd of 3
1841 I	Gx	2 45.6	+ 18 56	z	Ari		15p	F, vS, R, gvlbM
1082	Gx	2 45.7	− 8 13	r	Eri		15p	eeF, pS, lE
1092	Gx	2 45.7	− 17 32	r	Eri		14p	vF, vS, R, sbMN, b of 2
1083	Gx	2 45.8	− 15 20	A	Eri		14p	eeF, pS, mE, sp of 2
1844 I	Gx	2 45.8	+ 3 15	m	Cet	0.7	15p	F, pF, E pf, dif
1084	Gx	2 46.0	− 7 35	s	Eri	2.9	10.6	vB, pL, E, gpmbM
1077	Gx	2 46.1	+ 40 05	r	Per		16p	vF, pL, E
1097	Gx	2 46.3	− 30 17	s	For	9.3	9.3	vB, L, vmE 151°, vbMN
1085	Gx	2 46.4	+ 3 37	s	Cet	1.7	14p	F, S, R, lbM, bet 2 st
1087	Gx	2 46.4	− 0 30	s	Cet	3.5	11.0	pB, cL, lE, mbM
1089	Gx	2 46.4	− 15 04	A	Eri		14p	eeF, S, R, nf of 2
1090	Gx	2 46.6	− 0 15	s	Cet	3.8	11.9	vF, pL, iR, bM
1088	Gx	2 47.0	+ 16 11	r	Ari		15p	vF, S, iF
1102	Gx	2 47.1	− 22 14	r	Eri		14p	eF, vS, R
255 I	Gx	2 47.1	+ 16 16	m	Ari	0.6	16p	vF, vS, R, ∗12 f 5ˢ
1094	Gx	2 47.5	− 0 17	s	Cet	1.4	14p	vF, S, R, 2 S st p
1095	Gx	2 47.6	+ 4 38	r	Cet		14p	eF, pS, R
1846 I	Gx	2 47.7	+ 13 15	u	Ari	1.1	15p	F, S, glbM
1086	Gx	2 47.9	+ 41 15	r	Per		13p	vF, pS, D∗ nr
1847 I	Gx	2 47.9	+ 14 30	z	Ari		16p	F, S, iF, r
1103	Gx	2 48.0	− 13 57	r	Eri		13p	eeF, S, E, ∗15 inv, ∗11 f
1853 I	Gx	2 48.0	− 13 59	m	Eri	0.8	14p	eF, vS, 1103 f 2ˢ, 2′ n
1093	Gx	2 48.2	+ 34 25	r	Tri		14p	eF, vS
1849 I		2 48.2	+ 9 22	d	Cet			F, vS, R, stell
1101	Gx	2 48.3	+ 4 34	r	Cet		15p	vF, eS, R, bM, ∗13 p
1119		2 48.3	− 18 01	D	Eri			F, eS, R (F∗?)
1104	Gx	2 48.6	− 0 16	s	Cet	1.3	15p	vF, vS, r, ∗14 s
1108	Gx	2 48.6	− 7 58	r	Eri			eF, pS, R
1850 I		2 48.7	+ 13 14	d	Ari			F, S, dif
1859 I	Gx	2 48.8	− 31 11	m	For	1.2	14p	pF, pS, R, 2nd of 3
1856 I	Gx	2 48.9	− 0 46	v	Cet	1.3		F, S, E 200°, gbMN
1852 I	Gx	2 49.0	+ 13 13	u	Ari	1.3	15p	F, pS, R, gbM
1109	Gx	2 49.1	+ 13 15	r	Ari		15p	vF
261 I		2 49.1	− 14 28	F	Eri			F, pL; = 1120
1858 I	Gx	2 49.1	− 31 17	c	For	1.7		vF, pS, R, 1st of 3
1114	Gx	2 49.2	− 17 00	r	Eri		13p	pF, pL, pmE, glbM
1120	Gx	2 49.2	− 14 27	r	Eri		14p	vF, S, R, bM
1107	Gx	2 49.3	+ 8 06	r	Cet		14p	F, vS, R
1110	Gx	2 49.3	− 7 51	t	Eri	2.7		eF, pL, E 348°
1854 I	Gx	2 49.3	+ 19 18	v	Ari			F, vS, R, bMN
1855 I		2 49.3	+ 13 22	d	Ari			F, pL, D ns, biN
1860 I	Gx	2 49.6	− 31 11	c	For	1.9		pF, pS, lE, 3rd of 3
1111	Gx	2 49.7	+ 13 08	r	Ari			F, vS, stellar
1857 I	Gx	2 49.7	+ 14 37	u	Ari	1.0	15p	F, S, R, glbM
256 I	Gx	2 49.8	+ 46 59	u	Per	2.5	14p	cF, lE, S, 1st of 3
258 I	Gx	2 49.8	+ 41 03	u	Per	1.7	16p	vF, vlbM, ∗9.5 f 2′

NGC	Type	α_{2000}	δ_{2000}	Const.	Size	Mag.	Description
		h m	° ′		′		
257 I		2 49.9	+ 46 59 d	Per			eF, pS, R, v diffic, 2nd of 3
1112	–	2 50.0	+ 13 13 r	Ari			F, pS
1118	Gx	2 50.0	– 12 09 r	Eri		14p	eF, vS, E pf
259 I		2 50.1	+ 41 04 d	Per			vF, double, dist 17″
1113	–	2 50.2	+ 13 18 r	Ari			vF
1115	Gx	2 50.5	+ 13 15 r	Ari		15p	vF
1106	Gx	2 50.6	+ 41 41 r	Per		13p	vF, vS, vF∗ att s
1116	Gx	2 50.6	+ 13 19 r	Ari		15p	vF
263 I		2 50.6	– 0 07 d	Cet			vF, vS, R, N = 14m
1121	Gx	2 50.8	– 1 44 r	Eri		13p	F, mE
1135	Gx	2 50.8	– 54 56 c	Hor	0.8		F, R, gbM
1136	Gx	2 50.9	– 55 04 v	Hor	1.7		F, R, gbM
264 I		2 50.9	– 0 10 d	Cet			vF, eS, R, stellar
260 I	Gx	2 51.1	+ 46 57 u	Per	1.8	15p	eeF, pS, 2 F st nr, 3rd of 3
1848 I	C+N	2 51.2	+ 60 26 s	Cas	60	6.5	Cl, st F, extends 8ᵐf, in F neby
1117	Gx	2 51.3	+ 13 11 r	Ari		15p	close to a S∗
1124	Gx	2 51.6	– 25 42 r	For		15p	eF, eS, iR, gbM, ∗9 nf 1′
262 I	Gx	2 51.7	+ 42 50 u	Per	2.3	15p	eeF, pS, R, bet 2 st, v diffic
1125	Gx	2 51.8	– 16 38 r	Eri		13p	vF, S, lE, gbM
1851 I	?	2 51.8	+ 58 19 z	Cas			∗6.2, neb att sp, 5′ l
1862 I	Gx	2 52.0	– 33 20 c	For	3.2		eeF, vS, lE, v diffic, ∗7 sf
1105	Gx	2 52.4	– 15 42 r	Eri		15p	vF, vS, R
1126	Gx	2 52.4	– 1 18 r	Eri		15p	eeF, S, R, 1132 f
1128	–	2 52.6	+ 6 03 r	Cet			eF, S, lE, 2 F st close p
1133	Gx	2 52.7	– 8 47 r	Eri		15p	vF, vS, lE 45°, 2 st np, nf
1122	Gx	2 52.8	+ 42 12 r	Per		13p	vF, pS, R, ∗ nr n
1123	–	2 52.8	+ 42 13 r	Per			cF, S, iR, vgbM, r; = 1122?
1127	Gx	2 52.9	+ 13 15 r	Ari		15p	vF
1132	Gx	2 52.9	– 1 16 r	Eri		14p	eF, pL, gbM, ∗8 f
1139	Gx	2 52.9	– 14 31 r	Eri		15p	vF, S, R, gbMN
1864 I		2 53.2	– 34 12 d	For			eF, S, R
1861 I		2 53.3	+ 25 29 d	Ari			F, pS, R, vgbM
1134	Gx	2 53.6	+ 13 00 s	Ari	2.5	13p	F, S, iR, r
267 I	Gx	2 53.8	+ 12 50 v	Ari	2.2		vF, pS, dif, 1134 np
1137	Gx	2 54.0	+ 2 57 r	Cet		13p	vF, pS, R, lbM
1130	Gx	2 54.4	+ 41 37 r	Per		13p	eF, eS
1129	Gx	2 54.5	+ 41 35 r	Per		14p	cF, pS, iR, vglbM, D or F∗ sp
1131	Gx	2 54.6	+ 41 34 r	Per		15p	eF, eS
1140	Gx	2 54.6	– 10 02 s	Eri	1.4	12.5	pB, S, R, stellar
1145	Gx	2 54.6	– 18 38 r	Eri		13p	F, pL, pmE, 2 S st f
265 I	Gx	2 54.7	+ 41 40 z	Per		16p	eeF, eS, R
1863 I	Gx	2 54.9	+ 8 47 z	Cet		16p	F, vS, R, gbMN
1866 I	Gx	2 54.9	– 15 38 m	Eri	0.4	14p	vF, eS, alm stell
266 I	Gx	2 55.0	+ 42 14 m	Per	0.3	15p	eF, eS, R
1143	Gx	2 55.1	– 0 10 s	Cet	1.1	13.5	eF, S, R, p of 2
1141		2 55.2	+ 0 28 F	Cet			vF, S, p of Dneb; prob = 1143
1142		2 55.2	+ 0 28 F	Cet			pF, S, R, f of Dneb; prob = 1144
1144	Gx	2 55.2	– 0 11 s	Cet	0.9	13.3	eF, S, R, f of 2
1147	–	2 55.3	– 9 07 r	Eri			eF, vS, E 0°, ∗9.5 f 6′
268 I	Gx	2 55.4	– 14 06 m	Eri	0.6	15p	vF, vS, irr R, lbM
269 I	Gx	2 55.4	– 14 04 m	Eri	1.0	15p	eF, vS, dif
1865 I	Gx	2 55.4	+ 8 49 u	Cet	1.6	15p	F, vS, R, gbM, r
270 I	Gx	2 55.7	– 14 12 m	Eri	1.2	14p	pB, vS, R
1867 I	Gx	2 55.9	+ 9 18 u	Cet	2.2	15p	F, S, pR, gbM
271 I	Gx	2 56.0	– 12 00 m	Eri	0.8	15p	vF, S, R

NGC	Type	α_{2000}	δ_{2000}	Const.	Size	Mag.	Description
		h m	o ′		′		
272 I	Gx	2 56.1	− 14 11 m	Eri	0.9	15p	vF, S, iF
1868 I		2 56.1	+ 9 21 d	Cet			F, vS, R, stell
1138	Gx	2 56.5	+ 43 03 r	Per		14p	vF, vS, R, gbM, 2 S st △
1181		2 57.0	− 15 02 D	Eri			eF, vS, R, bMN
1148	Gx	2 57.1	− 7 42 r	Eri		15p	eF, pS, R, v diffic, np of 2
1150	Gx	2 57.1	− 15 03 r	Eri		15p	vF, S, R, sbMN
1151	Gx	2 57.1	− 15 00 r	Eri			eF, S, R (neb?), nr 1150
1180		2 57.1	− 15 00 D	Eri			eF, vS, R, bMN
273 I	Gx	2 57.1	+ 2 47 u	Cet	1.8	14p	F, pS, lE 235°, bM
1158	Gx	2 57.3	− 14 23 r	Eri		15p	eF, S, R, sbMN
1149	Gx	2 57.4	− 0 18 r	Cet		15p	vF, vS, R, bM, S∗ p 30″
1146	−	2 57.5	+ 46 27 r	Per			Cl, vS, vF + neb
1152	Gx	2 57.6	− 7 47 r	Eri		15p	eeF, S, R, v diffic, sf of 2, ∗ s
1870 I	Gx	2 57.9	− 2 21 t	Eri	2.9		vF, R, vgbM, v diffic
1153	Gx	2 58.1	+ 3 22 r	Cet		13p	F, vS, ilE, sbM, er
1154	Gx	2 58.1	− 10 21 r	Eri		14p	eF, S, lbM, sp of 2
1869 I	Gx	2 58.1	+ 5 50 z	Cet		16p	F, eS, like neb D∗
1155	Gx	2 58.2	− 10 20 r	Eri		14p	eF, S, lbM, nf of 2
1157	Gx	2 58.2	− 15 07 r	Eri			eF, pS, E 0°, sbMN
1165	Gx	2 58.7	− 32 07 v	For	3.1		vF, pL, E, vlbM
276 I	Gx	2 58.7	− 15 41 m	Eri	2.0	14p	pB, S, mbM
1162	Gx	2 58.9	− 12 24 r	Eri		13p	F, R, glbM, stellar
1156	Gx	2 59.7	+ 25 14 s	Ari	3.1	11.7	pB, cL, pmE 0°, bet 2 st
277 I	Gx	2 59.8	+ 2 46 v	Cet	1.6		pB, pS, R, N = 12.5
274 I		3 00.1	+ 44 13 d	Per			eeF, pS, R, v diffic
1163	Gx	3 00.3	− 17 09 v	Eri	3.4		vF, pS, mE 75°
1166	Gx	3 00.6	+ 11 51 r	Ari		15p	eF, S
1159	Gx	3 00.7	+ 43 10 r	Per		14p	vF, S, R, vlbM
1168	Gx	3 00.8	+ 11 47 r	Ari		15p	eF
275 I		3 00.9	+ 44 21 d	Per			eeF, pS, R, bet 2 st
1160	Gx	3 01.2	+ 44 58 s	Per	1.6	13p	F, E
1161	Gx	3 01.2	+ 44 55 s	Per	3.1	13p	F, pS, lE, sbM
279 I	Gx	3 01.2	+ 16 13 z	Ari		15p	vF, vS, R, dif
278 I	Gx	3 01.5	+ 37 47 u	Per	2.3	15p	vF, ∗10 p 95″, F∗ 12″ sp
1172	Gx	3 01.6	− 14 50 s	Eri	2.2	12.0	pF, pL, R, psbM
1167	Gx	3 01.7	+ 35 12 s	Per	3.1	12.3	vF, pL, R, spmbM
1164	Gx	3 01.9	+ 42 36 r	Per		14p	eF, vS
1205		3 02.4	− 9 40 D	Eri			eF, pS, E 25°, ∗9.5 3′ sp; = 1182
1170	−	3 02.5	+ 27 04 r	Ari			eL, dif
1179	Gx	3 02.6	− 18 54 s	Eri	4.6	12p	eF, pS, gbM, ∗12 f 1′
1187	Gx	3 02.6	− 22 52 s	Eri	5.0	11p	pF, cL, pmE, gbM ∗16, r
1185	Gx	3 03.0	− 9 08 r	Eri		15p	eF, pS, E 15°
1877 I	Gx	3 03.2	− 50 31 c	Hor	3.0		eF, vS, E 170°, prob neb
280 I	Ast	3 03.3	+ 42 21 x	Per			eF, pS, R
1189	Gx	3 03.4	− 15 37 r	Eri		14p	eF, vS, R, p 1209
1195	Gx	3 03.4	− 12 02 r	Eri		14p	eF, eS, ∗12 sf, 1196 sf
1182	Gx	3 03.5	− 9 40 r	Eri			eF, pS, E 120°, ∗10 sp 2′.5
1190	Gx	3 03.5	− 15 39 r	Eri		15p	eF, vS, R, p 1209
1196	Gx	3 03.5	− 12 05 r	Eri		14p	vF, sp of 2
1169	Gx	3 03.6	+ 46 23 s	Per	4.4	11.7	pF, pS, iF, sbM
1191	Gx	3 03.6	− 15 40 r	Eri		15p	eF, vS, R, p 1209
1199	Gx	3 03.6	− 15 37 s	Eri	2.2	11.5	cB, pS, iR, smbM
1188		3 03.7	− 15 30 D	Eri			eF, vS, R, p 1209
1192	Gx	3 03.7	− 15 40 r	Eri		15p	eF, vS, R, p 1209
1878 I		3 03.7	− 52 06 d	Hor			eeF, eS, cE 5°, prob neb

NGC	Type	α_{2000}		δ_{2000}		Const.	Size	Mag.	Description
		h	m	o	$'$		$'$		
1194	Gx	3	03.8	$-$ 1	05 r	Cet		14p	F, S, R, glbM
1200	Gx	3	03.8	-11	59 r	Eri		13p	pF, cL, iR, bM, nf of 2
1873 I		3	03.8	$+$ 9	31 d	Cet			F, S, E 200°
283 I	Gx	3	03.9	$-$ 0	12 m	Cet	0.4	15p	pB, eS, R
1875 I	Gx	3	03.9	-39	26 c	For	1.8		eF, pS, R, FD∗ sf in line
1879 I		3	03.9	-52	06 d	Hor			eeF, eS, mE 135°, stell N
1171	Gx	3	04.0	$+43$	24 s	Per	3.2	13p	vF, pL, iF
1201	Gx	3	04.1	-26	04 s	For	4.4	10.6	cB, pS, vlE, r, S∗ nr
285 I	Gx	3	04.1	-12	01 m	Eri	1.0	15p	F, vS, dif, 1200 p
1173	$-$	3	04.2	$+41$	22 r	Per			eF, vS, stellar Nucl
1175	Gx	3	04.5	$+42$	20 s	Per	2.5	12.8	F, cL, E
1176	$-$	3	04.5	$+41$	23 r	Per			∗13 in vF neb
281 I		3	04.5	$+42$	21 x	Per			eeF, vS, ∗ close n, 1175 nr; = 1177
1876 I	Gx	3	04.5	-27	26 s	For	0.7	14.4	eeF, S, R, F∗ nr sf
1177	Gx	3	04.6	$+42$	22 r	Per		15p	vF, S, R, nf 1175; = IC 281
1178	$-$	3	04.6	$+41$	18 r	Per			∗13 in vF neb (?)
1204	Gx	3	04.6	-12	20 r	Eri		15p	eF, E 45°, r, sev st inv
1872 I	OC	3	04.6	$+42$	49 x	Per			Cl
1183	$-$	3	04.7	$+41$	22 r	Per			∗13 inv in neb
286 I		3	04.8	$-$ 6	29 d	Eri			vF
1202	Gx	3	04.9	$-$ 6	29 r	Eri			eF, S, 2 st 4$'$ nf
287 I		3	05.0	-12	05 d	Eri			F, vS, R, stellar
1203	Gx	3	05.2	-14	22 r	Eri		15p	vF, S, R, bMN (neb?)
282 I		3	05.2	$+41$	51 d	Per			eF, S, R, bet 2 st nr
1174		3	05.5	$+42$	49 D	Per			pF, pS, lE, pB∗ close p; prob = 1186
1186	Gx	3	05.5	$+42$	50 s	Per	3.3	13p	F∗ with neb appendages
1193	OC	3	05.8	$+44$	23 s	Per	2	13p	F, cL, er
1209	Gx	3	06.0	-15	37 s	Eri	2.6	11.4	B, S, cE, psbM
1206	Gx	3	06.1	$-$ 8	50 F	Eri			eF, vS, vlE 0°
1197	$-$	3	06.2	$+44$	04 r	Per			pF, pS, cE, sev vF st nr
1198	Gx	3	06.2	$+41$	52 r	Per		14p	neb ∗11
1208	Gx	3	06.2	$-$ 9	32 r	Eri		14p	pB, S, lE 80°±, lbM
1217	Gx	3	06.2	-39	01 r	For			pF, S, R, psbM
284 I	Gx	3	06.2	$+42$	23 s	Per	4.9	13p	eeF, pL, lE, D∗ np, bet 2 st
1871 I	?	3	06.4	$+60$	41 x	Cas	4		∗9.3 nebs, chiefly f
1874 I	Gx	3	06.4	$+36$	00 m	Per	0.9	14p	F, vS, vlbM, dif
1244	Gx	3	06.5	-66	47 c	Hor	2.0		F, S, pmE, gbM
1880 I	Gx	3	06.5	$-$ 9	43 m	Eri	1.0	15p	eF, S, ∗9 f 8^s
1885 I	Gx	3	06.7	-32	52 c	For	1.5		vF, vS, mE 140°, gbM
1210	Gx	3	06.8	-25	42 r	For		13p	eF, vS, iR, gbMN
1211	Gx	3	06.9	$-$ 0	47 r	Cet		13p	pB, vS, R, mbMN = ∗9-10
1214	Gx	3	06.9	$-$ 9	32 r	Eri		14p	F, pS, iR, 1208 p
1246	Gx	3	07.0	-66	56 c	Hor	1.5		pF, S, R, glbM
1215	Gx	3	07.1	$-$ 9	35 r	Eri		14p	eF, vS, R
1216	Gx	3	07.3	$-$ 9	36 r	Eri		15p	eF, S, stellar, 3rd of 3
291 I	Gx	3	07.4	-12	37 m	Eri	0.8	14p	F, S, R, bM
288 I	OC	3	07.5	$+42$	22 x	Per			vF, vS, R, 2 st nf; S Cl?
1882 I	Gx	3	07.8	$+$ 3	09 u	Cet	1.0	15p	F, pL, E 210°
1886 I	Gx	3	08.0	$-$ 4	24 m	Eri	0.3	15p	vF, S, vmbM, ∗13 s 1$'$.2
1896 I		3	08.0	-54	14 d	Hor			eeF, eS, cE 10°, stell N
1221	Gx	3	08.1	$-$ 4	15 r	Eri		15p	eF, vS, E 170°, ∗ s
1207	Gx	3	08.2	$+38$	23 r	Per		13p	cF, vS, R, psb in npp end
1228	Gx	3	08.2	-22	55 r	Eri		14p	eF, eS, gbM, p of 2
1229	Gx	3	08.2	-22	58 s	Eri	1.9	14p	eF, eS, R, gbM, f of 2
1223		3	08.3	$-$ 4	09 D	Eri			eF, S, R, gbMN, p of 2

NGC	Type	α_{2000}	δ_{2000}	Const.	Size	Mag.	Description
		h m	° ′		′		
1230	Gx	3 08.3	− 23 00 r	Eri		15p	*12 in eF neb
1218	Gx	3 08.4	+ 4 07 s	Cet	1.3	12.8	pF, pS, R
1892 I	Gx	3 08.4	− 23 03 c	Eri	1.9		vF, L, nr 1230
1219	Gx	3 08.5	+ 2 09 r	Cet		13p	F, pL, R
1212	Gx	3 08.6	+ 40 51 r	Per			eF, S, R, Algol nr
1225		3 08.8	− 4 06 D	Eri			eF, vS, R, f of 2
1222	Gx	3 08.9	− 2 58 s	Eri	1.3	14p	vF* in pF, S, R neb
1213	Gx	3 09.2	+ 38 39 r	Per		15p	eF, lE, * close n, diffic
1881 I	Gx	3 09.2	+ 38 38 u	Per	3.0	16p	vF, pS, v dif (= 1213?)
1231	−	3 09.6	− 15 35 r	Eri			eF, pL, E (neb?)
1234	Gx	3 09.6	− 7 51 r	Eri		15p	eF, S, iR, * or st inv
1895 I	Gx	3 09.6	− 25 15 c	For	1.8		eeF, pS, 2 st close p
290 I	Gx	3 09.7	+ 40 59 u	Per	1.2	15p	eeF, S, R
1883 I	Gx	3 09.7	+ 40 54 u	Per	1.1	16p	S, R, vgbM
1884 I		3 09.7	+ 40 59 d	Per			S, E npsf, diffic, *12 close f
1232	Gx	3 09.8	− 20 35 s	Eri	7.8	9.9	pB, cL, R, gbM, r
1890 I	Gx	3 10.0	+ 19 13 m	Ari	0.2	15p	pB, pL, iF, N, r
1249	Gx	3 10.1	− 53 21 s	Hor	5.2	12p	B, L, vmE 80°, vgbM
1887 I		3 10.2	+ 40 45 d	Per			*12 close sf
1891 I		3 10.2	+ 19 36 d	Ari			vF, S, bM, dif
289 I	Pl	3 10.3	+ 61 19 s	Cas	0.6	12p	pB, pL, R, bet 2 vF st
292 I	Gx	3 10.3	+ 40 46 v	Per	1.2		eF, pS, R, * s, bet 2 st
1893 I		3 10.3	+ 19 37 d	Ari			ef, vS, diffic
1898 I	Gx	3 10.3	− 22 24 c	Eri	3.2		neb line at 60°, susp
1252		3 10.5	− 58 08 r	Hor			Cl of 18 or 20 st
1894 I	Gx	3 10.5	+ 19 36 z	Ari		16p	F, S, vlbM, dif
1237	D*	3 10.7	− 8 40 F	Eri			vF, S, E 170°; D*?
1897 I	Gx	3 10.8	− 10 49 m	Eri	0.5	14p	eF, vS, nr 1238
1238	Gx	3 10.9	− 10 45 r	Eri		14p	vF, pS, R, 1247 nf
293 I	Gx	3 10.9	+ 41 07 m	Per	0.2	15p	eF, S, R
294 I		3 10.9	+ 40 38 d	Per			vF, pS, irr R
1239	Gx	3 11.0	− 2 31 r	Eri		15p	eF, stellar (RA 30ˢgreater?)
295 I		3 11.0	+ 40 37 d	Per			eF, pS, R
299 I		3 11.0	− 13 07 d	Eri			vF, vS, R, lbM
1888 I		3 11.0	+ 41 08 d	Per			vF, S
1889 I		3 11.0	+ 40 37 d	Per			F, R, vgbM
1226	Gx	3 11.1	+ 35 24 r	Per		14p	F, vS, R, bM
296 I	Gx	3 11.1	+ 40 37 u	Per	2.8	16p	eF, pS, irr R, F D* p
1227	Gx	3 11.2	+ 35 20 r	Per		15p	vF, vS
1224	Gx	3 11.3	+ 41 22 s	Per	1.7	16p	eF, vS, R
1241	Gx	3 11.3	− 8 55 s	Eri	3.0	13p	F, pL, R, vglbM, *9 n
1242	Gx	3 11.3	− 8 54 s	Eri	1.3	14p	vF, S
298 I	Gx	3 11.3	+ 1 19 v	Cet			F, pL, 2 B points inv
1243	Gx	3 11.4	− 8 57 h	Eri	0.4	14p	F, vS, R
1236	Gx	3 11.6	+ 10 49 r	Ari		15p	eF, vS, R
1220	OC	3 11.7	+ 53 20 s	Per	2	12p	Cl, vS, st vF
1899 I		3 11.8	− 25 19 d	For			eeF, S, R, 2 F st sp in line
1247	Gx	3 12.2	− 10 29 s	Eri	3.6	13p	F, pL, E 80°
1261	Gb	3 12.3	− 55 13 s	Hor	6.9	8.4	⊕, B, L, R, rr
1233	Gx	3 12.5	+ 39 19 s	Per	2.1	13.2	F, vS, R, diff
303 I		3 12.7	− 11 42 d	Eri			eF, eS, stellar
1235	*⋆*	3 12.8	+ 38 56 r	Per			vF, S, lE
1248	Gx	3 12.8	− 5 13 s	Eri	1.3	14p	cF, S, lE, bM, *9 n 5′
302 I	Gx	3 12.8	+ 4 42 v	Cet	2.1		pF, pS, R, vSN
1240	*	3 12.9	+ 30 34 r	Ari			eF, vS; vS st?

NGC	Type	α_{2000}	δ_{2000}	Const.	Size	Mag.	Description
		h m	o ′		′		
306 I		3 13.0	− 11 43 d	Eri			eF, S, R, diffic
1903 I		3 13.1	− 50 36 d	Hor			2 F neb, E
297 I	D*	3 13.3	+ 42 06 x	Per			eeF, pS, R, v diffic, F* sp
1255	Gx	3 13.5	− 25 44 s	For	4.1	11.1	F, pL, F* close p
307 I	Gx	3 13.8	− 0 13 u	Cet	1.9	15p	pB, vS, r
1256	Gx	3 13.9	− 21 58 r	Eri		14p	F, S, E, alm stell, *8 np
1258	Gx	3 13.9	− 21 45 r	Eri		13p	eF, pS, vlE, 12′ n of 1256
1251	D*	3 14.1	+ 1 28 F	Cet			F
1253	Gx	3 14.1	− 2 49 s	Eri	4.8	12p	*12 with neb f, 90″ l
300 I	Gx	3 14.3	+ 42 25 x	Per			eF, S, R, *9 sp, np of 2
1254	Gx	3 14.4	+ 2 42 r	Cet		15p	F, vS, stellar
1245	OC	3 14.7	+ 47 15 s	Per	10	8.4	Cl, pL, Ri, C, iR, st 12...15
301 I	Gx	3 14.8	+ 42 13 x	Per			eF, pS, R, sf of 2
304 I	Gx	3 15.0	+ 37 54 u	Per	1.3	15p	vF, * 76″ sf, np of 2
1904 I	Gx	3 15.0	− 30 43 c	For	1.8		eF, vS, mE 80°, stell N
305 I	Gx	3 15.1	+ 37 51 m	Per	1.0	15p	vF, * 49″ nf
1908 I	Gx	3 15.1	− 54 49 c	Hor	1.6		vF, vS, spir branch
1250	Gx	3 15.4	+ 41 21 s	Per	2.7	14p	vF, vS, R
1262	Gx	3 15.7	− 15 52 r	Eri		14p	eF, pS, iR, sbMN
1263	Gx	3 15.8	− 15 06 r	Eri		15p	vF, S, lE, sbM
1266	Gx	3 16.0	− 2 24 r	Eri		14p	vF, pS, *13 sp 2′
1900 I	Gx	3 16.0	+ 37 08 m	Per	0.6	15p	F, S, pR, gbMN
309 I	Gx	3 16.1	+ 40 48 v	Per	1.0		eeF, pS, R, bet 2 st
1901 I		3 16.1	+ 37 07 d	Per			F, vS, R, gbMN
1906 I	Gx	3 16.1	− 34 22 c	For	1.5		vF, vS, vmE 60°, gbM
1902 I	Gx	3 16.2	+ 37 11 z	Per		16p	F, vS, R, sbM *14
308 I	Gx	3 16.3	+ 41 11 x	Per			eF, pS, iR, r?
1257	Gx	3 16.4	+ 41 31 r	Per		14p	stellar neb
1184	Gx	3 16.6	+ 80 48 s	Cep	3.0	13p	F, pL, mE
310 I	Gx	3 16.7	+ 41 20 v	Per	1.6		vF, pS, R, 1259 and 1260 near
311 I	Gx	3 16.8	+ 40 01 u	Per	1.9	16p	eF, pS, iR, bet 2 st, vF* v close f
1912 I		3 16.8	− 50 39 d	Hor			S, E ns
1259	Gx	3 17.0	+ 41 21 r	Per		15p	vF, S, R, vlbM
1288	Gx	3 17.2	− 32 35 s	For	2.3	12.1	vF, L, R, vglbM, cE ns
1269		3 17.3	− 41 06 c	Eri			vB, R, gmbM; = 1291
1291	Gx	3 17.3	− 41 08 s	Eri	10.5	8.5	⊕ , vB, pL, R, mbM, er
1909 I	Gx	3 17.3	− 33 41 c	For	1.3		vF, vS, cE 45°, stell N
1260	Gx	3 17.5	+ 41 24 s	Per	1.7	14p	vF, S, R
1284	Gx	3 17.6	− 10 18 r	Eri		14p	eF, vS, 2 st s
1285	Gx	3 17.8	− 7 20 r	Eri		14p	pF, S
1286	Gx	3 17.8	− 7 39 r	Eri		15p	eF, eS, R, 4 B st s
1264	Gx	3 17.9	+ 41 26 r	Per		15p	vF, S, vlbM
1280	Gx	3 18.0	− 0 10 r	Cet		14p	vF, vS, R, gbM, r
1910 I		3 18.0	− 21 26 d	Eri			2 eF, eS, neb susp
312 I	Gx	3 18.1	+ 41 45 v	Per	1.5		eeF, pS, R, nearly bet 2 st
1292	Gx	3 18.2	− 27 37 s	For	3.2	13p	F, pS, lE, vgbM, S D* nr
1265	Gx	3 18.3	+ 41 52 s	Per	2.1	15p	vF, vS, mbM
1313	Gx	3 18.3	− 66 30 s	Ret	8.5	9p	pB, L, E, vgbM, r
1287	Gx	3 18.6	− 2 45 r	Eri			vF, vS, iR
1267	Gx	3 18.7	+ 41 28 s	Per	1.4	15p	F, vS, R, stell
1268	Gx	3 18.8	+ 41 29 s	Per	1.2	15p	eF, S, lE, com
314 I	Gx	3 18.8	− 1 58 u	Eri	2.1	14p	*13 in vF, S neb
1905 I	*⃰*	3 18.8	+ 41 22 x	Per			Cl, S, vF; neb?
1289	Gx	3 18.9	− 1 59 r	Eri		14p	vF, S, R, 4 st f; = IC 314
1296	Gx	3 18.9	− 13 04 r	Eri		14p	eF, vS, R

NGC	Type	α_{2000}	δ_{2000}	Const.	Size	Mag.	Description
		h m	o '		'		
1270	Gx	3 19.0	+ 41 28 s	Per	1.1	12.9	vF, S, R
317 I	Gx	3 19.0	− 12 45 m	Eri	0.8	14p	vF, pL, R
315 I	Gx	3 19.1	+ 4 02 z	Cet		15p	vF, S, dif, vlbM
1271	Gx	3 19.2	+ 41 21 s	Per		16p	vF, vS
1297	Gx	3 19.2	− 19 06 s	Eri	2.3	13p	F, pS
1272	Gx	3 19.3	+ 41 29 s	Per	2.5	15p	F, S, R
1273	Gx	3 19.4	+ 41 32 s	Per	1.4	12.9	vF, vS
1290		3 19.4	− 13 59 D	Eri			eF, eS
1914 I	Gx	3 19.4	− 49 36 c	Hor	3.8		spiral?
1913 I	Gx	3 19.6	− 32 28 c	For	1.7		vF, vS, mE 155°, cbM
1274	Gx	3 19.7	+ 41 33 s	Per	0.6	15p	vF, vS
1300	Gx	3 19.7	− 19 25 s	Eri	6.5	10.4	cB, vL, vmE, psvmbM
1915 I		3 19.7	− 50 42 d	Hor			E ns
1275	Gx	3 19.8	+ 41 31 s	Per	2.6	11.6	F, S
1277	Gx	3 19.8	+ 41 34 s	Per	0.8	13.5	vF, vS, np 1278
1276	Gx	3 19.9	+ 41 33 r	Per			vF, vS
1278	Gx	3 19.9	+ 41 33 s	Per	1.7	12.6	pB, pS, R, bM
1302	Gx	3 19.9	− 26 04 s	For	4.4	11p	S, R, psvmbM, *9 np 1'
1907 I	Gx	3 19.9	+ 41 33 z	Per			vF, S, vmbM
1279	Gx	3 20.1	+ 41 28 r	Per			vF, vS
1281	Gx	3 20.1	+ 41 38 s	Per	0.7	13.5	vF, S, *11 p 1'
1295		3 20.1	− 14 00 D	Eri			eF, vS, gbMN, *10 f 3'
1299	Gx	3 20.1	− 6 17 r	Eri		14p	vF, S, vlE, gbM, er
1311	Gx	3 20.1	− 52 10 r	Hor			F, pL, mE 37°, gbM
1282	Gx	3 20.2	+ 41 22 s	Per	1.7	14p	vF, S, lbMN
1298	Gx	3 20.2	− 2 06 s	Eri	1.5	14p	F, pS, R, *13 sp
1283	Gx	3 20.3	+ 41 24 s	Per	1.3	16p	vF, S, vlbM
1916 I		3 20.3	− 49 03 d	Hor			F, S, R, 2 st sp
1301	Gx	3 20.5	− 18 45 r	Eri		13p	vF, mE 135°
1303	Gx	3 20.7	− 7 25 r	Eri		15p	vF, sev st inv
318 I	Gx	3 20.8	− 14 34 m	Eri	0.8	14p	F, S, dif, lbM
1911 I		3 20.8	+ 35 18 d	Per			neb, not well seen
1304	Gx	3 21.0	− 4 35 r	Eri		14p	eF, vS
1306	Gx	3 21.0	− 25 31 c	For	1.4		vF, vS, gbM, *10.5 f 4'
1310	Gx	3 21.0	− 37 08 s	For	2.3		⊕ , vF, pL, R, vgvlbM
313 I	Gx	3 21.0	+ 41 54 v	Per	1.6		eeF, vS, R, close D* nr s
1305	Gx	3 21.4	− 2 19 s	Eri	1.9	15p	pB, pS, R, *16 att
316 I	Gx	3 21.4	+ 41 56 x	Per			eeF, pS, R
1293	Gx	3 21.6	+ 41 24 s	Per	1.1	15p	vF, R, bM, np of 2
1294	Gx	3 21.7	+ 41 22 s	Per	1.8	13.1	vF, R, bM, sf of 2
1309	Gx	3 22.1	− 15 24 s	Eri	2.3	11.6	cB, cL, iR, gbM, *8 sp 4'
1307	−	3 22.2	− 4 33 r	Eri			eF, vS, R, *9.5 nf
1917 I		3 22.2	− 53 12 d	Hor			E ns
1308	Gx	3 22.5	− 2 45 r	Eri		15p	eF, S, iF, am 3 or 4 st
1314	Gx	3 22.6	− 4 11 r	Eri		15p	*10 with eF, cL, E neb s
1316	Gx	3 22.7	− 37 12 s	For	7.1	8.9	vB, cL, vlE, vsvmbMN
1317	Gx	3 22.8	− 37 06 s	For	3.2	11.0	pB, pS, psbM
1318	−	3 22.8	− 37 07 r	For			F; = 1317
1315	Gx	3 23.1	− 21 23 s	Eri	1.8	13p	pB, S, R, gbM
319 I	Gx	3 23.4	+ 41 24 x	Per			stellar, = 13m
1312	D*	3 23.7	+ 1 11 F	Tau			F
1319	Gx	3 23.9	− 21 32 s	Eri	1.3	14p	F, S, R, bM, p of 2
1326	Gx	3 23.9	− 36 28 s	For	4.0	10.5	○ ? pS, vsvmbMN
1920 I		3 24.2	− 52 43 d	Hor			stellar
1325	Gx	3 24.4	− 21 33 s	Eri	4.6	11.6	F, mE 239°, com, *9.5 att

NGC	Type	α_{2000}	δ_{2000}	Const.	Size	Mag.	Description
		h m	° ′		′		
321 I	Gx	3 24.5	− 15 00 m	Eri	0.4	15p	pB, vS, R
1327	−	3 24.7	− 25 40 r	For			eF, vS, 3 vF st close (no neb)
1921 I		3 24.7	− 50 42 d	Hor			stellar
1922 I		3 24.7	− 50 44 d	Hor			stellar
1320	Gx	3 24.8	− 3 01 s	Eri	1.9	14p	F, S, R, bM
1923 I		3 24.8	− 50 34 d	Hor			stellar
1321	Gx	3 24.9	− 3 00 r	Eri		14p	F, S, E pf, D or biN
1322	Gx	3 25.0	− 2 54 r	Eri		15p	vF, vS, R, bM
1323	Gx	3 25.0	− 2 49 r	Eri			eF, eS, *13 sp 25″ ±
1324	Gx	3 25.0	− 5 45 r	Eri		14p	vF, pS, pmE
1924 I		3 25.0	− 51 41 d	Hor			E, stellar
1926 I		3 25.2	− 51 41 d	Hor			E, stell
1927 I		3 25.2	− 51 43 d	Hor			vF
1925 I		3 25.3	− 51 15 d	Hor			E npsf, stell
1929 I		3 25.5	− 51 15 d	Hor			E npsf
1328	Gx	3 25.6	− 4 08 r	Eri			vF, eS, R, bMN
1933 I	Gx	3 25.7	− 52 47 s	Hor	2.5	13p	lE spnf
1329	Gx	3 25.9	− 17 37 r	Eri		14p	F, pS, R, glbM
322 I	Gx	3 25.9	+ 3 40 z	Tau		15p	vF, pL, vlbM, diffic
1932 I		3 25.9	− 51 20 d	Hor			E ns
320 I	Gx	3 26.0	+ 40 47 x	Per			eF, pS, R, vF* close p
1919 I	Gx	3 26.0	− 32 54 c	For	2.0		eF, pS, lE, sev st n
1918 I	Gx	3 26.2	+ 4 32 z	Tau		15p	F, S, glbM, dif
1935 I	Gx	3 26.2	− 50 01 c	Hor	1.3		stell, E, spir?
1332	Gx	3 26.3	− 21 20 s	Eri	4.6	10.3	vB, S, E 114°, smbMN
1936 I		3 26.4	− 51 19 d	Hor			stell, E npsf
1331	Gx	3 26.5	− 21 21 s	Eri	1.1	14p	vF, vS; = IC 324
324 I	Gx	3 26.5	− 21 21 c	Eri	0.9		F, pS, dif, bM; = 1331
1336	Gx	3 26.6	− 35 44 r	For			vF, S, vlE, gbM
1937 I		3 26.8	− 48 42 d	Hor			vF, vS, R, bM
1938 I		3 27.2	− 53 01 d	Hor			perhaps D*
1928 I	Gx	3 27.5	− 21 34 c	Eri	1.5		vF, vS, mE 20°, cbM
1940 I		3 27.7	− 52 08 d	Hor			bM
1939 I		3 27.8	− 51 04 d	Hor			E pf
1341	Gx	3 28.0	− 37 09 s	For	1.6	13p	F, S, mE 140°, *12 sf
1942 I		3 28.0	− 52 40 d	Hor			stell, E ns
1337	Gx	3 28.1	− 8 23 s	Eri	6.8	11.7	eF, vL, mE ns
1339	Gx	3 28.1	− 32 17 s	For	2.3	13p	cB, pS, R, psbM, D* p
1340	−	3 28.3	− 30 54 D	For			nonexistent; = 1344
1344	Gx	3 28.3	− 31 04 s	For	3.9	10.3	cB, pL, iR, vgbM
1930 I		3 28.8	+ 4 24 d	Tau			F, S, R, gbM, *8 p 3ˢ, s 1′.6
1931 I	Gx	3 28.8	+ 1 43 m	Tau	0.8	14p	vF, dif
1338	Gx	3 29.0	− 12 10 r	Eri		13p	vF, S, iR, lbM, r
1330	Gx	3 29.3	+ 41 22 r	Per		15p	vF st in vF, S neb
1333	Nb	3 29.3	+ 31 25 s	Per	9		F, L, *10 nf
1945 I		3 29.3	− 52 38 d	Hor			stell
1345	Gx	3 29.4	− 17 48 s	Eri	1.4	13.7	vF, S, R, pslbM
1946 I		3 29.4	− 52 37 d	Hor			stell
323 I		3 29.5	+ 41 52 d	Per			eF, pS, R, p of 2
1347	Gx	3 29.7	− 22 16 r	Eri		13p	eF, pS, E 130°, sbMN
1944 I		3 29.7	− 48 00 d	Hor			eF, eS, lE 20°
1334	Gx	3 30.1	+ 41 50 r	Per		15p	eF, pL, lbM
1346	Gx	3 30.1	− 5 33 r	Eri		15p	eF, eS, R, bM, *13 p
1335	Gx	3 30.4	+ 41 35 r	Per		15p	vF * in vF, eS neb
1351	Gx	3 30.5	− 34 52 s	For	1.8	13p	pB, pS, R, psbM

NGC	Type	α_{2000}	δ_{2000}	Const.	Size	Mag.	Description
		h m	° ′		′		
1947 I		3 30.6	− 50 19 *d*	Hor			stell
1356	Gx	3 30.7	− 50 17 *r*	Hor			vF, pL, iR, gbM, * nr
326 I	Gx	3 30.7	− 14 26 *m*	Eri	0.4	15p	vF, pL, E ns
325 I		3 30.8	− 7 03 *d*	Eri			vF, S, R, vlbM
1948 I		3 30.9	− 47 58 *d*	Hor			eeF, S, R
1949 I		3 31.0	− 47 59 *d*	Hor			cF, vS, spir, cbM
1350	Gx	3 31.1	− 33 38 *s*	For	4.3	10.5	B, L, mE, vmbMRN
327 I	Gx	3 31.1	− 14 43 *m*	Eri	0.6	15p	ef, vS, dif, v diffic
1950 I	Gx	3 31.1	− 50 26 *c*	Hor	1.3		E npsf
1951 I		3 31.1	− 53 08 *d*	Hor			E spnf
328 I	Gx	3 31.2	− 14 40 *m*	Eri	0.5	14p	vF, eS, R
1349	Gx	3 31.4	+ 4 22 *r*	Tau		15p	eeF, S, R, bet 2 st
1934 I	Gx	3 31.4	+ 42 48 *u*	Per	1.3	16p	eF, pS, lbM, *12 dist 34″
1955 I		3 31.4	− 57 13 *d*	Ret			eF, vS, R
1352	Gx	3 31.5	− 19 16 *r*	Eri		15p	eF, pslbM, diff, *8 sf
1342	OC	3 31.6	+ 37 20 *s*	Per	14	6.7	Cl, vL, ab 60 st
1954 I	Gx	3 31.6	− 51 55 *s*	Hor	3.6	12p	F, pL, R, spir
1353	Gx	3 32.1	− 20 49 *s*	Eri	3.4	11.4	pB, cL, iE, mbM
329 I	Gx	3 32.1	+ 0 16 *z*	Tau		15p	F, vS, R, lbM
330 I	Gx	3 32.2	+ 0 21 *u*	Tau	1.0	15p	F, vS, R, lbM
1941 I		3 32.2	+ 24 26 *d*	Tau			vF, S, vmE 0° (prob neb)
1957 I		3 32.2	− 52 27 *d*	Hor			E spnf
1354	Gx	3 32.4	− 15 13 *r*	Eri		14p	vF, S, lE, glbM
331 I	Gx	3 32.4	+ 0 17 *z*	Tau		15p	*13 in neb
1960 I	Gx	3 32.6	− 57 12 *c*	Ret	1.2		eF, eS, R
332 I	Gx	3 32.7	+ 1 23 *z*	Tau		15p	F, vS, R, sbM
1958 I		3 32.8	− 51 27 *d*	Hor			stell
1357	Gx	3 33.2	− 13 40 *t*	Eri	2.4	13p	pF, pL, R, lbM, *9 nf
1959 I	Gx	3 33.2	− 50 25 *c*	Hor	2.5		E npsf
1965 I	Gx	3 33.2	− 56 33 *c*	Ret	1.3		eF, vS, R, cbM
1360	Pl	3 33.3	− 25 51 *s*	For	6.5		*8 in B, L neb, E ns
1355	Gx	3 33.4	− 5 00 *s*	Eri	1.8	13.1	pF, S
1952 I	Gx	3 33.4	− 23 43 *c*	Eri	2.4		cF, S, vmE 140°, * 1′ sf
1365	Gx	3 33.6	− 36 08 *s*	For	9.8	9.5	!! vB, vL, mE, rN
1961 I		3 33.6	− 48 57 *d*	Hor			eF, vS, cE 20°
1964 I		3 33.6	− 53 10 *d*	Ret			E pf
1358	Gx	3 33.7	− 5 05 *s*	Eri	2.8	12.1	vF, S, bet 2 st
1953 I	Gx	3 33.7	− 21 29 *s*	Eri	2.8	12p	vF, cL, spir or annular
1348	OC	3 33.8	+ 51 26 *r*	Per			Cl, lRi, st L
1359	Gx	3 33.8	− 19 29 *s*	Eri	1.9	12.2	F, L, R, vglbM
1362	Gx	3 33.8	− 20 17 *r*	Eri		14p	vF, S, R
1366	Gx	3 33.9	− 31 12 *s*	For	2.7	13p	vF, S, iF, lbM
333 I		3 34.0	− 5 07 *d*	Eri			eF, *8.8 nf 4′
1369	−	3 34.1	− 36 17 *r*	For			F
1966 I		3 34.1	− 51 19 *d*	Hor			stell
1361	Gx	3 34.2	− 6 15 *r*	Eri			eF, eS, gbMN
1367	−	3 34.7	− 24 56 *r*	For			vF; = 1371
1968 I		3 34.7	− 50 38 *d*	Hor			stell
1363	Gx	3 34.8	− 9 50 *r*	Eri			vF, S, R, *7 sp 3′.5, sp of 2
1364	Gx	3 35.0	− 9 50 *r*	Eri			vF, S, vlE, nf of 2
1368	Gx	3 35.0	− 15 38 *r*	Eri		15p	vF, vS, R, lbM
1371	Gx	3 35.0	− 24 56 *s*	For	5.4	11p	pB, pL, vlE, psbM
1373	Gx	3 35.1	− 35 11 *r*	For			eF, vS, p of 3
1370	Gx	3 35.2	− 20 22 *r*	Eri		14p	vF, S, R, bet 2 st 14
1375	Gx	3 35.2	− 35 16 *s*	For	1.9		B, S, lE, pmbM, 3rd of 3

NGC	Type	α_{2000}	δ_{2000}	Const.	Size	Mag.	Description
		h m	° ′		′		
1374	Gx	3 35.3	− 35 14 *s*	For	1.8	12*p*	vB, pL, lE, gmbM, 2nd of 3
335 I	Gx	3 35.5	− 34 27 *c*	For	3.0		pF, pS, eE pf
1963 I	Gx	3 35.5	− 34 27 *c*	For	3.0		pB, S, eE 90°; = IC 335
1956 I	Gx	3 35.6	+ 5 05 *u*	Tau	1.4	16*p*	F, S, E 200°, 2 vF Nuclei
1962 I	Gx	3 35.6	− 21 17 *c*	Eri	2.3		eF, S, mE 175°, gbM
1378	D*	3 35.9	− 35 12 *r*	For			F
1971 I		3 36.0	− 52 38 *d*	Hor			E pf
1379	Gx	3 36.1	− 35 27 *s*	For	2.0	12*p*	⊕, B, pL, R, gpmbM
1969 I		3 36.2	− 45 11 *d*	Hor			eF, vS, ce 50°, cbM
1972 I		3 36.4	− 52 01 *d*	Hor			E
1973 I		3 36.4	− 51 59 *d*	Hor			E
1380	Gx	3 36.5	− 34 59 *s*	For	4.9	11*p*	vB, L, R, psbM
1970 I	Gx	3 36.5	− 43 57 *c*	Hor	3.3		eF, vS, ee 75°
1381	Gx	3 36.6	− 35 18 *s*	For	2.9	12*p*	F
1377	Gx	3 36.7	− 20 54 *r*	Eri		14*p*	F, S, R, gbM
1974 I		3 36.7	− 49 34 *d*	Hor			E npsf
1979 I		3 36.7	− 57 56 *d*	Ret			eeF, es, vmE 20°
1392	Gx	3 36.8	− 36 16 *r*	Eri			vF, pS, R
1386	Gx	3 36.9	− 36 00 *s*	Eri	3.5	12*p*	F
1372	Gx	3 37.0	− 15 53 *r*	Eri			vF, vS, R, glbM
1387	Gx	3 37.0	− 35 31 *s*	For	2.4	12*p*	⊕, vB, pL, R, gmbM
1980 I	Gx	3 37.0	− 57 58 *c*	Ret	1.2		eF, cS, vmE 25°
1376	Gx	3 37.1	− 5 03 *s*	Eri	2.0	13*p*	eF, pL, iR, bM, r
1382	Gx	3 37.1	− 35 12 *c*	For	2.1		F
337 I		3 37.1	− 6 43 *d*	Eri			eeF, pL, 3 st nr
1978 I	Gx	3 37.1	− 50 09 *c*	Hor	1.2		E ns
1389	Gx	3 37.2	− 35 45 *s*	Eri	2.1	13*p*	F
1976 I		3 37.2	− 47 26 *d*	Hor			eF, es, R
1385	Gx	3 37.5	− 24 30 *s*	For	3.0	11.2	pB, pS, R, gpmbM
1383	Gx	3 37.6	− 18 20 *r*	Eri		14*p*	pF, S, R, psmbM
338 I	Gx	3 37.6	+ 3 08 *z*	Tau		15*p*	vF, S, dif, vF* close
1967 I	Gx	3 37.7	+ 3 17 *m*	Tau	0.8	14*p*	vF, S, R, *13 nr
1982 I	Gx	3 37.7	− 57 47 *c*	Ret	1.4		cF, es, R
1343	Gx	3 37.8	+ 72 34 *s*	Cas	2.8	12.3	F, vS, iR, gbM, D* vnr
1390	Gx	3 37.9	− 19 00 *r*	Eri		15*p*	vF, pS, E 260°
1396	−	3 38.1	− 35 40 *r*	Eri			F
339 I	*	3 38.1	− 18 23 *z*	Eri			eF, es, stell N
336 I		3 38.2	+ 23 28 *d*	Tau			vF, eeL, v dif
1388	Gx	3 38.3	− 15 53 *r*	Eri			vF, vS, R, lbM
1391		3 38.5	− 18 21 *D*	Eri			eF, S, R, gbMN
1395	Gx	3 38.5	− 23 02 *s*	Eri	3.2	11*p*	B, pS, E, psmbM
1399	Gx	3 38.5	− 35 27 *s*	Eri	3.2	9.9	⊕, vB, pL, psbM, rr
1393	Gx	3 38.6	− 18 26 *s*	Eri	1.8	14*p*	F, S, R, glbM
1943 I	Gx	3 38.7	− 44 06 *c*	Hor	2.1		pB, S, R; = 1411
1411	Gx	3 38.8	− 44 05 *s*	Hor	2.8	12*p*	B, pS, R, smbM
1398	Gx	3 38.9	− 26 20 *s*	For	6.6	9.7	cB, cL, R, vmbM
1404	Gx	3 38.9	− 35 35 *s*	For	2.5	10.3	vB, pL, R, psmbM
1394	Gx	3 39.1	− 18 17 *s*	Eri	1.5	14*p*	vF, vS, E 170°, sbMN
1975 I		3 39.1	− 15 30 *d*	Eri			eF, vS, v diffic, nr 1405
1384	Gx	3 39.2	+ 15 50 *r*	Tau		15*p*	neb *13
1403	Gx	3 39.3	− 22 23 *r*	Eri		14*p*	vF, es, neb*
1401	Gx	3 39.4	− 22 44 *s*	Eri	2.8	13*p*	vF, vS, R
1402	Gx	3 39.4	− 18 31 *r*	Eri		15*p*	eF, vS, R
1406	Gx	3 39.4	− 31 19 *s*	For	3.9	13*p*	F, cL, vmE, vglbM, *7 np
1408	−	3 39.4	− 35 31 *r*	For			F

NGC	Type	α_{2000}	δ_{2000}	Const.	Size	Mag.	Description
		h m	° ′		′		
1400	Gx	3 39.5	− 18 41 s	Eri	1.9	11.1	cB, pS, R, psmbM
340 I	Gx	3 39.5	− 13 07 m	Eri	1.4	15p	F, pS, E pf, *14 at end
1397	Gx	3 39.6	− 4 40 r	Eri		14p	vF, vS, lE
1984 I		3 39.9	− 47 05 d	Hor			eeF, eS, mE 150°
343 I	Gx	3 40.1	− 18 27 c	Eri	1.8		eF, vS, lE 90°, dif
1405	Gx	3 40.2	− 15 30 r	Eri		16p	eF, pL, mE 150°, glbM, F st inv
1407	Gx	3 40.2	− 18 35 s	Eri	2.5	9.8	vB, L, R, svmbMN
1987 I	Gx	3 40.2	− 55 03 c	Ret	1.5		eF, vS, R
1413	Gx	3 40.3	− 15 35 r	Eri			eF, vS, R, lbM
1981 I	Gx	3 40.5	− 26 52 c	For	1.9		eF, eS, lE, * close nf; = 1412
1412	−	3 40.6	− 26 13 r	For			F, S, E, gbM, * sf 2′
1419	Gx	3 40.6	− 37 31 r	Eri			pF, pS, R, psbM
1986 I		3 40.6	− 45 22 d	Hor			eF, eS, cE 135°
1977 I	Gx	3 40.8	+ 17 45 u	Tau	1.7	15p	F, S, R, dif, *13.5 nr
1983 I	Gx	3 40.9	− 22 34 c	Eri	4.0		vF, pS, R
1415	Gx	3 41.0	− 22 34 s	Eri	3.6	12p	pB, S, lE, pglbM, * sf
1416	Gx	3 41.0	− 22 43 s	Eri	1.5	14p	eF, S, R, *8.6 n 2′
1409	Gx	3 41.2	− 1 17 s	Tau	1.3	15p	eF, stellar or lE
1410	Gx	3 41.2	− 1 17 v	Tau			makes Dneb with 1409, pos 0°
341 I		3 41.2	+ 21 57 d	Tau			vF, eeL, v dif
345 I	Gx	3 41.2	− 18 19 m	Eri	0.4	15p	eF, vS, iR, gbM
1414		3 41.5	− 21 41 D	Eri			eF, pS, mE 0°, bMN
1422	Gx	3 41.5	− 21 41 s	Eri	2.1	13p	eF, pS, E 80°
344 I	Gx	3 41.5	− 4 39 x	Eri			eeF, pL, R, 1417 f
346 I	Gx	3 41.7	− 18 16 c	Eri	1.9		eF, pL, E 80°, dif
1989 I	Gx	3 41.9	− 50 57 c	Hor	1.2		stell
1417	Gx	3 42.0	− 4 42 s	Eri	2.8	12.0	pF, pL, lE, lbM, * sf
1433	Gx	3 42.0	− 47 13 s	Hor	6.8	10.0	vB, L, pmE, vsvmbM *10
1425	Gx	3 42.2	− 29 54 s	For	5.4	12p	F, pL, iR, gbM
1418	Gx	3 42.3	− 4 44 s	Eri	1.5	15p	vF, S, E, *11 sf 1′
1427	Gx	3 42.3	− 35 25 s	For	2.8	12p	pF, S, R, psmbM
1428	Gx	3 42.4	− 35 10 s	For	1.8		F
1421	Gx	3 42.5	− 13 29 s	Eri	3.6	11.4	F, cL, mE 0°, r
347 I	Gx	3 42.5	− 4 17 m	Eri	0.7	13p	eF, vS, R, stellar
1423	Gx	3 42.6	− 6 22 r	Eri		15p	eeF, S, R, v diffic
1420	*⁎*	3 42.7	− 5 51 F	Eri			F, vS, *13 p
1426	Gx	3 42.8	− 22 07 s	Eri	2.1	11.4	pF, S, lE, bM
1988 I		3 42.8	− 39 53 d	Eri			eF, pL, R, 2 st nr f, 2 st np
1424	Gx	3 43.2	− 4 44 s	Eri	2.1	15p	vF, *10-11 np
1430	−	3 43.4	− 18 14 r	Eri			eF, S, E 20°, sbMN
1436	Gx	3 43.6	− 35 51 c	Eri			⊕, vB, pmE, pgbM; = 1437
1437	Gx	3 43.6	− 35 52 s	Eri	2.9	12p	F, vL, R, glbM
1429	*	3 44.0	− 4 43 r	Eri			eF, vS, E 0°, gbMN, f of 2
1434	−	3 44.4	− 9 41 r	Eri			eF, S, R, *8.5 f 25ˢ, n 3′
1448	Gx	3 44.5	− 44 39 s	Hor	8.1	11p	pB, L, vmE 222°; = 1457
1457	Gx	3 44.5	− 44 38 D	Hor			pF, pL, eE 42°, vgpmbM; = 1448
1466	Gb	3 44.5	− 71 41 s	Hyi	2.3	11.4	pF, pS, iR, glbM, *7 f
348 I	C+N	3 44.5	+ 32 17 s	Per	10	7.3	pB, vL, vgbM
1431	Gx	3 44.6	+ 2 51 r	Tau		15p	eF, pL, iR
1985 I		3 44.6	+ 32 10 d	Per			*8 in F, eL neb
350 I	Gx	3 44.7	− 11 49 m	Eri	0.8	14p	F, S, R, v dif
1991 I		3 44.7	− 51 33 d	Hor			stell, E spnf
1439	Gx	3 44.8	− 21 55 s	Eri	2.3	12p	F, pS, gpmbM
1445	Gx	3 44.9	− 9 50 r	Eri			vF, S, R, *9 np 2′
1997 I	Gx	3 44.9	− 59 08 c	Ret	1.3		eF, vS, R, cbM, stell N

NGC	Type	α_{2000}	δ_{2000}	Const.	Size	Mag.	Description
		h m	o ′		′		
1440	Gx	3 45.0	− 18 16 s	Eri	2.3	13p	pB, pS, R, smbM *13
1442	Gx	3 45.0	− 18 16 c	Eri			pB, vS, bM; = 1440
1996 I		3 45.0	− 57 20 d	Ret			eeF, eS, eE 95°
1992 I		3 45.1	− 51 01 d	Hor			stell
334 I	Gx	3 45.2	+ 76 38 s	Cam	6.0	12p	pB, S, *13 inv sf
1438	Gx	3 45.4	− 23 01 v	Eri	2.6		eF, mE, N, *10 f 1′
1452	Gx	3 45.4	− 18 38 s	Eri	1.7	13p	F, R, lbM, hazy *
1455	Gx	3 45.4	− 18 38 c	Eri	2.6		vF, S, lE 30°, sbMN; = 1452
1450	Gx	3 45.6	− 9 13 r	Eri			eF, pS, R (D, dist 0′.4?)
1441	Gx	3 45.7	− 4 06 s	Eri	1.5	12.9	vF, S, iE, *12 f
1443	*	3 45.7	− 4 01 F	Eri			vF, nf 1441
1432	Nb	3 45.8	+ 24 22 s	Tau	30		eF, vL, dif (Maia, in Pleiades)
1447	Gx	3 45.8	− 8 59 r	Eri			vF, S, R, neb? *7-8 f 3′
1994 I		3 45.8	− 51 40 d	Hor			E ns
1454	−	3 45.9	− 20 41 r	Eri			vF, eS, R, (*?), *9.5 sp 3′
1446	Gx	3 46.0	− 4 04 m	Eri	0.4	14p	eF, f 1441
1449	Gx	3 46.0	− 4 08 s	Eri	1.1	13.5	vF, vS, vlE
1435	Nb	3 46.1	+ 23 47 s	Tau	30		vF, vL, dif (Merope)
1451	Gx	3 46.1	− 4 04 s	Eri	0.7	13.3	vF, vS, lE
1460	Gx	3 46.1	− 36 41 r	Eri			F, S, R, * att
1463	Gx	3 46.2	− 59 48 r	Ret			cF, S, R, glbM, am 7 B st
349 I	Nb	3 46.3	+ 23 56 s	Tau			eF, vS, pos 165°, dist 36″ from Merope
1453	Gx	3 46.4	− 3 58 s	Eri	2.1	11.6	pB, S, R, *17 in M
342 I	Gx	3 46.8	+ 68 06 s	Cam	17.8	9p	pB, vS, *12 close n
1458	−	3 47.0	− 18 15 D	Eri			nonexistent
1459	Gx	3 47.0	− 25 31 r	For		14p	eF, pS, gbM
1993 I	Gx	3 47.1	− 33 43 c	For	2.5		eF, L, cE, *7.5 att, v diffic
1473	Gx	3 47.4	− 68 12 r	Hyi			cF, pL, R, gvlbM
351 I	Pl	3 47.5	+ 35 03 s	Per	0.1	12p	plan = *10, *9 p 14s, 2′ s
1990 I		3 47.5	+ 24 37 d	Tau			vL, mE pf, 15′ l
352 I		3 47.6	− 8 44 d	Eri			F, vS, R, bM
1999 I		3 47.7	− 56 57 d	Ret			eeF, vS, cE 140°
1456	−	3 48.2	+ 22 34 r	Tau			D* 10-12, comp nebulous at 130°, 9″
1461	Gx	3 48.5	− 16 24 s	Eri	3.3	11.7	pB, S, lE, mbMN
2000 I	Gx	3 49.1	− 48 52 c	Hor	3.8		cB, L, eE 80°, vmbM
1444	OC	3 49.4	+ 52 40 s	Per	4	6.6	Cl of ab 30 st 12...14
1462	Gx	3 50.3	+ 6 59 r	Tau		15p	vF, S, vlE
1995 I		3 50.3	+ 25 35 d	Tau			*6 in eF, eeL neb
2001 I		3 50.9	− 48 38 d	Hor			eF, vS, R, 3 st nr
1464	Gx	3 51.4	− 15 25 r	Eri			pF, S, R, 2 st nr
1998 I	Gx	3 51.5	+ 1 11 z	Tau		16p	F, S, R, bMN
2004 I		3 51.8	− 49 25 d	Hor			eF, S
1467	Gx	3 51.9	− 8 51 r	Eri		15p	eF, vS, R, *9 s 4′
2010 I	Gx	3 52.0	− 59 56 c	Ret	1.2		eF, S, E 70°
2051 I	Gx	3 52.0	− 83 50 c	Men	2.6		! vF, vS, stell N ellipt ring
1476	Gx	3 52.1	− 44 32 c	Hor	1.7		cF, S, E 90°, gbM
1468	Gx	3 52.2	− 6 21 r	Eri		15p	vF, vS, R, bM
1470	Gx	3 52.2	− 9 01 r	Eri		15p	eF, S, E 0°
2011 I		3 52.5	− 57 29 d	Ret			eeF, vS, R
1483	Gx	3 52.7	− 47 29 v	Hor			cF, pL, R, vglbM
2012 I		3 52.8	− 58 38 d	Ret			eeF, eS, cE ns
1471	−	3 53.1	− 15 24 r	Eri			vF, vS, E 45°; = 1464?
354 I		3 53.3	+ 23 25 d	Tau			vF, eeL, v dif
1490	Gx	3 53.5	− 66 02 r	Ret			pB, S, vlE, pmbM
1465	Gx	3 53.6	+ 32 28 r	Per		15p	pF, pS, R, pB* nr p

NGC	Type	α_{2000}	δ_{2000}	Const.	Size	Mag.	Description
		h m	° ′		′		
2009 I	Gx	3 53.6	− 48 59 c	Hor	1.9		eF, S
1472	Gx	3 53.7	− 8 35 r	Eri			vF, eS, stell N, 1st of 3
355 I		3 53.8	+ 20 00 d	Tau			vF, S, R, dif
1477	Gx	3 54.0	− 8 35 r	Eri			eF, vS, 2nd of 3
1475	−	3 54.1	− 8 07 r	Eri			eF, eS, R, *14 np 4′
1478	Gx	3 54.1	− 8 34 r	Eri			eF, vS, 3rd of 3
2006 I	Gx	3 54.1	− 35 59 s	Eri	2.3	12p	pB, S, R, * nr nf, D* sp
1474	Gx	3 54.2	− 10 25 r	Eri		14p	vF, S, R
1484	Gx	3 54.2	− 37 00 r	Eri			vF, L, E, vgvlbM
1479	−	3 54.4	− 10 12 r	Eri			eF, S, E, p of 2
1481	Gx	3 54.4	− 20 25 r	Eri		15p	eF, S, R, 2 B st f, p of 2
2002 I	Gx	3 54.4	+ 10 43 u	Tau	1.4	15p	F, E ns, dif, *14 n
1480		3 54.5	− 10 16 d	Eri			eF, S, iR, f of 2, *10 f 30ˢ
1482	Gx	3 54.7	− 20 30 s	Eri	1.5	14p	F, S, vlE, 2 st 10 nr, f of 2
353 I	Nb	3 55.0	+ 25 29 s	Tau	180		vF, eeL, v dif
2007 I	Gx	3 55.4	− 28 10 c	Eri	1.8		eF, S, R, F* att nf
2008 I		3 55.4	− 28 10 c	Eri			eF, vS, eF* v close nf; = IC 2007
2014 I	Gx	3 55.4	− 56 45 c	Ret	1.4		eeF, vS, R
1487	Gx	3 55.8	− 42 22 s	Eri	2.0	12p	pB, pL, R, gbM, 2 st △
1486	Gx	3 56.3	− 21 49 r	Eri		15p	eF, vS, R
2003 I	Pl	3 56.4	+ 33 52 s	Per	0.1	13p	pB, eS, lE ns, *13 n 4″, *12 sp 18″
1503	Gx	3 56.5	− 66 02 r	Ret			eF, pS, R, *10 np
2013 I		3 56.7	− 17 06 d	Eri			cB, cL, mE 170°, cbM, susp
2017 I	Gx	3 56.7	− 59 24 c	Ret	1.3		eF, vS, R
1493	Gx	3 57.5	− 46 12 s	Hor	2.6	12p	F, cL, R, vglbM
1520	OC	3 57.5	− 76 50 A	Men			Cl, pL, lRi, st 9-10
1489	Gx	3 57.6	− 19 14 r	Eri		14p	eF, pS, E 190°
2005 I	Gx	3 57.6	+ 36 48 z	Per		16p	F, vS, R, stell
1494	Gx	3 57.7	− 48 54 s	Hor	2.6	12p	F, L, R, vgvlbM, 3 st n
2018 I	Gx	3 57.9	− 52 47 c	Dor	1.2		eF, vS, R
2015 I		3 58.0	− 40 27 d	Hor			eF, S, R, bM, susp
1488	Gx	3 58.1	+ 18 34 r	Tau		15p	*12 inv in neb
1492	Gx	3 58.1	− 35 27 r	Eri			vF, vS, R
1500	Gx	3 58.2	− 52 19 r	Dor			F, vS, R, pmbM, *8 np
1495	Gx	3 58.4	− 44 28 c	Hor	2.9		eF, S, lE 90°, vgvlbM
2022 I		3 58.7	− 59 02 d	Ret			eeF, eS, mE 5°, cbM
2020 I		3 59.0	− 54 03 d	Ret			eF, vS, R
2021 I		3 59.4	− 52 40 d	Dor			eF, vS, R
1511	Gx	3 59.5	− 67 38 s	Hyi	3.3	12p	pB, pS, mE 121°.5, gbM
2023 I		3 59.7	− 52 41 d	Dor			eF, vS, R
2024 I	Gx	4 00.1	− 53 22 c	Ret	1.1		eF, vS, cE 35°
1506	Gx	4 00.4	− 52 34 r	Dor			eeeF, S, R, bet 2 st 12 & 13
2025 I	Gx	4 00.4	− 53 04 c	Ret	1.1		eF, vS, cE 135°
1469	Gx	4 00.5	+ 68 35 s	Cam	2.3	15p	vF, vS, R, B* nr
1498	−	4 00.5	− 12 01 r	Eri			Cl, S, C
1499	Nb	4 00.7	+ 36 37 s	Per	145		vF, vL, E ns, dif
2028 I	Gx	4 01.3	− 52 42 c	Dor	1.1		cF, vS, R
2029 I	Gx	4 01.3	− 52 48 c	Dor	1.3		eF, vS, R
2016 I	Gx	4 01.9	+ 20 13 z	Tau		16p	eF, vS, *15 s 30″
2019 I	Gx	4 02.0	+ 5 38 u	Tau	1.1	15p	F, S, R, stell, r
1497	Gx	4 02.1	+ 23 08 r	Tau		14p	eF, vS, iR, mbM
1504	Gx	4 02.5	− 9 19 r	Eri		15p	eF, S, R, gbM
1505	Gx	4 02.7	− 9 18 r	Eri		15p	eF, S, R, gbM
1491	Nb	4 03.4	+ 51 19 s	Per	3		vB, S, iF, bM, r, * inv
1510	Gx	4 03.5	− 43 25 s	Hor	1.0	13.0	F, pL, R, vgmbM

NGC	Type	α_{2000}	δ_{2000}	Const.	Size	Mag.	Description
		h m	° ′		′		
358 I	Gx	4 03.7	+ 19 53 u	Tau	1.4	15p	vS, dif, lbM
357 I	Gx	4 03.8	+ 22 09 u	Tau	1.3	14p	F, S, R, N = 13.5
1512	Gx	4 03.9	− 43 21 s	Hor	4.0	10.6	eF ⊚, B, cL, R, bM
2026 I		4 03.9	− 11 11 d	Eri			vF, vS, stell
1509	Gx	4 04.0	− 11 12 r	Eri		15p	vF, vS, lE, F∗ nr p
1515	Gx	4 04.1	− 54 06 s	Dor	5.4	11.0	B, L, vmE 10°, bM
1496	OC	4 04.4	+ 52 37 s	Per	6	10p	Cl, segment of a ring
1507	Gx	4 04.5	− 2 11 s	Eri	3.4	12.2	vF, pL, mE, vlbM, er
2030 I		4 04.9	− 19 14 d	Eri			cF, vS, ee 135°, susp
1485	Gx	4 05.1	+ 71 00 s	Cam	2.4	14p	eF, pS, R
1526	Gx	4 05.2	− 65 50 r	Ret			eF, vS, R, glbM
1508	Gx	4 05.8	+ 25 24 r	Tau		15p	vF, vS, R, bM, r
2031 I		4 05.9	− 5 37 d	Eri			eF, vS, dif, lbM, ∗11 nf 3′
1522	Gx	4 06.1	− 52 40 r	Dor			eF, vS, R, vlbM
1523	Ast	4 06.2	− 54 06 D	Dor			only 3 vF st (not a neb)
2034 I	Gx	4 06.6	− 57 58 c	Ret	1.2		eeF, vS, cE 115°
2027 I	Gx	4 06.7	+ 37 07 u	Per	1.2	16p	F, vS, R, vlbM
1518	Gx	4 06.8	− 21 11 s	Eri	3.0	11.8	B, L, pmE, gbM, ∗8 sp
1501	Pl	4 07.0	+ 60 55 s	Cam	0.9	13p	◯ , pB, pS, vlE, 1′ diam
2032 I	Gx	4 07.1	− 55 20 c	Dor	1.5		eF, vS, R
1529	Gx	4 07.2	− 62 54 r	Ret			vF, S, R, gbM
2033 I	Gx	4 07.2	− 53 41 c	Dor	1.3		eF, vS, cE 130°
2054 I		4 07.2	− 78 15 d	Men			eeF, eS, vF∗ 1′ nf, susp
1502	OC	4 07.7	+ 62 20 s	Cam	8	5.7	Cl, pRi, cC, iF
356 I	Gx	4 07.8	+ 69 49 s	Cam	5.2	11p	pF, pL, bM, ∗8.5 4′ n
1516	Gx	4 08.1	− 8 53 r	Eri		15p	eeF, S, E, psmbM, er
1519	Gx	4 08.1	− 17 12 s	Eri	2.0	13p	vF, S, lE, vS∗ inv
1521	Gx	4 08.3	− 21 03 s	Eri	2.9	11.4	pB, R, bM
2037 I	Gx	4 08.3	− 58 45 c	Ret	1.5		eF, vS, eE 90°, cbM
1527	Gx	4 08.4	− 47 53 s	Hor	3.4	12p	pB, pS, E 77°, vsmbMRN
1534	Gx	4 08.8	− 62 47 r	Ret			F, S, R, vS∗ $\frac{3}{4}$ d sf
2038 I	Gx	4 08.9	− 56 00 c	Dor	1.7		eF, vS, eE 145°
2035 I	Gx	4 09.0	− 45 31 s	Hor		12p	F, vS, R
2039 I	Gx	4 09.0	− 56 01 c	Dor	1.3		eF, vS, R
1514	Pl	4 09.2	+ 30 47 s	Tau	1.9	10p	∗9 in neb 3′ diam
1517	Gx	4 09.3	+ 8 39 r	Tau		14p	vF, vS, R, r, ∗9-10 sf
1533	Gx	4 09.9	− 56 07 s	Dor	2.9	10.9	vB, vL, R, smbM, 2 st 10 nf
1513	OC	4 10.0	+ 49 31 s	Per	9	8.4	Cl, L, vRi, pC, st vL
2036 I		4 10.0	− 39 42 d	Hor			eeF, pS, R, v diffic, ∗9 f
1524	−	4 10.3	− 8 48 r	Eri			eF, pS, R, gbM, Dneb with 1525
1525	−	4 10.3	− 8 48 r	Eri			eF, pS, R, gbM, at 340°, 0′.5 from 1524
1536	Gx	4 11.0	− 56 29 s	Ret	2.0	13p	vF, R, pL, vlbM
2043 I	Gx	4 11.2	− 53 41 c	Dor	1.3		eF, vS, eE 5°, vmbM
2044 I		4 11.2	− 54 31 d	Dor			eF, vS, R
2046 I		4 11.4	− 54 40 d	Dor			vF, vS, R
2042 I		4 11.7	− 47 16 d	Hor			∗9 in neb 1′ diam
1531	Gx	4 12.0	− 32 51 s	Eri	1.3	12.1	pB, pL, R, bM, np of 2
1532	Gx	4 12.1	− 32 52 s	Eri	5.6	11p	B, vL, vmE 32°, psmbM
2049 I	Gx	4 12.1	− 58 33 c	Ret	1.1		eF, vS, R
2041 I	Gx	4 12.6	− 32 49 c	Eri	1.5		eF, vS, R, ∗10 close s
1543	Gx	4 12.8	− 57 44 s	Ret	3.9	10.6	B, pL, E, smbMN = ∗11
360 I	Nb	4 13.0	+ 25 38 s	Tau	180		vF, eeL, v dif
2040 I	Gx	4 13.0	− 32 33 c	Eri	1.6		vF, vS, R, rr?, 1531-32 s
1557	−	4 13.3	− 70 25 r	Hyi			Cl, vlC, ab 20 sc st
1537	Gx	4 13.7	− 31 39 s	Eri		12p	vB, pS, lE, psvmbM

NGC	Type	α_{2000}	δ_{2000}	Const.	Size	Mag.	Description
		h m	° ′		′		
2050 I	Gx	4 13.9	− 53 29 c	Dor	1.4		F, vS, cE 60°
1535	Pl	4 14.2	− 12 44 s	Eri	0.7	10p	◯ , vB, S, R, pS, vsbM, r
2048 I	?	4 14.3	− 33 07 x	Eri			eeF, eS, B∗ f, v diffic
1546	Gx	4 14.6	− 56 04 s	Dor	3.2	11.6	pB, lE, gbMEN, $*$ p
2045 I		4 14.6	− 13 10 d	Eri			eF, eS, alm stell, nr 1538
1538	Gx	4 14.7	− 13 12 r	Eri		15p	eF, vS, R, gbM
2047 I		4 14.9	− 13 11 d	Eri			eF, eS, diffic, nr 1538
2052 I		4 15.0	− 54 20 d	Dor			vF, vS, mE
1540	Gx	4 15.2	− 28 29 c	Eri	1.2		vF, vS, E, gvlbM, r
1528	OC	4 15.4	+ 51 14 s	Per	24	6.4	Cl, B, vRi, cC
1549	Gx	4 15.7	− 55 36 s	Dor	3.7	9.9	B, pS, R
2053 I		4 15.8	− 49 22 d	Dor			eF, S, cE 140°, susp
1553	Gx	4 16.2	− 55 47 s	Dor	4.1	9.5	vB, pS, R, gmbM, am 3 st; a Dneb
2056 I	Gx	4 16.5	− 60 13 s	Ret	1.9	12p	F, pL, R, bM
362 I	Gx	4 16.7	− 12 13 m	Eri	0.3	14p	pB, vS, bM
1541	Gx	4 17.0	+ 0 50 r	Tau		15p	vF, S
1542	Gx	4 17.2	+ 4 48 r	Tau		15p	vF, S, E
1547		4 17.2	− 17 53 D	Eri			pF, pS, iR, Cl
1559	Gx	4 17.6	− 62 47 s	Ret	3.3	10.5	vB, vL, mE, vgpmbM, ∗14 att n
1556	Gx	4 17.7	− 50 10 D	Dor			cF, S, E 165°, vglbM
2055 I		4 17.8	− 48 55 d	Dor			F, S, cE ns, susp
2058 I	Gx	4 17.9	− 55 56 c	Dor	2.7		cB, cL, eE 10°
2060 I	Gx	4 17.9	− 56 37 c	Ret	1.3		F, S, bM
363 I		4 18.9	+ 3 03 d	Tau			eF, ∗9 nf 3′
1539	Gx	4 19.0	+ 26 51 r	Tau		15p	vF, vS, gbM
359 I	Nb	4 19.0	+ 28 12 s	Tau	15		eeF, pL, R
361 I	OC	4 19.0	+ 58 18 s	Cam	6	11.7	F, L (neb Cl?)
364 I	Gx	4 19.1	+ 3 10 z	Tau		15p	vF, vS, R, sbM
365 I	Gx	4 19.2	+ 3 20 m	Tau	0.6	14p	pB, S, iF, sbM
1558	Gx	4 19.3	− 45 02 v	Hor			pF, S, E, gbM
1550	Gx	4 19.6	+ 2 26 r	Tau		14p	vF, vS, R, ∗13 nr
1551	−	4 19.6	+ 1 25 r	Tau			F, vS, R, probably = 1550
366 I		4 19.6	+ 2 21 d	Tau			eF, 3′ sf of 1550
1566	Gx	4 20.0	− 54 56 s	Dor	7.6	9.4	B, vL, VG, svmbM, 15^{s}d in RA
1552	Gx	4 20.3	− 0 40 r	Eri		14p	cF, pS, lE, vgbM, ∗11 sp
2059 I	Gx	4 20.4	− 31 44 c	Eri	1.4		eeF, pL, R
367 I	Gx	4 20.6	− 14 47 m	Eri	0.3	15p	pB, pL, dif
1545	OC	4 20.9	+ 50 15 s	Per	18	6.2	Cl, pRi, lC, st L
1548	OC	4 21.0	+ 36 56 r	Per			Cl, vL, lRi, lC, st 10...12
1567	Gx	4 21.1	− 48 15 c	Cae	1.2		F, S, R, bM
2065 I	Gx	4 21.5	− 55 56 c	Dor	1.2		vF, vS, vmE 45°, pmbM
1562	Gx	4 21.7	− 15 45 r	Eri			vF, eS, R, glbM
1554	Nb	4 21.8	+ 19 32 s	Tau	var		!!! var, S, R, Nn = ∗13
2057 I	Gx	4 21.9	+ 4 03 z	Tau		15p	pB, pS, R, gbM, r
1574	Gx	4 22.0	− 56 58 s	Ret	2.0	10.5	pB, S, R, pgbM, 2 S st sf
1570	Gx	4 22.1	− 43 38 c	Cae			F, S, R, gbM; = 1571
1571	Gx	4 22.2	− 43 38 r	Cae			vF, S, R, gbM, $*$ nf
1572	Gx	4 22.6	− 40 36 r	Cae			pF, S, R, ∗13 nf 1′
368 I	Gx	4 22.7	− 12 37 m	Eri	0.8	14p	eS, R, bM
1555	Nb	4 22.9	+ 19 32 r	Tau			!!! vF, S, variable
1563		4 22.9	− 15 44 D	Eri			eF, vS, R, lbM, D with 1564
1564	Gx	4 22.9	− 15 44 r	Eri			eF, vS, R, lbM, D with 1563
2063 I		4 22.9	− 15 44 F	Eri			eF, vS, nr 1561-65
1561	Gx	4 23.0	− 15 51 r	Eri		15p	vF, vS, lE 170°, glbM, ∗8 p 6^s
1530	Gx	4 23.4	+ 75 18 s	Cam	4.9	12p	pB, L

NGC	Type	α_{2000}	δ_{2000}	Const.	Size	Mag.	Description
		h m	° ′		′		
1565	Gx	4 23.4	− 15 45 r	Eri		15p	eF, pS, lE
369 I	Gx	4 23.5	− 11 47 m	Eri	0.5	15p	F, S, R, stellar
2064 I		4 23.5	− 15 41 d	Eri			susp, nf 1565
2066 I		4 23.5	− 54 45 d	Dor			eeF, vS, R
1578	Gx	4 23.8	− 51 35 r	Dor			pF, S, R, bM
2061 I		4 24.0	+ 21 05 d	Tau			F, cS, R, susp
370 I	Gx	4 24.1	− 9 23 m	Eri	1.2	14p	eF, S, dif
1568	Gx	4 24.4	− 0 45 r	Eri		15p	eF, vS, R, nearly bet 2 st
2070 I	Gx	4 24.6	− 57 59 c	Dor	1.7		vF, vS, cbM
1581	Gx	4 24.7	− 54 56 r	Dor			F, S, E, glbM
2069 I		4 25.9	− 48 12 d	Cae			eeF, S, R, susp
1576	Gx	4 26.2	− 3 37 r	Eri		15p	eF, bM, bet 2 st
2071 I		4 26.2	− 53 08 d	Dor			eeF, vS, cE 80°
1575	Gx	4 26.3	− 10 07 D	Eri		13p	vF, pS, R, *9.5 s 2′; = 1577
1577	Gx	4 26.3	− 10 07 D	Eri		13p	vF, pL, R, lbM, * nr s
2068 I	Gx	4 26.6	− 42 06 c	Cae	1.3		eF, pL, R, 1585 f
2073 I	Gx	4 26.6	− 53 11 c	Dor	1.4		vF, vS, ee 60°, stell N
2072 I		4 26.9	− 48 22 d	Cae			cF, S, R, susp
1585	Gx	4 27.5	− 42 09 r	Cae			pF, S, R, gbM, *12 288°
1596	Gx	4 27.6	− 55 02 s	Dor	3.9	11.0	B, pL, mE 15°, smbM, p of 2
1602	Gx	4 27.9	− 55 03 v	Dor			eF, pL, lE, f of 2
1584	Gx	4 28.1	− 17 32 r	Eri			F, eS, R, sbMN
2076 I		4 28.1	− 48 13 d	Cae			vF, vS, cE 130°, susp
1580	Gx	4 28.2	− 5 11 r	Eri		14p	vF, vS, R, r
1583	Gx	4 28.3	− 17 37 r	Eri		15p	F, vS, R, sbMN
1595	Gx	4 28.4	− 47 49 c	Cae	1.5		vF, S, R, bM
2079 I	Gx	4 28.5	− 53 44 c	Dor	1.3		eF, vS, E 130°
1598	Gx	4 28.6	− 47 47 c	Cae	1.6		F, S, R, bM
2081 I	Gx	4 29.0	− 53 37 c	Dor	1.5		eF, vS, R, bet 2 F st
2082 I	Gx	4 29.1	− 53 50 s	Dor		12.8	cF, S, R
1629	OC	4 29.3	− 71 50 r	Hyi			vF, pL, R, glbM
1591	Gx	4 29.4	− 26 44 r	Eri		13p	pF, pS, R, gbM
1592		4 29.6	− 26 58 D	Eri			only F st
372 I	?	4 30.1	− 5 01 n	Eri			F, vS, R, lbM
1579	Nb	4 30.2	+ 35 16 s	Per	12		pB, vL, iR, mbM, *8 350°, 2′
371 I		4 30.2	− 0 33 d	Eri			stellar, eS (neb?)
1586	Gx	4 30.7	− 0 19 r	Eri		14p	vF, iF, vlbM, bet * & *14
1587	Gx	4 30.7	+ 0 40 s	Tau	2.0	13p	F, pS, R, r, p of Dneb
373 I	Gx	4 30.7	− 4 52 m	Eri	1.0	15p	F, vS, R, mbM
2083 I	Gx	4 30.7	− 53 59 c	Dor	1.1		eF, vS, R
1569	Gx	4 30.8	+ 64 51 s	Cam	2.9	11.2	pB, S, lE, BNM, *9.5 n 1′
1588	Gx	4 30.8	+ 0 39 s	Tau	1.8	14p	F, vS, R, r, f of Dneb
1589	Gx	4 30.8	+ 0 51 s	Tau	3.1	14p	F, pL, lE 132°, * 42°, 80″
1594	Gx	4 30.8	− 5 48 r	Eri		14p	vF, pS
2067 I		4 30.8	+ 35 27 d	Per			vF, R, *15 inv n, *17 close np
2075 I	Gx	4 31.0	− 5 48 v	Eri	2.0		eF, pL, vlbM
375 I		4 31.1	− 12 58 d	Eri			vF, dif, lbM
376 I	Gx	4 31.1	− 12 27 m	Eri	0.8	14p	F, iF
1590	Gx	4 31.2	+ 7 37 s	Tau	1.3	15p	F, S, *12 nf
1597	Gx	4 31.2	− 11 17 r	Eri		15p	eF, vS, R, gbM
377 I		4 31.3	− 12 27 d	Eri			F, iF
2074 I	OC	4 31.3	+ 7 42 z	Tau			vF, S, st inv; S Cl?
2085 I	Gx	4 31.4	− 54 25 c	Dor	2.4		eF, vS, eE 110°
378 I		4 31.5	− 12 18 d	Eri			* strongly nebs
1599	Gx	4 31.6	− 4 35 s	Eri	1.1	15p	vF, vS, R, vlbM

NGC	Type	α_{2000}	δ_{2000}	Const.	Size	Mag.	Description
		h m	o ′		′		
2086 I		4 31.6	− 53 38 d	Dor			eeF, vS, R
1600	Gx	4 31.7	− 5 05 s	Eri	2.5	11.1	pB, pL, R, gmbM
1603	Gx	4 31.7	− 5 06 r	Eri		15p	vF, vS
1617	Gx	4 31.7	− 54 36 s	Dor	4.7	10.4	B, L, mE 106°, vg, vsmbMN 5″
380 I	Gx	4 31.7	− 12 56 m	Eri	0.6	15p	vF, bM
1601	Gx	4 31.8	− 5 06 s	Eri	1.0	13.8	vF, vS
1593	Gx	4 31.9	+ 0 34 A	Tau			vF; = 1608
1604	Gx	4 31.9	− 5 22 r	Eri		14p	eF, S, R, bet * & D*
1608	Gx	4 31.9	+ 0 35 r	Tau		15p	pF, cS, *12 2′ n; = IC 2077
379 I	Gx	4 31.9	− 7 15 m	Eri	0.9	15p	vF, S, R, dif
2078 I		4 31.9	− 4 41 d	Eri			eF, pS
1582	OC	4 32.0	+ 43 51 s	Per	37	7p	Cl, vL, pRi, lC, st L
1607	Gx	4 32.0	− 4 27 r	Eri		15p	F, S, R, lbM
1606	Gx	4 32.1	− 5 02 v	Eri			eF
2077 I		4 32.1	+ 0 34 x	Tau			F, vS, gbMN; = 1608
2084 I		4 32.1	− 48 17 d	Cae			F, S, R, susp
2080 I		4 32.3	− 5 45 d	Eri			eF, vS, 1594 p about 90ˢ, 3′ s
374 I	Gx	4 32.5	+ 16 38 x	Tau		16p	F, S, R, mbM
1609	Gx	4 32.6	− 4 22 r	Eri		15p	vF, eS, *17 45″ n
2089 I		4 32.6	− 75 33 d	Men			eeF, vS, R, F* 1′ f, susp
1616	Gx	4 32.7	− 43 43 r	Cae			F, S, E, vglbM
1560	Gx	4 32.8	+ 71 53 s	Cam	9.8	11.5	vF, L, E, *9.3 sp
2062 I	Gx	4 32.8	+ 71 54 t	Cam	8.8	12p	eF; = 1560
1611	Gx	4 33.0	− 4 17 r	Eri		15p	eF, S, E 90°±
1612	Gx	4 33.1	− 4 10 r	Eri		15p	vF, vS, R, gmbM
1613	Gx	4 33.3	− 4 15 r	Eri		15p	F, vS, mbM
1614	Gx	4 34.0	− 8 35 s	Eri	1.3	12.9	pF, S, R, lbM
1610	Gx	4 34.1	− 4 42 r	Eri			eF, vS, R, bMN
1623	Gx	4 34.9	− 13 31 r	Eri			eF, vS, R, gbMN
1573	Gx	4 35.0	+ 73 15 s	Cam	2.2	14p	vF, S, *9.5 f
1605	OC	4 35.0	+ 45 15 s	Per	5	10.7	Cl, vF, pS, C, st eS
1615	Gx	4 36.0	+ 19 57 s	Tau	1.6	15p	vF, vS, R, lbM, vS* inv
1618	Gx	4 36.1	− 3 09 s	Eri	2.8	12.6	F, S, iF, lbM, 2 st sf
1641	OC	4 36.1	− 65 46 r	Dor			Cl, pL, pRi, pmC, st 11...16
1619	−	4 36.2	− 4 50 r	Eri			eeF, S, R; nonexistent?
1621	Gx	4 36.3	− 4 58 r	Eri		14p	eF, S, R, lbM
1620	Gx	4 36.6	− 0 09 s	Eri	3.0	14p	vF, pL, mE 140°, B* nf
1622	Gx	4 36.6	− 3 11 s	Eri	3.9	12.3	vF, S, *20 p 5ˢ, 1618 p
1625	Gx	4 37.1	− 3 18 s	Eri	2.7	12.4	vF, E 141°, sbM, F* att np, *6 p 48ˢ
1626	−	4 37.2	− 5 00 r	Eri			eF, vS, R, *8 np
1630	Gx	4 37.3	− 18 54 r	Eri			eF, eS, R
1627	Gx	4 37.5	− 4 51 r	Eri		13p	eF, pL, R, 2 st sf, s of 2
1628	Gx	4 37.5	− 4 42 r	Eri		14p	vF, pS, mE ns, n of 2
1651	Gb	4 37.5	− 70 35 r	Men			pF, L, vlE, vglbM
1632	Gx	4 37.9	− 9 31 r	Eri		13p	eF, vS, R
382 I	Gx	4 37.9	− 9 31 m	Eri	2.0	13p	pB, pL, R, SN
1644	Gb	4 38.0	− 66 12 r	Dor		13p	F, S, R, gbM
1649	−	4 38.1	− 68 49 r	Dor			F, pS, R, gbM; = 1652?
1652	Gb	4 38.1	− 68 40 r	Dor			vF, S, R, glbM
1631	Gx	4 38.4	− 20 40 r	Eri		14p	vF, S
383 I		4 39.0	+ 9 54 d	Tau			vF, S, dif, *11.5 f
384 I		4 39.3	− 7 50 d	Eri			F, eS, R, *11 n
385 I		4 39.5	− 7 06 d	Eri			vF, vS, R, dif
2103 I	Gx	4 39.8	− 76 50 c	Men	1.7		cF, vS, eE 80°, stell N
1633	Gx	4 40.0	+ 7 21 r	Tau		14p	eF, S, R, *8 sp, p of Dneb

NGC	Type	α_{2000}	δ_{2000}	Const.	Size	Mag.	Description
		h m	o ′		′		
1634	Gx	4 40.0	+ 7 20 r	Tau		15p	eF, vS, f of Dneb
386 I		4 40.0	− 9 27 d	Eri			vF, vS, vlbM
2087 I	Nb	4 40.0	+25 44 s	Tau	4		eeF, in hole of eL neby
1635	Gx	4 40.1	− 0 33 s	Eri	1.7	14p	F, S, R, bM, *11 nf 12ˢ
1624	C+N	4 40.4	+50 27 s	Per	5	10.4	F, cL, iF, 6 or 7 st + neb
1636	Gx	4 40.7	− 8 36 r	Eri		14p	vF, pS, R, vgbM, r, * nf 1′
1639	*⁎*	4 40.9	−17 00 D	Eri			only 3 st 12.5 forming equilateral △
1637	Gx	4 41.5	− 2 51 s	Eri	3.3	10.9	cB, L, R, vgbM
1638	Gx	4 41.6	− 1 49 s	Eri	2.5	12.1	F, pL, lE
387 I	Gx	4 41.7	− 7 05 v	Eri	1.5		eF, pL, v dif, diffic
388 I	Gx	4 42.0	− 7 18 m	Eri	0.4	15p	vF, v dif, S* inv
389 I	Gx	4 42.0	− 7 18 m	Eri	0.4	15p	F, S, R, stellar
390 I	Gx	4 42.1	− 7 13 m	Eri	0.7	15p	vF, vS, R
1640	Gx	4 42.2	−20 26 s	Eri	2.8	11.7	vF, pS, E 40°, gbM
1673	OC	4 42.4	−69 51 r	Men			vF, S, att to *10
1642	Gx	4 42.9	+ 0 37 s	Tau	2.0	14p	F, R, cometary, △ with 2 st 18 f
1669	Gx	4 43.0	−65 48 r	Dor			eF, S, R
1643	Gx	4 43.6	− 5 17 r	Eri		14p	F, vS, iR, bM
1676	OC	4 43.7	−68 50 r	Dor			vF, pL, iR, r
2088 I		4 43.7	+27 16 d	Tau			eeL, 3° long
1645	Gx	4 44.0	− 5 26 r	Eri		14p	vF, pS, R (1643 np)
1658	Gx	4 44.0	−41 27 r	Cae			F, pS, pmE, glbM
1660	Gx	4 44.2	−41 29 r	Cae			vF, S, lE, glbM
1646	Gx	4 44.3	− 8 33 r	Eri		14p	F, vS, iR, bM, *7 np
381 I	Gx	4 44.4	+75 39 s	Cam	3.4	14p	F, S, bM, *12 np
1648	Gx	4 44.5	− 8 29 r	Eri		16p	eeF, pS, v diffic, 1646 sp
2090 I		4 44.7	−34 00 d	Cae			vF, pS, R, 3 st sp
1841	Gb	4 45.	−84 00 r	Men		12p	pF, L, iR, vsbM, r
1650	Gx	4 45.1	−15 51 r	Eri		14p	vF, pS, E 0°, bMN
1672	Gx	4 45.7	−59 15 s	Dor	4.8	11p	B, L, smbMN
1653	Gx	4 45.8	− 2 25 s	Eri	2.0	13p	F, cS, R, lbM
1654	Gx	4 45.8	− 2 06 s	Eri	1.0	14p	F, S, R, lbM, r? p of 2
1656	Gx	4 45.8	− 5 08 r	Eri		14p	L, stell N in F neb E npsf
1647	OC	4 46.0	+19 04 s	Tau	45	6.4	Cl, vL, st L, sc
1668	Gx	4 46.1	−44 43 r	Cae			eF, R, att to *14
1655		4 46.2	+20 56 D	Tau			hazy *
1657	Gx	4 46.2	− 2 04 r	Eri		15p	fainter but larger than 1654
392 I	Gx	4 46.4	+ 3 30 u	Ori	1.5	15p	pB, S, R, N = 12.5
1659	Gx	4 46.5	− 4 47 s	Eri	1.7	12.5	pF, pS, iE 90°±, bM
2091 I	Ast	4 46.6	− 4 41 x	Eri			F, stell N
2092 I	D*	4 46.8	− 4 57 x	Eri			S, spiral, stell N
1661	Gx	4 47.2	− 2 03 r	Ori		14p	vF, vS, bM
1693	OC	4 47.5	−69 21 r	Dor			F, S, R
1695	OC	4 47.6	−69 24 r	Dor			F, S, R
2093 I	D*	4 47.6	− 2 43 F	Ori			vF, stell
393 I	Gx	4 47.9	−15 32 m	Eri	0.3	15p	F, vS, iF, lbM
1696	OC	4 48.0	−68 16 r	Dor			vF, E, vlbM
1665	Gx	4 48.2	− 5 25 r	Eri		14p	eF, pL, R, lbM
1688	Gx	4 48.4	−59 48 s	Dor	2.4	12p	pB, pL, iR, pgmbM
2094 I		4 48.4	− 5 22 d	Eri			spiral, F stell N
1662	OC	4 48.5	+10 56 s	Ori	20	6.4	Cl of L & S sc st
1666	Gx	4 48.5	− 6 34 s	Eri	1.3	14p	vF, pS, R
1663	OC	4 48.6	+13 10 r	Ori			Cl, lRi, st L & S
1667	Gx	4 48.6	− 6 19 s	Eri	1.5	12.1	pF, pS, R, r?
1680	Gx	4 48.6	−47 49 c	Pic	1.3		vF, S, R, r or st inv

NGC	Type	α_{2000}	δ_{2000}	Const.	Size	Mag.	Description
		h m	o ′		′		
1697	OC	4 48.6	− 68 32 r	Dor			⊕, pB, L, R, rr
2095 I	Gx	4 48.7	− 5 08 m	Eri	1.3	15p	F, S, E spnf, spiral?
394 I	?	4 48.9	− 6 17 x	Eri			vF, dif (vS Cl?)
1702	OC	4 49.3	− 69 51 r	Men			Cl, vF, S
1698	Nb	4 49.4	− 69 10 r	Dor			pB, pS, R, glbM
2105 I	Nb	4 49.4	− 69 12 x	Dor			◯, stellar
395 I		4 49.6	+ 0 15 D	Ori			eF, vS, R, F∗ close f
2096 I	∗*∗	4 49.6	− 4 59 F	Eri			S, E, spiral, stell N
1704	OC	4 49.7	− 69 45 r	Dor			F, pS, lE, r
1670	Gx	4 49.9	− 2 44 r	Ori		14p	vF, vS
1679	Gx	4 50.0	− 31 59 t	Cae	3.2		vB, L, iR, 4 st inv
1671	−	4 50.3	− 0 46 r	Ori			pF, pS, R
2097 I		4 50.3	− 5 05 d	Eri			F, E npsf, spiral, lbM
1711	OC	4 50.5	− 70 00 r	Men		10p	⊕, B, S, iR, rrr, st 14
2098 I	Gx	4 50.7	− 5 26 m	Eri	2.0	14p	F, spiral, lbM
1677	Gx	4 50.8	− 4 52 r	Eri		15p	pF, pL, lE
2099 I	Gx	4 50.8	− 4 54 m	Eri	0.6	15p	S, mbMN
1664	OC	4 51.1	+ 43 42 s	Aur	18	7.6	Cl, lRi, lC, pL
2100 I	D∗	4 51.2	− 4 50 F	Eri			vF, S, lE stell
1687	Gx	4 51.3	− 33 56 r	Cae			vF, S, R, vglbM
1712	C+N	4 51.3	− 69 28 r	Dor			Cl, pB, S
2101 I	Gx	4 51.6	− 6 15 m	Eri	1.5	14p	F, E npsf, bM, prob spir
1678	Gx	4 51.7	− 2 38 r	Ori		14p	vF, S
1681	Gx	4 51.7	− 5 49 r	Eri		13p	vF, S, R, vlbM
2102 I	Gx	4 51.9	− 4 58 m	Eri	1.1	15p	vF, lbM, prob spir
2111 I	Nb	4 51.9	− 69 24 x	Dor			◯, stellar
1714	Nb	4 52.1	− 66 56 r	Dor			vB, S, E or biN, bM, sp of 2
1715	Nb	4 52.1	− 66 55 r	Dor			vF, S, R, sbM, 2 st nr, nf of 2
1718	OC	4 52.2	− 67 04 r	Dor			F, pS, R, vglbM
1722	C+N	4 52.2	− 69 24 r	Dor			Cl, pF, S, R, 2nd of 3
1727	C+N	4 52.2	− 69 21 r	Dor			Cl, pB, pS, pmE, st 12
1682	Gx	4 52.3	− 3 06 r	Ori		14p	vF, vS, 1684 f 12ˢ±, ∗9 s 4′.5
1683	Gx	4 52.3	− 3 01 r	Ori			vF, R
1674	−	4 52.4	+ 23 54 r	Tau			1st of 2 F neb in same field
1675	−	4 52.4	+ 23 54 r	Tau			2nd of 2 F neb in same field
1684	Gx	4 52.5	− 3 06 r	Ori		13p	pF, pS, R, bM, ∗9, 225°±
1706	Gx	4 52.5	− 62 59 c	Dor	1.4		F, pS, R, vglbM
1685	Gx	4 52.6	− 2 57 r	Ori		14p	F
1686	Gx	4 52.8	− 15 22 r	Eri		14p	eF, vS, mE 30°
1703	Gx	4 52.8	− 59 45 v	Dor	3.2		F, L, R, vglbM, ∗ att
1732	OC	4 52.9	− 68 40 r	Dor			S, R, close ∗∗ in M
1736	Nb	4 53.1	− 68 04 r	Dor			B, R, r
1734	OC	4 53.3	− 68 47 r	Dor			pB, L, R, gmbM
1731	C+N	4 53.4	− 66 56 r	Dor			Cl, pL, lRi, lC, st 10...15
1689	−	4 53.6	− 6 20 r	Eri			pB, pS, lE; = 1667?
1733	OC	4 53.9	− 66 41 r	Dor			eF, pS, R, gbM
1735	C+N	4 53.9	− 67 07 r	Dor			pF, pS, R, 2 st att
1743	C+N	4 54.0	− 69 12 r	Dor			B, pL, R, gbM, r, 2nd of 4
1705	Gx	4 54.2	− 53 22 s	Pic	1.8	12.3	pF, S, R, pmbM
1751	Gb	4 54.2	− 69 49 r	Men			eF, pL, iR
1690	Gx	4 54.3	+ 1 38 s	Ori	1.3	14p	vF, vS, am vS st, L∗ sp
1737	C+N	4 54.3	− 69 12 r	Dor			vF, S, 1st of 4
1745	C+N	4 54.3	− 69 12 r	Dor			F, S, 3rd of 4
1748	C+N	4 54.4	− 69 12 r	Dor			pB, vS, R, 4th of 4
1754	Gb	4 54.4	− 70 27 r	Men			F, S, R, ∗13 att, 135°

NGC	Type	α_{2000}	δ_{2000}	Const.	Size	Mag.	Description
		h m	° ′		′		
1691	Gx	4 54.6	+ 3 15 r	Ori		13p	F, S, *11 inv
1749	OC	4 54.6	− 68 12 r	Dor			vF, R, p of 2
1756	OC	4 54.6	− 69 15 r	Dor			vF, S, R
2114 I		4 54.6	− 69 12 x	Dor			◯ , stellar; = 1748
1747	C+N	4 54.9	− 67 11 r	Dor			Cl, pS, lRi, st vS
1755	OC	4 55.0	− 68 11 s	Dor	2	9.9	vB, pL, R, gbM, f of 2
1694	Gx	4 55.2	− 4 39 r	Eri		15p	vF, vS, R, sbM
1692	Gx	4 55.4	− 20 34 c	Lep	1.3		eF, vS, R
1701	Gx	4 55.8	− 29 53 r	Cae		14p	F, S, vlE, glbM, *10 75″ sf
1766	OC	4 55.8	− 70 14 r	Men			cF, S, gbM
1777	OC	4 55.8	− 74 17 r	Men			eF, E, att, f
1764	OC	4 56.2	− 67 41 r	Dor			vF, S, R
1767	C+N	4 56.3	− 69 24 r	Dor			no descr (in LMC)
1761	C+N	4 56.4	− 66 30 r	Dor			Cl, L, mC, m
1760	C+N	4 56.5	− 66 32 r	Dor			vF, S, 3 vS st inv
2104 I	Gx	4 56.5	− 15 47 v	Lep	2.2		F, E, gbM
2106 I	Gx	4 56.6	− 28 30 c	Cae	2.0		eeF, pL, D* 24ˢf
1768	OC	4 56.7	− 68 15 r	Dor			F, S, R, gbM
1772	C+N	4 56.7	− 69 34 r	Dor			pB, pS, iR, rr
1763	Nb	4 56.8	− 66 24 s	Dor	25		vB, vL, vimE
1775	OC	4 56.8	− 70 26 r	Men			eF, pL, iR
1700	Gx	4 56.9	− 4 52 s	Eri	2.9	11.0	cB, S, mbM*
1699	Gx	4 57.0	− 4 45 s	Eri	1.1	15p	eeF, pS, R, bet 2 st, n of 1700
1770	C+N	4 57.0	− 68 25 r	Dor		9p	Cl + neb, pL, pRi, st 11...18
2115 I	Nb	4 57.1	− 66 24 x	Dor			◯ , stellar
2117 I	Nb	4 57.2	− 68 27 x	Dor			◯ , stellar
1710	Gx	4 57.3	− 15 18 D	Lep		14p	vF, vS, R, bMN, *13 inv
2108 I	Gx	4 57.3	− 15 17 m	Lep	1.2	14p	vF, pS, R, mbM, *9.5 sf 1′.3
391 I	Gx	4 57.4	+ 78 11 s	Cam	1.7	12.7	F, S, R
2116 I	Nb	4 57.4	− 66 25 x	Dor			◯ , stellar
1782	C+N	4 57.6	− 69 23 r	Dor			⊕ , pB, S, R, pmbM, rr
1769	C+N	4 57.7	− 66 28 r	Dor			B, L, iR, vsmbM
1774	OC	4 57.8	− 67 15 r	Dor		10p	B, S, R, smbM, ⁎ + neb
1789	OC	4 57.8	− 71 54 r	Men			vF, pS, R, vglbM
396 I	Gx	4 58.0	+ 68 19 s	Cam	3.0	13p	F, S, R, bMN, FD* sf
398 I	Gx	4 58.2	− 7 47 v	Eri	1.5		eF, pL, E 5°, dif
1773	C+N	4 58.3	− 66 21 r	Dor			pF, pL, iR, 2 or 3 B st nr
2107 I	?	4 58.3	+ 8 15 x	Ori			Cl, vF, vS, R
1716	Gx	4 58.4	− 20 24 r	Lep		14p	pF, pL, R, glbM
1765	Gx	4 58.4	− 62 02 r	Dor			cF, S, R, glbM
1776	OC	4 58.4	− 66 26 r	Dor			vF, S, R, gbM
1785	−	4 58.6	− 68 52 r	Dor			no descr, in LMC
1709	Gx	4 58.8	− 0 29 r	Ori		15p	vF, vS, np 1713
1707	−	4 58.9	+ 8 14 r	Ori			S, R, rrr; = IC 2107
1713	Gx	4 58.9	− 0 30 r	Ori		14p	F, S, R, bM
1771	Gx	4 58.9	− 63 18 v	Dor			vF, mE, glbM, *7-8 np
1783	Gb	4 58.9	− 66 00 r	Dor		11p	cB, L, R, vgpmbM, r
1791	Nb	4 59.0	− 70 10 r	Men			eF, S, R
2109 I		4 59.0	− 0 19 d	Ori			vF*, nebs?
2110 I		4 59.0	− 0 19 d	Ori			vF*, nebs?
1786	Gb	4 59.1	− 67 45 s	Dor	1.2	10.1	vB, pS, lE, vsvmbM *9
1787	OC	4 59.1	− 65 44 r	Dor			Cl, vL, pRi
1717	*	4 59.2	− 0 15 A	Ori			np 1719 (F*?)
1721	Gx	4 59.2	− 11 08 r	Eri		13p	vF, vS, R
1720	Gx	4 59.3	− 7 52 s	Eri	1.8	13p	pF, pL, lbM, 1726 nr

NGC	Type	α_{2000}	δ_{2000}		Const.	Size	Mag.	Description
		h m	° ′			′		
1725	Gx	4 59.3	− 11 08	D	Eri		13p	eF, vS, R
1723	Gx	4 59.4	− 10 59	s	Eri	3.7	12p	F, bet 2 st 9-10 n & s, 3rd * f
1728	Gx	4 59.4	− 11 08	D	Eri		13p	vF, vS, R
1793	OC	4 59.4	− 69 33	r	Dor			F, S, R, glbM
1795	Gb	4 59.5	− 69 48	r	Dor			F, pL, lE
1719	Gx	4 59.6	− 0 16	r	Ori		14p	pF, S, iR, pslbM
1730	Gx	4 59.6	− 15 50	s	Lep	3.0	13p	F, pS, lE, bet 2 F st
2113 I	Gx	4 59.6	− 15 50	m	Lep	2.3	13p	no descr
1726	Gx	4 59.7	− 7 45	s	Eri	1.4	12.1	F, R, *13, s
1744	Gx	5 00.0	− 26 01	s	Lep	6.8	11.2	F, vL, vmE, vgvlbM
1729	Gx	5 00.1	− 3 21	r	Ori		13p	vF, pL, 2 B st vnr
1801	OC	5 00.5	− 69 38	r	Dor			F, pL, R, vglbM, p of 2
2112 I	Gx	5 00.5	+ 4 23	z	Ori		15p	vF, pS, dif
1759	Gx	5 00.8	− 38 43	r	Cae			vF, pL, vglbM
1804	OC	5 00.9	− 69 05	r	Dor			F, S, R, bM
397 I		5 01.1	+ 40 26	d	Aur			F, S
1741	Gx	5 01.6	− 4 16	s	Eri	1.7	13.4	vF, vS, vS excent pt inv; = IC 339
1738	Gx	5 01.7	− 18 11	r	Lep		13p	vF, S, E 45°
1739	Gx	5 01.7	− 18 12	r	Lep		14p	eF, vS, lE, in field with 1738
1742	*	5 01.7	− 3 18	F	Ori			vF, vS, 3ˢ.6 f 1740
399 I	Gx	5 01.8	− 4 18	s	Eri		14.5	vF, vS, sf of 1741
1740	Gx	5 01.9	− 3 18	r	Ori		15p	eF, vS, *12 sp
1806	Gb	5 01.9	− 67 59	r	Dor		11p	pB, L, gbM
1809	Gx	5 02.0	− 69 34	r	Dor			pF, S, R, gbM, 2nd of 2
1752	Gx	5 02.1	− 8 14	s	Eri	2.6	13p	F, pL, pmE, 2 or 3 st 11 nf
1805	OC	5 02.2	− 66 06	r	Dor		10p	B, vS, vsmbM, st + neb
1815	OC	5 02.3	− 70 37	r	Men			F, vS, R, vlbM, am st
1753	Gx	5 02.4	− 3 21	r	Ori		15p	eeF, pS, R, sf 1740
1708	−	5 02.6	+ 52 53	r	Cam			Cl, vL, pRi, lC, st L & S
1757	−	5 02.6	− 4 44	r	Eri			vL dif neb in zigzags??
1813	OC	5 02.6	− 70 19	r	Men			vF, S, R, r
1796	Gx	5 02.7	− 61 08	s	Dor	2.0	13p	pF, pS, pmE, vglbM
1544	Gx	5 03.	+ 86 13	r	Cep		14p	vF, vS
1810	OC	5 03.1	− 66 22	r	Dor			cF, S, R, lbM, ⊕ f
1724	OC	5 03.5	+ 49 30	o	Aur		10p	Cl, vS, st + neb?
1823	OC	5 03.5	− 70 21	r	Men			Cl, pF, L, iF, st 12...15
1746	OC	5 03.6	+ 23 49	s	Tau	42	6p	Cl, P
1762	Gx	5 03.6	+ 1 34	r	Ori		13p	vF, vS
400 I		5 03.7	− 15 46	d	Lep			eF, eS
1814	C+N	5 03.8	− 67 17	r	Dor		9p	vF, R, s of 2 in Cl
1816	C+N	5 03.8	− 67 17	r	Dor		9p	vF, R, 2nd neb in Cl
1820	OC	5 03.8	− 67 17	r	Dor		9p	Cl, pL, Ri, C, iF
1750	OC	5 03.9	+ 23 39	s	Tau			Cl, st L, vc sc
1825	OC	5 04.1	− 68 55	r	Dor			no descr, in LMC
1828	OC	5 04.1	− 69 23	r	Dor			F, S, R, 1st of 3
1818	OC	5 04.2	− 66 24	s	Dor	3	9.8	⊕, vB, pL, R, vmC, rr
1833	C+N	5 04.3	− 70 43	r	Men			vF, pL, 1st of sev
401 I		5 04.3	− 10 05	d	Eri			vF, vS, R, vSN
1758	OC	5 04.4	+ 23 46	r	Tau			Cl, pC, st L and S
1830	OC	5 04.5	− 69 20	r	Dor			F, pS, R, 2nd of 3
1829	C+N	5 04.7	− 68 03	r	Dor		8p	F, pL, R, r
1837	C+N	5 04.7	− 70 42	r	Men			Cl, L, Ri, st sc
1822	OC	5 05.0	− 66 12	r	Dor			vF, S, p of 2
1792	Gx	5 05.2	− 37 59	s	Col	4.0	10.2	vB, vL, mE 314°, glbM, rr
1835	Gb	5 05.2	− 69 24	s	Dor	1.2	9.8	cB, S, R, gmbM, 3rd of 3

NGC	Type	α_{2000}	δ_{2000}	Const.	Size	Mag.	Description
		h m	o ′		′		
1779	Gx	5 05.3	− 9 09 s	Eri	2.6	13p	pB, S, R, gpmbM
1834	*⁎*	5 05.3	− 69 13 r	Dor			plan? B, eS, lE
1836	OC	5 05.3	− 68 37 r	Dor			st + neb, 1st of sev
1784	Gx	5 05.4	− 11 52 s	Lep	4.2	11.8	pB, pL, vlE, vgbM, am st
1803	Gx	5 05.4	− 49 34 c	Pic	1.1		F, S, R, vglbM, *11 sf; neb?
1826	OC	5 05.4	− 66 13 r	Dor			vF, S, f of 2
1838	OC	5 05.9	− 68 27 r	Dor			Cl, L, vlC
1839	C+N	5 05.9	− 68 37 r	Dor			st + neb, pB, iF, 2nd of sev
1831	OC	5 06.1	− 64 55 r	Dor		11p	B, L, R, glbM, r
1845	OC	5 06.3	− 70 28 r	Men			Cl, vlCM, st 9, 11...16
402 I		5 06.3	− 9 08 d	Eri			eF, pL, iR, dif
1780	Gx	5 06.4	− 19 29 r	Lep		15p	eF, eS, gbM
1800	Gx	5 06.4	− 31 57 s	Col	1.6	12.6	pB, pmE, gpmbM, *13 f
1840	OC	5 06.4	− 71 49 r	Men			F, R, bM, r
1788	Nb	5 06.9	− 3 21 s	Ori	8		B, cL, R, bM *⁎* ; *10 inv in the neby
1824	Gx	5 06.9	− 59 43 r	Dor			vF, pL, vmE 162°
1847	OC	5 06.9	− 68 59 r	Dor			B, S, lE, ⁎̣ in M
2118 I	Nb	5 06.9	− 7 13 s	Eri	180		F, eL, iF, 1779 inv s
1842	OC	5 07.1	− 67 16 r	Dor			vvF, R, p of 2
1844	OC	5 07.2	− 67 19 r	Dor			pF, pL, R, gbM, f of 2
2119 I		5 07.2	− 20 21 F	Lep			eeF, pS, v diffic, 2 st 12.5 nr
1848	C+N	5 07.3	− 71 11 r	Men			Cl, vlC, st 9...
1846	Gb	5 07.6	− 67 28 r	Dor		11p	pB, cL, R, vglbM, r
1797	Gx	5 07.7	− 8 02 r	Eri		15p	eeF, S, R, vF* np
1799	Gx	5 07.7	− 7 58 r	Eri		15p	vF, vS, vlE
1808	Gx	5 07.7	− 37 31 s	Col	7.2	9.9	B, L, E, psbM
1781		5 07.9	− 18 10 D	Lep			eF, vS, stellar; = 1794
1794	Gx	5 07.9	− 18 10 D	Lep		14p	vF, eS, gbM
1778	OC	5 08.1	+ 37 03 s	Aur	7	7.7	Cl, pC, lRi, iF, st L
1850	OC	5 08.5	− 68 46 s	Dor	3	9.3	⊕! vB, L, lE, vmCM, rr
1811	Gx	5 08.7	− 29 17 r	Col		15p	cF, S, lE, p of 2
1812	Gx	5 08.9	− 29 16 r	Col		14p	F, S, R, glbM, f of 2
1852	C+N	5 09.0	− 67 47 r	Dor			F, pL, R, vglbM
1854	OC	5 09.1	− 68 51 r	Dor		10p	⊕ , cB, S, R, gbM, 2nd of 3
1849	OC	5 09.2	− 66 18 r	Dor			vF, S, lE, glbM
1855	−	5 09.4	− 68 51 r	Dor			Cl, vB, L, R, st 12; = 1854?
1856	OC	5 09.4	− 69 08 r	Dor		10p	B, pL, R, gbM, 12ˢdiam RA
1858	C+N	5 09.7	− 68 54 r	Dor			B, L, iE, biN, Cl + neb
1827	Gx	5 10.1	− 36 58 t	Col	3.4		vF, vmE, long ray, *11 inv
1861	OC	5 10.1	− 70 46 r	Men			eF, pL, R, gvlbM
1802	−	5 10.2	+ 24 06 r	Tau			Cl, st c sc
1860	OC	5 10.4	− 68 46 r	Dor			F, pL, R, vgbM
1807	OC	5 10.7	+ 16 32 s	Tau	17	7.0	Cl, pRi, st L & S
1790	−	5 11.3	+ 52 04 r	Aur			Cl, group of 8 or 9 st 10
1859	OC	5 11.4	− 65 13 r	Dor			F, S, R, vgbM, *7 nf 6′
1863	OC	5 11.4	− 68 47 r	Dor			vB, vS, R, r or stellar
1798	−	5 11.6	+ 47 40 r	Aur			S, Cl or Cl + neb
1819	Gx	5 11.7	+ 5 12 r	Ori		13p	vF, S, R
1821	Gx	5 11.7	− 15 07 r	Lep		14p	vF, vS, lE
1817	OC	5 12.1	+ 16 42 s	Tau	16	7.7	Cl, L, Ri, lC, st 11...14
1832	Gx	5 12.1	− 15 41 s	Lep	2.8	11.4	pB, iR, mbM, c* nf 1′
1862	OC	5 12.2	− 66 08 r	Dor			pF, L, iR, vgbM
1865	OC	5 12.2	− 68 47 r	Dor			vF, pL, R, vglbM
1853	Gx	5 12.3	− 57 24 c	Dor	2.0		F, S, mE 45°, vgvlbM, *11 nf
1864	OC	5 12.5	− 67 38 r	Dor			F, pS, iR, bM, r or stellar

NGC	Type	α_{2000}	δ_{2000}	Const.	Size	Mag.	Description
		h m	° ′		′		
1878	OC	5 12.6	− 70 28 r	Men			vF, lE, gvlbM, R
1870	OC	5 13.0	− 69 08 r	Dor			B, S, R, glbM
1872	C+N	5 13.0	− 69 20 r	Dor			pB, R, gbM, 1st of group
1874	C+N	5 13.2	− 69 23 r	Dor			neb and Cl, biN
1876	C+N	5 13.2	− 69 23 r	Dor			pB, iR, biN, 2nd in group
1877	C+N	5 13.2	− 69 23 r	Dor			vF, 3rd of group in Cl
1881	C+N	5 13.2	− 69 21 r	Dor			vF, * p
404 I	Gx	5 13.3	+ 9 45 z	Ori		16p	vF, vS, stellar, *13 close
1866	OC	5 13.5	− 65 28 s	Dor	5	9.8	vB, L, R, vgmbM, r
1867	OC	5 13.5	− 66 17 r	Dor			eF, pL, R
1880	C+N	5 13.6	− 69 23 r	Dor			4th of group in Cl
1871	C+N	5 13.7	− 67 28 r	Dor			Cl, lRi, 2nd of sev
1873	C+N	5 13.7	− 67 20 r	Dor			Cl, 3rd of sev
1869	C+N	5 13.8	− 67 23 r	Dor			Cl, L, pRi, st sc
1890	OC	5 13.9	− 72 04 r	Men			vF, S, R, glbM
1843	Gx	5 14.1	− 10 38 t	Ori	1.8		F, S, R, lbM
1851	Gb	5 14.1	− 40 03 s	Col	11.0	7.3	⊕ ! vB, vL, R, vsvvbM, rrr
1868	Gb	5 14.5	− 63 57 r	Dor			pB, pL, R, vglbM
1885	OC	5 15.0	− 68 58 r	Dor			pB, vS, R, bM
1882	OC	5 15.2	− 66 07 r	Dor			pF, R, vgvlbM, r
403 I		5 15.3	+ 39 58 d	Aur			eF, eS, R
1894	OC	5 15.7	− 69 27 r	Dor			F, pL, R, sbM, r, st inv
1887	OC	5 15.8	− 66 18 r	Dor			vF, vS, R, * p 25″
1884	−	5 15.9	− 66 10 r	Dor			eF, pL
405 I	Nb	5 16.2	+ 34 16 s	Aur	30		*6.7 with pB, vL neb
1898	Gb	5 16.7	− 69 36 r	Dor		11p	F, pS, R
1895	Nb	5 16.9	− 67 19 r	Dor			pF, pL, R, gvlbM
1892	Gx	5 17.1	− 64 57 r	Dor			cF, pL, E 90°±, vglbM
1903	OC	5 17.2	− 69 18 r	Dor		12p	vB, S, R, gmbM
1897	OC	5 17.4	− 67 26 r	Dor			eF, S, R
1916	OC	5 17.5	− 69 22 r	Dor			B, S, R, vgvmbM, r
1914	C+N	5 17.6	− 71 14 r	Men			F, L, iE
407 I		5 17.7	− 15 31 d	Lep			F, lE ns
1899	Nb	5 17.8	− 67 53 r	Dor			F, pS, R, vglbM, 3 st 10 p
1901	OC	5 17.8	− 68 26 r	Dor			Cl, bM, lRi, st 7...
406 I	OC	5 17.8	+ 39 53 z	Aur			eF, neb or eS neb Cl
408 I		5 17.9	− 25 05 d	Lep			vF, pS, E, *8.5 south 5′
1902	OC	5 18.1	− 66 37 r	Dor			⊕, pB, pL, R, pmbM, rr
1910	OC	5 18.1	− 69 13 s	Dor	1		Cl, L, pRi, iR, st 11...16
1905	OC	5 18.2	− 67 15 r	Dor			F, S, R, r
2120 I	Pl	5 18.2	+ 37 36 s	Aur	0.8		eF
1913	OC	5 18.4	− 69 33 r	Dor			no descr, in LMC
1900	OC	5 19.0	− 63 02 r	Dor			F, pL, lE, vgvlbM, *7 np
1917	Gb	5 19.0	− 69 00 r	Dor			vF, L, R, vglbM
2122 I	Gx	5 19.0	− 37 05 c	Col	2.0		pB, eS, R, 3 st nf
1918	C+N	5 19.1	− 69 39 r	Dor			no descr, in LMC
1911	−	5 19.2	− 66 46 r	Dor			F, R, gbM, am st
1921	Nb	5 19.3	− 69 48 r	Dor			vF, pS, lE, r
1915	−	5 19.6	− 66 48 r	Dor			eF, pL
409 I	Gx	5 19.6	+ 3 18 m	Ori	0.6	15p	pB, R, biN?
1922	OC	5 19.7	− 69 29 r	Dor			no descr, in LMC
1956	Gx	5 19.7	− 77 45 r	Men			vF, hazy * inv in neb
2121 I	Gx	5 19.7	− 25 04 c	Lep	2.1		eef, S, R, v diffic, *7 p 14ˢ, 3′.6 s
1879	Gx	5 19.8	− 32 09 s	Col	2.2	13p	vF, L, R, vgvlbM, *12 p
1919	C+N	5 20.0	− 66 55 r	Dor			Cl, eF, L, iR, mC, rr

NGC	Type	α_{2000}	δ_{2000}	Const.	Size	Mag.	Description
		h m	° /		/		
1857	OC	5 20.2	+ 39 21 s	Aur	6	7.0	Cl, pRi, pC, st 7...
411 I	Gx	5 20.3	− 25 20 m	Lep	0.5	15p	vF, vS, R, 2 others in field
1926	OC	5 20.5	− 69 30 r	Dor			pB, pL, iR, r, in dif n
1920	Nb	5 20.6	− 66 48 r	Dor			pB, pL, R, vgbM
1928	OC	5 20.8	− 69 29 r	Dor			pF, pL, R, gbM
1923	C+N	5 21.0	− 65 30 r	Dor			vF, pS, R
1891	−	5 21.3	− 35 44 r	Col			Cl, L, sc, * taken
415 I		5 21.3	− 15 33 d	Lep			vF, vS, R, dif
1938	OC	5 21.4	− 69 55 r	Men			pB, pS, R, glbM, D with 1939, pos 339°
1939	OC	5 21.4	− 69 56 r	Men			F, S, R, glbM, D with 1938
1929	C+N	5 21.6	− 67 56 d	Dor			F, p of group
1875	Gx	5 21.8	+ 6 41 s	Ori		15p	eF, S, R
1886	Gx	5 21.8	− 23 49 c	Lep	2.6		vF, pL, E 240°, *9 p 11ˢ, 0′.9 s
1925	C+N	5 21.8	− 65 48 r	Dor			Cl, vlRi, lC, st 10
1934	C+N	5 21.8	− 67 56 r	Dor			2nd neb of group
1935	C+N	5 21.9	− 67 58 r	Dor			pF, S, R, 3rd of group; = IC 2126
1944	OC	5 21.9	− 72 30 r	Men			pB, pL, R, bM
412 I	Gx	5 21.9	+ 3 29 u	Ori	1.6	14p	vF, vS, stellar, IC 413 at pos 115°, dist 36″
414 I	Gx	5 21.9	+ 3 20 m	Ori	0.4	15p	eF, *9 sf 2′
2123 I		5 21.9	+ 3 30 d	Ori			vS, R, mbM, S* close n
2124 I		5 21.9	+ 3 30 d	Ori			vS, R, mbM, S* close n
2126 I		5 21.9	− 67 57 x	Dor			◯, stellar; = 1935
2127 I		5 21.9	− 67 58 x	Dor			◯ stellar; = 1936
413 I	Gx	5 22.0	+ 3 29 u	Ori	1.2	14p	eF, vS, stellar
1936	C+N	5 22.1	− 67 59 r	Dor			!, pB, S, R, 4th of group; = IC 2127
1933	OC	5 22.2	− 66 09 D	Dor			eF, R, stellar, D with 1932
1937	C+N	5 22.3	− 67 55 r	Dor			vF, pL, follows a group
1932	OC	5 22.4	− 66 09 D	Dor			pB, S, R, smbM, D with 1933, pos 260°, 80″
1888	Gx	5 22.5	− 11 30 s	Lep	3.0	12.0	pB, pL, R, r
1889	Gx	5 22.5	− 11 29 s	Lep	0.8	14p	makes a close Dneb with 1888
1940	OC	5 22.6	− 67 12 r	Dor			pB, vS, R, bM, 2 st 9 & 10 f
2012	Gx	5 22.6	− 79 51 c	Men	1.5		vF, S, lE, bM, 2 st 9 nf
410 I	C+N	5 22.6	+ 33 31 s	Aur	40		dif, many st inv
1893	OC	5 22.7	+ 33 24 s	Aur	11	7.5	Cl, L, Ri, lC
1943	C+N	5 22.7	− 70 10 r	Men		12p	pF, pS, iR, vglbM, *15 at 191°, 60″
2128 I	Nb	5 22.8	− 68 03 x	Dor			Cl, few st and neb (in LMC)
2134 I		5 23.0	− 75 27 d	Men			cF, vS
1941	Nb	5 23.1	− 66 23 r	Dor			vS, neb + st
416 I	Gx	5 23.9	− 17 16 c	Lep	1.7		F, S, gbM
2125 I		5 24.4	− 26 59 d	Lep			eeF, vS, R, v diffic
1904	Gb	5 24.5	− 24 33 s	Lep	8.7	8.0	⊕, pL, eRi, eC, rrr; = M79
1950	OC	5 24.5	− 69 57 r	Men			the 1st of a group of 7!
1942	OC	5 24.7	− 63 56 r	Dor			eF, stell, *14 + neb
1906		5 24.8	− 15 58 D	Lep			eF, pS, E 0°, glbM
1946	OC	5 25.1	− 66 25 r	Dor			pF, R, gbM, r
1949	Nb	5 25.1	− 68 29 r	Dor			pB, S, R, psbM
1896	−	5 25.4	+ 20 10 r	Tau			Cl, vL, Ri, vlC, st 9...12
1945	Nb	5 25.4	− 66 21 r	Dor			eeeF, vvL, irr dif
1953	Gb	5 25.4	− 68 48 r	Dor			pB, S, R, glbM
1948	C+N	5 25.5	− 66 15 r	Dor			Cl, cL, Ri, st 13
1958	OC	5 25.5	− 69 50 r	Dor			F, pL, iR, vgbM, 2nd of group!
1959	OC	5 25.8	− 69 56 r	Men			F, vL, vgbM, 3rd of group!
1883	OC	5 25.9	+ 46 33 s	Aur	3	12p	Cl, vF, pRi, pC, iF
1909	−	5 25.9	− 8 08 r	Ori			eL, strongly susp (2° in decl)
1930	Gx	5 25.9	− 46 44 r	Pic			pF, S, R, bM, 4 B st p

NGC	Type	α_{2000}	δ_{2000}	Const.	Size	Mag.	Description
		h m	o ′		′		
1951	OC	5 25.9	− 66 36 r	Dor		10p	B, lE, sbM & 11
1908	−	5 26.0	− 2 32 r	Ori			v diffused neb susp
1955	C+N	5 26.1	− 67 29 r	Dor		9p	Cl, Ri, 2nd of sev
1962	C+N	5 26.5	− 68 47 r	Dor		8p	vF, pL, R, 1st of 4!
1965	C+N	5 26.5	− 68 47 r	Dor		8p	F, S, 2nd of 4!
1967	OC	5 26.5	− 69 04 r	Dor			no descr, in LMC
1969	OC	5 26.5	− 69 49 r	Dor			F, S, 4th of gr of 7
1970	C+N	5 26.5	− 68 47 r	Dor		8p	4th of 4
1971	OC	5 26.7	− 69 51 r	Dor			5th of gr of 7
1972	OC	5 26.7	− 69 49 r	Dor			6th of gr of 7! D, a vS neb np
1947	Gx	5 26.8	− 63 46 s	Dor	3.0	10.8	pB, L, R, glbM, *9 np
1966	Nb	5 26.8	− 68 49 s	Dor	13		pB, R, pslbM, 3rd of 4, in pL, irr Cl
1968	C+N	5 27.2	− 67 26 r	Dor		9p	Cl, Ri, 3rd of sev
1987	Gb	5 27.2	− 70 46 r	Men		12p	F, L, iR, 3 st p
2000	OC	5 27.4	− 71 55 r	Men			F, pL, R, vlbM
1983	C+N	5 27.5	− 68 57 r	Dor		8p	Cl, vL, pRi, iF
1984	C+N	5 27.5	− 69 06 r	Dor			Cl, place of ⁑
1986	OC	5 27.5	− 69 58 r	Men		11p	B, pL, R, gbM
418 I	Pl	5 27.5	− 12 42 s	Lep	0.2	11p	plan = *9.2 (gaseous sp)
1924	Gx	5 27.9	− 5 19 r	Ori		13p	vF, pL, iR, st nr
1974	C+N	5 27.9	− 67 24 r	Dor		9p	Cl, L, irr
1907	OC	5 28.0	+ 35 19 s	Aur	7	8.2	Cl, pRi, pC, R, st 9...12
417 I	Nb	5 28.1	+ 34 26 s	Aur	13		vL, dif, *6 inv
1994	OC	5 28.2	− 69 07 r	Dor			Cl, eS, st 11...16
1978	Gb	5 28.6	− 66 14 s	Dor	2.7	9.9	vB, vL, lE, vgpmbM
1912	OC	5 28.7	+ 35 50 s	Aur	21	6.4	Cl, B, vL, vRi, iF, st L & S; = M38
1927	−	5 28.7	− 8 23 r	Ori			diffused nebulosity
1991	−	5 29.0	− 67 26 r	Dor			Cl, 4th of sev
2001	C+N	5 29.1	− 68 44 r	Dor			Cl, st 13m
2005	OC	5 30.0	− 69 44 r	Dor			no description, in LMC
2002	OC	5 30.2	− 66 52 r	Dor			vB, S, R, ⁑ + neb in vLCl
1997	OC	5 30.5	− 63 12 r	Dor			eF, cS, R
2004	OC	5 30.6	− 67 17 s	Dor		9.8	⊕ , B, pL, pRi, C, st 12
2010	OC	5 30.6	− 70 49 r	Men			F, cL, R, vglbM
2018	Nb	5 30.6	− 71 04 s	Men	25		pB, pL, R, pglbM, *10 p inv
2003	OC	5 30.7	− 66 27 r	Dor			B, S, stellar, r
2009	OC	5 30.8	− 69 09 r	Dor			pF, pS, R, glbM, in Cl
419 I		5 31.0	+ 30 09 d	Aur			pB, L, mE
2006	OC	5 31.2	− 66 57 r	Dor			Cl, eL, vRi, vBvSNM
2129 I		5 31.3	− 23 04 d	Lep			eeF, pS, R, *7 ssf
1931	C+N	5 31.4	+ 34 15 s	Aur	3	11.3	vB, L, R, B** in M
2016	OC	5 31.5	− 69 56 r	Men			F, vL, iR, gbM
2019	Gb	5 31.7	− 70 10 r	Men		11p	B, pL, gbM
2130 I	Gx	5 31.8	− 23 09 c	Lep	2.2		eF, pL, R, *7.5 nf
2015	C+N	5 31.9	− 69 13 r	Dor			Cl, vL, Ri, vlC
2011	C+N	5 32.1	− 67 31 r	Dor		9p	vB, S, R, psmbM
2014	C+N	5 32.2	− 67 40 r	Dor		8p	Cl, pL, pC, iF, st 9...15
421 I		5 32.2	− 8 05 d	Ori			vF, L
420 I		5 32.3	− 4 30 d	Ori			vF, spp *9 (not verified)
422 I		5 32.3	− 17 13 d	Lep			pB, vS, R, sbM
2131 I		5 32.3	− 17 13 d	Lep			pB, vS, R
1995	D*	5 32.5	− 48 42 A	Pic			eeF, R, bM, diffic, p of 2
2132 I	Gx	5 32.5	− 13 55 m	Lep	1.3	14p	vF, S
1954	Gx	5 32.8	− 14 04 s	Lep	4.1	13p	vF, S, R, smbM
1957	Gx	5 32.9	− 14 07 A	Lep			eF, pS, R, bMN, *15 inv

NGC	Type	α_{2000}	δ_{2000}	Const.	Size	Mag.	Description
		h m	o ′		′		
2020	Nb	5 33.1	− 67 42 *r*	Dor			F, vL, vlE, vglbM
2025	OC	5 33.1	− 71 44 *r*	Men			vB, vS, lE, gmbM, r
2142 I		5 33.1	− 78 00 *d*	Men			eF, vS, lE 25°, lbM
2135 I	Gx	5 33.2	− 36 24 *c*	Col	2.5		eeF, eS, eE, v diffic
2136 I	Gx	5 33.2	− 36 24 *c*	Col	2.5		eF, pS, eE; = IC 2135
2140 I	OC	5 33.2	− 75 22 *x*	Men			eF, vS; eS Cl?
1963	Gx	5 33.3	− 36 25 *t*	Col	3.5		Cl, st 8...11
1998	Gx	5 33.3	− 48 41 *A*	Pic			vF, R, gbM, st s, f of 2
1964	Gx	5 33.4	− 21 57 *s*	Lep	6.2	10.8	F, L, R, vsvmbM *12, 3 st inv
2021	C+N	5 33.4	− 67 26 *r*	Dor			vF, S, R, in pLCl
423 I	Nb	5 33.4	− 0 37 *s*	Ori	6		vF, L, oval ring
2028	OC	5 33.7	− 69 56 *r*	Men			vF
2031	OC	5 33.7	− 70 59 *r*	Men			⊕, B, pL, R, gbM, rr
424 I		5 33.7	− 0 19 *d*	Ori			vF, L, brightest f
1979	Gx	5 33.8	− 23 19 *r*	Lep		13*p*	vF, vS, stellar; = IC 2137
2137 I		5 34.3	− 23 20 *d*	Lep			eF, vS, R, *8 f 10ˢ, 1979 nr
2138 I	Gx	5 34.3	− 23 33 *m*	Lep	1.0	14*p*	eF, S, 2 st inv 0′.5 apart, *7 p
1989	Gx	5 34.4	− 30 48 *c*	Col	1.8		vF, S, R, lbM, st nr
2036	OC	5 34.4	− 70 04 *r*	Men			vF, pL, R, gbM
1952	Nb	5 34.5	+ 22 01 *s*	Tau	6	8.4	vB, vL, E 135°±, vglbM, r; = M1
1992	Gx	5 34.5	− 30 56 *r*	Col		15*p*	eeF, vS
2033	C+N	5 34.5	− 69 44 *r*	Dor			Cl, in LMC
2038	OC	5 34.5	− 70 33 *r*	Men			pB, S, R, gbM, *9 np 5′
2037	C+N	5 34.7	− 69 45 *r*	Dor			Cl, in LMC
2007	Gx	5 35.0	− 50 56 *r*	Pic			eF, pL, R
1973	Nb	5 35.1	− 4 44 *s*	Ori	5		*8-9 inv in neb (1977)
2008	Gx	5 35.1	− 50 59 *r*	Pic			eF, pL, R, vlbM
2027	C+N	5 35.1	− 66 55 *r*	Dor			Cl, vL, Ri, st 9...11
1981	OC	5 35.2	− 4 26 *s*	Ori	25	4.6	Cl, vB, lRi, st L, sc
2048	Nb	5 35.2	− 69 46 *s*	Dor	18		vF, L, pmE
2032	C+N	5 35.3	− 67 34 *r*	Dor			B, L, E, 2nd of 3
2035	C+N	5 35.3	− 67 34 *r*	Dor			B, L, R, bM, 3rd of 3
2046	OC	5 35.3	− 70 14 *r*	Men			vF, R, gbM, 1st of 7
2139 I	*⋆*	5 35.3	− 17 56 *F*	Lep			Cl, vvS (12″), looks nebs
1975	Nb	5 35.4	− 4 41 *s*	Ori	10		B⁎ inv in neb (1977)
1976	Nb	5 35.4	− 5 27 *s*	Ori	66	4	!!! θ^1 Ori and the great neb; = M42
1980	Nb	5 35.4	− 5 54 *s*	Ori	14		vF, vvL, 44 Ori inv
2029	C+N	5 35.4	− 67 33 *r*	Dor			pB, pL, R, gbM, in cLCl
2030	C+N	5 35.4	− 66 01 *r*	Dor			pB, L, iR, gbM, 1st of 3
1977	Nb	5 35.5	− 4 52 *s*	Ori	20		!!, 42 Ori and neb
1993	Gx	5 35.5	− 17 49 *r*	Lep		14*p*	eF, vS, stellar
1982	Nb	5 35.6	− 5 16 *s*	Ori	20	9	! vB, vL, R with tail, mbM *8-9; = M43
2047	OC	5 35.6	− 70 11 *r*	Men			F, S, lE, 2nd of 7
2034	C+N	5 35.7	− 66 56 *r*	Dor			Cl, vL, Ri
2042	C+N	5 35.8	− 68 54 *r*	Dor			Cl, vL, Ri, st 12...15
2044	C+N	5 35.9	− 69 11 *r*	Dor			Cl, in LMC
1960	OC	5 36.1	+ 34 08 *s*	Aur	12	6.0	Cl, B, vL, vRi, lC, st 9...11 sc; = M36
2040	C+N	5 36.1	− 67 33 *r*	Dor			F, L, iR, glbM, r
1990	Nb	5 36.2	− 1 12 *s*	Ori	50		!!!, eL, E, ϵ Ori inv p
2043	−	5 36.2	− 70 05 *r*	Men			S, E group of F st inv in F neby
2051	OC	5 36.2	− 71 00 *r*	Men			pB, S, R, gbM
2041	OC	5 36.4	− 66 58 *r*	Dor		10*p*	B, S, R, vglbM
1999	Nb	5 36.5	− 6 42 *s*	Ori	16		*10-11 inv in neb
2050	C+N	5 36.5	− 69 22 *r*	Dor			Cl + neb, mC, iF, st vS
2056	OC	5 36.5	− 70 40 *r*	Men			pB, R, bM, p of 2, *9 bet

NGC	Type	α_{2000}	δ_{2000}	Const.	Size	Mag.	Description
		h m	° ′		′		
2058	OC	5 36.6	− 70 08 r	Men		12p	vB, pL, R, gbM, 4th of 7
427 I		5 36.6	− 6 40 d	Ori			L, prob conn with Great Neb
428 I		5 36.6	− 6 31 d	Ori			L, prob conn with Great Neb
2057	OC	5 36.7	− 70 15 r	Men			pF, S, R, gbM, 3rd of 7
2059	OC	5 36.7	− 70 06 r	Men			vF, 5th of 7
426 I	Nb	5 36.8	− 0 15 s	Ori	5		vF, 5′ diam
2055	C+N	5 37.0	− 69 24 r	Dor			Cl, vL, Ri, st 10...15
425 I		5 37.1	+ 32 26 d	Aur			F, vvL
2052	Nb	5 37.3	− 69 45 r	Dor			eF, vvS, vglbM
2053	OC	5 37.3	− 67 24 r	Dor			F, pL, lE, gbM
2065	OC	5 37.3	− 70 13 r	Men		11p	B, R, 6th of 7
1988	*	5 37.5	+ 21 14 r	Tau			!!!, variable (?)
2066	OC	5 37.5	− 70 10 r	Men			vF, vS, E, 7th of 7
2060	C+N	5 37.6	− 69 10 r	Dor			neb, no descrip, in LMC
1985	Nb	5 37.7	+ 32 00 A	Aur			cF, S, R, psbM
2146 I	OC	5 37.8	− 74 46 x	Men			Cl, vF, bet 2 st
2072	OC	5 38.1	− 70 14 r	Men			vF, S
1996	−	5 38.2	+ 25 49 r	Tau			Cl, L, lC, lRi
2075	C+N	5 38.2	− 70 40 r	Men			B, R, bM, rr, f of 2
429 I		5 38.3	− 7 03 d	Ori			vF, vS, R (inv in f one?)
2069	Nb	5 38.5	− 69 05 r	Dor			F, L, E
430 I	Nb	5 38.5	− 7 05 s	Ori	11		neb band 10′ l, np *5
2070	C+N	5 38.6	− 69 05 s	Dor	40	8.2	!!! vB, vL, looped
2074	C+N	5 38.9	− 69 29 d	Dor			pB, pL, mE, 5 st inv
2148 I		5 39.2	− 75 31 d	Men			vF, vS, bM
2017	−	5 39.4	− 17 51 r	Lep			Cl of L st
2077	C+N	5 39.6	− 69 40 d	Dor	15		F, R, p of Dneb
2078	C+N	5 39.6	− 69 45 d	Dor			neb, np of gr of 7
2079	C+N	5 39.6	− 69 47 d	Dor			neb, sp of gr of 7
2080	C+N	5 39.7	− 69 39 d	Dor			B, R, f of Dneb
2083	C+N	5 39.9	− 69 45 r	Dor			neb, nf of gr of 7
2084	C+N	5 39.9	− 69 45 r	Dor			neb, sf of gr of 7
2062	OC	5 40.0	− 66 53 r	Dor			vF, pS, E, glbM, 2 st 10 s
2081	C+N	5 40.1	− 69 24 r	Dor			Cl, vF, mC, st + neb
2085	C+N	5 40.2	− 69 39 r	Dor			vF, R, *10 vnr
431 I	Nb	5 40.3	− 1 27 s	Ori	5		neb *8.6
2086	C+N	5 40.4	− 69 39 r	Dor			B, pS, R, lbM, *10 p
2145 I	Nb	5 40.4	− 69 40 x	Dor			◯ , stellar
433 I	Gx	5 40.5	− 11 38 m	Lep	0.4	14p	F, S, dif, gbM
2088	OC	5 40.8	− 69 28 r	Dor			vF, S, R
2091	OC	5 40.9	− 69 26 r	Dor			vF, S, mE, glbM; D?
432 I	Nb	5 40.9	− 1 29 s	Ori	8		neb, lE, *8.4 inv
2144	Gx	5 41.0	− 82 07 c	Men	1.6		F, pS, iR, bM
434 I	Nb	5 41.0	− 2 24 s	Ori	60		neb, 60′ l, south from ς Ori
2092	OC	5 41.5	− 69 13 r	Dor			vF, pL, R, rr
2093	C+N	5 41.5	− 68 55 r	Dor			vF, S, R
2023	Nb	5 41.6	− 2 14 s	Ori	10		B* in M of L, lE neb
2103	C+N	5 41.6	− 71 20 r	Men			pB, L, pmE, gbM *13
2082	Gx	5 41.8	− 64 18 s	Dor	1.6	13p	pF, L, R, glbM
2024	Nb	5 41.9	− 1 51 d	Ori	30		! irr, B, vvL, black sp incl
2100	OC	5 42.0	− 69 14 s	Dor	2	9.6	⊕ , B, pL, irr R, rr
1961	Gx	5 42.1	+ 69 23 s	Cam	4.3	11.1	cF, pL, iF, mbM, er, * inv
2022	Pl	5 42.1	+ 9 05 s	Ori	0.3	12p	◯ , pB, vS, vlE
2094	OC	5 42.1	− 68 21 r	Dor			vF, S, R
2096	OC	5 42.2	− 68 28 r	Dor			neb, no descrip, in LMC

NGC	Type	α_{2000}	δ_{2000}	Const.	Size	Mag.	Description
		h m	o ′		′		
2102	OC	5 42.2	− 69 29 r	Dor			neb, no descrip, in LMC
2133 I	?	5 42.2	+ 69 23 x	Cam			vF, pL, *13 sf 0′.7
2141 I		5 42.3	− 51 02 d	Pic			F, vS, R, bM
2098	C+N	5 42.5	− 68 16 r	Dor			⊕, B, S, rr
2095	OC	5 42.7	− 67 19 r	Dor			Cl, F, cS, irr
435 I	Nb	5 43.0	− 2 19 s	Ori	5		neb, *8.5
2026	−	5 43.1	+ 20 07 r	Tau			Cl, lRi, lC, st pL
2107	OC	5 43.2	− 70 37 r	Men		11p	pB, pS, R, gbM
2049	Gx	5 43.4	− 30 06 r	Col		14p	vF, S, R, bM
2108	Gb	5 43.8	− 69 12 r	Dor			eF, pL, lE
2061	−	5 43.9	− 33 57 r	Col			Cl, L, lC, st 13
2039	−	5 44.1	+ 8 38 r	Ori			Cl, vL, lRi, lC
2097	OC	5 44.1	− 62 47 r	Dor			vF, pS, iR, pslbM *16
2105	OC	5 44.2	− 66 25 r	Dor			F, pS, R, gbM
2087	Gx	5 44.3	− 55 32 c	Pic	1.1		eF, pS, R, vlbM
2013	−	5 44.4	+ 55 48 r	Aur			Cl, vlRi, st 11
2109	C+N	5 44.4	− 68 32 r	Dor			F, pS, R, vglbM
2111	OC	5 44.7	− 70 57 r	Men			vF, S, R, gbM
2045		5 45.0	+ 12 53 d	Tau			*8-9 with F neb
2054	Ast	5 45.2	− 10 05 D	Ori			only 3 S st and no neb
2113	C+N	5 45.5	− 69 45 r	Dor			Cl, F, S, iF, vlC, rr
2114	OC	5 45.8	− 68 03 r	Dor			eF, pL, iR
2073	Gx	5 45.9	− 21 59 r	Lep		13p	eF, vS, R, gbM
2064	Nb	5 46.3	+ 0 00 s	Ori	12		eF, vS, *9-10 np 4′
2101	Gx	5 46.4	− 52 05 A	Pic	1.9		eF, pS, R, 3 st 10 sp
2067	Nb	5 46.5	+ 0 06 s	Ori	8		F, pL, M78 s
2068	Nb	5 46.7	+ 0 03 s	Ori	8	8	B, L, wisp, gmbN, 3 st inv, r; = M78
2063	−	5 46.8	+ 8 48 r	Ori			Cl, poor, S sc st
2076	Gx	5 46.8	− 16 46 r	Lep		14p	vF, pS, iE, bM
2116	OC	5 46.9	− 68 32 r	Dor			F, S, R, *11 p
2143 I	Gx	5 46.9	− 18 44 c	Lep	2.5		eF, pS, vmE 45°, 3 st sf
2090	Gx	5 47.0	− 34 14 s	Col	4.5	12p	B, pL, iR, gbM, stell N, cE 10°
2104	Gx	5 47.1	− 51 33 c	Pic	2.0		pB, pS, R, glbM
2071	Nb	5 47.2	+ 0 18 s	Ori	4		D* (10 & 14m) with vF, L chev
2118	OC	5 47.2	− 69 09 r	Dor			⊕, vB, vS, vsmbM, rr
2117	OC	5 47.3	− 67 28 r	Dor			F, pL, iR, vlbM, rrr
2089	Gx	5 47.8	− 17 36 r	Lep		14p	vF, eS, stellar
2147 I		5 47.8	− 30 30 d	Col			eeF, pS, R, F* np
2121	Gb	5 48.0	− 71 28 s	Men	1.8	11.2	vF, cL, vgbM
2122	C+N	5 48.7	− 70 04 r	Men			Cl, pB, iF, gvmCM, st 15
2134	OC	5 50.1	− 71 07 r	Men		11p	⊕, B, pL, R, gmbM, r
2144 I		5 50.2	+ 23 52 d	Tau			pF, eS, *12 nnp 2′, *12 s 1′
2120	Gb	5 50.6	− 63 41 r	Dor			cF, pL, R, vglbM
2106	Gx	5 50.7	− 21 35 r	Lep		13p	vF, S, vlE, gbM
2125	OC	5 50.7	− 69 29 r	Dor			vF, pS, R, gbM
2127	OC	5 51.1	− 69 22 r	Dor			pB, vS, R, gmbM
2115	Gx	5 51.3	− 50 35 c	Pic	1.2		eeF, vS, 3 st 10 sp
2150 I	Gx	5 51.3	− 38 19 c	Col	2.3		eeF, S, vmE, v diffic, 3 st s
2133	Gb	5 51.4	− 71 11 r	Men			F, pL, R, gpmbM
437 I		5 51.6	− 12 34 d	Lep			vF, vS, R, dif
2123	OC	5 51.7	− 65 19 r	Dor			pB, vS, R, gbM
2130	OC	5 52.1	− 67 20 r	Dor			F, pS, R, glbM
2110	Gx	5 52.2	− 7 27 F	Ori		14p	eF, cS, lE, pslbM, er
2099	OC	5 52.4	+ 32 33 s	Aur	24	5.6	Cl, Ri, pCM, st L & S; = M37
2151 I	Gx	5 52.6	− 17 47 c	Lep	2.1		eF, pS, nr IC 438

NGC	Type	α_{2000}	δ_{2000}	Const.	Size	Mag.	Description
		h m	° ′		′		
2136	OC	5 52.8	− 69 30 r	Dor		10p	⊕ , pB, R, gmbM, rr, st 14...16
438 I	Gx	5 53.0	− 17 53 c	Lep	3.2		eeF, pS, E ns, 2 st p
2135	OC	5 53.1	− 67 26 r	Dor			F, pS, R, r, am st
2137	OC	5 53.2	− 69 29 r	Dor			vF, S, R, f of 2
436 I		5 53.7	+ 38 38 d	Aur			eF
2112	OC	5 53.9	+ 0 24 s	Ori	11	9p	Cl, pL, lRi, pC, st S
2140	OC	5 54.0	− 68 36 r	Dor			pF, pS, iR, bM
2138	OC	5 54.5	− 65 50 r	Dor			eF, S, R
2145	OC	5 54.5	− 70 55 r	Men			F, lE, r
2132	Ast	5 55.2	− 59 55 A	Pic			Cl, vlC, st L & S
2160 I	Gx	5 55.5	− 76 55 c	Men	1.9		vF, vS, stell N
2161	Gb	5 55.6	− 74 21 r	Men			F, pL, R, gpmbM
2150	Gx	5 55.9	− 69 34 r	Dor			F, vS, R, vsmbM, stellar
2147	C+N	5 56.0	− 68 12 r	Dor			eF, S, R, bM
2151	OC	5 56.3	− 69 01 r	Dor			F, pS, R, bM
2149 I	Pl	5 56.3	+ 46 07 s	Aur	0.1	11p	○ , stellar
439 I		5 56.6	+ 32 02 d	Aur			eeL, eE 150°±
2161 I		5 57.2	− 75 08 d	Men			eF, vS, bM, susp
2157	OC	5 57.3	− 69 11 r	Dor		10p	⊕ , vB, S, R, vgvmbM, rr
2119	Gx	5 57.4	+ 11 57 r	Ori			F, vS, R, bM
2153	OC	5 57.5	− 66 24 r	Dor			eeF, lE, *16 att
2154	Gb	5 57.5	− 67 15 r	Dor			F, pL, R, vglbM
2156	OC	5 57.6	− 68 27 r	Dor			pB, S, R, gbM, 1st of 3
2124	Gx	5 57.9	− 20 04 r	Lep		13p	F, S, E, r
2159	OC	5 57.9	− 68 38 r	Dor			pF, S, R, gbM, *15 att nf
2152 I	Gx	5 57.9	− 23 11 c	Lep	1.9		pB, pS, R, sev B st f
2160	OC	5 58.0	− 68 17 r	Dor			pF, pS, R, gbM
2173	Gb	5 58.1	− 72 59 r	Men			pF, pL, R, gmbM
2155	Gb	5 58.4	− 65 28 r	Dor			F, pL, R, vglbM
2171	Gx	5 58.6	− 70 41 r	Men			eF, L, R, glbM
2131	Gx	5 58.7	− 26 38 r	Lep			vF, pS, R, gbM
2148	Gx	5 58.7	− 59 07 r	Pic			eF, S, R, *12 vnr
2164	OC	5 58.7	− 68 31 r	Dor		10p	⊕ , vB, R, mCM, rr
2166	OC	5 59.3	− 67 56 r	Dor			F, S, R, gbM
2172	OC	5 59.9	− 68 38 r	Dor			F, cL, R, lbM
2153 I	Gx	6 00.1	− 33 55 c	Col	2.5		eF, vS, susp
2162	Gb	6 00.5	− 63 45 r	Dor			F, pL, R, vglbM
2190	Gb	6 00.8	− 74 43 r	Men			vF, pL, R, glbM
2155 I		6 00.8	− 34 01 d	Col			eF, vS, R, susp
2152	Gx	6 00.9	− 50 44 c	Pic	1.3		eeF, R, *15 att
2129	OC	6 01.0	+ 23 18 s	Gem	7	6.7	Cl, pL, 40 or 50 st 8...15
2177	OC	6 01.0	− 67 43 r	Dor			F, vS, iR, lbM, r
2139	Gx	6 01.1	− 23 40 s	Lep	2.2	11.7	F, S; = IC 2154
2154 I	Gx	6 01.1	− 23 40 c	Lep	3.3		pF, pS, R, * nf, 2 st np; = 2139
2176	OC	6 01.4	− 66 51 r	Dor			eeF, pL, R, gbM
2142	−	6 01.9	− 10 36 r	Mon			* (3 Mon) inv in pL, F, neb
2181	OC	6 02.6	− 65 15 r	Dor			vF, S, R
441 I	Gx	6 02.7	− 12 30 m	Lep	1.1	14p	eF, vS, diffic, vF* close
2178	Gx	6 02.8	− 63 46 c	Pic	1.0		eF, vS, R
2126	OC	6 03.0	+ 49 54 s	Aur	6	10p	Cl, not Ri, *7 n
2143	−	6 03.0	+ 5 43 r	Ori			Cl, L, pRi, vlC, st 10
2141	OC	6 03.1	+ 10 26 s	Ori	10	9.4	F, pS, dif
2149	Nb	6 03.5	− 9 44 s	Mon	3		F, *12 inv
2187	Gx	6 03.9	− 69 34 r	Dor			pB, pS, R, gbM, Dneb (comp vF, R, glbM)
2128	Gx	6 04.7	+ 57 39 r	Cam		13p	vF, vS, vlE

NGC	Type	α_{2000}	δ_{2000}	Const.	Size	Mag.	Description
		h m	o ′		′		
2199	Gx	6 04.7	− 73 24 r	Men			F, vS, R, bM
2203	OC	6 04.7	− 75 26 r	Men			F Cl
2156 I	OC	6 04.8	+ 24 09 z	Gem			Cl, nebs?
2157 I	OC	6 05.0	+ 24 00 s	Gem	7	8.4	Cl, S
2158 I	Gx	6 05.3	− 27 51 c	Col	1.6		vF, pS, lE, brush, * att nf
2197	OC	6 05.9	− 67 05 r	Dor			vF, pS, R, gbM
2193	Gb	6 06.2	− 65 05 r	Dor			F, iF, glbM, 2 or 3 st inv
2167	−	6 06.9	− 6 12 r	Mon			nebulous *7, am 3 st
2164 I	Gx	6 06.9	− 75 22 c	Men	1.3		eF, eeS, R, stell N
2158	OC	6 07.5	+ 24 06 s	Gem	5	8.6	Cl, pS, mC, vRi, irr △ st eS
2170	Nb	6 07.5	− 6 24 s	Mon	2		*9 in vF, pL neb, E 170°
2163		6 07.8	+ 18 40 D	Ori			eF, E, dif, *11 att s
2179	Gx	6 08.0	− 21 45 s	Lep	1.5	12.5	F, pS, bet 2 st, glbM
2169	OC	6 08.4	+ 13 57 s	Ori	7	5.9	Cl, S, lRi, pmC, ⁎ (ADS 4728)
2191	Gx	6 08.4	− 52 31 c	Car	1.9		pB, vS, E, vsbM, *9 p 5ˢ
2209	Gb	6 08.7	− 73 51 r	Men			vF, cL, R, gvlbM
2168	OC	6 08.9	+ 24 20 s	Gem	28	5.1	Cl, vL, cRi, pC, st 9...16; = M35
2182	Nb	6 09.5	− 6 20 s	Mon	3		pB⁎ , L* neb, E 90°±
2180	−	6 09.6	+ 4 43 r	Ori			Cl, pRi, lC, st L and S
2174	Nb	6 09.7	+ 20 30 s	Ori	40		eF, bet 3 vF st
2175	OC	6 09.8	+ 20 19 s	Ori	18	6.8	*8 in neb
2159 I	Nb	6 09.9	+ 20 24 z	Ori			vF, vL, dif
2188	Gx	6 10.1	− 34 06 s	Col	3.7	11.8	pF, pL, vmE, gvlbM
2205	Gx	6 10.6	− 62 32 c	Pic	1.4		pF, S, R, bM
2213	Gb	6 10.7	− 71 33 r	Men			vF, S, R, glbM, *⁎* p
2183	Nb	6 10.8	− 6 13 s	Mon	1		eF, S, lE, *11-12 sp
2184	OC	6 10.9	− 3 31 F	Ori			Cl, L, vlC
2165	−	6 11.1	+ 51 41 r	Aur			Cl, pL, poor, st 11
2185	Nb	6 11.1	− 6 13 s	Mon	3		*11 and 4 S st in vF, L neb
2210	Gb	6 11.5	− 69 08 s	Dor	1.7	10.2	vB, pL, R, mbM, r
2186	OC	6 12.2	+ 5 27 s	Ori	4	8.7	Cl, pL, pRi, pC, st L and S
2196	Gx	6 12.2	− 21 48 s	Lep	2.8	11.2	pF, pS, vlE, pmbM, st nr
2189	−	6 12.3	+ 1 08 r	Ori			2 clusters nr 2 st 9-10 & 10-11
2214	OC	6 12.8	− 68 16 r	Dor		11p	B, pS, lE, gbM, rrr
2162 I	Nb	6 12.9	+ 17 59 s	Ori	15		vF, pL, R, *10 inv p
2200	Gx	6 13.4	− 43 39 r	Pup			eF, pS, R, vlbM
2201	Gx	6 13.4	− 43 41 r	Pup			eF, S, R, pslbM
2194	OC	6 13.8	+ 12 48 s	Ori	10	8.5	Cl, L, Ri, gvmCM
2198	−	6 13.9	+ 1 00 r	Ori			Cl, bet 2 st 9-10 & 10-11
2195	Nb	6 14.4	+ 17 39 s	Ori			F, S, 2 S st inv, *10 n 31″
2192	OC	6 15.2	+ 39 51 s	Aur	6	11p	Cl, cL, C, iF, st vS
2204	OC	6 15.7	− 18 39 s	CMa	13	8.6	Cl, L, pRi, lC
2206	Gx	6 16.0	− 26 46 s	CMa	2.3	13p	F, pS, vlE, pslbM
2207	Gx	6 16.4	− 21 22 s	CMa	4.3	10.7	pB, pL, mE 87°, pslbMRN, biN, ring surr
2163 I	Gx	6 16.5	− 21 23 c	CMa			eF, pS, 2207 p 7ˢ
2202	−	6 16.9	+ 5 59 r	Ori			⁎ chief of Cl
443 I	Nb	6 16.9	+ 22 47 s	Gem	50		F, narrow, curved
2211	Gx	6 18.4	− 18 34 r	CMa		14p	vF, pS, E 45°, bMN
2212	Gx	6 18.5	− 18 33 r	CMa		14p	eF, vS, R, in field with 2211
2146	Gx	6 18.7	+ 78 21 s	Cam	6.0	10.5	pB, 2′ l, lE
440 I	Gx	6 18.9	+ 80 04 u	Cam	2.1	14p	vF, S
2221	Gx	6 20.2	− 57 35 c	Pic	1.5		vF, lE, vgbM, p of 2
2222	Gx	6 20.3	− 57 32 c	Pic	1.1		vF, lE, vgvlbM, f of 2
2231	Gb	6 20.4	− 67 32 r	Dor			F, pL, R, gvlbM, ⁎ f
444 I	Nb	6 20.4	+ 23 16 s	Gem	8		neb, *9.5 inv

NGC	Type	α_{2000}	δ_{2000}	Const.	Size	Mag.	Description
		h m	o ′		′		
2215	OC	6 21.0	− 7 17 s	Mon	11	8.4	Cl, cL, pRi, pC, st 11...15
2228	Gx	6 21.2	− 64 27 r	Dor			F, S, R, glbM
2229	Gx	6 21.3	− 64 58 r	Dor			eF, vS, R, 1st of 3
2230	Gx	6 21.4	− 65 00 r	Dor			eF, S, lE, 2nd of 3
2216	Gx	6 21.6	− 22 05 r	CMa		14p	vF, pL, R, vglbM
2217	Gx	6 21.7	− 27 14 s	CMa	4.8	10.4	vB, S, R, psmbM, r
2233	Gx	6 21.7	− 65 03 r	Dor			eF, S, 3rd of 3
2165 I	Pl	6 21.7	− 12 59 s	CMa	0.1	13p	◯ , stellar
2220	Ast	6 21.8	− 44 46 A	Pup			Cl, B, P, st 8...
2235	Gx	6 22.3	− 64 57 r	Dor			vF, S, R, ∗12 nr
2208	Gx	6 22.5	+ 51 55 r	Aur		14p	pF, pS, lE
2241	OC	6 22.7	− 68 57 r	Dor			vF, pL, R, glbM
2219	−	6 23.4	− 4 41 r	Mon			Cl, P, vlC, st 6, 11...12
2223	Gx	6 24.6	− 22 50 s	CMa	3.3	11.4	F, pL, R, vglbM, 2 st inv
2218	−	6 24.7	+ 19 20 r	Gem			F Cl
2227	Gx	6 25.9	− 21 59 s	CMa	2.3	14p	eF, R, ⚹ p 270°, 90″
2249	Gb	6 25.9	− 68 48 r	Dor			pB, pL, R, vgbM, ⚹ p
2225	OC	6 26.6	− 9 39 F	Mon			Cl, P, lCM, st 12...15
2232	OC	6 26.6	− 4 45 s	Mon	30	3.9	B∗ (10 Mon) + Cl
2226	−	6 26.7	− 9 39 r	Mon			S, v diffic, ∗10 close s
2166 I	Gx	6 27.0	+ 59 05 s	Lyn	2.9	13p	neb; F∗ p 1′, D∗ f 3′
2224	−	6 27.6	+ 12 38 r	Gem			Cl, pC, with neb?
2234	−	6 29.3	+ 16 41 r	Gem			Cl, eL, pRi, lC, st L & S
2236	OC	6 29.7	+ 6 50 s	Mon	7	8.5	Cl, pRi, pC, st 10, 12...15
2243	OC	6 29.8	− 31 17 s	CMa	5	9.4	F Cl, st 9...11
2237	Nb	6 30.3	+ 5 03 d	Mon			pB, vvL, dif, part of eL nebs ring ar 2239
2257	Gb	6 30.4	− 64 19 s	Dor	3.4	13.5	F, cL, R, vglbM, r, 17^{s}d
2238	C+N	6 30.6	+ 5 01 D	Mon			S∗ in neby, part of eL nebs ring ar 2239
2239	OC	6 31.0	+ 4 57 s	Mon	16		∗8 in L, P, B Cl
446 I	Nb	6 31.0	+ 10 27 s	Mon	5		neb ∗10; = IC 2167
447 I		6 31.2	+ 10 02 x	Mon			vF, eeL, dif; = IC 2167
2169 I	Nb	6 31.2	+ 9 54 s	Mon	25		F, L, dif, sev st 9-10 inv
2167 I		6 31.3	+ 10 27 d	Mon			∗9.5 in F, L neb
2244	OC	6 32.4	+ 4 52 s	Mon	24	4.8	Cl, beautiful, st sc (12 Mon)
2246	Nb	6 32.4	+ 5 07 r	Mon			eeF, L, irr R, e diffic
2245	Nb	6 32.7	+ 10 10 s	Mon	5		pL, com, mbN sf alm ∗, ∗7-8 nf
448 I	Nb	6 32.7	+ 7 19 s	Mon	15		neby, np ∗5
2250	OC	6 32.8	− 5 02 s	Mon	8	9p	Cl, pRi, lC, iF, st 8, 12...14
2240	−	6 32.9	+ 35 12 r	Aur			Cl, pL, P, vlC, st 7, 10...15
2247	Nb	6 33.2	+ 10 20 s	Mon	4		neb∗ in eF, eL neby, nf 2245
2168 I	OC	6 33.8	+ 44 41 x	Aur			Cl, S, F neby
2242	Pl	6 34.0	+ 44 46 A	Aur		14p	eeF, vS, R, F∗ nf
2255	Gx	6 34.0	− 34 47 r	Col			eF, S, lE, vlbM
2170 I		6 34.1	+ 44 42 d	Aur			eF, S, r, ∗13 spp 0′.8
2248	−	6 34.6	+ 26 19 r	Gem			small cluster
2251	OC	6 34.7	+ 8 22 s	Mon	10	7.3	Cl, vL, E, Ri, lC
2252	OC	6 35.0	+ 5 23 s	Mon	20	8p	Cl, vL, pRi, lC, st S
2254	OC	6 36.0	+ 7 40 s	Mon	4	9.7	Cl, S, pC, iF, st 11...13
442 I	Gx	6 36.5	+ 82 58 u	Cam	1.4	14p	F, S, R, mbM
445 I	Gx	6 37.3	+ 67 51 u	Cam	1.2	14p	eF, S, R, B∗ sf
2260	−	6 38.1	− 1 28 r	Mon			Cl, vL, P, vlC, st L & S
2262	OC	6 38.4	+ 1 11 s	Mon	4	11p	Cl, vC, iR, bM, st eS
2263	Gx	6 38.4	− 24 49 r	CMa		13p	pF, lE, bet 2 vS st, pslbM
2259	OC	6 38.6	+ 10 53 s	Mon	5	11p	Cl, cRi, eC, iF, st eS
2261	Nb	6 39.2	+ 8 44 s	Mon	2		B, vmE 330°, N com = ∗11

NGC	Type	α_{2000}	δ_{2000}	Const.	Size	Mag.	Description
		h m	° ′		′		
2267	Gx	6 40.8	− 32 29 r	CMa		14p	two neb close together
2264	C+N	6 41.1	+ 9 53 s	Mon	60	3.9	eL neb, 3° diam, densest 12′ sp 15 Mon
2265	−	6 41.5	+ 11 56 r	Gem			Cl, P, 30 or 40 st 12...13
2253	OC	6 42.4	+ 66 20 A	Cam			vF, st eS
2272	Gx	6 42.7	− 27 27 s	CMa	2.1	11.9	pF, pS, vlE, bM, r
2271	Gx	6 42.8	− 23 28 r	CMa		14p	pF, S, R, gbM, am st
2266	OC	6 43.2	+ 26 58 s	Gem	7	10p	Cl, pS, eC, Ri, st 11...15
2269	OC	6 43.9	+ 4 34 s	Mon	4	10.0	Cl, vmC, not Ri, st vS
2270	−	6 43.9	+ 3 26 r	Mon			Cl, lC, not Ri
2297	Gx	6 44.4	− 63 43 c	Pic	1.6		vF, S, R, vglbM
2171 I	Gx	6 44.4	− 17 56 c	CMa	1.8		F, 3 st 10 around
2280	Gx	6 44.8	− 27 38 s	CMa	5.6	12p	pF, pL, lE, gbM
449 I	Gx	6 45.7	+ 71 21 v	Cam	2.0		pF, S, R, bM, bet 2 D st
2283	Gx	6 45.9	− 18 14 r	CMa		13p	3 or 4 S st + neb
2282	Nb	6 46.9	+ 1 19 s	Mon	3		*10 in F, R neby
2172 I		6 46.9	+ 1 20 d	Mon			neb*
2287	OC	6 47.0	− 20 44 s	CMa	38	4.5	Cl, vL, B, lC, st 8...; = M41
2256	Gx	6 47.2	+ 74 14 s	Cam	2.6	14p	F, R, *9.5 3′ sf
2274	Gx	6 47.2	+ 33 34 r	Gem		13p	F, S, bM
2275	Gx	6 47.2	+ 33 36 r	Gem		14p	eF, vS
2295	Gx	6 47.3	− 26 44 r	CMa		14p	eF, S, R, bet st, Dneb f
2286	OC	6 47.6	− 3 10 s	Mon	15	7.5	Cl, L, C, ab 100 st 9...15
2292	Gx	6 47.6	− 26 45 r	CMa		14p	eF, R, gbM, D with 2293, am st
2293	Gx	6 47.7	− 26 45 r	CMa		13p	pB, R, gbM, D with 2292, am st
2258	Gx	6 47.8	+ 74 29 s	Cam	2.6	13p	F, 2 st 10-11 f
2277	−	6 47.8	+ 33 26 r	Gem			Cl, vS, lRi
2278	−	6 48.3	+ 33 24 r	Gem			vF, vS; = 2274?
2279	−	6 48.4	+ 33 24 r	Gem			vF, vS, stellar Nucl; = 2275?
2296	Gx	6 48.6	− 16 55 r	CMa		13p	vF, vS, R; = IC 452
2305	Gx	6 48.6	− 64 16 c	Vol	2.0		vF, vS, R, 2 st △
452 I	Gx	6 48.6	− 16 54 c	CMa			*13.5 in S neby; = 2296
2307	Gx	6 48.8	− 64 20 c	Vol	1.6		vF, pS, vlE 90°
2298	Gb	6 49.0	− 36 00 s	Pup	6.8	9.4	⊕, B, pL, iR, gbM, rr
2284	−	6 49.1	+ 33 13 r	Gem			F, r
453 I	*	6 49.1	− 17 02 F	CMa			2 or 3 st close?
2281	OC	6 49.3	+ 41 04 s	Aur	15	5.4	Cl, pRi, vlC, st pL
2285	−	6 49.4	+ 33 21 r	Gem			eF, eS, r?
2273	Gx	6 50.1	+ 60 51 s	Lyn	3.5	12p	F, S, iR, r?
2288	Gx	6 50.7	+ 33 26 A	Gem		14p	eF, vS
2289	Gx	6 50.7	+ 33 27 A	Gem		15p	cF, S, R
2173 I		6 50.8	+ 33 26 x	Gem			eF, neb*, 2288 close, *12 nnp 1′; = 2291
2290	Gx	6 51.0	+ 33 26 s	Gem	1.5	15p	F, S, gbM
2291	Gx	6 51.0	+ 33 32 s	Gem	1.3	16p	eF, vS; = IC 2173
2299	−	6 51.1	− 7 00 r	Mon			Cl of 30 or 40 st
454 I		6 51.1	+ 12 54 D	Gem			eeF, S, e diffic, one or 2 st inv
2294	Gx	6 51.2	+ 33 32 s	Gem	1.1	15p	eeF
2301	OC	6 51.8	+ 0 28 s	Mon	12	6.0	Cl, Ri, L, iF, st L & S
2302	OC	6 51.9	− 7 04 s	Mon	3	8.9	Cl, L, P, lC
450 I	Gx	6 52.2	+ 74 26 v	Cam	1.3		vF, S
451 I	Gx	6 52.9	+ 74 29 v	Cam	1.6		vF, S
2310	Gx	6 54.0	− 40 52 s	Pup	5.0	12p	pB, pL, vmE 45°, pslbM
2306	−	6 54.6	− 7 11 r	Mon			Cl, P, vlC
2304	OC	6 55.0	+ 18 01 s	Gem	5	10p	Cl, pL, Ri, mC, st vS
2303	Gx	6 56.2	+ 45 30 r	Aur		14p	eF, vS, R, sev st nr
2309	OC	6 56.2	− 7 12 s	Mon	3	11p	Cl, pL, pRi, mC, st 13

NGC	Type	α_{2000}	δ_{2000}	Const.	Size	Mag.	Description
		h m	° ′		′		
2311	OC	6 57.8	− 4 35 s	Mon	7	10p	Cl, lC, not Ri
2313	Nb	6 58.0	− 7 57 F	Mon			F, vS, R
2308	Gx	6 58.6	+ 45 13 r	Lyn		14p	eF, vS, vF* inv
2312	−	6 58.8	+ 10 16 r	Mon			Cl, P
2317	−	6 58.8	− 7 46 r	Mon			close Dneb with 2316
2318	OC	6 59.5	− 13 42 F	CMa			Cl, L, sc st 8...9
2316	Nb	6 59.7	− 7 46 s	Mon	4		pF, S, R, r, S st inv
2175 I		6 59.7	+ 35 17 d	Gem			eF, pL, r, nebs?
456 I	Gx	7 00.3	− 30 10 c	CMa	2.3		vF, pS, R, B st nf and np
2319	−	7 01.1	+ 3 04 r	Mon			Cl of v sc st 8, 9...
2315	Gx	7 02.5	+ 50 36 r	Lyn		14p	eF
2328	Gx	7 02.5	− 42 03 r	Pup			vF, S, vlE, bM, am st
2325	Gx	7 02.7	− 28 42 s	CMa	2.3	11.2	pB, pL, lE, gbM
2348		7 03.1	− 67 23 r	Vol			Cl, P, lC, 30 st ±
2323	OC	7 03.2	− 8 20 s	Mon	16	5.9	! Cl, vL, Ri, pC, E, st 12...16; = M50
2324	OC	7 04.2	+ 1 03 s	Mon	8	8.4	Cl, L, Ri, cC, st 12...16
2327	Nb	7 04.3	− 11 18 r	CMa			pB* inv in S, vF, neb
2177 I	Nb	7 05.1	− 10 42 s	Mon	120		pB, eL, iR, v dif.
2320	Gx	7 05.6	+ 50 36 r	Lyn		14p	pB, S, iR, gbM, *8 at 120°
2321	Gx	7 05.9	+ 50 46 r	Lyn		15p	vF, 12′n of 2320
2322	Gx	7 05.9	+ 50 31 r	Lyn		14p	vF, vS, lE
2335	OC	7 06.6	− 10 05 s	Mon	12	7.2	Cl, L, lC
2331	OC	7 07.2	+ 27 21 s	Gem	18	9p	Cl, L, vlC, S Cl inv
2176 I	Gx	7 07.5	+ 32 28 m	Gem	0.4	15p	vF, vS, R, stell
2178 I	Gx	7 07.6	+ 32 31 z	Gem		16p	vF, vS, R, bMN
2338	Ast	7 07.7	− 5 37 F	Mon			Cl, vlC
2339	Gx	7 08.3	+ 18 47 s	Gem	2.8	11.6	pB, pL, R, glbM
2343	OC	7 08.3	− 10 39 s	Mon	7	6.7	Cl, cL, P, lC
2345	OC	7 08.3	− 13 10 s	CMa	12	7.7	Cl, pL, pRi, gbM, st 10...14
2326	Gx	7 08.4	+ 50 44 r	Lyn		14p	vF, pL, iR, psmbM, st p
2333	Gx	7 08.4	+ 35 11 r	Gem		14p	vF, S, R, bM
466 I	Nb	7 08.6	− 4 19 s	Mon	1		*11.5 in vF neb
2174 I	Gx	7 09.1	+ 75 21 v	Cam	1.2		eF, S, bM
2329	Gx	7 09.2	+ 48 37 s	Lyn	1.6	14p	vF, vS, stellar
2341	Gx	7 09.3	+ 20 35 s	Gem	1.1	14p	vF, vS
2342	Gx	7 09.4	+ 20 38 s	Gem	1.6	13p	pF, S, lE, vlbM
2346	Pl	7 09.4	− 0 48 s	Mon	0.9		*10 att with S, vF, neb
457 I	Gx	7 09.4	+ 50 09 m	Lyn	0.3	16p	eF, sp 2332
2330	Gx	7 09.5	+ 50 12 r	Lyn		14p	vF, vS, v stellar
2332	Gx	7 09.5	+ 50 11 r	Lyn		14p	F, S, R, psbM
2334	−	7 09.9	+ 50 12 r	Lyn			vF, bet 2 st 12
2349	−	7 10.0	− 8 37 r	Mon			Cl, cL, P, cC
2337	Gx	7 10.2	+ 44 27 s	Lyn	2.6	13p	eF, S, E
2314	Gx	7 10.5	+ 75 20 s	Cam	2.1	11.9	vF, S, R
458 I	Gx	7 10.5	+ 50 06 u	Lyn	1.0	14p	F, bM
459 I		7 10.6	+ 50 11 d	Lyn			eF
460 I	Gx	7 10.7	+ 50 13 m	Lyn	0.4	16p	vF (not seen at Birr)
461 I	Gx	7 10.7	+ 50 05 m	Lyn	0.6	16p	vF, 3 F st f
463 I	Gx	7 10.9	+ 50 08 z	Lyn		15p	eF
2340	Gx	7 11.0	+ 50 10 r	Lyn		14p	pF, S, R, glbM, r
462 I		7 11.0	+ 50 11 d	Lyn			vF (not seen at Birr)
464 I	Gx	7 11.0	+ 50 09 m	Lyn	0.6	15p	F
2180 I	Gx	7 11.3	+ 26 23 u	Gem	1.2	15p	F, S, iF, dif
465 I	Gx	7 11.5	+ 50 15 m	Lyn	0.8	15p	F
2344	Gx	7 12.5	+ 47 10 s	Lyn	2.0	12.1	pB, pS, R, lbM

NGC	Type	α_{2000}	δ_{2000}	Const.	Size	Mag.	Description
		h m	° '		'		
2350	Gx	7 13.2	+ 12 15 r	CMi		14p	eF, eS, iR
2181 I	Gx	7 13.2	+ 19 00 u	Gem	1.0	15p	F, S, R, stell
2351		7 13.5	− 10 29 F	Mon			Cl, lC, ⁎ taken
2352	−	7 13.6	− 24 06 r	CMa			Cl, pRi, pC
2268	Gx	7 14.	+ 84 23 s	Cam	3.4	11.5	pF, pL, lE
2182 I		7 14.2	+ 18 57 d	Gem			vF, vS, dif, ⁎12 att
2354	OC	7 14.3	− 25 44 s	CMa	20	6.5	Cl, cRi, lC
2353	OC	7 14.6	− 10 18 s	Mon	20	7.1	Cl, L, lC, one vB⁎
2179 I	Gx	7 15.5	+ 64 56 s	Cam	1.0	12.6	⁎13 in vF, vS neb (= 2347?)
2347	Gx	7 16.1	+ 64 43 s	Cam	2.0	12.5	vF, S, R, lbM
2369	Gx	7 16.6	− 62 21 s	Car	4.6	13p	pB, pL, iE, glbM
2358	−	7 16.8	− 17 03 r	CMa			Cl, P, lC
2355	OC	7 16.9	+ 13 47 s	Gem	9	10p	Cl, pS, pRi, mC, st 15...16
2183 I		7 16.9	− 20 25 d	CMa			wisp 2' ns, 3 st n, susp
2356	−	7 17.1	+ 13 58 r	Gem			Cl, lC
468 I	Nb	7 17.5	− 13 09 s	CMa	20		vF neby, perhaps 2 or 3 st inv
2357	Gx	7 17.6	+ 23 22 s	Gem	4.5	14p	eF, L, mE, bM, F st inv
2360	OC	7 17.8	− 15 37 s	CMa	13	7.2	Cl, vL, Ri, pC, st 9...12
2361	D⁎?	7 18.4	− 13 13 F	CMa			vvF, vS; part of 2359
2359	Nb	7 18.6	− 13 12 s	CMa	8		!!, vF, vvL, viF
2362	C+N	7 18.8	− 24 57 s	CMa	8	4.1	Cl, pL, Ri (30 CMa)
2381	Gx	7 20.0	− 63 04 c	Car	1.6		vF, vS, R, am st
2367	OC	7 20.1	− 21 56 s	CMa	4	7.9	Cl, S, P, lC
2364	OC	7 20.8	− 7 34 F	Mon			Cl, pC, st pL, bifid
2368	OC	7 21.0	− 10 23 s	Mon	5	12p	Cl, S, pRi, st 15
2397	Gx	7 21.3	− 69 00 s	Vol	2.2	13p	pB, cL, cE 117°, lbM
2365	Gx	7 22.5	+ 22 04 r	Gem		14p	vF, pS, R, psbM
2186 I		7 22.7	+ 21 32 d	Gem			F, S, R, gbM, r
2187 I		7 22.7	+ 21 29 d	Gem			F, S, R, dif, ⁎11.5 vnr
2188 I		7 22.7	+ 21 30 d	Gem			F, S, dif, FN
2185 I	Gx	7 23.2	+ 32 30 m	Gem	0.5	15p	F, S, R
470 I		7 23.5	+ 46 05 d	Lyn			eF, eS, stellar
2380	Gx	7 23.9	− 27 31 r	CMa		13p	pF, pS, R, vsmbM, am st
2382		7 23.9	− 27 32 D	CMa			pF, S, R, bM; = 2380
2374	OC	7 24.0	− 13 16 s	CMa	19	8.0	Cl, vL, pRi, lC, st L
2383	OC	7 24.8	− 20 56 s	CMa	6	8.4	Cl, pS, pmC, st 12
2377	Gx	7 24.9	− 9 40 s	Mon	1.8	15p	eF, vS⁎ inv, ⁎11 s
2370	Gx	7 25.0	+ 23 47 r	Gem		14p	eF, vS, E
2189 I		7 25.0	+ 8 55 d	CMi			◯ stell
2384	OC	7 25.1	− 21 02 s	CMa	3	7.4	Cl, lC, bifid, ⁎
2371	Pl	7 25.6	+ 29 29 s	Gem	0.9	13p	B, S, R, bMN, p of Dneb
2372	Pl	7 25.6	+ 29 30 d	Gem			pB, S, R, bMN, f of Dneb
2373	Gx	7 26.5	+ 33 48 r	Gem		14p	eF, vS
2376	Gx	7 26.6	+ 23 04 r	Gem		14p	eF, vS
2276	Gx	7 27.	+ 85 45 s	Cep	2.6	11.4	F, 60″, lbM
2336	Gx	7 27.1	+ 80 11 s	Cam	6.9	10.5	pB, pL, R, 2 st 11 nr
2375	Gx	7 27.1	+ 33 49 r	Gem		14p	eF, vS, 2379 f 17ˢ, 1' s
2395	OC	7 27.1	+ 13 35 s	Gem	12	8.0	Cl, pRi, C
2378	−	7 27.4	+ 33 50 r	Gem			2 vF close st in eF neb, 2379 f 2ˢ, 1' s
2379	Gx	7 27.4	+ 33 49 s	Gem	1.1	13.5	vF, vS
2202 I	Gx	7 27.9	− 67 34 c	Vol	2.1		eF, eS, R
2396	OC	7 28.1	− 11 44 s	Pup	10	7p	Cl, vL, vlC
2200 I	Gx	7 28.3	− 62 22 c	Car	1.1		eF, eS, eE 65°, bet 2 st, susp
2385	Gx	7 28.4	+ 33 50 r	Gem		15p	vF, vS, R, bM
2195 I		7 28.4	− 51 15 d	Car			cB, S, R, bM, susp

NGC	Type	α_{2000}	δ_{2000}	Const.	Size	Mag.	Description
		h m	o ′		′		
2386	*ᐧ*	7 28.6	+ 33 46 r	Gem			stellar
2394	−	7 28.6	+ 7 02 r	CMi			Cl, L, P, vlC, st L
2363	Gx	7 28.7	+ 69 04 A	Cam			neb* or vFvS, 2366 sf
2388	Gx	7 28.8	+ 33 49 r	Gem		14p	vF, S, R, bM
2366	Gx	7 28.9	+ 69 13 s	Cam	7.6	10.9	vF, pL, mbM, vS* inv, curved tails
2387	Gx	7 29.0	+ 36 52 r	Aur		15p	pB, S, stellar
2390	*	7 29.0	+ 33 50 r	Gem			vF
2389	Gx	7 29.1	+ 33 51 s	Gem	2.1	12.8	vF, S, R, psbM
2391	−	7 29.2	+ 33 49 r	Gem			eF
2392	Pl	7 29.2	+ 20 55 s	Gem	0.7	10p	B, S, R, *9 M, *8 nf 100″
2401	OC	7 29.4	− 13 58 s	Pup	2	13p	Cl, S, cRi, cC, st vS
2184 I	Gx	7 29.4	+ 72 08 v	Cam	1.3		vF, S, stell, r
2399	*ᐧ*	7 29.9	− 0 13 F	CMi			1st of 2 F neb (vS clusters?)
2190 I		7 29.9	+ 37 31 d	Aur			F, pS, dif
2393	Gx	7 30.0	+ 34 01 r	Gem		15p	eF, pS, lE, dif, r?
2400	*ᐧ*	7 30.0	− 0 13 F	CMi			2nd of 2 F neb (vS clusters?)
467 I	Gx	7 30.0	+ 79 52 s	Cam	3.5	12p	vF, pS, ssF of 2336
2417	Gx	7 30.1	− 62 15 v	Car	2.2		vF, L, R, gbM, r
2398	Gx	7 30.3	+ 24 29 r	Gem		15p	vF, eS, bM, Dneb?
2191 I	Gx	7 30.3	+ 24 18 m	Gem	0.7	15p	F, vS, R, stell
2402	Gx	7 30.8	+ 9 39 r	CMi		15p	eF, S, R, lbM, * inv
2409	−	7 31.6	− 17 11 r	Pup			Cl, S but B, st 8...10
2406	Gx	7 31.9	+ 18 18 r	Gem		15p	eF, eS, vSN?
2407	Gx	7 31.9	+ 18 21 r	Gem		15p	eF, eS, vSN?
2300	Gx	7 32.	+ 85 43 s	Cep	3.1	11.0	pB, pL, lE, bM
2405	Gx	7 32.2	+ 25 55 r	Gem		14p	vF, S, iR
2413	−	7 33.3	− 13 06 r	Pup			Cl, vL, P, vlC
2414	OC	7 33.3	− 15 27 s	Pup	4	7.9	Cl, P, lC, st 9...
2192 I		7 33.3	+ 31 22 d	Gem			F, vS, R, *14 nearly in cont
2193 I		7 33.3	+ 31 27 d	Gem			close p *10 (= IC 2192?)
2194 I	Gx	7 33.7	+ 31 19 m	Gem	1.0	15p	F, S, R, gbM, r
2196 I	Gx	7 34.1	+ 31 24 u	Gem	1.5	14p	F, S, pR, gbM, r, 3 st 2′ p
2198 I	Gx	7 34.1	+ 23 58 z	Gem		15p	F, S, R, gbM, r
2197 I	Gx	7 34.3	+ 31 24 m	Gem	0.5	14p	vvF
2412	−	7 34.4	+ 8 33 r	CMi			vF, *8 f 59ˢ, 1′.5 s, *13 s 10″
2411	Gx	7 34.6	+ 18 17 r	Gem		14p	*14 slightly nebs
2434	Gx	7 34.9	− 69 17 s	Vol	2.5	11.2	pB, S, R, pmbM, 3 st 11 n
2199 I		7 34.9	+ 31 13 d	Gem			F, S
455 I	Gx	7 35.	+ 85 33 u	Cep	1.2	14p	vF, eS, sf 2300
2410	Gx	7 35.0	+ 32 50 r	Gem		14p	eF, vS, sev vF st inv, 1′ long, gbM, r
2416	Gx	7 35.7	+ 11 37 r	CMi		14p	eF, S
2201 I	Gx	7 36.2	+ 33 07 u	Gem	1.3	15p	F, vS, R, gbM, r
2421	OC	7 36.3	− 20 37 s	Pup	10	8.3	Cl, L, cRi, st 11...13
2443	−	7 36.3	− 69 32 r	Vol			pL, vF, R, D with 42, D* inv M
2442	Gx	7 36.4	− 69 32 s	Vol	6.0	11p	Cl, vF, R, D with 43, D* inv M
2418	Gx	7 36.5	+ 17 54 r	Gem		13p	vF, eS, bM
2427	Gx	7 36.5	− 47 38 s	Pup	5.6	11.6	eF, L, pmE, gmbM, 2 st inv
2422	OC	7 36.6	− 14 30 s	Pup	30	4.4	Cl, B, vL, pRi, st L and S; = M47
2403	Gx	7 36.9	+ 65 36 s	Cam	17.8	8.4	!! cB, eL, vmE, vgmbMN
2415	Gx	7 36.9	+ 35 15 s	Lyn	1.0	12.4	pB, cS, R, vgvlbM, r, alm ○
2404	Kt	7 37.1	+ 65 42 A	Cam			vF, vS
2423	OC	7 37.1	− 13 52 s	Pup	19	6.7	Cl, vL, Ri, pC, st vS
2419	Gb	7 38.1	+ 38 53 s	Lyn	4.1	10.4	pB, pL, lE 90°, vgbM, *7-8 267°, 4′ dist
2425	OC	7 38.3	− 14 52 s	Pup	3		Cl, P, S, st vS
2420	OC	7 38.5	+ 21 34 s	Gem	10	8.3	Cl, cL, Ri, C, st 11...18

NGC	Type	α_{2000}	δ_{2000}	Const.	Size	Mag.	Description
		h m	o ′		′		
2428	−	7 39.2	− 16 31 r	Pup			Cl, vL, vlC
2430	−	7 39.4	− 16 21 r	Pup			Cl, vL, vlC
2408	Ast	7 40.5	+ 71 39 A	Cam			Cl, vlC
2203 I	Gx	7 40.6	+ 34 13 u	Gem	1.2	14p	F, S, R, gbM, r
2424	Gx	7 40.7	+ 39 14 s	Lyn	4.0	12.6	vF, pS, mE, lbM, r?
2439	OC	7 40.8	− 31 39 s	Pup	10	6.9	Cl, B, pRi, pL, lC, st 9, 12...14
2432	OC	7 40.9	− 19 05 s	Pup	8	10p	Cl, pL, pC, E 0°, st L and S
2204 I	Gx	7 41.2	+ 34 13 u	Gem	1.1	15p	F, vS, R, efN, r
2437	OC	7 41.8	− 14 49 s	Pup	27	6.1	!, Cl, vB, vRi, vL, inv ◯ ; = M46
2438	Pl	7 41.8	− 14 44 s	Pup	1.1	10p	◯ , pB, pS, vlE, r, 3ˢ.75 d
2440	Pl	7 41.9	− 18 13 s	Pup	0.5	11p	◯ , cB, not v well def
473 I		7 42.4	+ 9 15 d	CMi			neb *14, 2433 nf
2433	Gx	7 43.0	+ 9 19 r	CMi			eF, *15, 90″ sp
2426	Gx	7 43.2	+ 52 49 r	Lyn		14p	cF, R, vgbM, r, *8 p
471 I	Gx	7 43.6	+ 49 39 u	Lyn	0.8	14p	eF, pS, R, np of 2
2429	Gx	7 43.7	+ 52 21 r	Lyn		14p	pF, pS, vmE, *12 att
472 I	Gx	7 43.8	+ 49 36 u	Lyn	1.9	14p	eeF, pS, R, sf of 2
2435	Gx	7 44.2	+ 31 38 r	Gem		13p	F, S, lbM
2447	OC	7 44.6	− 23 52 s	Pup	22	6.2	Cl, L, pRi, lC, st 8...13; = M93
2448	−	7 44.6	− 24 41 r	Pup			Cl of 18 or 20 st 11...13
2466	Gx	7 45.2	− 71 24 v	Vol	1.5		vF, S, R, lbM
2431	Gx	7 45.3	+ 53 04 r	Lyn		14p	eF, vS, R, bM
2451	OC	7 45.4	− 37 58 s	Pup	45	2.8	Cl, vvL, vlC, one *4.5
2206 I		7 45.8	− 34 22 d	Pup			◯ , stell, 9.5m
2436	*	7 46.1	+ 52 04 r	Lyn			vF, vS, R, bM
474 I		7 46.1	+ 26 29 d	Gem			pB, vS, dif
2444	Gx	7 46.9	+ 39 02 s	Lyn	2.3	12.9	vF, mbM
2445	Gx	7 46.9	+ 39 01 s	Lyn	2.1	13.0	vF, mbM, S* att s
2205 I	Gx	7 46.9	+ 26 53 z	Gem		15p	F, vS, neb D*
475 I	Gx	7 47.2	+ 30 31 m	Gem	0.5	15p	vF, vS, dif
2449	Gx	7 47.3	+ 26 55 r	Gem		14p	eF, eS, R, bM, r
476 I	Gx	7 47.3	+ 26 57 z	Gem		15p	vS, vF, lbM, diffic
2452	Pl	7 47.4	− 27 20 s	Pup	0.3	13p	◯ , F, S, lE, am 60 st
2450	Gx	7 47.5	+ 27 00 r	Gem		15p	eF, vS, S* inv
2453	OC	7 47.8	− 27 14 s	Pup	5	8.3	Cl, S, pRi, pC
2446	Gx	7 48.7	+ 54 36 r	Lyn		14p	F, am 4 st
2455	OC	7 49.0	− 21 18 s	Pup	8	10p	Cl, cL, pRi, lC, st 12
2207 I	Gx	7 49.8	+ 33 57 u	Gem	2.0	15p	vF, vS, dif, *15 vnr
2454	Gx	7 50.5	+ 16 22 r	Gem		14p	vF, eS, R, bM
2459		7 52.0	+ 9 33 D	CMi			only a couple of F st
477 I	Gx	7 52.1	+ 23 28 z	Gem		15p	F, pL, R, dif
2441	Gx	7 52.2	+ 73 02 s	Cam	2.2	12.2	vF, pS
2477	OC	7 52.3	− 38 33 s	Pup	27	5.8	!, Cl, B, Ri, L, lC, st 12
2208 I		7 52.5	+ 27 30 d	Gem			F, S, R, dif
2467	C+N	7 52.6	− 26 23 s	Pup	16	7p	pB, vL, R, er, *8 M
478 I	Gx	7 53.7	+ 26 29 z	Gem		15p	vF, vS, dif
2456	Gx	7 54.1	+ 55 29 r	Lyn		14p	vF, R, vgbM
2470	Gx	7 54.3	+ 4 27 s	CMi	2.2	14p	eF, S, lE, bet 2 st
479 I	Gx	7 54.4	+ 27 00 z	Gem		15p	pF, vS, R
2457	Gx	7 54.7	+ 55 32 r	Lyn		15p	F, pL, R, 2456 sp
2478	−	7 54.7	− 15 25 r	Pup			cluster
2482	OC	7 54.9	− 24 18 s	Pup	12	7.3	Cl, L, cRi, vlC
2479	OC	7 55.1	− 17 43 s	Pup	7	10p	Cl, pL, pRi, pC, st S
480 I		7 55.3	+ 26 47 d	Gem			vF, pL, E ns, dif
2458	Gx	7 55.4	+ 56 43 r	Lyn			vF, *12 close

NGC	Type	α_{2000}	δ_{2000}	Const.	Size	Mag.	Description
		h m	o '		'		
2483	OC	7 55.9	− 27 56 s	Pup	10	7.6	Cl, L, lC
2502	Gx	7 55.9	− 52 18 c	Car	2.1		pF, S, R, vgpmbM
469 I	Gx	7 56.	+ 85 10 v	Cep	2.3		F, S, E, sf 2300
2461	Gx	7 56.0	+ 56 41 r	Lyn		15p	*13 slightly nebulous
2489	OC	7 56.2	− 30 04 s	Pup	8	7.9	Cl, pL, cRi, pC, st 11...13
2209 I	Gx	7 56.2	+ 60 18 s	Cam	1.1	13.8	vF, S, lbM
2462	Gx	7 56.7	+ 56 39 r	Lyn		14p	vF, vS, vlbM
2476	Gx	7 56.7	+ 39 56 r	Lyn		13p	vS* in eF, S neb
2485	Gx	7 56.7	+ 7 29 r	CMi		13p	neb *12
2220 I	Nb	7 56.8	− 59 07 x	Car			!! L, E, spiral, * inv
2460	Gx	7 56.9	+ 60 21 s	Cam	2.9	11.7	F, S, R, S* in centre
2463	Gx	7 57.1	+ 56 40 r	Lyn		15p	eF, R
2210 I	Gx	7 57.1	+ 56 40 z	Lyn		15p	eF, stell, *13 np
2464	Gx	7 57.2	+ 56 41 m	Lyn	0.4	15p	pS Cl, st eF, nebulous
2480	Gx	7 57.2	+ 23 47 r	Gem		15p	vF, E np sf, close np 2481
2481	Gx	7 57.3	+ 23 46 r	Gem		13p	F, S, lE, bM, er
2465	−	7 57.7	+ 56 45 r	Lyn			*, nebulous?
2211 I	Gx	7 57.7	+ 32 34 u	Gem	0.8	14p	pB, S, R, FN, r
2474	Gx	7 57.9	+ 52 51 s	Lyn	0.6	14p	F, pS, E?, bM vS*? L* nf
2486	Gx	7 57.9	+ 25 09 r	Gem		14p	vF, S, psbM
2468	Gx	7 58.0	+ 56 22 s	Lyn	1.3	15p	F, R, bM
2475	Gx	7 58.0	+ 52 51 s	Lyn	0.8	14p	makes a Dneb with 2474
2469	Gx	7 58.1	+ 56 41 s	Lyn	1.1	13p	F, vS, R, *9 sf
2471	*	7 58.3	+ 56 45 r	Lyn			*13, slightly nebulous
2487	Gx	7 58.3	+ 25 08 s	Gem	2.8	14p	vF, S, gbM
2516	OC	7 58.3	− 60 52 s	Car	30	3.8	Cl, vB, vL, pRi, st 7...13
2473	−	7 58.4	+ 56 41 r	Lyn			1 of 10 neb, in line with 2463, 69; = 2472?
2491	Gx	7 58.4	+ 7 59 r	CMi		15p	only a few st 14, v diffic, *10 p
2484	Gx	7 58.5	+ 37 47 s	Lyn	1.6	15p	vF, vS, R, bM, r?
2472	Gx	7 58.6	+ 56 42 r	Lyn		15p	1 of 10 neb, in line with 2463, 2469
2496	Gx	7 58.6	+ 8 02 r	CMi		15p	vF, pS, R, lbM, *11 3ˢp
2501	Gx	7 58.6	− 14 22 r	Pup		14p	cF, S, vlE 90°, glbM, am st
2499	Gx	7 58.8	+ 7 30 r	CMi		15p	eF, pS, iR
481 I	Gx	7 59.0	+ 24 09 u	Gem	1.1	15p	vF, vS, dif
2212 I	Gx	7 59.0	+ 32 37 m	Gem	0.5	15p	F, pL, vlbM, dif
2213 I	Gx	7 59.0	+ 27 28 m	Gem	0.7	15p	F, S, R, lbMN
2490	Gx	7 59.2	+ 27 05 r	Gem		15p	vF, S, R, *13 1' f, p of 2
2494	Gx	7 59.2	− 0 38 r	Mon		14p	F, S, lE; = IC 487
487 I		7 59.2	− 0 40 x	Mon			eeF, vS, E 110°; = 2494
2492	Gx	7 59.4	+ 27 02 r	Gem		14p	vF, S, R, bM, f of 2
2216 I		7 59.5	+ 5 36 d	CMi			vF, eS, sbM
2498	Gx	7 59.6	+ 24 58 r	Gem		14p	vF, vS, R, bMN
2215 I	OC	7 59.6	+ 24 55 x	Gem			Cl, vS, 30''
2504	Gx	7 59.8	+ 5 37 r	CMi		14p	vF, S, R
482 I	Gx	7 59.8	+ 25 21 m	Gem	0.6	15p	vF, S, dif, diffic
483 I		7 59.9	+ 25 55 d	Gem			F, S, bM, F* nf
484 I	Gx	7 59.9	+ 26 40 z	Gem		15p	F, vS, R, bM
2214 I	Gx	7 59.9	+ 33 18 u	Lyn	0.8	14p	pB, S, R, gbMN
2506	OC	8 00.2	− 10 47 s	Mon	7	7.6	Cl, pL, vRi, C, st 11...20
485 I	Gx	8 00.3	+ 26 42 u	Gem	1.4	15p	vF, vS, R, sbM
486 I	Gx	8 00.3	+ 26 37 u	Gem	1.0	15p	F, S, dif, gbM
2493	Gx	8 00.4	+ 39 50 s	Lyn	2.5	13p	cB, S, R, sbM
2495	Gx	8 00.6	+ 39 50 v	Lyn	0.4		follows 2493 2' or 3', eF, vS
2503	Gx	8 00.6	+ 22 24 r	Cnc		15p	eF, S, glbM
2509	OC	8 00.7	− 19 04 s	Pup	8	9p	Cl, B, pRi, lC, st S

NGC	Type	α_{2000}	δ_{2000}	Const.	Size	Mag.	Description
		h m	° '		'		
488 I		8 00.8	+ 25 54 d	Cnc			vF, S, dif, *13 sp
2217 I	Gx	8 00.8	+ 27 30 u	Cnc	0.6	14p	F, pS, R, dif, r
2507	Gx	8 01.6	+ 15 43 s	Cnc	2.5	14p	pB, pL, iR, vgbM, er, * at 232°, 80''
489 I		8 01.6	+ 26 00 D	Cnc			vF, vS, sbM
2218 I	Gx	8 01.6	+ 24 26 z	Cnc		16p	F, S, R, *14 vnr
2488	Gx	8 01.8	+ 56 34 r	Lyn		14p	vF, vS, R, glbM
2500	Gx	8 01.9	+ 50 44 s	Lyn	2.9	11.6	F, L, R, vgbM, r, am st
2508	Gx	8 02.0	+ 8 34 r	CMi		14p	F, vS, vlE, 2 st p
2510	Gx	8 02.2	+ 9 29 r	CMi		14p	no description
2497	Gx	8 02.3	+ 56 57 r	Lyn		14p	ef, vS
2511	Gx	8 02.3	+ 9 24 r	CMi		15p	eF, 2513 nf
2513	Gx	8 02.5	+ 9 25 r	Cnc		13p	F, S, R, psmbM, r
2520		8 02.5	− 28 11 A	Pup			Cl, B, pRi, pC; = 2527
2219 I	Gx	8 02.6	+ 27 27 u	Cnc	1.5	14p	F, pS, E 135°, gbM, r
2514	Gx	8 02.8	+ 15 49 s	Cnc	1.4	14p	eF, pS, irrR, dif
2517	Gx	8 02.8	− 12 19 s	Pup	0.8	12.3	F, vS, R, bet 3 st 13-14
2512	Gx	8 03.1	+ 23 24 s	Cnc	1.7	14p	vF, S, iR
490 I	Gx	8 03.3	+ 25 48 z	Cnc		16p	eF, eS, S* f
2515		8 03.4	+ 20 11 d	Cnc			vF, cometic
491 I	Gx	8 03.8	+ 26 32 z	Cnc		15p	vF, eS, R
2505	Gx	8 04.0	+ 53 34 r	Lyn		14p	eF, vS
2221 I		8 05.1	+ 37 27 d	Lyn			vF, vS, R, diffic
2222 I		8 05.2	+ 37 29 d	Lyn			F, S, R, dif, r
2527	OC	8 05.3	− 28 10 s	Pup	22	6.5	Cl, vL, pRi, lC, st 10...15
2525	Gx	8 05.6	− 11 26 s	Pup	2.9	11.6	cF, pL, R, vgvlbM, am st
492 I	Gx	8 05.7	+ 26 10 v	Cnc	1.3		pB, vgbM, E ns, *13.5 sf
2223 I		8 05.8	+ 37 28 d	Lyn			F, S, R, dif
2224 I		8 05.8	+ 37 28 d	Lyn			vF, vS, R, vlbM, diffic
2522	Gx	8 06.1	+ 17 43 r	Cnc		14p	vF, vS, E, psbM
2226 I	Gx	8 06.2	+ 12 32 v	Cnc	1.4		F, S
494 I	Gx	8 06.4	+ 1 02 u	CMi	1.4	14p	vF, pS, bM
2225 I		8 06.4	+ 35 56 d	Lyn			F, pS, gbM, r
2526	Gx	8 06.9	+ 8 01 r	Cnc		14p	vF, S, mE
2533	OC	8 07.0	− 29 54 s	Pup	4	7.6	Cl, pL, Ri, C, st 9, 13...14
2228 I	Gx	8 07.1	+ 8 02 m	Cnc	0.4	15p	eF, S, r
2518	Gx	8 07.3	+ 51 09 r	Lyn		14p	1st of 2 neb, F, L, R, gbM
2227 I		8 07.3	+ 36 02 d	Lyn			F, vS, gbMN, r, *13.5 vnr
2528	Gx	8 07.4	+ 39 13 r	Lyn		13p	F, S, R, bM
493 I		8 07.4	+ 25 06 d	Cnc			pB, E ns
2529	Gx	8 07.8	+ 17 50 r	Cnc		14p	eF (suspected)
2530		8 07.9	+ 17 49 d	Cnc			eF, lE, vS* n
2519		8 08.0	+ 51 07 d	Lyn			F, L, R, gbM, 42^{s}f 2518
2531		8 08.0	+ 17 49 d	Cnc			vF
2524	Gx	8 08.1	+ 39 10 r	Lyn		13p	vF, S
495 I	Gx	8 08.3	+ 9 00 z	Cnc		15p	vF, vS, R, gvlbM
2521	Gx	8 08.8	+ 57 46 s	Lyn	1.5	14p	pF, pL, R, psbM, *9 np 3'
498 I	Gx	8 09.4	+ 5 16 u	CMi	1.4	15p	F, pS, R
496 I	Gx	8 09.7	+ 25 52 m	Cnc	0.3	15p	pF, S, E pf, lbM
2229 I		8 09.7	+ 25 53 d	Cnc			F, S, R, lbMN, r
497 I	Gx	8 10.1	+ 24 53 m	Cnc	0.5	15p	F, S, R, lbM
2532	Gx	8 10.2	+ 33 57 s	Lyn	2.2	12.4	pB, pL, R, vglbM, r, 2 st nf
2539	OC	8 10.7	− 12 50 s	Pup	22	6.5	Cl, vL, Ri, lC, st 11...13
2547	OC	8 10.7	− 49 16 s	Vel	20	4.7	Cl, B, L, lC, st 7...16
2230 I	Gx	8 10.9	+ 25 41 z	Cnc		16p	F, vS, dif
2231 I	Gx	8 11.0	+ 5 05 u	CMi	2.0	15p	F, vS, R, dif, *14 att

NGC	Type	α_{2000}	δ_{2000}		Const.	Size	Mag.	Description
		h m	o ′			′		
2535	Gx	8 11.2	+ 25 12	s	Cnc	3.0	12.6	eF, vS, R
2536	Gx	8 11.3	+ 25 11	s	Cnc	0.9	14.1	vF, vS, R
2542	–	8 11.3	– 12 56	r	Pup			nebulous *5
2538	Gx	8 11.4	+ 3 37	r	CMi		14p	vF, vS, R, mbM
2546	OC	8 12.4	– 37 38	s	Pup	41	6.3	Cl, B, L, lC, iE, st 9...12
500 I	Gx	8 12.6	– 16 03	m	Pup	0.7	15p	vF, dif, vF* att
2540	Gx	8 12.8	+ 26 21	r	Cnc		14p	vF, pL, iR, bM, r
2534	Gx	8 12.9	+ 55 40	s	Lyn	1.7	14p	pF, pL, R, psbM, *8 164°
2232 I		8 12.9	+ 36 15	x	Lyn			F, pS, R, gbMN; = 2543
2543	Gx	8 13.0	+ 36 15	s	Lyn	2.5	13p	F, pL, iR, vgbM, D* nr; = IC 2232
2537	Gx	8 13.2	+ 46 00	s	Lyn	1.7	11.7	⊕, pB, pL, R, rrr, st 20
2235 I		8 13.6	+ 24 05	d	Cnc			pB, S, E 135°, dif
2236 I		8 13.6	+ 24 03	d	Cnc			pB, E 0°, dif
2548	OC	8 13.8	– 5 48	s	Hya	54	5.8	Cl, vL, pRi, pmC, st 9...13; = M48
2234 I		8 13.9	+ 35 30	d	Lyn			pF, vS, dif, vFN
2233 I	Gx	8 14.0	+ 45 44	s	Lyn	4.7	13.0	pB, L, E np sf; 2537 np
2237 I		8 14.1	+ 24 41	d	Cnc			vF, pS, p dif
2238 I		8 14.1	+ 24 40	d	Cnc			pF, S, dif
2239 I	Gx	8 14.1	+ 23 52	m	Cnc	1.0	15p	pB, S, R, stell N
2545	Gx	8 14.2	+ 21 21	s	Cnc	2.2	12.4	F, S, lE 45°, *8 np 4′
2541	Gx	8 14.7	+ 49 04	s	Lyn	6.6	11.8	F, L, E, vgbM
2240 I		8 14.8	+ 24 28	d	Cnc			vF, S, E 155°, dif
2523	Gx	8 15.0	+ 73 35	s	Cam	3.0	12.0	pB, pL, lE, lbM, * nr
2241 I		8 15.1	+ 24 08	d	Cnc			pB, S, dif
2242 I		8 15.2	+ 24 08	d	Cnc			pF, S, dif
2243 I		8 15.3	+ 23 58	d	Cnc			F, S, dif, biN
2244 I		8 15.4	+ 24 33	d	Cnc			vF, S, E 0°
2245 I		8 15.5	+ 24 32	d	Cnc			vF, S, iF
2246 I		8 16.0	+ 23 51	d	Cnc			pB, S, dif, bf
2247 I		8 16.1	+ 24 12	d	Cnc			pF, E 135°, biN
2248 I	Gx	8 16.1	+ 23 08	m	Cnc	0.4	15p	pB, pL, E 90°, Nn
2250 I		8 16.5	+ 23 38	d	Cnc			F, S, dif
2253 I	Gx	8 16.5	+ 21 25	z	Cnc		15p	F, vS, R, stell
2249 I		8 16.6	+ 24 30	d	Cnc			F, vS, iF, att* sp
2251 I		8 16.7	+ 23 57	d	Cnc			pF, pS, dif
2252 I		8 16.7	+ 24 42	d	Cnc			pF, S, R
2254 I	Gx	8 16.7	+ 24 47	z	Cnc		15p	F, S, R, stell, *13.5 vnr
2255 I		8 16.7	+ 23 27	d	Cnc			vF, pL, N
2256 I	Gx	8 16.8	+ 24 11	m	Cnc	0.6	15p	B, pS, E 205°
2559	Gx	8 17.1	– 27 28	t	Pup	5.6		F, pL, gmbM, am 60 st
2257 I		8 17.2	+ 23 39	d	Cnc			F, S, lbM
2258 I		8 17.3	+ 23 35	d	Cnc			pF, S, mE 0°, biN
2259 I		8 17.3	+ 23 34	d	Cnc			vF, S, dif, diffic
2262 I	?	8 17.4	+ 18 27	x	Cnc			pB, S, B* nf
2260 I		8 17.5	+ 24 40	d	Cnc			pF, S, R, dif
2261 I		8 17.6	+ 23 31	d	Cnc			vF, mE 45°, B* 1′ f
2553	Gx	8 17.7	+ 20 54	r	Cnc		15p	vF, S, glbM
2263 I		8 17.7	+ 23 35	d	Cnc			vF, S, E 0°, vlbM
2266 I	?	8 17.7	+ 18 25	x	Cnc			pB, vS, mE, B* att
2264 I		8 17.8	+ 23 43	d	Cnc			pB, S, stell N
2265 I		8 17.8	+ 24 12	d	Cnc			pF, vS, R, dif
2554	Gx	8 17.9	+ 23 28	s	Cnc	3.4	14p	F, S, R, mbM, r
2555	Gx	8 18.0	+ 0 44	r	Hya		13p	vF, cS, iF, 3 S st inv?
2568	OC	8 18.0	– 37 06	r	Pup			vF, pL, F* inv
2267 I	Gx	8 18.0	+ 24 44	u	Cnc	2.3	15p	pB, mE 137°

NGC	Type	α_{2000}	δ_{2000}	Const.	Size	Mag.	Description
		h m	° ′		′		
2270 I	?	8 18.0	+ 19 06 x	Cnc			pB, S, * vnr np
2268 I	Gx	8 18.1	+ 24 48 z	Cnc		15p	pF, S, R, glbM
2272 I	?	8 18.1	+ 18 44 x	Cnc			vF, vS, gbM, * att
2269 I	Gx	8 18.2	+ 23 03 z	Cnc		16p	pF, S, E 25°
2273 I	?	8 18.2	+ 18 24 x	Cnc			pF, S, bM
2274 I	*∗*	8 18.2	+ 18 40 x	Cnc			pB neb∗, 2 spir branches
2275 I	?	8 18.2	+ 18 25 x	Cnc			pB, S, gbM
2271 I	Gx	8 18.4	+ 24 31 z	Cnc		15p	pB, S, bM
2276 I	?	8 18.5	+ 18 29 x	Cnc			iF, conn with IC 2278, 80
2277 I	?	8 18.5	+ 18 39 x	Cnc			pF, vS, iF
2564	Gx	8 18.6	− 21 49 r	Pup			vF, S, R, gbM, am many st
2567	OC	8 18.6	− 30 38 s	Pup	10	7.4	Cl, pL, pRi, lC, iR, st 11...14
2278 I	?	8 18.6	+ 18 28 x	Cnc			iF, conn with IC 2276, 80
2279 I	?	8 18.6	+ 18 34 x	Cnc			F, S, dif
2566	Gx	8 18.7	− 25 29 s	Pup	3.1	15p	vF, cL, er, vS neb or neb ∗11 with ∗12 close
2280 I	?	8 18.7	+ 18 27 x	Cnc			pF, iF, conn with IC 2276, 78
501 I	Gx	8 18.8	+ 24 32 z	Cnc		15p	F, R, lbM
2311 I	Gx	8 18.8	− 25 22 c	Pup	2.2		pB, vS, R, lbM, 6′ n of 2566
2571	OC	8 18.9	− 29 44 s	Pup	13	7.0	Cl, vL, cRi, lC, st 9...
2281 I	?	8 18.9	+ 18 55 x	Cnc			* att 51°, spir br
2549	Gx	8 19.0	+ 57 48 s	Lyn	4.2	11.1	pB, S, mE 0°, psmbM
2284 I	?	8 19.0	+ 18 36 x	Cnc			F, S, dif, stell N, * vnr sf
2285 I		8 19.1	+ 18 55 d	Cnc			pF, S, curved N, conn with IC 2281
2286 I		8 19.1	+ 18 57 d	Cnc			pB, vS, E 50°
2287 I		8 19.1	+ 19 24 d	Cnc			vF, pS, lbM, dif
2289 I	?	8 19.1	+ 18 32 x	Cnc			pF, S, iF
2556	Gx	8 19.2	+ 20 55 r	Cnc		15p	vF, vS
2557	Gx	8 19.2	+ 21 27 s	Cnc	1.4	15p	eF, eS, R, lbM
2552	Gx	8 19.3	+ 50 01 s	Lyn	3.2	12.2	eF, cL, lE 45°
2282 I		8 19.3	+ 24 48 d	Cnc			pF, L, dif, * sf
2283 I		8 19.3	+ 24 47 d	Cnc			pF, pS, R, ∗9 f 4ˢ.6, 35″ s
2288 I	Gx	8 19.3	+ 23 46 m	Cnc	0.3	15p	F, S, E 90°, bM, dif
2290 I	?	8 19.3	+ 19 19 x	Cnc			pF, pS, dif, others nr
2291 I	?	8 19.3	+ 18 30 x	Cnc			vF, S, mE 125°, gbM
2558	Gx	8 19.4	+ 20 30 r	Cnc		14p	vF, vS, R, sbM, stellar
2292 I		8 19.4	+ 19 34 d	Cnc			pF, vS, E 135°, bM
2294 I		8 19.4	+ 18 59 d	Cnc			pF, vS, iF
2295 I		8 19.4	+ 18 25 d	Cnc			F, vS, E 90°, vF stell N, B∗ sf
2296 I		8 19.5	+ 18 54 d	Cnc			pF, vS, iF, vlbM
2561	Gx	8 19.6	+ 4 39 r	Hya		14p	vF, S, R, 2 st △
2293 I	Gx	8 19.6	+ 21 23 m	Cnc	0.8	15p	F, pS, dif
2565	Gx	8 19.8	+ 22 02 s	Cnc	1.9	14p	F, biN
2560	Gx	8 19.9	+ 20 59 s	Cnc	1.7	15p	F, pL
2297 I		8 20.1	+ 18 23 d	Cnc			pB, S, others nr
2298 I		8 20.1	+ 18 24 d	Cnc			pF, vS, iF, Ns, * close nf
2299 I		8 20.2	+ 19 20 d	Cnc			F, vME 60°
2300 I		8 20.2	+ 18 25 d	Cnc			F, pS, iF, arms n and p
2301 I		8 20.2	+ 18 26 d	Cnc			vF, S, mE, exc N, * sf
2302 I		8 20.3	+ 19 21 d	Cnc			F, vS, R, vlbM
2303 I		8 20.3	+ 19 25 d	Cnc			F, vS, mE 0°
2562	Gx	8 20.4	+ 21 08 s	Cnc	1.4	12.9	vF, cS, R
2563	Gx	8 20.6	+ 21 04 s	Cnc	2.3	12.3	cF, S, R, bM
2304 I		8 20.6	+ 19 26 d	Cnc			B, vS, neb∗
2305 I		8 20.7	+ 19 27 d	Cnc			vF, S, N
2306 I		8 20.7	+ 19 07 d	Cnc			F, vS, R, bM

NGC	Type	α_{2000}	δ_{2000}	Const.	Size	Mag.	Description
		h m	∘ ′		′		
2307 I		8 20.7	+ 19 26 d	Cnc			pB, pS, dif, E 0°
2574	Gx	8 20.8	− 8 57 r	Hya		14p	eF, pS, rr, *7.5 nf 5′
2309 I	Gx	8 20.8	+ 18 23 z	Cnc		16p	vF, pS, E 165°
2310 I		8 20.8	+ 18 28 d	Cnc			pB, pS, mE 40°, curved mbM
2308 I	Gx	8 20.9	+ 19 21 m	Cnc	0.3	16p	pB, vS, iF, bM
2312 I		8 20.9	+ 18 31 d	Cnc			vF, S, E 45°, dif, vlbM
2313 I		8 20.9	+ 18 31 d	Cnc			vF, vS, vF stell N
2579	C+N	8 21.1	− 36 11 s	Pup	10	7.5	D* in pS neb, am 70 st
2314 I		8 21.1	+ 18 46 d	Cnc			F, S, spir, vlbM
2315 I		8 21.2	+ 18 55 d	Cnc			F, vS, R, dif, N
2316 I		8 21.3	+ 19 46 d	Cnc			pB, S, R, exc stell N
2572	Gx	8 21.4	+ 19 08 r	Cnc		15p	eF, vS, iF, *13 att
2578	Gx	8 21.4	− 13 19 s	Pup	2.4	12.4	F, vlE, gbM, r, am 50 st
2317 I		8 21.4	+ 18 51 d	Cnc			F, vS, dif, vF stell N
2327 I	Gx	8 21.4	+ 3 10 u	Hya	1.5	14p	F, S, dif
2569	Gx	8 21.5	+ 20 52 r	Cnc		15p	vF, cE, 3 vS st f
2570	Gx	8 21.5	+ 20 55 r	Cnc		15p	eeF, L, R, n of 2
2318 I		8 21.5	+ 18 37 d	Cnc			F, vS, N
2580	OC	8 21.6	− 30 19 s	Pup	8	10p	Cl, cL, pRi, pC, R, st 12
2319 I		8 21.6	+ 18 29 d	Cnc			F, S, R
2320 I		8 21.6	+ 18 40 d	Cnc			F, vS, N
2544	Gx	8 21.7	+ 73 59 s	Cam	1.1	12p	eeF, pS, R, sev B st around
2321 I		8 21.7	+ 18 28 d	Cnc			pB, vS, R
2322 I		8 21.7	+ 18 29 d	Cnc			F, S, dif
2323 I		8 21.7	+ 18 37 d	Cnc			pF, S, R
502 I	Gx	8 22.0	+ 8 45 k	Cnc	0.4	15p	F, vS, dif
2324 I		8 22.0	+ 19 12 d	Cnc			pF, S, mE 155°, sev N
2325 I		8 22.1	+ 18 55 d	Cnc			vF, pL, iF, F* att f
503 I	Gx	8 22.2	+ 3 15 u	Hya	1.1	14p	vF, S, lE
2326 I		8 22.2	+ 19 01 d	Cnc			vF, mE 90°, dif, sev N
2328 I		8 22.3	+ 19 37 d	Cnc			pB, pS, mE 65°
2329 I	Gx	8 22.4	+ 19 24 u	Cnc	2.2	15p	pF, pS, mE 110°, stell N
2330 I		8 22.4	+ 18 51 d	Cnc			B, vS, stell, 2 spir branches
504 I	Gx	8 22.6	+ 4 15 u	Hya	1.1	14p	vF, pS, R, 4 st f
2331 I		8 22.6	+ 19 41 d	Cnc			vF, pL, R, dif
2577	Gx	8 22.7	+ 22 33 s	Cnc	2.1	13p	F, S, iF, r
2332 I		8 22.7	+ 19 55 d	Cnc			pB, vS, R, stell N, F* att s
2575	Gx	8 22.8	+ 24 17 s	Cnc	2.5	14p	eF, pL, iR, sev F st inv
2576	Gx	8 22.9	+ 25 44 r	Cnc		15p	eF, eS, stellar
2333 I		8 23.0	+ 19 05 d	Cnc			F, S, R, N
2334 I		8 23.0	+ 18 37 d	Cnc			pF, S, R
2335 I		8 23.1	+ 19 25 d	Cnc			F, pS, vlbM, dif, biN
2583	Gx	8 23.2	− 5 01 s	Hya	0.7	13.5	vF, S, R, sbMN, 1st of 4
2584	Gx	8 23.2	− 5 00 r	Hya		14p	vF, S, R, 2nd of 4
2588	OC	8 23.2	− 32 59 s	Pup	2	12p	Cl, F, S, R, gbM, st 15
505 I	Gx	8 23.3	+ 4 22 u	Hya	1.4	15p	eF, S, R, lbM
2336 I		8 23.3	+ 18 32 d	Cnc			vF, vS, R
2337 I		8 23.3	+ 18 32 d	Cnc			F, vS, R
2585	Gx	8 23.4	− 4 56 r	Hya		14p	vF, S, R, 3rd of 4
506 I	Gx	8 23.4	+ 4 18 m	Hya	0.4	15p	eeF, eS, R, v diffic
2587	OC	8 23.5	− 29 30 s	Pup	9	9p	Cl, pmCM, iF, st 9...13
2342 I		8 23.5	+ 18 35 d	Cnc			pB, S, R, *12 att 112°
2338 I	Gx	8 23.6	+ 21 20 v	Cnc	0.6		F, vS, bMN
2339 I	Gx	8 23.6	+ 21 20 v	Cnc	1.2		F, S, R, bMN
2340 I	Gx	8 23.6	+ 18 44 m	Cnc	0.8	15p	pF, pS, dif, bMN

NGC	Type	α_{2000}	δ_{2000}	Const.	Size	Mag.	Description
		h m	o ′		′		
2341 I	Gx	8 23.7	+ 21 26 v	Cnc	1.6		F, S, R, bMN
2343 I		8 23.9	+ 19 01 d	Cnc			F, pS, lbM, dif
2344 I		8 23.9	+ 18 39 d	Cnc			pF, pS, R, lbM
2345 I		8 24.1	+ 19 57 d	Cnc			F, S, E 90°, att B∗ sp
2346 I		8 24.2	+ 19 42 d	Cnc			vF, S, R, bM, 2nd vnr sf
2347 I		8 24.2	+ 18 46 d	Cnc			vF, S, iF, dif
2367 I	Gx	8 24.2	− 18 46 c	Pup	2.3		pB, S
2349 I		8 24.3	+ 19 00 d	Cnc			pF, L, lbM, dif
2586	∗∗	8 24.4	− 4 56 F	Hya		15p	eF, pS, R, 4th of 4 (neb?)
2348 I	Gx	8 24.4	+ 20 32 m	Cnc	0.6	16p	F, pS, mE 45°, bM
2581	Gx	8 24.5	+ 18 35 r	Cnc		14p	vF, vS, R, vF∗ inv, F∗ att
2589	−	8 24.5	− 8 46 r	Hya			pF, pS, lE; nonexistent?
2350 I		8 24.5	+ 19 33 d	Cnc			vF, S, gbMN, B∗ s
2550	Gx	8 24.6	+ 74 01 s	Cam	1.2	13p	eeF, pS, cE
2351 I	Gx	8 24.6	+ 18 36 u	Cnc	1.1	14p	pF, pS, iF, F stell N, 2581 f
2353 I		8 24.6	+ 18 39 d	Cnc			pB, S, R, spir br
2352 I		8 24.7	+ 19 36 d	Cnc			F, S, lbM, S neb f
2354 I		8 24.7	+ 18 40 d	Cnc			vF, vS, dif, vFN
2551	Gx	8 24.8	+ 73 25 s	Cam	1.9	12.0	vF, S, F∗ in centre
2355 I		8 24.9	+ 20 28 d	Cnc			pB, S, R, stell N
2356 I		8 25.0	+ 19 30 d	Cnc			F, vS, mE, lbM
2590	Gx	8 25.1	− 0 36 r	Hya		14p	F∗ inv in vF, vS, lE neb
2357 I		8 25.1	+ 19 31 d	Cnc			pF, S, R, dif, stell N
2358 I		8 25.1	+ 19 30 d	Cnc			F, S, E 135°, FN, vS neb f
2360 I		8 25.2	+ 19 27 d	Cnc			F, S, dif, vFN exc
2582	Gx	8 25.3	+ 20 20 s	Cnc	1.3	14p	vF, pS, R, glbM, ∗ p 75″; = IC 2359
2359 I	Gx	8 25.3	+ 20 20 u	Cnc	1.1	14p	F, vS, E 160°, stell N exc nf
2601	Gx	8 25.5	− 68 07 v	Vol	2.0		F, pS, R, gbM
507 I	?	8 25.6	− 0 27 x	Hya			eeF, pS, vlE, bet 2 st
2361 I	Gx	8 25.7	+ 27 53 u	Cnc	1.7	15p	F, pS, lE ns, gbM, r
2362 I		8 25.7	+ 19 57 d	Cnc			pF, pL, dif, bet 4 B st
2363 I	Gx	8 25.8	+ 19 27 v	Cnc			pF, pL, dif
2364 I		8 25.9	+ 19 46 d	Cnc			pF, S, R, bM
2368 I		8 26.0	+ 19 53 d	Cnc			pF, vS, bMNE 170°
2365 I		8 26.3	+ 27 52 d	Cnc			pB, vS, R, stell
2366 I	Gx	8 26.3	+ 27 50 u	Cnc	1.4	15p	pB, vS, R, bMN
2369 I		8 26.3	+ 20 14 d	Cnc			pB, S, R, stell N
2375 I		8 26.3	− 13 18 d	Pup			F, vS, E 90°, 1st of 3
2370 I		8 26.4	+ 19 38 d	Cnc			pB, vS, iF, N
2377 I		8 26.4	− 13 18 d	Pup			eF, vS, 2nd of 3
2379 I		8 26.4	− 13 18 d	Pup			vF, vS, 3rd of 3
2371 I		8 26.6	+ 19 48 d	Cnc			pB, S, lE 90°
2372 I		8 26.7	+ 19 53 d	Cnc			F, S, lE 135°, B∗ sf
2593	Gx	8 26.8	+ 17 22 r	Cnc		15p	eF, vS
2373 I	Gx	8 26.9	+ 20 22 u	Cnc	1.4	15p	F, S, dif, exc N
2592	Gx	8 27.1	+ 25 58 r	Cnc		13p	pF, S, R, vsbM ∗
2594	Gx	8 27.3	+ 25 52 r	Cnc		15p	eF
2596	Gx	8 27.4	+ 17 17 r	Cnc		14p	vF, S, lE
2595	Gx	8 27.7	+ 21 29 s	Cnc	3.1	14p	vF, pL, iF, R, D∗ sp 2′
2374 I		8 28.3	+ 30 26 d	Cnc			pF, S, R, dif, ∗11.5 close
508 I	Gx	8 28.4	+ 25 07 z	Cnc		15p	F, L, R
2376 I		8 28.4	+ 30 24 d	Cnc			F, vS, R, ∗14 close
2381 I		8 28.4	+ 19 47 d	Cnc			pF, S, R bM, dif
2378 I	Gx	8 28.5	+ 30 26 v	Cnc	0.9		F, S, R, glbM, r
2380 I	Gx	8 28.6	+ 30 25 m	Cnc	0.4	15p	F, S, R, lbM, r

NGC	Type	α_{2000}	δ_{2000}	Const.	Size	Mag.	Description
		h m	o ′		′		
2382 I	Gx	8 28.7	+ 22 04 m	Cnc	0.4	15p	F, S, R, r, *12.5 close
2609	OC	8 29.5	− 61 06 A	Car			Cl, pS, lRi, lC
2383 I	Gx	8 29.6	+ 30 41 z	Cnc		16p	F, vS, R, bMN
2597	Gx	8 30.0	+ 21 30 u	Cnc	1.4	15p	eF, vS
2598	Gx	8 30.0	+ 21 29 s	Cnc	1.3	13.7	F, S
509 I	Gx	8 32.0	+ 24 00 v	Cnc	1.9		vF, pL, dif, lbM
510 I	Gx	8 32.1	− 2 10 u	Hya	1.1	15p	F, vS, R, dif
2599	Gx	8 32.2	+ 22 34 s	Cnc	2.4	13p	vF, S, stellar
513 I	Gx	8 33.0	− 12 21 m	Hya	0.6	14p	F, S, dif, r
2604	Gx	8 33.3	+ 29 33 r	Cnc		13p	vF, pL, R, lbM, r, D* nr
2610	Pl	8 33.4	− 16 09 s	Hya	0.6	14p	F, S, att to *13, *7 nf
2613	Gx	8 33.4	− 22 58 s	Pyx	7.2	10.4	cB, L, vmE 110°
2612	Gx	8 33.8	− 13 09 s	Hya	3.2	13p	F, S, E, psbM, bet 2 st
2607	Gx	8 33.9	+ 26 59 r	Cnc		15p	eF
2384 I	Gx	8 34.5	+ 32 26 m	Cnc	0.4	16p	F, S, R, stell
2615	Gx	8 34.6	− 2 32 r	Hya		13p	F, pS, lE, lbM, F* inv r
2600	Gx	8 34.8	+ 52 44 r	UMa		15p	no description
2386 I		8 34.8	+ 25 49 d	Cnc			eF, L, e dif
2385 I	Gx	8 35.1	+ 37 17 m	Lyn	0.6	15p	F, S, R, dif, r
2602	Gx	8 35.2	+ 52 50 r	UMa		15p	eF, S, R, * 95°
2608	Gx	8 35.3	+ 28 28 s	Cnc	2.5	12.1	F, vlE, mbM, r
2605	−	8 35.4	+ 52 51 r	UMa			F, S, lbM
514 I	Gx	8 35.4	− 2 03 z	Hya		15p	vF, E ns
2603	Gx	8 35.5	+ 52 47 r	UMa		15p	eF, vS
2611	Gx	8 35.5	+ 25 02 r	Cnc		15p	vF, S, pmE, gbM
515 I	Gx	8 35.5	− 1 54 u	Hya	1.2	16p	vF, vS, dif, 2616 nf
2616	Gx	8 35.6	− 1 51 s	Hya	1.3	12.6	vF, S, R, * nr nf
2626	Nb	8 35.6	− 40 40 s	Vel	5		*9 inv in pB, pL, R neb
2606	Gx	8 35.7	+ 52 48 r	UMa		15p	cF, S, R, * 310°
2617	Gx	8 35.7	− 4 03 r	Hya		15p	eF, vS, 2 vF st inv
516 I	Gx	8 35.8	− 1 52 z	Hya		16p	vF, vS, dif, 2616 p
2618	Gx	8 36.2	+ 0 42 D	Hya		14p	eF, pL, iF
517 I	Gx	8 36.3	− 2 04 z	Hya		15p	vF, S, iF
518 I	OC	8 37.1	+ 0 41 x	Hya			vF (vS Cl?)
2627	OC	8 37.3	− 29 57 s	Pyx	11	8p	Cl, cL, pRi, pC, st 11...13
2591	Gx	8 37.4	+ 78 02 s	Cam	3.2	13p	F, S, E, lbM
2640	Gx	8 37.4	− 55 07 c	Car	2.5		pB, S, R, 3 or 4 vS st p nr
2620	Gx	8 37.5	+ 24 57 r	Cnc		15p	F, S, E
2619	Gx	8 37.6	+ 28 43 r	Cnc		13p	F, pS, R, bM, r
2621	Gx	8 37.7	+ 25 00 r	Cnc		15p	vF, S, R
2624	Gx	8 38.1	+ 19 44 r	Cnc		14p	eF
2622	Gx	8 38.3	+ 24 55 r	Cnc		15p	F, S, R
2623	Gx	8 38.4	+ 25 45 s	Cnc	0.6	13.8	vF, vS, R, bM, r
2625	Gx	8 38.4	+ 19 42 s	Cnc	0.4		eF, vS
2635	OC	8 38.5	− 34 46 s	Pyx	3	11.2	Cl, pmC, irr △ , st 13...
2387 I	Gx	8 38.6	+ 30 47 u	Cnc	1.2	15p	F, pS, E ns, gbM
2645	−	8 38.9	− 46 13 r	Vel			Cl, S, st L and S
2388 I	Gx	8 40.0	+ 19 38 z	Cnc		16p	eF, S, dif (FN?); *10 n 90″
2632	OC	8 40.1	+ 19 59 s	Cnc	95	3.1	Praesepe; = M44
2391 I	OC	8 40.2	− 53 04 s	Vel	50	2.5	Cl, co, incl *3.7 (o Vel)
2628	Gx	8 40.5	+ 23 33 r	Cnc		14p	eF, S
519 I	Gx	8 40.6	+ 2 36 z	Hya		15p	vF, vS, R, diffic, *14 close
2642	Gx	8 40.7	− 4 07 s	Hya	2.3	13p	vF, pL, gbM, 2 B st s, one f
511 I	Gx	8 40.8	+ 73 29 v	Cam	1.7		vF, S, cE, 2 st sf
2637	Gx	8 41.1	+ 19 42 r	Cnc			eeF, vS

NGC	Type	α_{2000}	δ_{2000}	Const.	Size	Mag.	Description
		h m	o ′		′		
2395 I	OC	8 41.1	− 48 12 s	Vel	8	4.6	Cl, co
2644	Gx	8 41.5	+ 4 59 r	Hya		13p	vF, pL, irr oval, sev S points
2643	Gx	8 41.7	+ 19 43 r	Cnc			eF neb*
2390 I	Gx	8 41.8	+ 19 42 z	Cnc		16p	iF, gbM, *10 sf 1′.5, *12 nf 1′
2660	OC	8 42.2	− 47 09 s	Vel	4	8.8	Cl, pS, mC, iR, gbM, st 13...15
2638	Gx	8 42.4	+ 37 13 r	Lyn		13p	vF, vS, iF
2647	Gx	8 42.6	+ 19 40 r	Cnc		15p	neb*
2659	OC	8 42.6	− 44 57 s	Vel	3	8.6	Cl, L, Ri, pmE, st 11...14
2648	Gx	8 42.7	+ 14 17 s	Cnc	3.6	13p	F, S, vlE 135°, psbM
2614	Gx	8 42.8	+ 72 59 s	UMa	2.8	14p	eF, pS, R
2652	−	8 43.3	− 3 37 D	Hya			F, pS, E 50°, gbM, stell N, *9 sp 50″; place?
2658	OC	8 43.4	− 32 39 s	Pyx	12	9p	Cl, pS, lRi, lC, iF, st 12-13
2639	Gx	8 43.6	+ 50 12 s	UMa	2.0	11.8	cB, S, E 130°, psmbM
2651	Gx	8 44.0	+ 11 47 r	Cnc		15p	eF, S, E
2649	Gx	8 44.1	+ 34 43 s	Lyn	1.9	13p	F, L, R, r
2392 I	Gx	8 44.5	+ 18 17 x	Cnc			pB, pS, E 180°, vlbM
2669	OC	8 44.9	− 52 58 s	Vel	12	6.1	Cl, L, P, lC, st 10...13
2663	Gx	8 45.1	− 33 48 v	Pyx			pF, pS, lE
2630	Gx	8 45.4	+ 73 02 r	UMa		16p	1st of 2 vF, vS, vnr 2629
2657	Gx	8 45.4	+ 9 40 r	Cnc		14p	vF, vS, iR, F* att f
2670	OC	8 45.5	− 48 47 s	Vel	9	7.8	Cl, pL, P, lC, st 13...
2662	Gx	8 45.7	− 15 08 r	Hya		15p	vF, vS, R, bM, *15 nr
499 I	Gx	8 46.	+ 85 43 m	Cam	1.9	14p	pF, S, mbM, * nf
2661	Gx	8 46.0	+ 12 38 r	Cnc		14p	eF, cL, R, lbM
2665	Gx	8 46.0	− 19 17 r	Hya		13p	F, S, R, gbMN
2671	OC	8 46.2	− 41 53 s	Vel	4	12p	Cl, pRi, lCM, st 12...13
2403 I		8 46.2	− 15 21 d	Hya			vF, eS, lE
2396 I	D*	8 46.7	+ 17 39 x	Cnc			vF, vS
2397 I	?	8 46.7	+ 17 40 x	Cnc			F, vS, R
2398 I	Gx	8 46.7	+ 17 45 x	Cnc			pB, S, R, bM
521 I		8 46.8	+ 2 33 d	Hya			neb *13
2393 I	Gx	8 46.8	+ 28 11 u	Cnc	1.4	15p	F, S, R, N, r
2631	Gx	8 47.1	+ 73 00 m	UMa	0.8	14p	2nd of 2 vF, vS, vnr 2629
2394 I	Gx	8 47.1	+ 28 16 u	Cnc	1.7	15p	F, S, R, gbM
2629	Gx	8 47.2	+ 72 59 s	UMa	2.6	13p	vF, S, stellar
2664	−	8 47.2	+ 12 36 r	Cnc			Cl, st 9...10
2656	Gx	8 47.8	+ 53 52 s	UMa	1.5	13.3	eF, psbM
2399 I	Gx	8 47.8	+ 18 54 x	Cnc			vF, pL, E 190°, bs
2389 I	Gx	8 48.0	+ 73 23 s	Cam	1.7	13.4	vF, S, lbM
2400 I	Gx	8 48.0	+ 38 06 m	Lyn	0.6	15p	F, S, stell
2633	Gx	8 48.1	+ 74 06 s	Cam	2.6	11.9	F, S, lE
2641	Gx	8 48.1	+ 72 54 r	UMa		15p	vF, S, stellar
2401 I	Gx	8 48.1	+ 37 45 u	Lyn	1.3	15p	F, S, R, N, r
2402 I	Gx	8 48.1	+ 31 49 m	Cnc	0.4	15p	F, S, R, gbMN, r
2404 I	Gx	8 48.1	+ 29 30 z	Cnc		15p	F, S, R, sbMN
2406 I	Gx	8 48.1	+ 17 42 x	Cnc			B, pS, E 165°
2407 I	Gx	8 48.1	+ 17 37 x	Cnc			pB, pS, mE 80°
2674	−	8 48.2	− 14 17 r	Hya			eF, S; nonexistent?
2667	Gx	8 48.3	+ 19 01 r	Cnc		15p	eF; = IC 2410
2408 I	*	8 48.3	+ 19 02 x	Cnc			pF, vS, R
2634	Gx	8 48.4	+ 73 58 s	Cam	2.2	13p	F, S, lE
2636	Gx	8 48.4	+ 73 40 s	Cam	0.5	14p	vF, S, 2 st 11-12 f
2409 I	Gx	8 48.4	+ 18 20 x	Cnc			pB, pL, bM, *15 p
2410 I	Gx	8 48.5	+ 19 01 x	Cnc			pB, S, E 90°, stell N
2411 I	Gx	8 48.5	+ 19 03 x	Cnc			vF, S, E 235°

NGC	Type	α_{2000}	δ_{2000}	Const.	Size	Mag.	Description
		h m	° ′		′		
2405 I	Gx	8 48.7	+ 37 14 m	Lyn	0.4	15p	F, S, R, gbM
2654	Gx	8 49.2	+ 60 13 s	UMa	4.3	11.8	pF, S, F* in M, F* close sp
2672	Gx	8 49.3	+ 19 04 s	Cnc	2.6	11.6	pB, pL, iR, mbM
2668	Gx	8 49.4	+ 36 41 r	Lyn		15p	vF, vS, R, r
2673	Gx	8 49.4	+ 19 04 s	Cnc	1.4	12.9	vF, vS, close f 2672
2412 I	D*	8 49.4	+ 18 33 z	Cnc			pB, S, R, N, *14 np
2413 I	D*	8 49.5	+ 18 45 z	Cnc			pF, vS, FN
2414 I	Gx	8 49.8	+ 18 48 z	Cnc			pF, vS, R, vlbM
2650	Gx	8 50.0	+ 70 18 s	UMa	1.9	14p	pB, pL, iF, er
2666	—	8 50.0	+ 47 03 r	UMa			Cl, lC
2677	Gx	8 50.0	+ 19 00 r	Cnc		15p	eF, vS, rr (vS Cl)
2415 I	***	8 50.0	+ 18 39 z	Cnc			F, vS, E 65°, FN
2678	—	8 50.2	+ 11 20 r	Cnc			Cl, vlC, P
2646	Gx	8 50.4	+ 73 28 s	Cam	1.7	12.0	vF, S, 2 F st 2′.5 sf
2682	OC	8 50.4	+ 11 49 s	Cnc	30	6.9	! Cl, vB, vL, eRi, lC, st 10...15; = M67
2416 I	D*	8 50.5	+ 18 34 z	Cnc			pB, S, R
2417 I	Gx	8 51.2	+ 18 48 z	Cnc			B, S, R, stell N
2418 I	Gx	8 51.4	+ 17 57 z	Cnc			vF, pL, R, 2nd vnr sf
2676	Gx	8 51.5	+ 47 33 s	UMa	1.5	14p	eeF, pS, R, 4 pB st nf
2679	Gx	8 51.5	+ 30 52 r	Cnc		14p	pF, pS, R, bM, D with 2680
2680	Gx	8 51.5	+ 30 52 r	Cnc		14p	vF, vS, R, bM, D with 2679
2420 I	Gx	8 51.5	+ 3 05 z	Hya		15p	F, S, gbMN
2675	Gx	8 51.9	+ 53 36 r	UMa		14p	vF, R, *15 p 12ˢ
2419 I	*	8 52.2	+ 18 06 z	Cnc			F, pS, E 0°, dif
2683	Gx	8 52.7	+ 33 25 s	Lyn	9.3	9.7	vB, vL, vmE 39°, gmbM
2690	Gx	8 52.7	− 2 37 r	Hya		14p	pF, S, E
523 I	Gx	8 53.2	+ 9 09 u	Cnc	1.4	15p	F, S, R, dif
2681	Gx	8 53.5	+ 51 19 s	UMa	3.8	10.3	vB, vL, vg, vsmbM *10
2714	Gx	8 53.5	− 59 13 t	Car			eF, S, R, pslbM
520 I	Gx	8 53.7	+ 73 29 s	Cam	2.3	13p	pB, pL, bM, * nr
2696	—	8 54.4	− 4 59 r	Hya			eF, vS, stellar
2421 I	Gx	8 54.4	+ 32 41 v	Cnc	2.6		vF, pS, dif, diffic
2422 I	Gx	8 54.4	+ 20 14 m	Cnc	0.4	16p	pF, S, R, dif, *14 close
2695	Gx	8 54.5	− 3 05 r	Hya		13p	pF, cS, R
522 I	Gx	8 54.5	+ 57 10 u	UMa	1.0	14p	pF, pS, R, bM (2 eF st inv?)
2684	Gx	8 54.8	+ 49 08 r	UMa		13p	F, pL, R, gbM, 4 S st nr
2691	Gx	8 54.8	+ 39 32 s	Lyn	1.6	14p	pF, vS, mbM
2423 I	Gx	8 54.8	+ 20 14 u	Cnc	1.1	15p	F, S, R, dif
2686	Gx	8 54.9	+ 49 08 r	UMa		16p	vF, vS, D or * close f
2687	Gx	8 55.0	+ 49 09 r	UMa		17p	vS
2697	Gx	8 55.1	− 3 00 r	Hya		13p	vF, vS, R
2689	Gx	8 55.2	+ 49 09 r	UMa			vvF, S
2688	Gx	8 55.3	+ 49 06 r	UMa		16p	vvF, S
2653	Ast	8 55.6	+ 78 25 r	Cam			vF, vS, F* close n, 2655 s
2655	Gx	8 55.6	+ 78 13 s	Cam	5.1	10.1	vB, cL, lE 90°, gsvmbM
2685	Gx	8 55.6	+ 58 44 s	UMa	5.2	11.1	pF, R, F* in centre
2698	Gx	8 55.6	− 3 11 s	Hya	1.8	13p	vF, pS, R, *9 np 4′
2700	—	8 55.7	− 5 06 r	Hya			eF, vS, 1′ n of 2699
2425 I	*	8 55.8	− 3 24 F	Hya			eF, neb?
2699	Gx	8 55.9	− 3 09 r	Hya		13p	vF, S, R, *15 np
2702	*	8 55.9	− 3 03 F	Hya			vF, vS, 4′ nf 2699
2703	D*	8 55.9	− 3 17 F	Hya			eF, lE, doubtful
2705	*	8 56.0	− 3 00 F	Hya			vF, vS, 3 st 14 f, nf
2708	Gx	8 56.1	− 3 22 s	Hya	3.0	14p	pF, pS, E, 2 st nr
2707	*	8 56.2	− 3 04 F	Hya			eF, S

NGC	Type	α_{2000}	δ_{2000}	Const.	Size	Mag.	Description
		h m	° /		/		
2706	Gx	8 56.3	− 2 35 r	Hya		14p	vF, pS, mE, * nr f
2709	Gx	8 56.3	− 3 16 r	Hya		15p	vF, pS, lE, nnf 2708
2424 I		8 56.8	+ 39 23 n	Lyn			vF, S, lbM; = 2704
2704	Gx	8 56.9	+ 39 22 r	Lyn		14p	vF, vS; = IC 2424?
2692	Gx	8 57.0	+ 52 04 s	UMa	1.5	14p	vF, S, R, psbM
2693	Gx	8 57.0	+ 51 21 s	UMa	2.2	11.7	pB, lE, psmbM
2694	Gx	8 57.0	+ 51 20 v	UMa	0.3	14.3	vF, vS, 1's of 2693
2717	Gx	8 57.0	− 24 40 r	Pyx		14p	pF, S, R, vgpmbM
2711	Gx	8 57.3	+ 17 17 r	Cnc		14p	vF, S, R
2713	Gx	8 57.3	+ 2 55 s	Hya	3.9	11.7	pB, iR, mbM
2716	Gx	8 57.6	+ 3 05 s	Hya	1.8	12.4	F, S, R, mbM
524 I		8 58.2	− 19 11 d	Hya			vF, vS, R, vF N?
2426 I	Gx	8 58.5	+ 2 54 m	Hya	0.3	15p	F, vS, R, stell
2722	Gx	8 58.8	− 3 43 v	Hya			vF, vS, stellar
2718	Gx	8 58.9	+ 6 18 s	Hya	2.5	13p	F, pL, E, am 3 st
2721	Gx	8 58.9	− 4 46 s	Hya	2.6	13p	cF, pL, R, vgbM
2701	Gx	8 59.1	+ 53 46 s	UMa	2.1	12.4	pB, fan-shaped, *11 att
2720	Gx	8 59.2	+ 11 10 r	Cnc		14p	F, S, R, bM
2712	Gx	8 59.5	+ 44 55 s	Lyn	2.9	12.0	pB, L, E, vgbM *18
2710	Gx	8 59.8	+ 55 41 r	UMa		14p	vF, S
2723	Gx	9 00.2	+ 3 11 s	Hya	1.3	15p	F, S, R
2719	Gx	9 00.3	+ 35 44 s	Lyn	1.3	14p	vF, S, E 110°, 2 vF st inv
2736	Gx	9 00.4	− 45 54 r	Vel			! eeF, vL, vvmE 19°
2724	Gx	9 01.0	+ 35 46 r	Lyn		15p	eF, S, stellar
2427 I	Gx	9 01.0	+ 37 52 z	Lyn		16p	F, vS, R, bM
2725	Gx	9 01.1	+ 11 05 r	Cnc		14p	F, pL, p of 2
2727	−	9 01.1	− 3 23 r	Hya			vF, L, R, bM
525 I	Gx	9 01.3	− 1 52 u	Hya	1.0	15p	F, S, E ns
2729	Gx	9 01.5	+ 3 43 r	Hya		14p	vF, vS, R
2728	Gx	9 01.8	+ 11 04 r	Cnc		15p	vF, pL, lE, f of 2
2731	Gx	9 02.1	+ 8 18 r	Cnc		14p	F, vS, R
2733	−	9 02.1	− 3 44 r	Hya			eF, R
2730	Gx	9 02.3	+ 16 50 r	Cnc		13p	vF, L, R
2735	Gx	9 02.6	+ 25 56 s	Cnc	1.2	14p	S* inv in vF, vS neb, E pf
526 I	Gx	9 02.6	+ 10 50 m	Cnc	0.7	15p	F, S, R
2734	Gx	9 03.0	+ 16 50 r	Cnc			eF, vS, R
2428 I	Gx	9 03.2	+ 30 35 u	Cnc	1.9	15p	F, pS, E pf, glbM
2429 I	Gx	9 03.8	+ 29 18 m	Cnc	0.4	15p	F, vS, R, bMN
2737	Gx	9 03.9	+ 21 54 r	Cnc		15p	vF, vS, D with 2738
2738	Gx	9 03.9	+ 21 58 r	Cnc		14p	pB, S, iF, D with 2737
512 I	Gx	9 04.	+ 85 30 s	Cam	3.6	12p	F, S, R, gbM
2741	−	9 04.3	+ 18 16 r	Cnc			vF, p of 2
2430 I	Gx	9 04.5	+ 27 57 u	Cnc	1.1	14p	F, S, R, gbM, r
2431 I	Gx	9 04.5	+ 14 36 u	Cnc	0.6	14p	F, S, R, N, r
2745	Gx	9 04.6	+ 18 15 r	Cnc		15p	eF, vS, stell, f of 2
2432 I	Gx	9 04.6	+ 5 31 z	Hya		15p	F, vS, R, dif
2744	Gx	9 04.7	+ 18 28 s	Cnc	1.8	13.4	vF, S, R, r, D* nr
2726	Gx	9 04.9	+ 59 56 s	UMa	1.5	13p	cF, pS, iR, er
2743	Gx	9 05.0	+ 25 00 r	Cnc		14p	eF, S, R, vlbM
2754	Gx	9 05.0	− 19 05 r	Hya			eF, S, R, 1st of 3
2747	Gx	9 05.3	+ 18 26 r	Cnc		15p	vF, vS, stellar
2749	Gx	9 05.4	+ 18 19 s	Cnc	2.0	12.0	pF, S, R, bMN = *15
2758	Gx	9 05.4	− 19 03 r	Hya		14p	eF, S, E 0°, 3rd of 3
2436 I	D*	9 05.4	− 19 10 F	Hya			eF, S, stell, susp
2751	Gx	9 05.5	+ 18 15 r	Cnc		15p	eF, eS, stellar

NGC	Type	α_{2000}	δ_{2000}		Const.	Size	Mag.	Description
		h m	o ′			′		
2757	D*	9 05.5	− 19 02	F	Hya			eF, 2nd of 3; only a D*, dist 12″
2433 I	Gx	9 05.5	+ 22 37	m	Cnc	0.8	15p	F, lE pf, dif
2437 I	Gx	9 05.5	− 19 12	c	Hya	2.4		F, vS, R, 10′ s of 2754, 57, 58
2750	Gx	9 05.7	+ 25 26	s	Cnc	2.3	12p	vF, cL, R, bMN, 2 c st p
2752	Gx	9 05.7	+ 18 20	s	Cnc	2.0	15p	pF, pL, vmE, gbM
2739	Gx	9 06.0	+ 51 45	r	UMa		15p	vF, S, R, np 2740
2746	Gx	9 06.0	+ 35 22	r	Lyn		14p	eF, S, R, vglbM, *12 nnp 50″
2740	Gx	9 06.1	+ 51 44	r	UMa		15p	vF, pS, R
2763	Gx	9 06.8	− 15 30	s	Hya	2.3	12.1	vF, pS, bM, S* 30″ n
2435 I	Gx	9 06.8	+ 26 16	u	Cnc	1.0	15p	F, S, R, gbM, r
2448 I	Pl	9 07.1	− 69 57	s	Car	0.1	12p	◯ , stell
2753	Gx	9 07.2	+ 25 20	r	Cnc		15p	vF, vS, *14 np 40″
2434 I	Gx	9 07.2	+ 37 12	u	Lyn	1.9	14p	F, pS, lbM, r
2761	Gx	9 07.5	+ 18 26	r	Cnc		15p	vF, S
2742	Gx	9 07.6	+ 60 29	s	UMa	3.1	11.7	cB, cL, E 90°, er
2765	Gx	9 07.6	+ 3 23	s	Hya	2.3	13p	vF, pL, E, gbM, er
2772	Gx	9 07.7	− 23 37	r	Pyx		15p	eF, lE, lbM
2755	Gx	9 07.9	+ 41 43	r	Lyn		14p	vF, S, iF, lbM, r
2715	Gx	9 08.1	+ 78 05	s	Cam	5.0	11.4	pB, L, E
2764	Gx	9 08.3	+ 21 27	s	Cnc	1.7	12.7	cF, vS, R, er, bet 2 pB st
2759	Gx	9 08.6	+ 37 37	r	Lyn		14p	vF, cS, R
2439 I	Gx	9 08.6	+ 32 35	z	Cnc		15p	F, S, dif, r
2766	Gx	9 08.8	+ 29 52	r	Cnc		14p	vF, vS, iF, bM
2756	Gx	9 09.0	+ 53 51	s	UMa	1.9	13p	pB, pS, E, vgbM
2788	Gx	9 09.0	− 67 56	v	Car			vF, vS, mE 105°
528 I	Gx	9 09.4	+ 15 48	u	Cnc	1.7	15p	pB, vS, R, N = 13m
2770	Gx	9 09.6	+ 33 07	s	Lyn	3.7	12p	F, L, mE 150°, r, 2 st n
2773	Gx	9 09.6	+ 7 11	r	Cnc		14p	vF, S, lE
527 I	Gx	9 09.6	+ 37 35	u	Lyn	1.9	15p	eeF, pL, R, e diffic
2762	Gx	9 09.8	+ 50 26	r	UMa		15p	vvF, S, R, 1st of 4
2441 I		9 10.0	+ 22 52	d	Cnc			F, S, R, glbM, D?
2767	Gx	9 10.1	+ 50 25	r	UMa		14p	vF, sbM *15, 2nd of 4
2442 I		9 10.1	+ 22 51	d	Cnc			vF, vS, R, vlbM
2775	Gx	9 10.3	+ 7 02	s	Cnc	4.5	10.3	cB, cL, R, vgvsmbM, r
2769	Gx	9 10.4	+ 50 27	r	UMa		14p	pF, S, E, pslbM, 3rd of 4
2771	Gx	9 10.5	+ 50 24	r	UMa		14p	vF, S, lE, 4th of 4
2774	Gx	9 10.6	+ 18 42	r	Cnc		15p	vF, S, R, am 5 S st
2777	Gx	9 10.7	+ 7 12	s	Cnc	1.0	14p	F, S
2781	Gx	9 11.5	− 14 49	s	Hya	3.9	11.5	B, S, vlE, psmbM
2443 I	Gx	9 11.5	+ 28 49	m	Cnc	0.6	15p	F, S, R, gbMN
2768	Gx	9 11.6	+ 60 02	s	UMa	6.3	10.0	cB, cL, lE, psbMLBN
2808	Gb	9 12.0	− 64 52	s	Car	13.8	6.3	! ⊕ , vL, eRi, vgeCM, 45ˢd, st 13...15
2776	Gx	9 12.2	+ 44 57	s	Lyn	2.9	11.6	pB, L, R, vgbM, r
2778	Gx	9 12.3	+ 35 01	s	Lyn	1.5	13p	pB, S, R, psmbM
2779	Gx	9 12.3	+ 35 03	r	Lyn		15p	eF, vS, 92″ nf 2778
2784	Gx	9 12.3	− 24 10	s	Hya	5.1	10.1	B, L, mE 64°, gmbM
2792	Pl	9 12.4	− 42 26	s	Vel	0.2	14p	! ◯ , pB = *9, vS, R, am st
2780	Gx	9 12.7	+ 34 55	s	Lyn	1.0	14p	vF, S, R, S D* p
2444 I	Gx	9 12.8	+ 30 14	m	Cnc	0.9	15p	F, vS, R, stell
2445 I	Gx	9 13.2	+ 31 48	u	Cnc	1.0	15p	F, S, R, dif, r
2732	Gx	9 13.4	+ 79 11	s	Cam	2.3	11.9	pB, S, E 45°, *13 nf
2446 I	Gx	9 13.5	+ 28 58	u	Cnc	1.7	15p	F, S, E 130°, bMN, r
2447 I		9 13.5	+ 28 45	d	Cnc			F, S, R, gbMN
2783	Gx	9 13.6	+ 29 59	r	Cnc		14p	vF, vS, R, 2 pB st sp
2748	Gx	9 13.7	+ 76 29	s	Cam	3.1	11.7	pB, pL, E, vglbM

NGC	Type	α_{2000}	δ_{2000}	Const.	Size	Mag.	Description
		h m	° ′		′		
2836	Gx	9 13.7	− 69 20 v	Car			F, pS, R, glbM
2786	−	9 14.0	+ 12 09 r	Cnc			vF, vS, mbM
2822	Gx	9 14.0	− 69 38 s	Car	2.1	12p	pF, vS, R, glbM
2438 I	OC	9 14.0	+ 73 26 x	Cam			Cl, 5 or 6 st 13... within 1′.5
2782	Gx	9 14.1	+ 40 07 s	Lyn	3.8	11.5	cB, R, mbMBN
2789	Gx	9 15.0	+ 29 44 r	Cnc		14p	pF, S, R, gbM
2790	Gx	9 15.0	+ 19 43 r	Cnc		14p	vF, S, R, lbM
2791	Gx	9 15.0	+ 17 36 r	Cnc		15p	F, R
2785	Gx	9 15.2	+ 40 55 r	Lyn		15p	eF, pS, iE, sev eF st inv
2449 I		9 15.2	+ 30 00 d	Cnc			vF, vS, lbM
530 I	Gx	9 15.3	+ 11 53 u	Cnc	2.1	14p	pB, S, E pf
2440 I		9 15.5	+ 73 28 d	Cam			vF, stell (13m), neb?
2842	Gx	9 15.6	− 63 04 t	Car			F, vS, bet 2 st
2760	−	9 15.7	+ 76 23 r	Cam			vF, S, R, nearly bet ∗8 & ∗9
2450 I		9 15.7	+ 25 27 d	Cnc			F, S, gbM, r
2451 I	Gx	9 15.7	+ 23 29 z	Cnc		16p	F, S, R, gbMN
2453 I	Gx	9 15.8	+ 20 56 z	Cnc		15p	F, S, R, gbM, r
2452 I	Gx	9 15.9	+ 23 27 z	Cnc		16p	F, S, R, gbMN
2794	Gx	9 16.0	+ 17 36 r	Cnc		14p	eF, vS, sp of 2
2818	OC	9 16.0	− 36 37 s	Pyx	9	8.2	! ⊕, pB, pL, R, vglbM, in L Cl
2454 I	Gx	9 16.0	+ 17 49 u	Cnc	1.2	14p	F, vS, gbMN
2795	Gx	9 16.1	+ 17 38 r	Cnc		14p	eF, vS, nf of 2
2811	Gx	9 16.2	− 16 19 s	Hya	2.7	11.3	pB, pS, E, psmbM
2815	Gx	9 16.3	− 23 38 s	Hya	3.5	13p	F, S, lE, gbM
2797	Gx	9 16.4	+ 17 44 r	Cnc		14p	eF, sev st nr
2796	Gx	9 16.7	+ 30 55 r	Cnc		14p	eF, S, R, lbM
2801	Gx	9 16.7	+ 19 56 r	Cnc		15p	eF, pL
2802	Gx	9 16.7	+ 18 58 r	Cnc		14p	vF, S, R, r, np of 2
2803	Gx	9 16.7	+ 18 58 r	Cnc		14p	vF, S, R, r, sf of 2
2793	Gx	9 16.8	+ 34 26 s	Lyn	1.3	14p	vF, S, R, D∗ p 5ˢ, n 5′
2804	Gx	9 16.8	+ 20 12 r	Cnc		14p	vF, S, R
2821	Gx	9 16.8	− 26 49 r	Pyx		14p	eF, ∗11 att
2455 I		9 16.8	+ 20 07 d	Cnc			F, R, gbMN, r
2806	Gx	9 17.0	+ 20 03 r	Cnc		15p	vF, stellar, p 2809
2807	Gx	9 17.0	+ 20 02 r	Cnc		15p	vF, vS, 2809 f 7ˢ, n 2′
2809	Gx	9 17.1	+ 20 04 r	Cnc		14p	vF, S, R
2457 I	Gx	9 17.1	+ 20 05 m	Cnc	1.2	14p	F, S, R, dif
2817	Gx	9 17.3	− 4 44 r	Hya		13p	vF, pS, R
2798	Gx	9 17.4	+ 42 00 s	Lyn	2.8	12.3	pB, S, stellar
2799	Gx	9 17.5	+ 42 00 s	Lyn	1.9	14p	F, cL, vmE, f 2798
2456 I		9 17.5	+ 34 47 d	Lyn			F, S, dif, r
2812	Gx	9 17.6	+ 19 55 r	Cnc		15p	eF
2813	Gx	9 17.7	+ 19 54 r	Cnc		15p	F
2835	Gx	9 17.9	− 22 21 s	Hya	6.3	11p	F, ∗10 inv f, bet 2 st 9
531 I	Gx	9 17.9	− 0 17 u	Hya	1.8	15p	F, vS, E pf, lbM
2819	Gx	9 18.2	+ 16 13 r	Cnc		14p	pB, vS, R
2837	Gx	9 18.4	− 16 30 h	Hya	0.3	14p	eF, R, bM, ∗ f 8ˢ.5
529 I	Gx	9 18.5	+ 73 46 s	Cam	3.7	13p	pF, pL, E
2800	Gx	9 18.6	+ 52 31 r	UMa		14p	vF, S, lE, ∗ att, ∗ inv
2845	Gx	9 18.6	− 38 00 r	Vel			vF, S, R, ∗12 att sf
2824	Gx	9 19.0	+ 26 16 s	Cnc	1.3	14p	Cl, S, st F, vC
532 I	?	9 19.0	− 16 46 x	Hya			pB, pL, E pf, bM
2459 I		9 19.1	+ 34 53 d	Lyn			eF, vS, diffic
2827	Gx	9 19.2	+ 33 52 r	Lyn		15p	vF, vS, R, 1st of 3
2787	Gx	9 19.3	+ 69 12 s	UMa	3.4	10.8	B, pL, lE 90°, mbM, r, vS∗ sf inv

NGC	Type	α_{2000}	δ_{2000}	Const.	Size	Mag.	Description
		h m	° ′		′		
2823	Gx	9 19.3	+ 34 00 s	Lyn	1.0	16p	vF, S, R
2849	OC	9 19.3	− 40 31 r	Vel			eF, cL, R, vglbM, rr
2460 I	?	9 19.3	+ 33 51 x	Lyn			F, vS, E pf, stell N
2825	Gx	9 19.4	+ 33 44 s	Lyn	1.1	16p	F, pS, lE, bM
2826	Gx	9 19.4	+ 33 37 s	Lyn	1.8	15p	vF, vS, R, 2825 n 7′
2828	Gx	9 19.5	+ 33 53 r	Lyn		15p	vF, vS, R, 2nd of 3
2829	Gx	9 19.5	+ 33 40 r	Lyn			eF, vS, R, nf 2826
2830	Gx	9 19.7	+ 33 44 A	Lyn	1.3	15p	F, S, lE, bM, 1st of 3
2831	Gx	9 19.7	+ 33 44 A	Lyn	0.8	13.6	F, vS, R, 2nd of 3
2832	Gx	9 19.8	+ 33 44 A	Lyn	3.3	11.5	cB, cL, E, 3rd of 3
2833	Gx	9 19.9	+ 33 56 r	Lyn		15p	F, pS, R, 3rd of 3 in line
2846		9 19.9	− 14 41 D	Hya			vS Cl (neb?), *10 sf 4′
2461 I	Gx	9 19.9	+ 37 10 u	Lyn	2.7	15p	F, vS, vlbM
2834	Gx	9 20.0	+ 33 43 r	Lyn		15p	vF, S, R, bM
2847	Gx	9 20.1	− 16 31 h	Hya	0.4	15p	vF, S, inv in 2848, np
2848	Gx	9 20.2	− 16 32 s	Hya	2.7	12.1	vF, cL, E 45°, glbM, *11 nf 3′
2805	Gx	9 20.3	+ 64 06 s	UMa	6.3	11.3	vF, L, R, mbM
2843	Gx	9 20.4	+ 18 57 r	Cnc			S* and neb
533 I		9 20.4	− 4 00 d	Hya			eF, S, dif
2839	Gx	9 20.6	+ 33 40 r	Lyn		15p	vF, S, R
2851	Gx	9 20.6	− 16 28 r	Hya		15p	eF, pS, mE, f 2848
2838	Gx	9 20.7	+ 39 19 r	Lyn		14p	vF, vS, R
2840	Gx	9 20.8	+ 35 23 r	Lyn		15p	cF, S, R, *10 np 2′
2850	Gx	9 21.0	− 4 55 r	Hya			vF, vS, R, mbM
2816	−	9 21.1	+ 60 27 r	UMa			F, pmE
2814	Gx	9 21.2	+ 64 15 s	UMa	1.4	13.8	F, S, iF, 1st of 2
534 I	Gx	9 21.2	+ 3 09 u	Hya	1.9	15p	vF, S, dif
2867	Pl	9 21.4	− 58 19 s	Car	0.2	10p	!! ○ = *8, vS, R, *15, 59°, 13″
2855	Gx	9 21.5	− 11 55 s	Hya	2.7	11.6	pB, pL, R, gmbMN
2458 I	Gx	9 21.6	+ 64 14 s	UMa	0.4	15p	eF, S, dif close to 2820
2820	Gx	9 21.8	+ 64 16 s	UMa	4.3	12.8	F, S, E, 2nd of 2
2844	Gx	9 21.8	+ 40 09 s	Lyn	1.9	12.9	cF, cS
2841	Gx	9 22.0	+ 50 58 s	UMa	8.1	9.3	vB, L, vmE 151°, vsmbM = *10
2866	−	9 22.0	− 51 05 r	Vel			Cl, lC
2810	Gx	9 22.1	+ 71 50 s	UMa	2.0	13p	F, cS, bM
535 I	Gx	9 22.2	− 1 03 z	Hya		16p	F, vS, R
2858	Gx	9 22.9	+ 3 09 r	Hya		14p	vF, S, mbM
2462 I		9 22.9	+ 22 41 d	Leo			vF, S, dif, r
2463 I	Gx	9 23.0	+ 22 37 z	Leo		16p	F, S, R, gbM, r
2469 I	Gx	9 23.0	− 32 27 c	Pyx	5.1		pF, cS, mE, *10 sp nr
2852	Gx	9 23.2	+ 40 10 s	Lyn	1.2	14p	vF, cS, R, *10 p 2′, 1st of 2
2853	Gx	9 23.3	+ 40 12 s	Lyn	2.0	14p	vF, S, vgbM, 2nd of 2
2887	Gx	9 23.3	− 63 49 t	Car			F, S, R, pmbM, B* nr
2868		9 23.4	− 10 25 D	Hya			eF, S, R, 10ˢp 2869
2464 I	Gx	9 23.4	+ 22 35 m	Leo	0.6	15p	pF, S, R, gbM, r
2865	Gx	9 23.5	− 23 10 s	Hya	2.0	11.4	B, S, R, gbM
2861	Gx	9 23.6	+ 2 08 r	Hya		14p	pF, S, iR, *14 f
2863	Gx	9 23.6	− 10 24 r	Hya		13p	cF, S, E, bet 2 st 12, 16
2869		9 23.6	− 10 26 D	Hya			eF, pS, E 170°, gbM, bet 2 F st; = 2863
2465 I		9 23.6	+ 24 27 d	Leo			F, S, dif
2466 I	Gx	9 23.7	+ 24 31 z	Leo		15p	vF, vS, dif, *13.5 att
2854	Gx	9 24.0	+ 49 13 r	UMa		14p	cF, cS, vlE, pglbM
2856	Gx	9 24.2	+ 49 15 r	UMa		14p	cF, cS, lE, bM
2864	Gx	9 24.2	+ 5 57 r	Hya		15p	vF, pL, lE
2859	Gx	9 24.3	+ 34 31 s	LMi	4.8	10.7	vB, pL, R, smbM

NGC	Type	α_{2000}	δ_{2000}	Const.	Size	Mag.	Description
		h m	° ′		′		
2857	Gx	9 24.5	+ 49 21 s	UMa	2.4	14p	vF, pL, 4 st p
536 I	Gx	9 24.6	+ 25 07 u	Leo	1.2	15p	F, S, R, lbM
2860	Gx	9 24.9	+ 41 04 r	Lyn		15p	vF, vS, R, gbM
2862	Gx	9 24.9	+ 26 46 r	Leo		14p	F, S, E, bM
2467 I		9 24.9	+ 38 20 d	LMi			F, vS, R, gbMN
2468 I		9 25.0	+ 38 20 d	LMi			vS, R, sbM ∗15
2470 I		9 25.0	+ 3 23 d	Hya			F, pS, iF, E 135°, r
2876	Gx	9 25.2	− 6 43 r	Hya		14p	F, S, sev vF st inv
2883	Gx	9 25.2	− 34 05 v	Pyx			vF, S, vglbM, rrr, st 15
2471 I	Gx	9 25.2	− 6 50 m	Hya	0.7	14p	vF, 2 or 3 st in neb; = 2876?
2879	∗*∗	9 25.4	− 11 40 F	Hya			vF, vS, R, lbM
537 I	Gx	9 25.4	− 12 23 m	Hya	1.0	14p	neb ∗14
2871		9 25.7	+ 11 27 D	Leo			eF, 2872 sf 1′
2872	Gx	9 25.7	+ 11 26 s	Leo	2.1	13p	pF, pS, R, bM
2874	Gx	9 25.8	+ 11 26 s	Leo	2.5	14p	vF, pL, mE
2875	Gx	9 25.8	+ 11 26 h	Leo	0.5	15p	eF, nf 2874
2877	Gx	9 25.8	+ 2 13 r	Hya		14p	vF, S, vlE
2878	Gx	9 25.8	+ 2 05 r	Hya		15p	vF, S, vlE
2873	Gx	9 25.9	+ 11 27 r	Leo		15p	vF, vS, R, n of E neb
2881	Gx	9 25.9	− 11 59 r	Hya		14p	eF, pS, 2 st 9.5 & 10.5 sf
2915	Gx	9 26.2	− 76 38 s	Cha	1.5	12.6	pF, pL, R, gbM
2888	Gx	9 26.3	− 28 02 s	Pyx	0.8	12.5	cF, S, R, gmbM
2884	Gx	9 26.4	− 11 33 s	Hya	2.6	13p	F, S, r?
2882	Gx	9 26.5	+ 7 56 r	Leo		13p	F, pL, E
2886	∗*∗	9 26.5	− 21 46 F	Hya			eeF, pL
2472 I	Gx	9 26.5	+ 21 23 z	Leo		15p	F, S, R, dif
2890	Gx	9 26.6	− 14 32 r	Hya		15p	eF, S, R, bMN
2891	Gx	9 26.8	− 24 49 r	Pyx		14p	F, S, R, bM
2484 I		9 26.8	− 42 51 d	Vel			pB, S, R, ∗7 nf, D∗ p
2899	Pl	9 27.0	− 56 06 s	Vel	2.0		F, pL, R, gmbM, am 80 st
2482 I	Gx	9 27.0	− 12 06 m	Hya	2.0	13p	F, vS, ∗10 p 7^s, 0′.8 n
2889	Gx	9 27.2	− 11 38 s	Hya	2.0	11.8	pF, pS, vlE, vglbM, r
2474 I		9 27.2	+ 23 02 d	Leo			∗13 in vS neb, IC 538 f
2485 I		9 27.2	− 39 17 d	Ant			eF, vS, R, st in neb, susp
538 I	Gx	9 27.4	+ 23 01 m	Leo	0.5		∗13 in vF neb; = 2885?
2473 I	Gx	9 27.4	+ 30 26 u	Leo	1.6	15p	F, pS, R, glbM
2481 I	Gx	9 27.4	+ 3 56 u	Hya	0.9	14p	F, S, E 150°, gbM, r
2488 I	OC	9 27.6	− 56 59 s	Vel	15	7p	Cl, co
2870	Gx	9 27.8	+ 57 23 s	UMa	2.6	14p	cF, S, E, vglbM
2475 I	Nb	9 27.9	+ 29 48 x	Leo	0.5		F, vS, R, lbM
2476 I	Gx	9 27.9	+ 29 59 v	Leo	1.7		F, S, R, bM
2477 I		9 27.9	+ 29 42 d	Leo			F, S, gbM, r
2478 I	Nb	9 27.9	+ 30 01 x	Leo	0.1		F, S, R, N
2479 I	Nb	9 28.1	+ 30 00 x	Leo	0.3		F, S, R, vlbM
2480 I	Nb	9 28.2	+ 29 43 x	Leo	0.2		F, vS, lE pf, gbM, r
539 I	Gx	9 29.1	− 2 33 u	Hya	1.2	14p	pB, S, R, gbM, r
2894	Gx	9 29.4	+ 7 43 r	Leo		13p	vF, E, er, 2 or 3 st inv
2483 I	Gx	9 29.5	+ 31 00 z	Leo		16p	F, S, R, lbM
2880	Gx	9 29.6	+ 62 30 s	UMa	2.6	11.6	B, cS, R, mbM, am st
2885	Gx	9 29.6	+ 22 57 r	Leo			eF, vS, E 90°
2897	Gx	9 29.8	+ 2 12 r	Hya			eF, S
2898	Gx	9 29.8	+ 2 03 r	Hya		15p	vF, vS, lE
2904	Gx	9 30.2	− 30 23 r	Ant		13p	F, S, lE, psbM
540 I	Gx	9 30.2	+ 7 54 u	Leo	1.4	15p	F, S, dif
2487 I	Gx	9 30.2	+ 20 06 v	Leo	2.0		F, L, mE 160°

NGC	Type	α_{2000}	δ_{2000}	Const.	Size	Mag.	Description
		h　m	o　　′		′		
2893	Gx	9 30.3	+ 29 32 s	Leo	1.4	13p	vF, S, R, vsbM *12
2896	Gx	9 30.3	+ 23 39 r	Leo		15p	F, vS, R, *17 att
2900	Gx	9 30.3	+ 4 08 r	Hya		14p	eeF, pL, R
2486 I	Gx	9 30.3	+ 26 39 u	Leo	1.1	15p	vF, cS, dif
2910	OC	9 30.4	− 52 54 s	Vel	5	7.2	Cl, cL, pRi, pC, st 10...14
541 I		9 30.5	− 4 15 d	Hya			eeF, pS, R, *10 s
2902	Gx	9 30.9	− 14 44 s	Hya	1.3	13p	vF, vS, stellar; = IC 543
543 I	Gx	9 30.9	− 14 44 t	Hya	1.2	13p	vF, pL, E, dif
542 I	Gx	9 31.2	− 13 10 m	Hya	1.0	15p	F, vS, E pf, lbM
2489 I		9 31.2	− 5 53 d	Hya			pF, R
2907	Gx	9 31.6	− 16 44 s	Hya	1.9	13p	pF, S, lE, mb sf
2903	Gx	9 32.2	+ 21 30 s	Leo	12.6	8.9	cB, vL, E, gmbM, r, sp of 2
2905	Gx	9 32.2	+ 21 31 u	Leo	13.3	10p	vF, cL, R, psbM, r, nf of 2
2906	Gx	9 32.2	+ 8 27 s	Leo	1.6	13p	F, pS, lE, gbM
2895	Gx	9 32.4	+ 57 29 r	UMa		14p	vF, vS, R, vgbM, D* 7′ s
2901	−	9 32.4	+ 31 07 r	Leo			no description
2892	Gx	9 32.9	+ 67 37 s	UMa	1.7	14p	pF, pS, R, lbM
2490 I	Nb	9 33.1	+ 29 55 x	Leo	0.3		F, S, gbM
2492 I		9 33.2	− 37 54 d	Ant			cF, vS, R, B* 1′ np, susp
2912	Gx	9 33.7	+ 10 09 r	Leo			eF, 2911 sp
2925	OC	9 33.7	− 53 26 s	Vel	12	8p	Cl, pRi, pC, D* taken
2911	Gx	9 33.8	+ 10 09 s	Leo	4.3	11.6	F, pL, R, gbM, p of 2
2913	Gx	9 34.0	+ 9 28 r	Leo		14p	vF, pL, iR
2914	Gx	9 34.0	+ 10 07 s	Leo	1.2	13.1	vF, S, R, bMN, f of 2
2920	Gx	9 34.3	− 20 51 r	Hya			eF, S, R, p of 2
2917	Gx	9 34.5	− 2 30 r	Hya		14p	pF, S, mbM
2921	Gx	9 34.7	− 20 57 r	Hya		13p	vF, pS, lE, vglbM, f of 2
2919	Gx	9 34.8	+ 10 17 s	Leo	1.9	14p	F, pS
546 I	Gx	9 34.9	− 16 23 m	Hya	0.6	14p	F, vS, iF, 2924 f
2916	Gx	9 35.0	+ 21 42 s	Leo	2.6	12.0	F, S, vlE
2924	Gx	9 35.2	− 16 24 s	Hya	1.6	13p	pB, S, R
2491 I	Gx	9 35.2	+ 34 44 u	LMi	1.1	15p	F, S, R, gbM, r
2932	−	9 35.3	− 46 57 r	Vel			Cl, eL, vRi, st L and S
2918	Gx	9 35.8	+ 31 42 r	Leo		13p	vF, cS, R, sbMN
544 I	Gx	9 35.9	+ 24 54 m	Leo	0.7	15p	vF, dif, diffic
2923	Gx	9 36.0	+ 16 45 r	Leo		15p	vF
545 I	Gx	9 36.1	+ 24 57 m	Leo	0.4	15p	F, E pf, F* f
2494 I		9 36.1	− 12 26 d	Hya			pB, pL, R, 2 st nr f
547 I	Gx	9 36.2	− 12 25 m	Hya	1.2	13p	pB, S, R, lbM
2493 I	Gx	9 36.3	+ 37 23 m	LMi	0.5	15p	F, vS, stell
2935	Gx	9 36.7	− 21 08 s	Hya	3.5	12p	pB, pS, vlE, gmbM
2922	Gx	9 36.8	+ 37 41 r	LMi		14p	vF, S, iR, lbM, r
2927	Gx	9 37.2	+ 23 35 r	Leo		14p	F, pL, R, lbM
2928	Gx	9 37.3	+ 16 58 r	Leo		15p	vF, S, R, bM
2929	Gx	9 37.4	+ 23 09 r	Leo		14p	eF, vS, lE, vlbM, 1st of 3
2926	Gx	9 37.5	+ 32 50 r	Leo		14p	vF
2930	Gx	9 37.5	+ 23 12 r	Leo		14p	eF, S, 2nd of 3
2931	Gx	9 37.6	+ 23 14 r	Leo		15p	eF, vS, 3rd of 3
2945	Gx	9 37.6	− 22 02 r	Hya		14p	F, S, R, glbM, 2 or 3 S st nr
2936	Gx	9 37.7	+ 2 44 s	Hya	1.7	13.1	vF, iR
2937	Gx	9 37.7	+ 2 44 s	Hya	1.0	13.6	F, S, like a neb*
2933	Gx	9 38.0	+ 17 01 r	Leo		15p	F, vS, lE, sp of 2
2934	Gx	9 38.0	+ 17 01 r	Leo		15p	eF, nf of 2
2973	Gx	9 38.0	− 30 08 r	Ant			eF, pS, *8 f
2939	Gx	9 38.1	+ 9 31 s	Leo	2.7	14p	vF, S, vlE, bM, △ st nf

NGC	Type	α_{2000}	δ_{2000}	Const.	Size	Mag.	Description
		h m	° ′		′		
2940	Gx	9 38.1	+ 9 36 s	Leo	1.3	15p	vF, S, 5′ n of 2939
2495 I	Gx	9 38.2	+ 28 03 m	Leo	0.7	15p	F, cS, R, gbMN
2938	Gx	9 38.3	+ 76 19 r	Dra		14p	ef, S, iF, D∗ f 3′
548 I	Gx	9 38.3	+ 9 26 z	Leo		15p	F, vS, ibM, 2939 np
2941	Gx	9 38.4	+ 17 03 r	Leo		15p	ef, vS, lE, p of 2
2947	—	9 38.4	− 12 26 r	Hya			ef, pL, iR, gbM
2943	Gx	9 38.6	+ 17 02 r	Leo		14p	F, S, iR, bM, f of 2
2504 I		9 38.6	− 69 05 d	Car			ef, vS, ee 170°, lbM, susp
2496 I	Gx	9 38.7	+ 34 43 z	LMi		15p	F, vS, R, r
2501 I	Pl	9 38.8	− 60 05 s	Car	0.4	11p	◯ , stell
2948	Gx	9 38.9	+ 6 57 r	Leo		14p	vF, pL, vgbM
2942	Gx	9 39.1	+ 34 00 s	LMi	2.2	13p	F, pL, vlE 0°, vglbM
2946	Gx	9 39.1	+ 17 01 r	Leo		15p	vF, S, E
2944	Gx	9 39.3	+ 32 19 s	Leo	1.3	15p	F, vS, lbM
2952	—	9 39.3	− 10 09 r	Hya			ef, pS, iR, sbM, ∗9.5 f 30ˢ
2956	Gx	9 39.3	− 19 06 r	Hya			vF, vS, R, ∗9.5 sf 4′
2951	Gx	9 39.7	− 0 14 r	Hya		15p	pF, S, E
2949	Gx	9 40.0	+ 16 47 r	Leo		15p	vF, double?
2972	OC	9 40.3	− 50 20 s	Vel	4	9.9	Cl, S, lRi, pC, st 13
2953	—	9 40.4	+ 14 50 r	Leo			eeF, suspected
2954	Gx	9 40.5	+ 14 55 r	Leo		13p	vF, S, R, n of 2
550 I	Gx	9 40.5	− 6 56 m	Hya	0.6	14p	F, eS, stellar
2958	Gx	9 40.6	+ 11 53 r	Leo		14p	vF, pS, R, vlbM
2960	Gx	9 40.6	+ 3 34 r	Hya		13p	vF, R, gbM
549 I		9 40.7	+ 3 59 d	Hya			vF, S, iF, bM
553 I	Gx	9 40.7	− 5 26 z	Hya			vF, vS, R, dif
2962	Gx	9 40.9	+ 5 10 s	Hya	3.3	11.7	F, vS, vlE, psbM
551 I	Gx	9 40.9	+ 6 56 u	Leo	0.9	14p	F, vS, R, N = 13m
2497 I		9 41.1	+ 34 42 d	LMi			vF, vS, R, r
2975	Gx	9 41.2	− 16 39 r	Hya			eeF, S, R, gbM
2955	Gx	9 41.3	+ 35 53 s	LMi	1.8	12.7	cF, pS, iR, glbM, r
552 I	Gx	9 41.3	+ 10 38 u	Leo	1.1	14p	F, vS, stell N = 14m
2498 I	Gx	9 41.3	+ 28 06 z	Leo		15p	F, S, E ns, r; biN?
2499 I		9 41.4	+ 27 54 d	Leo			F, vS, dif, v diffic
2969	Gx	9 41.8	− 8 37 r	Sex		13p	vF, pS, iR, vglbM
554 I		9 41.8	+ 12 26 d	Leo			eeF, eS, alm stell
555 I	Gx	9 41.9	+ 12 17 u	Leo	1.3	14p	pB, vS, R, bM
2967	Gx	9 42.1	+ 0 20 s	Sex	3.0	11.6	pF, pL, R, vglbM
2966	Gx	9 42.2	+ 4 40 r	Sex		14p	vF∗ in vF, lE neb, F∗ p 30″
2500 I	?	9 42.3	+ 36 20 z	LMi			vF, pS, R, mbM
2982	—	9 42.4	− 44 12 r	Vel			Cl, P, E, st 10...11
2950	Gx	9 42.6	+ 58 51 s	UMa	3.2	11.0	B, pS, R, vgvmbMN
2974	Gx	9 42.6	− 3 42 s	Sex	3.4	10.8	B, cS, iR, bM, ∗9 sp 43″
2964	Gx	9 42.9	+ 31 51 s	Leo	3.0	11.3	B, vL, lE, vgbM, sp of 3
2979	Gx	9 43.1	− 10 23 r	Sex		14p	pF, pS, vlE, psbM
2965	Gx	9 43.2	+ 36 14 r	LMi		14p	ef, vS, R, bM, r
2968	Gx	9 43.2	+ 31 56 s	Leo	2.2	11.8	pB, pL, lE, vglbM, 2nd of 3
2980	Gx	9 43.2	− 9 37 s	Sex	1.8	13p	vF, pS, lE 0°, vglbM
2502 I		9 43.2	+ 33 08 d	LMi			F, S, R, gbM, diffic
2503 I		9 43.2	+ 33 11 d	LMi			vF, vS, dif, v diffic
2978	Gx	9 43.3	− 9 45 s	Sex	1.2	14p	ef, S, R, 2980 n 10′
2908	Gx	9 43.5	+ 79 41 r	Dra		14p	ef, vS
2970	Gx	9 43.5	+ 31 59 s	Leo	1.0	14p	F, nf of 3
2984	Gx	9 43.6	+ 11 04 r	Leo		14p	ef, vS, R, bM; = IC 556
2971	Gx	9 43.7	+ 36 10 r	LMi		15p	ef, pS, iR, vlbM

NGC	Type	α_{2000}	δ_{2000}	Const.	Size	Mag.	Description
		h m	° ′		′		
2983	Gx	9 43.7	− 20 29 s	Hya	2.6	11.7	F, pS, R, bM, r, stellar
556 I	Gx	9 43.7	+ 11 04 u	Leo	0.9	14p	F, vS, R, N = 14m
2977	Gx	9 43.8	+ 74 52 s	Dra	1.7	13p	cB, pL, iF
2909	Gx	9 44.0	+ 65 59 r	UMa		14p	eF, S, psbM
2995	−	9 44.1	− 54 47 r	Vel			Cl, P, lC
557 I	Gx	9 44.1	+ 10 59 m	Leo	0.5	15p	F, vS, R, vlbM
2986	Gx	9 44.3	− 21 17 s	Hya	2.5	10.9	pB, pS, iR, mbM
2507 I	Gx	9 44.6	− 31 47 c	Ant	1.7		vF, S, R, *12.5 nr nf, *9 np
559 I	Gx	9 44.7	+ 9 37 m	Leo	0.8	15p	F, pS, R, dif
2981	Gx	9 45.0	+ 31 06 r	Leo		15p	vF
558 I	Gx	9 45.0	+ 29 27 m	Leo	0.9	15p	F, R, bM
2959	Gx	9 45.1	+ 68 36 s	UMa	1.5	14p	F, pL, R, vglbM, st n
2505 I		9 45.1	+ 27 16 d	Leo			F, S, R, vlbM
2999	−	9 45.2	− 50 26 r	Vel			Cl, S, lRi, iF, st 12...15
2506 I		9 45.2	+ 27 15 d	Leo			F, S, R, glbM, r
2961	Gx	9 45.4	+ 68 36 v	UMa	0.9		cF, S, lE, nf 2959
2989	Gx	9 45.4	− 18 23 s	Hya	1.4	13p	F, R, gbM, D* f
2987	Gx	9 45.6	+ 4 56 r	Sex		14p	eF, S, iF, sev vF st inv
2997	Gx	9 45.6	− 31 11 s	Ant	8.1	11p	! vF, vL, vgvsbMN 4″, 19ˢ.5 d
2992	Gx	9 45.7	− 14 20 s	Hya	4.1	11.9	cF, S, R, bM, stellar, p of 2
2993	Gx	9 45.8	− 14 22 s	Hya	1.6	12.6	cF, S, R, bM, stellar, f of 2
560 I	Gx	9 45.9	− 0 16 u	Sex	1.5	15p	F, S, dif, *10 near
561 I	Gx	9 46.0	+ 3 08 m	Sex	0.4	15p	pF, dif
562 I	Gx	9 46.1	− 3 58 v	Sex	1.5		vF, pL, E ns, gbM
2990	Gx	9 46.3	+ 5 43 s	Sex	1.3	12.8	F, pS, lE 90°
3001	Gx	9 46.3	− 30 26 s	Ant	3.1	13p	F, S, R, *12 att 320°
563 I	Gx	9 46.3	+ 3 03 v	Sex	1.1		pB, S, dif, gbM
564 I	Gx	9 46.4	+ 3 04 v	Sex	1.9		pB, pL, E pf
2996	Gx	9 46.5	− 21 36 r	Hya		14p	vF, S, *9 f 1′
2988	Gx	9 46.8	+ 22 01 r	Leo		14p	eF, p 2991
2991	Gx	9 46.8	+ 22 01 r	Leo		14p	F, vS, bM, sp of 2
2509 I	*	9 46.9	+ 5 43 z	Sex			eF, neb?
2508 I	Gx	9 47.1	+ 33 30 z	LMi		16p	F, vS, R, dif, r
2994	Gx	9 47.2	+ 22 06 r	Leo		14p	F, S, R, bM, nf of 2
2976	Gx	9 47.3	+ 67 55 s	UMa	4.9	10.2	B, vL, mE 152°, st inv
3007	Gx	9 47.6	− 6 26 r	Sex		15p	eF, S, iR, lbM, r
2510 I	Gx	9 47.7	− 32 50 c	Ant	1.5		eF, vS, cE 140°, bM, susp
2963	Gx	9 47.8	+ 72 58 s	Dra	1.4	14p	vF, vS, R, bM
565 I	Gx	9 47.8	+ 15 51 u	Leo	1.7	15p	F, S, dif
2957	Gx	9 47.9	+ 72 58 r	Dra		15p	eF, *13 nr
3003	Gx	9 48.6	+ 33 25 s	LMi	5.9	11.7	! cB, L, vmE 90°
2998	Gx	9 48.7	+ 44 05 s	UMa	3.0	13p	pF, pL, E 51°, bMN, r
3029	Gx	9 48.7	− 8 03 r	Sex			pF, pS, R
3033	OC	9 48.8	− 56 25 s	Vel	5	8.8	Cl, pL, pRi, iF, st 11...12
3002	Gx	9 49.0	+ 44 03 r	UMa		16p	eeF, vS
3000	D*	9 49.1	+ 44 08 r	UMa			vF, S, iR, r
3017	Gx	9 49.1	− 2 50 r	Sex		14p	eF, vS, *11 np 3′
3004	D*	9 49.2	+ 44 07 r	UMa			eF, suspected
3005	Gx	9 49.2	+ 44 08 r	UMa		16p	vF, pS, E nnp ssf
3014	Gx	9 49.2	− 4 44 r	Sex		14p	eF, pL, p of 2
3006	Gx	9 49.3	+ 44 01 r	UMa		15p	vF, S, stellar
3036	OC	9 49.3	− 62 41 A	Car			Cl, cL, lC
3015	Gx	9 49.4	+ 1 08 r	Sex		14p	F, vS, alm stellar
2511 I	Gx	9 49.4	− 32 51 c	Ant	3.1		pB, pS, eE, *7 np, np of 2
2512 I	Gx	9 49.4	− 32 51 c	Ant	3.1		eeF, pS, mE, bet 2 st, sf of 2; = IC 2511

NGC	Type	α_{2000}	δ_{2000}	Const.	Size	Mag.	Description
		h m	° ′		′		
3025	Gx	9 49.5	− 21 45 r	Hya		15p	eF, vS, R, ∗9 s
3008	Gx	9 49.6	+ 44 05 r	UMa		15p	pF, S, E, ∗13-14 p 1′
3011	Gx	9 49.7	+ 32 13 s	Leo	1.2	14p	eeF, eS, stellar
3016	Gx	9 49.7	+ 12 42 r	Leo		13p	vF, S, R, p of 2
3018	Gx	9 49.7	+ 0 37 r	Sex		14p	vF, vS, bM
3012	Gx	9 49.8	+ 34 42 r	LMi		15p	vF, pL, R, com
3022	Gx	9 49.8	− 5 09 r	Sex		14p	F, R, vglbM, f of 2
3023	Gx	9 49.9	+ 0 37 s	Sex	3.1	13p	pF, pL, iR, lbM, dif
3028	Gx	9 49.9	− 19 10 r	Hya			F, S, R, lbM
3019	Gx	9 50.0	+ 12 44 r	Leo		15p	eF, f of 2
566 I	Gx	9 50.0	− 0 14 z	Sex		15p	vF, vS, R, bM
2513 I	Gx	9 50.0	− 32 53 c	Ant	3.0		eeF, eS, R, D∗ nr sf, sp of 2; = IC 2514
2514 I	Gx	9 50.0	− 32 53 c	Ant	3.0		eeF, eS, 3 F st nr f, nf of 2
3013	Gx	9 50.1	+ 33 34 r	LMi		15p	pF, pS, R, bM, 3021 f
3020	Gx	9 50.1	+ 12 49 s	Leo	3.2	13p	eF, pS, lE 0°, r
3009	Gx	9 50.2	+ 44 18 r	UMa		14p	pF, R, bM, r, p of 2
3030	Gx	9 50.2	− 12 14 r	Hya		15p	eF, vS, R, bM
3059	Gx	9 50.2	− 73 55 s	Car	3.2	12p	F, L, iR, glbM, S∗ inv
2985	Gx	9 50.4	+ 72 17 s	UMa	4.3	10.5	vB, cL, R, psmbM, ∗ inv f
3024	Gx	9 50.5	+ 12 46 s	Leo	2.2	14p	eF, pL, E, r
567 I		9 50.5	+ 12 49 d	Leo			vF, suspected, 2′ from 3024
3010	Gx	9 50.6	+ 44 20 r	UMa		14p	F, psbM, rr, f of 2
3026	Gx	9 50.9	+ 28 33 s	Leo	2.2	13p	eeF, pS, lE, v diffic
3021	Gx	9 51.0	+ 33 33 s	LMi	1.7	13p	pB, pS, vlE, mbM, ∗10, 140°
568 I	Gx	9 51.1	+ 15 44 u	Leo	1.5	15p	F, pL, E pf, gbM
3038	Gx	9 51.3	− 32 45 s	Ant	2.6	13p	pB, pS, R
3037	Gx	9 51.4	− 27 02 r	Hya		14p	F, pS, R, lbM
569 I	Gx	9 51.5	+ 10 55 m	Leo	0.2	15p	vF, dif, vlbM
3035	Gx	9 51.8	− 6 49 r	Sex		13p	pF, pL, R, sev vF st inv
570 I	Gx	9 51.8	+ 15 46 z	Leo		16p	pF, S, R, gbM
3032	Gx	9 52.1	+ 29 14 s	Leo	2.5	11.9	F, S, sbM ∗12, bet 2 B st
3039	Gx	9 52.5	+ 2 09 s	Sex	1.3	14p	vF, S, iR
571 I	Gx	9 52.5	+ 15 46 m	Leo	0.3	15p	pB, S, R, N = 12.5
572 I	Gx	9 52.5	+ 15 50 m	Leo	0.4	15p	F, S, R, gbM
2517 I		9 52.7	− 33 44 d	Ant			eeF, S, R, susp
3040	Gx	9 53.0	+ 19 26 r	Leo		14p	vF, vS, bM, r
3041	Gx	9 53.1	+ 16 41 s	Leo	3.7	11.5	⊕, F, L, R, vglbM, rr, 2 B st sp
3045	Gx	9 53.2	− 18 39 r	Hya		14p	vF, pS, R, lbM, sp of 2
3046	∗	9 53.3	− 27 19 r	Ant			pF, R, sp of 2
3042	Gx	9 53.4	+ 0 42 r	Sex		14p	pB, S, vlE, gbM
3058	Gx	9 53.5	− 12 30 r	Hya		15p	eF, pL, D or biN, pos 210°, dist 20″; = IC 573
573 I	Gx	9 53.6	− 12 31 m	Hya	1.2	15p	eF, vS, R, vS∗ close
3044	Gx	9 53.7	+ 1 35 s	Sex	4.8	12.0	vF, vL, vmE 122°
3051	Gx	9 53.8	− 27 17 r	Ant		14p	pF, S, R, gbM, nf of 2
3050	−	9 54.3	− 10 22 r	Sex			vF, pS, vlE, gbMN
574 I	Gx	9 54.4	− 6 58 m	Sex	0.5	15p	pB, S, R, mbM, ∗ 12ˢ
3052	Gx	9 54.5	− 18 38 s	Hya	2.1	13p	F, pL, R, glbM, nf of 2
3054	Gx	9 54.5	− 25 42 s	Hya	3.9	12p	pB, L, irr oblong
3056	Gx	9 54.5	− 28 18 s	Ant	2.0	13p	pB, S, R, vgmbM, ∗11 att 204°
3047	Gx	9 54.6	− 1 18 r	Sex		14p	vF, S, R
575 I	Gx	9 54.6	− 6 51 a	Sex			F, S, R, gbM
2515 I	Gx	9 54.6	+ 37 24 u	LMi	1.1	15p	F, cS, E ns, r, biN?
3049	Gx	9 54.8	+ 9 16 r	Leo		13p	vF, vS, F∗ vnr
2516 I	Gx	9 54.8	+ 37 41 z	LMi		15p	F, S, R, gbM
3048	Gx	9 55.0	+ 16 28 r	Leo		15p	eF

NGC	Type	α_{2000}	δ_{2000}	Const.	Size	Mag.	Description
		h m	° ′		′		
576 I	Gx	9 55.1	+ 11 02 z	Leo		15p	vF, vS, R
2522 I	Gx	9 55.2	− 33 08 s	Ant	2.8	13p	vF, cL, R, ∗8 n, susp
2523 I	Gx	9 55.2	− 33 13 c	Ant	1.6		vF, vS, cE 20°, susp
3055	Gx	9 55.3	+ 4 16 s	Sex	2.2	12.1	F, pL, vlE, vgbM, rr, ∗7 f 92ˢ
3031	Gx	9 55.6	+ 69 04 s	UMa	25.7	6.9	! eB, eL, E 156°, gsvmbMBN; = M81
3053	Gx	9 55.6	+ 16 26 r	Leo		13p	vF, S, vlE, gbM
3064	Gx	9 55.6	− 6 22 r	Sex		14p	eF, vS, E 45°
3027	Gx	9 55.7	+ 72 12 s	UMa	4.7	12p	vF, vL, lE, r
3034	Gx	9 55.8	+ 69 41 s	UMa	11.2	8.4	vB, vL, vmE (ray); = M82
2518 I	Gx	9 56.0	+ 37 09 z	LMi		16p	F, S, R, lbM
2519 I	Gx	9 56.0	+ 34 02 z	LMi		16p	F, vS, R, dif
577 I	Gx	9 56.1	+ 10 30 u	Leo	0.7	14p	F, vS, iF, F∗ n
3043	Gx	9 56.2	+ 59 18 s	UMa	2.0	14p	cF, pS, lE, vgbM, ∗10 n 7′
3061	Gx	9 56.2	+ 75 52 s	Dra	2.0	14p	vF, pL, r
578 I	Gx	9 56.3	+ 10 29 u	Leo	1.3	15p	F, vS, R, lbM
3060	Gx	9 56.4	+ 16 51 r	Leo		14p	vF, cS, vlE, er
2520 I	Gx	9 56.4	+ 27 14 u	Leo	0.7	14p	F, vS, R, gbMN, r
3062	Gx	9 56.6	+ 1 26 r	Sex		15p	vF, vS, alm stellar
579 I		9 56.6	− 14 09 d	Hya			pF, pS, R
2526 I	Gx	9 57.1	− 32 15 c	Ant	1.9		vF, S, R, ∗7.5 nf
2521 I	Gx	9 57.3	+ 34 01 m	LMi	0.5	15p	F, S, dif
2524 I	Gx	9 57.5	+ 33 37 s	LMi	0.7	15p	F, vS, R, stell
3072	Gx	9 57.6	− 19 21 r	Hya		13p	vF, pS, lE, glbM
3076	Gx	9 57.7	− 18 11 r	Hya		14p	eF, S, R
3069	Gx	9 57.9	+ 10 27 r	Leo		15p	vF, vS; = IC 580
3070	Gx	9 58.0	+ 10 22 r	Leo		13p	pB, pS, R, gmbMN, am 3 st
580 I	Gx	9 58.0	+ 10 27 m	Leo	0.6	15p	pF, vS, iF
581 I	Gx	9 58.2	+ 15 56 u	Leo	1.1	15p	pB, S, dif, N = 13 inv
3067	Gx	9 58.4	+ 32 22 s	Leo	2.5	11.7	pB, pL, E 106°, gbM, ∗9, 74°, 4′
3078	Gx	9 58.4	− 26 56 s	Hya	1.9	11.1	pB, S, R, mbM
2525 I	Gx	9 58.4	+ 37 06 z	LMi		16p	F, S, R, gbM
3068	Gx	9 58.5	+ 28 53 r	Leo		15p	eeF, eS, stellar (?)
3071	Gx	9 58.9	+ 31 37 r	Leo		15p	neb ∗13
3082	Gx	9 58.9	− 30 20 r	Ant		14p	vF, S, R, D∗ att
3075	Gx	9 59.0	+ 14 25 r	Leo		14p	vvF, ∗14 att, ∗11 f
3084	Gx	9 59.0	− 27 08 r	Ant		14p	vF, S, R, ∗13 att sf
582 I	Gx	9 59.0	+ 17 49 u	Leo	1.1	15p	pB, S, iF, gbm
583 I	Gx	9 59.1	+ 17 50 u	Leo	1.0	15p	F, vS, gbM
584 I	Gx	9 59.1	+ 10 22 m	Leo	0.3	15p	eF, S, R, dif, 3070 p
2528 I	Gx	9 59.1	− 27 08 c	Ant	2.0		eeF, eS, R, v diffic, eF D∗ s; = 3084
3087	Gx	9 59.2	− 34 13 s	Ant	1.9	13p	pB, S, R, pmbM, bet 2 st
3081	Gx	9 59.5	− 22 50 s	Hya	2.2	12p	vF, cS, lbM, △ S st np; = IC 2529
2529 I	Gx	9 59.5	− 22 50 c	Hya	2.3		eeF, eS, eF∗ att; = 3081
3085	Gx	9 59.6	− 19 29 r	Hya		14p	vF, S, mE 90°
3089	Gx	9 59.6	− 28 20 s	Ant	1.9	13p	pF, pS, R, vS st inv
3074	Gx	9 59.7	+ 35 24 s	LMi	2.5	15p	vF, pL, iR, vgvlbM
585 I	Gx	9 59.7	+ 13 02 n	Leo	0.2	15p	∗13 in eF, S neb
3080	Gx	9 59.9	+ 13 03 r	Leo		14p	vF
3083	Gx	9 59.9	− 2 52 r	Sex		14p	eF, S, E
586 I	Gx	9 59.9	− 6 55 m	Sex	0.4	15p	F, vS, mottled
2531 I	Gx	9 59.9	− 29 37 c	Ant	6.3		eeF, pS, cE, 4 st n, nf, D∗ np
3095	Gx	10 00.1	− 31 33 s	Ant	3.2	13p	F, L, E, vgvlbM
2527 I	Gx	10 00.1	+ 38 10 z	LMi		15p	F, vS, R, N
2532 I	Gx	10 00.1	− 34 14 c	Ant	1.8		cB, S, stell N
3086	Gx	10 00.2	− 2 58 r	Sex		14p	eF, S, iR

NGC	Type	α_{2000}	δ_{2000}	Const.	Size	Mag.	Description
		h m	o ′		′		
3091	Gx	10 00.2	− 19 38 s	Hya	2.2	13p	pB, pS, iR, bM, p of 2
2533 I	Gx	10 00.5	− 31 15 c	Ant	1.7		cB, S, R
3090	Gx	10 00.6	− 2 57 r	Sex		14p	vF, vS
3096	Gx	10 00.7	− 19 39 r	Hya		15p	eF, R, lbM, f of 2
3100	Gx	10 00.7	− 31 40 s	Ant	2.8	13p	pB, pS, R, gpmbM
3103	Gx	10 00.7	− 31 40 D	Ant			eF, pL, R; = 3100
3105	OC	10 00.8	− 54 46 s	Vel	2	9.7	Cl, C, lE, st 13...16
3073	Gx	10 00.9	+ 55 37 s	UMa	1.5	13p	vF, S, vglbM
3092	Gx	10 00.9	− 3 00 r	Sex		14p	eF, S
3093	Gx	10 01.0	− 2 57 r	Sex		15p	eF, vS
3088	Gx	10 01.1	+ 22 24 r	Leo		15p	vF, S
3094	Gx	10 01.5	+ 15 47 r	Leo		13p	F, bM, *9 0′.5 sf
2530 I	Gx	10 01.5	+ 37 12 z	LMi		15p	F, vS, stell
2534 I	Gx	10 01.5	− 34 07 c	Ant	2.8		cB, S, R
3063	D*	10 01.6	+ 72 08 r	UMa			F, pS, R
3101	Gx	10 01.7	− 2 59 r	Sex		15p	eF
3065	Gx	10 01.9	+ 72 10 s	UMa	2.0	12.0	pF, vS, R, bM, *11 nr
3079	Gx	10 02.0	+ 55 41 s	UMa	7.6	10.6	vB, L, mE 135°
3066	Gx	10 02.2	+ 72 07 s	UMa	1.2	12.9	vF, vS, vglbM
588 I	Gx	10 02.2	+ 3 03 u	Sex	1.1	15p	F, S, R, mottled
3098	Gx	10 02.3	+ 24 43 s	Leo	2.6	12.0	pB, S, E 85°, psbMN
3108	Gx	10 02.6	− 31 41 r	Ant		13p	F, S, R, glbM
3099	Gx	10 02.7	+ 32 42 r	LMi		15p	eF, S
3114	OC	10 02.7	− 60 07 s	Car	35	4.2	Cl, eL, lC, B, st 9...14
587 I		10 03.0	− 2 24 F	Sex			F, pL, R
3109	Gx	10 03.1	− 26 09 s	Hya	14.5	10p	cF, vL, vmE 82°, lbM
3077	Gx	10 03.3	+ 68 44 s	UMa	4.6	9.9	cB, cL, mbM, R with ray
3107	Gx	10 03.3	+ 13 38 d	Leo		13p	pF, pL, iR, *8, 148°, 112″
2536 I	Gx	10 03.5	− 33 57 c	Ant	1.9		F, S, E 50°, cbM
3149	Gx	10 03.8	− 80 25 c	Cha	2.1		F, S, lE, vlbM, *15 inv
3104	Gx	10 03.9	+ 40 45 s	LMi	3.2	13p	eF, pL, E, vF* inv
3106	Gx	10 03.9	+ 31 11 r	LMi		14p	F, S, R, sbM
2537 I	Gx	10 03.9	− 27 34 s	Ant	2.7	12.2	eeF, L, cE
2538 I	Gx	10 03.9	− 34 48 c	Ant	1.6		vF, vS, R, cbM
3112	Gx	10 04.0	− 20 46 r	Hya			eF, eS, R; neb?
3110	Gx	10 04.1	− 6 28 r	Sex		13p	F, vS, iR, r
3097	−	10 04.3	+ 60 08 r	UMa			neb*? 2′ np 3102
2539 I	Gx	10 04.3	− 31 22 c	Ant	1.7		cF, vS, cE 30°, vmbM
3113	Gx	10 04.4	− 28 27 s	Ant	3.2	14p	eF, L, △ 2 st 8m
589 I		10 04.4	− 5 41 d	Sex			vF, vS, biN?
2535 I	Gx	10 04.5	+ 38 03 m	LMi	0.7	14p	pB, pS, E 110°, gbM, r
3102	Gx	10 04.6	+ 60 07 r	UMa		14p	vF, vS, R, bM, *11, 142°
3115	Gx	10 05.2	− 7 43 s	Sex	8.3	9.2	vB, L, vmE 46°, vgsmbMEN
3120	Gx	10 05.4	− 34 13 r	Ant			F, pS, R, gbM
3057	Gx	10 05.6	+ 80 17 s	Dra	2.5	14p	eF, pL, vlbM, 2 S st s
3136	Gx	10 05.8	− 67 23 s	Car	2.5	11.0	pB, pS, R, gbM, *13 n
2541 I	Gx	10 05.8	− 17 27 m	Hya	1.2	14p	F, eE 5°, vmbM
3128	Gx	10 05.9	− 16 07 r	Hya		14p	eF, pL, mE 170°, lbM
590 I	Gx	10 05.9	+ 0 38 u	Sex	1.1	14p	F, dif; neb D*?
3111	Gx	10 06.2	+ 47 16 r	UMa		14p	pB, S, R, smbM *12
3117	Gx	10 06.2	+ 2 54 r	Sex		14p	vF, vS, R, S* inv
3127	Gx	10 06.3	− 16 07 r	Hya		14p	eF, pL, mE 45°
3122	Gx	10 06.5	− 6 32 r	Sex			F, S, lE, er
3116	Gx	10 06.6	+ 31 06 r	LMi		15p	neb *13
3119	Gx	10 06.6	+ 14 19 r	Leo		15p	vF

NGC	Type	α_{2000}	δ_{2000}	Const.	Size	Mag.	Description
		h m	° ′		′		
3125	Gx	10 06.6	− 29 56 s	Ant	1.5	13p	cF, S, R, vgbM
2545 I		10 06.6	− 33 51 d	Ant			eF, eS, cE 25°, 2 st
3124	Gx	10 06.7	− 19 13 s	Hya	3.2	12p	F, pL, R, lbM, D∗ s
3121	Gx	10 06.8	+ 14 23 r	Leo		14p	pF, pL, glbM, ∗9.5 np
2540 I	Gx	10 06.9	+ 31 28 m	LMi	0.8	15p	F, vS, R, gbMN
3123	−	10 07.0	+ 0 04 r	Sex			neb, no description
3132	Pl	10 07.0	− 40 26 s	Vel	0.8	8p	!! ◯ , vB, vL, lE ∗9 M, 4ˢd
2546 I		10 07.1	− 33 15 d	Ant			vF, vS, R, bet 2 st
3133	Gx	10 07.2	− 11 57 r	Hya			eF, vS, R
3118	Gx	10 07.3	+ 33 02 r	LMi		14p	S group of vF st in vF neb
591 I	Gx	10 07.5	+ 12 16 s	Leo	1.4	14p	pF, S, R
592 I	Gx	10 07.9	− 2 30 u	Sex	1.0	14p	F, S, R, dif
2542 I		10 07.9	+ 34 10 d	LMi			F, pS, glbM
2548 I	Gx	10 07.9	− 35 14 c	Ant	2.4		eF, vS, R, bM, dif
3126	Gx	10 08.2	+ 31 52 r	LMi		13p	F, S, lE, N = ∗15
3130	Gx	10 08.2	+ 9 59 r	Leo		14p	eF, S, psbM, ∗5 sf
593 I	Gx	10 08.3	− 2 32 u	Sex	0.8	14p	F, S, R, gbM
3129	−	10 08.4	+ 18 25 r	Leo			eF, cS, vlE, r
2543 I	Gx	10 08.4	+ 37 50 z	LMi		16p	F, S, R, N, r
2544 I	Gx	10 08.4	+ 33 21 z	LMi		15p	F, S, dif
594 I	Gx	10 08.6	− 0 40 u	Sex	1.1	15p	F, S, R, gbM, r
3131	Gx	10 08.7	+ 18 15 r	Leo		14p	pB, pS, pmE, gbM
2554 I	Gx	10 08.9	− 67 02 c	Car	2.7		cF, S, cE 10°, N, spir
3138	Gx	10 09.1	− 11 58 r	Hya		15p	eF, vS, R, 1st of 2
3137	Gx	10 09.2	− 29 04 t	Ant	6.8		vF, S, lE
3141	−	10 09.3	− 16 38 r	Hya			eF, S, R, 2nd of 2
2553 I	Pl	10 09.3	− 62 37 s	Car	0.2	13p	◯ , stellar
3134	−	10 09.5	+ 12 20 r	Leo			vF, disc
3140	Gx	10 09.5	− 16 37 s	Hya	1.4	14p	eF, pS, R, sbMN, 1st of 2
3195	Pl	10 09.5	− 80 52 s	Cha	0.6		! ◯ , pB, S, lE, 13ˢd, 3 S st nr
595 I	Gx	10 09.7	+ 11 00 z	Leo		15p	F, vS, R, lbM
3139	Gx	10 10.1	− 11 47 r	Hya		15p	eF, vS, R, 2nd of 2
3142	Gx	10 10.1	− 8 29 r	Sex		14p	F, R
3143	Gx	10 10.1	− 12 35 s	Hya	0.9	14p	F, S
2547 I		10 10.1	+ 36 31 d	LMi			F, S, R, dif
3145	Gx	10 10.2	− 12 26 s	Hya	3.3	12p	F, pL, mE, vgslbM, λ Hya np
597 I		10 10.2	− 6 54 d	Sex			F, vS, R
2549 I		10 10.2	+ 36 28 d	LMi			F, S, R, gvlbM
2550 I	Gx	10 10.4	+ 27 57 u	LMi	1.1	15p	F, cS, R, dif
596 I	Gx	10 10.6	+ 10 02 m	Leo	0.8	15p	F, S, dif
2551 I	Gx	10 10.7	+ 24 25 u	Leo	1.3	15p	F, vS, R, stell
2552 I	Gx	10 10.8	− 34 51 c	Ant	1.8		cB, S, R, bM
3135	Gx	10 10.9	+ 45 58 r	UMa		14p	F, S, R, gbM
3146	Gx	10 11.2	− 20 52 r	Hya		13p	eF, S, R, gbM
2555 I	Gx	10 11.7	− 31 39 c	Ant	2.4		eF, vS, eE 45°, cbM; = 3157
3157	Gx	10 11.8	− 31 38 A	Ant			vF, pS, E, ∗8-9 sp
2556 I	Gx	10 12.6	− 34 44 c	Ant	2.1		eF, S, stell N
3156	Gx	10 12.7	+ 3 08 s	Sex	2.1	13p	F, cS, R, psbM, ∗9-10 sf 2′
3153	Gx	10 12.9	+ 12 40 s	Leo	2.3	13p	eF, pL, vlE, r, st inv
3154	Gx	10 13.1	+ 17 03 r	Leo		14p	F, S, R, lbM
598 I		10 13.1	+ 43 14 d	UMa			vF, vS, R, bM, alm stell
599 I	Gx	10 13.3	− 5 38 m	Sex	1.0	14p	pF, S, vlbM
3148	Gx	10 13.4	+ 50 28 r	UMa		16p	∗7 in photosphere 2′ or 3′ d
3150	Gx	10 13.4	+ 38 41 r	LMi		15p	vF, S
3151	Gx	10 13.5	+ 38 37 s	LMi	1.0	15p	vF, vS

NGC	Type	α_{2000}	δ_{2000}	Const.	Size	Mag.	Description
		h m	° ′		′		
3162	Gx	10 13.5	+ 22 44 s	Leo	3.1	11.6	pF, cL, R, vglbM, r, S∗ inv
3165	Gx	10 13.5	+ 3 23 s	Sex	1.6	15p	vF, mE 0°, 1st of 3
3152	Gx	10 13.6	+ 38 50 v	LMi	1.0		eF, vS, iR, eF∗ close sp
3158	Gx	10 13.8	+ 38 46 s	LMi	2.3	11.8	cB, cS, R, psbM, r
3166	Gx	10 13.8	+ 3 26 s	Sex	5.2	10.6	B, pS, R, psmbM, 2nd of 3
3159	Gx	10 13.9	+ 38 39 s	LMi	1.3	13.4	vF, vS, stellar
3160	Gx	10 13.9	+ 38 52 r	LMi		15p	vF, vS, lE
3161	Gx	10 14.0	+ 38 39 v	LMi	1.0		vF, vS
3163	Gx	10 14.1	+ 38 39 s	LMi	1.4	13.1	F, S, R, gbM
3169	Gx	10 14.2	+ 3 28 s	Sex	4.8	10.5	B, pL, vlE, pgmbM, ∗11, 78°, 80″, 3rd of 3
3197	Gx	10 14.4	+ 77 49 r	Dra		14p	vF, vS [place??]
3173	Gx	10 14.5	− 27 41 r	Ant		14p	eF, S, R, 2 B st f
3167	−	10 14.6	+ 29 36 r	LMi			F, S; vS Cl of vF st?
3175	Gx	10 14.7	− 28 52 s	Ant	4.8	11.3	cB, L, mE 51°, vglbM
2558 I	Gx	10 14.7	− 34 20 c	Ant	1.6		cF, vS, cE 10°, cbM
2559 I	Gx	10 14.8	− 34 04 c	Ant	1.8		eF, S, lE 10°, cbM
3164	Gx	10 15.2	+ 56 41 r	UMa		14p	eF, S, R, vglbM
3176	−	10 15.3	− 19 01 r	Hya			eF, pS, iR; neb?
3144	Gx	10 15.5	+ 74 13 s	Dra	1.4	14p	vF, S, R, ∗13 att f
3171	Gx	10 15.6	− 20 39 F	Hya			eF, S, R, gbM
3170	−	10 16.1	+ 46 36 r	UMa			F, S, R
3178	Gx	10 16.1	− 15 47 r	Hya		13p	pB, pL, gpmbM
2557 I	Gx	10 16.1	+ 38 05 m	LMi	0.3	15p	vF, vS, R
2560 I	Gx	10 16.3	− 33 34 c	Ant	4.1		eF, pS, am 4 st
3168	Gx	10 16.4	+ 60 14 r	UMa		14p	F, psbM, stellar, ∗7-8 np 5′
3177	Gx	10 16.6	+ 21 07 s	Leo	1.7	12.3	cF, S, R, psbM
3147	Gx	10 16.9	+ 73 24 s	Dra	4.0	10.7	vB, L, R, vgvsvmbM
3199	Nb	10 17.1	− 57 55 s	Car	22		! vB, vL, falcate, D∗ inv
600 I	Gx	10 17.2	− 3 30 t	Sex	2.3		F, pS, R, gbM
3155	Gx	10 17.6	+ 74 21 r	Dra		14p	vF, S, R
3185	Gx	10 17.6	+ 21 41 s	Leo	2.3	12.2	pF, pL, gmbM
3186	Gx	10 17.6	+ 6 57 r	Leo		15p	pF, vS, gbM, sev F st nr
3201	Gb	10 17.6	− 46 25 s	Vel	18.2	6.8	⊕, vL, iR, lCM, st 13...16
3187	Gx	10 17.8	+ 21 52 s	Leo	3.3	13.1	vF, E
3211	Pl	10 17.8	− 62 40 s	Car	0.2	12p	plan = ∗10, R, am 150 st
3179	Gx	10 18.0	+ 41 06 r	UMa		14p	S, R, bMN, in line with 2 st
3180	−	10 18.1	+ 41 25 r	UMa			vF, E, connected with 3184
3190	Gx	10 18.1	+ 21 50 s	Leo	4.6	11.0	B, pS, E, psbMN
3181	−	10 18.2	+ 41 24 r	UMa			vF, E, connected with 3184
3189	Gx	10 18.2	+ 21 50 u	Leo	4.5	12p	vvF, mE, parallel to 3190
601 I	Gx	10 18.2	+ 7 02 m	Leo	0.6	15p	vF, vS, dif, sbM
3184	Gx	10 18.3	+ 41 25 s	UMa	6.9	9.8	pB, vL, R, vgbM
602 I	Gx	10 18.3	+ 7 03 v	Leo	1.1		pB, S, E ns
3193	Gx	10 18.4	+ 21 54 s	Leo	2.8	10.9	B, S, vlE, pslbM, ∗9.5 354°, 80″
3200	Gx	10 18.6	− 17 59 s	Hya	4.8	12p	pB, E 160°, bMN
3196	Gx	10 18.8	+ 27 40 r	Leo		15p	eeF, pS, lE
2562 I	Gx	10 18.8	+ 16 08 m	Leo	0.6	15p	F, S, gbM, dif
2563 I	Gx	10 18.9	− 32 36 c	Ant	1.6		eF, vS, eE 110°, eF∗ s
3192	Gx	10 19.0	+ 46 27 A	UMa			eF, vS; = 3191
3191	Gx	10 19.1	+ 46 28 s	UMa	0.8	14p	F, S, R, bM
2561 I	Gx	10 19.1	+ 34 40 u	LMi	1.1	15p	F, S, E 200°, gbM
603 I	Gx	10 19.4	− 5 39 m	Sex	0.4	14p	F, vS, R, N = 13.5
3182	Gx	10 19.5	+ 58 12 s	UMa	2.3	13p	cB, cL, iR, vgbM
3203	Gx	10 19.6	− 26 42 s	Hya	3.0	13p	pB, S, cE, gbM
3188	Gx	10 19.7	+ 57 25 s	UMa	1.1	15p	vF, pL, r

NGC	Type	α_{2000}	δ_{2000}	Const.	Size	Mag.	Description
		h m	° ′		′		
3208	Gx	10 19.7	− 25 51 s	Hya	1.9	14p	eF, pL, iR, gbM
3198	Gx	10 19.9	+ 45 33 s	UMa	8.3	10.4	pB, vL, mE 45°, vgbM
3204	Gx	10 20.2	+ 27 49 r	Leo		15p	eF, pL, gbM
3202	Gx	10 20.5	+ 43 01 s	UMa	1.4	14p	cF, S, R, vgbM, 1st of 3
3209	Gx	10 20.6	+ 25 29 r	Leo		14p	F, S, R, has a *
3174	−	10 20.8	+ 75 09 r	Dra			cF, S, stellar, S* f nr; = 3144?
3205	Gx	10 20.8	+ 42 57 r	UMa		14p	cF, S, R, vgbM, 2nd of 3
3207	Gx	10 21.0	+ 42 58 r	UMa		14p	cF, S, R, stellar, 3rd of 3
3213	Gx	10 21.3	+ 19 39 s	Leo	1.2	14p	vF, vS, R, r
2565 I	Gx	10 21.3	+ 27 56 v	LMi			F, vS, R, stell
3217	−	10 21.4	+ 10 53 r	Leo			vF disc
2564 I		10 21.4	+ 36 27 d	LMi			F, S, R, gbM stell N
3223	Gx	10 21.6	− 34 16 s	Ant	4.1	12p	pB, vL, vlE, pslbMN; = IC 2571
3224	Gx	10 21.6	− 34 42 r	Ant			vF, pS, R, vgmbM
2570 I	Gx	10 21.6	− 33 37 c	Ant	1.3		eF, eS, mE 150°, 3 st sf
2571 I	Gx	10 21.6	− 34 16 c	Ant	4.3		vF, cS, R, mbM, *9 f 9ˢ; = 3223
3216	Gx	10 21.7	+ 23 54 r	Leo		15p	vF, pS, R, bM
3183	Gx	10 21.8	+ 74 10 s	Dra	2.5	13p	F, pL, E, lbM
3206	Gx	10 21.8	+ 56 56 s	UMa	3.0	12p	pB, cL, E, vglbM
3228	OC	10 21.8	− 51 43 s	Vel	18	6.0	Cl, 9 L and a few S st
3233	Gx	10 22.0	− 22 16 r	Hya		14p	eF, pL, iF, stell N
2567 I	Gx	10 22.0	+ 24 39 m	Leo	0.7	16p	F, vS, R, r
3221	Gx	10 22.3	+ 21 34 s	Leo	3.3	14p	eF, mE, ray
605 I	Gx	10 22.4	+ 1 12 u	Sex	0.7	14p	f, S, R, gbM
2566 I	Gx	10 22.4	+ 36 36 m	LMi	0.7	15p	F, S, R, gbM, r
2568 I		10 22.5	+ 36 38 d	LMi			F, S, R, N, r
3222	Gx	10 22.6	+ 19 53 s	Leo	1.3	12.8	F, lbM, rr; biN?
3219	Gx	10 22.7	+ 38 34 r	LMi		15p	eF, S, R, lbM
2569 I		10 22.9	+ 24 36 d	Leo			R, vS, R, stell
3194	−	10 23.0	+ 74 47 r	Dra			vF, vS; = 3155?
3214	Gx	10 23.1	+ 57 02 s	UMa	1.0	15p	cB, vS, R, sbM, 5′ p 3220
3226	Gx	10 23.4	+ 19 54 s	Leo	2.8	11.4	pB, cL, R, D with 3227, pos 159°, 138″
3229	D*	10 23.4	+ 0 04 A	Sex			F
3227	Gx	10 23.5	+ 19 52 s	Leo	5.6	10.8	pB, cL, R, D with 3226
606 I	Gx	10 23.5	+ 10 58 m	Leo	0.4	15p	vF, vS, R, dif
2573 I	Gx	10 23.5	− 35 27 c	Ant	1.5		eF, vS, eE 0°
3220	Gx	10 23.7	+ 57 02 s	UMa	1.6	14p	pF, cL, E 92°, *9 f 9′.5
3230	Gx	10 23.7	+ 12 33 r	Leo		14p	pF, pS, sbM *14, *9-10 s 19″
604 I		10 23.8	+ 57 02 d	UMa			eeF, vS, vmE (sev eF st in line?)
607 I	Gx	10 24.2	+ 16 45 u	Leo	1.5	15p	eeF, pS, R, v diffic, * sp
3232	Gx	10 24.3	+ 28 01 r	LMi		15p	eF, *11 p 150″, ls, p of 2
3241	Gx	10 24.3	− 32 29 s	Ant	1.5	12.7	F, pmE, glbM, *11 np
608 I	Gx	10 24.3	− 6 02 m	Sex	0.7	15p	F, S, R
3240	Gx	10 24.5	− 21 47 r	Hya		14p	eF, S, R, * nr
3242	Pl	10 24.8	− 18 38 s	Hya	20.8	9p	! ◯ , vB, lE 147°, 45″ d, blue
3234		10 24.9	+ 27 01 D	Leo			pB, pS, R, psbM
3235	Gx	10 24.9	+ 28 01 r	LMi		14p	F, S, f of 2
2572 I	Gx	10 25.0	+ 28 06 u	LMi	1.0	16p	pF, S, iF
3225	Gx	10 25.1	+ 58 09 s	UMa	2.3	13p	cF, pL, lE, vgbM
3239	Gx	10 25.1	+ 17 10 s	Leo	5.2	12p	vF, *9 inv nr M
2575 I		10 25.4	− 32 39 d	Ant			eF, vS, R
3244	Gx	10 25.5	− 39 50 v	Ant	1.9		vF, *11 n 90″
609 I	Gx	10 25.5	− 2 13 u	Sex	1.6	14p	F, pL, R
3237	Gx	10 25.8	+ 39 39 r	UMa		14p	vF, vS, R, pgbM
3247	C+N	10 25.9	− 57 56 s	Car	7	7.6	st inv in neb

NGC	Type	α_{2000}	δ_{2000}	Const.	Size	Mag.	Description
		h m	o ′		′		
2576 I		10 26.0	− 32 55 d	Ant			F, S, R
3249	Gx	10 26.3	− 34 58 r	Ant			eF, pL, R, vgvlbM
3243	Gx	10 26.4	− 2 38 r	Sex		14p	vF, S, lE, bet 2 st
3218	−	10 26.5	+ 74 39 r	Dra			cB, cL, er [place??]
3250	Gx	10 26.5	− 39 57 s	Ant	3.2	11.0	pB, pL, R, vgpsbM, *13, 45°
3255	OC	10 26.5	− 60 40 s	Car	2	11.0	Cl, pS, vC, st 15
610 I	Gx	10 26.5	+ 20 14 v	Leo	2.1		eeF, pS, cE, e diffic; = IC 611
611 I	Gx	10 26.5	+ 20 14 x	Leo			eF, S, lE
3231	−	10 26.7	+ 66 48 r	UMa			Cl, cL, P, lC, st 10...12
3238	Gx	10 26.7	+ 57 14 s	UMa	1.6	14p	F, S, R, pslbM
3246	Gx	10 26.7	+ 3 52 s	Sex	2.3	13p	eF, S, R, 2 st △ , *6, 300°, 8′
3236	Gx	10 26.8	+ 61 16 r	UMa		15p	eF, vS, psbM, 2 st 11-12 f
614 I	Gx	10 26.9	− 3 27 m	Sex	0.7	15p	vF, dif
612 I	Gx	10 27.1	+ 11 03 m	Leo	0.3	15p	F, vS, dif, vlbM
613 I	Gx	10 27.1	+ 11 01 m	Leo	0.3	15p	F, vS, R
3210	Gx	10 27.2	+ 79 51 a	Dra			stellar, 1st of 3 in line, 1′ apart
3245	Gx	10 27.3	+ 28 30 s	LMi	3.2	10.8	vB, pL, E 0°, smbMEN
615 I	Gx	10 27.3	+ 11 05 u	Leo	1.4	15p	vF, S, R
2578 I	Gx	10 27.4	− 33 53 c	Ant	1.4		eF, vS, eE 135°
2581 I	OC	10 27.4	− 57 38 s	Car	8	4.3	Cl, around *5.4m
3248	Gx	10 27.8	+ 22 50 r	Leo		14p	pB, S, R, psbM
3256	Gx	10 27.8	− 43 54 s	Vel	3.5	11.3	cB, S, R, gmbM
2577 I	Gx	10 28.0	+ 32 46 m	LMi	0.5	15p	F, cS, r, *12 nr
3212	Gx	10 28.1	+ 79 47 r	Dra		14p	vF, S, 2nd of 3
2580 I	Gx	10 28.3	− 31 31 c	Ant	2.1		cB, S, bM
2574 I	Gx	10 28.4	+ 68 25 s	UMa	12.3	10.6	vF, vL, iF
3253	Gx	10 28.5	+ 12 42 s	Leo	1.4	14p	vF, pS, R
3257	Gx	10 28.8	− 35 40 s	Ant	1.1		vF, vS, R, psbM, 1st of 4
3258	Gx	10 28.9	− 35 36 s	Ant	1.8	11.7	cF, S, R, pslbM, 2nd of 4
3215	Gx	10 29.0	+ 79 46 r	Dra		14p	vF, S, 3rd of 3
3261	Gx	10 29.0	− 44 39 s	Vel	4.1	12p	F, S, R, am st
3260	Gx	10 29.1	− 35 36 s	Ant	1.3		vvF, vS, R, pslbM, 3rd of 4
3262	Gx	10 29.2	− 44 10 v	Vel	1.2		eF, S, R
2582 I	Gx	10 29.2	− 30 21 c	Ant	1.5		bM, indistinct (corner of plate)
3251	Gx	10 29.3	+ 26 05 r	Leo		14p	vF, pL, 3 B st sp; = IC 2579
3254	Gx	10 29.3	+ 29 30 s	LMi	5.1	11.5	cB, L, mE 45°, psmbMN
3263	Gx	10 29.3	− 44 08 v	Vel	3.6		F, S, mE 280°, psbM
2579 I		10 29.3	+ 26 07 x	Leo			pB, pL, E 260°, bM; = 3251?
3267	Gx	10 29.8	− 35 19 s	Ant	2.4	13p	eF, vS, R, 1st of 4
2584 I	Gx	10 29.9	− 34 55 c	Ant	1.5		cB, bM
3268	Gx	10 30.0	− 35 20 s	Ant	2.0	11.8	F, S, R, 2nd of 4
3269	Gx	10 30.0	− 35 13 s	Ant	3.1	13p	F, S, R, bM, 3rd of 4
2585 I	Gx	10 30.4	− 35 22 c	Ant	2.7		cB, bM; = 3271
3271	Gx	10 30.5	− 35 22 s	Ant	2.3	11.7	pF, S, E, pmbM, 4th of 4
3273	Gx	10 30.5	− 35 37 s	Ant	2.3	13p	vF, vS, R, pslbM, 4th of 4
3275	Gx	10 30.9	− 36 44 s	Ant	2.8	12p	F, L, vlE, pslbM
2586 I	Gx	10 31.0	− 28 43 c	Hya	1.6		pF, vS, R, 4 st nr sp
2587 I	Gx	10 31.0	− 34 34 c	Ant	2.4		cB, bM
3265	Gx	10 31.1	+ 28 48 s	LMi	1.2	14p	pF, S, R, psbM, * sf
3276	Gx	10 31.1	− 39 57 r	Ant			F, S, *8 p
2583 I	Gx	10 31.2	+ 26 03 m	Leo	0.3	15p	F, vS, R, stell
3270	Gx	10 31.5	+ 24 51 r	Leo		14p	cF, vS, E, glbM
3278	Gx	10 31.6	− 39 57 r	Ant			F, S, R, D* nf
2588 I	Gx	10 31.8	− 30 23 c	Ant	1.5		eeF, pL, R, D* nr sf
3281	Gx	10 31.9	− 34 51 s	Ant	3.3	11.7	eF, pL, E, glbM

NGC	Type	α_{2000}	δ_{2000}	Const.	Size	Mag.	Description
		h m	° ′		′		
2589 I		10 32.1	− 24 03 d	Hya			eeF, eS, v diffic, *13 sf, *9 p 1′
3272	Gx	10 32.2	+ 28 27 r	LMi			F, vS, iR, 3277 nf
3274	Gx	10 32.3	+ 27 40 s	Leo	2.2	12.8	F, pL, R, glbM, D* f
3282	Gx	10 32.3	− 22 18 r	Hya		14p	eF* in eF, vS neb, bet 2 st
3264	Gx	10 32.4	+ 56 05 s	UMa	3.4	13p	eF, bet 2 S st
3259	Gx	10 32.6	+ 65 03 s	UMa	2.3	13p	F, S, R, gbM
3280	Gx	10 32.6	− 12 39 r	Hya		16p	F, biN
3295	Gx	10 32.7	− 12 38 D	Hya			eF, pL, bM, D or st inv; = 3280
3296	Gx	10 32.7	− 12 43 r	Hya			eF, pS, R, bM
616 I	Gx	10 32.8	+ 15 52 u	Leo	1.1	15p	F, pS, R
617 I	Gx	10 32.8	− 12 38 m	Hya	0.1	16p	vF, vS, R, bM
618 I		10 32.8	− 12 44 d	Hya			F, S, E pf, lbM
3277	Gx	10 32.9	+ 28 31 s	LMi	2.0	11.7	cB, cS, R, pgmbM
3283		10 32.9	− 46 05 r	Vel			pF, S, R, gbM
3266	Gx	10 33.3	+ 64 45 s	UMa	1.7	14p	cF, vS, R, psmbM *
621 I	Gx	10 33.3	+ 2 40 z	Sex		15p	F, S, R
619 I		10 33.5	+ 12 33 d	Leo			eeF, S, R, 3 F st f
620 I	Gx	10 33.5	+ 11 53 z	Leo		15p	vF, vS
3285	Gx	10 33.6	− 27 27 s	Hya	2.5	13p	pB, S, lE, gbM, 1st of 9
3289	Gx	10 34.2	− 35 20 s	Ant	2.2		eF, vS, R
2596 I	Gx	10 34.2	− 73 14 c	Car	1.4		eF, pS, bM
3252	Gx	10 34.4	+ 73 46 s	Dra	2.1	14p	eF, pS, mE, r
3279	Gx	10 34.6	+ 11 12 r	Leo		14p	F, mE
622 I	Gx	10 34.6	+ 11 11 u	Leo	2.9	14p	vF, pS, E, * 9ˢ
3287	Gx	10 34.8	+ 21 39 s	Leo	2.2	13p	F, pL, D* p 24ˢ, s 4′
3290	Gx	10 35.1	− 17 16 s	Hya	1.4	14p	eF, S, lE 0°, gbM, B* n 6′
2592 I	Gx	10 35.1	− 43 42 c	Vel	1.9		F, pL, cE 15°, spir?; = 3366
3366	Gx	10 35.2	− 43 41 r	Vel			F, E, gbM, *6-7 vnr
3297	−	10 35.4	− 12 42 r	Hya			eF, S, iR
623 I	Gx	10 35.4	+ 3 33 u	Sex	1.1	15p	F, S, R
3292	Gx	10 35.6	− 6 11 r	Sex		14p	vF, vS, lE
3293	C+N	10 35.8	− 58 14 s	Car	40	4.7	Cl, B, Ri, pL
3302	Gx	10 35.8	− 32 22 r	Ant		14p	eF, S, R
3284	*	10 36.0	+ 58 32 r	UMa			eF, vS
3291	Gx	10 36.1	+ 37 15 h	LMi	1.0	14p	*13 inv in vF neb
2594 I	Gx	10 36.1	− 24 19 c	Hya	2.2		eF, pS, R, bet 2 wide D st
3286	Gx	10 36.3	+ 58 37 r	UMa		14p	vF, pS, R, pslbM
3294	Gx	10 36.3	+ 37 20 s	LMi	3.3	11.7	cB, L, mE 135°, glbM
3305	Gx	10 36.3	− 27 10 s	Hya		14p	vF, S, R, 2nd of 9
3307	Gx	10 36.3	− 27 32 s	Hya	1.0	16p	eeF, 3rd of 9
624 I	Gx	10 36.3	− 8 21 v	Sex	3.3		F, vS, R
2590 I	Gx	10 36.3	+ 26 58 u	Leo	1.1	15p	F, S, R, gbM, *12 close
2593 I		10 36.3	− 12 43 d	Hya			eF, cS; *?
3288	Gx	10 36.4	+ 58 33 s	UMa	1.2	15p	eF, cS, R, vglbM
3299	Gx	10 36.4	+ 12 42 s	Leo	2.1	13p	eF, cL, R, vgbM, r
3308	Gx	10 36.4	− 27 26 s	Hya	2.0	12.2	F, S, R, 4th of 9
625 I		10 36.5	− 23 55 d	Hya			eF, pL, E 110°, dif
3300	Gx	10 36.6	+ 14 10 s	Leo	2.1	13p	cF, cS, R, pmbM, r, am B st
3309	Gx	10 36.6	− 27 31 s	Hya	1.9	11.9	B, L, R, p of Dneb, 5th of 9
2591 I	Gx	10 36.6	+ 35 02 u	LMi	1.5	14p	F, cS, E 200°
3311	Gx	10 36.7	− 27 32 s	Hya	2.5	11.6	B, L, R, f of Dneb, 6th of 9
3301	Gx	10 36.9	+ 21 53 s	Leo	3.6	11.4	cB, S, lE 53°, psbM, r
3760		10 36.9	+ 21 53 D	Leo			B, pS, mbMN = *13, *11 p 4ˢ, s 175″; = 3301
3312	Gx	10 37.0	− 27 34 s	Hya	3.6	12p	cF, E, gbM, 7th of 9; = IC 629
626 I	Gx	10 37.0	− 7 01 m	Sex		14p	F, S, R, r

NGC	Type	α_{2000}	δ_{2000}	Const.	Size	Mag.	Description
		h m	° ′		′		
629 I	Gx	10 37.0	− 27 34 c	Hya	3.0		vF, vS st inv, Cl?; = 3312
3303	Gx	10 37.1	+ 18 08 s	Leo	3.0	15p	vF, vS, vlE, glbM, r
3298	Gx	10 37.2	+ 50 06 r	UMa		15p	vF, pS, iE
3306	Gx	10 37.2	+ 12 39 s	Leo	1.5	14p	F, S, R
3314	Gx	10 37.2	− 27 41 s	Hya	2.0	14p	8th of 9 neb
3315		10 37.3	− 27 46 A	Hya			vF, pL, iR, gvlbM, * 1′ np; = 3314
3318	Gx	10 37.3	− 41 38 s	Vel	2.6	12p	cF, pL, pmE, lbM
3324	C+N	10 37.3	− 58 38 s	Car	16	6.7	pB, vvL, iF, D* inv
627 I	Gx	10 37.3	− 3 22 m	Sex	0.4	14p	F, S, r
3317	Gx	10 37.4	− 27 29 m	Hya	0.6	14p	neb*, 5′ n of 3316
2599 I		10 37.4	− 58 37 d	Car			*8.5 in neb, 3324 f 6ˢ, 6′ s
3313	Gx	10 37.5	− 25 19 r	Hya		13p	eF, pS, iR, gbMN, *15 s 3″
3304	Gx	10 37.6	+ 37 27 s	LMi	1.7	14p	vF, cS, psbM, er
3316	Gx	10 37.6	− 27 36 s	Hya	1.2	15p	F, S, R, bM, 9th of 9
628 I	Gx	10 37.6	+ 5 35 u	Sex	1.0	15p	vF, vS, iF
2595 I		10 37.6	− 11 07 d	Sex			cB, eS, R, alm stell
2597 I	Gx	10 37.8	− 27 05 c	Hya	3.0		pB, pS, D* nr p
630 I	Gx	10 38.5	− 7 10 m	Sex		13p	F, eS, stellar, *9.5 sp 1′.5
3330	OC	10 38.6	− 54 09 s	Vel	7	7.4	Cl, P, st 9...
3310	Gx	10 38.7	+ 53 30 s	UMa	3.6	10.9	cB, pL, R, vg, vsmbMN 15″
3321	Gx	10 38.8	− 11 39 t	Hya	2.7		eF, pS, mE 160°, * np end
3322		10 38.8	− 11 39 D	Hya			F, iF, * p; = 3321
3331	Gx	10 39.0	− 23 49 D	Hya		14p	vF, S, vlE 0°
631 I		10 39.0	− 7 03 d	Sex			vF, vS, dif
3319	Gx	10 39.2	+ 41 41 s	UMa	6.8	11.3	cF, L, iE, mb, s of M
632 I	Gx	10 39.2	− 0 25 u	Sex	1.0	15p	F, S, R, gbM
3325	Gx	10 39.3	− 0 13 r	Sex		14p	F, vS, vS* inv
633 I	Gx	10 39.4	− 0 24 u	Sex	0.6	14p	vF, vS, R, SN
3326	Gx	10 39.5	+ 5 06 r	Sex		14p	vF, eS, stellar
3320	Gx	10 39.6	+ 47 24 s	UMa	2.2	13p	F, pS, mE, *10 nf
3335	Gx	10 39.6	− 23 56 r	Hya		14p	vF, S, iR, gbM
3323	Gx	10 39.7	+ 25 19 r	LMi		14p	vF, vS, R, lbM
3328		10 39.7	+ 9 13 D	Leo			vS Cl, not nebs
2598 I	Gx	10 39.7	+ 26 44 z	LMi		15p	F, S, R, N, r
3333	Gx	10 39.9	− 36 03 v	Ant			eF, vS, mE, *15 att
3327	Gx	10 40.0	+ 24 05 r	LMi		14p	vF, S, R, gbM, vS* att
3336	Gx	10 40.3	− 27 46 r	Hya		13p	vF, pL, lE, glbM
3332	Gx	10 40.4	+ 9 11 r	Leo		13p	vF, S, lE 130°
634 I	Gx	10 40.9	+ 5 59 u	Sex	1.3	15p	vF, S, r
3334	Gx	10 41.4	+ 37 18 r	LMi		14p	cF, vS, R, bM
635 I	Gx	10 41.7	+ 15 39 u	Leo	1.3	15p	F, S, R, gbM
3337	Gx	10 41.8	+ 4 59 r	Sex		15p	eF, vS, alm stellar
636 I	Gx	10 41.9	+ 4 20 u	Sex	1.1	15p	vF, vS, r
3338	Gx	10 42.1	+ 13 45 s	Leo	5.5	10.8	F, cL, E, vgbM, *7 p 10ˢ
3339	*	10 42.2	− 0 22 A	Sex			eF, stellar
3340	Gx	10 42.3	− 0 23 A	Sex		13p	F, S, R
3436	Gx	10 42.4	+ 7 56 r	Leo			eS
637 I	Gx	10 42.4	+ 15 20 z	Leo		15p	F, vS, in line w 3 st
3341	Gx	10 42.6	+ 5 02 r	Sex		15p	vF, vS
3342	*	10 42.7	+ 9 26 r	Leo			eF, eS
3347	Gx	10 42.8	− 36 22 s	Ant	4.4	13p	pF, S, mE 0°±, vsvmbM, 1st of 3
3354	Gx	10 43.1	− 36 22 s	Ant		14p	F, S, vlE, psbM, 2nd of 3
2602 I	OC	10 43.2	− 64 24 s	Car	50	1.9	Cl, co, incl θ Car
3344	Gx	10 43.5	+ 24 55 s	LMi	6.9	10.0	cB, L, gbM, * inv, 2 st f
3355	−	10 43.5	− 23 12 r	Hya			neb, no description

NGC	Type	α_{2000}	δ_{2000}	Const.	Size	Mag.	Description
		h m	° ′		′		
3345	D*	10 43.6	+ 11 59 r	Leo			eeF (if anything)
3358	Gx	10 43.6	− 36 23 s	Ant	3.8	13p	cF, vS, vlE, vS* att, 3rd of 3
3346	Gx	10 43.7	+ 14 52 s	Leo	2.8	12p	cF, vL, R, vgvlbM, er
3349	Gx	10 43.8	+ 6 45 r	Leo		15p	eF, vS
3372	Nb	10 43.8	− 59 52 s	Car	120		! great neb, η Car
638 I	Gx	10 43.8	+ 15 53 z	Leo		15p	F, vS, R
3351	Gx	10 44.0	+ 11 42 s	Leo	7.4	9.7	B, L, R, pgmbMN; = M95
3356	Gx	10 44.2	+ 6 45 r	Leo		13p	vF, pS, R, bM, *9 s 150″ ±
3352	Gx	10 44.3	+ 22 22 r	Leo		14p	pB, S, R, bMN
3360		10 44.3	− 11 36 D	Sex			vF, R, pair with 3361
3350	Gx	10 44.4	+ 30 43 r	LMi		15p	eF, vS, 2 st 9-10 s
3357	Gx	10 44.4	+ 14 05 s	Leo	1.9	15p	F, S, mbM
3361		10 44.4	− 11 37 D	Sex			mE 160°, brighter than 3360
3329	Gx	10 44.7	+ 76 49 s	Dra	2.1	13p	pB, S, lE, psmbM
3362	Gx	10 44.8	+ 6 36 r	Leo		13p	vF, pS, R, lbM, r
3363	Gx	10 45.3	+ 22 04 r	Leo		14p	F, pS, iR, lbM, r
3353	Gx	10 45.4	+ 55 58 s	UMa	1.5	12.7	F, cS, R, pgbM, * s 90″
639 I	Gx	10 45.9	+ 16 56 m	Leo	0.7	15p	eF, S, mE ns, *10 nf 5′
3343	Gx	10 46.1	+ 73 21 s	Dra	1.6	15p	pF, S, R, gbM
3365	Gx	10 46.3	+ 1 49 s	Sex	4.7	13p	eF, L, eE 159°, vgvlbM
3359	Gx	10 46.6	+ 63 13 s	UMa	6.8	10.5	pB, L, E 0°, glbM
3367	Gx	10 46.6	+ 13 45 s	Leo	2.3	11.5	pB, cL, iR, vglbM, r, 1st of 3
3378	Gx	10 46.6	− 40 01 r	Ant			cF, S, R, glbM
3369	Gx	10 46.7	− 25 15 r	Hya		15p	eF, vS, R
2600 I	Gx	10 46.7	+ 72 19 m	UMa	0.4	16p	eF, S, v dif
3368	Gx	10 46.8	+ 11 49 s	Leo	7.1	9.2	vB, vL, lE, vsvmbM, r; = M96
640 I		10 46.8	+ 34 45 d	LMi			vF, pS, E, D ?
3371	*	10 47.0	+ 13 48 r	Leo			eF, R, 2nd of 3
3375	Gx	10 47.0	− 9 57 r	Sex		13p	F, S, R, gmbM
3370	Gx	10 47.1	+ 17 16 s	Leo	3.1	12p	cB, pL, vlE, gbM, r
2601 I	Gx	10 47.1	+ 72 18 z	UMa		15p	eF, pS, sev eF st inv
3348	Gx	10 47.2	+ 72 50 s	UMa	2.2	11.2	B, S, ilE, psbM, *11 282°, 21ˢ
3373	*	10 47.2	+ 13 40 r	Leo			F, R, 3rd of 3
3383	Gx	10 47.3	− 24 27 r	Hya		13p	F, pL, iR, glbM
3376	Gx	10 47.4	+ 6 03 r	Sex		14p	vF, S
3377	Gx	10 47.7	+ 13 59 s	Leo	4.4	10.2	vB, cL, lE, svmbMBN
3379	Gx	10 47.8	+ 12 35 s	Leo	4.5	9.3	vB, cL, R, psbM, r; = M105
641 I		10 47.8	+ 34 40 d	LMi			vS, pS, dif
3374	Gx	10 47.9	+ 43 10 r	UMa		14p	vF, cS, iR
3390	Gx	10 48.1	− 31 32 s	Hya	4.0	12.2	F, S, pmE 0°
3450	Gx	10 48.1	− 20 51 s	Hya	2.7	14p	vF, L, R, vglbM, r
642 I	Gx	10 48.1	+ 18 11 u	Leo	1.6	14p	vF, pS, lE, 2 st f
3380	Gx	10 48.2	+ 28 36 s	LMi	1.9	14p	pB, pS, R, sbM
3385	Gx	10 48.2	+ 4 55 r	Sex		13p	vF, S, R, s of 2
3386	Gx	10 48.2	+ 5 00 r	Sex		15p	vF, S, lE, bM, n of 2
3387	Gx	10 48.2	+ 5 00 r	Sex		15p	eF, eS
3384	Gx	10 48.3	+ 12 38 s	Leo	5.9	10.0	vB, L, R, psmbM, 2nd of 3
3388	−	10 48.3	+ 8 36 r	Leo			F, R
3393	Gx	10 48.3	− 25 10 r	Hya		13p	F, S, R, psbM, 2 st 10 f
3381	Gx	10 48.4	+ 34 42 s	LMi	2.4	13p	pF, cL, iR, vglbM, 1st of 3
2603 I	*	10 48.4	+ 32 56 z	LMi			vF, pL, biN or D pf, bf
3364	Gx	10 48.5	+ 72 25 s	UMa	1.9	14p	vF, L, R, vgbM, r, D* sf
3382	−	10 48.5	+ 36 44 r	LMi			F, S, iR; S Cl?
3389	Gx	10 48.5	+ 12 32 s	Leo	2.7	11.8	F, L, E pf, vglbM, 3rd of 3
3391	Gx	10 48.9	+ 14 13 r	Leo		13p	F, S, R, bet 2 st, nr

NGC	Type	α_{2000}	δ_{2000}	Const.	Size	Mag.	Description
		h m	° ′		′		
3399	Gx	10 49.4	+ 16 13 r	Leo		14p	F, vS
643 I	Gx	10 49.4	+ 12 13 z	Leo		15p	pF, S, E ns, lbM
2604 I	Gx	10 49.4	+ 32 47 v	LMi	1.4		F, cS, dif
3405	Gx	10 49.7	+ 16 14 r	Leo		14p	F, eS, alm stell, close to S*
3395	Gx	10 49.8	+ 32 59 s	LMi	1.9	12.1	cB, pS, ilE, 1st of 2
2605 I	?	10 49.8	+ 32 58 x	LMi			eF, S, 0′.3 ssp 3395
3396	Gx	10 49.9	+ 32 59 s	LMi	2.8	12.2	pB, pS, ilE, 2nd of 2
3402	Gx	10 50.0	− 12 40 r	Hya			F, R
3420	Gx	10 50.1	− 17 15 r	Hya		14p	eF, vS, R, pgbMN, *8.5 s 6′
3409	Gx	10 50.2	− 17 03 r	Hya		15p	eF, S, E 200°, 2 vF st inv
645 I		10 50.2	− 6 03 d	Sex			F, S, R
3404	Gx	10 50.3	− 12 07 s	Hya	2.6	14p	pB, vL, E pf; = IC 2609?
3411	Gx	10 50.3	− 12 51 r	Hya		13p	F, S, R, lbM
2606 I	Gx	10 50.3	+ 37 57 z	LMi		15p	F, S, E ns, dif
2607 I	Gx	10 50.3	+ 38 00 m	LMi	0.7	15p	vF, vS, vlbM, diffic
2608 I	Gx	10 50.3	+ 32 46 x	LMi			F, vS, R, *14 att
2609 I		10 50.3	− 12 06 x	Hya			vf, S, bM; = 3404
3401	−	10 50.4	+ 5 48 r	Sex			eF (not verified)
3394	Gx	10 50.6	+ 65 43 r	UMa		13p	cF, S, lE, vgbM
647 I		10 50.6	− 12 52 d	Hya			eF, vS, dif, 3411 p
650 I		10 50.7	− 13 27 d	Hya			pF, vS, R
3400	Gx	10 50.8	+ 28 28 s	LMi	1.4	14p	pF, S, R, bM
3421	Gx	10 50.8	− 12 27 r	Hya		14p	F, R
3412	Gx	10 50.9	+ 13 25 s	Leo	3.6	10.6	B, S, lE 135°±, smbMN
3429	Gx	10 50.9	+ 9 15 r	Leo			pF, R
649 I	Gx	10 50.9	+ 1 11 m	Sex	0.6	15p	F, S, lbM, *10.5 sp
3392	Gx	10 51.0	+ 65 46 r	UMa		15p	vF, S, psbM, st nr
3417	Gx	10 51.0	+ 8 29 r	Leo		15p	eF, vS, alm stell
648 I	Gx	10 51.0	+ 12 17 m	Leo	0.8	15p	eF, vS, vF* inv, diffic
651 I	Gx	10 51.0	− 2 08 v	Sex	0.8		pB, pS, gbM, r
652 I		10 51.0	− 12 38 d	Hya			F, vS, R, bM
3422	Gx	10 51.1	− 12 24 r	Hya		15p	F, R, only susp
3423	Gx	10 51.2	+ 5 50 s	Sex	3.9	11.2	F, vL, R, vgbM, rr
3431	Gx	10 51.2	− 17 01 r	Crt		14p	eF, S, E 130°, gbM
3413	Gx	10 51.3	+ 32 46 s	LMi	2.4	13p	F, S
3414	Gx	10 51.3	+ 27 59 s	LMi	3.6	10.8	B, pL, R, mbM
3418	Gx	10 51.3	+ 28 07 u	LMi	1.2	14p	cF, S, R, bM
3419	Gx	10 51.3	+ 13 57 s	Leo	1.1	13p	F, vS, R, alm stell, S* vnr
3425	Gx	10 51.4	+ 8 34 r	Leo		14p	eF, eS, R
3427	Gx	10 51.4	+ 8 18 r	Leo		14p	neb, no descr
3428	Gx	10 51.4	+ 9 17 r	Leo		14p	vF, S, lE, glbM
3398	Gx	10 51.5	+ 55 23 v	UMa	1.3		vF, S, E, er
644 I	Gx	10 51.5	+ 55 23 x	UMa			eeF, pS, lE, B* sf, sp of 2
3426	Gx	10 51.6	+ 18 28 r	Leo		14p	pF, S, R, D* n
646 I	Gx	10 51.6	+ 55 28 x	UMa			eeF, pS, R, nf of 2
3415	Gx	10 51.7	+ 43 43 s	UMa	2.4	13p	pB, S, vlE, stell, 3 S st nr
3416	Gx	10 51.7	+ 43 46 r	UMa		15p	eF (F*?), n of 3415
3406	Gx	10 51.8	+ 51 02 r	UMa		13p	pB, R, pgbM
3424	Gx	10 51.8	+ 32 54 s	LMi	3.0	13p	pF, pL, lE, sp of 3
3410	Gx	10 51.9	+ 51 01 r	UMa		15p	F, pS, dif, 2′ sf 3406
3434	Gx	10 52.0	+ 3 48 r	Leo		13p	F, pS, R, vglbM
3433	Gx	10 52.1	+ 10 09 s	Leo	3.5	12p	vF, vL, R, vgbM
3446	OC	10 52.1	− 45 09 A	Vel			Cl, pL, P, lC, iF, st 9...13
3408	Gx	10 52.2	+ 58 26 s	UMa	1.0	14p	vF, cS, R, 2 pB st s
3430	Gx	10 52.2	+ 32 57 s	LMi	3.9	11.5	pB, L, iE, gbM, 2nd of 3

NGC	Type	α_{2000}	δ_{2000}	Const.	Size	Mag.	Description
		h m	° ′		′		
653 I	Gx	10 52.2	− 0 33 u	Leo	2.3	14p	F, S, R, dif
2610 I	?	10 52.2	+ 33 04 x	LMi			vF, S, lbM, * 25″ p
3407	Gx	10 52.3	+ 61 23 s	UMa	1.7	15p	vF, vS, R, vS* nr
3438	Gx	10 52.4	+ 10 34 r	Leo		14p	vF, eS, alm stell
3439	Gx	10 52.4	+ 8 34 r	Leo		15p	eeF, vS, alm stell
3432	Gx	10 52.5	+ 36 37 s	LMi	6.2	11.3	pB, pL, vmE 40°, ⁑ close sp
3441	Gx	10 52.5	+ 7 14 r	Leo		14p	pB
3437	Gx	10 52.6	+ 22 56 s	Leo	2.6	13p	pB, pL, lE 120°, gbM
2611 I	*	10 52.7	+ 10 07 x	Leo			eF
3449	Gx	10 52.9	− 32 56 s	Ant	2.6	13p	F, S, R, *6-7 sf
3443	Gx	10 53.0	+ 17 34 s	Leo	2.5	14p	eeF, vS, R
3444	Gx	10 53.0	+ 10 13 v	Leo	1.2		eF, vS, pmE
3442	Gx	10 53.1	+ 33 55 s	LMi	0.7	13p	F, vS, R, mbM, r?
3447	Gx	10 53.4	+ 16 46 s	Leo	3.8	13p	eF, vL, vgvlbM, B ⁑ sp
2612 I	Gx	10 53.6	+ 32 46 x	LMi			F, S, R, dif
3453	Gx	10 53.7	− 21 47 r	Hya			F, S, R, bM
3403	Gx	10 53.9	+ 73 41 s	Dra	3.1	13p	pF, L, iE, vgbM
3440	Gx	10 53.9	+ 57 07 s	UMa	2.3	14p	vF, S, lE
654 I		10 53.9	− 11 44 d	Crt			vF, S, diffic
3452	Gx	10 54.1	− 11 24 r	Crt		15p	eF, R, n of S*
3456	Gx	10 54.1	− 16 02 s	Crt	2.1	13p	eF, att to *12 f
3397	−	10 54.2	+ 77 17 r	Dra			cB, vS, iF; = 3329?
2613 I		10 54.3	+ 32 58 x	LMi			B, pL, E 200°, gmbM dif N; = 3430
3451	Gx	10 54.4	+ 27 14 r	LMi		13p	F, pL, vlE, vlbM
655 I	Nb	10 54.4	− 0 22 x	Leo	1		eF, iF
3454	Gx	10 54.5	+ 17 21 s	Leo	2.2	14p	pF, lE, np of 2
3455	Gx	10 54.5	+ 17 17 s	Leo	2.8	13p	pF, S, E, gbM, r, sf of 2
3445	Gx	10 54.6	+ 56 59 s	UMa	1.6	12.4	cB, pL, iR, vglbM, *10 nf 2′
3448	Gx	10 54.7	+ 54 19 s	UMa	5.4	11.7	B, pL, mE 67°, gbM
3457	Gx	10 54.7	+ 17 37 r	Leo		13p	2 or 3 S st and neb
3459	Gx	10 54.7	− 17 04 r	Crt		14p	vF, S, E, gbM
3464	Gx	10 54.7	− 21 04 s	Hya	2.8	13p	eF, pL, E 125°
3435	Gx	10 54.8	+ 61 18 r	UMa		14p	cF, pS, lE, vgbM
3460		10 54.8	+ 17 36 A	Leo			pB, R, no * nr; = 3457
3461	Gx	10 54.9	+ 17 39 r	Leo			F neb 5′ nf 3460
3463	Gx	10 55.1	− 26 07 r	Hya		14p	F, S, R, glbM
656 I	OC	10 55.1	+ 17 36 x	Leo			vS, Cl, neb?
3462	Gx	10 55.3	+ 7 42 r	Leo		13p	vF, vS, vlE, psbM
3458	Gx	10 56.0	+ 57 07 s	UMa	1.7	13p	vB, vS, R, stellar
3466	Gx	10 56.3	+ 9 45 s	Leo	1.3	15p	vF, *9 90°, p of 2
3467	Gx	10 56.7	+ 9 46 r	Leo		14p	vF, R, vsmbM *12, f of 2
3469	Gx	10 56.9	− 14 18 r	Crt		14p	eeF, S
3472	−	10 57.3	− 19 38 r	Crt			eF, S, R, gbM
3468	Gx	10 57.4	+ 40 57 r	UMa		14p	F, eS, R, bM
657 I		10 57.9	− 4 54 d	Leo			F, pS, lE ns
3473	Gx	10 58.0	+ 17 07 r	Leo		15p	vF, E, bet 2 st
3474	Gx	10 58.1	+ 17 05 r	Leo		15p	vF, pS, R, s of 3473
3476	Gx	10 58.1	+ 9 17 r	Leo		15p	eF, vS, alm stell
659 I		10 58.1	− 6 16 d	Leo			F, S, R, bM
3477	Gx	10 58.2	+ 9 13 r	Leo		15p	eeF, eS, stell
3475	Gx	10 58.3	+ 24 14 r	Leo		14p	vF, R, gbM, *13 1′ n (2′ s?)
658 I	Gx	10 58.3	+ 8 15 m	Leo	0.3	15p	F, vS, R, stellar
660 I	Gx	10 58.5	+ 1 23 z	Leo		16p	vF, S, r
3482	Gx	10 58.6	− 46 35 c	Vel	2.0		eF, S, R, gbM
3470	Gx	10 58.7	+ 59 31 s	UMa	1.7	14p	vF, S, R, vgbM

NGC	Type	α_{2000}	δ_{2000}	Const.	Size	Mag.	Description
		h m	o ′		′		
3479	Gx	10 58.9	− 14 58 r	Crt		13p	ef, pS, E 90°, gbMN
3480	−	10 58.9	+ 9 21 r	Leo			S, stellar
661 I	Gx	10 58.9	+ 1 40 z	Leo		16p	ef, vS, R, diffic
3483	Gx	10 59.0	− 28 28 r	Hya		13p	pF, S, R, bM, am st
3471	Gx	10 59.1	+ 61 32 s	UMa	2.0	13p	vF, S, R, bM
3465	Gx	10 59.3	+ 75 12 r	Dra		14p	ef, pL, R, vglbM, * nf
662 I	Gx	10 59.4	+ 1 36 z	Leo		16p	vF, SN, diffic
3478	Gx	10 59.5	+ 46 07 s	UMa	2.8	13p	ef, S, R
3481	Gx	10 59.5	− 7 31 r	Crt		14p	ef, vS, rr, prob vF Cl, *9 5′ sf
3496	OC	10 59.8	− 60 20 s	Car	9	8.2	Cl, pL, pRi, lC, st 13
3490	Gx	10 59.9	+ 9 22 r	Leo		15p	vF, S
3485	Gx	11 00.0	+ 14 50 s	Leo	2.5		F, L, R, glbM, r
3489	Gx	11 00.3	+ 13 54 s	Leo	3.7	10.3	vB, pL, lE 80°±, smbMN
2621 I	Pl	11 00.3	− 65 15 s	Car	0.1		◯, stell, 10.5m
3486	Gx	11 00.4	+ 28 58 s	LMi	6.9	10.3	cB, cL, R, gmbM
665 I		11 00.5	− 13 52 d	Crt			F, vS, R, bM
3491	Gx	11 00.6	+ 12 10 r	Leo		14p	ef, cS, R, bMN
663 I	Gx	11 00.6	+ 10 27 z	Leo		16p	ef, vS, R, 2 st s, 1st of 4
3487	Gx	11 00.7	+ 17 35 r	Leo		14p	eef, pS, R, v diffic
664 I	Gx	11 00.7	+ 10 33 m	Leo	1.0	15p	ef, vS, R, lbM, 3492 f
3492	Gx	11 00.9	+ 10 30 r	Leo		14p	pF, S, *9.5 p 20ˢ, 1′ s
3494	−	11 01.2	+ 3 43 r	Leo			vS, 3495 6′ s
3495	Gx	11 01.3	+ 3 38 s	Leo	4.6	13p	vF, pL, mE
3503	Nb	11 01.3	− 59 51 s	Car	3		3 S st 10 in vF neb
666 I	Gx	11 01.3	+ 10 29 z	Leo		15p	ef, vS, iF, 4th of 4
3488	Gx	11 01.4	+ 57 41 s	UMa	2.0	14p	ef or cB, vlE, pS, *13 s att
3497	−	11 01.4	− 19 28 r	Crt			vF, vS, iR, glbM; = 3528?
3493	Gx	11 01.5	+ 27 44 r	LMi		15p	vF, R, bM, * sp
2614 I		11 01.6	+ 38 48 d	UMa			vF, vS, R
3500	Gx	11 01.7	+ 75 13 A	Dra		15p	vF & ef, Dneb, v near
3498	*⁎	11 01.9	+ 14 23 r	Leo			ef, pL
2615 I		11 02.0	+ 37 56 d	UMa			F, vS, R, lbM
2618 I		11 02.0	+ 27 46 d	LMi			vS neb?
3502	Gx	11 02.1	− 14 08 r	Crt		14p	ef, pL, iR, glbM
2616 I	Gx	11 02.2	+ 38 46 m	UMa	0.2	15p	F, S, R, gbM, r
2617 I	Gx	11 02.2	+ 38 39 m	UMa	0.8	15p	F, S, R, FN
2619 I	Gx	11 02.2	+ 37 57 z	UMa		16p	F, vS, R stell
2620 I	Gx	11 02.3	+ 38 30 u	UMa	1.1	15p	F, S, R, N, r
3505	−	11 02.7	− 15 29 r	Crt			pF, S, R, glbM, *14 nr
3523	Gx	11 02.8	+ 75 08 r	Dra		14p	F, pL, lbM (place doubtful)
3501	Gx	11 02.9	+ 17 59 s	Leo	3.7	13p	vF, mE ns, gbM, 3′ long
3508	Gx	11 02.9	− 16 18 r	Crt		14p	F, S, bM, * 0′.5 nf
3484	−	11 03.0	+ 75 49 r	Dra			very doubtful object
3499	Gx	11 03.2	+ 56 13 s	UMa	1.0	14p	vF, vS, stellar
3504	Gx	11 03.2	+ 27 58 s	LMi	2.7	11.1	B, L, E, mbMN, rr, p of 2
3506	Gx	11 03.2	+ 11 05 s	Leo	1.3	13p	vF, cS, R, vgvlbM
3511	Gx	11 03.4	− 23 05 s	Crt	5.4	12p	vF, vL, mE
3507	Gx	11 03.5	+ 18 08 s	Leo	3.5	11p	cF, pL, R, sbMS *, *9 att 25°
2622 I		11 03.5	− 16 14 d	Crt			eeF, eS, like D*
3510	Gx	11 03.7	+ 28 53 s	LMi	3.8	12.9	F, L, cE, *7, 310°, 8′
3513	Gx	11 03.8	− 23 15 s	Crt	2.8	12p	vF, vL, mE
2623 I		11 03.8	− 20 06 d	Crt			vF, vS
3514	Gx	11 03.9	− 18 49 r	Crt		13p	vF, pL, R, vgvlbM
3512	Gx	11 04.0	+ 28 02 s	LMi	1.7	12.4	F, pS, R, pgbM, f of 2
3519	−	11 04.0	− 61 22 r	Car			Cl, pRi, pC

NGC	Type	α_{2000}	δ_{2000}	Const.	Size	Mag.	Description
		h m	° ′		′		
3518	Gx	11 04.3	− 6 28 r	Leo			eF, eS, lE
3509	Gx	11 04.4	+ 4 50 s	Leo	2.3	14p	eF, S, lE?
3515	Gx	11 04.6	+ 28 14 s	LMi	1.1	15p	vF, S, R, sev eF st inv
3520	Ast	11 05.5	− 17 56 F	Crt			eF, vS, iR, gbM, sev vF st inv
3517	Gx	11 05.6	+ 56 31 s	UMa	1.2	14p	eF, S, R, vgbM
3521	Gx	11 05.8	− 0 02 s	Leo	9.5	8.9	cB, cL, mE 140°±, vsmbMN
3525	−	11 06.4	− 19 27 r	Crt			F, pS, gbMN
3532	OC	11 06.4	− 58 40 s	Car	55	3.0	!!, Cl, eL, R, lC, st 8...12
3524	Gx	11 06.5	+ 11 24 r	Leo		13p	F, S, lE, psbM, 2 st np in line
667 I	Gx	11 06.5	+ 15 05 z	Leo		15p	vF, vS, R, vlbM
3522	Gx	11 06.6	+ 20 04 r	Leo		14p	pF, vS, lE
668 I	Gx	11 06.6	+ 15 02 m	Leo	0.6	15p	vF, vS, R, bM
3516	Gx	11 06.8	+ 72 34 s	UMa	2.3	11.6	pB, vS, iR, psmbM *
3531		11 06.9	+ 7 10 D	Leo			E 50°, *11 at sp end; = 3526
3526	Gx	11 07.0	+ 7 10 r	Leo		13p	eF, vmE 50°±
3533	Gx	11 07.2	− 37 10 v	Cen	2.6		eeF, vS* att
3527	Gx	11 07.3	+ 28 32 r	UMa		15p	eF, S, *10 p 60″
3528	Gx	11 07.3	− 19 28 c	Crt	3.0		F, S, R, pslbM, p of 2
3529	Gx	11 07.3	− 19 33 c	Crt	1.5		eF, S, R, vlbM, f of 2
669 I	Gx	11 07.3	+ 6 18 u	Leo	1.6	14p	pB, vS, R, sbM
2624 I	Gx	11 07.3	− 19 28 c	Crt	3.0		cB, pS, R, n of 2; = 3528
2625 I	Gx	11 07.3	− 19 33 c	Crt	1.5		eeF, vS, R, s of 2; = 3529
670 I	Gx	11 07.4	+ 6 43 u	Leo	1.3	15p	F, pS, R, bM
671 I	Gx	11 07.6	+ 0 47 u	Leo	1.6	15p	vF, pS, R
672 I	Gx	11 08.0	− 12 29 m	Crt	0.5	15p	vF, vS
3535	Gx	11 08.5	+ 4 50 r	Leo		14p	cF, vS, R, bM, r
3537	Gx	11 08.6	− 10 26 r	Crt		14p	vF, S, vF st inv
3530	Gx	11 08.7	+ 57 14 r	UMa		14p	vF, S, R, pgbM
3534	Gx	11 08.7	+ 26 36 r	Leo		15p	vF, *9 np 3′
3536	Gx	11 08.8	+ 28 29 r	UMa		15p	F, S, R, bM
3541	Gx	11 08.8	− 10 56 r	Crt		15p	nebulous *
2626 I	Gx	11 09.0	+ 26 55 z	Leo		16p	F, vS, dif, diffic
3539	Gx	11 09.1	+ 28 40 r	UMa		15p	eF
3540	Gx	11 09.3	+ 36 01 r	UMa		14p	vF, R, psbM, *7 p 7′
673 I		11 09.5	− 0 05 d	Leo			vF, vS, E pf, r
3551	Gx	11 09.6	+ 21 43 r	Leo		15p	eeF, vS, R, sp of 2
3555	Gx	11 09.7	+ 21 44 r	Leo		15p	vF, R, nf of 2
3546	Gx	11 09.8	− 13 23 r	Crt		14p	neb* 12, *12 2′ nf
2631 I		11 09.8	− 76 37 d	Cha			*9 in L neb
3547	Gx	11 09.9	+ 10 43 s	Leo	2.2	12.8	F, S, lE, vlbM
3565	−	11 09.9	− 20 02 r	Crt			vF, vS, R, gbMN, 1st of 2
3566	−	11 09.9	− 20 02 r	Crt			eeF, eS, R, gbM, 2nd of 2
2627 I	Gx	11 09.9	− 23 44 s	Crt	2.7	12.0	eF, L, R, stell N
3542	Gx	11 10.0	+ 36 57 r	UMa		15p	vF, S, irrR, lbM, r
3557	Gx	11 10.0	− 37 32 s	Cen	4.0	10.4	B, S, R, pgmbM, 1st of 3
3545	Gx	11 10.2	+ 36 58 r	UMa		15p	vF, vS, irrR, lbM, r
3548	−	11 10.4	+ 36 02 r	UMa			eF, S, *8, p; = 3540?
3572	C+N	11 10.4	− 60 14 s	Car	20	6.6	Cl, pRi, lC
3550	Gx	11 10.6	+ 28 46 s	UMa	1.4	14p	F (var?), S, R, bM, *9 f 1′, 1st of 4
3552	Gx	11 10.6	+ 28 42 r	UMa		15p	eF, vS, 2nd of 4
3553	Gx	11 10.6	+ 28 42 r	UMa		15p	eF, vS, forms Dneb with 3552
3564	Gx	11 10.6	− 37 33 s	Cen	2.1	12.2	pF, S, R, bM, 2nd of 3
3554	Gx	11 10.7	+ 28 40 r	UMa		15p	vF, pS, R, bM, 3rd of 4
3559	Gx	11 10.7	+ 12 01 s	Leo	1.5	14p	eF, pS, lE, r
3560	*	11 10.7	+ 11 11 r	Leo			F, S, R, gbM

NGC	Type	α_{2000}	δ_{2000}	Const.	Size	Mag.	Description
		h m	° ′		′		
675 I		11 10.7	+ 3 41 d	Leo			pB, pL, E ns, biN?
3543	Gx	11 10.8	+ 61 22 r	UMa		15p	eF, vS, E 0°±, r
3568	Gx	11 10.8	− 37 27 v	Cen	2.4		vF, pL, R, * inv, 3 B st nr, 3rd of 3
3549	Gx	11 10.9	+ 53 23 s	UMa	3.2	12p	cB, cL, cE 160°
3558	Gx	11 10.9	+ 28 33 s	UMa	1.3	15p	pF, S
674 I	Gx	11 11.1	+ 43 38 u	UMa	1.8	14p	pF, R, bM, D* sf
3561	Gx	11 11.2	+ 28 43 s	UMa	1.1	15p	vF, pL, 4th of 4
3567	Gx	11 11.3	+ 5 50 r	Leo		14p	eF, R, sbM, r
3573	Gx	11 11.3	− 36 51 r	Cen			eF, S, R, glbM, 3 st 11 f
3563	Gx	11 11.4	+ 26 58 s	Leo	1.4	15p	pF, pL, *8 2′ n
3538	−	11 11.5	+ 75 34 r	Dra			vF, pL, *17 nr
3544	Gx	11 11.5	− 18 17 c	Crt			vF, L, mE 95°, bM; = 3571
3556	Gx	11 11.5	+ 55 40 s	UMa	8.3	10.1	cB, vL, vmE 79°, pbM, r; = M108
3571	Gx	11 11.5	− 18 17 s	Crt	3.3	13p	pF, pL, iF, bM
2628 I	Gx	11 11.6	+ 12 08 z	Leo		15p	pF, pS, R, bM, spir
3576	Nb	11 11.8	− 61 23 d	Car	20		F, lE, 1st of 6
3579	Nb	11 11.9	− 61 14 d	Car			F, lE, sbM, 2nd of 6
3569	Gx	11 12.1	+ 35 27 r	UMa		14p	F, vS, stell
3570	Gx	11 12.1	+ 27 35 s	Leo	1.3	15p	vF, vS, R, bM
3581	Nb	11 12.1	− 61 18 r	Car			*12 with fan-shaped neb att, 3rd of 6
3574	Gx	11 12.2	+ 27 37 v	Leo	0.5		eF
3582	Nb	11 12.3	− 61 16 r	Car			B, bM*, 4th of 6
3584	Nb	11 12.4	− 61 12 r	Car			F, L, E 0°, bM, 5th of 6
3586	Nb	11 12.6	− 61 21 r	Car			eF, S, E 160°±, 6th of 6
2629 I		11 12.6	+ 12 06 d	Leo			F, S, R, bM
676 I	Gx	11 12.7	+ 9 04 u	Leo	2.2	13p	vF, pS, lE, bet 2 dist st
2630 I		11 12.7	+ 12 19 d	Leo			F, vS, R, spir
3578	−	11 12.8	− 15 57 r	Crt			doubtful object, probably a neb
3562	Gx	11 12.9	+ 72 53 r	Dra		13p	pF, pS, lE, gbM, *15, 22°, 70″
3590	OC	11 12.9	− 60 47 s	Car	4	8.2	Cl, pRi, C, E
3575	−	11 13.1	+ 22 40 r	Leo			pB, pL, R, *11 p
2632 I		11 13.1	+ 11 40 d	Leo			F, S, R, bM
2633 I		11 13.2	+ 11 36 d	Leo			F, cS, iF
3580	Gx	11 13.3	+ 3 40 r	Leo		14p	vF, *14 f
3585	Gx	11 13.3	− 26 45 s	Hya	2.9	10.0	B, pL, E, vsmbMN, 2 B st △
2634 I	Gx	11 13.5	+ 10 30 m	Leo	0.4	15p	cB, cS, R, gbM
2635 I		11 13.5	+ 11 28 d	Leo			F, S, stell N
2636 I		11 13.6	+ 11 27 d	Leo			F, S, bM
3577	Gx	11 13.8	+ 48 16 s	UMa	1.7	15p	eF, vS, p of 2
2637 I	Gx	11 13.8	+ 9 36 u	Leo	0.9	14p	pB, cS, R, bM
677 I	Gx	11 13.9	+ 12 19 u	Leo	1.6	14p	F, pL, gbM
2638 I	Gx	11 13.9	+ 10 34 u	Leo	1.1	15p	cB, pS, E 100°, bM
2639 I		11 13.9	+ 9 39 d	Leo			F, S, R, bM, spir
3588	Gx	11 14.0	+ 20 24 r	Leo		15p	vF, cS, 4ˢf δ Leo (& 8′ s)
3591	Gx	11 14.1	− 14 04 r	Crt		14p	vF, S, iR, lbM
678 I	Gx	11 14.1	+ 6 35 m	Leo	0.2	15p	F, S, r, N = 13.5
2640 I		11 14.1	+ 11 00 d	Leo			F, S, iF
3583	Gx	11 14.2	+ 48 19 s	UMa	2.8	12p	pB, pL, R, vgmbM
2641 I		11 14.2	+ 9 24 d	Leo			F, S, iF
2642 I		11 14.2	+ 10 16 d	Leo			vF, vS, R, bM, spir
3592	Gx	11 14.4	+ 17 16 s	Leo	2.0	15p	eF, S, pmE 60°
2643 I		11 14.5	+ 10 08 d	Leo			cF, S, R, bM
2644 I		11 14.5	+ 10 46 d	Leo			F, S, R
2645 I	Gx	11 14.5	+ 11 54 z	Leo		16p	pF, S, R, bM
3593	Gx	11 14.6	+ 12 49 s	Leo	5.8	11.0	B, cL, E 90°±, psmbM

NGC	Type	α_{2000}	δ_{2000}	Const.	Size	Mag.	Description
		h m	° ′		′		
3597	Gx	11 14.6	− 23 43 r	Crt		13p	vF, pS, R, bM
2646 I		11 14.6	+ 12 32 d	Leo			vF, vS, iF
2647 I		11 14.7	+ 12 09 d	Leo			eF, pL, iF
2648 I	Gx	11 14.7	+ 10 14 z	Leo		16p	cF, cS, R, bM
3587	Pl	11 14.8	+ 55 01 s	UMa	3.2	11.2	!!, ○ , vB, vL, R, vvg, vsbM, 150″ d; = M97
2649 I	Gx	11 14.8	+ 11 08 m	Leo	0.6	15p	pB, S, R, bM, spir
2650 I		11 14.9	+ 13 51 d	Leo			F, S, bM, iF
2651 I		11 14.9	+ 12 15 d	Leo			F, S, R, bM
2652 I		11 14.9	+ 12 27 d	Leo			vF, S, R, bM, spir
2653 I		11 14.9	+ 10 33 d	Leo			vF, S, R
3596	Gx	11 15.1	+ 14 47 s	Leo	4.2	12p	pF, L, R, glbM
3603	C+N	11 15.1	− 61 15 s	Car	12	9.1	⊕ and neb, st 15...18
2654 I		11 15.1	+ 12 30 d	Leo			vF, S, E 120°
2655 I		11 15.1	+ 12 10 d	Leo			eF, S, iF
2656 I		11 15.1	+ 12 23 d	Leo			vF, S, iF, E 120°
3589	Gx	11 15.2	+ 60 42 s	UMa	1.7	15p	vF, L, E, vgbM, in △ of L st
3598	Gx	11 15.2	+ 17 16 r	Leo		13p	F, vS, stell, ∗ n
2657 I		11 15.2	+ 13 42 d	Leo			F, pL, dif, bet 2 st
2658 I	∗	11 15.2	+ 13 00 x	Leo			vF, cS, R, bM
3595	Gx	11 15.4	+ 47 27 s	UMa	1.7	13p	vF, vS, vlE, stellar, cB∗ n
3599	Gx	11 15.4	+ 18 07 s	Leo	2.8	11.9	B, pS, R, pgmbM
3601	Gx	11 15.5	+ 5 07 r	Leo		14p	vF, pS, alm stell
2659 I	∗	11 15.5	+ 12 53 x	Leo			F, vS, R, bM, spir
2660 I		11 15.5	+ 12 26 d	Leo			vF, S
2661 I	Gx	11 15.5	+ 13 37 z	Leo		15p	F, pS, E 100°, bM
2662 I	∗	11 15.5	+ 12 46 x	Leo			F, vS, R, bM
2668 I	Gx	11 15.5	− 14 11 m	Crt	1.0	14p	eF, S
2663 I	∗	11 15.6	+ 12 36 x	Leo			pB, vS, R, sbM ∗
2664 I	∗	11 15.6	+ 12 34 x	Leo			F, vS, lE 80°, bM
2665 I		11 15.7	+ 11 43 d	Leo			vF, pL, iF, N, 2 st 13 att
2666 I	Gx	11 15.7	+ 13 47 m	Leo	0.7	15p	cB, cS, E 20°, bM
2667 I		11 15.7	+ 12 07 d	Leo			F, vS, R, bM, spir
3600	Gx	11 15.8	+ 41 36 s	UMa	4.3	12p	pF, S, lE 0°±, vgbM
3602	Gx	11 15.8	+ 17 25 r	Leo		15p	eeF, vS, alm stell
2669 I		11 15.9	+ 13 26 d	Leo			F, S, E 50°, bM
2670 I		11 16.0	+ 11 47 d	Leo			F, vS, R, bM, spir
3594	Gx	11 16.1	+ 55 42 r	UMa		15p	vF, vS, stellar
3620	Gx	11 16.1	− 76 13 c	Cha	2.8		F, pS, pmE, gbM
2671 I		11 16.1	+ 13 08 d	Leo			F, vS, R, bM
2672 I		11 16.1	+ 10 10 d	Leo			F, vS, R, bM
2673 I		11 16.1	+ 10 10 d	Leo			F, pL, iF, N, ∗11 f 1′
3606	Gx	11 16.2	− 33 49 r	Hya			eF, S, R, gbM
2674 I	Gx	11 16.2	+ 11 03 u	Leo	1.4	15p	F, pS, R, bM, spir
2675 I		11 16.2	+ 12 15 d	Leo			F, vS, R
3604	−	11 16.3	+ 4 31 r	Leo			pB, S, lE, mbM; = 3611?
2676 I		11 16.3	+ 9 50 d	Leo			F, S, iF, ∗11 sf 0′.5
2677 I		11 16.3	+ 12 13 d	Leo			F, vS, R, bM, in L, E neby
2678 I		11 16.4	+ 11 57 d	Leo			F, vS, E 110°, bM
2679 I		11 16.4	+ 12 01 d	Leo			F, S, R, bM, spir, ∗13 sp 20″
2680 I		11 16.4	+ 9 49 d	Leo			cF, S, iF, N, ∗11 np
679 I		11 16.6	− 13 58 d	Crt			F, S, R, sbM
2681 I	Gx	11 16.6	+ 11 12 z	Leo		15p	cB, vS
2682 I		11 16.6	+ 9 25 d	Leo			pF, S, E, bM
3605	Gx	11 16.8	+ 18 01 s	Leo	1.7	13p	F, S, R, sp of 3
3607	Gx	11 16.9	+ 18 03 s	Leo	3.7	10.0	vB, L, R, vmbM, 2nd of 3

NGC	Type	α_{2000}	δ_{2000}	Const.	Size	Mag.	Description
		h m	° ′		′		
2683 I		11 16.9	+ 12 06 d	Leo			F, pL, iF, N
3608	Gx	11 17.0	+ 18 09 s	Leo	3.0	11.0	B, pL, R, psbM, 3rd of 3
2684 I	Gx	11 17.0	+ 13 06 z	Leo		15p	F, pS, R, bM
2685 I		11 17.0	+ 10 06 d	Leo			F, vS, R, sbM *14
2686 I		11 17.1	+ 12 57 d	Leo			F, S, iF, att *14 sf
2687 I		11 17.2	+ 10 10 d	Leo			vF, vS, R, bM, spir
2688 I		11 17.3	+ 13 29 d	Leo			vF, S, E 30°, bM
2689 I		11 17.3	+ 12 58 d	Leo			F, S, E 40°
2690 I		11 17.4	+ 12 59 d	Leo			vF, S, iF, diffic
2691 I		11 17.4	+ 12 02 d	Leo			F, S, R, mbM
3611	Gx	11 17.5	+ 4 33 s	Leo	2.4	12.2	pF, cS, iR, psmbM, *10 np 3′
2692 I		11 17.6	+ 10 46 d	Leo			F, vS
2693 I		11 17.6	+ 13 33 d	Leo			vF, S, R, bM
2694 I	Gx	11 17.6	+ 13 23 z	Leo		15p	pB, S, E 90°, bM
3609	Gx	11 17.8	+ 26 38 r	Leo		14p	pF, S, bM
3617	Gx	11 17.8	− 26 07 r	Hya		13p	F, S, R, gbM
2695 I		11 17.8	+ 13 44 d	Leo			F, S, R, bM
2696 I		11 17.8	+ 12 45 d	Leo			F, vS, R, bM
2697 I		11 17.9	+ 13 24 d	Leo			F, S, iF, N, bet 2 st
2698 I		11 17.9	+ 11 53 d	Leo			F, pS, iF, biN
2699 I		11 17.9	+ 11 55 d	Leo			F, eS, R, bM
2700 I		11 17.9	+ 12 03 d	Leo			vF, vS, iF, N
2714 I	OC	11 17.9	− 62 42 s	Car	12	8p	Cl, pC
3615	Gx	11 18.0	+ 23 24 r	Leo		14p	cF, vS, smbM, stellar, p of 2
680 I	Gx	11 18.0	− 1 56 m	Leo	0.6	15p	F, S, R, gbM
2701 I		11 18.0	+ 11 07 d	Leo			F, vS, iF
2702 I		11 18.0	+ 9 25 d	Leo			vF, S, E
2703 I	Gx	11 18.1	+ 17 39 z	Leo			vF, S
2704 I	Gx	11 18.1	+ 12 28 z	Leo		15p	F, S, E 70°, bM
2705 I		11 18.1	+ 11 54 d	Leo			eF, eS, R, bM, diffic
3612	Gx	11 18.2	+ 26 38 r	Leo		15p	pL, dif, *10-11 nf 2′
3616	−	11 18.2	+ 14 44 r	Leo			eF, pL; nonexistent?
3614	Gx	11 18.3	+ 45 45 s	UMa	4.6	12p	F, pL, lE 90°±, glbM, r
3621	Gx	11 18.3	− 32 49 s	Hya	10.0	10p	cB, vL, E 160°, am 4 st
3610	Gx	11 18.4	+ 58 47 s	UMa	3.2	10.8	vB, pS, lE 90°±, vsvmbMSN
3618	Gx	11 18.5	+ 23 29 r	Leo		14p	vF, S, f of 2
2706 I		11 18.5	+ 12 33 d	Leo			F, vS, E 60°, bM
2707 I		11 18.5	+ 9 29 d	Leo			F, vS, R, bM, spir, *13 sf
3613	Gx	11 18.6	+ 58 00 s	UMa	3.6	12p	vB, cL, mE 305°, smbMN
681 I		11 18.6	− 12 09 d	Crt			vF, S, iF, diffic
2708 I	Gx	11 18.6	+ 12 43 z	Leo		15p	pB, vS, R, bM
2709 I		11 18.7	+ 12 34 d	Leo			eF, pL, iF, *13 n
3624	Gx	11 18.8	+ 7 32 r	Leo		14p	eF
2710 I		11 18.8	+ 13 34 d	Leo			B, vS, R, bM
2711 I		11 18.8	+ 13 44 d	Leo			F, vS, R, bM
3623	Gx	11 18.9	+ 13 05 s	Leo	10.0	9.3	B, vL, mE 165°±, gbMBN; = M65
2712 I		11 18.9	+ 9 38 d	Leo			F, vS, R, bM
2713 I		11 19.2	+ 12 10 d	Leo			cF, vS, R, bM
2715 I		11 19.2	+ 11 57 d	Leo			vF, S, iF
2716 I		11 19.3	+ 11 42 d	Leo			vF, S, iF
2717 I		11 19.3	+ 12 03 d	Leo			vF, vS, R, bM, diffic
3619	Gx	11 19.4	+ 57 46 s	UMa	3.1	13p	cB, cL, R, vgmbM
2718 I		11 19.4	+ 12 01 d	Leo			F, vS, iF
2719 I		11 19.5	+ 12 04 d	Leo			vF, S, iF, N
2720 I		11 19.6	+ 12 05 d	Leo			cF, vS, R, bM

NGC	Type	α_{2000}	δ_{2000}	Const.	Size	Mag.	Description
		h m	o ′		′		
2721 I		11 19.7	+ 12 09 d	Leo			eF, pS, dif
2722 I		11 19.7	+ 13 58 d	Leo			F, S, iF
2723 I		11 19.8	+ 12 02 d	Leo			F, vS, E 200°, diffic
2724 I		11 19.8	+ 10 43 d	Leo			cF, vF, R, bM, *13 p 20″
2725 I		11 20.0	+ 13 26 d	Leo			vF, S, iF, diffic
2726 I	*	11 20.0	+ 13 25 x	Leo			vF, vS, iF, diffic
2727 I		11 20.0	+ 12 02 d	Leo			F, vS, iF, N, diffic
3626	Gx	11 20.1	+ 18 21 s	Leo	3.1	10.9	B, S, vlE, sbM
2728 I	*	11 20.1	+ 13 25 x	Leo			vF, S, iF, N, diffic
2729 I		11 20.1	+ 13 25 d	Leo			vF, S, iF, diffic
2730 I		11 20.1	+ 12 22 d	Leo			F, eS, E 90°, bM
3622	Gx	11 20.2	+ 67 15 r	UMa		13p	pB, S, R, gbM
3627	Gx	11 20.2	+ 12 59 s	Leo	8.7	9.0	B, vL, mE 150°, mbM, 2 st np; = M66
2731 I	*	11 20.2	+ 13 34 x	Leo			F, S, R, bM, spir
2732 I		11 20.2	+ 12 24 d	Leo			vF, S, R, bM
3628	Gx	11 20.3	+ 13 36 s	Leo	14.8	9.5	pB, vL, vmE 102°
3630	Gx	11 20.3	+ 2 58 s	Leo	2.3	13p	pB, S, R, smbMN
3638	Gx	11 20.3	− 8 06 r	Crt		15p	eF, vS, 2 st 10 f
3633	Gx	11 20.4	+ 3 35 s	Leo	1.4	14p	vF, S, R, 2 st nr
3636	Gx	11 20.4	− 10 17 s	Crt	1.1	13p	F, vS, R, lbM, *7 f, p of 2
2733 I	D*	11 20.4	+ 13 52 x	Leo			vF, cS, iF, N, *14 n
2734 I		11 20.4	+ 12 27 d	Leo			F, S, iF, N
3625	Gx	11 20.5	+ 57 47 s	UMa	2.2	14p	F, S, lE 135°±
3629	Gx	11 20.5	+ 26 58 s	Leo	2.2	13p	cF, L, R, vgvlbM
3632	−	11 20.5	+ 18 09 r	Leo			pB, * inv; = 3626?
3634	Gx	11 20.6	− 9 01 r	Crt		15p	eF, eS, R, bMN, D with 3635, 85°, dist 0′.4
3635	Gx	11 20.6	− 9 01 r	Crt		16p	eF, eS, R, bMN, D with 3634
3637	Gx	11 20.7	− 10 16 s	Crt	1.7	13p	F, vS, R, psbM, *7 p, f of 2
2736 I		11 20.9	+ 12 25 d	Leo			vF, S, iF, N
3631	Gx	11 21.0	+ 53 10 s	UMa	4.6	10.4	pB, L, R, svmbMrN
2735 I	Gx	11 21.0	+ 34 21 u	UMa	1.2	15p	pB, cS, E pF, N, r
3640	Gx	11 21.1	+ 3 14 s	Leo	4.1	10.3	B, pL, R, psbM
2737 I		11 21.1	+ 14 18 d	Leo			F, cS, R, bM
3641	Gx	11 21.2	+ 3 12 s	Leo	1.1	14p	F, vS, alm stell, 3640 2′ n
682 I		11 21.2	+ 20 13 d	Leo			eF, eS, R, vF* close np
2739 I		11 21.2	+ 11 55 d	Leo			F, vS, annular?
2738 I	Gx	11 21.3	+ 34 22 v	UMa	0.6		F, S, R, gbMN
2740 I		11 21.3	+ 8 45 d	Leo			vF, S, dif, diffic
2741 I		11 21.3	+ 9 09 d	Leo			vF, pS, iF, sev N
2742 I		11 21.3	+ 10 27 d	Leo			F, S, iF
3643	Gx	11 21.4	+ 3 01 s	Leo	1.1	15p	eF, vS
683 I	Gx	11 21.4	+ 2 45 x	Leo			neb object 13.5m
2743 I		11 21.4	+ 8 42 d	Leo			F, vS, R, bM, spir
3639	Gx	11 21.5	+ 18 28 r	Leo		14p	pF, S, R, vlbM, 15′ f 3626
3644	Gx	11 21.5	+ 2 49 r	Leo		15p	vF, vS; = IC 684
2745 I	Gx	11 21.5	+ 13 26 x	Leo		15p	pB, Sp, E 70°, bM, *12 att sf
3645	Gx	11 21.6	+ 2 59 r	Leo		15p	pB, S, E, bM
3647	Gx	11 21.6	+ 2 54 r	Leo		15p	eF neb*
684 I		11 21.6	+ 2 50 x	Leo			F, S, * sp 0′.5; = 3644
2746 I		11 21.6	+ 11 44 d	Leo			F, vS, R, bM
3646	Gx	11 21.7	+ 20 10 s	Leo	3.9	11.2	cF, cL, lE, gbM, sp of 2
2744 I	Gx	11 21.7	+ 34 22 m	UMa	0.4	15p	F, S, gbM, r
2747 I		11 21.7	+ 8 48 d	Leo			vF, vS, iF, 2 st p
2748 I		11 21.7	+ 8 48 d	Leo			F, vS, iF
2749 I	Gx	11 21.7	+ 8 35 x	Leo		16p	F, S, dif (D*?)

NGC	Type	α_{2000}	δ_{2000}	Const.	Size	Mag.	Description
		h m	° ′		′		
2750 I		11 21.9	+ 9 40 d	Leo			vF, vS, iF
2752 I	Nb	11 22.0	+ 14 08 z	Leo	0.3		F, S, R, bM
2753 I		11 22.0	+ 9 53 d	Leo			cF, vS, R, bM
2754 I	Nb	11 22.0	+ 14 09 z	Leo	0.5		F, S, iF, N, diffic
2755 I	*	11 22.0	+ 13 48 z	Leo			F, vS, R, bM
2756 I		11 22.0	+ 9 58 d	Leo			vF, vS, E 120°, bM
2757 I	Gx	11 22.0	+ 8 24 z	Leo		15p	F, S, iF, N
2758 I	Gx	11 22.0	+ 7 49 z	Leo		15p	F, cS, R, bM, diffic
685 I	Gx	11 22.1	+ 17 45 z	Leo			eeF, pS, R, * nf
2751 I	Gx	11 22.1	+ 34 23 z	UMa		16p	F, S, R, 2 st 15 inv
3649	Gx	11 22.2	+ 20 13 s	Leo	1.6	15p	vF, pS, R, gbM, nf of 2
2759 I		11 22.2	+ 24 19 d	Leo			cF, stell, *13 npp 2′.5
2760 I		11 22.2	+ 12 40 d	Leo			vF, S, R, bM
3642	Gx	11 22.3	+ 59 05 s	UMa	5.8	11.1	pB, pL, R, vgbM
2761 I	Nb	11 22.3	+ 14 11 z	Leo	0.1		F, S, R, bM, diffic
2762 I	Gx	11 22.3	+ 12 44 z	Leo		15p	cF, pS, mE 150°, bM, *12 p
2763 I		11 22.3	+ 13 04 d	Leo			cF, pS, E 95°, long N
3651	Gx	11 22.4	+ 24 18 r	Leo		14p	cF, vS, R, bM, np of 2
2765 I	Nb	11 22.4	+ 14 13 z	Leo	0.1		vF, vS, iF, N
2766 I		11 22.4	+ 12 54 d	Leo			vF, S, iF
2767 I		11 22.4	+ 13 05 d	Leo			vF, vS, iF
2768 I		11 22.4	+ 12 32 d	Leo			vF, vS, iF, N
2769 I	Nb	11 22.4	+ 14 12 z	Leo	0.1		F, cS, R, bM
2770 I		11 22.4	+ 9 13 d	Leo			F, S, iF
3653	Gx	11 22.5	+ 24 16 r	Leo		15p	vF, vS, sf of 2
2771 I		11 22.5	+ 12 31 d	Leo			vF, vS, iF, N, diffic
2772 I		11 22.5	+ 13 36 d	Leo			vF, eS, iF, N
3648	Gx	11 22.6	+ 39 53 r	UMa		13p	pB, S, pmE, bMN = close ⁎⁎ ?
3650	Gx	11 22.6	+ 20 42 s	Leo	1.9	15p	eF, S, R, bet 2 st
3652	Gx	11 22.6	+ 37 46 s	UMa	2.4	13p	pF, cL, lE, vgbM
2773 I		11 22.6	+ 13 34 d	Leo			vF, S, viF, diffic
2774 I		11 22.6	+ 12 31 d	Leo			vF, vS, iF, N, diffic
2775 I		11 22.7	+ 12 31 d	Leo			vF, vS, iF, N, diffic
2776 I		11 22.7	+ 13 20 d	Leo			pF, pS, R, bM, spir
2777 I	Gx	11 22.7	+ 12 02 z	Leo		15p	pF, vS, R, bM
2778 I		11 22.7	+ 12 31 d	Leo			vF, vS, iF, N, diffic
2779 I		11 22.8	+ 13 21 d	Leo			cF, eS, R
2780 I		11 22.8	+ 10 09 d	Leo			F, vS, R, bM, *15 n 15″
2781 I		11 22.8	+ 12 21 d	Leo			F, vS, iF, fainter one 2′ nf
3655	Gx	11 22.9	+ 16 35 s	Leo	1.6	11.6	pB, pS, iR, bM, r
2782 I	Gx	11 22.9	+ 13 27 u	Leo	1.1	15p	cF, cS, R, bM
2783 I		11 22.9	+ 8 53 d	Leo			F, vS, R, bM, spir
686 I	Gx	11 23.1	+ 5 39 z	Leo		15p	eF, vS, R, v diffic
2784 I		11 23.2	+ 13 07 d	Leo			pB, eS, R, bM, *13 p 20″
2785 I		11 23.3	+ 13 23 d	Leo			pF, S, R, bM
2786 I		11 23.3	+ 13 23 d	Leo			cF, S, E 110°, bM
2787 I	Gx	11 23.3	+ 13 39 u	Leo	1.0	15p	cF, S, R, bM
2788 I		11 23.4	+ 12 42 d	Leo			vF, S, R
2789 I	D*	11 23.5	+ 14 11 z	Leo			pB, S, R, bM
3656	Gx	11 23.6	+ 53 51 s	UMa	1.7	13p	pB, S, R, vgbM, *12 p
3660	Gx	11 23.6	− 8 40 s	Crt	2.8	13p	F, pL, iR, vgbM
689 I		11 23.6	− 13 50 z	Crt			eF, vS, r, dif; = 3661
2790 I		11 23.6	+ 9 33 d	Leo			vF, S, iF
2791 I		11 23.6	+ 12 54 d	Leo			vF, vS, iF, diffic
3661	Gx	11 23.7	− 13 48 r	Crt		14p	F, S, R, stellar, p of 2; = IC 689

NGC	Type	α_{2000}	δ_{2000}		Const.	Size	Mag.	Description
		h　m	°　′			′		
688 I		11 23.7	− 9 48	d	Crt			eF, vS, R
2792 I		11 23.7	+ 11 24	d	Leo			F, S, R
3659	Gx	11 23.8	+ 17 49	s	Leo	2.1	13p	cF, S, lE, r
3662	Gx	11 23.8	− 1 06	s	Leo	1.6	14p	vF, S, att to *13
2793 I		11 23.8	+ 9 27	d	Leo			vF, S, iF, diffic
3657	Gx	11 23.9	+ 52 55	s	UMa	1.8	12p	cF, vS, R, stellar
3658	Gx	11 24.0	+ 38 34	s	UMa	2.1	13p	F, S, R, svmbMN = *14
3663	Gx	11 24.0	− 12 17	r	Crt		13p	eF, fan shaped, * close
3654	Gx	11 24.1	+ 69 26	r	UMa		13p	F, S, lE 15°±
2794 I		11 24.1	+ 12 48	d	Leo			F, eS, R, bM
2795 I		11 24.1	+ 12 08	d	Leo			F, vS, R
2796 I		11 24.1	+ 9 21	d	Leo			vF, S, iF
3667	Gx	11 24.3	− 13 49	r	Crt		13p	pF, pL, iR, vlbM
687 I	Gx	11 24.3	+ 47 51	m	UMa	0.7	15p	eF, eS, R, stell N, F* f
690 I		11 24.3	− 8 21	d	Crt			pB, S, R, N = 12m
3664	Gx	11 24.4	+ 3 20	s	Leo	2.0	13p	pF, biN
3666	Gx	11 24.4	+ 11 21	s	Leo	4.2	12p	F, E 90°±, *6 f 34ˢ, 5′ n
2797 I		11 24.4	+ 11 42	d	Leo			F, vS, R, bM
2798 I		11 24.4	+ 12 25	d	Leo			vF, S, iF, N, diffic
2799 I	Nb	11 24.4	+ 13 51	x	Leo	0.4		F, S, iF, N
2800 I		11 24.5	+ 12 12	d	Leo			vF, S, R, bM
2801 I		11 24.5	+ 10 11	d	Leo			F, S, R, bM, spir
2802 I		11 24.5	+ 12 13	d	Leo			vF, vS, iF, N, v diffic
2803 I		11 24.6	+ 9 51	d	Leo			F, vS, E 70°
3665	Gx	11 24.7	+ 38 46	s	UMa	3.2	10.8	cB, cL, iR, pgmbM
3670	Gx	11 24.7	+ 23 57	r	Leo		14p	vF, vS, R
2804 I	Gx	11 24.9	+ 13 13	m	Leo	0.8	15p	pB, cS, E 10°, exc N
3672	Gx	11 25.0	− 9 48	s	Crt	4.1	11p	pB, L, E 0°±, gbM
2805 I	*	11 25.0	+ 14 01	x	Leo			vF, S, R, bM, diffic
3673	Gx	11 25.2	− 26 44	s	Hya	3.5	12p	F, vL, gvlbM, *7 s 6′
2806 I		11 25.3	+ 9 39	d	Leo			vF, S, iF; annular?
2807 I		11 25.3	+ 11 32	d	Leo			F, S, iF, *14 att p
3669	Gx	11 25.4	+ 57 43	s	UMa	2.3	13p	vF, pL, pmE 135°±, er
3668	Gx	11 25.5	+ 63 27	r	UMa		13p	F, pS, iR, gbM, *9 np
2808 I		11 25.5	+ 9 08	d	Leo			vF, vS, R, bM, spir
3676	−	11 25.6	− 10 37	r	Crt			eF, vS, R, 2 st 10 nf, sf
2809 I		11 25.6	+ 8 32	d	Leo			F, S, R, bM; spir?
3680	OC	11 25.7	− 43 15	s	Cen	12	7.6	Cl, cL, pRi, lC, st 10...14
3671	Gx	11 25.8	+ 60 29	r	UMa		15p	vF, vS, 2 vS st inv
2810 I	Nb	11 25.8	+ 14 40	x	Leo	1		pF, pS, R, bM, *14 sf
2811 I		11 25.8	+ 9 10	d	Leo			F, S, iF, *14 f 30″
692 I	Gx	11 25.9	+ 9 59	u	Leo	0.8	14p	F, vS, R, *12 sf 2′
2812 I		11 25.9	+ 11 32	d	Leo			F, S, E 10°
3675	Gx	11 26.1	+ 43 35	s	UMa	5.9	11p	vB, cL, vmE 0°±, vsmbMN, many st p
2813 I		11 26.1	+ 11 15	d	Leo			F, vS, R, bM, spir
2814 I		11 26.1	+ 9 40	d	Leo			pF, vS, R, bM, *14 nf 30″
3678	Gx	11 26.2	+ 27 53	r	Leo		14p	vF, S, psbM, *12 nf
3679	Gx	11 26.2	− 5 35	r	Leo		15p	eF, cL, R, r (v near vB*)
3685	−	11 26.2	+ 4 08	r	Leo			eF, vS
3677	Gx	11 26.3	+ 46 58	s	UMa	2.0	14p	eF, S, R, vsbM *, 2 st 11 nf
2815 I		11 26.3	+ 12 48	d	Leo			F, eS, R, bM
2816 I		11 26.3	+ 10 38	d	Leo			cF, vS, R, bM, spir
2817 I		11 26.3	+ 9 09	d	Leo			F, vS, iF, N
3674	Gx	11 26.4	+ 57 03	s	UMa	2.0	13p	pF, iF
2820 I		11 26.4	+ 10 14	d	Leo			pF, vS, *16 att n

NGC	Type	α_{2000}	δ_{2000}	Const.	Size	Mag.	Description
		h m	° ′		′		
3681	Gx	11 26.5	+ 16 52 s	Leo	2.5	11.7	B, pS, R, bM
2818 I		11 26.5	+ 12 55 d	Leo			F, vS, R, bM
2819 I	Gx	11 26.5	+ 13 51 z	Leo		16p	cF, S, E 60°, bM
2821 I		11 26.6	+ 13 58 d	Leo			F, S
2822 I	Gx	11 26.6	+ 11 26 u	Leo	1.7	15p	F, pL, E 110°, bM, *14 s
691 I	Gx	11 26.7	+ 59 09 s	UMa	0.7	14p	pF, pS, R, 2 st nr
2823 I	Gx	11 26.7	+ 12 50 z	Leo		15p	pF, S, E 20°, biN?
693 I	Gx	11 26.8	− 5 00 m	Leo	0.6	15p	F, pS, R, gbM, r
2825 I		11 27.0	+ 8 27 d	Leo			F, S, iF, N, *15 att sf
2764 I	Gx	11 27.1	− 28 59 c	Hya	1.7		pB, pS, R, *10 nr nf, *7 f
2824 I		11 27.1	+ 14 05 d	Leo			pF, S, R, bM
2826 I	Gx	11 27.1	+ 13 14 z	Leo		15p	pF, cS, N
3684	Gx	11 27.2	+ 17 02 s	Leo	3.2	11.7	pB, pL, E, vgbM
2827 I		11 27.2	+ 11 31 d	Leo			F, eS, *14 sf
2828 I	Gx	11 27.2	+ 8 43 m	Leo	1.0	15p	pF, cS, E 65°, bM 2 st p
2829 I	Gx	11 27.2	+ 10 18 z	Leo		15p	cF, vS, R, bM, spir, *12 s
2830 I	Gx	11 27.4	+ 7 48 z	Leo		15p	F, S, R, bM
2831 I		11 27.4	+ 8 59 d	Leo			F, vS, R
2832 I		11 27.4	+ 13 59 d	Leo			pF, S, R, bM
2833 I		11 27.4	+ 13 36 d	Leo			vF, S, iF, diffic, *14 att(?) np
3683	Gx	11 27.5	+ 56 53 s	UMa	2.0	13p	cB, pL, E
2834 I		11 27.5	+ 13 34 d	Leo			vF, S, iF, diffic, other neb att f
2835 I		11 27.5	+ 12 09 d	Leo			cF, vS, R, bM, *14 f
2836 I		11 27.6	+ 9 05 d	Leo			F, vS, neb *15 n 1′
3682	Gx	11 27.7	+ 66 35 s	Dra	2.0	13p	cB, S, iR, spmbMN
3686	Gx	11 27.7	+ 17 13 s	Leo	3.3	11.4	pB, L, vlE, vgbM, r
2837 I		11 27.7	+ 10 19 d	Leo			cF, vS, R, bM, spir
2884 I		11 27.7	− 79 44 d	Cha			eeF, eS, cE 145°, susp
3688	Gx	11 27.8	− 9 10 r	Crt		15p	eF, eS, lE 0°, gbM
2838 I		11 27.8	+ 14 01 d	Leo			F, S
2839 I		11 27.8	+ 10 49 d	Leo			vF, S, iF
2840 I		11 27.8	+ 13 26 d	Leo			vF, S, iF, N
2841 I		11 27.8	+ 12 36 d	Leo			F, vS, R, bM, diffic
2842 I		11 27.8	+ 9 39 d	Leo			vF, S, iF
3687	Gx	11 28.0	+ 29 31 s	UMa	2.0	13p	pB, pS, R, lbM, r
3699	Pl	11 28.0	− 59 57 s	Cen	1.1		B, pL, iR, pgpmbM
695 I		11 28.0	− 11 43 d	Crt			eF, S, v diffic
2843 I	Gx	11 28.0	+ 13 11 z	Leo		15p	F, cS, R, bM, diffic, *8.7 f 2′
2844 I		11 28.0	+ 11 27 d	Leo			F, S, iF
2845 I		11 28.0	+ 12 32 d	Leo			F, vS, iF, N
2846 I		11 28.0	+ 11 09 m	Leo	0.8	15p	pB, vS, R, bM, *12 f
2847 I		11 28.1	+ 13 56 d	Leo			vF, vS, iF, diffic
3689	Gx	11 28.2	+ 25 40 s	Leo	1.6	12.3	pB, pL, lE, bM
3691	Gx	11 28.2	+ 16 55 s	Leo	1.3	14p	F, pS, lE, r
3693	Gx	11 28.2	− 13 10 r	Crt		13p	cF, S, E, gbM
2848 I		11 28.2	+ 13 02 d	Leo			vF, S, iF
2849 I		11 28.2	+ 9 06 d	Leo			pF, vS, R, bM
2850 I		11 28.2	+ 9 04 d	Leo			pB, S, E 120°, bM, *13 sf
2852 I		11 28.2	+ 9 48 d	Leo			F, vS, R, bM, spir; neb*?
2856 I	Gx	11 28.2	− 12 53 m	Crt	0.7	14p	vF, vS, cE 30°, cbM, susp
2851 I		11 28.3	+ 11 24 d	Leo			F, S
2853 I	Gx	11 28.3	+ 9 08 u	Leo	1.0	15p	pB, pS, E 160°, bM
2854 I		11 28.3	+ 8 58 d	Leo			F, vS, R, bM, spir
3692	Gx	11 28.4	+ 9 24 s	Leo	3.3	13p	F, mE, r
2855 I		11 28.4	+ 9 41 d	Leo			F, vS, iF, N

NGC	Type	α_{2000}	δ_{2000}	Const.	Size	Mag.	Description
		h m	o ′		′		
3690	Gx	11 28.5	+ 58 33 s	UMa	2.4	12p	pB, pS, vlE 80°±, pgbM, S st sf nr
694 I	Gx	11 28.5	+ 58 34 v	UMa	1.2		vS, forms Dneb with 3690
2857 I		11 28.5	+ 9 06 d	Leo			F, pL, mE 160°, bM
696 I	Gx	11 28.6	+ 9 05 u	Leo	1.0	14p	vF, pS, R, vlbM
697 I	Gx	11 28.6	− 1 37 z	Leo		15p	F, S, R, gbM
2858 I		11 28.6	+ 13 40 d	Leo			F, S, R, bM
3697	Gx	11 28.7	+ 20 48 r	Leo		14p	eF, vS, E 90°
2859 I		11 28.7	+ 9 07 d	Leo			cF, vS, R, bM
2860 I		11 28.7	+ 14 02 d	Leo			vF, S, iF, N
2862 I		11 28.7	+ 10 08 d	Leo			F, S, iF
3696	Gx	11 28.8	− 11 15 r	Crt			eF, eS, R, bMN
3694	Gx	11 28.9	+ 35 24 s	UMa	1.0	13p	cF, S, R, mbM
2863 I		11 28.9	+ 9 06 d	Leo			pF, vS, E 110°, bM
3698	−	11 29.0	+ 35 40 r	UMa			eF, vS
698 I	Gx	11 29.0	+ 9 06 u	Leo	1.0	14p	F, vS, R, bM
2861 I	Gx	11 29.0	+ 38 51 m	UMa	0.2	14p	F, S, R, dif
2864 I		11 29.0	+ 12 22 d	Leo			F, vS, iF
2865 I	*	11 29.0	+ 9 07 x	Leo			vF, S, dif
2866 I	*	11 29.0	+ 9 03 x	Leo			vS, vF, iF
2867 I		11 29.0	+ 9 05 d	Leo			cF, S, iF, v diffic, *14 np
2872 I	Nb	11 29.0	− 62 57 s	Cen	12		vL, mE, bM
699 I	Gx	11 29.1	+ 8 59 u	Leo	1.3	15p	F, vS, lE ns
2868 I		11 29.1	+ 9 06 x	Leo			vF, S, iF, N; = IC 698
2869 I		11 29.1	+ 9 01 d	Leo			vF, S, R, bM, spir
2870 I	Gx	11 29.1	+ 11 52 u	Leo	1.4	18p	F, pL, dif, diffic
3695	Gx	11 29.2	+ 35 35 r	UMa		15p	eF, pS, 3694 4′ s
700 I	Gx	11 29.3	+ 20 33 m	Leo	0.8	15p	pS, R, lbM
2871 I	Gx	11 29.3	+ 8 36 m	Leo	0.7	15p	F, cS, E 85°
3701	Gx	11 29.4	+ 24 05 r	Leo		14p	pF, pL, lE
3711	Gx	11 29.4	− 11 04 r	Crt		15p	eF, vS, *9 s 4′
3700	Gx	11 29.5	+ 35 31 r	UMa		15p	eF, 3694 p
2873 I	Gx	11 29.5	+ 13 12 m	Leo	0.6	15p	pF, cS, E 5°, bM
2874 I	OC	11 29.5	+ 10 38 x	Leo			F, pS, iF; Cl?
3703	−	11 29.6	− 8 37 r	Crt			eF, vS, gbMN
2875 I		11 29.6	+ 12 59 d	Leo			F, vS, R, bM, *9 sp
2876 I		11 29.6	+ 9 01 d	Leo			vF, S, dif
2877 I	Gx	11 29.6	+ 12 51 z	Leo		16p	F, S, R, lbM
2878 I		11 29.6	+ 9 58 d	Leo			pF, vS, iF, N
3706	Gx	11 29.7	− 36 25 s	Cen	2.9	12p	pB, cS, R, psmbM
2879 I		11 29.7	+ 9 01 d	Leo			vF, S, dif
2880 I		11 29.9	+ 13 12 d	Leo			pF, vS, R, bM
2881 I		11 29.9	+ 12 31 d	Leo			F, vS
3704	Gx	11 30.0	− 11 30 r	Crt		14p	vF, pS, *9-10 2′ ssf
3705	Gx	11 30.1	+ 9 17 s	Leo	5.0	11p	pF, pL, R, vsmbM, r
3707	−	11 30.1	− 11 32 r	Crt			vF, S, *15 (neb?) 2ˢf
3702	Gx	11 30.2	− 8 52 r	Crt		15p	eF, eS, R, glbM
2882 I		11 30.2	+ 11 59 d	Leo			vF, S, R, bM, diffic
2883 I		11 30.3	+ 10 55 d	Leo			F, vS, R, bM
2885 I		11 30.4	+ 9 46 d	Leo			F, vS, R, bM, spir
2886 I		11 30.4	+ 11 34 d	Leo			F, vS, R, bM, spir, *12 sf
2887 I	Gx	11 30.5	+ 9 23 z	Leo		15p	F, pS, E, curved, *10 nf 1′
2888 I		11 30.6	+ 9 55 d	Leo			pF, vS, E 130°
2889 I		11 30.6	− 13 05 d	Crt			eF, vS, cE 165°, bM, susp
3708	−	11 30.7	− 3 13 r	Leo			vF, S, R, gbM
3709	−	11 30.7	− 3 15 r	Leo			eF, eS

NGC	Type	α_{2000}	δ_{2000}	Const.	Size	Mag.	Description
		h m	o '		'		
701 I	Gx	11 30.8	+ 20 28 v	Leo	0.7		eF, vS, R, 2 pB st sf
2890 I		11 30.8	+ 13 11 d	Leo			vF, S, iF, N
2891 I		11 30.8	+ 12 41 d	Leo			F, S, iF, N, diffic
2892 I		11 30.8	+ 10 35 d	Leo			F, vS, iF
702 I		11 30.9	− 4 56 d	Leo			F, vS, R, N = 13.5
2893 I	Gx	11 30.9	+ 13 23 z	Leo		16p	F, eS, E 345°
3710	Gx	11 31.0	+ 22 46 r	Leo		14p	F, S, ∗7-8 nf 5′
2894 I	Gx	11 31.0	+ 13 13 z	Leo		16p	vF, cS, R, bM
2895 I		11 31.0	+ 9 59 d	Leo			F, vS, R, bM
3712	Gx	11 31.1	+ 28 34 r	UMa		15p	F, vS, R, smbM
2896 I		11 31.2	+ 12 21 d	Leo			pB, vS, annular?
2897 I		11 31.3	+ 11 33 d	Leo			cF, vS, R, bM, ∗14 p
2898 I		11 31.3	+ 13 20 d	Leo			vF, S, iF, ∗14 nf
2899 I		11 31.3	+ 10 38 d	Leo			F, S, E 350°; st?
3715	Gx	11 31.5	− 14 12 r	Crt		13p	pF, S, R, vgvlbM
3717	Gx	11 31.5	− 30 19 s	Hya	5.8	12p	pB, S, mE, ∗13 att
2900 I		11 31.5	+ 13 10 d	Leo			vF, S, R, bM
2901 I		11 31.5	+ 12 42 d	Leo			F, S, iF, N
3713	Gx	11 31.6	+ 28 09 r	Leo		14p	F, cS, R, sbMN
2902 I		11 31.6	+ 14 13 d	Leo			F, S, R, bM, diffic
3716	Gx	11 31.7	+ 3 30 r	Leo		14p	vF, vS
2903 I		11 31.7	+ 12 38 d	Leo			F, vS, iF, N
2904 I		11 31.7	+ 13 11 d	Leo			FN in vF, dif neb
3714	Gx	11 31.8	+ 28 22 r	UMa		14p	F, S, R, psbM
703 I		11 31.8	− 11 36 d	Crt			eeF, S, R, p of 2
2905 I		11 31.8	+ 9 06 d	Leo			vF, S, R, bM, ∗14 nf
2906 I		11 31.8	+ 13 08 d	Leo			F, vS, R, bM
2907 I		11 31.8	+ 9 54 d	Leo			vF, S, iF, N
2908 I		11 31.8	+ 12 56 d	Leo			vF, S, iF, ∗13 sp
2909 I		11 31.8	+ 11 28 d	Leo			vF, S, R, vlbM
2913 I	Gx	11 31.8	− 30 25 m	Hya	0.4	14p	B, pS, R, sf 3717
704 I		11 31.9	− 11 33 d	Crt			eF, vS (close D?), f of 2
2910 I	Gx	11 31.9	− 9 45 m	Crt	0.3	15p	vF, vS, sbM ∗13
2911 I		11 32.1	+ 12 59 d	Leo			vF, cS, iF, other nf
2912 I		11 32.1	+ 11 43 d	Leo			F, S, R, bM, diffic
3719	Gx	11 32.2	+ 0 49 s	Leo	2.0	14p	vF, np of 2
2914 I	Gx	11 32.2	+ 13 30 z	Leo		15p	F, S, R, bM
2915 I		11 32.3	+ 14 29 d	Leo			F, cS, R, bM
2916 I		11 32.3	+ 11 41 d	Leo			F, S, R, bM
2917 I		11 32.3	+ 10 57 d	Leo			vF, pS, iF
3720	Gx	11 32.4	+ 0 48 s	Leo	1.1	13.3	vF, sf of 2
3723	Gx	11 32.4	− 9 58 r	Crt		14p	F, S, R
2918 I		11 32.4	+ 13 15 d	Leo			vF, S, E 100°, bM
3718	Gx	11 32.6	+ 53 04 s	UMa	8.7	10.5	pB, vL, R, vglbM
2919 I		11 32.6	+ 14 11 d	Leo			pF, cS, R, bM
2920 I		11 32.8	+ 12 34 d	Leo			F, vS, iF, N
2921 I		11 32.8	+ 10 18 d	Leo			cF, S, R, bM, spir
705 I	Gx	11 32.9	+ 50 14 m	UMa	0.3	15p	eeF, vS, R
2922 I		11 32.9	+ 12 55 d	Leo			pB, vS, R, bM
2923 I		11 32.9	+ 13 10 d	Leo			vF, cS, iF, N, diffic, ∗10 sf
2924 I		11 32.9	+ 9 01 d	Leo			vF, S, iF, N, ∗11 nf
706 I	Gx	11 33.1	− 13 22 m	Crt	1.2	15p	eF, vS, lbM
2926 I		11 33.1	+ 12 26 d	Leo			pF, vS, R, stell N, spir
2927 I		11 33.1	+ 13 05 d	Leo			vF, vS, iF
3728	Gx	11 33.2	+ 24 27 r	Leo		14p	F, S, R, bM

NGC	Type	α_{2000}	δ_{2000}	Const.	Size	Mag.	Description
		h m	o '		'		
2925 I		11 33.2	+ 34 16 d	UMa			F, S, R, gbM, biN
3726	Gx	11 33.3	+ 47 02 s	UMa	6.0	10.4	pB, vL, lE 0°, vsmbM *15, *11 n
2928 I	Gx	11 33.5	+ 34 18 u	UMa	1.2	15p	F, cS, R, gbMN
2929 I		11 33.5	+ 12 08 d	Leo			F, pS, dif
707 I	Gx	11 33.6	+ 21 22 u	Leo	0.6	14p	pF, pS, bM
3725	Gx	11 33.7	+ 61 53 s	UMa	1.4	14p	cF, S, R, gvlbM, r
3727	Gx	11 33.7	− 13 52 r	Crt			eF, eS, R, gbMN, *11 sf 1'
2930 I	Gx	11 33.7	+ 10 05 z	Leo		16p	F, cS, E 60°, bM
3729	Gx	11 33.8	+ 53 08 s	UMa	3.1	11.4	pB, pL, lE 0°±, gbM, *12 nr
2931 I		11 33.8	+ 12 28 d	Leo			F, cS, N; neb*(?) 15m np 20''
708 I	Gx	11 33.9	+ 49 03 u	UMa	1.7	14p	eF, S, R, 1st of 4
2932 I		11 33.9	+ 10 33 d	Leo			pB, S, R, bM
3731	Gx	11 34.2	+ 12 32 r	Leo		14p	vF, vS, R
3732	Gx	11 34.2	− 9 51 s	Crt	1.3	13p	F, S, R, psbM, *14 sp 225°
709 I	Gx	11 34.2	+ 49 02 z	UMa		15p	eeF, S, R, 2nd of 4
2933 I	Gx	11 34.2	+ 34 18 u	UMa	1.4	15p	F, cS, E ns, gbMN
2934 I	Gx	11 34.3	+ 13 20 m	Leo	0.6	15p	F, S, iF, *14 nf 0'.5
3721	Gx	11 34.4	− 9 35 r	Crt		15p	eF, eS, R, gbM
710 I	Gx	11 34.4	+ 25 51 z	Leo		16p	F, vS, R, lbM
3722	Gx	11 34.5	− 9 39 r	Crt		16p	eF, vS, R, sbMN, 1st of 2
3724	Gx	11 34.5	− 9 41 r	Crt		15p	eF, vS, R, sbMN, 2nd of 2
3730	Gx	11 34.7	− 9 37 r	Crt			eF, S, lE 140°, glbnM
3734	Gx	11 34.7	− 14 06 r	Crt		14p	eF, S, R, gbM
711 I	Gx	11 34.7	+ 48 57 z	UMa		15p	eeF, pS, R, F, * close sp
712 I	Gx	11 34.8	+ 49 04 v	UMa	1.6		eF, S, R, pB, * nf
713 I		11 34.8	+ 16 51 d	Leo			eF, susp, 3' nnf from *6
2935 I		11 34.8	+ 10 15 d	Leo			cF, cS, E 130°, bM
2936 I		11 34.9	+ 13 01 d	Leo			F, S, R, bM
3733	Gx	11 35.0	+ 54 51 s	UMa	4.8	12p	eF, S, iR, *6 sf
2937 I		11 35.1	+ 10 06 d	Leo			F, S, R, bM
3742	Gx	11 35.4	− 37 56 r	Cen			pF, pL, vlE, glbM
3736	Gx	11 35.6	+ 73 28 r	Dra		15p	vF, vS, R
3737	Gx	11 35.6	+ 54 57 s	UMa	1.3	14p	vF, stellar
3739	Gx	11 35.6	+ 25 04 r	Leo		15p	vF, bet 2 st 12
2938 I	Gx	11 35.6	+ 13 41 z	Leo		15p	cF, pS
2939 I		11 35.6	+ 10 42 d	Leo			cF, S, R, bM
3738	Gx	11 35.8	+ 54 31 s	UMa	2.6	11.7	pB, pL, bM
3743	Gx	11 35.8	+ 21 44 r	Leo		15p	F, S, R, *9 1' sf
3744	Gx	11 35.8	+ 23 00 r	Leo		15p	eF, S, R, lbM
3749	Gx	11 35.8	− 37 59 r	Cen			F, cS, lE, gvlbM
3735	Gx	11 36.0	+ 70 32 s	Dra	4.2	12p	pB, L, mE 130°, mbM
3741	Gx	11 36.0	+ 45 18 r	UMa		14p	vF, S, R, vgbM
2940 I	D*	11 36.0	+ 21 46 x	Leo			eF, susp [not seen at Birr]
3766	OC	11 36.1	− 61 37 s	Cen	12	5.3	Cl, pL, pRi, pC, st 8...13
3777	Gx	11 36.1	− 12 34 r	Crt		14p	eF, pS, iR, gbM, S* or neb f
3740	Gx	11 36.2	+ 59 59 r	UMa		15p	vF, vS, R, vgbM
2941 I	Gx	11 36.2	+ 10 03 m	Leo	0.8	15p	F, pL R, bM, spir
2942 I		11 36.2	+ 11 49 d	Leo			cF, cS, R, bM
3758	Gx	11 36.4	+ 21 36 r	Leo		15p	pB, S, R, bM, *8.5 3' f
3763	Gx	11 36.4	− 9 50 r	Crt		13p	F, dif, sp 7 st; = IC 714?
714 I		11 36.5	− 9 51 d	Crt			vF, pS, lE 170°, gbMN
3755	Gx	11 36.6	+ 36 25 s	UMa	3.2	13p	eF, pL, pmE, gbM
2944 I	C+N	11 36.6	− 63 02 s	Cen	75	4.5	*3.4 in eL neb
2943 I	Gx	11 36.7	+ 54 51 v	UMa	0.4	14.8	pF, S
3756	Gx	11 36.8	+ 54 18 s	UMa	4.4	11.5	pF, L, lE

NGC	Type	α_{2000}	δ_{2000}	Const.	Size	Mag.	Description
		h m	° ′		′		
3761	Gx	11 36.8	+ 23 00 r	Leo		15p	vF, S, R, bM
3759	Gx	11 36.9	+ 54 49 s	UMa	1.5	14p	F, S, iR, *11 nr
3764	Gx	11 36.9	+ 17 54 r	Leo		15p	F, S, R
715 I		11 36.9	− 8 22 d	Crt			F, pS, R
3757	Gx	11 37.1	+ 58 26 r	UMa		13p	vF, R, stellar, vS* 1 d sf
3765	Gx	11 37.1	+ 24 07 r	Leo		15p	vF, S, R
2945 I	Gx	11 37.1	+ 12 55 u	Leo	1.2	15p	pF, pS
3768	Gx	11 37.2	+ 17 51 r	Leo		13p	vF, eS, stellar
3767	Gx	11 37.3	+ 16 53 r	Leo		14p	vF, S, bM
3747	−	11 37.5	+ 74 59 r	Dra			eF, S, place doubtful
3762	Gx	11 37.5	+ 61 46 r	UMa		13p	F, vlE, gbM
2946 I	Gx	11 37.5	+ 32 14 z	UMa		15p	F, S, R, gvlbM
2947 I	Gx	11 37.5	+ 31 22 m	UMa	0.6	15p	F, cS, R, gbM, r
3752		11 37.6	+ 75 17 d	Dra			pB, pL
3745	Gx	11 37.7	+ 22 01 s	Leo	0.4		pB, pS, R
3746	Gx	11 37.7	+ 22 00 s	Leo	1.3	15p	pB, pS, R
3769	Gx	11 37.7	+ 47 54 s	UMa	3.2	12p	pB, S, pmE
3748	Gx	11 37.8	+ 22 02 s	Leo	0.8		pB, pS, R
3772	Gx	11 37.8	+ 22 42 r	Leo		14p	vF, S, E, r
3750	Gx	11 37.9	+ 21 58 s	Leo	0.9		pB, R, cbM, 1st of 3 in line
3751	Gx	11 37.9	+ 21 56 s	Leo	0.4	15p	F, L, E 45°
3753	Gx	11 37.9	+ 21 59 s	Leo	2.0	15p	pB, pL, 2nd of 3 in line
3754	Gx	11 37.9	+ 21 59 s	Leo	0.4		vF, R, 3rd of 3 in line
3770	Gx	11 38.0	+ 59 37 r	UMa		13p	pF, S, R, gbM, r
3789	Gx	11 38.1	− 9 36 F	Crt		16p	eF, vS, E 0°, gbM
3773	Gx	11 38.2	+ 12 07 s	Leo	1.6	13p	cF, cS, R, psbM
3775	Gx	11 38.3	− 10 37 r	Crt		15p	pB, bMN
3776	Gx	11 38.3	− 3 20 r	Vir			eF, vS
3771	Gx	11 38.4	− 9 20 r	Crt			vF, eS, R, *10 p 15ˢ
3778	Gx	11 38.4	− 50 43 c	Cen	1.4		eF, S, am 50 S st
3774	Gx	11 38.6	− 8 59 r	Crt		15p	eF, vS, E 75°, *9 np 3′
2948 I	Nb	11 38.8	− 63 32 z	Cen	60		eeL
3779		11 38.9	− 10 37 D	Crt			eeF
3781	Gx	11 39.0	+ 26 22 r	Leo		15p	vF, vS, R, bM
3783	Gx	11 39.0	− 37 45 s	Cen	1.9	13p	cB, R, sbMN *, *9 sf
716 I	Gx	11 39.1	− 0 13 u	Vir	1.7	15p	vF, S, lbM
3782	Gx	11 39.3	+ 46 31 s	UMa	1.7	13p	F, S, att to *15, another * inv
3780	Gx	11 39.4	+ 56 16 s	UMa	3.1	12p	pF, L, vlE, vgbM, r
3784	Gx	11 39.4	+ 26 20 r	Leo		15p	vF, vS, R, gmbM
3793	Gx	11 39.4	+ 31 52 r	UMa		15p	vS, f 3788
717 I	?	11 39.4	− 10 39 z	Crt			eF, pS, E pf, dif
3785	Gx	11 39.5	+ 26 19 r	Leo		15p	vF, eS, R, bM
3794	Gx	11 39.6	+ 55 11 r	UMa		15p	cF, pS, vS* vnr
3786	Gx	11 39.7	+ 31 55 s	UMa	2.4	13p	pB, pL, E 57°, gbM, p of 2
3787	Gx	11 39.7	+ 20 29 r	Leo		14p	vF, vS, R, *15 p
3788	Gx	11 39.7	+ 31 56 s	UMa	2.2	13p	cB, pL, pmE 177°, pgbM
3790	Gx	11 39.8	+ 17 43 r	Leo		14p	cF, vS, pmE, sbM, 2 S st f, 1st of 3
3791	Gx	11 39.8	− 9 23 r	Crt		14p	vF, vS, R, gbM, *8 s 6′
3792	−	11 39.8	+ 5 00 r	Vir			vF, dif
718 I	Gx	11 39.9	+ 8 52 u	Vir	1.2	15p	vF, S
3795	Gx	11 40.1	+ 58 37 s	UMa	2.4	14p	vF, S, mE
3797	Gx	11 40.1	+ 31 54 h	UMa	0.2	15p	vS, f 3788
3798	Gx	11 40.2	+ 24 43 r	Leo		14p	F, cS, lE, stellar, r
3799	Gx	11 40.2	+ 15 20 s	Leo	0.9	14p	cF, R, p of 2
3800	Gx	11 40.2	+ 15 21 s	Leo	2.1	13p	F, pS, E, pglbM, r, f of 2

NGC	Type	α_{2000}	δ_{2000}	Const.	Size	Mag.	Description
		h m	° ′		′		
3801	Gx	11 40.3	+ 17 44 s	Leo	3.2	12.1	pF, pL, R, bM, r, 2nd of 3
3802	Gx	11 40.3	+ 17 46 s	Leo	1.4	13.6	vF, pS, r, 2 vB st p, 3rd of 3
3803	Gx	11 40.3	+ 17 49 r	Leo			vF, S, R
719 I	Gx	11 40.3	+ 9 00 s	Vir	1.7	14p	F, pL, lE 45°, bM
3796	Gx	11 40.6	+ 60 18 r	UMa		13p	F, cS, R, mbM
3808	Gx	11 40.7	+ 22 27 s	Leo	0.7	11.9	vF, vS
3805	Gx	11 40.8	+ 20 22 r	Leo		14p	cB, cS, R, bM, r
3806	Gx	11 40.8	+ 17 48 r	Leo		14p	F, pL, *9-10 s 5′
3807	Gx	11 40.8	+ 17 47 u	Leo	1.5	15p	vF, S, R (vF*?)
3804	Gx	11 40.9	+ 56 12 s	UMa	2.4	13p	pB, E
2949 I		11 40.9	− 46 29 d	Cen			no descr
3810	Gx	11 41.0	+ 11 28 s	Leo	4.3	10.8	B, L, vlE
3812	Gx	11 41.1	+ 24 51 r	Leo		14p	cF, vS, R, 1st of 3, *6 sf 3′
3809	Gx	11 41.3	+ 59 54 r	UMa		13p	pB, S, R, glbM
3811	Gx	11 41.3	+ 47 42 s	UMa	2.4	13p	F, S, vlE, glbM
3813	Gx	11 41.3	+ 36 33 s	UMa	2.3	11.7	cB, pL, pmE 83°, bM
3814	Gx	11 41.5	+ 24 49 r	Leo		15p	vS, nebs*, p 3815
2950 I	Gx	11 41.6	+ 37 58 z	UMa		15p	F, cS, lE pf, gbM, r
3815	Gx	11 41.7	+ 24 49 r	Leo		14p	cF, S, 3rd of 3
3816	Gx	11 41.8	+ 20 07 r	Leo		13p	F, S, bM
3817	Gx	11 41.9	+ 10 19 r	Leo		14p	F, 1st of 4
3818	Gx	11 42.0	− 6 09 s	Vir	2.1	11.8	F, pS, R, psbM
3819	Gx	11 42.1	+ 10 22 r	Leo		15p	vF, 2nd of 4
3820	Gx	11 42.1	+ 10 24 r	Leo		15p	eF, vS, 3819 s
3821	Gx	11 42.2	+ 20 20 r	Leo		14p	vF, cS, R, bM, bet 2 st
3822	Gx	11 42.2	+ 10 17 r	Vir		13p	pF, pS, 3rd of 4
3823	Gx	11 42.2	− 13 51 r	Crt		14p	F, cS, lE, pslbM
720 I	Gx	11 42.3	+ 8 46 m	Vir	1.0	15p	F, S, R
3825	Gx	11 42.4	+ 10 17 r	Vir		14p	pF, pS, 4th of 4
3826	Gx	11 42.4	+ 26 30 r	Leo		14p	pF, S, R, psbM, stellar
721 I	Gx	11 42.5	− 8 22 m	Crt	1.1	15p	pF, pL, E pf
3827	Gx	11 42.6	+ 18 51 r	Leo		13p	F, S, lbM
722 I		11 42.6	+ 9 04 d	Vir			eF, vS, *10 nf 2′
3824	Gx	11 42.8	+ 52 47 s	UMa	1.6	15p	vF, cS, pmE
3828	Gx	11 42.9	+ 16 30 r	Leo		15p	vF, S, dif
3901	Gx	11 43.0	+ 77 24 r	Cam		14p	pF, pL, r; place doubtful
723 I		11 43.0	− 8 19 d	Crt			pB, S, N = 12.5, r
3830	Gx	11 43.2	+ 26 35 r	Leo		14p	eF
3831	Gx	11 43.2	− 12 52 r	Crt			F, vS, R, bM
724 I		11 43.4	+ 9 02 d	Vir			F, lE 45°, S, bM
2951 I	Gx	11 43.4	+ 19 44 u	Leo	1.4	15p	*14 in neb
3829	Gx	11 43.5	+ 52 43 s	UMa	1.2	15p	vF, vS
3832	Gx	11 43.5	+ 22 44 r	Leo		14p	vF, pL, 2 suspected neb nr
3833	Gx	11 43.5	+ 10 10 r	Vir		14p	eF, pS
3836	Gx	11 43.5	− 16 48 r	Crt		13p	F, S, F* close n
725 I		11 43.5	− 1 40 z	Vir		15p	F, vS, lE ns, *11 n 1′
3834	Gx	11 43.6	+ 19 05 v	Leo	1.9		vF, vS, slbMN *13
3848	Gx	11 43.7	+ 10 16 r	Vir		15p	eF, vS
726 I		11 43.8	+ 33 18 d	UMa			vF, pL, R
3837	Gx	11 43.9	+ 19 54 r	Leo		14p	cF, S, R, 1st of 5
3839	Gx	11 43.9	+ 10 48 r	Leo		13p	vF, S, R, lbM
3840	Gx	11 43.9	+ 20 05 r	Leo		14p	F, S, lE
3843	Gx	11 43.9	+ 7 56 r	Vir		14p	F, E sp nf, *11 p
3841	Gx	11 44.0	+ 19 59 r	Leo		15p	cF, S, R, 2nd of 5
3842	Gx	11 44.0	+ 19 57 s	Leo	1.2	13p	F, S, R, vglbM, 3rd of 5

NGC	Type	α_{2000}	δ_{2000}	Const.	Size	Mag.	Description
		h m	o /		/		
3844	Gx	11 44.0	+ 20 02 r	Leo		15p	vF, pS, lE
3835	Gx	11 44.1	+ 60 07 s	UMa	2.0	13p	pB, E, gbM, sf 5'
3845	Gx	11 44.1	+ 20 00 r	Leo		15p	vF, pS, 4th of 5
3838	Gx	11 44.2	+ 57 57 s	UMa	1.7	13p	pB, cS, E, psbM *12
3847		11 44.2	+ 33 21 D	UMa			F, S, R, psbM
3849	–	11 44.2	+ 3 10 r	Vir			F, S, F* 2' ssp
3851	Gx	11 44.3	+ 19 59 r	Leo		15p	eF, vS, R, 5th of 5
3855		11 44.3	+ 33 20 D	UMa			eF, vS
2952 I		11 44.3	+ 33 20 d	UMa			pF, S, dif, vlbM
3852	–	11 44.4	+ 10 18 r	Vir			eF, vS; = 3848?
3853	Gx	11 44.4	+ 16 34 r	Leo		13p	S, R, bM
3856		11 44.4	+ 33 20 D	UMa			vF, R, bM
2953 I		11 44.4	+ 33 20 d	UMa			F, cS, dif, vlbM
3846	Gx	11 44.5	+ 55 40 s	UMa	1.2	15p	F, pL, R, vgbM
3854	–	11 44.5	– 9 22 r	Crt			eF, vS, lE 70°, bMN
727 I	Gx	11 44.5	+ 10 46 u	Leo	1.6	15p	vF, eS, R, 3839 p
3860	Gx	11 44.6	+ 19 49 r	Leo		14p	vF, vS, r
3857	Gx	11 44.8	+ 19 33 r	Leo		15p	vF, vS, mbM
3861	Gx	11 44.8	+ 20 00 r	Leo		14p	F, S, R, bM
3858	Gx	11 44.9	– 9 16 m	Crt	1.9	13p	eF, eS, R, gbM, *9.5 p 3ˢ
3859	Gx	11 44.9	+ 19 28 r	Leo		15p	eF, vS, R, lbM, r?
3865	Gx	11 44.9	– 9 14 s	Crt	2.3	13p	F, pL, dif
728 I	Gx	11 44.9	– 1 36 u	Vir	1.3	15p	vF, S, R
3862	Gx	11 45.1	+ 19 36 s	Leo	1.6	12.6	vF, vS, R, *17 n
3863	Gx	11 45.1	+ 8 29 r	Vir		14p	vF, 2' l, mE 70°, glbM
2955 I	Gx	11 45.1	+ 19 36 u	Leo	1.3	14p	eF, close to 3862
3864	Gx	11 45.2	+ 19 24 r	Leo		15p	eF, vS, R
729 I	Gx	11 45.2	+ 33 19 z	UMa		15p	F, pS, R
2954 I	Gx	11 45.2	+ 26 46 u	Leo	1.3	15p	F, S, R, gbM, stell
2956 I	Gx	11 45.2	+ 26 46 u	Leo	1.3	15p	pF, cS, lbM
3866	Gx	11 45.3	– 9 20 r	Crt		14p	sf 3865, not so L
3867	Gx	11 45.4	+ 19 24 r	Leo		14p	F, S, irrR, mbM, s of 2
3868	Gx	11 45.4	+ 19 27 r	Leo		15p	vF, vS, R, mbM, n of 2
3876	Gx	11 45.4	+ 9 11 D	Vir		13p	vF, r
3850	Gx	11 45.6	+ 55 53 s	UMa	2.3	14p	eF, pL, lE
730 I	Gx	11 45.6	+ 3 13 m	Vir	0.6	15p	F, vS, R, gbM, R
2957 I		11 45.6	+ 33 18 d	UMa			F, S, R, *14 nr f
3873	Gx	11 45.7	+ 19 47 r	Leo		14p	vF, pS, lE, 3875 sf
2958 I	Gx	11 45.7	+ 33 09 m	UMa	0.5	16p	F, S, dif
3869	Gx	11 45.8	+ 10 50 r	Leo		13p	F, S, iR, psbM
3872	Gx	11 45.8	+ 13 46 s	Leo	2.2	11.7	B, S, R, smbM *
3874	D*	11 45.8	+ 8 33 r	Vir			vF, vS, suspected
3875	Gx	11 45.8	+ 19 46 r	Leo		15p	vF, vS, r
3870	Gx	11 45.9	+ 50 12 s	UMa	1.3	13p	cF, cS, R, psbM
731 I		11 46.0	+ 49 34 d	UMa			vF, vS, R
732 I	Gx	11 46.0	+ 20 26 h	Leo	0.4	15p	vF, v dif
733 I		11 46.0	– 8 10 d	Crt			F, vS, R, gbM, r
3877	Gx	11 46.1	+ 47 30 s	UMa	5.4	12p	B, L, mE 37°
3882	Gx	11 46.1	– 56 22 A	Cen			vF, lE, 2 st inv
2959 I	Gx	11 46.1	+ 33 06 u	UMa	1.1	15p	vF, S, R, r
3871	Gx	11 46.2	+ 33 05 D	UMa		15p	eF, R, gbM, 1st of 4
3878	Gx	11 46.2	+ 33 12 r	UMa		15p	vF, R, 2nd of 4
3884	Gx	11 46.2	+ 20 25 r	Leo		14p	cF, S, iR, gbM, r, *7 sp 6'
734 I	Gx	11 46.2	– 8 17 m	Crt	0.8	16p	F, S, dif
3880	Gx	11 46.3	+ 33 10 r	UMa		15p	vF, R, gbM, 3rd of 4

NGC	Type	α_{2000}	δ_{2000}	Const.	Size	Mag.	Description
		h m	o ′		′		
2960 I	Gx	11 46.3	+ 34 59 z	UMa		16p	F, S, dif, vlbM
3881	Gx	11 46.5	+ 33 07 r	UMa		15p	vF, R, gbM, 4th of 4
3883	Gx	11 46.8	+ 20 42 r	Leo		14p	vF, cL
3885	Gx	11 46.8	− 27 55 s	Hya	1.7	13p	cF, vS, vlE, bM, vF∗ sf
3879	Gx	11 46.9	+ 69 24 r	Dra		13p	F, pL, mE 105°±
3886	Gx	11 47.1	+ 19 51 r	Leo		14p	F
3887	Gx	11 47.1	− 16 51 s	Crt	3.3	11.0	pB, L, iR, vgpmbM
3888	Gx	11 47.6	+ 55 58 s	UMa	1.8	13p	pB, S, lE, pgbM
2961 I	Gx	11 47.8	+ 31 21 z	UMa		15p	F, S, R, lbM
3889	Gx	11 47.9	+ 56 02 A	UMa		16p	vF, vS, 5′ nf 3888
3891	Gx	11 48.0	+ 30 23 r	UMa		13p	pB, S, bM
3892	Gx	11 48.0	− 10 58 s	Crt	2.8	12p	pB, pL, R, gbM, r
735 I		11 48.2	+ 10 13 d	Vir			eF, S, iF
736 I	Gx	11 48.4	+ 12 43 m	Leo	0.4	15p	vF, eS, R
737 I	Gx	11 48.5	+ 12 43 m	Leo	0.6	15p	vF, eS, R, N = 14
3893	Gx	11 48.6	+ 48 43 s	UMa	4.4	11p	B, pL, R, mbM
3894	Gx	11 48.8	+ 59 25 s	UMa	2.4	13p	B, pL, iR, pgmbM, p of 2
3896	Gx	11 48.9	+ 48 41 s	UMa	1.7	14p	F, vS
738 I		11 48.9	− 4 41 d	Vir			F, S, R, N = 14m
3897	Gx	11 49.0	+ 35 01 s	UMa	2.1	14p	F, S, R, bM .
3895	Gx	11 49.1	+ 59 26 s	UMa	1.4	14p	pF, pL, vlE, gbM, f of 2
3903	Gx	11 49.1	− 37 30 r	Cen			pB, cS, vlE, lbM
3905	Gx	11 49.1	− 9 44 s	Crt	1.8		vF, L, dif
2962 I		11 49.1	− 12 19 d	Crt			eF, cL, iR, 2 st n, f
3898	Gx	11 49.2	+ 56 05 s	UMa	4.4	10.8	B, pL, lE, svmbM
3899	−	11 49.2	+ 26 28 r	Leo			pB, R, smbM; = 3912?
3900	Gx	11 49.2	+ 27 01 s	Leo	3.5	11.4	B, pL, vlE 0°±, bMN
3904	Gx	11 49.2	− 29 17 s	Hya	2.2	11.0	pB, S, R, mbM
3902	Gx	11 49.3	+ 26 07 s	Leo	1.8	14p	F, pS, lE, vglbM
3890	Gx	11 49.4	+ 74 20 r	Dra		14p	vF, S, R, bM
3911	Gx	11 49.4	+ 24 57 r	Leo		15p	vF, S, p of 2
2963 I	Gx	11 49.4	− 5 07 m	Vir	1.1	14p	v diffic, ∗12 npp 20″
3907	Gx	11 49.5	− 1 04 r	Vir		14p	eF, S, psbM
3909	OC	11 49.6	− 48 15 A	Cen			Cl, vL, lC, st 9...14
3906	Gx	11 49.7	+ 48 26 s	UMa	1.9	14p	eF, pL
2964 I		11 49.8	+ 12 02 d	Leo			eeF, eF ∗ 3ˢf, 3′ s
3908	Gx	11 49.9	+ 12 11 r	Leo			F, vS, R, mbM
3172	Gx	11 50.	+ 89 07 s	UMi	0.7	13.6	vF, R, gbM, ∗11 s 2′, Polarissima Borealis
3910	Gx	11 50.0	+ 21 22 r	Leo		14p	S, R, mbM, ∗10-11 s 50″
3912	Gx	11 50.1	+ 26 29 s	Leo	1.7	13p	F, pL, R, pgbM
3920	Gx	11 50.1	+ 24 57 r	Leo		14p	neb, f of 2
3918	Pl	11 50.3	− 57 11 s	Cen	0.2	8p	◯, !, S, R, blue, = ∗7, d = 1ˢ.5
739 I		11 50.4	+ 23 49 d	Leo			vF, S, R, ∗10.5 f
2966 I	Nb	11 50.4	− 64 54 s	Mus	3		pL, bM
741 I	Gx	11 50.5	− 4 49 m	Vir	0.5	15p	pB, S, R, sbMN = 12m
3913	Gx	11 50.6	+ 55 21 s	UMa	2.6	13p	F, E
3914	Gx	11 50.6	+ 6 35 r	Vir		14p	F, vS, R, lbM, ∗13 np 80″
3915	−	11 50.6	− 5 08 r	Vir			eF, eS, bet 2 st
3919	Gx	11 50.6	+ 20 01 r	Leo		14p	F, S, R
740 I	Gx	11 50.6	+ 55 21 t	UMa	2.7	13p	eeF, pL, iR, 3916 s; = 3913
3916	Gx	11 50.8	+ 55 09 s	UMa	1.8	15p	eF, R, gbM
3917	Gx	11 50.8	+ 51 50 s	UMa	4.9	12p	F, L, vmE, vgbM
2967 I	Gx	11 50.8	+ 30 52 m	UMa	0.3	15p	pB, vS, stell N
3960	OC	11 50.9	− 55 42 s	Cen	7	8.3	Cl, pL, pRi, gpmbM, st 13
3923	Gx	11 51.0	− 28 48 s	Hya	2.9	10.1	B, pL, lE, gmbM, r, vS∗ sp inv

NGC	Type	α_{2000}	δ_{2000}	Const.	Size	Mag.	Description
		h m	° ′		′		
742 I	Gx	11 51.0	+ 20 48 u	Leo	1.3	15p	eeF, pS, R, pB* sp
3921	Gx	11 51.1	+ 55 05 s	UMa	2.2	13p	pF, S, R, pspmbM
3922	Gx	11 51.2	+ 50 11 r	UMa		14p	vF, vS
3931	Gx	11 51.2	+ 52 00 s	UMa	1.4	15p	eF, S
3925	Gx	11 51.3	+ 21 55 r	Leo		15p	vF, vS
3942	Gx	11 51.4	− 11 24 r	Crt		14p	eF, pS, E 160°, gvlbM
3926	Gx	11 51.5	+ 22 03 r	Leo		14p	eF, eS, vlE, er, st nr
3927	−	11 51.6	+ 28 09 r	Leo			pF, pS
3929	Gx	11 51.7	+ 21 01 r	Leo		14p	Cl, S, st F, vC
3928	Gx	11 51.8	+ 48 41 s	UMa	1.8	13p	pF, S, R, pspmbM
3930	Gx	11 51.8	+ 38 01 s	UMa	3.8	12p	eF, cL, iF, glbM, *7 (Grb 1830) f
3933	Gx	11 52.0	+ 16 49 r	Leo		14p	pF, lE
3934	Gx	11 52.2	+ 16 52 r	Leo		15p	eF, R
3936	Gx	11 52.3	− 26 54 s	Hya	4.0	13p	vF, cL, vmE 59°
3935	Gx	11 52.4	+ 32 25 r	UMa		14p	pF, S, lE, psbM
3932	Gx	11 52.5	+ 48 28 r	UMa		15p	vF, v diffic, 3928 np
3924	Gx	11 52.6	+ 50 01 s	UMa	1.9	15p	pB, S, iF, bM
2968 I	Gx	11 52.6	+ 20 36 m	Leo	0.4	14p	eF, vS, 3937 f 12″
2969 I	Gx	11 52.6	− 3 52 F	Vir			eF, pS, R, B* f 55″, np of 2
3937	Gx	11 52.7	+ 20 39 r	Leo		14p	vF, cS, R; = IC 2968
3940	Gx	11 52.7	+ 21 01 r	Leo		14p	vF, cS, R
3938	Gx	11 52.8	+ 44 07 s	UMa	5.4	10.4	B, vL, R, bMpBN, er
3941	Gx	11 52.9	+ 36 59 s	UMa	3.8	11p	vB, pL, R, smbM *9
3943	Gx	11 52.9	+ 20 30 r	Leo		14p	pF, pS, E, *8 p 24″
3944	Gx	11 53.1	+ 26 14 r	Leo		14p	pF, pS, R, psbM
3939	−	11 53.2	+ 75 07 r	Dra			eF, vS, R (place doubtful)
3945	Gx	11 53.2	+ 60 41 s	UMa	5.5	10.6	B, pL, R, gmbM, r, *12 sp
2970 I	**	11 53.2	− 23 03 x	Crt			pB, S, R, 3955 f
3946	Gx	11 53.4	+ 21 03 r	Leo		15p	vF, vlbM, dif
3947	Gx	11 53.4	+ 20 45 s	Leo	1.6	14p	F, pS, iE, lbM, ⁑ p
3948	Gx	11 53.4	+ 20 59 m	Leo	0.5	15p	vF, stellar
743 I		11 53.4	− 13 16 d	Crt			F, S, dif
2971 I	Gx	11 53.5	+ 30 41 z	UMa		16p	F, S, R, psbM
3949	Gx	11 53.7	+ 47 52 s	UMa	3.0	11.0	cB, pL, pmE, vgbM
3950	Gx	11 53.7	+ 47 56 r	UMa		15p	eF, 2′.6 n of 3949
3951	Gx	11 53.7	+ 23 24 r	Leo		14p	vF, cS, vlE
3952	Gx	11 53.7	− 4 00 s	Vir	1.5	13p	cF, cS, lE 90°±, bM, r
3954	Gx	11 53.7	+ 20 54 r	Leo		14p	eF, R
2972 I	Gx	11 53.7	− 3 59 m	Vir	0.9	14p	vF, pS, R, 2 B st n, np, sf of 2
3953	Gx	11 53.8	+ 52 20 s	UMa	6.6	10.1	cB, L, E 0°±, vsbMLrN
2973 I	Gx	11 53.8	+ 33 21 u	UMa	1.5	14p	F, cS, dif
2974 I	Gx	11 53.9	− 5 09 v	Vir	2.8		eeF, vS, lE
3955	Gx	11 54.0	− 23 10 s	Crt	3.2	11.9	cF, S, E 170°±, lbs
3956	Gx	11 54.0	− 20 34 s	Crt	3.5	13p	cF, pL, pmE 57°
3957	Gx	11 54.0	− 19 34 s	Crt	3.5	13p	F, S, E, r
2965 I	Gx	11 54.0	− 19 34 c	Crt	2.5		B, S, vmE, ray; = 3957
744 I	Gx	11 54.1	+ 23 12 z	Leo		16p	eF, vS, v diffic
2975 I		11 54.2	− 5 47 d	Vir			eeF, vS, lE, 3 B st in line n, circle of st n
745 I	Gx	11 54.3	+ 0 08 s	Vir	0.7	14p	F, vS, stellar, N = 14
2976 I		11 54.5	− 2 43 d	Vir			vF, vS, R, vF* nr nf
3958	Gx	11 54.6	+ 58 22 s	UMa	1.6	13p	pF, pS, pmE, vgbM
3959	Gx	11 54.6	− 7 44 r	Crt		14p	vF, S, bet 2 vF st
3962	Gx	11 54.7	− 13 58 s	Crt	2.9	10.6	cB, pL, iR, gmbM, △ 2 st
3964	Gx	11 54.8	+ 28 16 r	Leo		15p	vF, S, E, *10 nf att
3961	Gx	11 55.0	+ 69 20 r	Dra		14p	eF, vS

NGC	Type	α_{2000}	δ_{2000}	Const.	Size	Mag.	Description
		h m	° ′		′		
3963	Gx	11 55.0	+ 58 30 s	UMa	2.8	12p	pF, cL, R, vg, sbM
3965	–	11 55.1	− 10 52 r	Crt			eF, eS, R, bMN, *9.5 np 4′
3969	Gx	11 55.1	− 18 56 r	Crt		14p	eF, vS, gbMN, *8.5 nearly n
3967	Gx	11 55.2	− 7 50 r	Crt		15p	vF, S, F* close p
2977 I	Gx	11 55.2	− 37 42 c	Cen	2.0		eF, vS, *7 sp
3970	Gx	11 55.3	− 12 02 r	Crt		14p	F, S, R, psbM, p of 2
3968	Gx	11 55.5	+ 11 58 s	Leo	3.0	13p	pB, L, iR, bM, *10, 65°, 3′
3971	Gx	11 55.6	+ 30 00 r	UMa		14p	pF, vS, R, bM
3973	Gx	11 55.6	+ 12 01 r	Leo		15p	eF, eS, *10 1′ sf (requires verification)
746 I	Gx	11 55.6	+ 25 53 u	Leo	1.3	14p	F, pS, R
3966	Gx	11 55.7	+ 32 12 r	UMa		14p	F, pL, lE, bM, *12 p
3974	Gx	11 55.7	− 12 00 r	Crt		14p	vF, S, R, bM, f of 2
3972	Gx	11 55.8	+ 55 19 s	UMa	4.0	13p	pB, E
3975	Gx	11 55.9	+ 60 32 s	UMa	0.8	15p	vF, vS, 3978 f 17^s
3976	Gx	11 56.0	+ 6 45 s	Vir	3.9	12p	B, pL, cE 30°, vsmbMN
3977	Gx	11 56.1	+ 55 24 s	UMa	1.7	13p	F, S
3979	Gx	11 56.1	− 2 42 r	Vir		14p	pF, *11-12 nf
3980	Gx	11 56.1	+ 55 23 u	UMa	1.8	15p	eF, pL, E, D* nr
3981	Gx	11 56.1	− 19 54 s	Crt	3.9	12p	vF, pL, iF
3978	Gx	11 56.2	+ 60 31 s	UMa	1.8	15p	cF, S, lE, bM, *8, 90°, 6′
3983	Gx	11 56.4	+ 23 53 r	Leo		15p	cF, cS, R, psbM
2978 I	Gx	11 56.4	+ 32 01 u	UMa	1.1	15p	vF, S, v dif
3982	Gx	11 56.5	+ 55 08 s	UMa	2.5	12p	B, pL, R, g, sbM disc
3985	Gx	11 56.7	+ 48 20 s	UMa	1.2	13p	vF, cS, another suspected
3986	Gx	11 56.7	+ 32 01 s	UMa	3.1	14p	pF, S, pmE 90° ±, *11 nr
2979 I		11 56.9	+ 33 09 d	UMa			F, S, R, lbM, r
747 I		11 57.1	− 8 18 d	Vir			F, vS, R, stellar
3987	Gx	11 57.3	+ 25 12 s	Leo	2.5	14p	F, mE
3988	Gx	11 57.4	+ 27 53 r	Leo		14p	vF, S, R, bM *, p of 2
3989	Gx	11 57.4	+ 25 14 r	Leo		15p	eF, vS, R
3991	Gx	11 57.5	+ 32 20 s	UMa	1.4	13.2	F, S, lE, 1st of 3
748 I	Gx	11 57.5	+ 7 28 m	Vir	0.3	15p	F, vS, R, sbMN = 13
2980 I	Gx	11 57.5	− 73 41 c	Mus	2.0		eeF, eS, R, cbM
3990	Gx	11 57.6	+ 55 28 s	UMa	1.7	12.6	pF, S, lE, pslbM
3992	Gx	11 57.6	+ 53 23 s	UMa	7.6	9.8	cB, vL, pmE, sbMBrN; = M109
3993	Gx	11 57.6	+ 25 15 s	Leo	1.9	15p	vF, pS, E, 3 st nr
3994	Gx	11 57.6	+ 32 17 s	UMa	1.1	12.7	pB, vS, 2nd of 3
3995	Gx	11 57.7	+ 32 18 s	UMa	2.8	12.6	F, pL, iR, bM, 3rd of 3
3984	Gx	11 57.8	+ 29 03 r	UMa		15p	eF, S, R, bM
3996	Gx	11 57.8	+ 14 19 r	Leo		14p	vF, pL, R, 2 st f
3997	Gx	11 57.8	+ 25 16 s	Leo	1.8	14p	pF, vS, E 25°, bet 2 st
2981 I		11 57.8	+ 33 11 d	UMa			F, S, R, gvlbM
2982 I		11 57.8	+ 27 49 d	Leo			vF, stell, *10 nr
3998	Gx	11 57.9	+ 55 27 s	UMa	3.1	10.6	cB, pS, R, vg, smbM
4000	Gx	11 58.0	+ 25 09 r	Leo		15p	vF, vS, lE, *8 2′ f, 4005 is sf
4002	Gx	11 58.0	+ 23 13 r	Leo		14p	vF, vS, R, n of 2
4003	Gx	11 58.0	+ 23 08 r	Leo		15p	vF, vS, R, s of 2
4001	Gx	11 58.1	+ 47 20 r	UMa		15p	S, R, 7′ np 4010
4004	Gx	11 58.1	+ 27 53 s	Leo	2.2	14p	F, vS, R, *12 near
4005	Gx	11 58.2	+ 25 08 r	Leo		14p	pF, vS, mbM, *7 np 2′
4006	Gx	11 58.2	− 2 05 r	Vir		14p	F, S, R, bM, *11 nf; = IC 2983
4007		11 58.2	+ 25 08 A	Leo			eF, vS; = 4005
4008	Gx	11 58.3	+ 28 12 s	Leo	2.5	12.0	pB, pS, E, psbM, * inv n
2983 I	*	11 58.3	− 2 05 F	Vir			eF
3999	Gx	11 58.4	+ 25 09 r	Leo		15p	vF, S

NGC	Type	α_{2000}	δ_{2000}	Const.	Size	Mag.	Description
		h m	o '		'		
4009	Gx	11 58.4	+ 25 13 r	Leo			vF, eS
4011	Gx	11 58.4	+ 25 07 r	Leo		15p	vF, vS, *12 np
4016	Gx	11 58.4	+ 27 31 s	Leo	1.5	15p	vF
4012	Gx	11 58.5	+ 10 02 r	Vir		14p	vF, S, lE
4013	Gx	11 58.5	+ 43 57 s	UMa	5.2	12p	B, cL, mE 62°, vsvmbM *10
4024	Gx	11 58.5	− 18 21 s	Crv	2.3	13p	F, vS, iF, bM
4010	Gx	11 58.6	+ 47 16 s	UMa	4.2	13p	F, pL, mE, vglbM
4014	Gx	11 58.6	+ 16 11 r	Com		13p	pB, pS, R, psbM
749 I	Gx	11 58.6	+ 42 44 s	UMa	2.5	12.2	pB, L, R, lbM
4015	Gx	11 58.7	+ 25 03 r	Com		14p	F, vS, E, mbM
4017	Gx	11 58.7	+ 27 26 s	Com	1.8	13p	F, L, E, gbfM
4018	Gx	11 58.7	+ 25 20 r	Com		14p	mE np sf, 2 st s
4019	−	11 58.9	+ 14 13 r	Com			ef, *9 sf 5'
4020	Gx	11 58.9	+ 30 25 s	UMa	2.1	13p	pB, pL, E 20°, biN
750 I	Gx	11 58.9	+ 42 43 s	UMa	2.9	11.8	pB, L, lE 35°, bM
751 I	Gx	11 58.9	+ 42 34 v	UMa	1.5		pF, pL, lE 45°, mbM
4021	Gx	11 59.0	+ 25 06 r	Com		15p	F, S, vlE
4022	Gx	11 59.0	+ 25 14 r	Com		14p	pF, vS, stellar
4023	Gx	11 59.1	+ 25 00 r	Com		14p	pF, pL, dif
2984 I		11 59.1	+ 30 42 d	UMa			F, cS, R, vlbM
4025	Gx	11 59.2	+ 37 48 s	UMa	3.3	15p	ef, pL, R
753 I	Gx	11 59.2	− 0 30 u	Vir	0.6	14p	pB, vS, R, vmbM, *11 nf
2985 I		11 59.2	+ 30 44 d	UMa			pF, S, dif
752 I	Gx	11 59.3	+ 42 33 z	UMa		15p	vF, S, iR, *13 nf 1'.5
4026	Gx	11 59.4	+ 50 58 s	UMa	5.1	12p	vB, cL, mE 176°, vsvmbMBN
754 I	Gx	11 59.4	− 1 38 u	Vir	0.9	14p	F, S, R, sbM
4027	Gx	11 59.5	− 19 16 s	Crv	3.0	11.1	⊕, pF, pL, R, rr, st 16
2986 I	Gx	11 59.8	+ 30 52 m	UMa	0.6	15p	F, vS, R, N, r
4028	−	11 59.9	+ 16 14 r	Com			vF, vS, vlE, r
4029	Gx	12 00.1	+ 8 12 r	Vir		14p	vF, vS, lE, stellar N
4030	Gx	12 00.4	− 1 06 s	Vir	4.3	12p	cB, L, vlE, psmbM, B st nr
4031	Gx	12 00.5	+ 31 57 r	UMa		14p	ef, vS, *17 vnr south
4035	Gx	12 00.5	− 15 57 v	Crv	1.4		ef, pL, *9 45°±
4032	Gx	12 00.6	+ 20 04 s	Com	2.1	13p	pF, pL, R, gbM, *12 nf
4033	Gx	12 00.6	− 17 51 s	Crv	2.5	13p	pB, S, lE, bM
755 I	Gx	12 01.2	+ 14 06 v	Com	2.7		eeF, S, E, bet 2 st
4036	Gx	12 01.4	+ 61 54 s	UMa	4.5	10.6	vB, vL, E
4037	Gx	12 01.4	+ 13 24 s	Com	2.7	13p	ef, pL, R, r
4034	Gx	12 01.5	+ 69 19 r	Dra			ef, S, iF, gvlbM
4038	Gx	12 01.9	− 18 52 s	Crv	2.6	10.7	pB, cL, R, vgbM
4039	Gx	12 01.9	− 18 53 s	Crv	3.2	13p	pF, pL
4052	OC	12 01.9	− 63 12 s	Cru	8	9p	Cl, pRi, lC
4040	Gx	12 02.2	+ 17 50 r	Com		15p	ef, pS, R, 3 st nr
4041	Gx	12 02.2	+ 62 08 s	UMa	2.8	11.1	B, cL, R, g, psvmbMrN
4042	−	12 02.4	+ 20 09 r	Com			vF, vS; = 4032?
4043	Gx	12 02.4	+ 4 21 r	Vir		14p	pF, S, R, psbM, ☆ f 30ˢ
4044	Gx	12 02.5	− 0 11 r	Vir		14p	cF, cS, R, bM
4045	Gx	12 02.7	+ 1 59 s	Vir	2.8	11.8	pF, L, R, sbM, * sf
4046	−	12 02.8	+ 1 45 r	Vir			F, pS, △ 2 F st; = 4045?
4047	Gx	12 02.9	+ 48 38 s	UMa	1.5	13p	pB, pS, R
4048	Gx	12 02.9	+ 18 01 r	Com		14p	vF, vS, R, psbM
4050	Gx	12 02.9	− 16 22 s	Crv	3.1	12p	F, cL, iR, lbM
4049	Gx	12 03.0	+ 18 46 r	Com		14p	ef, pS, R, glbM
756 I	Gx	12 03.0	+ 4 50 u	Vir	2.1	15p	vF, pL
4051	Gx	12 03.2	+ 44 32 s	UMa	5.0	10.3	B, vL, E, vgvsmbM *11

NGC	Type	α_{2000}	δ_{2000}	Const.	Size	Mag.	Description
		h m	o '		'		
4053	Gx	12 03.2	+ 19 44 r	Com		14p	F, vS, vlE, alm stell
4054	Gx	12 03.2	+ 57 54 r	UMa		15p	eF, S
757 I	D∗	12 03.4	+ 52 39 z	UMa		13p	susp, close to ∗12
2987 I	Gx	12 03.4	+ 38 49 v	UMa			F, S, N, dif
4055	–	12 03.7	+ 21 04 r	Com			pB (decl very doubtful)
2988 I		12 03.7	+ 3 24 d	Vir			eF, r, ∗11.5 sf 2'.7
4058	Gx	12 03.8	+ 3 34 r	Vir		14p	vF, pS, R, bM
4059	–	12 03.9	+ 21 19 r	Com			pB (decl very doubtful)
4056	Gx	12 04.0	+ 20 19 r	Com			eF, vS
4068	Gx	12 04.0	+ 52 35 s	UMa	3.2	13p	pF, S, stellar
4060	Gx	12 04.1	+ 20 21 r	Com		15p	eF
4061	Gx	12 04.1	+ 20 13 s	Com	1.5	14p	vF, S, R, p of Dneb, pos 80°
4062	Gx	12 04.1	+ 31 54 s	UMa	4.3	11.2	pB, vL, mE 97°, vgbM
4063	Gx	12 04.1	+ 1 52 r	Vir		15p	eF, vS, B pts inv
4064	Gx	12 04.2	+ 18 27 s	Com	4.5	11.5	B, E, gbM
4065	Gx	12 04.2	+ 20 13 s	Com	1.5	14p	pF, R, f of Dneb
4066	Gx	12 04.2	+ 20 22 r	Com		14p	pB
4067	Gx	12 04.2	+ 10 51 s	Vir	1.5	13p	F, pS, R, gbM
4069	Gx	12 04.2	+ 20 20 r	Com			vF, vS
4070	Gx	12 04.2	+ 20 26 r	Com		14p	F, vS
4071	Pl	12 04.2	− 67 18 s	Mus	1.3		vF, vS, R, bM∗, am st
758 I	Gx	12 04.2	+ 62 30 s	UMa	2.0	13p	eeF, pS, R, bet 2 distant st
4072	Gx	12 04.3	+ 20 13 r	Com		15p	eF, sf 4061, 4062, 4065
4073	Gx	12 04.5	+ 1 54 s	Vir	2.5	13p	F, pS, R, pgbM, np of 2
4074	Gx	12 04.6	+ 20 20 r	Com		15p	eF, vS
4076	Gx	12 04.6	+ 20 12 r	Com		14p	vF, vS
4081	Gx	12 04.6	+ 64 26 s	UMa	1.8	14p	F, S, mE, D∗ nr
4075	Gx	12 04.7	+ 2 05 r	Vir		14p	F, S, R
4077	Gx	12 04.7	+ 1 48 r	Vir		14p	cF, cS, vlE, bM, sf of 2
2989 I	Gx	12 04.7	+ 1 47 u	Vir	1.1	14p	vF, S, bM or 2 or 3 eF st inv
2990 I	Gx	12 04.7	+ 11 02 m	Vir	0.6	15p	eF, R, poss ◯
4078	Gx	12 04.8	+ 10 36 r	Vir		14p	F, vS, R, glbM
4079	Gx	12 04.8	− 2 23 s	Vir	2.4	14p	F, L, R, ∗10 n 1'
4080	Gx	12 05.0	+ 27 00 r	Com		14p	cF, pS, E, gbM
2991 I		12 05.1	+ 10 37 d	Vir			eF, S, E 10°, bet 4082 and 83
759 I		12 05.2	+ 20 15 d	Com			pB, pL, E pf
2992 I		12 05.2	+ 30 21 d	UMa			F, S, R, gbMN, r
2993 I		12 05.2	+ 32 52 d	UMa			F, S, N, dif, r
4057	Gx	12 05.3	+ 20 19 r	Com			pB (decl very doubtful)
4082	Gx	12 05.3	+ 10 41 r	Vir		15p	vF, vS, lE, lbM
4083	Gx	12 05.3	+ 10 37 r	Vir		15p	eF, vS
4084	Gx	12 05.3	+ 21 14 r	Com		15p	F, S
4085	Gx	12 05.4	+ 50 21 s	UMa	2.8	12.3	B, pL, pmE 78°, vsbM
4086	Gx	12 05.5	+ 20 15 r	Com		15p	F, pS, R
4090	Gx	12 05.5	+ 20 19 r	Com		15p	vF, vS, ∗15 f 1'; = IC 2997
2994 I	Gx	12 05.5	+ 12 41 z	Vir		16p	eF, R, bM
4087	Gx	12 05.6	− 26 33 r	Hya		13p	pB, S, R, bM
4088	Gx	12 05.6	+ 50 33 s	UMa	5.8	10.5	B, cL, E 55°, lbM
4089	Gx	12 05.6	+ 20 34 r	Com		15p	vF, S, R, p of 2
4091	Gx	12 05.7	+ 20 34 r	Com		15p	vF, S, R, f of 2
2995 I	Gx	12 05.8	− 27 56 s	Hya	3.1	13p	vF, L, cE 120°, ∗8 f
2997 I		12 05.8	+ 20 17 d	Com			eF, ∗12 sf 2'; = 4090?
4092	Gx	12 05.9	+ 20 30 r	Com		14p	F, pS, R, ∗11 np
4093	Gx	12 05.9	+ 20 33 r	Com		15p	eF, vS
4094	Gx	12 05.9	− 14 32 s	Crv	4.2	12p	eF, L, pmE, vgbM, 2 st 11 nr

NGC	Type	α_{2000}	δ_{2000}	Const.	Size	Mag.	Description
		h m	° ′		′		
760 I	Gx	12 05.9	− 29 18 c	Hya	1.6		F, S, R, bM, E 150°?
2996 I	Gx	12 05.9	− 30 00 m	Hya	0.8	14p	F, vS, E 20°, * sp
2998 I		12 05.9	+ 20 45 d	Com			vF, others near
2999 I	Gx	12 05.9	+ 31 21 z	UMa		16p	vF, vS, N
4095	Gx	12 06.0	+ 20 35 r	Com		14p	vF, vS
4096	Gx	12 06.0	+ 47 29 s	UMa	6.5	10.6	pB, vL, mE 32°
761 I	Gx	12 06.0	− 12 40 m	Crv	0.6	15p	neb *14
4097	Gx	12 06.1	+ 36 52 r	UMa		14p	eF, vS, R, stellar, *10 sp 2′
4098	Gx	12 06.1	+ 20 37 r	Com		14p	eF, eS, R, bM
4099	−	12 06.1	+ 20 39 r	Com			eF, eS
3000 I		12 06.1	− 29 41 d	Hya			F, indistinct (defect?)
4100	Gx	12 06.2	+ 49 35 s	UMa	5.2	12p	pB, vL, vmE 161°, vgvlbM
4101	Gx	12 06.2	+ 25 34 r	Com		14p	eF, vS, R, vgbM
3001 I	Gx	12 06.2	+ 33 31 m	UMa	0.7	15p	F, S, R, gbM
4102	Gx	12 06.4	+ 52 43 s	UMa	3.2	12p	B, pS, R, bMBN, *12 sp, vnr
4104	Gx	12 06.6	+ 28 10 s	Com	3.0	14p	pB, pS, lE, bM
4103	OC	12 06.7	− 61 15 s	Cru	7	7p	Cl, pL, pC, iR, st 10...14
4105	Gx	12 06.7	− 29 46 s	Hya	2.4	12p	pF, pS, R, psbM, r, p of 2
4107		12 06.7	+ 10 36 D	Vir			pB, S, lE, *10-11 np
4106	Gx	12 06.8	− 29 46 s	Hya	1.9	11.4	pF, pS, R, pgbM, f of 2
4108	Gx	12 06.8	+ 67 10 s	Dra	1.9	13p	B, S, R, gbM
4109	Gx	12 06.9	+ 43 00 s	CVn	0.8	15p	vF, 4111 nnf 6′
4110	Gx	12 07.1	+ 18 32 r	Com		14p	F, S
4111	Gx	12 07.1	+ 43 04 s	CVn	4.8	10.8	vB, pS, mE 151°
4112	Gx	12 07.1	− 40 11 r	Cen			F, S, vlE, glbM, 3 B st nr
3002 I	Gx	12 07.1	+ 33 22 m	CVn	0.5	15p	F, cS, R, gbM, r
3003 I		12 07.1	+ 32 51 d	Com			F, S, dif, N, r
4113	−	12 07.2	+ 34 00 r	CVn			eF; nonexistent?
4114	Gx	12 07.2	− 14 11 s	Crv	2.3	13p	cF, S, iR, gbM
4115	−	12 07.2	+ 14 25 r	Com			eF, suspected
4122	Gx	12 07.2	+ 33 00 r	Com		15p	eF, vS, R, mbM
3004 I	Gx	12 07.2	+ 13 14 m	Vir	0.9	16p	R, bM, mag 15
3005 I	Gx	12 07.2	− 30 01 c	Hya	2.2		F, S, eE 160°, stell N
3006 I		12 07.4	+ 12 59 d	Vir			R, bM, mag 15
3007 I	Gx	12 07.4	+ 31 21 z	Com		15p	vF, vS, diffic
4116	Gx	12 07.6	+ 2 42 s	Vir	3.8	11.9	vF, E (hook shape), sp of 2
4117	Gx	12 07.8	+ 43 08 s	CVn	2.8	14p	vF, vS
4118	Gx	12 07.9	+ 43 07 s	CVn	0.9	16p	eF, vS, 1′ s of 4117
4119	−	12 07.9	+ 9 33 r	Vir			lE; nonexistent?
4121	Gx	12 07.9	+ 65 07 s	Dra	0.6	14p	F, vS, lE, r
3010 I	Gx	12 07.9	− 30 20 c	Hya	1.9		eF, cS, R, 2 st 10 sf 8′
3008 I	Gx	12 08.0	+ 13 33 m	Com	0.8	15p	R, bM, mag 13.5
3009 I	?	12 08.0	+ 12 39 x	Vir			pB, cS
4125	Gx	12 08.1	+ 65 11 s	Dra	5.1	9.8	pB, pL, cE, mbM
762 I	Gx	12 08.1	+ 25 45 m	Com	0.6	15p	pB, S, R, N = 12m
4123	Gx	12 08.2	+ 2 53 s	Vir	4.5	11.2	cF, vL, E 90°±, bMN
4124	Gx	12 08.2	+ 10 23 s	Vir	4.6	12p	pB, pL, mE 118°, bM, r; = IC 3011
763 I	Gx	12 08.2	+ 25 49 m	Com	0.8	15p	F, vS, N = 13m
3011 I	Gx	12 08.2	+ 10 22 t	Vir	3.8	12p	pF, pS, E 110°; = 4124
4127	Gx	12 08.4	+ 76 48 s	Cam	2.3	13p	F, pL, vlE, glbM
4120	Gx	12 08.5	+ 69 33 s	Dra	1.9	14p	eF, vS, E
4128	Gx	12 08.5	+ 68 46 s	Dra	2.8	13p	cB, lE, bM
3012 I	Gx	12 08.5	+ 11 10 z	Vir		15p	R, ○ ?, mag 15
3013 I	Gx	12 08.5	+ 10 01 m	Vir	0.8	15p	bM, mag 15
3014 I	Gx	12 08.5	+ 38 49 u	CVn	1.1	14p	pB, cS, R, gbM, r

NGC	Type	α_{2000}	δ_{2000}	Const.	Size	Mag.	Description
		h m	° ′		′		
4133	Gx	12 08.6	+ 74 56 r	Dra		13p	pB, cL, R, gmbM
4126	Gx	12 08.7	+ 16 09 r	Com		14p	vF, S, R, pslbM, bet 2 vS st
4131	Gx	12 08.7	+ 29 18 s	Com	1.6	14p	cF, S, R, 1st of 3
4129	Gx	12 08.9	− 9 02 s	Vir	2.6	12.6	F, pL, pmE 95°±, vglbM
4130	−	12 08.9	− 4 00 r	Vir			pE, lbM, *13 p 5′
4132	Gx	12 09.0	+ 29 14 s	Com	1.1	15p	cF, S, iR, 2nd of 3
3015 I	Gx	12 09.0	− 31 31 c	Hya	3.0		pB, mE 45°, *10.5 sf 1′
4134	Gx	12 09.2	+ 29 11 r	Com		14p	pF, pL, lE, 3rd of 3
4135	Gx	12 09.2	+ 44 00 s	CVn	1.0	15p	vF, pS, R, 2 F st inv
4136	Gx	12 09.3	+ 29 56 s	Com	4.1	12p	F, vL, vgmbM
4137	Gx	12 09.3	+ 44 06 s	CVn	1.2	15p	vF, pS, R, l fainter than 4135
3016 I	Gx	12 09.4	+ 11 25 z	Vir		16p	S, R, bM
3017 I		12 09.4	+ 13 36 d	Com			R, bM, dif, mag 14.5
3019 I	Gx	12 09.4	+ 14 00 x	Com			R, bM, dif, mag 14.5
4138	Gx	12 09.5	+ 43 41 s	CVn	2.9	12p	B, pL, lE, vgbM, * np
4142	Gx	12 09.5	+ 53 06 s	UMa	2.3	14p	vF, S, iF, vglbM, er
3018 I	?	12 09.5	+ 14 04 x	Com			R, lbM, mag 13.5
4139	−	12 09.6	+ 1 49 r	Vir			F, S, diffic, p of Dneb
4143	Gx	12 09.6	+ 42 32 s	CVn	2.9	12p	cB, R, vg, vsbMN
3020 I		12 09.6	+ 14 13 d	Com			R, bM, mag 14
4140	−	12 09.7	+ 1 48 r	Vir			F, S, diffic, f of Dneb
4141	Gx	12 09.7	+ 58 51 r	UMa		14p	vF, pS, lE, gbM, r
3022 I	Gx	12 09.9	+ 38 43 m	CVn	0.2	14p	pB, pS, gbM
4144	Gx	12 10.0	+ 46 27 s	UMa	5.9	12p	pF, cL, vmE 109°, vgbM
4145	Gx	12 10.0	+ 39 53 s	CVn	5.8	11.0	B, vL, vglbM
3021 I	Gx	12 10.0	+ 13 01 u	Vir	1.8	15p	R, bM, v dif, mag 14.5
4147	Gb	12 10.1	+ 18 33 s	Com	4.0	10.3	⊕, vB, pL, R, gbM, rrr
4148	Gx	12 10.1	+ 35 52 s	CVn	1.8	15p	F, S, *12 sf
3023 I		12 10.1	+ 14 21 d	Com			R, bM, dif, mag 15
764 I	Gx	12 10.2	− 29 44 s	Hya	4.8	12p	eF, pL, E ns, lbM
4146	Gx	12 10.3	+ 26 26 s	Com	1.6	14p	vF, pS
3024 I	Gx	12 10.3	+ 12 18 u	Vir	1.2	15p	R, bM, mag 13.5
4149	Gx	12 10.4	+ 58 19 r	UMa		14p	F, S, E
3025 I	Gx	12 10.4	+ 10 11 m	Vir	0.4	15p	S, E, bM
4151	Gx	12 10.5	+ 39 24 s	CVn	5.9	10.4	vB, S, R, vsmbMBN, p of 2
765 I	D*	12 10.5	+ 16 08 x	Com			vF, susp 6′ n of 4152
3027 I	?	12 10.5	+ 14 11 x	Com			bM, mag 14
3028 I		12 10.5	+ 11 45 d	Vir			bM, mag 15
4150	Gx	12 10.6	+ 30 24 s	Com	2.5	11.7	B, S, R, pgmbM
4152	Gx	12 10.6	+ 16 02 s	Com	2.3	12.0	pB, pL, R, pgmbM, r
3026 I	*	12 10.6	− 29 56 x	Hya			vF, vS, mE 40°, bet 2 st
4154	*	12 10.7	+ 58 21 r	UMa			vF, S, E 90°±
4159	Gx	12 10.7	+ 76 09 r	Dra		14p	eF, pS, R, △ 2 st
4153	−	12 10.8	+ 18 22 r	Com			B, pL, E, bM
4155	Gx	12 10.8	+ 19 03 r	Com		14p	eF, vS
4156	Gx	12 10.8	+ 39 28 s	CVn	1.5	13.0	pF, S, E, vgbM, f of 2
3029 I	Gx	12 10.8	+ 13 19 u	Com	1.5	15p	E 35°, mag 13.5
766 I	Gx	12 10.9	− 12 40 m	Crv	1.2	14p	pB, E ns, sbMN = 14m
4157	Gx	12 11.1	+ 50 29 s	UMa	6.9	12p	pF, cL, vmE 60°±(double?)
767 I	Gx	12 11.1	+ 12 05 m	Vir	0.6	15p	F, vS, stell, N = 14m
3030 I		12 11.1	+ 14 08 d	Com			R, bM, mag 14
3031 I		12 11.1	+ 13 18 d	Vir			vF, wisp at 35°
3032 I	Gx	12 11.1	+ 14 16 z	Com		15p	R, bM, mag 13.5
3033 I	Gx	12 11.1	+ 13 35 u	Com	1.2	15p	bM, wisps ns 0′.5, mag 13.5
4158	Gx	12 11.2	+ 20 11 s	Com	2.0	13p	F, pS, lE, bM, pB* sf

NGC	Type	α_{2000}	δ_{2000}	Const.	Size	Mag.	Description
		h m	° ′		′		
4161	Gx	12 11.4	+ 57 44 r	UMa		13p	F, S, R
4160	−	12 11.6	+ 43 45 r	CVn			neb *13
4162	Gx	12 11.9	+ 24 07 s	Com	2.5	11.5	B, L, iE, bM
768 I	Gx	12 11.9	+ 12 08 u	Vir	1.6	15p	vF, pS, R, gbM
3034 I		12 11.9	+ 14 11 d	Com			vF, E, bM
4164	Gx	12 12.1	+ 13 12 r	Vir		15p	vF, 2′-3′ s of 4165
4163	Gx	12 12.2	+ 36 10 s	CVn	1.9	13p	vF, pL, vlE, r
4165	Gx	12 12.2	+ 13 15 s	Vir	1.5	13.6	eF, *10 np, 4168 f; = IC 3035
4166	Gx	12 12.2	+ 17 46 r	Com		14p	vF, S
4167	−	12 12.2	+ 36 31 r	CVn			F, pL, R, vgbM, * s; = 4163?
4169	Gx	12 12.2	+ 29 10 s	Com	2.1	13p	F, S, 1st of 4
4172	Gx	12 12.2	+ 56 11 r	UMa		14p	F, S, lE, gbM
3035 I		12 12.2	+ 13 15 z	Vir			F, cS; = 4165
3036 I	Gx	12 12.2	+ 12 28 u	Vir	1.8	15p	vF, spir
4168	Gx	12 12.3	+ 13 12 s	Vir	2.8	11.3	pB, pL, iF, psbM, r, * inv
4170	Gx	12 12.3	+ 29 12 D	Com		13p	eF, vnr 4169, 4173-5
4171	Gx	12 12.3	+ 29 12 u	Com	5.1	14p	eF, vnr 4169, 4173-5
4173	Gx	12 12.3	+ 29 11 s	Com	4.8	13p	F, S, 2nd of 4
4174	Gx	12 12.4	+ 29 08 s	Com	0.8	14p	F, S, 3rd of 4
3037 I	Gx	12 12.4	+ 9 59 z	Vir		15p	R, ○ ?, mag 16
4175	Gx	12 12.5	+ 29 09 s	Com	2.0	14p	F, eS, 4th of 4
769 I	Gx	12 12.5	+ 12 07 s	Vir	2.5	13p	vF, pS, vlbM
3039 I	Gx	12 12.5	+ 12 18 m	Vir	1.0	15p	S, R, bM
3038 I	Gx	12 12.6	+ 11 20 z	Vir		16p	R, bM, ○ ?, mag 16
4176	Gx	12 12.7	− 9 08 r	Vir			eF, vS, R, slbM, *10
3040 I	Gx	12 12.7	+ 11 04 m	Vir	0.6	16p	R, ○ ?, mag 16
3041 I		12 12.7	+ 12 44 d	Vir			S, E
4177	Gx	12 12.8	− 14 00 r	Crv		13p	vF, pL, R, vgbM
4178	Gx	12 12.8	+ 10 52 s	Vir	5.0	11.4	vF, vL, E 45°±, *7 f; = IC 3042
3042 I		12 12.8	+ 10 52 x	Vir			pF, cL; = 4178
3043 I		12 12.8	+ 10 00 d	Vir			cS, E ns, mag 15
3044 I	Gx	12 12.8	+ 13 59 v	Com	2.1		F, stell
4179	Gx	12 12.9	+ 1 18 s	Vir	4.2	10.9	pB, pS, pmE 135°±, bMN
770 I		12 13.0	− 4 33 d	Vir			vF, vS, R, *13.5 n 1′
3045 I	?	12 13.0	+ 12 47 x	Vir			pF, cS, Ns = 10.5m
4180	Gx	12 13.1	+ 7 02 s	Vir	1.8	13p	pF, S, lE 0°±, r
3046 I	Gx	12 13.1	+ 12 55 u	Vir	1.2	15p	vF, pS, spir
4183	Gx	12 13.3	+ 43 42 s	CVn	5.0	13p	vF, cL, mE 170°±
3047 I		12 13.3	+ 12 58 d	Vir			R, bM, mag 14.5
4181	Gx	12 13.4	+ 50 46 r	CVn		14p	eF, S, stellar
4182	−	12 13.4	+ 4 03 r	Vir			vS (vS Cl?)
4185	Gx	12 13.4	+ 28 31 r	Com		13p	cF, L, R, gbM
4187	Gx	12 13.4	+ 50 44 r	CVn		14p	pB, S, lE
3048 I	D*	12 13.4	+ 13 04 x	Vir			F, S; *13?
3049 I	Gx	12 13.5	+ 14 29 u	Com	1.1	16p	R, ○ ?, mag 16
4184	−	12 13.6	− 62 42 r	Cru			Cl, mC, st eS
4190	Gx	12 13.7	+ 36 38 s	CVn	1.7	13p	cF, pS, R, vglbM, r
3050 I	Gx	12 13.7	+ 13 26 t	Com	2.0	13p	pB, cL, gbM; = 4189
4189	Gx	12 13.8	+ 13 26 s	Com	2.5	11.7	F, L, lE, vglbM, r; = IC 3050
4192	Gx	12 13.8	+ 14 54 s	Com	9.5	10.1	B, vL, vmE 152°, vsvmbM; = M98
4191	Gx	12 13.9	+ 7 12 r	Vir		14p	cF, R, bM, near S*
4193	Gx	12 13.9	+ 13 10 s	Vir	2.3	12.4	vF, pL, E, vgbM; = IC 3051
3051 I		12 13.9	+ 13 10 x	Vir			pB, pS; = 4193
3052 I		12 13.9	+ 12 40 d	Vir			R, ○ ?, mag 16.5
3053 I		12 14.0	+ 14 12 d	Com			R, bM, ○ ?, mag 16

NGC	Type	α_{2000}	δ_{2000}	Const.	Size	Mag.	Description
		h m	o /		/		
4186	Gx	12 14.1	+ 14 44 s	Com	1.4	14p	pF, S, R, sp M98
4188	Gx	12 14.2	− 12 33 r	Crv		14p	eF, pS
4194	Gx	12 14.2	+ 54 32 s	UMa	2.5	12.4	pB, vS, vsbM ∗12
4195	Gx	12 14.2	+ 59 37 r	UMa		15p	eF
4198	Gx	12 14.3	+ 56 01 r	UMa		14p	pF, pS, lE, gbM
3054 I		12 14.3	+ 13 31 d	Com			R, ○ ?, mag 16.5
4196	Gx	12 14.4	+ 28 25 s	Com	1.6	14p	pB, S, R, vsmbM ∗
3055 I		12 14.4	+ 12 04 d	Vir			bM, mag 15
4197	Gx	12 14.6	+ 5 48 s	Vir	3.5	13p	pF, pmE, vgbM
3056 I	?	12 14.6	+ 13 47 x	Com			pL, vmE 50°
4201	Gx	12 14.7	− 11 34 r	Vir		14p	eF, eS, R, bMN
4199	Gx	12 14.8	+ 59 54 r	UMa		15p	vF, S
4200	Gx	12 14.8	+ 12 11 r	Vir		14p	cF, lE, lbM
4205	Gx	12 14.9	+ 63 48 r	Dra		14p	pB, pS, R, ∗12 f, ln
3058 I		12 14.9	+ 14 04 d	Com			R, ○ ?, mag 16
3059 I	Gx	12 14.9	+ 13 28 v	Com	1.7		vF, spir, doubtful
3057 I		12 15.0	− 44 29 d	Cen			cF, S, R (defect?)
3060 I	Gx	12 15.0	+ 12 31 m	Vir	0.3	15p	vF, S, lE 0°; ∗14?
4203	Gx	12 15.1	+ 33 12 s	Com	3.6	10.7	vB, S, R, psmbM
3061 I	Gx	12 15.1	+ 14 02 s	Com	2.3	13.6	F, pL, spir
3062 I	Gx	12 15.1	+ 13 35 m	Com	1.0	15p	F, S
3063 I	Gx	12 15.1	+ 12 00 u	Vir	1.0	15p	bM, mag 14.5
4204	Gx	12 15.2	+ 20 39 s	Com	4.2	13p	vF, cL, iR, vgbM
771 I	Gx	12 15.2	+ 13 11 z	Vir		15p	vF, S, R, ∗ 3′ south
772 I	Gx	12 15.2	+ 23 57 z	Com		15p	vF, vS, stell
3064 I	Gx	12 15.2	+ 13 01 t	Vir	5.3	13p	cF, cL, E 5°; = 4206
3065 I	Nb	12 15.2	+ 14 26 x	Com	0.5		R, ○ ?, mag 14
3067 I	Gx	12 15.2	+ 23 57 z	Com		15p	vF, vS, stell
4206	Gx	12 15.3	+ 13 02 s	Vir	5.2	12.1	F, vmE
4210	Gx	12 15.3	+ 65 59 s	Dra	2.2	13p	pF, pS, R, vgbM
3066 I	Gx	12 15.3	+ 13 28 u	Com	1.0	15p	pL, E 160°, spir
4208		12 15.4	+ 13 54 D	Com			nonexistent
3068 I		12 15.4	+ 11 30 d	Vir			bM, mag 16
3069 I		12 15.4	+ 10 10 d	Vir			bM, mag 15.5
3070 I	∗	12 15.4	+ 13 02 x	Vir			vF, vS
4207	Gx	12 15.5	+ 9 35 s	Vir	1.8	13p	pF, pS, lE, ∗14 np
4209	−	12 15.5	+ 28 31 r	Com			F, pS
3071 I	?	12 15.5	+ 9 33 z	Vir			eF, eS
4211	Gx	12 15.6	+ 28 11 s	Com	1.4	14p	vF, eS, mbM
4214	Gx	12 15.6	+ 36 20 s	CVn	7.9	9.7	cB, cL, iE, biN
3072 I	?	12 15.6	+ 9 33 x	Vir			eF, eS, ?
3073 I	Gx	12 15.6	+ 13 36 u	Com	1.0	16p	bM, mag 16
4212	Gx	12 15.7	+ 13 54 s	Com	3.0	11.2	B, L, E 107°, g, sbM, r
4213	Gx	12 15.7	+ 23 59 r	Com		14p	cF, vS, R
3074 I	Gx	12 15.7	+ 10 41 s	Vir	2.3	14p	cF, pL, E 170°
4217	Gx	12 15.8	+ 47 06 s	CVn	5.5	12p	pF, L, mE 45°, ⁜ n, p of 2
4218	Gx	12 15.8	+ 48 08 s	CVn	1.2	13p	vF, vS
3075 I	Gx	12 15.8	+ 23 35 m	Com	0.7	15p	F, vS, R, stell
4215	Gx	12 15.9	+ 6 24 s	Vir	1.9	13p	B, pS, E, sbM ∗11
4216	Gx	12 15.9	+ 13 09 s	Vir	8.3	10.0	vB, vL, vmE 17°, sbMN
4221	Gx	12 16.0	+ 66 14 s	Dra	2.3	14p	pB, S, R, psbM
3076 I	?	12 16.1	+ 9 05 x	Vir			vF, vS
3077 I	Nb	12 16.1	+ 14 24 x	Com	0.2		bM, mag 15
3078 I		12 16.1	+ 12 39 d	Vir			bM, mag 14
3079 I	Gx	12 16.1	+ 11 31 z	Vir		15p	bM, mag 14

NGC	Type	α_{2000}	δ_{2000}	Const.	Size	Mag.	Description
		h m	° ′		′		
4220	Gx	12 16.2	+ 47 53 s	CVn	4.1	12p	cB, pL, pmE 134°, psbM
3080 I	Nb	12 16.2	+ 14 13 x	Com	0.3		bM, mag 14
3081 I		12 16.2	+ 12 40 d	Vir			bM, mag 15
3082 I		12 16.2	+ 23 51 d	Com			vF, vS, dif, *5 n 6′
3084 I	Gx	12 16.3	+ 23 54 m	Com	0.4	16p	F, vS, R, dif
4219	Gx	12 16.4	− 43 20 s	Cen	4.5	12p	pF, pL, pmE, vglbM
4222	Gx	12 16.4	+ 13 19 s	Com	3.3	14p	vF, pS, R
4226	Gx	12 16.4	+ 47 02 s	CVn	1.3	14p	F, S, lE, f of 2
3083 I	?	12 16.4	+ 12 35 x	Vir			bM, mag 15
3085 I	*	12 16.4	+ 9 28 x	Vir			cF, vS, = *13
3089 I	Gx	12 16.4	+ 23 49 m	Com	0.4	16p	vF, S, vlbM, dif
4223	−	12 16.5	+ 6 42 r	Vir			pF, pL, R, r; = 4241?
4227	Gx	12 16.5	+ 33 31 s	CVn	1.8	14p	F, vS, vlE, psbM, sp of 2
3086 I	?	12 16.5	+ 9 01 x	Vir			eF, vS
3087 I	D*	12 16.5	+ 13 17 x	Vir			F, S, eE 30°, neb?
3088 I	*	12 16.5	+ 9 28 x	Vir			vF, vS, = *14
3090 I	D*	12 16.5	+ 9 26 x	Vir			vF, vS
4224	Gx	12 16.6	+ 7 28 s	Vir	2.4	11.8	pB, pS, lE, gbM, r
4228	−	12 16.6	+ 36 20 r	CVn			vF, L, R, gbM; = 4214?
3091 I	D*	12 16.6	+ 13 59 x	Com			bM, mag 14
3092 I		12 16.6	+ 10 03 d	Vir			bM, mag 15.5
4225	Gx	12 16.7	− 12 18 r	Crv		14p	F, eS, R, * 170°, 60″
4229	Gx	12 16.7	+ 33 34 r	CVn		14p	cF, vS, lE, psbM, nf of 2
4236	Gx	12 16.7	+ 69 28 s	Dra	18.6	9.7	vF, eL, mE 160°±, vgbM
3093 I	Nb	12 16.7	+ 14 17 x	Com			bM, mag 14
4231	Gx	12 16.8	+ 47 27 s	CVn	1.4	15p	vF, vS, n of Dneb
4232	Gx	12 16.8	+ 47 26 s	CVn	1.5	15p	vF, vS, s of Dneb
4238	Gx	12 16.9	+ 63 25 s	Dra	1.9	14p	vF, pS, iR, vglbM
3094 I	Gx	12 16.9	+ 13 37 u	Com	0.6	14p	F, S, bM
3095 I	Gx	12 16.9	+ 23 56 m	Com	0.5	16p	pF, S, vlE pf, bM, *5 p 35ˢ, 1′ s
3096 I	Nb	12 16.9	+ 14 31 x	Com	1		bM, mag 14.5
3097 I	Gx	12 17.0	+ 9 24 z	Vir		15p	vF, S, lbM
4233	Gx	12 17.1	+ 7 37 s	Vir	2.3	11.9	pF, R, vsbMSN
3099 I	Gx	12 17.1	+ 12 27 u	Vir	2.1	15p	vF, pL, lE 0°
4234	Gx	12 17.2	+ 3 41 s	Vir	1.3	12.9	pB, L, R, gbM
4235	Gx	12 17.2	+ 7 11 s	Vir	4.3	11.6	pB, pL, pmE, bM, p of 2
4237	Gx	12 17.2	+ 15 19 s	Com	2.3	11.7	pB, pL, lE, vgbM, r
3098 I		12 17.2	+ 7 12 x	Vir			pF, pS, E 45°; = 4235
3100 I		12 17.2	+ 12 15 d	Vir			bM, wisps 45°?, mag 14.5
4230	OC	12 17.3	− 55 08 s	Cen	6	9p	Cl, F, pL, iF, st 13...15
4239	Gx	12 17.3	+ 16 32 r	Com		13p	F, pL, R
3101 I	Gx	12 17.3	+ 11 56 z	Vir		15p	bM, mag 15
4240	Gx	12 17.4	− 9 56 r	Vir		14p	pB, S, *12 sp 0′.5
4241	Gx	12 17.4	+ 6 41 s	Vir	2.5	12.0	vF, L, vgbM, *7 s; = IC 3102
4250	Gx	12 17.4	+ 70 48 s	Dra	2.7	13p	pB, S, R, pgbM
3102 I		12 17.4	+ 6 41 x	Vir			pF, pS, *?; = 4241
4242	Gx	12 17.5	+ 45 37 s	CVn	4.8	11.0	vF, cL, iR, vgbM, r
4244	Gx	12 17.5	+ 37 49 s	CVn	16.2	10.2	pB, vL, eE 43°, vgbM
3103 I	*	12 17.5	+ 9 22 x	Vir			vF, vS, stell
4243	−	12 17.6	− 11 19 r	Vir			pB, eS, pB* close p
4245	Gx	12 17.6	+ 29 36 s	Com	3.3	11.4	cB, pL, vlE, smbM, r
3105 I	Gx	12 17.6	+ 12 23 u	Vir	1.8	15p	vF, pS, E 40°
3110 I		12 17.7	+ 37 23 d	CVn			vF, S, dif
4248	Gx	12 17.8	+ 47 25 s	CVn	3.0	12.6	vF, S, pmE, psbM
3106 I		12 17.8	+ 9 37 d	Vir			vF, vS, E 95°

NGC	Type	α_{2000}	δ_{2000}	Const.	Size	Mag.	Description
		h m	° ′		′		
3107 I	Gx	12 17.8	+ 10 50 u	Vir	1.5	14p	F, vS, lE, mbM
3108 I		12 17.8	+ 13 21 d	Com			R, bM, mag 14
3109 I		12 17.8	+ 13 08 d	Vir			bM, mag 14
3111 I	Gx	12 17.8	+ 8 26 z	Vir		15p	eF, S?
3112 I	Gx	12 17.8	+ 26 01 v	Com	1.3		F, S, iF, N
3114 I	?	12 17.9	+ 9 08 x	Vir			cF, vS, stell
4246	Gx	12 18.0	+ 7 11 s	Vir	2.5	12.7	eF
4247	Gx	12 18.0	+ 7 16 s	Vir	0.7	15p	F, S, R, bM, 6′ n of 4246
4249	Gx	12 18.0	+ 5 36 r	Vir		15p	F
3113 I		12 18.0	+ 7 11 x	Vir			cF, pL, E; = 4246
3115 I	Gx	12 18.0	+ 6 39 s	Vir	1.7	13.1	vF, pL, E
3116 I		12 18.0	+ 25 05 d	Com			vF, cS, R, bM
4251	Gx	12 18.1	+ 28 10 s	Com	4.2	12p	vB, S, E, vsvmbMN, *6-7 f 90^s
773 I	Gx	12 18.1	+ 6 08 v	Vir	1.8		F, vS, dif, 2 vF st inv
3117 I	?	12 18.1	+ 9 04 x	Vir			eF, S, E 30°
3119 I	Gx	12 18.1	+ 24 41 z	Com		15p	pF, cS, R, bM
4202	Gx	12 18.2	− 1 04 F	Vir		14p	F, irr, cometary, F* 1′ nf
3118 I	Gx	12 18.2	+ 9 30 u	Vir	1.6	15p	vF, cS, lE, dif
3122 I	Gx	12 18.3	+ 25 13 u	Com	1.5	15p	pF, pL, E 150°, pLN
4253	Gx	12 18.4	+ 29 49 s	Com	1.1	14p	vF, vS, R
3120 I		12 18.4	+ 13 42 d	Com			R, bM, mag 14.5
3121 I		12 18.4	+ 13 14 d	Vir			eF, lE, mag 15
3123 I	*	12 18.4	+ 8 04 x	Vir			neb, or *
3125 I		12 18.4	+ 24 22 d	Com			F, S, R, bM
4252	Gx	12 18.5	+ 5 34 s	Vir	1.5	15p	F, E
3124 I	*	12 18.5	+ 9 35 x	Vir			cF, S, = *13
3127 I	Gx	12 18.5	+ 11 51 m	Vir	0.6	16p	R, bM, mag 16
3126 I		12 18.6	+ 13 48 d	Com			R, bM, mag 15
4256	Gx	12 18.7	+ 65 54 s	Dra	4.6	12p	pB, L, cE 38°, bMBN
3128 I		12 18.7	+ 11 43 d	Vir			lE, D?, mag 14.5
3129 I	*	12 18.7	+ 9 36 x	Vir			vF, eS, = *14
4254	Gx	12 18.8	+ 14 25 s	Com	5.4	9.8	!! B, L, R, gbM, r, 3-branched spiral; = M99
774 I		12 18.8	− 6 46 d	Vir			F, vS, R, gbM
3104 I	Gx	12 18.8	− 79 44 c	Cha	4.7		eeF, cS, or vS Cl, *12 sp 0′.5
3130 I	?	12 18.8	+ 8 14 x	Vir			eF, pS, mE 140°, ?
3131 I	Gx	12 18.8	+ 7 51 m	Vir	0.6	15p	vF, S
3132 I		12 18.8	+ 7 52 x	Vir			vF, S, stell; = IC 3131
775 I	Gx	12 18.9	+ 12 55 s	Vir	1.4	13.3	vF, S, stell, N
3133 I	?	12 18.9	+ 7 39 x	Vir			eF, S, dif
3134 I	Gx	12 18.9	+ 8 58 z	Vir		15p	vF, vS, E 0°
3135 I		12 18.9	+ 27 30 d	Com			vF, S, iF
3141 I	Gx	12 18.9	+ 24 11 z	Com		16p	F, S, R, bM
4255	Gx	12 19.0	+ 4 48 r	Vir		13p	S, pmbM
4258	Gx	12 19.0	+ 47 18 s	CVn	18.2	8.3	vB, vL, vmE 0°, sbMBN; = M106
776 I	Gx	12 19.0	+ 8 51 s	Vir	2.1	14p	F, pL, R
3136 I	Gx	12 19.0	+ 6 11 v	Vir	1.2		F
3137 I		12 19.0	+ 12 27 d	Vir			pL, E 45°
3138 I		12 19.0	+ 12 25 d	Vir			R, bM, mag 15.5
3139 I	*	12 19.0	+ 9 08 x	Vir			eF, vS
3140 I		12 19.0	+ 27 08 d	Com			vF, pS, iF, dif
4257	Gx	12 19.1	+ 5 44 s	Vir	1.2	15p	vF, pS, R, *18 s 2′
3142 I	Nb	12 19.1	+ 13 59 x	Com			R, bM, mag 14.5
3143 I	Gx	12 19.1	+ 27 18 z	Com		16p	vF, S, R
3144 I		12 19.2	+ 25 18 d	Com			vF, S, R, bM
3145 I		12 19.2	+ 24 18 d	Com			F, S, R, bM

NGC	Type	α_{2000}	δ_{2000}	Const.	Size	Mag.	Description
		h m	° ′		′		
3146 I		12 19.2	+ 25 43 d	Com			eF, S, iF
3147 I		12 19.3	+ 12 01 d	Vir			vF, vS, stell
3148 I	Gx	12 19.3	+ 7 52 m	Vir	0.8	15p	vF, S
3149 I	Gx	12 19.3	+ 12 18 m	Vir	0.5	16p	vF, vS
4259	Gx	12 19.4	+ 5 23 s	Vir	1.1	13.6	F, pS, R
4260	Gx	12 19.4	+ 6 06 s	Vir	2.6	11.8	pB, E, psbM
4261	Gx	12 19.4	+ 5 49 s	Vir	3.9	10.3	pB, pS, R, gbM
777 I	Gx	12 19.4	+ 28 18 u	Com	1.3	14p	vF
778 I		12 19.4	+ 56 00 d	UMa			eF, pS, r, bet 2 st
4262	Gx	12 19.5	+ 14 53 s	Com	2.2	11.5	B, S, R, r
3150 I	?	12 19.5	+ 7 48 x	Vir			vF, S
3151 I		12 19.5	+ 9 24 d	Vir			R, bM, mag 13.5
4264	Gx	12 19.6	+ 5 51 s	Vir	1.1	12.9	F, pS, R, gbM
4271	Gx	12 19.6	+ 56 45 r	UMa		13p	pB, pL, iF
3152 I	Gx	12 19.6	− 26 09 c	Hya	2.0		pB, S, R, 4 st sf, *8 np
3153 I	Gx	12 19.6	+ 5 23 z	Vir		15p	vF, S, 4273 f
3154 I		12 19.6	+ 25 35 d	Com			F, S, R, bM
4263	Gx	12 19.7	− 12 15 D	Crv		14p	vF, pL, iF; = 4265
4265	Gx	12 19.7	− 12 15 D	Crv		14p	vF, pS, R
4266	Gx	12 19.7	+ 5 32 s	Vir	2.1	15p	pF
3156 I	Gx	12 19.7	+ 9 09 m	Vir	0.6	15p	vF, vS
3157 I	Gx	12 19.7	+ 12 25 z	Vir		15p	R, bM, mag 14
4267	Gx	12 19.8	+ 12 48 s	Vir	3.5	10.9	pB, vS, R, vsmbM
4268	Gx	12 19.8	+ 5 17 s	Vir	1.6	12.7	pF, S, 2nd of 6 neb
4269	Gx	12 19.8	+ 6 01 s	Vir	1.5	14p	pF, S, R, *9 f 1^s.7, n 85″
4270	Gx	12 19.8	+ 5 28 s	Vir	2.2	12.2	pB, S, R
4272	Gx	12 19.8	+ 30 20 z	Com		14p	cF, S, iR, gmbM
4274	Gx	12 19.8	+ 29 37 s	Com	6.9	10.4	vB, vL, E 90°, mbMN
779 I		12 19.8	+ 29 53 d	Com			F
3155 I	Gx	12 19.8	+ 6 00 v	Vir	1.1		cF, S, sbM; vF st inv?
3158 I	*	12 19.8	+ 9 18 x	Vir			eF, cS, ??
4273	Gx	12 19.9	+ 5 21 s	Vir	2.3	11.9	pB, L, E, gbM
4275	Gx	12 19.9	+ 27 37 s	Com	1.0	13p	F, S, vlE, gbM, *15 nr
780 I	Gx	12 19.9	+ 25 46 u	Com	1.3	14p	pB, S, R, N = 12.5m
3159 I		12 19.9	+ 11 39 d	Vir			R, mbM, mag 15
3166 I		12 19.9	+ 60 42 d	UMa			eeF, S, p of 2
3160 I	*	12 20.0	+ 9 06 x	Vir			eF, cS
3161 I	D*	12 20.0	+ 9 00 x	Vir			eF, vS, *?, conn w f one
3162 I	D*	12 20.0	+ 9 00 x	Vir			eF, vS, *?, conn w p one
3163 I	D*	12 20.0	+ 9 15 x	Vir			neb or *?
3165 I	Gx	12 20.0	+ 27 58 u	Com	2.0	15p	F, cS, iF, lbM
4277	Gx	12 20.1	+ 5 21 s	Vir	0.9	13.5	vF, eS
4278	Gx	12 20.1	+ 29 17 s	Com	3.6	10.2	vB, pL, R, mbM, r, 1st of 3
781 I	Nb	12 20.1	+ 14 58 x	Com	1		vF, S, dif
3164 I		12 20.1	+ 24 57 d	Com			eF, S, iF; D*?
4276	Gx	12 20.2	+ 7 42 r	Vir		14p	pF, pL
4284	Gx	12 20.2	+ 58 06 r	UMa		14p	cF, lE, p of 2
3167 I	Gx	12 20.2	+ 9 32 z	Vir		15p	vF, vS, lE 65°, bM
4283	Gx	12 20.3	+ 29 19 s	Com	1.4	12.0	B, S, R, bM, 2nd of 3
4291	Gx	12 20.3	+ 75 22 s	Dra	2.2	12p	pB, vS, R, lbM, 3 st f
3168 I	Gx	12 20.3	+ 27 55 z	Com		16p	F, cS, E 45°, bM
3171 I	Gx	12 20.3	+ 25 32 m	Com	0.3	15p	pB, S, R, bM
4279	Gx	12 20.4	− 11 40 r	Vir		14p	eeF, vS, R
4280	−	12 20.4	− 11 41 r	Vir			eF, vS, R
4281	Gx	12 20.4	+ 5 23 s	Vir	3.1	11.3	B, vL, R, pgbM

NGC	Type	α_{2000}	δ_{2000}	Const.	Size	Mag.	Description
		h m	° ′		′		
4282	Gx	12 20.4	+ 5 35 r	Vir		14p	pF
3169 I		12 20.4	+ 26 36 d	Com			vF, vS, R, bM
3170 I	Gx	12 20.4	+ 9 25 m	Vir	0.4	15p	F, S, R, bM
3172 I		12 20.4	+ 27 49 d	Com			vF, S, iF
3174 I	Gx	12 20.4	+ 10 14 z	Vir		16p	eF, vS, *13 att sp
3175 I	Gx	12 20.4	+ 9 50 z	Vir		15p	R, bM, mag 13
3180 I		12 20.4	+ 60 42 d	UMa			vF, pL, R, *7.5 s, f of 2
3173 I	Gx	12 20.5	+ 11 20 z	Vir		16p	R, bM, mag 13
3176 I		12 20.5	+ 25 31 d	Com			vF, vS, R, bM
4288	Gx	12 20.6	+ 46 17 s	CVn	2.3	13p	vF, pS, R, vgbM, r
3177 I		12 20.6	+ 14 07 d	Com			L, vmE 45°, 2′.5 l
3178 I		12 20.6	+ 26 10 d	Com			F, vS, iF, N
3179 I		12 20.6	+ 26 10 d	Com			F, vS, iF, N
4285	Gx	12 20.7	− 11 39 r	Vir		14p	eeF, pS, R
4286	Gx	12 20.7	+ 29 21 s	Com	1.9	15p	vF, 3rd of 3; = IC 3181
3181 I		12 20.7	+ 29 21 z	Com			pF, pL, lE 150°; = 4286
3184 I	Gx	12 20.7	+ 24 55 z	Com		16p	pF, cS, E 40°, bM
4287	Gx	12 20.8	+ 5 39 r	Vir		15p	pF
4290	Gx	12 20.8	+ 58 06 s	UMa	2.5	12p	pB, L, R, gmbM
3182 I	***	12 20.8	+ 12 44 x	Vir			vF, S, biN
3183 I	*	12 20.8	+ 6 41 z	Vir			vF, cS, st?
3185 I		12 20.9	+ 25 26 d	Com			F, vS, R, bM
3186 I	Gx	12 20.9	+ 24 40 m	Com	0.4	15p	pB, S, R, bM
3187 I	Gx	12 20.9	+ 11 10 z	Vir		16p	vlE, bM, mag 14.5
3188 I	Gx	12 20.9	+ 11 01 m	Vir	0.4	15p	R, bM, mag 13.5
3189 I		12 20.9	+ 25 26 d	Com			F, vS, R, bM
3193 I	Gx	12 20.9	+ 27 54 m	Com	0.8	16p	F, S, iF; D* ?
4289	Gx	12 21.0	+ 3 43 s	Vir	3.9	14p	vF, S, *8.5 12″f
3190 I	*	12 21.0	+ 9 34 z	Vir			eF, eS
3191 I	?	12 21.1	+ 7 42 x	Vir			vF, vS, R
3192 I		12 21.1	+ 11 44 d	Vir			lbM, ○ ?, mag 15
4293	Gx	12 21.2	+ 18 23 s	Com	6.0	11p	F, vL, E, lbM, r
4295	Gx	12 21.2	+ 28 09 v	Com			vF, S
3194 I		12 21.2	+ 25 08 d	Com			F, vS, R, bM
4292	Gx	12 21.3	+ 4 36 s	Vir	2.1	14p	F, S, R, vglbM, *9 np 72″
4294	Gx	12 21.3	+ 11 31 s	Vir	3.1	12.1	F, L, mE 135°±, biN, p of 2
3195 I		12 21.3	+ 25 48 d	Com			vF, S, iF
3197 I		12 21.4	+ 25 27 d	Com			F, vS, R, bM
4296	Gx	12 21.5	+ 6 40 r	Vir		14p	vF, vS
4297	Gx	12 21.5	+ 6 40 r	Vir		14p	eF, eS
4298	Gx	12 21.5	+ 14 36 s	Com	3.2	11.4	F, L, E, vgbM, p of 2
3196 I		12 21.5	+ 11 44 d	Vir			bM, mag 14
3198 I		12 21.5	+ 26 22 d	Com			eF, S, iF
4301	Gx	12 21.6	+ 4 47 s	Vir	1.4	15p	F, E, 10′ nf 4292
782 I	Gx	12 21.6	+ 5 45 m	Vir	0.6	15p	eF, S, R
783 I	Gx	12 21.6	+ 15 45 s	Com	1.5	13.6	eF, S, R
3200 I		12 21.6	+ 26 46 d	Com			vF, S, iF, N
4299	Gx	12 21.7	+ 11 30 s	Vir	1.7	12.5	F, L, lE, vgbM, f of 2
4300	Gx	12 21.7	+ 5 23 r	Vir		14p	F, lE, vgbM
4302	Gx	12 21.7	+ 14 36 s	Com	5.2	11.6	L, vmE 177°, f of 2
4319	Gx	12 21.7	+ 75 19 s	Dra	3.1	12p	pB, pS, vlE, sbM
3199 I	Gx	12 21.7	+ 10 36 u	Vir	1.1	15p	R, bM, mag 14
3201 I		12 21.7	+ 25 43 d	Com			vF, S, R, bM
3202 I		12 21.7	+ 27 03 d	Com			eF, S, iF
3203 I	Gx	12 21.7	+ 25 53 u	Com	1.5	16p	pF, S, E 150°

NGC	Type	α_{2000}	δ_{2000}	Const.	Size	Mag.	Description
		h m	° ′		′		
3204 I		12 21.8	+ 24 15 d	Com			F, S, E
3205 I		12 21.8	+ 26 20 d	Com			cF, S, iF, N
3206 I		12 21.8	+ 26 22 d	Com			cF, S, iF, N
4303	Gx	12 21.9	+ 4 28 s	Vir	6.0	9.7	vB, vL, vsbM∗, biN; = M61
4308	Gx	12 21.9	+ 30 03 s	Com	1.0	14p	vF, S, vF st inv, np 4314
3207 I		12 21.9	+ 24 21 d	Com			F, S, E 100°
3208 I		12 22.0	+ 11 57 d	Vir			F, pL, vmE 70°
3210 I	Gx	12 22.0	+ 28 26 z	Com		15p	F, S, R, bM, spir
4305	Gx	12 22.1	+ 12 44 s	Vir	2.2	12.6	vF, R
4306	Gx	12 22.1	+ 12 47 s	Vir	1.6	14p	vF, pL, R, 4305 sp
4307	Gx	12 22.1	+ 9 02 s	Vir	3.7	13p	pF, L, mE, 3 knots
3209 I	Gx	12 22.1	+ 11 45 z	Vir		15p	pL, E 140°, sbM ∗, spir
3211 I	Gx	12 22.1	+ 8 59 u	Vir	1.1	15p	eF, S
3212 I	Gx	12 22.1	+ 28 11 z	Com		16p	F, S, R, glbM
3213 I	Gx	12 22.1	+ 23 52 z	Com		16p	pF, S, R, bM, ∗12 att np
3215 I	Gx	12 22.1	+ 26 03 u	Com	2.0	16p	vF, pS, E 95°, bM
4304	Gx	12 22.2	− 33 29 s	Hya	2.4	12.0	vF, vL, R, vgvlbM, r
4309	Gx	12 22.2	+ 7 09 s	Vir	2.0	14p	F, S, ∗11 f 12^s
3214 I		12 22.2	+ 27 14 d	Com			vF, vS, R, bM
3216 I		12 22.2	+ 25 17 d	Com			F, vS, R, bM
3217 I		12 22.2	+ 26 23 d	Com			cF, S, R, bM, spir
3218 I	Gx	12 22.2	+ 6 55 m	Vir	0.6	16p	vF, pL, biN?
3219 I		12 22.3	+ 25 57 d	Com			eF, vS, R, bM, spir
3221 I		12 22.3	+ 25 17 d	Com			eF, S, iF, v diffic
3222 I	Gx	12 22.3	+ 28 50 u	Com	1.1	16p	F, cS, dif
4310	Gx	12 22.4	+ 29 12 s	Com	2.6	13p	F, cL, lE, n of 2
4311	Gx	12 22.4	+ 29 12 u	Com	2.3	13p	F, s of 2
4331	Gx	12 22.4	+ 76 11 s	Dra	2.0	15p	eF, E 0°±
3220 I		12 22.4	+ 10 35 d	Vir			R, bM, mag 14.5
4312	Gx	12 22.5	+ 15 32 s	Com	4.7	11.8	pB, cL, E, gbM
3223 I	∗	12 22.5	+ 9 29 x	Vir			vF, pS, am 3 vF st
4313	Gx	12 22.6	+ 11 48 s	Vir	3.9	13p	vF, L, E 135°±, r
4314	Gx	12 22.6	+ 29 53 s	Com	4.8	10.5	cB, L, E 150°±, sbM, ∗ np
4317	∗	12 22.6	+ 31 03 r	Com			F, S
784 I		12 22.6	− 4 39 D	Vir			vF, pL, mE, pB∗ s
3224 I		12 22.6	+ 12 09 d	Vir			R, bM, mag 14.5
3225 I		12 22.6	+ 6 41 d	Vir			F, S; st?
3226 I		12 22.6	+ 26 04 d	Com			vF, vS, bM ∗, spir
3227 I		12 22.6	+ 24 05 d	Com			F, S, iF
4315	−	12 22.7	+ 9 19 r	Vir			vF, vS
4318	Gx	12 22.7	+ 8 12 s	Vir	0.9	14p	eF, ∗8 n 5′
4345	∗	12 22.7	+ 75 20 r	Dra			F, pL, gbM
3228 I		12 22.7	+ 24 20 d	Com			F, vS, E 150°, bM
3229 I		12 22.7	+ 6 41 d	Vir			eF, cS, dif, ?
3230 I		12 22.7	+ 27 45 d	Com			F, vS, iF
3231 I		12 22.7	+ 24 49 d	Com			pF, S, iF, bM
4316	Gx	12 22.8	+ 9 21 r	Vir		14p	vF, S, mE, 2 knots
4332	Gx	12 22.8	+ 65 51 s	Dra	2.3	13p	pF, S, vlE, vgbM
3232 I		12 22.8	+ 24 26 d	Com			F, eS, neb∗
4321	Gx	12 22.9	+ 15 49 s	Com	6.9	9.4	!! pF, vL, R, vg, psbMrN, 2-br spir; = M100
4323	−	12 22.9	+ 15 54 r	Com			2nd of 2, vF, n of M100; = 4322?
3233 I		12 22.9	+ 12 34 d	Vir			R, bM, mag 15
3234 I		12 22.9	+ 28 07 d	Com			F, S, R, bM
4322	Gx	12 23.0	+ 15 54 s	Com	1.3	13.9	1st of 2, vF, n of M100
4335	Gx	12 23.0	+ 58 27 s	UMa	2.2	14p	pB, S, E, gbM

NGC	Type	α_{2000}	δ_{2000}	Const.	Size	Mag.	Description
		h m	o ′		′		
785 I	Gx	12 23.0	− 13 14 m	Crv	0.8	15p	F, vS, R, stell
3235 I		12 23.0	+ 13 32 d	Com			lE, bM, mag 15
3236 I		12 23.0	+ 10 05 d	Vir			R, bM, mag 14
3237 I		12 23.0	+ 28 30 d	Com			F, cS, iF, eFN, att *14 sp
4320	Gx	12 23.1	+ 10 33 r	Vir		15p	F, vS, sp of 2
4324	Gx	12 23.1	+ 5 15 s	Vir	2.5	13p	pB, R or lE, bM
4338	Gx	12 23.1	+ 28 55 r	Com		15p	vF, lE, com; = IC 3247
3238 I	Gx	12 23.1	+ 14 25 m	Com	0.6	15p	R, bM, 14m
3239 I	Gx	12 23.1	+ 11 43 z	Vir		16p	E, lbM, mag 15
3241 I		12 23.1	+ 26 54 d	Com			F, vS, R, bM
4325	Gx	12 23.2	+ 10 38 r	Vir		15p	vF, vS, iR, nf of 2
4326	Gx	12 23.2	+ 6 04 s	Vir	1.7	14p	vF, S, R, bM, 1st of 3
4327	−	12 23.2	+ 15 47 r	Com			vF, s of 4328
786 I	Gx	12 23.2	− 13 13 m	Crv	1.0	15p	vF, eS, R, stell
3240 I		12 23.2	+ 10 20 d	Vir			R, bM, mag 15
3242 I		12 23.2	+ 26 15 d	Com			vF, S, iF
3243 I	Gx	12 23.2	+ 27 45 z	Com		16p	F, S, iF, dif
3244 I	Gx	12 23.2	+ 14 23 v	Com	0.7		R, bM, mag 14
4328	Gx	12 23.3	+ 15 48 s	Com	1.5	13.5	F, S, R, r
4330	Gx	12 23.3	+ 11 23 r	Vir		14p	vF, L, mE
3245 I	?	12 23.3	+ 9 07 x	Vir			vF, pL, bM; defect?
3246 I		12 23.3	+ 13 03 d	Vir			eF, pL, vmE 145°, ?
3247 I	Gx	12 23.3	+ 28 53 u	Com	2.4	16p	pF, pS, E 170°, bM
3248 I		12 23.3	+ 25 33 d	Com			eeF, S, R, bM
3249 I		12 23.3	+ 25 27 d	Com			eeF, S, iF
3250 I		12 23.3	+ 25 38 d	Com			eeF, S, R, bM
3251 I		12 23.3	+ 25 39 d	Com			eeF, S, R, bM
4329	Gx	12 23.4	− 12 34 s	Crv	1.2	14p	vF, vS, R, bMN
4333	Gx	12 23.4	+ 6 02 s	Vir	1.1	14p	F, pS, R, bM, 2nd of 3
4334	Gx	12 23.4	+ 7 28 s	Vir	2.4	14p	pF, S, R, * vnr
3252 I	OC	12 23.4	+ 28 37 x	Com			F, S, iF; Cl?
4346	Gx	12 23.5	+ 47 00 s	CVn	3.5	12p	vF, S, mE 100°±, vsmbMBN
4363	Gx	12 23.5	+ 74 57 s	Dra	1.5	15p	eF, pL, iF
3254 I		12 23.5	+ 19 27 x	Com			B, S, R, ◯ ; = 4336
4336	Gx	12 23.6	+ 19 27 r	Com		13p	vF, pL, iR, biN?
4339	Gx	12 23.6	+ 6 05 s	Vir	2.3	11.4	B, pL, R, bM, 3rd of 3
4340	Gx	12 23.6	+ 16 43 s	Com	4.1	11.0	pB, S, R, psbM
4342	Gx	12 23.6	+ 7 03 t	Vir	1.1	14p	eF, vS, R; = IC 3256
4344	Gx	12 23.6	+ 17 32 s	Com	1.9	13p	vF, pS, R, vglbM, △ 2 st
3255 I	Gx	12 23.6	+ 9 37 z	Vir		15p	R, bM, mag 13
4343	Gx	12 23.7	+ 6 57 s	Vir	2.8	12.1	pF, S, E; D?
3253 I	Gx	12 23.7	− 34 38 s	Cen	3.3	12p	eF, vL, mE 20°, lbM
3256 I	Gx	12 23.7	+ 7 03 s	Vir	1.4	12.6	*12 in S neb [= 4341 or 42?]
3257 I	?	12 23.7	+ 7 16 x	Vir			eF
3258 I	Gx	12 23.7	+ 12 28 s	Vir	1.9	14p	cF, cS, R, exc N s
3259 I	Gx	12 23.8	+ 7 11 s	Vir	1.8	13.6	F, cS, R, bM
3262 I	OC	12 23.8	+ 27 24 x	Com			F, S, iF, Cl?
3263 I	Gx	12 23.8	+ 28 12 m	Com	0.6	15p	pF, S, R, bM, spir, 2nd sp att
4337	OC	12 23.9	− 58 08 s	Cru	4	8.9	Cl, pRi, lC, st 12...14
4347	−	12 23.9	− 3 14 r				no description
4348	Gx	12 23.9	− 3 27 s	Vir	3.5	13p	F, pL, E 70°±, vlbM
3260 I	Gx	12 23.9	+ 7 07 s	Vir	1.9	13.3	F, cS, R, bM
3261 I		12 23.9	+ 11 28 d	Vir			pS, F* M, spir, doubtful
3264 I		12 23.9	+ 25 34 d	Com			vF, S, R, bM
4341	Gx	12 24.0	+ 7 07 r	Vir		14p	eF, vS, R; = IC 3260

NGC	Type	α_{2000}	δ_{2000}	Const.	Size	Mag.	Description
		h m	o /		/		
4350	Gx	12 24.0	+ 16 42 s	Com	3.2	11.1	cB, vS, mE, vsbM
4351	Gx	12 24.0	+ 12 12 s	Vir	2.0	12.7	F, pL, iR, bM
4353	Gx	12 24.0	+ 7 47 s	Vir	1.3	14p	no description; = IC 3266
4357	Gx	12 24.0	+ 48 46 s	CVn	3.8	14p	F, pS, gbM; = 4381?
4358	Gx	12 24.0	+ 58 24 r	UMa		14p	cF, cS, lE
4364	Gx	12 24.0	+ 58 24 r	UMa		14p	cF, cS, R
3265 I	?	12 24.0	+ 7 48 x	Vir			pF, S, N; *?
3266 I		12 24.0	+ 7 47 x	Vir			cF, S, biN, st?; = 4353
4352	Gx	12 24.1	+ 11 13 s	Vir	1.9	12.7	cF, cS, lE
4354	−	12 24.1	+ 12 12 r	Vir			eeF, pL, v diffic; = 4351?
3267 I	Gx	12 24.1	+ 7 03 s	Vir	1.1	13.5	pF, cS, R
3268 I	Gx	12 24.1	+ 6 36 s	Vir	0.7	14p	pB, *?
3269 I		12 24.1	+ 27 26 d	Com			eF, S, iF
3270 I		12 24.1	+ 27 35 d	Com			vF, vS, iF
4355	−	12 24.2	− 1 00 r	Vir			eF, S, R
4359	Gx	12 24.2	+ 31 31 s	Com	3.5	13p	cF, pmE 90°, vlbM
4362	Gx	12 24.2	+ 58 22 r	UMa		15p	vF, cS, R, r
3271 I	Gx	12 24.2	+ 7 57 u	Vir	1.1	15p	eF, pS, dif, ??
3272 I		12 24.2	+ 23 18 d	Com			vF, S, iF, *13 att n
3276 I		12 24.2	+ 25 49 d	Com			vF, vS, R, bM
4356	Gx	12 24.3	+ 8 33 r	Vir		14p	vF; = IC 3273
4360	Gx	12 24.3	+ 9 17 s	Vir	1.7	13p	F, F st inv, *9.5 np
3273 I		12 24.3	+ 8 32 x	Vir			cF, pL, E 48°, *10.5 inv; = 4356
3274 I	Gx	12 24.3	+ 9 17 u	Vir	1.4	14p	eF, vS, ?
3275 I		12 24.3	+ 10 25 d	Vir			R, bM, mag 14.5
3277 I		12 24.3	+ 25 34 d	Com			eF, cS, dif
3278 I		12 24.3	+ 27 25 d	Com			vF, S, iF, N
3279 I	*	12 24.4	+ 12 51 x	Vir			pF, S; 2 st?
3280 I	Gx	12 24.4	+ 13 14 m	Vir	0.7	15p	S, R, bM, mag 15.5
4349	OC	12 24.5	− 61 54 s	Cru	16	7.4	Cl, vB, vL, lC, st 12...14
4361	Pl	12 24.5	− 18 48 s	Crv	1.8	10p	vB, L, R, vsmbMN, r
4365	Gx	12 24.5	+ 7 19 s	Vir	6.2	11p	cB, pL, vlE, gl, smbM
4386	Gx	12 24.5	+ 75 32 s	Dra	3.0	12p	pB, cL, lE, psmbM
3281 I	?	12 24.5	+ 7 49 x	Vir			pB, pS, N, stell
3282 I		12 24.5	+ 25 40 d	Com			eF, vS, R, bM
3283 I		12 24.5	+ 27 13 d	Com			vF, S, R, bM, spir
4367	−	12 24.6	+ 12 11 r	Vir			vF, S, R
4369	Gx	12 24.6	+ 39 23 s	CVn	2.5	12p	cB, S, R, mbMN, r
3284 I		12 24.6	+ 10 49 d	Vir			vS, R, bM, mag 14
3285 I		12 24.6	+ 24 52 d	Com			vF, vS, R, bM, in dif neb E 25°
3286 I		12 24.6	+ 23 45 d	Com			S, pR
3287 I		12 24.6	+ 24 36 d	Com			eF, cS, iF, in dif neby
4368	−	12 24.7	+ 10 36 r	Vir			vF, vS
3288 I		12 24.7	+ 24 57 d	Com			vF, vS, R, bM
3292 I	Gx	12 24.8	+ 18 11 x	Com		15p	F, vS, R, bM
3294 I		12 24.8	+ 25 36 d	Com			eF, cS, dif
3295 I		12 24.8	+ 28 42 d	Com			cF, S, R, bM
4370	Gx	12 24.9	+ 7 27 s	Vir	1.6	14p	pF, pS, lE, bM
4371	Gx	12 24.9	+ 11 42 s	Vir	3.9	10.8	B, pS, R, gbM
3291 I		12 24.9	+ 12 00 d	Vir			R, bM, mag 14
3293 I		12 24.9	+ 17 26 d	Com			F, eS, R, ○
4366	?	12 25.0	+ 7 27 A	Vir			eF; evidently not 4370
4375	Gx	12 25.0	+ 28 33 s	Com	1.6	14p	F, S, R, bM, * nf 90″
3289 I	Gx	12 25.0	− 26 02 m	Hya	0.8	14p	eF, vS, R, v diffic, *7 nf, *8 np
3296 I	Gx	12 25.0	+ 24 23 x	Com		16p	cF, neb *13, *13 sp

NGC	Type	α_{2000}	δ_{2000}	Const.	Size	Mag.	Description
		h m	o ′		′		
3297 I		12 25.0	+ 26 46 d	Com			vF, pL, R, bM, spir
3298 I		12 25.0	+ 17 02 d	Com			S, E 150°, bM
3300 I	Gx	12 25.0	+ 25 57 u	Com	1.1	15p	pF, pS, E 80°, bM
4374	Gx	12 25.1	+ 12 53 s	Vir	5.0	9.3	vB, pL, R, psbM, r; = M84
4381	−	12 25.1	+ 48 50 r	CVn			F, S; = 4357?
3299 I		12 25.1	+ 27 23 d	Com			vF, vS, R, bM, spir
4377	Gx	12 25.2	+ 14 46 s	Com	1.8	11.8	B, S, R, smbM
4379	Gx	12 25.2	+ 15 36 s	Com	2.1	11.7	pS, R, psbMN
4384	Gx	12 25.2	+ 54 30 s	UMa	1.5	13p	cF, S, iR
4392	Gx	12 25.2	+ 45 52 r	CVn		14p	cF, S, R, vgbM
3290 I	Gx	12 25.2	− 39 47 c	Cen	1.6		pF, vS, R, * att, 4373 f
3301 I		12 25.2	+ 14 09 d	Com			vF, vS, R
3302 I		12 25.2	+ 25 53 d	Com			eF, vS, iF
3303 I	Gx	12 25.2	+ 12 43 v	Vir	1.4		vF, vS
3304 I		12 25.2	+ 25 25 d	Com			eF, S, R
3305 I	Gx	12 25.2	+ 11 50 u	Vir	1.1	15p	vlE, bM, mag 15
3306 I		12 25.2	+ 27 24 d	Com			vF, vS, iF, N
4373	Gx	12 25.3	− 39 45 s	Cen	3.2	11.1	pB, S, R, pgvmbM
4376	Gx	12 25.3	+ 4 56 r	Vir		14p	F, S
4378	Gx	12 25.3	+ 4 55 s	Vir	3.3	12p	B, S, *8-9 sf 3′
4391	Gx	12 25.3	+ 64 56 s	Dra	1.4	14p	cF, S, R, sbM, *̈* sp
3308 I	Gx	12 25.3	+ 26 42 u	Com	1.5	15p	F, cS, E 70°, bM
4380	Gx	12 25.4	+ 10 01 s	Vir	3.7	12p	vF, pL, R, lbM
4382	Gx	12 25.4	+ 18 11 s	Com	7.1	9.2	vB, pL, R, bM, * np; = M85
4383	Gx	12 25.4	+ 16 28 s	Com	2.2	13p	eS, stellar or neb* 11-12
3307 I	*	12 25.4	+ 14 09 x	Com			R, bM, mag 15
3309 I	Gx	12 25.4	+ 28 23 u	Com	1.4	16p	F, pS, R, bM, spir
787 I	Gx	12 25.5	+ 16 06 m	Com	1.0	15p	eF, pS, R, B* n, 4405 f
3310 I	*	12 25.5	+ 15 40 x	Com			vF, S, dif, sbM
3311 I	Gx	12 25.5	+ 12 15 u	Vir	2.1	15p	vF, cS, mE 135°
3312 I		12 25.5	+ 23 35 d	Com			eF, S, R, bM, v diffic
3313 I		12 25.5	+ 15 50 d	Com			F, vS, R, ◯, IC 3310 ssp
3314 I		12 25.5	+ 23 35 d	Com			vF, S, R, bM
4389	Gx	12 25.6	+ 45 41 s	CVn	2.7	12p	pB, pL, iE, vglbM
3316 I		12 25.6	+ 26 10 d	Com			eF, vS, bM; neb?
3317 I		12 25.6	+ 25 21 d	Com			eF, S, E
4385	Gx	12 25.7	+ 0 34 s	Vir	2.3	12.4	vF, vS, alm stell
4387	Gx	12 25.7	+ 12 49 s	Vir	1.9	12.0	pF, vS, R, *13 90″ np, np of 2
3315 I		12 25.7	+ 12 18 d	Vir			E, bM, mag 15
4372	Gb	12 25.8	− 72 40 s	Mus	18.6	7.8	⊕, pF, L, R, st 12...16
4388	Gx	12 25.8	+ 12 40 s	Vir	5.1	11.1	vF, E, sf of 2
4390	Gx	12 25.8	+ 10 27 s	Vir	1.8	13p	vF, pL, R; = IC 3319-20
4393	Gx	12 25.8	+ 27 33 s	Com	3.3	13p	vF, vL, iF, B* p; = IC 3323, IC 3329
4395	Gx	12 25.8	+ 33 33 s	CVn	12.9	10.2	eF, vL, np of Dneb
3318 I	*	12 25.8	+ 9 46 x	Vir			pB, S; = *10.5
3319 I		12 25.8	+ 10 23 x	Vir			pF, pS; = 4390
3320 I		12 25.8	+ 10 27 x	Vir			pF, pS, iF, FN; = 4390
3321 I		12 25.8	+ 26 05 d	Com			vF, vS, R; D*?
3323 I	Gx	12 25.8	+ 27 33 t	Com	3.1	13p	cF, vS, R, bM, neb* att
3324 I		12 25.8	+ 26 44 d	Com			cF, vS, R, bM, spir
3325 I		12 25.8	+ 23 54 d	Com			F, S
4394	Gx	12 25.9	+ 18 13 s	Com	3.9	10.9	pB, lE, bM
4399	−	12 25.9	+ 33 34 r	CVn			vF, forms trapezium with 4395, 4400, 4401
4400	−	12 25.9	+ 33 34 r	CVn			vF
4401	−	12 25.9	+ 33 31 r	CVn			vF, vL, pslbM, sf of Dneb

NGC	Type	α_{2000}	δ_{2000}	Const.	Size	Mag.	Description
		h m	° ′		′		
3322 I	Gx	12 25.9	+ 7 33 v	Vir	2.5		cF, pS, mE 130°
3326 I		12 25.9	+ 23 46 d	Com			F, S, iF
3328 I	Gx	12 25.9	+ 10 03 m	Vir	0.6	15p	vF, vS, bM
3329 I		12 25.9	+ 27 34 d	Com			vF, S, iF, att 4393
3330 I	Gx	12 25.9	+ 30 51 v	Com	1.4		F, cS, E pf, gbM
4396	Gx	12 26.0	+ 15 40 s	Com	3.5	13p	vF, pL, mE
4397	**	12 26.0	+ 18 19 r	Com			vF, S, 4394 sp
3327 I	Gx	12 26.0	+ 14 52 z	Com		15p	bM, mag 15
3331 I	Gx	12 26.0	+ 11 48 m	Vir	0.2	15p	eF, cS, E 78°, bM
4398	*	12 26.1	+ 10 42 r	Vir			F, pS, 4390 p 14^s, 14′ s
4402	Gx	12 26.1	+ 13 07 s	Vir	4.1	11.7	F, L, mE 90°
4405	Gx	12 26.1	+ 16 11 s	Com	2.0	13p	pF, S, R, vsbM, r; = IC 788?
788 I		12 26.1	+ 16 12 z	Com			pB, pL, R, 4405 south; = 4405?
3332 I		12 26.1	+ 25 17 d	Com			vF, vS, iF, N
4406	Gx	12 26.2	+ 12 57 s	Vir	7.4	9.2	vB, L, R, gbMN, r; = M86
4408	Gx	12 26.2	+ 27 53 r	Com		15p	F, S, r
3333 I	*	12 26.2	+ 13 08 z	Vir			vF, vS; *14?
3334 I		12 26.2	+ 28 28 d	Com			vF, pS, R, bM
4403	Gx	12 26.3	− 7 41 r	Vir		14p	vF, vS, E
4407	−	12 26.3	+ 12 39 r	Vir			f of 2 neb; = 4413?
789 I	Gx	12 26.3	+ 7 27 z	Vir		15p	F, vS, R, N = 14m, vF* close
3335 I		12 26.3	+ 26 08 d	Com			eF, vS, R, bM; neb?
3336 I	Gx	12 26.3	+ 26 49 z	Com		15p	pB, vS, R, bM
4404	Gx	12 26.4	− 7 41 r	Vir		14p	vF, vS, E
4414	Gx	12 26.4	+ 31 13 s	Com	3.6	10.3	vB, L, E, g, vsmbM *
3337 I		12 26.4	+ 25 19 d	Com			eF, vS, R, bM, spir
3338 I		12 26.4	+ 25 53 d	Com			F, vS, R, bM, spir
3341 I		12 26.4	+ 27 45 d	Com			vF, cS, dif
4409	−	12 26.5	+ 2 30 r	Vir			vF, pS, r; = 4420?
4410	Gx	12 26.5	+ 9 01 s	Vir	1.3	14p	pF, vL, R, gbM
4411	Gx	12 26.5	+ 8 52 s	Vir	2.2	12.8	vF, L, 2′.5; = IC 3339
4413	Gx	12 26.5	+ 12 37 s	Vir	2.5	13p	cF, S, gbM, 2 st n, np
790 I	Gx	12 26.5	+ 9 01 m	Vir	0.5	15p	vF, vS, f 4410
3339 I		12 26.5	+ 8 52 z	Vir			*11 with neb nf; = 4411
3340 I	Gx	12 26.5	+ 16 50 m	Com	0.7	15p	vS, E 200°
3342 I		12 26.5	+ 27 08 d	Com			vF, vS, R, spir, sbM *
3344 I	Gx	12 26.5	+ 13 34 m	Com	0.5	15p	R, bM, mag 14.5
3345 I		12 26.5	+ 24 22 d	Com			eF, S, iF
4412	Gx	12 26.6	+ 3 58 s	Vir	1.5	13p	F, pL, R, gbM, r
4415	Gx	12 26.6	+ 8 25 s	Vir	1.5	14p	eF, pS
3343 I	?	12 26.6	+ 8 53 z	Vir			eF, vS, ??
3348 I		12 26.6	+ 25 37 d	Com			eF, vS, iF
3346 I		12 26.7	+ 11 21 d	Vir			eS, R, bM, mag 15.5
3347 I		12 26.7	+ 10 53 d	Vir			R, bM, mag 15
3349 I	Gx	12 26.7	+ 12 27 z	Vir		15p	vS, R, lbM, mag 15
3351 I		12 26.7	+ 27 36 d	Com			eF, S, iF
3353 I		12 26.7	+ 27 55 d	Com			eF, S, iF
4416	Gx	12 26.8	+ 7 56 r	Vir		13p	vF, L, R, *7 sp 5′
4417	Gx	12 26.8	+ 9 35 s	Vir	3.6	11.2	F, pL, E, lbp
3350 I	*	12 26.8	+ 9 27 z	Vir			*10.5 with neb sp
3352 I	?	12 26.8	+ 8 45 z	Vir			F, pS, E
3355 I	Gx	12 26.8	+ 13 11 v	Vir	1.3		eF, pS, E 168°
3356 I	Gx	12 26.8	+ 11 34 t	Vir	1.4	15p	R, bM, mag 16
3357 I	Gx	12 26.8	+ 9 45 z	Vir		15p	R, bM, mag 15
3360 I		12 26.8	+ 26 03 d	Com			eF, vS, iF

NGC	Type	α_{2000}	δ_{2000}		Const.	Size	Mag.	Description
		h m	° ′			′		
4418	Gx	12 26.9	− 0 51	r	Vir		14p	F or vF, S or cL, R or mE, ∗ nr
4419	Gx	12 26.9	+ 15 03	s	Com	3.4	11.1	B, pmE 135°±, sbM
3354 I	∗	12 26.9	+ 12 06	x	Vir			eF, S, ?
3358 I	Gx	12 26.9	+ 11 39	u	Vir	1.2	15p	vF, S
3359 I		12 26.9	+ 23 30	d	Com			F, S, iF, N, ∗14 np
3362 I		12 26.9	+ 26 41	d	Com			F, vS, bM, spir
4420	Gx	12 27.0	+ 2 30	s	Vir	2.2	13p	F, pL, lE, r; = 4409?
4421	Gx	12 27.0	+ 15 28	s	Com	2.7	11.6	pB, pL, pgbM, B∗ np
791 I	Gx	12 27.0	+ 22 38	u	Com	1.2	14p	BN = 12m
3361 I		12 27.0	+ 10 38	d	Vir			R, bM, mag 15.5
3363 I	Gx	12 27.0	+ 12 33	z	Vir		15p	E, bM, mag 15
4423	Gx	12 27.1	+ 5 52	s	Vir	2.3	14p	vF, vS, E
792 I	Gx	12 27.1	+ 16 20	u	Com	1.8	15p	F, S, gbM
3364 I		12 27.1	+ 25 34	d	Com			vF, vS, R, bM
3365 I	Gx	12 27.1	+ 15 54	s	Com	1.9	14p	pL, vmE 240°
4424	Gx	12 27.2	+ 9 25	s	Vir	3.7	11.6	F, pL, iR, bM
4425	Gx	12 27.2	+ 12 44	s	Vir	3.4	11.9	pF, S, R, bM
4426	D∗	12 27.2	+ 27 51	r	Com			Cl, F, S
4427	D∗	12 27.2	+ 27 51	r	Com			vF; 2 or 3 F st in neb?
3367 I	Gx	12 27.2	+ 26 57	z	Com		16p	F, vS, R, att 2nd np
4422	Gx	12 27.3	− 5 49	r	Vir		14p	F, vS, R, psbM, 2 S st nr
4441	Gx	12 27.3	+ 64 48	s	Dra	4.7	14p	pB, S, iR, bM
3366 I	?	12 27.3	+ 9 25	x	Vir			vF, vS
3368 I		12 27.3	+ 16 25	d	Com			vS, vlE, ○
3369 I		12 27.3	+ 16 02	d	Com			vF, bM, mag 14
3371 I	Gx	12 27.3	+ 10 52	u	Vir	1.9	15p	F, pL, vmE 225°
4429	Gx	12 27.4	+ 11 07	s	Vir	5.5	10.2	B, L, cE, psbM, ∗10 nf
4430	Gx	12 27.4	+ 6 15	s	Vir	2.7	12p	cF, L, R, gbM
3372 I		12 27.4	+ 25 17	d	Com			vF, vS, bM, spir
4428	Gx	12 27.5	− 8 10	s	Vir	1.9	13p	vF, pL
4431	Gx	12 27.5	+ 12 18	s	Vir	2.0	12.8	vF, vS, cE, gbM
4434	Gx	12 27.5	+ 8 09	s	Vir	1.6	13p	pF, vS
3373 I		12 27.5	+ 25 27	d	Com			F, cS, iF
3374 I		12 27.5	+ 9 59	z	Vir		16p	R, bM, mag 15.5
4432		12 27.6	+ 6 14	r	Vir		15p	2 st in eF neb
4433	Gx	12 27.6	− 8 17	s	Vir	2.3	13p	pF, pL, lE
3370 I	Gx	12 27.6	− 39 20	s	Cen	2.8	11.1	pB, pL, R, ∗8.5 p 4′
4435	Gx	12 27.7	+ 13 05	s	Vir	3.0	10.9	vB, cL, R, np of 2
4436	Gx	12 27.7	+ 12 19	s	Vir	1.9	13.1	cF, S, gbM
3375 I		12 27.7	+ 27 22	d	Com			F, vS, R, att ∗14 sp
4438	Gx	12 27.8	+ 13 01	s	Vir	9.3	10.1	B, cL, vlE, r, sf of 2
4456	Gx	12 27.8	− 30 07	r	Hya		15p	eeF, vS, ∗13 att
3376 I	Gx	12 27.8	+ 26 59	u	Com	1.8	14p	pB, S, R, bM
4440	Gx	12 27.9	+ 12 18	s	Vir	2.0	11.8	B, pS, R, bM, r
3377 I		12 27.9	+ 24 56	d	Com			pF, vS, R, bM
793 I		12 28.0	+ 9 26	x	Vir			eF, S, mE, 3 others in field; = 4445
4442	Gx	12 28.1	+ 9 48	s	Vir	4.6	10.5	vB, pL, R, smbM
4443	∗	12 28.1	+ 13 08	r	Vir			F, S
794 I	Gx	12 28.1	+ 12 06	v	Vir	1.7		F, S, E pF, bM
3378 I		12 28.1	+ 17 18	d	Com			1st of 2 neb, 1′apart, mag 15.5
3379 I		12 28.1	+ 17 18	d	Com			2nd of 2 neb, 1′apart, mag 15.5
3380 I		12 28.1	+ 26 40	d	Com			F, vS, bM, spir
4446	Gx	12 28.2	+ 13 55	r	Com		15p	eeF, pS, R
4448	Gx	12 28.2	+ 28 37	s	Com	4.0	11.1	B, L, E 90°, sbM
4449	Gx	12 28.2	+ 44 06	s	CVn	5.1	9.4	vB, cL, mE, D or bifid, rrr, ∗9 f 5′

NGC	Type	α_{2000}	δ_{2000}	Const.	Size	Mag.	Description
		h m	° ′		′		
3382 I	Gx	12 28.2	+ 13 33 u	Com	1.0	16p	F, pS, mE 150°
3383 I	Gx	12 28.2	+ 10 17 m	Vir	0.7	15p	R, bM, mag 15
3384 I		12 28.2	+ 25 05 d	Com			eF, vS, iF
3385 I		12 28.2	+ 25 26 d	Com			ef, pS, R, bM, dif
4445	Gx	12 28.3	+ 9 26 s	Vir	2.8	12.8	vF, pL, mE; = IC 793
4447	Gx	12 28.3	+ 13 54 r	Com		15p	eeF, pS, R
3381 I	Gx	12 28.3	+ 11 47 v	Vir	1.5		eF, vS, stell
3387 I		12 28.3	+ 28 00 d	Com			vF, S, viF
4439	OC	12 28.4	− 60 06 s	Cru	4	8.4	Cl, S, st 11...12
3386 I		12 28.4	+ 13 11 d	Vir			vF, cS, E 90°
3388 I	Gx	12 28.4	+ 12 49 z	Vir		15p	vS, R, lbM, mag 15
3389 I		12 28.4	+ 27 51 d	Com			vF, S, iF
3391 I	Gx	12 28.4	+ 18 24 u	Com	1.1	14p	cS, vlE, sbMF∗; spir?
4450	Gx	12 28.5	+ 17 05 s	Com	4.8	10.1	B, L, R, gvmbM ∗, r, B∗ sp
795 I	Gx	12 28.5	+ 23 18 z	Com		15p	pB, S, stellar, 13m
3390 I		12 28.5	+ 24 49 d	Com			vF, vS, R, bM
4444	Gx	12 28.6	− 43 16 t	Cen	1.6		eF, L, R, vgbM
4451	Gx	12 28.7	+ 9 16 s	Vir	1.5	12.5	pB, pS, R, bM, ∗13 s
4452	Gx	12 28.7	+ 11 45 s	Vir	2.4	12.4	pB, S, vmE
4453	Gx	12 28.7	+ 6 30 v	Vir	0.6		F, pS, bM, r
4455	Gx	12 28.7	+ 22 49 s	Com	2.8	13p	F, L, E, gbM, 2 B st nf
3392 I	Gx	12 28.7	+ 15 00 v	Com	2.4		B, L, mE 225°, mbM
3393 I	Gx	12 28.7	+ 12 55 v	Vir	1.4		S, E 125°, bM, mag 14
3395 I		12 28.7	+ 25 02 d	Com			vF, vS, R, bM
3396 I		12 28.7	+ 25 03 d	Com			vF, vS, R, bM, others n
4454	Gx	12 28.8	− 1 56 s	Vir	2.2	12.1	F, L, R, gbM, er
4460	Gx	12 28.8	+ 44 52 s	CVn	4.4	12p	B, pL, E 123°, psbM
3394 I	Gx	12 28.8	+ 26 47 m	Com	0.4	16p	F, S, bM, spir
3397 I		12 28.8	+ 25 44 d	Com			F, S, v iF
4484	Gx	12 28.9	− 11 39 r	Vir		14p	pF, S, R, gbM
3399 I		12 28.9	+ 25 42 d	Com			vF, vS, R, bM
4457	Gx	12 29.0	+ 3 34 s	Vir	3.0	10.8	cB, pS, R, smbMN
4458	Gx	12 29.0	+ 13 15 s	Vir	1.9	12.1	pB, S, R, bM, p of 2
4459	Gx	12 29.0	+ 13 59 s	Com	3.8	10.4	pB, pL, iR, bM, r, ∗8 sf 2′
4461	Gx	12 29.0	+ 13 11 s	Vir	3.7	11.2	pF, S, R, bM, f of 2
3398 I	∗	12 29.0	+ 13 34 z	Com			cF, vS
3400 I	?	12 29.0	+ 9 24 z	Vir			cB, cS, = ∗10
3401 I		12 29.0	+ 26 28 d	Com			vF, vS, R
3402 I	Gx	12 29.0	+ 28 51 u	Com	1.0	16p	vF, cL, E 10°, ∗ np, conn?
3403 I	Gx	12 29.0	+ 24 38 z	Com		16p	cF, S, pR, bM
3405 I		12 29.0	+ 37 44 d	CVn			F, S, R, vlbM
3407 I	Gx	12 29.0	+ 27 47 u	Com	1.2	15p	cF, cS, E 150°, bM; spir?
3406 I	Gx	12 29.1	+ 27 38 m	Com	0.5	16p	cF, S, bM, spir
3410 I	Gx	12 29.1	+ 19 00 z	Com		16p	bM, mag 15.5
3404 I	?	12 29.2	+ 7 09 x	Vir			cB, cS, R, mbM
3411 I		12 29.2	+ 24 35 d	Com			eF, S, iF, neby sf
4462	Gx	12 29.3	− 23 10 s	Crv	3.7	12p	pB, pS, E 130°, sbM
3408 I	∗	12 29.3	+ 11 53 z	Vir			B, stell; ∗9.5?
3412 I	Gx	12 29.3	+ 9 59 z	Vir		15p	eF, cS
4464	Gx	12 29.4	+ 8 10 s	Vir	1.1	12.7	F, vS, R, pgbM
4465	Gx	12 29.4	+ 8 02 r	Vir		15p	vF, v dif
796 I	Gx	12 29.4	+ 16 24 u	Com	1.4	14p	F, S, E ns, r
3409 I	Gx	12 29.4	+ 14 46 m	Com	0.6	17p	bM, mag 15
3413 I	Gx	12 29.4	+ 11 26 v	Vir	1.6		vF, vS, R, bM
3414 I	Gx	12 29.4	+ 6 46 v	Vir	1.7		cF, cS, mbM

NGC	Type	α_{2000}	δ_{2000}	Const.	Size	Mag.	Description
		h m	o /		/		
3415 I		12 29.4	+ 26 46 d	Com			F, vS, bM, spir; neb*?
4466	Gx	12 29.5	+ 7 42 s	Vir	1.4	15p	vF, pS, iR
4467	Gx	12 29.5	+ 8 00 v	Vir	0.7	14.5	vF, vS, lE
4468	Gx	12 29.5	+ 14 03 s	Com	1.5	13.0	F, cL
4469	Gx	12 29.5	+ 8 45 s	Vir	3.9	12p	pF, pL, mE, bM, r
4470	Gx	12 29.6	+ 7 49 s	Vir	1.5	13p	F, pL, iR, bM; = IC 3417
3416 I	Gx	12 29.6	+ 10 47 m	Vir	0.1	15p	S, mE 250°
3421 I	OC	12 29.6	+ 26 14 x	Com			Cl, F, cS, R, bM
4471	Gx	12 29.7	+ 7 55 h	Vir	0.2	15p	vF, vS
3417 I	*	12 29.7	+ 7 52 x	Vir			eF, vS, ?*
3418 I	Gx	12 29.7	+ 11 24 v	Vir	1.5		vF, wisp
3419 I		12 29.7	+ 15 02 d	Com			vF, R, mag 16
3420 I	*	12 29.7	+ 13 27 x	Com			vF, S, R, ??
3422 I		12 29.7	+ 14 42 d	Com			bM, mag 15
3424 I		12 29.7	+ 24 24 d	Com			eF, pS, iF
4472	Gx	12 29.8	+ 8 00 s	Vir	8.9	8.4	vB, L, R, mbM, r; = M49
4473	Gx	12 29.8	+ 13 26 s	Com	4.5	10.2	pB
4475	Gx	12 29.8	+ 27 15 s	Com	2.1	15p	eF, pL, R
4481	Gx	12 29.8	+ 64 03 r	Dra		15p	pF, vS, R, *13 att
3423 I	?	12 29.8	+ 13 40 x	Com			vF, vS
4474	Gx	12 29.9	+ 14 04 s	Com	2.3	11.8	pF, R, r
3425 I	Gx	12 29.9	+ 10 36 u	Vir	1.9	15p	bM, mag 14
4463	OC	12 30.0	− 64 48 s	Mus	5	7.2	Cl, P, vlC
4476	Gx	12 30.0	+ 12 21 s	Vir	1.9	12.3	F, S, R, bM, 1st of 3
4477	Gx	12 30.0	+ 13 38 s	Com	4.0	10.4	pB, cL
3426 I	*	12 30.0	+ 13 36 x	Com			vF, vS
3427 I	Gx	12 30.1	+ 10 46 x	Vir		14p	F, vS, exc Nf
3428 I		12 30.1	+ 23 40 d	Com			F, S, R, bM
3429 I		12 30.1	+ 23 33 d	Com			vF, S, iF, N
4482	Gx	12 30.2	+ 10 47 r	Vir		14p	eF, pL; = IC 3427
3430 I	Gx	12 30.2	+ 9 04 u	Vir	1.2	15p	eF, cS, dif
4478	Gx	12 30.3	+ 12 20 s	Vir	2.0	11.2	pB, S, R, psbM, 2nd of 3
4479	Gx	12 30.3	+ 13 35 s	Com	1.8	12.5	pB, pL
4480	Gx	12 30.4	+ 4 15 s	Vir	2.6	12.4	pF, pS, E, bs
3431 I	*	12 30.4	+ 11 35 x	Vir			vS, R
3432 I	Gx	12 30.4	+ 14 10 m	Com	0.6	15p	B, S, R
3433 I		12 30.4	+ 17 18 d	Com			bM, mag 14.5
4485	Gx	12 30.5	+ 41 42 s	CVn	2.4	12.0	B, pS, iR, np of 2
3434 I	Gx	12 30.5	+ 18 48 z	Com		15p	bM, mag 15
3436 I	Gx	12 30.5	+ 19 39 m	Com	0.4	15p	bM, mag 14
4490	Gx	12 30.6	+ 41 38 s	CVn	5.9	9.8	vB, vL, mE 130°, r, sf of 2
3435 I	Gx	12 30.6	+ 15 07 u	Com	1.2	16p	S, mE 135°, sbM
4483	Gx	12 30.7	+ 9 01 s	Vir	1.8	13p	pB, pS, R, bM
4486	Gx	12 30.8	+ 12 24 s	Vir	7.2	8.6	vB, vL, R, mbM, 3rd of 3; = M87
4489	Gx	12 30.8	+ 16 45 s	Com	2.2	13p	pF, cS, R, gbM
3437 I	Gx	12 30.8	+ 11 20 z	Vir		15p	bM, mag 15
4488	Gx	12 30.9	+ 8 22 s	Vir	3.6	13p	vF, vS, lE
4491	Gx	12 31.0	+ 11 29 s	Vir	1.9	12.5	F, L, R
4492	Gx	12 31.0	+ 8 05 s	Vir	2.0	12.5	pF, pL, vglbM, 2 st nr; = IC 3438
3438 I		12 31.0	+ 8 05 x	Vir			cF, S, FN; = 4492
3439 I		12 31.0	+ 25 34 d	Com			vF, cS, iF, sev N
4487	Gx	12 31.1	− 8 03 s	Vir	4.1	11p	F, vL, er
3440 I		12 31.1	+ 12 02 d	Vir			eF, pS, lE 30°
4493	Gx	12 31.2	+ 0 37 r	Vir		15p	vF, vS, iR
3441 I	Gx	12 31.2	+ 28 51 m	Com	0.4	15p	F, S, bM, spir

NGC	Type	α_{2000}	δ_{2000}	Const.	Size	Mag.	Description
		h m	° ′		′		
3444 I		12 31.2	+ 27 33 d	Com			vF, vS, bM, spir
4495	Gx	12 31.3	+ 29 09 r	Com		14p	pF, cS, R, pslbM
3442 I	Gx	12 31.3	+ 14 07 v	Com	1.5		F, vS, R, lbM
3443 I	Gx	12 31.3	+ 12 19 m	Vir	0.2	16p	bM, mag 15.5
3445 I		12 31.3	+ 12 44 d	Vir			F, eS, R
3446 I	Gx	12 31.3	+ 11 29 z	Vir		15p	bM, mag 14
4494	Gx	12 31.4	+ 25 47 s	Com	4.8	9.9	vB, pL, R, vsmbMN
4500	Gx	12 31.4	+ 57 58 s	UMa	1.9	13p	B, cS, E, pgbM, *9 f 50″
3447 I	*	12 31.4	+ 10 40 x	Vir			F, eS, R
3448 I		12 31.4	+ 17 12 d	Com			vF, vlE
3449 I	D*	12 31.4	+ 25 55 z	Com			eF, vS, bM, spir
3450 I	Gx	12 31.4	+ 26 48 z	Com			vF, vS, spir, ? (4494 sp)
3451 I	Gx	12 31.4	+ 28 51 m	Com	0.5	15p	F, S, bM, spir
4497	Gx	12 31.5	+ 11 37 s	Vir	2.3	12.6	vF or pF; = IC 3452
3452 I		12 31.5	+ 11 37 x	Vir			pF, pS, E 100°; = 4497
3453 I	Gx	12 31.5	+ 14 51 s	Com	1.2	15p	F, S, E 160°, lbM
4496	Gx	12 31.6	+ 3 56 s	Vir	3.9	12p	F, cL, biN or Dneb
3454 I	Gx	12 31.6	+ 27 30 u	Com	1.3	16p	F, S, iF, dif, att *11 n
4498	Gx	12 31.7	+ 16 51 s	Com	3.2	13p	vF, pL, E; biN?
4510	Gx	12 31.7	+ 64 15 r	Dra		14p	Cl, vS, st F, mC
3455 I	?	12 31.7	+ 25 47 x	Com			eF, S, iF
3456 I		12 31.7	+ 28 21 d	Com			vF, pS, iF
3458 I		12 31.7	+ 28 09 d	Com			F, S, bM, spir
4529	Gx	12 31.8	+ 20 30 r	Com		15p	eF, L
3460 I		12 31.8	+ 27 23 d	Com			F, S, iF
4513	Gx	12 31.9	+ 66 20 r	Dra		14p	F, R (vS Cl?)
797 I	Gx	12 31.9	+ 15 07 u	Com	1.2	14p	F, S, R, gbM
3457 I	Gx	12 31.9	+ 12 39 v	Vir	1.6		S, R, lbM
3459 I	Gx	12 31.9	+ 12 10 u	Vir	1.2	15p	vF, pS, dif
4501	Gx	12 32.0	+ 14 25 s	Com	6.9	9.5	B, vL, vmE; = M88
3461 I	Gx	12 32.0	+ 11 53 m	Vir	0.6	15p	vF, vS
3462 I		12 32.0	+ 15 18 d	Com			vF, eS, R
3464 I	*	12 32.0	+ 26 00 x	Com			eF, vS, bM, spir
4499	Gx	12 32.1	− 39 58 r	Cen			vF, L, R, vglbM
4502	Gx	12 32.1	+ 16 42 r	Com		15p	vF, S
4503	Gx	12 32.1	+ 11 11 s	Vir	3.5	11.1	pB, S, R, gbM
3463 I	D*	12 32.1	+ 12 19 x	Vir			vF, cS, E 40°
4506	Gx	12 32.2	+ 13 25 s	Com	1.6	14p	cF, pmE 90°±, gbM, *9 p 8^s
4511	Gx	12 32.2	+ 56 29 r	UMa		14p	pF, vS, iR, vgbM
3465 I		12 32.2	+ 12 04 d	Vir			bM, mag 16
3466 I		12 32.2	+ 11 48 d	Vir			bM, mag 15
3469 I		12 32.2	+ 25 48 d	Com			eF, S, E 50°
4504	Gx	12 32.3	− 7 34 s	Vir	4.0	12p	pB, cL, iE, gvlbM, er
4505	−	12 32.3	+ 3 59 r	Vir			vF, cL, r, f of 2; = 4496?
3467 I		12 32.3	+ 11 47 d	Vir			cS, vmE 255°, sbM *
3468 I	Gx	12 32.3	+ 10 14 x	Vir			bM, mag 13.5
3471 I	Gx	12 32.3	+ 16 01 m	Com	0.7	16p	F, vS, R
3472 I		12 32.3	+ 24 44 d	Com			eF, S, iF
3473 I	Gx	12 32.3	+ 18 14 u	Com	1.1	15p	S, R, lbM
4508	−	12 32.4	+ 5 50 r	Vir			vS, R, sbM *13
3470 I	Gx	12 32.4	+ 11 15 x	Vir			bM, mag 13.5
4514	Gx	12 32.5	+ 29 44 r	Com		14p	eF, vS, R, bM
798 I	Gx	12 32.5	+ 15 24 z	Com		15p	vF, eS, R
4512	Gx	12 32.6	+ 63 54 r	Dra		14p	pB, S, R, psbM
3474 I	Gx	12 32.6	+ 2 40 v	Vir	2.2		pF, E spnf, dif, *17 np, B* sf

NGC	Type	α_{2000}	δ_{2000}	Const.	Size	Mag.	Description
		h m	° ′		′		
3477 I	*	12 32.6	+ 26 03 x	Com			vF, vF, bM, spir
3475 I	Gx	12 32.7	+ 12 46 s	Vir	2.6	13.3	vF, pS, R, dif
3476 I	Gx	12 32.7	+ 14 03 s	Com	2.2	12.7	pF, pL, lbM
3478 I	Gx	12 32.7	+ 14 12 v	Com	1.3		vF, vS, bM
3479 I		12 32.7	+ 25 24 d	Com			vF, vS, iF
3480 I		12 32.7	+ 26 50 d	Com			vF, S, E 90°, bM
4437		12 32.8	+ 0 07 A	Vir			F, eE 75°, *10 nf, place that of *; = 4517
4517	Gx	12 32.8	+ 0 07 s	Vir	10.2	10.5	cB, vL, vmE 89°, pB* in cont
4521	Gx	12 32.8	+ 63 57 r	Dra		13p	pB, S, pmE, pgbM, *10 p 12ˢ
3481 I	Gx	12 32.9	+ 11 24 s	Vir	0.7	14.0	bM, mag 13
3568 I	Pl	12 32.9	+ 82 33 s	Cam	0.1	12p	◯ or neb *9.5; *13 p 15″
4515	Gx	12 33.0	+ 16 15 s	Com	1.6	13p	F, vS, bM *
3482 I		12 33.0	+ 27 50 d	Com			vF, S, bM, spir
4509	Gx	12 33.1	+ 32 06 s	CVn	1.1	14p	vF, S, R, lbM
4516	Gx	12 33.1	+ 14 34 s	Com	1.9	14p	F, pS, R, r
3484 I	Gx	12 33.1	+ 17 24 m	Com	0.6	15p	S, R, bM
3488 I	Gx	12 33.1	+ 26 21 x	Com			F, S, R, bM
4518	Gx	12 33.2	+ 7 51 r	Vir		15p	F, S, R, bM
3483 I	Gx	12 33.2	+ 11 21 s	Vir	0.5	15.0	bM, mag 14
3485 I	*	12 33.2	+ 9 13 x	Vir			eF, S; ?
3486 I		12 33.2	+ 12 52 d	Vir			F, S, R, dif
3487 I		12 33.2	+ 9 24 d	Vir			vF, vS
3489 I	Gx	12 33.2	+ 12 14 m	Vir	0.6	15p	bM, mag 13
3490 I	Gx	12 33.2	+ 10 55 z	Vir	0.6	16p	vF, S, vmE 240°
3491 I	Gx	12 33.2	+ 27 06 x	Com			F, S, iF
3492 I	Gx	12 33.2	+ 12 51 s	Vir		15p	sbM, prob spiral
3494 I	Gx	12 33.2	+ 27 35 x	Com			vF, vS, neb*, *15 np
3493 I	*	12 33.4	+ 9 23 x	Vir			eF, vS
4519	Gx	12 33.5	+ 8 39 s	Vir	3.1	11.7	F, pL, R, bM, r
3495 I	Gx	12 33.5	+ 26 47 x	Com			vF, cS, iF, diffic
3496 I	Gx	12 33.5	+ 26 44 x	Com			vF, cS, iF, *15 np
3497 I		12 33.5	+ 25 29 d	Com			vF, vS, R, bM
3498 I	*	12 33.5	+ 26 44 x	Com			vF, S, iF
4522	Gx	12 33.7	+ 9 10 s	Vir	3.7	13p	eF, pL, lE, vlbM
799 I		12 33.7	− 7 24 x	Vir			eF, eS, R (eF* att p?); = 4520
3499 I	Gx	12 33.7	+ 10 59 s	Vir	1.6	13.3	cS, E (wisps) 130°, bM
3502 I	Gx	12 33.7	+ 26 37 x	Com			eF, S, iF
4520	Gx	12 33.8	− 7 23 s	Vir			vF, S, 2 vS st inv
4523	Gx	12 33.8	+ 15 10 s	Com	2.6	14p	Cl + neb, close to a ⁎
4524	Gx	12 33.8	− 12 01 r	Crv		14p	vF, iF, bM
4525	Gx	12 33.8	+ 30 17 s	Com	2.9	13p	F, pL, iR, bM
4530	−	12 33.8	+ 41 21 r	CVn			nebulous * 4 mag ??? (8 CVn)
801 I	Gx	12 33.8	+ 52 15 u	CVn	1.2	15p	eeF, S, R, * close n
3500 I	Gx	12 33.8	+ 13 58 z	Com		15p	S, E 90°, sbM *
3501 I	Gx	12 33.8	+ 13 19 m	Com	0.6	15p	F, S, R, bMN
3503 I		12 33.8	+ 37 47 d	CVn			eF, vS, bMN
800 I	Gx	12 33.9	+ 15 21 v	Com	1.7		F, S, R, gbM
4526	Gx	12 34.0	+ 7 42 s	Vir	7.2	9.6	vB, vL, mE 120°±, psmbM, bet 2 st 7m
4527	Gx	12 34.1	+ 2 39 s	Vir	6.3	10.4	pB, L, pmE 69°, mbM
4528	Gx	12 34.1	+ 11 19 s	Vir	1.8	11.7	pF, cS, R, bM, *9 f 30ˢ
4534	Gx	12 34.1	+ 35 31 s	CVn	3.0	12p	cF, L, lE, vglbM, r
3504 I	?	12 34.1	+ 6 53 x	Vir			eF, vS, nr *10
3505 I	Gx	12 34.1	+ 15 57 m	Com	0.8	15p	F, S, E
3507 I		12 34.1	+ 25 22 d	Com			vF, vS, iF
3508 I	Gx	12 34.1	+ 26 40 x	Com			cF, S, bM, spir

NGC	Type	α_{2000}	δ_{2000}	Const.	Size	Mag.	Description
		h m	° ′		′		
3506 I		12 34.2	+ 12 44 d	Vir			vF, R
3511 I	?	12 34.2	+ 27 21 x	Com			vF, S, iF, N
3512 I	?	12 34.2	+ 27 22 x	Com			vF, S, iF, N
3513 I	?	12 34.2	+ 27 20 x	Com			vF, S, iF, N
4531	Gx	12 34.3	+ 13 05 s	Vir	3.0	13p	F, pL, R, vgbM
4532	Gx	12 34.3	+ 6 28 s	Vir	2.9	11.9	pB, pL, pmE, vgbM, r
4535	Gx	12 34.3	+ 8 12 s	Vir	6.8	9.8	pF, vL, r, spiral neb
3509 I	Gx	12 34.3	+ 12 04 z	Vir		15p	bM, mag 14
3510 I	Gx	12 34.3	+ 11 04 u	Vir	1.1	15p	eF, bM, mag 15, *10 nf
3514 I	D*	12 34.3	+ 26 42 x	Com			vF, vS, bM, spir
3515 I		12 34.3	+ 27 52 d	Com			F, S, iF
3516 I	Gx	12 34.3	+ 27 27 x	Com			vF, S, iF, N
4533	Gx	12 34.4	+ 2 20 s	Vir	2.0	15p	F, 4536 sf
4536	Gx	12 34.5	+ 2 11 s	Vir	7.4	10.4	B, vL, mE 110°, sbM, er
3517 I	Gx	12 34.5	+ 9 09 u	Vir	1.5	15p	eF, pS, mE 28°; ?
3518 I	Gx	12 34.5	+ 9 37 u	Vir	1.3	15p	cS, mE 210°, bM
3519 I	?	12 34.5	+ 15 34 x	Com			vF, vS, R
3520 I	Gx	12 34.5	+ 13 30 z	Com		15p	vF, R
4539	Gx	12 34.6	+ 18 12 s	Com	3.5	12.0	pB, pmE
4545	Gx	12 34.6	+ 63 31 s	Dra	2.8	13p	F, L, iR, vgbM, S* nf
3521 I	Gx	12 34.6	+ 7 09 x	Vir			pF, cS, E 45°, bM
4538	Gx	12 34.7	+ 3 20 r	Vir		15p	eF, vS, nearly R
3523 I		12 34.7	+ 14 01 d	Com			vF, R
3524 I	D*	12 34.7	+ 14 14 x	Com			cF, S; *12.5?
3526 I		12 34.7	+ 25 41 d	Com			F, vS, R, bM
3527 I	D*	12 34.7	+ 26 09 x	Com			F, vS, R, bM *
4540	Gx	12 34.8	+ 15 33 s	Com	2.0	12p	F, pS, bM, r
4542	Gx	12 34.8	+ 50 50 r	CVn		15p	eF, pL, R
4547	Gx	12 34.8	+ 58 56 r	UMa		15p	vF, pS, E, vgbM, *9 f 2′, p of 2
4549	Gx	12 34.8	+ 58 56 r	UMa		15p	eF, pS, E, f of 2
3522 I	Gx	12 34.8	+ 15 13 v	Com	1.5		vF, S, mE 90°
3525 I		12 34.8	+ 10 10 d	Vir			vF, R
3529 I		12 34.8	+ 25 42 d	Com			F, vS, R, bM
3530 I	Gx	12 34.8	+ 17 48 z	Com		15p	F, vS, R
3528 I	Gx	12 34.9	+ 15 34 v	Com	0.7		bM, mag 14
3531 I	Gx	12 34.9	+ 26 38 x	Com			vF, vS, bM, spir
3532 I		12 35.0	+ 25 53 d	Com			vF, vS, bM, spir
3533 I	Gx	12 35.0	+ 25 46 z	Com		16p	pF, vS, R, bM
4537	Gx	12 35.2	+ 50 50 r	CVn		16p	eeF, S, R, nearly bet 2 st
4541	Gx	12 35.2	− 0 13 s	Vir	1.8	14p	F, S, R, gbM
3534 I		12 35.2	+ 15 00 d	Com			vF, cS, R
3535 I		12 35.2	+ 25 44 d	Com			F, vS, R, bM
3536 I	Gx	12 35.2	+ 26 32 x	Com			vF, S, iF
3538 I	*	12 35.2	+ 26 14 x	Com			eF, S, iF
3539 I		12 35.3	+ 23 59 d	Com			eF, S, R, bM, *13 sp
4543	Gx	12 35.4	+ 6 07 r	Vir		14p	pF, cS, R, bM
4548	Gx	12 35.4	+ 14 30 s	Com	5.4	10.2	B, L, lE, lbM; = M91
3537 I	D*	12 35.4	+ 7 39 x	Vir			vF, S, ?
3540 I	Gx	12 35.4	+ 12 45 m	Vir	0.4	15p	vS, R, sev condens
3541 I		12 35.4	+ 23 58 d	Com			eF, S, R
4546	Gx	12 35.5	− 3 48 s	Vir	3.5	10.3	vB, cL, pmE 78°, vsmbMN
4550	Gx	12 35.5	+ 12 13 s	Vir	3.5	11.6	pB, S, vlE, sp of 2
4507	Gx	12 35.6	− 39 55 s	Cen	2.3	13p	pB, S, psmbM *16
4544	Gx	12 35.6	+ 3 02 s	Vir	2.1	14p	vF, S, R, bet 2 st
4551	Gx	12 35.6	+ 12 16 s	Vir	2.0	11.9	pB, S, R, bM, nf of 2

NGC	Type	α_{2000}	δ_{2000}	Const.	Size	Mag.	Description
		h m	o ′		′		
4562	Gx	12 35.6	+ 25 51 s	Com	2.5	14p	S, sp 4565
4552	Gx	12 35.7	+ 12 33 s	Vir	4.2	9.8	pB, pS, R, gmbM; = M89
4554	−	12 35.7	+ 11 11 r	Vir			vF
4555	Gx	12 35.7	+ 26 31 s	Com	1.7	14p	B, pS, iR, vsmbM *12
3543 I	Gx	12 35.7	+ 26 17 v	Com	1.1		vF, S, lE 150°
3545 I		12 35.7	+ 26 31 x	Com			pB, S, R, bM; = 4555
3546 I	Gx	12 35.7	+ 26 13 x	Com			F, S, lE 150°
4556	Gx	12 35.8	+ 26 54 s	Com	1.5	14p	F, pL
4558	Gx	12 35.8	+ 27 01 r	Com		15p	vF, nf of 2 (or 3?); = IC 3556
802 I	Nb	12 35.8	+ 74 15 x	Dra	1		vF, S, stellar
3542 I		12 35.8	+ 11 40 d	Vir			bM, mag 14.5
3544 I	D*	12 35.8	+ 14 18 x	Com			cF, vS; *12.5?
3547 I	D*	12 35.8	+ 26 20 x	Com			vF, vS, iF
3549 I	*	12 35.8	+ 26 24 x	Com			vF, vS, bM, spir
4563	Gx	12 35.9	+ 26 59 r	Com		15p	F, vS, R, mbM
4566	Gx	12 35.9	+ 54 13 s	UMa	1.5	14p	pF, S, iR, gbM
4572	Gx	12 35.9	+ 74 15 r	Dra		15p	eF, S
3548 I		12 35.9	+ 10 57 d	Vir			vF, eS, R
3550 I		12 35.9	+ 27 56 d	Com			N inv in 4559
3551 I		12 35.9	+ 27 58 d	Com			N inv in 4559
3552 I		12 35.9	+ 28 00 d	Com			N inv in 4559
3553 I	?	12 35.9	+ 26 12 x	Com			vF, vS, R, bM
3554 I		12 35.9	+ 27 56 d	Com			N inv in 4559 (2ˢp, 1′.8 s)
3555 I		12 35.9	+ 28 00 d	Com			N inv in 4559 (1ˢ.5 p, 2′.0 n)
4559	Gx	12 36.0	+ 27 58 s	Com	10.5	9.9	vB, vL, mE 150°, gbM, 3 st f
3556 I	Gx	12 36.0	+ 26 58 x	Com			F, S, R, bM
4553	Gx	12 36.1	− 39 27 v	Cen	2.1		F, vlE, glbM
4557	Gx	12 36.1	+ 26 57 r	Com		15p	nebulous *
4560	−	12 36.1	+ 7 41 r	Vir			cB, pL, R, gbM
4561	Gx	12 36.1	+ 19 20 s	Com	1.5	13p	pB, pL, vlE, lbM, r; = IC 3569
3557 I	Gx	12 36.1	+ 16 38 m	Com	0.7	15p	bM, mag 15.5
3559 I	Gx	12 36.1	+ 26 59 x	Com			vF, vS, R, bM
3560 I	Gx	12 36.1	+ 27 05 x	Com			vF, vS, R, bM
3561 I	Gx	12 36.1	+ 26 54 x	Com			cF, vS, R, bM *
3563 I		12 36.1	+ 27 56 d	Com			N inv in 4559
3569 I	Gx	12 36.1	+ 19 19 t	Com	1.3	13p	cS, spir, 2 br, F* M, F* inv; = 4561
3558 I		12 36.2	+ 11 51 d	Vir			D; F, R, dist 12″ n & s
3562 I	Gx	12 36.2	+ 9 55 z	Vir		16p	E 220°
3564 I		12 36.2	+ 27 56 d	Com			N inv in 4559
3565 I	Gx	12 36.2	+ 26 45 x	Com			vF, S, E 148°; st?
4565	Gx	12 36.3	+ 25 59 s	Com	16.2	9.6	B, eL, eE 135°, vsbMN = *10-11
3566 I	?	12 36.3	+ 11 09 x	Vir			com, R with tail 1′ at 110°
3570 I		12 36.3	+ 24 05 d	Com			eF, S, iF, *13 np
3571 I	Gx	12 36.3	+ 26 05 x	Com			eF, S, iF, others nr
4564	Gx	12 36.4	+ 11 26 s	Vir	3.1	11.1	pB, S, lE, psbM
3567 I	Gx	12 36.4	+ 13 36 z	Com		15p	F, vS, R, bM
4567	Gx	12 36.5	+ 11 15 s	Vir	3.0	11.3	vF, L, np of Dneb (4568 at 160° ±)
3572 I	*	12 36.5	+ 11 37 x	Vir			eF, vS, ??
3573 I		12 36.5	+ 11 46 d	Vir			F, vS, R
3574 I		12 36.5	+ 12 24 d	Vir			vF, vS; *14?
3575 I		12 36.5	+ 13 45 d	Com			vF, vS, R
3579 I	*	12 36.5	+ 26 06 x	Com			eF, S, iF, others nr
3582 I	Gx	12 36.5	+ 26 12 v	Com	0.5		F, vS, com, bM, others nr
4568	Gx	12 36.6	+ 11 14 s	Vir	4.6	10.8	vF, L, sf of Dneb
3576 I	Gx	12 36.6	+ 6 37 s	Vir	3.0	14p	F, pS, dif

NGC	Type	α_{2000}	δ_{2000}	Const.	Size	Mag.	Description
		h m	° ′		′		
3577 I	D*	12 36.6	+ 11 54 x	Vir			vF, pS, dif, *13 inv nf
3578 I	Gx	12 36.6	+ 11 06 u	Vir	1.0	15p	S, E 125°
3580 I		12 36.6	+ 18 17 d	Com			F, vS, R
3581 I	Gx	12 36.6	+ 24 24 m	Com	0.4	15p	pB, S, E 50°, bM
3583 I	Gx	12 36.7	+ 13 15 s	Vir	2.2	14p	vmE, *13 att sf, 2 st 12 nr
3585 I	Gx	12 36.7	+ 26 50 v	Com	1.4		cF, S, neb*
4569	Gx	12 36.8	+ 13 10 s	Vir	9.5	9.5	pL, bMN; = M90
3584 I	*	12 36.8	+ 12 14 x	Vir			vF, vS; *14?
3587 I	Gx	12 36.8	+ 27 33 u	Com	1.5	16p	vF, S, lE 120°, *15 nf
4570	Gx	12 36.9	+ 7 15 s	Vir	4.1	10.9	cB, pS, mE 0°±, sbMrN
4571	Gx	12 36.9	+ 14 13 s	Com	3.8	11.3	vF, L, E, vgbM, *9 nf nr; = IC 3588
3586 I	Gx	12 36.9	+ 12 32 m	Vir	0.6	15p	vF, cS, dif
3588 I	?	12 36.9	+ 14 13 x	Com			cF, pL, lbM
3590 I		12 36.9	+ 27 17 d	Com			vF, S, viF
3592 I	Gx	12 36.9	+ 27 53 u	Com	1.3	15p	pF, S, lE 140°
3594 I	*	12 36.9	+ 26 07 x	Com			eF, vS, iF
3589 I		12 37.0	+ 6 56 d	Vir			vF, S, R, stell
3591 I		12 37.0	+ 6 56 d	Vir			F, pS, nr *14
3593 I	Gx	12 37.0	+ 27 46 m	Com	0.4	15p	pF, S, iF, N
3595 I		12 37.1	+ 23 47 d	Com			eF, S, iF
3596 I	D*	12 37.3	+ 26 31 x	Com			vF, S, iF, nr D*
4589	Gx	12 37.4	+ 74 12 s	Dra	3.0	12p	cB, L, lE, pgmbM
3597 I		12 37.4	+ 23 52 d	Com			eF, S, R
3598 I	Gx	12 37.4	+ 28 12 v	Com	1.7		pF, vS, sbM *, *15 nf 100″
4577	—	12 37.5	+ 6 04 r	Vir			vF, vS; = 4543?
4578	Gx	12 37.5	+ 9 33 s	Vir	3.6	11.4	pF, pS, R, sbMN, * np
4576	Gx	12 37.6	+ 4 22 s	Vir	1.4	13.5	F, *7 sf
3600 I	Gx	12 37.6	+ 27 08 v	Com	0.6		F, vS, neb*
4573	Gx	12 37.7	− 43 37 r	Cen			vF, S, *10 n 30″
4574	Gx	12 37.7	− 35 30 r	Cen			vF, L, lE, vglbM
4579	Gx	12 37.7	+ 11 49 s	Vir	5.4	9.8	B, L, iR, vmbM, r; = M58
3599 I	Gx	12 37.7	+ 26 42 v	Com			cF, S, R, bM
4580	Gx	12 37.8	+ 5 22 s	Vir	2.4	13p	pB, L, vgbM
3601 I	PD	12 37.8	+ 15 12 x	Com			bM, mag 15
4575	Gx	12 37.9	− 40 32 s	Cen	2.2	13p	F, S, pmE, 2 st p
4583	Gx	12 38.0	+ 33 28 r	CVn		14p	cF, S, lE, bM
4585	Gx	12 38.1	+ 28 57 r	Com		14p	vF, eS
3602 I	Gx	12 38.1	+ 10 05 z	Vir		15p	F, eS, R, lbM
4581	Gx	12 38.2	+ 1 28 r	Vir		13p	F, S, bM, stell N
4582	*	12 38.2	+ 0 11 F	Vir			*12 in F neb
3603 I		12 38.2	+ 15 32 d	Com			eF, bM, mag 15
4584	Gx	12 38.3	+ 13 07 s	Vir	1.5	14p	vF, S, R
3605 I		12 38.3	+ 19 31 d	Com			vF, vS, R
3604 I		12 38.4	+ 11 43 d	Vir			F, vS, R, lbM
3606 I		12 38.4	+ 12 36 d	Vir			F, vlE
4586	Gx	12 38.5	+ 4 19 s	Vir	4.4	11.6	pB, L, E, psbM
3607 I	?	12 38.5	+ 10 22 x	Vir			F, eS, R
3609 I	Gx	12 38.5	+ 14 22 z	Com		15p	B, vS, R; ○ ?
4587	Gx	12 38.6	+ 2 40 r	Vir		14p	F, pS, mbM
3608 I	Gx	12 38.6	+ 10 29 u	Vir	3.5	15p	vS, R, wisps pf, 1′ each
4588	Gx	12 38.8	+ 6 46 r	Vir		15p	vF, eS
3610 I		12 38.8	+ 26 52 d	Com			eF, S, viF
3614 I		12 39.0	+ 26 18 d	Com			eF, pS, gbM, spir
3615 I	Gx	12 39.0	+ 18 11 u	Com	1.3	15p	S, E 185°, bM
3611 I	Gx	12 39.1	+ 13 22 x	Com			pF, cS, E 130°

NGC	Type	α_{2000}	δ_{2000}	Const.	Size	Mag.	Description
		h m	° ′		′		
3612 I		12 39.1	+ 14 43 d	Com			B, vS, R; ○ ?
3613 I		12 39.1	+ 13 44 d	Com			F, eS, R, lbM
3616 I	?	12 39.2	+ 14 44 x	Com			bM, mag 14
3618 I	Gx	12 39.2	+ 26 41 v	Com			F, vS, R, bM
4591	Gx	12 39.3	+ 6 01 r	Vir		14p	vF, cS
4592	Gx	12 39.3	− 0 32 s	Vir	4.6	12p	F, L, E 90°±, vgbM
3619 I		12 39.3	+ 24 08 d	Com			vF, cS, E 160°, bM
3620 I	Gx	12 39.3	+ 27 55 v	Com			F, S, iF, bM, sev neb st nr
3617 I	Gx	12 39.4	+ 7 58 s	Vir	1.1	15p	vF, S
3623 I	Gx	12 39.4	+ 27 07 v	Com			cF, S, R, bM
4590	Gb	12 39.5	− 26 45 s	Hya	12.0	8.2	⊕, L, eRi, vC, iR, rrr, st 12; = M68
3621 I		12 39.5	+ 15 29 d	Com			bM, mag 14
3622 I		12 39.5	+ 15 25 d	Com			vF, S, R
3626 I	Gx	12 39.5	+ 25 41 z	Com		16p	vF, S, bM, spir
3627 I		12 39.5	+ 27 30 d	Com			F, S, iF, N
803 I	Gx	12 39.6	+ 16 36 m	Com	0.7	15p	eF, S, v diffic
3624 I		12 39.6	+ 11 59 d	Vir			F, S, E 180°
4593	Gx	12 39.7	− 5 21 s	Vir	4.0	12p	pB, cL, E, sbMN = *
3625 I		12 39.7	+ 10 58 d	Vir			vF, R
3628 I		12 39.7	+ 26 15 d	Com			eF, S, R
3629 I		12 39.8	+ 13 31 d	Com			S, mE 245°, lbM
3630 I		12 39.8	+ 25 26 d	Com			vF, vS, lE; D*?
3631 I	Gx	12 39.8	+ 12 59 x	Vir		14p	bM, mag 13
4595	Gx	12 39.9	+ 15 18 s	Com	1.8	13p	pF, pL, R, gbM
4596	Gx	12 39.9	+ 10 11 s	Vir	3.9	10.5	B, pS, R, gmbM, r, 3 st f
4594	Gx	12 40.0	− 11 37 s	Vir	8.9	8.3	!, vB, vL, eE 92°, vsmbMN; = M104
4605	Gx	12 40.0	+ 61 37 s	UMa	5.5	11p	B, L, vmE 118°, glbM
3632 I		12 40.0	+ 26 41 d	Com			eF, cS, iF
4597	Gx	12 40.2	− 5 48 s	Vir	3.6	12p	F, vL, bM
3633 I	Gx	12 40.2	+ 9 53 z	Vir		15p	vS, ○ , lbM
3634 I		12 40.2	+ 9 50 d	Vir			vF, R, dif
3635 I	Gx	12 40.2	+ 12 53 u	Vir	1.2	15p	F, vS, R, bM
3636 I		12 40.2	+ 22 04 d	Com			eF, vS, E 0°, bM
4598	Gx	12 40.3	+ 8 23 r	Vir		14p	eF, L, R, vlbM
3637 I	Gx	12 40.3	+ 14 43 z	Com		16p	vF, vS, R, dif
3638 I	Gx	12 40.3	+ 10 31 m	Vir	0.6	15p	B, S, R, lbM
4600	Gx	12 40.4	+ 3 08 r	Vir		13p	F, S, R, 2 st 8 f
3640 I		12 40.4	+ 26 31 d	Com			vF, R neb 30″ np IC 3641
3641 I		12 40.4	+ 26 31 d	Com			F, S, bM, spir
3642 I		12 40.4	+ 26 44 d	Com			vF, cS, iF, dif
4599	Gx	12 40.5	+ 1 11 r	Vir		13p	vF, vS
3645 I	Gx	12 40.5	+ 26 32 v	Com	0.7		F, vS, R, bM
3646 I	Gx	12 40.5	+ 26 31 v	Com	1.3		F, S, E 65°, bM
4602	Gx	12 40.6	− 5 08 s	Vir	3.6	12p	F, L, E, vglbM
3644 I		12 40.6	+ 26 30 d	Com			vF, S, iF
4604	−	12 40.7	− 5 09 r	Vir			no description
3643 I		12 40.7	+ 12 24 d	Vir			F, vlE
3650 I	Gx	12 40.7	+ 26 30 m	Com	0.8	15p	eF, vS, bM, spir
4601	Gx	12 40.8	− 40 54 v	Cen	2.2		eF, L, R, pslbM, p of 2
3649 I		12 40.8	+ 21 06 d	Com			F, vS, iF, N
3651 I	Gx	12 40.8	+ 26 44 v	Com	1.3		pF, cS, R, spir
4603	Gx	12 40.9	− 40 59 s	Cen	3.8	12p	F, L, R, vgbM, r
3639 I	Gx	12 40.9	− 36 45 c	Cen	1.4		pF, pS, *12.5 ssp
3647 I	?	12 40.9	+ 10 28 x	Vir			F, cS, mE 135°
3648 I	?	12 40.9	+ 12 59 x	Vir			eF, S; ??

NGC	Type	α_{2000}	δ_{2000}	Const.	Size	Mag.	Description
		h m	° ′		′		
4606	Gx	12 41.0	+ 11 55 s	Vir	2.8	11.9	vF, pS, E, 2 or 3 vS st inv
3652 I	Gx	12 41.0	+ 11 11 u	Vir	1.0	15p	S, R, mbM
4617	Gx	12 41.1	+ 50 26 s	CVn	3.1	14p	pF, S, iR, er
4607	Gx	12 41.2	+ 11 53 s	Vir	3.2	12.9	F, mE, 3′ or 4′ f 4606
4608	Gx	12 41.2	+ 10 09 s	Vir	3.2	11.1	pB, pL, R, psbM, r, *12 np 1′
3653 I	Gx	12 41.2	+ 11 24 x	Vir		15p	bM, mag 13
3654 I		12 41.2	+ 22 35 d	Com			F, S, iF, N
3655 I		12 41.2	+ 20 40 d	Com			vF, vS, iF, *16 inv, other neb nr
3656 I		12 41.2	+ 22 36 d	Com			F, S, iF, N
804 I	Gx	12 41.3	− 5 01 x	Vir			vF, vS, R
805 I		12 41.3	+ 13 44 x	Com			vF, pL, R, 2 st n & nf; = 4611
3657 I		12 41.3	+ 21 41 d	Com			vF, vS, N; neb*?
3658 I	Gx	12 41.3	+ 14 42 z	Com		15p	F, S, E 240°
4610	−	12 41.4	+ 7 43 r	Vir			F, vL; = 4470?
4613	Gx	12 41.4	+ 26 05 r	Com		15p	vF, S, lE, 1st of 3
4614	Gx	12 41.4	+ 26 02 r	Com		14p	F, S, R, *12 np, 2nd of 3
4611	Gx	12 41.5	+ 13 44 r	Com		15p	eF, S, lE, bet 2 vF st; = IC 805
4612	Gx	12 41.5	+ 7 19 s	Vir	2.2	13p	pB, S, R, psmbM
4615	Gx	12 41.5	+ 26 04 r	Com		14p	F, pL, E, 3rd of 3
4618	Gx	12 41.5	+ 41 09 s	CVn	4.4	10.8	B, L, E, mbM, curved branch n
3659 I		12 41.5	+ 22 56 d	Com			cF, S, E 50°
3667 I		12 41.5	+ 41 09 d	CVn			cB, pL, E 55°, bM
3668 I		12 41.5	+ 41 08 d	CVn			pF, pS, iF, N
3660 I		12 41.6	+ 21 06 d	Com			F, vS, iF, N
3661 I		12 41.6	+ 22 30 d	Com			cF, S, iF, N
3662 I	Gx	12 41.6	+ 23 25 m	Com	0.6	15p	F, S, R, bM, spir
3669 I		12 41.6	+ 41 08 d	CVn			F, pS, iF, N
4619	Gx	12 41.7	+ 35 04 s	CVn	1.5	14p	F, pS, R, lbM, *8-9 f
3663 I		12 41.7	+ 12 14 d	Vir			F, S, R, dif
3664 I		12 41.7	+ 19 57 d	Com			vF, vS, iF, N
4648	Gx	12 41.8	+ 74 25 s	Dra	2.2	13p	pB, cS, R, gbM, * p
3665 I	Gx	12 41.8	+ 11 30 u	Vir	1.0	15p	F, S, R, dif
3671 I	Gx	12 41.8	+ 23 31 m	Com	0.5	15p	cF, cS, lE 230°, bM
4625	Gx	12 41.9	+ 41 16 s	CVn	2.4	12.3	pF, S, R
808 I	OC	12 41.9	+ 19 57 x	Com			S nebs Cl
3666 I		12 41.9	+ 7 51 d	Vir			eF, vS, ?
3670 I		12 41.9	+ 11 45 d	Vir			vS, R, bM
3675 I	Gx	12 41.9	+ 41 17 t	CVn	2.0	13p	pB, pL, iF, N; = 4625
4620	Gx	12 42.0	+ 12 57 s	Vir	2.0	13p	vF, S, R, vgbM
4621	Gx	12 42.0	+ 11 39 s	Vir	5.1	9.8	B, pL, lE, vsvmbM, 2 st p; = M59
4627	Gx	12 42.0	+ 32 34 s	CVn	2.7	12.3	F, S, R, np of 2
3680 I		12 42.0	+ 39 06 d	CVn			F, S, iF, N
3681 I		12 42.0	+ 39 05 d	CVn			cF, vS, E 135°, bM, *13 sp
4631	Gx	12 42.1	+ 32 32 s	CVn	15.1	9.3	!, vB, vL, eE 70°±, bMN, *12 att n
809 I	Gx	12 42.1	+ 11 45 u	Vir	1.1	15p	eF, pS, R, M59 s
810 I	Gx	12 42.1	+ 12 36 u	Vir	1.7	15p	eF, pS, mE
3672 I	Gx	12 42.1	+ 11 45 x	Vir			vF, vS, R, stell; IC 809 n
3673 I		12 42.1	+ 21 08 d	Com			F, vS, iF, N
3674 I		12 42.1	+ 22 31 d	Com			pF, S, exc N, *11 sp
3687 I	Gx	12 42.1	+ 38 30 s	CVn	3.5	13p	vF, cL, dif, sev N
4623	Gx	12 42.2	+ 7 41 s	Vir	2.6	13p	cF, pL, E, pslbM, r
806 I	Gx	12 42.2	− 17 20 m	Crv	0.6	15p	eF, eS, R, *12 close
3676 I	*	12 42.2	+ 13 33 x	Com			vF, vS; *13?
3677 I		12 42.2	+ 20 53 d	Com			F, vS, iF, N
3678 I		12 42.2	+ 20 53 d	Com			vF, vS, iF, N

NGC	Type	α_{2000}	δ_{2000}	Const.	Size	Mag.	Description
		h m	° ′		′		
3679 I		12 42.2	+ 22 49 d	Com			F, S, iF, N
4609	OC	12 42.3	− 62 58 s	Cru	5	6.9	Cl, pL, pC, cE, st 10
4616	Gx	12 42.3	− 40 39 s	Cen	1.6		eF, vS, R, * att nf, p of 2
4624	−	12 42.3	+ 3 04 r	Vir			B, E; = 4636?
807 I	Gx	12 42.3	− 17 22 m	Crv	0.3	15p	pF, vS, R, gbM
3682 I		12 42.3	+ 20 52 d	Com			F, vS, iF, N
3683 I		12 42.3	+ 20 52 d	Com			F, vS, iF, N
4626	Gx	12 42.4	− 7 02 r	Vir		14p	vF, cS, lE, glbM
4628	Gx	12 42.4	− 6 57 r	Vir		14p	cF, S, E, gbM
3684 I		12 42.4	+ 11 43 d	Vir			vF, vS, R
4630	Gx	12 42.5	+ 3 58 s	Vir	1.7	13p	cF, S, R, lbM
4632	Gx	12 42.5	− 0 05 s	Vir	3.2	12p	pB, L, E 45°±
3685 I		12 42.5	+ 6 52 d	Vir			vF, pL
4622	Gx	12 42.6	− 40 45 s	Cen	2.1		pF, S, R, pslbM, f of 2
4629	D*	12 42.6	− 1 21 F	Vir			pB, pL, E, lbM; biN?
4633	Gx	12 42.6	+ 14 21 s	Com	2.1	13.2	eeF, pS, F* close p, 4634 s; = IC 3688
4635	Gx	12 42.6	+ 19 57 s	Com	2.0	13p	vF, L, vglbM
3686 I	Gx	12 42.6	+ 10 34 m	Vir	1.5	16p	F, S, R
3688 I		12 42.6	+ 14 22 z	Com			cF, pS; = 4633
3689 I		12 42.6	+ 20 51 d	Com			F, vS, iF, N
4634	Gx	12 42.7	+ 14 18 s	Com	2.4	12.4	vF, L, mE 135°±, vgbM
4644	Gx	12 42.7	+ 55 09 s	UMa	1.8	14.0	vF, S, R, gbM
4636	Gx	12 42.8	+ 2 41 s	Vir	6.2	9.6	B, L, iR, vgvmbM, r
4638	Gx	12 42.8	+ 11 26 s	Vir	2.8	11.3	F, R, gbM
3690 I	Gx	12 42.8	+ 10 22 u	Vir	1.3	15p	B, vS, R
3691 I		12 42.8	+ 22 47 d	Com			F, S, iF, N
4637	Gx	12 42.9	+ 11 26 s	Vir	1.5	15p	cB, S, like a *10; makes a Dneb with 4638?
4639	Gx	12 42.9	+ 13 15 s	Vir	2.9	11.5	pB, S, E, r, *12 sf 1′
4646	Gx	12 42.9	+ 54 51 s	UMa	0.7	14p	F, S, 4 vS st sp
3692 I	Gx	12 42.9	+ 21 00 u	Com	1.0	15p	pF, S, bM, spir
3693 I		12 43.0	+ 10 40 d	Vir			F, vS, R, lbM
3697 I	Gx	12 43.0	+ 39 50 m	CVn	0.7	17p	vF, S, N; neb*?
4640	Gx	12 43.1	+ 12 18 r	Vir		15p	eF, pL, lE, * nr p
3694 I	Gx	12 43.1	+ 11 13 m	Vir	0.7	15p	bM, mag 13.5
3695 I		12 43.1	+ 22 45 d	Com			vF, vS, iF, N
4641	Gx	12 43.2	+ 11 03 r	Vir		15p	eF, pL, R, F* nr f
3696 I		12 43.2	+ 19 56 d	Com			vF, vS, iF, N
4642	Gx	12 43.3	− 0 39 s	Vir	2.0	14p	vF, cS, E
4643	Gx	12 43.3	+ 1 59 s	Vir	3.4	10.6	cB, pS, lE, mbM
4652	Gx	12 43.3	+ 58 58 r	UMa		15p	pF, pL, gbM, 2 B st 6′ np
3698 I	Gx	12 43.3	+ 11 13 m	Vir	0.5	15p	S, R, mbM
3699 I		12 43.3	+ 19 00 d	Com			F, S, iF, N, 3 st n, np
3700 I		12 43.3	+ 19 16 d	Com			F, S, dif
3703 I		12 43.4	+ 37 59 d	CVn			F, vS, iF, N, 2 st 11 sf
4647	Gx	12 43.5	+ 11 35 s	Vir	3.0	11.4	pF, pL, lE 115°±, np of Dneb
3701 I		12 43.5	+ 11 02 d	Vir			F, vS, R, dif
3702 I	Gx	12 43.5	+ 10 53 z	Vir		15p	B, vS, R
3707 I		12 43.5	+ 37 59 d	CVn			pF, vS, bM*
4655	Gx	12 43.6	+ 41 02 r	CVn		15p	vF, vS, stellar, *15 f
4649	Gx	12 43.7	+ 11 33 s	Vir	7.2	8.8	vB, pL, R, f of Dneb; = M60
4651	Gx	12 43.7	+ 16 24 s	Com	3.8	10.7	cB, L, E 90°, gbM, r
3704 I	Gx	12 43.7	+ 10 47 u	Vir	1.3	15p	F, pL, mE 225°
3705 I		12 43.7	+ 19 20 d	Com			eF, S, iF
3706 I	*	12 43.8	+ 9 14 z	Vir			vF, cS, dif
4653	Gx	12 43.9	− 0 34 s	Vir	2.6	12.3	vF, pL

NGC	Type	α_{2000}	δ_{2000}	Const.	Size	Mag.	Description
		h m	° ′		′		
3708 I		12 43.9	+ 13 08 x	Vir			pB, cL, E; = 4654
4654	Gx	12 44.0	+ 13 08 s	Vir	4.7	10.5	F, vL, pmE (D?), 3 st nr; = IC 3708
4656	Gx	12 44.0	+ 32 10 s	CVn	13.8	10.4	!, pB, L, vmE 34°, sp of 2
3709 I	Gx	12 44.0	+ 9 04 z	Vir		15p	vF, cS, dif
3710 I	Gx	12 44.1	+ 12 08 x	Vir			vF, cS, R, dif
3713 I	Gx	12 44.1	+ 41 10 m	CVn	0.6	15p	F, pS, dif, *13 sf 1′
4645	Gx	12 44.2	− 41 45 s	Cen	2.2	13p	pB, S, psbM
4657	Gx	12 44.2	+ 32 12 v	CVn	1.2		!, pF, L, E 90°±, nf of 2
3711 I		12 44.2	+ 11 10 d	Vir			vF, vS, R, dif
4650	Gx	12 44.3	− 40 44 s	Cen			vF, R, bM, r
3712 I	?	12 44.3	+ 10 22 x	Vir			vF, pS, E 42°; ?
3714 I	Gx	12 44.4	+ 10 11 m	Vir	0.8	16p	S, R
3715 I		12 44.4	+ 19 51 d	Com			vF, vS, iF, N
3717 I	Gx	12 44.4	+ 39 30 m	CVn	0.6	16p	F, cS, E 150°, bM, *15 np
4659	Gx	12 44.5	+ 13 31 s	Com	1.8	13p	F, cS, R, bM, r
4660	Gx	12 44.5	+ 11 11 s	Vir	2.8	11.0	vB, S, vsvmbMN
4662	Gx	12 44.5	+ 37 07 s	CVn	2.5	14p	pF, pL, R, gbM, r
3723 I	Gx	12 44.5	+ 40 44 v	CVn	0.4		pF, vS, R, bM
4658	Gx	12 44.6	− 10 05 s	Vir	2.2	13p	vF, L, E, *16 att, *9 p
3726 I	Gx	12 44.7	+ 40 42 u	CVn	1.7	16p	F, cS, E 145°, bM
4663	Gx	12 44.8	− 10 12 s	Vir	1.4	14p	vF, S, *13-14 f; = IC 811
4669	Gx	12 44.8	+ 54 53 s	UMa	1.7	15p	F, E; r?
811 I		12 44.8	− 10 12 x	Vir			nebs *13, sf 4658; = 4663
3716 I		12 44.8	+ 8 06 d	Vir			vF, vS, sp of 2
3718 I	Gx	12 44.8	+ 12 21 v	Vir	3.0		F, pS, E 90°
3719 I		12 44.8	+ 8 06 d	Vir			eF, vS, ??, nf of 2
3720 I	Gx	12 44.8	+ 12 04 v	Vir	2.8		eF, S, dif
3721 I		12 44.8	+ 18 45 d	Com			bM, mag 13.5
812 I		12 44.9	− 4 26 d	Vir			pB, S, R, N = 13m
3722 I	*	12 44.9	+ 11 47 x	Vir			vF, vS, = *13
3724 I	Gx	12 44.9	+ 10 17 z	Vir		16p	S, R
3725 I		12 44.9	+ 18 45 x	Com			pF, cS, E, bM; = IC 3721
3729 I	Gx	12 44.9	+ 39 20 m	CVn	0.2	16p	F, vS, iF, N, neb st np
4664		12 45.1	+ 3 03 A	Vir			pB, 2 S st in M, S* p; = 4665
4665	Gx	12 45.1	+ 3 03 s	Vir	4.2	12p	B, pL, iR, mbM, *10 sp
4666	Gx	12 45.1	− 0 28 s	Vir	4.5	10.8	B, vL, mE 45°±, psbM
4727 I	Gx	12 45.1	+ 10 54 u	Vir	1.6	16p	F, S, R, lbM
3728 I		12 45.1	+ 20 58 d	Com			vF, vS, iF, N
3730 I	Gx	12 45.1	+ 21 11 v	Com	0.4	14.6	pB, vS, R, bM, in dif neb
4661	Gx	12 45.2	− 40 49 c	Cen	1.1		F, pL, R, gbM
813 I	Gx	12 45.2	+ 23 03 u	Com	1.1	14p	F, pS, iR, bM
3731 I		12 45.2	+ 12 25 d	Vir			bM, mag 14.5
3732 I		12 45.2	+ 10 18 d	Vir			vS, R
3734 I		12 45.2	+ 23 02 d	Com			*15 in dif neb; IC 813 f 0′.5
4667	−	12 45.3	+ 11 26 r	Vir			B, S, R, psbM; nonexistent?
4670	Gx	12 45.3	+ 27 08 s	Com	1.8	12.7	pF, cS, R, bM, r, p of 2
3733 I		12 45.3	+ 6 58 d	Vir			eF, S, = *14
3735 I	Gx	12 45.3	+ 13 42 m	Com	0.4	15p	F, S, R
3736 I	Gx	12 45.3	+ 21 31 m	Com	0.5	16p	pF, vS, E 155°, bM
3737 I		12 45.3	+ 21 58 d	Com			F, vS, iF, N
3738 I		12 45.4	+ 19 14 d	Com			neb *15
4668	Gx	12 45.5	− 0 32 s	Vir	1.4	13.1	vF, S, iF
3739 I	?	12 45.5	+ 13 00 x	Vir			cF, cS, biN
3740 I	Gx	12 45.5	+ 20 49 z	Com		16p	pF, cS, E 0°, bM
3742 I	Gx	12 45.5	+ 13 20 v	Com	1.9		pL, mE 225°, bM

NGC	Type	α_{2000}	δ_{2000}	Const.	Size	Mag.	Description
		h m	° ′		′		
4673	Gx	12 45.6	+ 27 04 s	Com	1.2	14p	F, vS, R, sbM *10, f of 2
4675	Gx	12 45.6	+ 54 44 s	UMa	1.6	15p	cF, S, lE
814 I		12 45.6	− 8 06 d	Vir			pB, vS, R, r
3741 I		12 45.6	+ 19 12 d	Com			neb *16
3745 I	Gx	12 45.6	+ 19 10 m	Com	0.3	15p	pF, vS, R, bM
3746 I	Gx	12 45.6	+ 37 49 z	CVn		16p	F, S, iF, N
3747 I		12 45.6	+ 37 58 d	CVn			F, vS, iF, N
3751 I	Gx	12 45.6	+ 37 49 z	CVn		16p	F, vS, iF, N, neb *15 p
3743 I	*	12 45.7	+ 11 06 x	Vir			vF, S
3744 I		12 45.7	+ 19 30 d	Com			F, vS, iF, N
4671	Gx	12 45.8	− 7 04 r	Vir		14p	pF, S, R, psmbM
3748 I		12 45.8	+ 19 26 d	Com			vF, vS, iF, N
3749 I		12 45.9	+ 19 32 d	Com			vF, eS, bM, spir
3758 I	Gx	12 45.9	+ 40 47 z	CVn		15p	pF, S, neb*
3750 I		12 46.0	+ 19 06 d	Com			eF, eS, iF, N
3757 I		12 46.0	+ 38 31 d	CVn			pF, S, iF, *13 inv
4674	Gx	12 46.1	− 8 39 s	Vir	1.9	15p	vF, cS, R, glbM
4676	Gx	12 46.1	+ 30 44 s	Com	2.8	14p	vF, pmE; biN?
3752 I		12 46.1	+ 19 01 d	Com			vF, vS, iF, neb *14 np 1′, *10 np 1′.5
3753 I		12 46.1	+ 19 07 d	Com			eF, S, E, *14 conn p
3755 I		12 46.1	+ 19 09 d	Com			F, vS, iF, N
3754 I	Gx	12 46.2	+ 8 21 u	Vir	1.4	15p	F, S
4672	Gx	12 46.3	− 41 43 v	Cen	1.9		eF, S, R, vgbM
3756 I	Gx	12 46.3	+ 11 53 m	Vir	0.3	15p	bM, mag 15
3759 I		12 46.3	+ 20 47 d	Com			vF, vS, iF, N, *15 sf 20″
815 I	Gx	12 46.4	+ 11 53 m	Vir	0.4	15p	F, vS, *14 inv
3760 I		12 46.4	+ 11 52 x	Vir			bM, mag 14; = IC 815
3761 I		12 46.5	+ 20 17 d	Com			vF, vS, R, bM, *12 sp
818 I	Gx	12 46.6	+ 29 44 v	Com	1.3		vS, R, bM, *12 nf 2′.5
3762 I		12 46.6	+ 22 15 d	Com			vF, S, iF, in gr of neb
3765 I		12 46.6	+ 38 34 d	CVn			vF, S, iF, N
4678	−	12 46.7	− 4 35 r	Vir			eF, eS, R (neb?), * 2ˢf
4686	Gx	12 46.7	+ 54 33 s	UMa	2.3	14p	pF, vS, vmE, vsmbM
816 I	Gx	12 46.7	+ 9 51 u	Vir	1.0	15p	eeF, vS, R, D* nf, np of 2
3768 I		12 46.7	+ 40 36 d	CVn			vF, S, iF, N
3763 I		12 46.8	+ 21 59 d	Com			F, S, iF
3769 I		12 46.8	+ 40 28 d	CVn			F, vS, iF, N
4680	Gx	12 46.9	− 11 37 r	Vir		13p	eF, S, 1 or 2 st inv
817 I	Gx	12 46.9	+ 9 52 m	Vir	0.3	15p	eeF, vS, R, sf of 2
3766 I		12 46.9	+ 19 07 d	Com			vF, vS, R, bM
3771 I		12 46.9	+ 39 10 d	CVn			vF, S, dif
3774 I	Gx	12 46.9	+ 36 17 u	CVn	1.1	16p	F, cS, iF, N
4677	Gx	12 47.0	− 41 35 s	Cen	2.9	12.7	eF, lE, vgbM
3764 I		12 47.0	+ 9 51 x	Vir			vF, cS; = IC 816
3767 I		12 47.0	+ 10 10 d	Vir			vF, bM, mag 16
3778 I	Gx	12 47.0	+ 40 37 z	CVn		16p	pF, S, R, bM
4685	Gx	12 47.1	+ 19 28 r	Com		14p	F, S, R, sbM*, rr
4693	Gx	12 47.1	+ 71 12 r	Dra		14p	vF, plE
3772 I	Gx	12 47.1	+ 36 34 m	CVn	0.6	16p	pF, cS, iF, N
3780 I		12 47.1	+ 40 14 d	CVn			F, vS, bM, spir
819 I		12 47.2	+ 30 44 d	Com			vF, vS, np & conn with IC 820
820 I		12 47.2	+ 30 43 x	Com			Dneb with IC 819 and brighter; = 4676
3773 I	Gx	12 47.2	+ 10 13 u	Vir	2.1	14p	vF, S, bM
3776 I		12 47.2	+ 22 29 d	Com			F, S, iF
4682	Gx	12 47.3	− 10 04 s	Vir	2.8	13p	cF, L, E 45°±, gvlbM

NGC	Type	α_{2000}	δ_{2000}	Const.	Size	Mag.	Description
		h m	° ′		′		
4684	Gx	12 47.3	− 2 43 s	Vir	2.9	13p	B, pL, pmE 25°
3770 I		12 47.3	+ 9 12 d	Vir			cF, cS, E 30°; ?
3775 I		12 47.3	+ 11 44 d	Vir			vF, bM, mag 16
3779 I	Gx	12 47.3	+ 12 10 z	Vir		15p	bM, mag 15
3782 I		12 47.3	+ 40 23 d	CVn			F, vS, R, bM
4687	Gx	12 47.4	+ 35 21 s	CVn	1.2	14p	vF, vS, R, psbM
821 I	Gx	12 47.4	+ 29 48 v	Com	1.4		R, pL, glbM, 2 st ssf
3777 I		12 47.4	+ 9 09 d	Vir			F, S
3781 I		12 47.4	+ 22 34 d	Com			vF, pS, iF, 2 st n and p
3783 I	Gx	12 47.4	+ 40 34 m	CVn	0.6	14p	pF, S, iF, N
4679	Gx	12 47.5	− 39 34 s	Cen	2.3	13p	eeF, pL, R
4681	Gx	12 47.5	− 43 20 r	Cen			pF, S, R, gbM
4695	Gx	12 47.5	+ 54 23 s	UMa	1.3	15p	eF, pS, vlE, mbMN
3791 I		12 47.5	+ 54 27 d	UMa			eeF, S, cE
3786 I		12 47.6	+ 39 03 d	CVn			vF, S, iF, p dif
4683	Gx	12 47.7	− 41 32 s	Cen	2.1	12.9	eF, pS, R, vgbM, S∗ sp
3787 I		12 47.7	+ 40 37 d	CVn			F, vS, iF, N
4688	Gx	12 47.8	+ 4 20 s	Vir	3.3	13p	eF, pL, ∗9-10 p 10ˢ
4689	Gx	12 47.8	+ 13 46 s	Com	4.0	10.9	pB, vL, E, vglbM, r
822 I	Gx	12 47.8	+ 30 05 m	Com	0.4	16p	F, eS, bM
823 I	?	12 47.8	+ 27 12 x	Com			susp, 2′ s of 4692
4690	Gx	12 47.9	− 1 38 r	Vir		14p	vF, S
4692	Gx	12 47.9	+ 27 13 s	Com	1.4	14p	F, cS, R, bM; = IC 823
3784 I		12 47.9	+ 19 23 d	Com			F, vS, E 70°, bM
3785 I		12 47.9	+ 19 17 d	Com			vF, vS, iF, N
3788 I	Gx	12 48.1	+ 18 52 m	Com	0.5	17p	F, S, R, ∗7 sp 2′
3789 I		12 48.1	+ 20 12 d	Com			F, cS, bM, spir, ∗13 sp 0′.5
3795 I	Gx	12 48.1	+ 40 43 m	CVn	0.5	16p	F, S, iF, N
4691	Gx	12 48.2	− 3 20 s	Vir	3.2	11.2	pB, pL, E 90°±, mbM
4694	Gx	12 48.2	+ 10 59 s	Vir	3.6	12p	pF, S, vlE
3790 I	∗	12 48.2	+ 11 07 x	Vir			eF, vS, ??
3793 I		12 48.2	+ 19 09 d	Com			vF, vS, iF, N
3792 I	?	12 48.3	+ 11 05 x	Vir			vF, S
4698	Gx	12 48.4	+ 8 29 s	Vir	4.3	10.7	cB, pL, iR, bM, r
4707	Gx	12 48.4	+ 51 10 s	CVn	2.3	14p	S, stellar
3794 I		12 48.4	+ 19 10 d	Com			F, spir, sbM ∗
3796 I		12 48.5	+ 20 02 d	Com			vF, eS, R, bM, D∗ 13 np
3800 I		12 48.5	+ 36 35 d	CVn			F, S, iF, N
4697	Gx	12 48.6	− 5 48 s	Vir	6.0	9.3	vB, L, lE 45°±, smbMN
3797 I	?	12 48.6	+ 11 36 x	Vir			F, pS, vmE, lbM
3798 I		12 48.7	+ 9 14 d	Vir			F, S
3802 I		12 48.7	+ 38 15 d	CVn			F, vS, R bM
3805 I		12 48.7	+ 38 15 d	CVn			gr of eF neb and st
4696	Gx	12 48.8	− 41 19 s	Cen	3.5	10.7	pB, L, R, gbM, r
4704	Gx	12 48.8	+ 41 55 s	CVn	1.2	15p	cF, S, R, gbM
3804 I	Gx	12 48.8	+ 35 20 v	CVn	1.6		pF, pL, E 40°, bM; = 4711
4711	Gx	12 48.9	+ 35 21 r	CVn		14p	F, S, E, glbM, er; = IC 3804
3806 I	Gx	12 48.9	+ 14 54 v	Com	1.7		vS, R, bM, mag 13.5
4699	Gx	12 49.0	− 8 40 s	Vir	3.5	9.6	vB, R, vmbMrN, r
4702	Gx	12 49.0	+ 27 11 r	Com		15p	pF, S, viF
3799 I	Gx	12 49.0	− 14 23 m	Crv	2.5	14p	vF, pL, vmE 210°, 1st of 7
3801 I	?	12 49.0	+ 10 57 x	Vir			cB, pS, stell
3808 I	Gx	12 49.0	+ 40 36 m	CVn	0.6	15p	pF, S, iF, N, ∗14 f 0′.5
4700	Gx	12 49.1	− 11 25 s	Vir	3.0	12p	F, L, mE 40°, vlbM, B∗ p
3803 I		12 49.1	+ 10 38 d	Vir			eF, pL, ?

NGC	Type	α_{2000}	δ_{2000}	Const.	Size	Mag.	Description
		h m	° ′		′		
3809 I		12 49.1	+ 36 29 d	CVn			pF, S, iF, N
3810 I		12 49.1	+ 40 39 d	CVn			cF, cS, iF, N
4701	Gx	12 49.2	+ 3 23 s	Vir	3.0	12.4	F, S
4703	Gx	12 49.3	− 9 07 s	Vir	2.8	15p	eF, cS, pmE
4705	Gx	12 49.4	− 5 12 s	Vir	3.0	14p	cF, pL, lE
3811 I		12 49.4	+ 21 28 d	Com			F, eS, iF, N
3807 I		12 49.5	− 4 24 d	Vir			eeF, L, mE, *7 sf
3814 I		12 49.5	+ 20 03 d	Com			vF, vS, E 110°
4710	Gx	12 49.6	+ 15 10 s	Com	5.1	11.0	cB, pL, vmE 28°, sbMN
4712	Gx	12 49.6	+ 25 28 s	Com	2.6	13.0	vF, pL
3815 I		12 49.6	+ 19 16 d	Com			vF, vS, R
3816 I	Gx	12 49.6	+ 37 15 m	CVn	0.5	15p	pF, vS, R
4708	Gx	12 49.7	− 11 06 s	Vir	1.6	14p	eF, S
824 I	Gx	12 49.7	− 4 34 m	Vir	0.5	15p	pB, pL, E pf, biN
3817 I		12 49.7	+ 22 50 d	Com			neb *15
3820 I		12 49.7	+ 37 07 d	CVn			vF, vS, iF, N
3823 I		12 49.7	+ 40 53 d	CVn			vF, vS, iF, N
4715	Gx	12 49.8	+ 27 49 s	Com	2.0	15p	F, S, R
3818 I		12 49.8	+ 21 45 d	Com			vF, S, iF, *14 p
4706	Gx	12 49.9	− 41 17 s	Cen	2.2	12.7	vF, vS, R, psbM
3812 I	Gx	12 49.9	− 6 42 m	Vir	0.8	15p	eeF, eS, cE 15°
4713	Gx	12 50.0	+ 5 19 s	Vir	2.8	11.8	pB, L, vlE, glbM
3813 I	Gx	12 50.0	− 25 55 c	Hya	1.5		eF, S, E, *8 nf
3821 I		12 50.0	+ 20 58 d	Com			vF, vS, iF, N
4709	Gx	12 50.1	− 41 23 s	Cen	2.7		pB, cS, R, gbM
4719	Gx	12 50.1	+ 33 09 s	CVn	1.8	14p	vF, stellar
4732	Gx	12 50.1	+ 52 52 r	UMa		15p	F, S, vsmbM
4750	Gx	12 50.1	+ 72 52 s	Dra	2.3	12p	pB, L, R, vg, vsbM
4721	Gx	12 50.2	+ 27 20 r	Com		15p	vF, vS; r?
4714	Gx	12 50.3	− 13 18 r	Crv		14p	F, pS, R, gbM
825 I		12 50.3	− 5 23 d	Vir			eeF, pS, R, nearly bet 2 st
3819 I		12 50.3	− 14 23 d	Crv			eF, vS, 2nd of 7
4725	Gx	12 50.4	+ 25 30 s	Com	11.0	9.2	vB, vL, E, vg, vsvmbMeBN
3822 I	Gx	12 50.4	− 14 19 m	Crv	1.1	15p	eF, vS, 3rd of 7
3828 I	D*	12 50.4	+ 37 57 x	CVn			F, vS, iF; neb*?
4716	Gx	12 50.5	− 9 26 r	Vir		15p	np part of Dneb, smbM
4718	Gx	12 50.5	− 5 17 s	Vir	2.1	15p	eF, vS, bet 2 st
4728	Gx	12 50.5	+ 27 26 v	Com	1.1		eF, eS
3824 I		12 50.5	− 14 26 d	Crv			eF, vS, 4th of 7
4717	Gx	12 50.6	− 9 26 r	Vir		15p	sf 4716 & fainter
3825 I		12 50.6	− 14 30 d	Crv			eeF, vS, *14?, 5th of 7
4720	Gx	12 50.7	− 4 07 r	Vir		15p	eF, S, bM
3826 I	Gx	12 50.7	− 9 00 m	Vir	0.6	15p	vF, vS, mbM
3827 I	Gx	12 50.8	− 14 29 m	Crv	0.8	14p	F, vS, R, *11 s 0′.6; 6th of 7
3832 I		12 50.8	+ 39 49 d	CVn			F, S, iF, p dif
4724	Gx	12 50.9	− 14 20 s	Crv	1.5	15p	F, vS, R, stellar, np of 2
4736	Gx	12 50.9	+ 41 07 s	CVn	11.0	8.2	vB, L, iR, vsvmbMBN, r; = M94
4737	Gx	12 50.9	+ 34 09 r	CVn		15p	eF, vS, pmE
4741	Gx	12 50.9	+ 47 40 r	CVn		14p	vF, S, R, psbM
3830 I		12 50.9	+ 19 50 d	Com			vF, eS, bM, spir
3835 I		12 50.9	+ 40 12 d	CVn			vF, vS, iF, N
4727	Gx	12 51.0	− 14 20 s	Crv	1.6	13p	F, pL, R, lbM, sf of 2
4731	Gx	12 51.0	− 6 24 s	Vir	6.5	11p	vF, pL, E
4735	Gx	12 51.0	+ 28 56 s	Com	0.7	15p	vF, vlbM
4723	Gx	12 51.1	− 13 15 r	Crv		15p	2nd of 2, vF, vS, f 4714; nonexistent?

NGC	Type	α_{2000}	δ_{2000}	Const.	Size	Mag.	Description
		h m	° ′		′		
4733	Gx	12 51.1	+ 10 55 s	Vir	2.3	13p	cF, pL, lE, r, *12 p
4738	Gx	12 51.1	+ 28 48 s	Com	2.3	15p	vF, E 30°, vlbM
3836 I		12 51.1	+ 40 11 d	CVn			vF, vS, iF, N
4734	Gx	12 51.2	+ 4 52 s	Vir	1.2	14p	vF, vS, R
4749	Gx	12 51.2	+ 71 38 s	Dra	1.9	14p	vF, cL, E 135°±
830 I	Gx	12 51.2	+ 53 41 m	UMa	0.8	14p	vF, vS, lE, stellar
4745	Gx	12 51.3	+ 27 26 v	Com	0.7		eF, *6 n
826 I	Gx	12 51.3	+ 31 04 m	Com	0.6	15p	F, pS, R, gbM
3831 I	Gx	12 51.3	− 14 34 m	Crv	1.4	14p	F, vS, R, bM, 7th of 7
4722	Gx	12 51.5	− 13 19 r	Crv		13p	vF, vS, f 4714, with *11 4^{s}f; = IC 3833
4726		12 51.5	− 14 13 r	Crv		14p	vF, 4′ n of Dneb; = IC 3834
4740		12 51.5	− 14 13 D	Crv			pF, pS, R, mbM; = 4726
3833 I	Gx	12 51.5	− 13 19 m	Crv	1.8	13p	vF, S, iF, bM
3834 I	Gx	12 51.5	− 14 13 m	Crv	0.7	14p	vF, lbM, *13 p 0′.8
3837 I		12 51.5	+ 19 43 d	Com			eF, vS, bM, spir
4739	Gx	12 51.6	− 8 25 s	Vir	1.7	14p	F, pL, lE, pglbM
3842 I		12 51.6	+ 40 22 d	CVn			vF, cS, dif; neb* np 0′.5
3843 I		12 51.7	+ 39 00 d	CVn			F, vS, mE 160°, am 3 st
4729	Gx	12 51.8	− 41 08 c	Cen	1.3		neb, 1st of 3, p & a little s of 4744
4742	Gx	12 51.8	− 10 27 s	Vir	2.3	11.1	pB, vS, vbMN = *11, *10 sf
4747	Gx	12 51.8	+ 25 47 s	Com	3.6	12.4	F, pL, lE
3839 I		12 51.8	+ 20 25 d	Com			vF, S, bM, spir
3840 I		12 51.8	+ 21 44 d	Com			vF, S, iF, * inv sp
3841 I		12 51.8	+ 22 21 d	Com			vF, vS, iF, ?
4746	Gx	12 51.9	+ 12 05 s	Vir	2.5	13p	pB, mE, r
4730	Gx	12 52.0	− 41 09 c	Cen	1.2		2nd of 3
827 I	Gx	12 52.0	+ 16 17 u	Com	1.0	15p	vF, S, E pf, dif
3838 I		12 52.0	− 14 28 d	Crv			vF, S, lbM, *13 s 0′.8
3844 I		12 52.1	+ 39 49 d	CVn			vF, S, iF, N
4748	Gx	12 52.2	− 13 24 r	Crv			F, vS, iR, gbM
3829 I	Gx	12 52.2	− 29 50 c	Hya	2.3		B, S, lE, *9 sf
3845 I		12 52.2	+ 38 37 d	CVn			vF, S, iF, N
4743	Gx	12 52.3	− 41 24 s	Cen			F, R, gbM
4752	*	12 52.3	+ 13 29 r	Com			vF, S, E, r
4754	Gx	12 52.3	+ 11 19 s	Vir	4.7	10.6	B, pL, R, psbM, p of 2
828 I		12 52.3	− 8 08 d	Vir			F, vS, R, N = 13.5m
4744	Gx	12 52.4	− 41 04 s	Cen			F, L, E, gbM, 3rd of 3
4753	Gx	12 52.4	− 1 12 s	Vir	5.4	9.9	cB, L, vlE, vglbM
829 I	Gx	12 52.4	− 15 31 m	Crv	0.4	15p	neb *13
3847 I		12 52.6	+ 22 04 d	Com			vF.vS, iF, neb *15 sp
3849 I		12 52.6	+ 40 46 d	CVn			vF, vS, iF, N, *14 nf
4758	Gx	12 52.7	+ 15 51 s	Com	3.2	14p	vF, pL, E?
831 I	Gx	12 52.7	+ 26 29 x	Com		15p	F, S, R, bM
3846 I		12 52.7	+ 13 39 d	Com			B, pS, N = *9.2
3848 I		12 52.7	+ 21 25 d	Com			vF, vS, E 120°
3850 I	Gx	12 52.7	+ 40 06 m	CVn	0.9	15p	pF, vS, iF, N
4757	Gx	12 52.8	− 10 19 s	Vir	1.8	15p	vF
4751	Gx	12 52.9	− 42 40 r	Cen			B, pS, R, vg, vsmbM
4756	Gx	12 52.9	− 15 25 s	Crv	2.0	13p	vF, pS, r
4762	Gx	12 52.9	+ 11 14 s	Vir	8.7	10.2	pB, vmE 31°, 3 B st s, f of 2
4759	Gx	12 53.1	− 9 11 r	Vir		15p	pL, double, *10 2′ sp
4760	Gx	12 53.1	− 10 30 s	Vir	1.8	13p	pB, R
4761	Gx	12 53.1	− 9 11 r	Vir		14p	eF, eS, 1′ f Dneb 4759
4766	Gx	12 53.1	− 10 23 s	Vir	1.6	15p	vF
3851 I		12 53.1	+ 21 55 d	Com			vF, vS, iF, ?, *12 s

NGC	Type	α_{2000}	δ_{2000}	Const.	Size	Mag.	Description
		h m	o ′		′		
3852 I	Gx	12 53.1	+ 35 47 u	CVn	1.4	16p	F, pS, E 60°, bM
4764	Gx	12 53.2	− 9 11 r	Vir		16p	eF, eS, sf Dneb 4759
4765	Gx	12 53.2	+ 4 28 s	Vir	1.4	13p	F, cS, R, gbM
4774	Gx	12 53.2	+ 36 49 s	CVn	0.6	14.4	eF, cS, R, bM
3853 I		12 53.2	+ 38 50 d	CVn			eF, S, p dif
3854 I		12 53.2	+ 40 51 d	CVn			vF, pL, dif, diffic, ∗15 f
4768	∗	12 53.3	− 9 32 F	Vir			vF, vS, p 4770 on parallel
4769	D∗	12 53.3	− 9 32 F	Vir			vF, vS, p 4770 on parallel
4763	Gx	12 53.4	− 17 00 s	Crv	1.7	13p	vF, S, lbM
4771	Gx	12 53.4	+ 1 16 s	Vir	4.0	13p	F, pL, mE, ∗9 p 90°
3855 I		12 53.4	+ 36 47 d	CVn			pF, eS, R, bM
4770	Gx	12 53.5	− 9 31 r	Vir		14p	vF, vS
4772	Gx	12 53.5	+ 2 10 s	Vir	3.3	13p	pF, pS, R, mbM
4785	Gx	12 53.5	− 48 46 r	Cen			vF, S, R, glbM
4755	OC	12 53.6	− 60 20 s	Cru	10	4.2	Cl, vL, st vB (κ Cru)
4773	Gx	12 53.6	− 8 38 s	Vir	2.0	15p	vF, S
4775	Gx	12 53.8	− 6 37 s	Vir	2.2	12p	F, cL, R, vglbM, r
4779	Gx	12 53.8	+ 9 44 s	Vir	2.3	13p	vF, pL, R, r
832 I	Gx	12 53.8	+ 26 27 v	Com			F, S, R, bM, D∗ nf
3856 I		12 53.8	+ 20 06 d	Com			vF, S, iF, ∗15 inv p
3862 I	Gx	12 53.8	+ 36 06 u	CVn	1.0	16p	vF, pS, dif, ∗15 att
4767	Gx	12 53.9	− 39 43 s	Cen	2.6	13p	B, pS, lE, mbM
3857 I		12 53.9	+ 19 36 d	Com			eF, vS, R, bM, 2 eF st nr
3858 I		12 53.9	+ 20 47 d	Com			F, vS, R, bM, neb ∗14 & ∗13 sp
3861 I		12 53.9	+ 38 17 d	CVn			F, eS; neb∗?
3863 I		12 53.9	+ 38 29 d	CVn			F, S, iF, ∗14 att
4777	Gx	12 54.0	− 8 47 s	Vir	2.3	15p	vF, S
4776	−	12 54.1	− 9 13 r	Vir			F, S, R, vlbM, p of Dneb
4778	−	12 54.1	− 9 12 r	Vir			vF, S, R, vlbM, f of Dneb
4780	Gx	12 54.1	− 8 37 s	Vir	2.1	14p	vF, f 4773 and 4777
4787	Gx	12 54.1	+ 27 04 r	Com		15p	vF, vS, 4789 f
3860 I		12 54.1	+ 19 18 d	Com			vF, vS, R, bM
4788	Gx	12 54.2	+ 27 19 r	Com		15p	vF, S
3864 I		12 54.2	+ 18 57 d	Com			vF, vS, iF, ∗14 s 30″; many other neb about
3865 I		12 54.2	+ 18 52 d	Com			vF, vS, R, bM
4789	Gx	12 54.3	+ 27 04 s	Com	1.7	12.0	F, R, ∗9 att 1′ n
3866 I	OC	12 54.3	+ 22 22 x	Com			vF, S, iF, N; Cl?
3867 I		12 54.3	+ 18 56 d	Com			vF, S, iF, N
3868 I		12 54.3	+ 19 00 d	Com			vF, vS, iF, N
4781	Gx	12 54.4	− 10 32 s	Vir	3.5	12p	cB, vL, mE
3859 I	OC	12 54.4	− 9 06 x	Vir			vF; eF Cl?
3869 I		12 54.4	+ 18 58 d	Com			vF, vS, iF, N
3870 I		12 54.4	+ 22 23 d	Com			vF, S, iF, p dif
3871 I		12 54.4	+ 18 56 d	Com			vF, vS, R, bM
4786	Gx	12 54.5	− 6 52 s	Vir	2.0	13p	pB, pS, mbM, r
3872 I		12 54.5	+ 18 58 d	Com			vF, vS, iF, N
3873 I		12 54.5	+ 18 53 d	Com			vF, vS, iF, N
3878 I		12 54.5	+ 40 04 d	CVn			vF, vS, bM, spir
3879 I	Gx	12 54.5	+ 38 38 m	CVn	0.6	16p	F, S, R, bM
4782	Gx	12 54.6	− 12 34 s	Crv	1.5	11.7	pF, pS, R, mbM, p of Dneb
4783	Gx	12 54.6	− 12 33 s	Crv	1.7	11.8	pF, pS, R, mbM, f of Dneb
4784	Gx	12 54.6	− 10 37 s	Vir	1.8	15p	eF, eS
4793	Gx	12 54.6	+ 28 56 s	Com	2.9	11.7	pB, pS, lE, ∗8 nf 1′
4800	Gx	12 54.6	+ 46 32 s	CVn	1.8	12p	pB, cS, R, psbM, ∗14 p
4801	Gx	12 54.6	+ 53 06 r	UMa		15p	eF, S, lE

NGC	Type	α_{2000}	δ_{2000}	Const.	Size	Mag.	Description
		h m	o ′		′		
3874 I		12 54.6	+ 18 57 d	Com			vF, vS, iF, *15 sf 20″
3875 I		12 54.6	+ 22 02 d	Com			vF, S, iF, N, *14 p
3885 I		12 54.7	+ 37 09 d	CVn			F, S, R, neb*
3887 I		12 54.7	+ 40 18 d	CVn			vF, vS, iF, N
3888 I	Gx	12 54.7	+ 39 34 m	CVn	0.9	16p	F, S, lE 60°, N
4791	Gx	12 54.8	+ 8 03 r	Vir		15p	eF, vS, lE, vlbM
4809	Gx	12 54.8	+ 2 39 s	Vir	1.9	14p	F, Dneb with 4810, E ⊥ to each other
4810	Gx	12 54.8	+ 2 38 s	Vir	0.8	15p	F, Dneb with 4809
3876 I		12 54.8	+ 19 01 d	Com			vF, vS, R, bM
3877 I		12 54.8	+ 19 18 d	Com			pF, cL, E 20°, bM
3880 I		12 54.8	+ 22 30 d	Com			vF, S, viF
3881 I	Gx	12 54.8	+ 19 11 s	Com	3.9	13p	vF, vS, R, bM
3890 I		12 54.8	+ 37 11 d	CVn			vF, S, iF, N
4790	Gx	12 54.9	− 10 15 s	Vir	1.8	13p	pF, pS, iR
4797	−	12 54.9	+ 27 21 r	Com			F, S, R, lbM; nonexistent?
3882 I		12 54.9	+ 22 34 d	Com			vF, vS, iF, N
3889 I		12 54.9	+ 36 01 d	CVn			vF, S, iF, diffic
4795	Gx	12 55.0	+ 8 04 s	Vir	1.7	13p	pB, pL, R, bM, r
4798	Gx	12 55.0	+ 27 25 s	Com	1.3	13.1	pF, pS, gbM
3884 I		12 55.0	+ 19 41 d	Com			F, S, R, bM, * 14ᵉ
3886 I		12 55.0	+ 19 01 d	Com			vF, S, iF, N
3891 I		12 55.0	+ 36 03 d	CVn			vF, S, iF, diffic
4792	Gx	12 55.1	− 12 30 v	Crv	1.1		vS, R, 7′ nnp of 4794
4796	Gx	12 55.1	+ 8 04 r	Vir		13p	eF, eS, alm stell, close f 4795
3892 I		12 55.1	+ 39 13 d	CVn			F, S, iF
3893 I		12 55.1	+ 38 34 d	CVn			vF, S, iF, N
4794	Gx	12 55.2	− 12 37 s	Crv	2.3	14p	vF, S, 2 or 3 st near
3895 I		12 55.2	+ 39 12 d	CVn			F, cS, iF, N, *15 nf conn
4799	Gx	12 55.3	+ 2 54 r	Vir		14p	cF, S, vS* att
3883 I		12 55.3	− 8 09 d	Vir			eF, vS, mE 5°
3897 I		12 55.3	+ 39 40 d	CVn			F, vS, E 40°, bM
4805	Gx	12 55.4	+ 27 57 r	Com			vF
4814	Gx	12 55.4	+ 58 21 s	UMa	3.2	13p	B, pS, vlE, vgbM
3898 I		12 55.4	+ 37 35 d	CVn			eF, vS, v diffic, att eF*
4807	Gx	12 55.5	+ 27 31 s	Com	1.2	14p	F, pS, R, bM
3894 I		12 55.5	+ 19 04 d	Com			vF, vS, iF, N
3902 I		12 55.6	+ 36 00 d	CVn			pF, vS, neb*
3903 I		12 55.6	+ 40 24 d	CVn			vF, vS, iF, N
4803	Gx	12 55.7	+ 8 14 r	Vir		15p	eF, eS, R, lbM
3899 I		12 55.7	+ 20 38 d	Com			vF, S
3900 I	Gx	12 55.7	+ 27 15 v	Com	0.7		pB, S, bMN
4802	Gx	12 55.8	− 12 03 s	Crv		12p	vF, S, *10 att
4808	Gx	12 55.8	+ 4 18 s	Vir	2.7	12p	pB, cL, E 135°±
3906 I		12 55.8	+ 40 28 d	CVn			vF, S, iF, N
4804	−	12 55.9	− 13 02 r	Crv			S, att to pB*; = 4802?
3901 I	*	12 55.9	+ 21 56 x	Com			eF, vS, E 95°
3904 I	Gx	12 55.9	+ 36 18 m	CVn	0.5	15p	F, S, bM, spir
836 I	Gx	12 56.0	+ 63 37 u	Dra	1.4	15p	eeF, vS, v diffic, bet 2 st
3909 I		12 56.0	+ 40 23 d	CVn			vF, vS, R, bM
3905 I		12 56.1	+ 19 51 d	Com			vF, S, iF
3910 I		12 56.1	+ 39 43 d	CVn			vF, vS, R, bM; neb D*?
3912 I		12 56.1	+ 39 55 d	CVn			F, vS, iF, N
4806	Gx	12 56.2	− 29 30 r	Hya		14p	F, cS, R, gvlbM
4816	Gx	12 56.2	+ 27 45 s	Com	1.6	15p	vF, pL
4817	−	12 56.2	+ 28 00 r	Com			vF, no N; nonexistent?

NGC	Type	α_{2000}	δ_{2000}	Const.	Size	Mag.	Description
		h m	° ′		′		
3911 I		12 56.2	+ 35 38 d	CVn			vF, pS, dif, diffic
3907 I		12 56.3	+ 18 47 d	Com			eF, S, iF, N, *13 sf 1′
4834	Gx	12 56.4	+ 52 18 r	CVn		15p	vF, S, iR, bM
3914 I		12 56.4	+ 36 22 d	CVn			eF, vS, iF, N
4819	Gx	12 56.5	+ 26 59 s	Com	1.2	14p	vF, pL, iF
4821	Gx	12 56.5	+ 26 57 s	Com	0.7	15p	vF, vS, 4819 np
834 I		12 56.5	+ 26 20 D	Com			pF, pS, sbM
3913 I	Gx	12 56.5	+ 27 17 m	Com	0.6	15p	F, S, R
3916 I	Gx	12 56.5	+ 38 37 u	CVn	1.1	16p	pF, S, bM, spir?
4813	Gx	12 56.6	− 6 48 r	Vir		15p	F, S, R, bM
4824	Gx	12 56.6	+ 27 31 r	Com			vF, vS
3896 I	Gx	12 56.6	− 50 19 s	Cen	2.2	13p	bM, mag 14
4826	Gx	12 56.7	+ 21 41 s	Com	9.3	8.5	! vB, vL, vmE 120°±, bMSBN; = M64
4827	Gx	12 56.7	+ 27 11 s	Com	1.7	13.0	F, cL
4828	Gx	12 56.7	+ 28 01 r	Com		15p	F, S, R
833 I		12 56.7	− 6 44 d	Vir			vF, S, R
3908 I		12 56.7	− 7 35 d	Vir			eF, eS, cE 160°; F trail?
3915 I		12 56.7	+ 20 07 d	Com			F, vS, spir, *14 inv s
4818	Gx	12 56.8	− 8 31 s	Vir	4.5	12p	pB, L, pmE 0°, gbM
3919 I		12 56.8	+ 38 32 d	CVn			F, vS, bM, spir
3920 I		12 56.8	+ 39 58 d	CVn			F, vS, iF, N
4811	Gx	12 56.9	− 41 48 r	Cen			eF, cS, R, gbM, p of 2
4812	Gx	12 56.9	− 41 49 r	Cen			eF, S, R, gbM, f of 2
4837	Gx	12 56.9	+ 48 18 s	CVn	1.4	14p	neb?
835 I	Gx	12 56.9	+ 26 29 v	Com	0.6		F, S, R
3917 I	Gx	12 56.9	+ 22 22 x	Com			eF, vS, iF, N
3918 I		12 56.9	+ 22 22 x	Com			pF, vS, bM, spir; = IC 3917
4820	Gx	12 57.0	− 13 42 r	Vir		15p	vS, sp of 4825
4822	Gx	12 57.0	− 10 45 r	Vir		14p	F, st inv
3921 I		12 57.0	+ 38 38 d	CVn			F, vS, bM, spir
3922 I		12 57.0	+ 38 29 d	CVn			vF, vS, iF
3923 I		12 57.0	+ 37 57 d	CVn			pF, eS, E, bM
4825	Gx	12 57.2	− 13 40 s	Vir	2.0	12.1	pB, iF, bM
4857	Gx	12 57.2	+ 70 12 r	Dra		14p	eF, vS, iR, vlbM
4829	Gx	12 57.3	− 13 44 r	Vir			vS, sf 4825
3925 I		12 57.3	+ 36 25 d	CVn			pF, vS, E 60°, bM
3928 I		12 57.3	+ 40 26 d	CVn			vF, pL, dif, *13 att
4823		12 57.4	− 13 44 F	Vir			vS, sp of 4825
4830	Gx	12 57.4	− 19 42 r	Vir		13p	F, L, st inv, *8 5′ sf
4839	Gx	12 57.4	+ 27 30 s	Com	4.2	14p	F, pL, R
3924 I		12 57.4	+ 18 47 d	Com			eF, S, R
3930 I		12 57.4	+ 38 46 d	CVn			F, vS, N; neb*?
4836	Gx	12 57.5	− 12 45 r	Vir		13p	vF, L, dif
4840	Gx	12 57.5	+ 27 37 s	Com	0.6	15p	vF, vS
4841	Gx	12 57.5	+ 28 29 s	Com	1.9	11.5	pF, pL, R, vS* att
837 I	Gx	12 57.5	+ 26 30 x	Com		15p	F, S, R
3926 I		12 57.5	+ 22 49 d	Com			vF, vS, iF, N
4831	Gx	12 57.6	− 27 18 r	Hya		14p	F, S, R, gbM
4842	Gx	12 57.6	+ 27 29 s	Com	0.6	15p	vF, vS, 4839 sp
3929 I		12 57.7	+ 20 24 d	Com			vF, vS, bM, spir
4832	Gx	12 57.8	− 39 44 A	Cen			pF, vS, R, sbM *17, *10 70°
4838	Gx	12 57.9	− 13 03 r	Vir		13p	vF, pS, R, 3 S st sp
4846	Gx	12 57.9	+ 36 22 r	CVn		14p	eF
3933 I		12 57.9	+ 36 39 d	CVn			F, vS, iF, N
4815	OC	12 58.0	− 64 57 s	Mus	3	8.6	Cl, pL, pRi, iF, st 10...18

NGC	Type	α_{2000}	δ_{2000}	Const.	Size	Mag.	Description
		h m	° ′		′		
4843	Gx	12 58.0	− 3 37 r	Vir		14p	cF, E, er, * sf 30″
4845	Gx	12 58.0	+ 1 35 s	Vir	5.0	12p	pF, pL, pmE, vgbM, * nf 30°
3931 I		12 58.0	+ 19 37 d	Com			cF, S, iF, N
4835	Gx	12 58.1	− 46 15 s	Cen	3.4	12p	F, pL, mE, vgbM
4844	*	12 58.1	− 13 04 A	Vir			F, S
4848	Gx	12 58.1	+ 28 15 s	Com	1.8	14p	pF, S, lE
3932 I		12 58.1	+ 19 35 d	Com			vF, es, R bM
4849	Gx	12 58.2	+ 26 24 s	Com	2.2	15p	pB, R, bM; = IC 3935
838 I	Gx	12 58.2	+ 26 24 x	Com		14p	vF, 1′.5 nf 4849
3927 I	Gx	12 58.2	− 22 53 c	Hya	1.4		vF, vS, *10 np, *7 s 10′
3935 I		12 58.2	+ 26 23 x	Com			pB, S, R, N, r, IC 838 f; = 4849
3941 I		12 58.2	+ 39 46 d	CVn			F, vS, iF, N
4851	Gx	12 58.3	+ 28 09 r	Com		15p	F, vS, r; = IC 839?
3934 I		12 58.3	+ 18 50 d	Com			F, S, iF
3936 I		12 58.3	+ 19 03 d	Com			neb *13, *12.5 f 1′
3940 I		12 58.3	+ 35 50 d	CVn			cF, vS, R, bM
3942 I		12 58.3	+ 36 06 d	CVn			eF, es, iF, N
4850	Gx	12 58.4	+ 27 58 s	Com	1.6	16p	F, S, R
839 I	Gx	12 58.4	+ 28 09 x	Com			stellar, 13m
3937 I		12 58.4	+ 18 49 d	Com			vF, vS, iF, N
3938 I		12 58.4	+ 18 45 d	Com			eF, vS, R, bM, *13 sp
4847	Gx	12 58.5	− 13 08 r	Vir			F, S neb*, *9 p 40ˢon parallel
3939 I		12 58.5	+ 18 45 d	Com			vF, es, bM, spir
3945 I		12 58.5	+ 39 56 d	CVn			F, vS, iF, N
4853	Gx	12 58.6	+ 27 36 s	Com	1.2	13.1	F, S, R, pslbM
3943 I		12 58.6	+ 28 07 x	Com			pF, vS, iF
840 I	Gx	12 58.7	+ 10 37 u	Vir	1.0	15p	F, S, R, lbM, r
3944 I		12 58.7	+ 23 47 d	Com			F, vS, iF, N
4854	Gx	12 58.8	+ 27 40 s	Com		15p	vF, pL, com
3946 I	Gx	12 58.8	+ 27 49 s	Com	1.0	13.9	F, pS, bM
3947 I	Gx	12 58.9	+ 27 47 v	Com			vF, S
3949 I	Gx	12 58.9	+ 27 50 v	Com	1.3		F, pS, E
3952 I		12 58.9	+ 38 52 d	CVn			F, cS, iF, N
3956 I		12 58.9	+ 37 24 d	CVn			F, vS, R, bM
4858	Gx	12 59.0	+ 28 07 s	Com	0.4	16p	F, vS, p of Dneb
4859	Gx	12 59.0	+ 26 49 s	Com	1.7	15p	F, vS, R
4861	Gx	12 59.0	+ 34 52 s	CVn	4.1	12.2	vF, pL, vmE 30°±, bet 2 st
3948 I		12 59.0	+ 24 04 d	Com			vF, vS, iF, N
4860	Gx	12 59.1	+ 28 07 s	Com	1.0	13.5	pF, S, R, f of Dneb
4868	Gx	12 59.1	+ 37 19 s	CVn	1.7	13p	pB, S, R, mbM
3950 I		12 59.1	+ 18 44 d	Com			F, vS, R, bM
3955 I	Gx	12 59.1	+ 28 00 v	Com			vF, S, N 14 mag
3957 I	Gx	12 59.1	+ 27 46 x	Com		16p	cF, vS, R, bM
3959 I	Gx	12 59.1	+ 27 47 v	Com	0.6		F, pS, R, lbM
3960 I	Gx	12 59.1	+ 27 51 v	Com	0.4		vF, pS, diffic
3961 I	Gx	12 59.1	+ 34 52 t	CVn	4.2	13p	pF, pL, lE 30°, bM; = 4861
4864	Gx	12 59.2	+ 27 59 s	Com	0.6	13.6	F, S, p of 2
3951 I		12 59.2	+ 18 46 d	Com			F, vS, iF, N; neb D*?
3953 I		12 59.2	+ 23 05 d	Com			vF, S, R, bM, dif
3954 I		12 59.2	+ 19 16 d	Com			F, vS, R, bM
3958 I		12 59.2	+ 24 02 d	Com			vF, vS, iF, N
3963 I	Gx	12 59.2	+ 27 47 v	Com	0.7		vF, vS, R, bM
3964 I	*	12 59.2	+ 27 51 x	Com			eF, vS
3967 I	Gx	12 59.2	+ 36 07 m	CVn	0.4	15p	pF, vS, iF, N
3970 I		12 59.2	+ 40 24 d	CVn			F, vS, E 120°, *15 att p

NGC	Type	α_{2000}	δ_{2000}	Const.	Size	Mag.	Description
		h m	o ′		′		
3975 I	Gx	12 59.2	+ 38 53 m	CVn	0.5	15p	pF, vS, E 40°, bM
4855	Gx	12 59.3	− 13 13 r	Vir		14p	F, S, st inv
4856	Gx	12 59.3	− 15 02 s	Vir	4.6	10.4	B, R, psmbM, *13 np
4865	Gx	12 59.3	+ 28 05 s	Com	1.4	13.3	vF, vS, *7-8 f 13^s
4867	Gx	12 59.3	+ 27 58 s	Com	1.1	16p	vF, vS, stellar, f 4864
4870	Gx	12 59.3	+ 37 00 r	CVn			pF, lE, bet 2 st
3962 I		12 59.3	+ 23 40 d	Com			vF neb*
3966 I	Gx	12 59.3	+ 35 52 m	CVn	0.4	15p	F, S, iF, N
3972 I		12 59.3	+ 37 17 d	CVn			vF, vS, R, bM
3977 I		12 59.3	+ 36 48 d	CVn			vF, S, iF, N
3980 I		12 59.3	+ 39 09 d	CVn			eF, vS, iF
3982 I		12 59.3	+ 40 05 d	CVn			F, vS, R, bM, bet 2 st 13
3983 I		12 59.3	+ 39 15 d	CVn			F, S, iF, N
4862	Gx	12 59.4	− 14 07 r	Vir		15p	eF, S, R
4869	Gx	12 59.4	+ 27 55 s	Com	1.1	13.5	cF, S, R, *7 n
3965 I		12 59.4	+ 18 51 d	Com			F, vS, iF, N
3968 I	Gx	12 59.4	+ 27 58 x	Com			eF, vS, *14 nr
3979 I		12 59.4	+ 36 20 d	CVn			F, eS, R, bM
3981 I		12 59.4	+ 37 14 d	CVn			eF, vS, iF, N, diffic
3987 I		12 59.4	+ 38 44 d	CVn			pF, vS, R, bM
4866	Gx	12 59.5	+ 14 10 s	Vir	6.5	11.0	B, pL, mE 90°, sbMN, S* inv
4871	Gx	12 59.5	+ 27 57 s	Com	0.5	15p	vF, vS, stell N
3969 I		12 59.5	+ 19 39 d	Com			eF, S, iF
3971 I		12 59.5	+ 22 51 d	Com			vF, vS, iF, N
3973 I	Gx	12 59.5	+ 27 53 v	Com			F, vS, R, N 13 mag
3976 I	Gx	12 59.5	+ 27 51 v	Com			*14 inv in vF neb
3988 I		12 59.5	+ 37 15 d	CVn			vF, S, iF
3989 I		12 59.5	+ 36 47 d	CVn			vF, vS, iF, N
3992 I		12 59.5	+ 36 46 d	CVn			F, vS, iF, N
3993 I		12 59.5	+ 40 36 d	CVn			F, vS, iF, N
3996 I		12 59.5	+ 40 28 d	CVn			F, vS, sbM *
4833	Gb	12 59.6	− 70 53 s	Mus	13.5	7.4	⊕, B, L, R, g, vsbM, st 12
4863	Gx	12 59.6	− 14 01 r	Vir		15p	eF, S, mE 45°, sbMN
4872	Gx	12 59.6	+ 27 57 s	Com	1.0	13.7	pF, pS, R
4873	Gx	12 59.6	+ 27 59 v	Com	0.8	14.2	vF, vS
4874	Gx	12 59.6	+ 27 58 s	Com	2.7	11.9	F, 4869 and 4872 p
4875	Gx	12 59.6	+ 27 54 s	Com		16p	vF, vS, stellar
3978 I		12 59.6	+ 19 38 d	Com			eF, S, iF
3990 I	Gx	12 59.6	+ 28 54 v	Com	1.3		F, S, R, N, r
3991 I	Gx	12 59.6	+ 28 56 x	Com		15p	F, S, R, FN, r
3995 I		12 59.6	+ 38 53 d	CVn			F, S, iF, N
3997 I		12 59.6	+ 36 42 d	CVn			vF, S, iF
4000 I		12 59.6	+ 39 35 d	CVn			vF, vS, iF; neb*?
4001 I		12 59.6	+ 38 52 d	CVn			pF, vS, R, bM
4876	Gx	12 59.7	+ 27 55 s	Com	0.4	15p	vF, vS, no Nucl
3984 I		12 59.7	+ 19 38 d	Com			eF, S, iF
3985 I		12 59.7	+ 19 35 d	Com			cF, eS, R, bM
4002 I		12 59.7	+ 36 46 d	CVn			pF, S, iF, N
4003 I		12 59.7	+ 38 49 d	CVn			pF, vS, iF, N
4004 I		12 59.7	+ 38 49 d	CVn			pF, vS, iF, N
841 I		12 59.8	+ 21 49 D	Com			vF
3994 I		12 59.8	+ 22 43 d	Com			eF, vS, iF; eF* inv?
3998 I	Gx	12 59.8	+ 27 58 v	Com		14.7	eF, pS
4006 I		12 59.8	+ 37 01 d	CVn			vF, S, iF
4883	Gx	12 59.9	+ 28 02 v	Com		14.3	vF, S, stellar

NGC	Type	α_{2000}	δ_{2000}	Const.	Size	Mag.	Description
		h m	° ′		′		
4901	Gx	12 59.9	+ 47 12 r	CVn		15p	pF, S, R, gbM
4009 I		12 59.9	+ 36 40 d	CVn			vF, vS, R, bM
4010 I		12 59.9	+ 37 53 d	CVn			F, vS, iF, N
4881	Gx	13 00.0	+ 28 15 s	Com	1.0	13.5	F, S, lE, *9 sp
4882		13 00.0	+ 27 59 A	Com			vF, S, others near
4884	−	13 00.0	+ 27 59 r	Com			chief one of mult neb; = 4889?
4886	Gx	13 00.0	+ 27 59 s	Com	0.8	13.9	F, S, R, 4889 f 4ˢ
4892	Gx	13 00.0	+ 26 54 s	Com	1.6	15p	vF
4005 I		13 00.0	+ 22 38 d	Com			vF, vS, iF, N
4013 I		13 00.0	+ 37 12 d	CVn			vF, vS, iF, N
4015 I		13 00.0	+ 37 12 x	CVn			n part of Dneb, eF, S, iF, N; = 4893
4016 I		13 00.0	+ 37 12 x	CVn			s part of Dneb, eF, S, iF, N; = 4893
4018 I		13 00.0	+ 40 29 d	CVn			vF, S, iF, N
4020 I		13 00.0	+ 38 36 d	CVn			eF, pL, dif
4852	OC	13 00.1	− 59 36 s	Cen	11	9p	Cl, L, pRi, iR, st 10
4889	Gx	13 00.1	+ 27 58 s	Com	3.0	11.4	pB, pmE, bM, *7 n
4893	Gx	13 00.1	+ 37 11 r	CVn		15p	vF, *20 sp, *17 nf; = IC 4015
4007 I		13 00.1	+ 19 58 d	Com			vF, vS, R, bM
4008 I		13 00.1	+ 22 21 d	Com			vF, vS, iF, N
4011 I	Gx	13 00.1	+ 28 00 v	Com		15.0	eF, vS, N 15m
4012 I	Gx	13 00.1	+ 28 05 v	Com		14.8	*14 in vF neb
4022 I		13 00.1	+ 38 29 d	CVn			eF, eS, iF, N
4024 I		13 00.1	+ 40 31 d	CVn			vF, vS, iF, N
4880	Gx	13 00.2	+ 12 29 s	Vir	3.3	12p	cF, pL, R, vglbM, r
4014 I		13 00.2	+ 22 30 d	Com			vF, vS, iF, N
4021 I	Gx	13 00.2	+ 28 02 v	Com	0.3	14.9	*14 in vF neb
4027 I		13 00.2	+ 37 08 d	CVn			F, S, iF, N, 4893 np
4029 I		13 00.2	+ 38 46 d	CVn			vF, vS, iF, N
4878	Gx	13 00.3	− 6 05 r	Vir		14p	vF, vS, p of 2
4894	Gx	13 00.3	+ 27 58 s	Com		16p	pF, S, R
4895	Gx	13 00.3	+ 28 12 s	Com	2.3	12.8	vF, S, R
4898	Gx	13 00.3	+ 27 57 s	Com		15p	vF, S, close to 4894
4017 I		13 00.3	+ 22 33 d	Com			vF, vS, E 80°, bM
4019 I		13 00.3	+ 23 43 d	Com			F, vS, iF, *14 att nf, * 11 sp
4028 I	Gx	13 00.3	+ 36 15 u	CVn	1.2	15p	F, cS, iF, N
4031 I		13 00.3	+ 39 09 d	CVn			vF, S, R, bM
4034 I		13 00.3	+ 37 03 d	CVn			cF, S, iF, N
4035 I		13 00.3	+ 40 18 d	CVn			vF, S, viF, diffic
4037 I		13 00.3	+ 39 00 d	CVn			F, vS, iF, N
4877	Gx	13 00.4	− 15 17 s	Vir	2.7	13p	pB, pL, mbM
4023 I		13 00.4	+ 19 06 d	Com			vF, vS, iF; ?
4026 I	Gx	13 00.4	+ 28 03 v	Com		14.7	*14 in vF neb
4032 I	Gx	13 00.4	+ 28 52 x	Com		15p	F, S, R, gbM
4036 I		13 00.4	+ 36 55 d	CVn			vF, vS, iF, N
4038 I		13 00.4	+ 37 02 d	CVn			F, vS, iF, N
4879	Gx	13 00.5	− 6 03 r	Vir		15p	vF, vS, f of 2
4885	Gx	13 00.5	− 6 50 r	Vir		15p	vF, S, E
4896	Gx	13 00.5	+ 28 21 s	Com	1.3	13.7	vF, vS, R, mbM
3999 I	Gx	13 00.5	− 14 18 x	Vir			eF, susp
4025 I		13 00.5	+ 19 06 d	Com			vF, vS, iF, N
4030 I	Gx	13 00.5	+ 27 57 x	Com			eF, vS, R, *15 inv
4033 I	Gx	13 00.5	+ 27 58 x	Com			eF, pS, R
4887	Gx	13 00.6	− 14 40 s	Vir	1.6	14p	vF, 4902 nf
4890	Gx	13 00.6	− 4 34 r	Vir		14p	cF, S, iR, bM
4900	Gx	13 00.6	+ 2 30 s	Vir	2.3	11.5	cB, cE, *10 att 135°±

NGC	Type	α_{2000}	δ_{2000}	Const.	Size	Mag.	Description
		h m	° ′		′		
842 I	Gx	13 00.6	+ 29 01 x	Com		15p	pF
4040 I	Gx	13 00.6	+ 28 03 v	Com	1.1		vF, S, R, gbM
4048 I		13 00.6	+ 39 50 d	CVn			vF, vS, iF, N
4906	Gx	13 00.7	+ 27 55 v	Com		14.2	vF, vS, ∗15 p
4914	Gx	13 00.7	+ 37 19 s	CVn	3.6	12p	pB, cS, R, smbM, ∗17 np
4916	Gx	13 00.7	+ 37 22 r	CVn			neb, nf 4914 (?)
4039 I		13 00.7	+ 21 41 d	Com			cF, vS, neb∗
4041 I	Gx	13 00.7	+ 28 00 v	Com	0.7		vF, pS
4042 I	Gx	13 00.7	+ 27 58 v	Com		14.3	F, S, bM
4043 I	Gx	13 00.7	+ 37 06 u	CVn	1.0	16p	vF, S, iF
4046 I		13 00.7	+ 36 41 d	CVn			F, vS, R, bM
4049 I	Gx	13 00.7	+ 36 21 u	CVn	1.2	15p	pB, vS, sbM ∗
4050 I		13 00.7	+ 36 40 d	CVn			vF, S, iF, N; D∗?
4052 I		13 00.7	+ 39 40 d	CVn			vF, vS, iF, N
4056 I	Gx	13 00.7	+ 39 45 u	CVn	1.1	16p	F, vS, exc N
4891	∗	13 00.8	− 13 26 A	Vir			F neb∗
4907	Gx	13 00.8	+ 28 09 s	Com	1.4	13.4	eF, vS, ∗13 att
4912	−	13 00.8	+ 37 23 r	CVn			neb n of and in line with 4914 (?)
4913	−	13 00.8	+ 37 21 r	CVn			nonexistent?
4044 I	Gx	13 00.8	+ 27 55 x	Com			eF, S, lbM
4045 I	Gx	13 00.8	+ 28 05 s	Com	0.7	13.9	pF, S, bM
4060 I	Gx	13 00.8	+ 40 35 m	CVn	0.7	15p	vF, cS, iF, N
4897	Gx	13 00.9	− 13 27 A	Vir	2.8	13p	F
4899	Gx	13 00.9	− 13 57 s	Vir	2.7	12p	pF, eL
4908	Gx	13 00.9	+ 28 02 s	Com	1.1	15p	vF, vS
4911	Gx	13 00.9	+ 27 47 s	Com	1.3	12.8	1st of 4, F, pL, ∗11 2′ np
4917	Gx	13 00.9	+ 47 14 r	CVn		15p	eF, S, E, bM
4051 I	Gx	13 00.9	+ 28 00 s	Com	1.3	13.4	pF, S, R, bM, 4908 np
4902	Gx	13 01.0	− 14 31 s	Vir	3.0	11.2	pB, pL, iR, st nr
4904	Gx	13 01.0	− 0 02 s	Vir	2.3	12.1	pB, pS, R, bM
4047 I	Gx	13 01.0	+ 19 41 x	Com		16p	cF, S, E 110°, bM
4053 I		13 01.0	+ 22 56 d	Com			eF, eS, R, bM; others nr?
4054 I		13 01.0	+ 22 54 d	Com			vF, eS, R, bM, ∗10 f 0′.5
4055 I		13 01.0	+ 22 54 d	Com			eF, vS, iF, N; ?
4061 I		13 01.0	+ 39 35 d	CVn			vF, S, iF
4062 I		13 01.0	+ 39 52 d	CVn			vF, cS, iF, N
4888	−	13 01.1	− 6 04 r	Vir			pF, cS, E, psbM, ⁎ np; = 4879?
4057 I		13 01.1	+ 23 09 d	Com			vF, vS, R
4063 I		13 01.1	+ 39 15 d	CVn			F, S, iF, N
4064 I		13 01.1	+ 39 50 d	CVn			pF, S, R, bM; spir?
4058 I		13 01.2	+ 19 30 d	Com			cF, vS, R, bM
4065 I	Gx	13 01.2	+ 39 44 m	CVn	0.7	15p	vF, vS, sbM ∗
4919	Gx	13 01.3	+ 27 48 s	Com	1.4	15p	vF, vS, 2nd of 4
4059 I		13 01.3	+ 19 16 d	Com			F, vS, iF, N
4067 I		13 01.3	+ 39 56 d	CVn			vF, vS, iF, N
4068 I		13 01.3	+ 39 54 d	CVn			vF, vS, iF, N
4903	Gx	13 01.4	− 30 56 r	Cen		15p	vF, cS, R, ∗ att, p of 2
4910	−	13 01.4	+ 1 40 r	Vir			eF, vL, rr
4921	Gx	13 01.4	+ 27 53 s	Com	2.7	12.1	F, pL, 3rd of 4
4922	Gx	13 01.4	+ 29 19 s	Com	2.1	14p	pB, S, R, lbM, ∗11-12 f
4069 I		13 01.4	+ 36 05 d	CVn			vF, vS, pR, eFN
4072 I		13 01.4	+ 37 21 d	CVn			eF, S, iF, diffic
4073 I		13 01.4	+ 39 55 d	CVn			F, vS, iF, N
4905	Gx	13 01.5	− 30 52 r	Cen		15p	vF, vS, R, slbM, f of 2
4915	Gx	13 01.5	− 4 33 s	Vir	1.7	11.9	pB, S, R, bM

NGC	Type	α_{2000}	δ_{2000}	Const.	Size	Mag.	Description
		h m	° ′		′		
4923	Gx	13 01.5	+ 27 51 s	Com	1.3	13.6	vF, 4th of 4
3986 I	Gx	13 01.5	− 32 17 c	Cen	2.0		eeF, pS, R, *10 nf
843 I	Gx	13 01.6	+ 29 08 x	Com		15p	F, bMN
4077 I		13 01.6	+ 37 23 d	CVn			F, S, R, bM
4082 I		13 01.6	+ 37 20 d	CVn			F, S, iF
4083 I		13 01.6	+ 38 09 d	CVn			F, vS, iF, neb*
4085 I		13 01.6	+ 39 42 d	CVn			vF, vS, R, bM
4066 I		13 01.7	+ 19 16 d	Com			vF, vS, iF
4070 I		13 01.7	+ 19 18 d	Com			F, S, iF, N
4078 I	Gx	13 01.7	+ 36 38 u	CVn	1.0	16p	pF, vS, iF, N
4084 I		13 01.7	+ 36 58 d	CVn			pF, vS, R, bM
4086 I	Gx	13 01.7	+ 36 38 u	CVn	1.0	16p	F, pS, iF, N, *15 n
4918	Gx	13 01.8	− 4 30 r	Vir			eF, eS, R, bMN, 4915 sp 4′
4074 I		13 01.8	+ 19 00 d	Com			F, S, iF, N
4075 I		13 01.8	+ 19 58 d	Com			F, vS, bM, spir
4076 I		13 01.8	+ 23 23 d	Com			F, vS, iF, N, Cl?; *15 np
4088 I	Gx	13 01.8	+ 29 03 x	Com		15p	eF, susp; *11 or 12 f 1′.4
4090 I		13 01.8	+ 36 50 d	CVn			vF, S, iF, N
4920	Gx	13 01.9	− 11 22 r	Vir		14p	vF
4926	Gx	13 01.9	+ 27 37 s	Com	1.4	12.9	pB, S, R, glbM
4079 I		13 01.9	+ 19 15 d	Com			vF, vS, att to IC 4080
4081 I		13 01.9	+ 22 46 d	Com			F, vS, R, bM
4909	Gx	13 02.0	− 42 46 r	Cen			eF, 3 or 4 st 11-12 f
4927	Gx	13 02.0	+ 28 00 s	Com		15p	vF
4071 I	Gx	13 02.0	− 7 35 m	Vir	0.5	15p	eeF, eS, cE 10°
4080 I		13 02.0	+ 19 15 d	Com			F, vS, *14 p 0′.3, *15 sf
4087 I		13 02.0	+ 20 00 d	Com			vF, vS, bM; spir?
4094 I		13 02.0	+ 37 48 d	CVn			F, vS, iF, N
4100 I	Gx	13 02.0	+ 40 25 u	CVn	1.5	15p	pF, cS, iF, 3 wings
4925	Gx	13 02.1	− 7 42 r	Vir		14p	cF, S
4089 I		13 02.1	+ 19 30 d	Com			eF, S, iF, N, bet 2 st 14
4093 I		13 02.1	+ 29 00 d	Com			susp, close p *8
4097 I		13 02.1	+ 36 36 d	CVn			pF, vS, iF, N
4098 I		13 02.1	+ 37 59 d	CVn			F, vS, R, bM
4924	Gx	13 02.2	− 14 58 s	Vir	0.7	14p	cF, L, vlE 45°±
4954	Gx	13 02.2	+ 75 24 r	Dra		14p	vF, S, R, vgbM
4091 I		13 02.2	+ 19 54 d	Com			vF, vS, iF, N
4092 I		13 02.2	+ 19 11 d	Com			vF, S, iF, N
4101 I		13 02.2	+ 39 56 d	CVn			vF, vS, iF, N
4095 I		13 02.3	+ 19 06 d	Com			F, S, iF, N
4096 I		13 02.3	+ 24 01 d	Com			F, S, iF, N
4102 I		13 02.3	+ 36 09 d	CVn			F, vS, R, sbM *
4104 I		13 02.3	+ 38 35 d	CVn			F, S, iF, N
4105 I		13 02.3	+ 38 16 d	CVn			vF, vS, iF, neb*
4099 I		13 02.4	+ 24 05 d	Com			vF, vS, iF, N
4103 I	Gx	13 02.4	+ 38 02 m	CVn	0.7	15p	F, vS, iF, N
4108 I		13 02.5	+ 38 29 d	CVn			F, vS, iF, N
4932	Gx	13 02.6	+ 50 27 r	CVn		14p	cF, S, R, vglbM
4106 I	Gx	13 02.6	+ 28 07 x	Com		15p	eF, pS, dif
4929	Gx	13 02.7	+ 28 03 s	Com	1.5	15p	F, S, *16 close p
4107 I		13 02.7	+ 22 00 d	Com			eF, cL, dif
4112 I		13 02.7	+ 37 13 d	CVn			F, S, iF, N, diffic
4114 I		13 02.7	+ 40 06 d	CVn			vF, S, viF, N
4115 I		13 02.8	+ 37 13 d	CVn			F, pL, iF, N
4117 I		13 02.8	+ 40 32 d	CVn			vF, S, iF, neb*

NGC	Type	α_{2000}	δ_{2000}	Const.	Size	Mag.	Description
		h m	° ′		′		
4111 I	Gx	13 02.9	+ 28 04 *z*	Com		16*p*	eF
4118 I		13 02.9	+ 38 18 *d*	CVn			F, vS, R, bM
4928	Gx	13 03.0	− 8 05 *s*	Vir	1.3	13*p*	F, pS, vlE, glbM
4931	Gx	13 03.0	+ 28 02 *s*	Com	2.0	13.5	F, S
4938	Gx	13 03.0	+ 51 20 *r*	CVn		15*p*	eF, R, psbM
4109 I		13 03.0	+ 19 00 *d*	Com			vF, S, iF
4110 I		13 03.0	+ 19 14 *d*	Com			eF, vS, R, *13 p
4120 I		13 03.0	+ 37 05 *d*	CVn			cF, vS, iF, N
4113 I		13 03.1	+ 20 28 *d*	Com			vF, vS, iF, N
4123 I		13 03.1	+ 38 19 *d*	CVn			F, S, fan, Ns
4116 I		13 03.2	+ 19 05 *d*	Com			F, S, R
4934	Gx	13 03.3	+ 28 01 *r*	Com		15*p*	F, S, lE
4935	Gx	13 03.3	+ 14 23 *r*	Com		14*p*	vF, vS, R, 3 st f
844 I	Gx	13 03.3	− 30 31 *c*	Cen	1.3		vF, vS, lbM
4119 I		13 03.3	+ 19 14 *d*	Com			eF, S, E 30°; ?
4127 I	Gx	13 03.3	+ 38 04 *m*	CVn	0.4	15*p*	F, vS, iF, neb*
4121 I		13 03.4	+ 19 17 *d*	Com			vF, vS, iF N
4122 I	Gx	13 03.4	+ 20 11 *z*	Com		15*p*	cF, S, bM, spir, *15 p 20″
4131 I		13 03.4	+ 38 57 *d*	CVn			F, cS, iF, N
4124 I		13 03.5	+ 22 51 *d*	Com			vF, vS, E 110°, bM
4125 I		13 03.6	+ 18 48 *d*	Com			F, S, iF, N
4126 I		13 03.6	+ 19 19 *d*	Com			eF, vS, iF, N
4132 I		13 03.6	+ 38 23 *d*	CVn			F, vS, R, bM
4135 I	Gx	13 03.6	+ 40 15 *u*	CVn	1.0	16*p*	vF, cS, iF, N
4128 I		13 03.7	+ 20 13 *d*	Com			F, S, bM, spir
4129 I		13 03.7	+ 18 53 *d*	Com			vF, S, iF
4943	Gx	13 03.8	+ 28 05 *r*	Com		15*p*	vF, vS
4944	Gx	13 03.8	+ 28 11 *s*	Com	1.9	13*p*	F, S, R, bM, *9 nf 1′
4130 I		13 03.8	+ 19 16 *d*	Com			cF, S, R
4133 I	Gx	13 03.8	+ 27 59 *z*	Com		15*p*	vF, vS, mbM
4142 I		13 03.8	+ 38 12 *d*	CVn			vF, vS, iF, N
4143 I		13 03.8	+ 40 12 *d*	CVn			F, S, iF
4145 I		13 03.8	+ 38 17 *d*	CVn			vF, S, iF
4933	Gx	13 03.9	− 11 29 *s*	Vir	2.5	13*p*	pB, pL, iR
4144 I	Gx	13 03.9	+ 36 57 *u*	CVn	1.1	16*p*	F, cS, iF
4137 I		13 04.0	+ 22 44 *d*	Com			cF, vS, iF, N
4138 I		13 04.0	+ 20 40 *d*	Com			F, vS, iF, N, *16 inv np; D*?
4149 I	Gx	13 04.0	+ 22 16 *m*	Com	0.4	15*p*	pF, vS, iF, N, *9 p 2′, *15 sf
4151 I		13 04.0	+ 36 51 *d*	CVn			vF, cS, iF
4152 I		13 04.0	+ 38 12 *d*	CVn			F, vS, iF, N
4930	Gx	13 04.1	− 41 25 *t*	Cen	3.6		vF, R, △ 2 st 8, 9, f
4139 I		13 04.1	+ 19 18 *d*	Com			F, S, iF, N, 2 st nf
4140 I		13 04.1	+ 20 06 *d*	Com			vF, vS, R; ?
4141 I		13 04.1	+ 19 13 *d*	Com			F, S, iF, N
4939	Gx	13 04.2	− 10 20 *s*	Vir	5.8	11*p*	pB, L, R, gmbM
4941	Gx	13 04.2	− 5 33 *s*	Vir	3.7	11.1	pF, L, E, gbMBN, r
4949	Gx	13 04.2	+ 29 02 *r*	Com			eF, S
4972	−	13 04.2	+ 75 18 *r*	UMi			vF, S, iR, bM
4146 I		13 04.2	+ 19 17 *d*	Com			F, vS, R, bM
4147 I		13 04.2	+ 20 15 *d*	Com			vF, S, dif
4148 I		13 04.2	+ 19 15 *d*	Com			eF, vS, R
4150 I		13 04.2	+ 21 59 *d*	Com			vF, vS, R
4155 I		13 04.2	+ 40 01 *d*	CVn			vF, S, iF, dif
4936	Gx	13 04.3	− 30 32 *s*	Cen	1.9	11.3	pB, S, R, bM, * f 6^s
4942	Gx	13 04.3	− 7 39 *s*	Vir	1.8	14*p*	vF, S

NGC	Type	α_{2000}	δ_{2000}	Const.	Size	Mag.	Description
		h m	° ′		′		
4157 I		13 04.3	+ 38 40 d	CVn			eF, pL, iF; biN?
4134 I		13 04.4	− 11 27 d	Vir			vF, S, mbM
4136 I	?	13 04.4	− 5 58 x	Vir			eeF, cS
4153 I		13 04.4	+ 19 03 d	Com			F, S, R, bM
4158 I		13 04.4	+ 36 29 d	CVn			F, S, iF, N
4154 I		13 04.5	+ 23 34 d	Com			pF, S, R
4161 I		13 04.6	+ 39 59 d	CVn			F, vS, iF, N
4937	−	13 04.7	− 47 13 r	Cen			eeF, S, R, p of 2
4159 I		13 04.8	+ 22 15 d	Com			F, vS, iF, N
4160 I		13 04.8	+ 22 54 d	Com			vF, S, iF, dif
4940	Gx	13 04.9	− 47 16 r	Cen			F, S, R, f of 2
4948	Gx	13 04.9	− 7 57 s	Vir	1.8	14p	eeF, pS, lE, 4958 f
4952	Gx	13 05.0	+ 29 08 s	Com	1.6	14p	F, S, R, psbM *11
4156 I	?	13 05.0	− 6 16 x	Vir			eeF, cS, mE 140°
4165 I		13 05.0	+ 39 55 d	CVn			F, cS, p dif
4951	Gx	13 05.1	− 6 30 s	Vir	3.3	12p	F, pL, lE, r
4956	Gx	13 05.1	+ 35 11 r	CVn		13p	pB, cS, R, smbM
4162 I		13 05.1	+ 20 33 d	Com			vF, S, iF, N, *14 sp
4163 I		13 05.1	+ 20 46 d	Com			F, vS, bM; spir?
4957	Gx	13 05.2	+ 27 34 s	Com	1.3	12.9	F, S, R
4164 I	OC	13 05.2	+ 20 33 x	Com			vF, S, neb Cl?; *14 n
4168 I		13 05.2	+ 40 13 d	CVn			F, vS, R, bM, *13 sp
4169 I		13 05.2	+ 38 46 d	CVn			vF, S, iF, N
845 I		13 05.3	+ 12 07 d	Vir			eeF, S, R, F* nr p; decl uncertain
846 I	Gx	13 05.3	+ 23 06 x	Com		15p	vF, R, lbM, diffic
3974 I	Gx	13 05.3	− 35 20 c	Cen	2.1		eeF, pS, lE; = 4947
4945	Gx	13 05.4	− 49 28 s	Cen	20.0	9p	B, vL, vmE 39°
4946	Gx	13 05.4	− 43 36 r	Cen			B, pS, R, gpmbM, p of 2
4947	Gx	13 05.4	− 35 20 s	Cen	2.8	12p	F, pL, R, vglbM
4964	Gx	13 05.4	+ 56 18 r	UMa		13p	eF, S, lE
4166 I	Gx	13 05.4	+ 31 27 u	CVn	1.0	15p	F, S, dif
4171 I	Gx	13 05.4	+ 36 07 u	CVn	1.0	16p	F, cS, E 60°, bM
4950	Gx	13 05.5	− 43 31 r	Cen			eF, S, R, pslbM, f of 2
4973		13 05.5	+ 53 41 D	UMa			vF, S
4167 I		13 05.5	+ 21 55 d	Com			vF, vS, iF, N
4174 I		13 05.5	+ 36 24 d	CVn			vF, S, iF, N
4170 I		13 05.6	+ 21 08 d	Com			F, vS, iF, N
4172 I		13 05.6	+ 22 51 d	Com			F, S, R, bM
4959	Gx	13 05.7	+ 33 11 r	CVn		15p	eF, S, R
4967	Gx	13 05.7	+ 53 34 r	UMa		15p	vF, S, E, * att
4178 I	Gx	13 05.7	+ 36 00 u	CVn	1.2	16p	vF, cS, R, bM, dif
4958	Gx	13 05.8	− 8 01 s	Vir	4.1	10.5	vB, pS, E, bMBN
4960	Gx	13 05.8	+ 27 33 r	Com			F, S, R, N = *16
4961	Gx	13 05.8	+ 27 44 s	Com	1.7	13.5	F, S, iF
4963	Gx	13 05.8	+ 41 43 r	CVn		14p	F, vS, R, stell, vS* s
4175 I		13 05.8	+ 20 22 d	Com			vF, S, R
4179 I		13 05.8	+ 37 12 d	CVn			F, vS, iF, N, *14 p
4182 I	Gx	13 05.8	+ 37 36 s	CVn	6.7	13p	cF, vL, iF, N
4962	−	13 05.9	+ 29 04 r	Com			eF, vS
4974		13 05.9	+ 53 40 D	UMa			vF, S; = IC 847
4184 I		13 05.9	+ 38 50 d	CVn			pF, S, iF, N
4190 I	Gx	13 05.9	+ 37 37 m	CVn	5.0	13p	vF, cS, iF, diffic
847 I		13 06.0	+ 53 41 x	UMa			vF, S, R, bet 2 st; = 4974
4186 I		13 06.0	+ 36 59 d	CVn			F, S, iF, N
4187 I		13 06.0	+ 36 18 d	CVn			F, S, iF, N, D* s

NGC	Type	α_{2000}	δ_{2000}	Const.	Size	Mag.	Description
		h m	° ′		′		
4188 I		13 06.0	+ 36 20 d	CVn			vF, S, iF, cF neb p 1′
4189 I	Gx	13 06.0	+ 35 58 v	CVn	1.6		pF, pS, E 60°, bM
4953	Gx	13 06.1	− 37 34 r	Cen			vF, pS, am 3 S st
4955	Gx	13 06.1	− 29 45 r	Hya		15p	F, cS, R, gbM
4181 I		13 06.1	+ 21 30 d	Com			cF, vS, R, bM
4192 I	?	13 06.1	+ 37 36 x	CVn			vF, S, iF, v diffic
4193 I	Gx	13 06.1	+ 39 26 z	CVn		16p	pF, S, iF, N, eF∗ att np
4194 I		13 06.1	+ 38 52 d	CVn			F, S, iF, N
4977	Gx	13 06.2	+ 55 39 r	UMa		14p	cF, S
4173 I		13 06.2	− 11 34 d	Vir			neb ∗13, sp of 2
4183 I		13 06.2	+ 21 30 d	Com			F, vS, iF, N
4185 I		13 06.2	+ 21 47 d	Com			vF, S, iF, att ∗15 n
4966	Gx	13 06.3	+ 29 04 s	Com	1.2	14p	vF, vS, vlE, vglbM, ∗∗ sp
4176 I		13 06.3	− 11 33 d	Vir			pF, pS, bM, nf of 2
4177 I	Gx	13 06.3	− 13 35 m	Vir	0.8	15p	vF, vS, R, susp
4195 I		13 06.3	+ 37 02 d	CVn			vF, S, iF
4971	Gx	13 06.9	+ 28 32 s	Com	1.3	15p	F, vS, lE, ∗∗ nr n
4180 I	Gx	13 06.9	− 23 55 c	Hya	1.5		eeF, eS, R, 1st of 3
4969	Gx	13 07.0	+ 13 39 r	Vir		15p	eeF, S, R, v diffic
848 I	Gx	13 07.0	+ 16 02 m	Com	0.8	15p	eF, vS, diffic
4968	Gx	13 07.1	− 23 41 r	Hya		14p	F, pL, R, glbM
4965	Gx	13 07.2	− 28 14 s	Hya	2.6	14p	vF, vL, cE, vgbM
4970	Gx	13 07.5	− 24 02 r	Hya		14p	vF, pL, iF
4199 I		13 07.5	+ 35 51 d	CVn			F, S, iF, N
4979	Gx	13 07.6	+ 24 49 r	Com		15p	eF, pL, lE; = IC 4198?
849 I	Gx	13 07.6	− 0 56 u	Vir	1.2	14p	F, pL, R, gbM
852 I	Gx	13 07.6	+ 60 09 u	UMa	1.1	15p	vF, pS, R, B∗ p
4196 I	Gx	13 07.6	− 24 01 c	Hya	2.0		eeF, eS, R, ∗11 p 4′; 2nd of 3; = 4970
4198 I	Gx	13 07.7	+ 24 49 u	Com	1.1	15p	F, cS, R, 4979 nr
4978	Gx	13 07.8	+ 18 25 r	Com		14p	F, vS, R, sbM, stellar
850 I	Gx	13 07.8	− 0 51 v	Vir	0.8		vF, S, R
4201 I	Gx	13 07.8	+ 35 50 m	CVn	0.4	15p	F, S, iF, N
4975	Gx	13 08.0	− 5 01 v	Vir	0.5		vF, vS, R, psbM
4987	Gx	13 08.0	+ 51 56 r	CVn		14p	vF, vS, stellar
4985	Gx	13 08.1	+ 41 41 r	CVn		15p	vF, vS, R, lbM
4197 I	Gx	13 08.1	− 23 48 c	Hya	1.7		eeF, eS, R, 3rd of 3, ∗8 f 37ˢ
4998	Gx	13 08.2	+ 50 40 r	CVn		15p	vF
4203 I		13 08.3	+ 40 26 d	CVn			eF, S, dif
4983	Gx	13 08.4	+ 28 19 r	Com		15p	vF
4986	Gx	13 08.4	+ 35 12 r	CVn		14p	vF, S, R, stellar
4202 I	Gx	13 08.4	+ 24 42 u	Com	1.8	15p	F, cS, E, gbM
4204 I	Gx	13 08.4	+ 39 27 u	CVn	1.5	16p	F, cS; spir?
851 I	Gx	13 08.5	+ 21 02 m	Com	1.0	15p	vF
4976	Gx	13 08.6	− 49 30 s	Cen	4.3	10.2	B, pL, R, gmbM
5003	Gx	13 08.6	+ 43 44 A	CVn		15p	vF, pS, lbM
853 I	Gx	13 08.6	+ 52 46 v	UMa	1.3		eeF, pS, R
4205 I		13 08.7	+ 52 52 d	UMa			vF, pL, R [= IC 853?]
4981	Gx	13 08.8	− 6 47 s	Vir	2.8	12p	B, pL, R, ∗10 1′ sf
4982	Ast	13 08.8	− 10 35 F	Vir			vF, S
4191 I	Pl	13 08.8	− 67 39 s	Mus	0.1	12p	◯ , stellar
4984	Gx	13 09.0	− 15 31 s	Vir	2.8	12p	B, pL, R, psmbM
4992	Gx	13 09.0	+ 11 38 r	Vir		14p	vF, S, lE, 2 S st s
4980	Gx	13 09.2	− 28 38 s	Hya	2.2	15p	eF, cS, R
4991	Gx	13 09.3	+ 2 21 r	Vir		15p	vF, vS
5007	Gx	13 09.3	+ 62 10 r	UMa		14p	vF, vS

NGC	Type	α_{2000}	δ_{2000}	Const.	Size	Mag.	Description
		h m	° ′		′		
4989	Gx	13 09.4	− 5 25 r	Vir		14p	pB, S, R, *4 sf
4990	Gx	13 09.4	− 5 16 r	Vir		15p	vF, vS
4206 I		13 09.4	+ 39 01 d	CVn			pF, S, iF, N
4207 I		13 09.5	+ 37 49 d	CVn			vF, cS, iF
4996	Gx	13 09.6	+ 0 53 r	Vir		14p	pB, S, R, bM
4999	Gx	13 09.6	+ 1 40 s	Vir	2.6	13p	cF, pL, R, lbM, er
5001	Gx	13 09.6	+ 53 29 r	UMa		14p	pF, S, iR, gbM
4200 I	Gx	13 09.6	− 51 58 c	Cen	1.4		F, bM, mag 14.5
4208 I		13 09.6	+ 37 15 d	CVn			F, cS, bM, spir
4993	Gx	13 09.7	− 23 24 r	Hya		14p	vF, vS
4995	Gx	13 09.7	− 7 50 s	Vir	2.5	11.0	pB, pL, R, vgpmbM, *8 np
4988	Gx	13 09.8	− 43 06 r	Cen			vF, S, E, r
4994	Gx	13 09.8	− 23 23 c	Hya			pF, cS, R, slbM, am st; = 4993
5000	Gx	13 09.8	+ 28 54 s	Com	1.9	14p	cF, pS, lE
854 I	Gx	13 09.8	+ 24 35 m	Com	0.6	15p	pF, vS, R, vlbM
4997	Gx	13 10.0	− 16 30 r	Vir		13p	no description, *6.5 2′ p
4209 I	Gx	13 10.4	− 7 10 v	Vir	1.6		eF, cS, cE 100°
855 I		13 10.6	− 4 29 d	Vir			F, S, *13.5 sp
5002	Gx	13 10.7	+ 36 37 r	CVn		14p	vF, pL, E, *13 att n
856 I		13 10.7	+ 20 32 d	Com			F, E, lbM
5009	Gx	13 10.8	+ 50 05 r	CVn		15p	vF, R, bet 2 vS st
4210 I	Nb	13 10.8	+ 29 42 x	Com	1		eF, S, dif
5005	Gx	13 10.9	+ 37 03 s	CVn	5.4	9.8	vB, vL, vmE 66°, vsbMN
4211 I	*	13 10.9	+ 37 11 x	CVn			cF, S, E 315°, bM
5004	Gx	13 11.1	+ 29 38 s	Com	1.9	14p	vF, vS, vlE
5008	−	13 11.3	+ 25 23 r	Com			pF, pL, R
5014	Gx	13 11.5	+ 36 17 s	CVn	1.7	13p	pF, S, E, psbM
5012	Gx	13 11.6	+ 22 55 s	Com	2.9	13p	pF, cL, E 17°, biN, *9 f
5006	Gx	13 11.8	− 19 14 r	Vir		14p	F* close p
5016	Gx	13 12.1	+ 24 06 s	Com	1.9	14p	pB, S
5021	Gx	13 12.1	+ 46 12 r	CVn		14p	pF, cS, R, *12 nf 90″
4212 I		13 12.1	− 6 59 F	Vir			eF, cS, cE 20°
4213 I	Gx	13 12.1	+ 35 40 s	CVn	2.6	14p	F, L, vmE ns, gvlbM
5013	Gx	13 12.2	+ 3 12 r	Vir		15p	vF, vS
5023	Gx	13 12.2	+ 44 02 s	CVn	6.5	12p	pF, L, mE 20°, vlbM
5034	Gx	13 12.2	+ 70 39 r	UMi		14p	vF, vS, R
5015	Gx	13 12.4	− 4 19 s	Vir	1.9	13p	eF, eS, cE 55°
5010	Gx	13 12.5	− 15 47 r	Vir		14p	vF, R, bM, *10 np 5′
5020	Gx	13 12.6	+ 12 36 r	Vir		13p	cF, cL, vlE, lbM
5029	Gx	13 12.6	+ 47 04 r	CVn		14p	F, vS, R, gbM
5019	Gx	13 12.8	+ 4 44 r	Vir		14p	eF, vS, R, er
5025	Gx	13 12.8	+ 31 48 r	CVn		14p	vF, S, lE, *13 n
5011	Gx	13 12.9	− 43 06 s	Cen	2.0	13p	pB, cS, R, am 4 st
5017	Gx	13 12.9	− 16 46 s	Vir	1.7	13p	vF, R, bM
5024	Gb	13 12.9	+ 18 10 s	Com	12.6	7.7	!, ⊕, B, vC, iR, vvmbM, st 12; = M53
5018	Gx	13 13.0	− 19 31 s	Vir	2.6	10.8	cB, S, R, mbMpBN
5027	Gx	13 13.4	+ 6 04 r	Vir		15p	vF, S, R, pgbM
5032	Gx	13 13.4	+ 27 48 r	Com		13p	vF, pL, iR
5033	Gx	13 13.4	+ 36 36 s	CVn	10.5	10.1	vB, pL, E 167°, smbMvBN, * np
5022	Gx	13 13.5	− 19 33 s	Vir	2.5	13p	vF, pL, E 30°, gbM, f 5018, F* close p
5040	Gx	13 13.6	+ 51 16 r	CVn		15p	F, S, iR, vgmbM
5028	Gx	13 13.8	− 13 03 s	Vir	1.7	14p	vF, S, *11-12 p
857 I		13 13.8	+ 17 05 d	Com			pF, vS, R, gvlbM
5030	Gx	13 13.9	− 16 30 s	Vir	1.9	14p	vF, S
5031	Gx	13 14.1	− 16 06 r	Vir		14p	vF, stellar

NGC	Type	α_{2000}	δ_{2000}	Const.	Size	Mag.	Description
		h m	° ′		′		
5026	Gx	13 14.2	− 42 58 s	Cen	2.3	13p	pB, pL, R, gbM, *7 nf
5041	Gx	13 14.6	+ 30 42 r	Com		14p	F, S, R
5036	Gx	13 14.7	− 4 11 r	Vir			eF, vS, R, gbM, 1st of 2
5035	Gx	13 14.8	− 16 30 s	Vir	1.6	14p	F, S, R, bMN
5039	Gx	13 14.9	− 4 10 r	Vir			eF, eS, E 45°, 2nd of 2
858 I	Gx	13 14.9	+ 17 13 u	Com	1.7	15p	F, vS, R, stellar, N = 12m
5037	Gx	13 15.0	− 16 35 s	Vir	2.5	13p	cF, pS, vlE, bM
859 I	Gx	13 15.0	+ 17 13 z	Com		15p	pF, R, N = 14m
5038	Gx	13 15.1	− 15 56 r	Vir		14p	pB, E 90°, stellar
860 I	Gx	13 15.1	+ 24 36 m	Com	0.5	15p	F, vS, R, N = 12m
861 I	Gx	13 15.1	+ 34 19 u	CVn	1.1	16p	F, vS, R, sbM
5044	Gx	13 15.4	− 16 23 s	Vir	2.6	11.0	pB, pL, R, bM
5042	Gx	13 15.5	− 23 59 s	Hya	4.2	13p	F, L, R, vgvlbM, *9 p
5052	Gx	13 15.6	+ 29 39 r	Com		14p	vF
5046	Gx	13 15.8	− 16 20 s	Vir	1.2	15p	F, vS, R, stellar Nucl
5047	Gx	13 15.8	− 16 31 s	Vir	3.0	13p	vF
5050	Gx	13 15.8	+ 2 52 r	Vir		14p	F, vS, stell
5055	Gx	13 15.8	+ 42 02 s	CVn	12.3	8.6	vB, L, pmE 120°±, vsmbMBN; = M63
5049	Gx	13 16.0	− 16 24 s	Vir	2.1	12.9	cF, S
5048	Gx	13 16.1	− 28 23 r	Hya		15p	pF, R, sp of 2
5056	Gx	13 16.2	+ 30 56 r	Com		13p	cF, cS, R, sp of 2
862 I	Gx	13 16.2	+ 20 02 k	Com	0.3	15p	pB, eS, R, N = 12m
4215 I	Gx	13 16.2	+ 25 24 u	Com	1.8	15p	F, S, E 210°
5051	Gx	13 16.3	− 28 17 c	Hya	1.4		neb, nf of 2
5053	Gb	13 16.4	+ 17 42 s	Com	10.5	9.8	Cl, vF, pL, iR, vgbM, st 15
5057	Gx	13 16.5	+ 31 01 r	Com		14p	cF, cS, R, nf of 2
5043	−	13 16.7	− 60 04 r	Cen			Cl, P, E, sc st 11
5058	Gx	13 16.8	+ 12 33 r	Vir		14p	vvF
5045	−	13 17.0	− 63 25 r	Cen			Cl, vL, vRi, st 11
5054	Gx	13 17.0	− 16 38 s	Vir	5.0	11p	F, pS, iR
5059	Gx	13 17.0	+ 7 50 r	Vir		15p	eF, S, lE
4216 I	Gx	13 17.0	− 10 46 m	Vir	1.8	13p	vF, cL, cE 40°
875 I	Gx	13 17.1	+ 57 32 s	UMa	1.9	13p	eF, S, R, stellar
4218 I	Gx	13 17.1	− 2 16 u	Vir	1.4	14p	eF, eS, cE 170°; susp
863 I	Gx	13 17.2	− 17 16 c	Vir	2.4		F, S, iF, biN
864 I	Gx	13 17.2	+ 20 42 u	Com	1.1	16p	vF, pS, R, bMSN
866 I	Gx	13 17.2	+ 20 42 u	Com	1.1	16p	vF, S, R, lbM
867 I	Gx	13 17.2	+ 20 39 u	Com	1.5	15p	vF, R, lbM
4217 I	Gx	13 17.2	− 13 09 m	Vir	0.6	15p	eF, eS, R
5060	Gx	13 17.3	+ 6 02 r	Vir		14p	F, S, lE
868 I	Gx	13 17.4	+ 20 36 z	Com		15p	vF, R, lbM
869 I		13 17.5	+ 20 41 d	Com			vF, S, R, lbM
870 I		13 17.5	+ 20 36 d	Com			vF, S, R, lbM
5065	Gx	13 17.6	+ 31 04 r	Com		14p	vF, cS
865 I		13 17.6	− 5 50 d	Vir			F, vS, R, stellar
4214 I	Gx	13 17.7	− 32 06 c	Cen	2.4		pB, pS, R, *9 sf
871 I	Gx	13 17.9	+ 4 24 u	Vir	2.1	15p	pB, pS, E pf, dif
4220 I	Gx	13 17.9	− 13 36 m	Vir	0.7	14p	eF, eS, cE 130°
5061	Gx	13 18.1	− 26 50 s	Hya	2.6	12p	vB, S, R, vsmbM, *10 f
872 I		13 18.2	+ 6 21 d	Vir			eeF, pS, R, lbM
873 I	Gx	13 18.3	+ 4 28 z	Vir		15p	F, vS, R, bMN = 13.5m
5062	Gx	13 18.4	− 35 26 r	Cen			eF, vS, E, r
5063	Gx	13 18.4	− 35 20 r	Cen			eF, vS, R, * nr
5066	Gx	13 18.4	− 10 14 r	Vir		14p	vF, vS
5067	D*	13 18.4	− 10 08 F	Vir			vF, vS

NGC	Type	α_{2000}	δ_{2000}	Const.	Size	Mag.	Description
		h m	o '		'		
5074	Gx	13 18.4	+ 31 28 s	CVn	1.0	14.0	eF, vS
876 I	Gx	13 18.5	+ 4 29 m	Vir	0.6	15p	F, pL, dif
4219 I	Gx	13 18.5	− 31 38 c	Cen	1.0		eeF, pL, R, *9 sp
4221 I	Gx	13 18.5	− 14 36 m	Vir	1.1	13p	cF, S, mE 165°, cbM
5069	−	13 18.7	− 10 12 r	Vir			eF, vS; = 5066?
5071	Gx	13 18.7	+ 7 56 r	Vir		15p	eF, eS, stell
5068	Gx	13 18.9	− 21 02 s	Vir	6.9	11p	F, L, iR, bM
4223 I	Gx	13 18.9	+ 7 47 z	Vir		15p	eF, S, r
5064	Gx	13 19.0	− 47 55 s	Cen	2.8	13p	B, S, R, pslbM
5083	Gx	13 19.0	+ 39 36 r	CVn		15p	pF, pL, R
874 I	Gx	13 19.0	− 27 38 c	Hya	1.2		vF, S, R, dif
877 I		13 19.0	+ 6 05 d	Vir			eeF, pS, pB* f 13^s
878 I		13 19.0	+ 6 07 d	Vir			eeF, pL, v diffic
5072	Gx	13 19.1	− 12 32 r	Vir		14p	F, S, *14 nf
880 I		13 19.1	+ 6 07 d	Vir			eeF, pS, E ns, pB* s, 5th of 5
4224 I	Gx	13 19.1	− 2 31 m	Vir	0.8	15p	eF, S, cE 110°, susp
5070	Gx	13 19.2	− 12 29 r	Vir		15p	eeF, eS, vF* nr, 5072 nr
5075	Gx	13 19.2	+ 7 49 r	Vir		15p	vF, eS, stell
5081	Gx	13 19.2	+ 28 30 r	Com		14p	pF, S, iR, *7-8 np
5073	Gx	13 19.4	− 14 52 s	Vir	3.5	13p	vF, pL, pmE 135°±
5076	Gx	13 19.4	− 12 45 r	Vir		13p	vF, cS, R, 1st of 3
5080	Gx	13 19.4	+ 8 25 r	Vir		14p	F, S, *7 nf
5077	Gx	13 19.5	− 12 39 s	Vir	2.0	11.5	pB, S, vlE, sbM, 2nd of 3
4222 I		13 19.5	− 28 26 d	Hya			eeF, eS, R
5079	Gx	13 19.6	− 12 42 s	Vir	1.7	12p	cF, pS, vlE, 3rd of 3
5089	Gx	13 19.6	+ 30 15 s	Com	2.1	14p	pF, pL, gbM
5093	Gx	13 19.6	+ 40 23 r	CVn		15p	vF, S, R, lbM
879 I	Gx	13 19.7	− 27 26 c	Hya	1.3		eF, pL, iR, dif
5078	Gx	13 19.8	− 27 24 s	Hya	3.2	12p	pB, pS, cE, psbM, *7-8 f
5092	Gx	13 19.9	+ 23 00 r	Com		14p	pB, pL, iR, *17 s
881 I	Gx	13 20.0	+ 15 51 u	Com	1.7	15p	F, vS, R, stellar
4225 I	Gx	13 20.0	+ 31 58 u	CVn	1.1	15p	F, cS, R
5096	Gx	13 20.2	+ 33 05 r	CVn		15p	vF, cS, R, bM, sp of 2
5098	Gx	13 20.2	+ 33 09 s	CVn	0.9	15p	vF, S, bet 2 st, nf of 2
882 I	Gx	13 20.2	+ 15 54 z	Com		15p	pF, vS, R, stellar
5084	Gx	13 20.3	− 21 50 s	Vir	4.8	12p	cB, cS, vlE 90°±, bf
5085	Gx	13 20.3	− 24 26 s	Hya	3.4	12p	F, L, R, vglbM
5088	Gx	13 20.3	− 12 34 s	Vir	2.7	13p	pB, pS, R, bM
5087	Gx	13 20.4	− 20 37 s	Vir	2.3	11.0	cF, vS, iF
5103	Gx	13 20.5	+ 43 04 r	CVn		13p	pB, cS, E
4226 I		13 20.5	+ 32 00 d	CVn			F, vS, stell N
5095	Gx	13 20.6	− 2 17 r	Vir		15p	vF, iR, *11 sp
883 I	Gx	13 20.6	+ 34 08 v	CVn	1.7		F, pS, iR, bM
5094	Gx	13 20.7	− 14 05 r	Vir		14p	cF, vS, R, gbM
5082	Gx	13 20.9	− 43 42 v	Cen	3.1		vF, S, R, 1st of 4
5097	Gx	13 20.9	− 12 29 r	Vir			eF, eS, R, stell, nearly bet 2 st
5109	Gx	13 20.9	+ 57 39 s	UMa	1.9	14p	cF, S, cE
4227 I	Gx	13 20.9	+ 32 11 z	CVn		16p	F, S, gbM, r
5090	Gx	13 21.1	− 43 44 s	Cen	2.6	13p	pB, pL, R, 3rd of 4
5100	Gx	13 21.1	+ 8 58 r	Vir		15p	vF, vS, lbM
5086	Gx	13 21.2	− 43 46 r	Cen			eF, vS, R, 2nd of 4
5091	Gx	13 21.2	− 43 44 s	Cen	2.2		cF, S, vlE, 4th of 4
5099	Gx	13 21.3	− 13 04 r	Vir			eF, eS, R
5104	Gx	13 21.4	+ 0 20 r	Vir		14p	F, S, lE
5107	Gx	13 21.4	+ 38 32 s	CVn	1.9	14p	vF, S, cE 0°±

NGC	Type	α_{2000}	δ_{2000}	Const.	Size	Mag.	Description
		h m	o /		/		
5113	Gx	13 21.4	+ 57 42 r	UMa		15p	cF, S, E (perhaps = 5109)
4228 I	Gx	13 21.6	+ 25 31 z	Com		15p	F, S, r
5106	*	13 21.7	+ 8 29 r	Vir			vF, vS; decl very doubtful
5101	Gx	13 21.8	− 27 26 s	Hya	5.5	12p	cB, pS, lE, psbM *
5105	Gx	13 21.8	− 13 13 s	Vir	2.6	13p	eF, pS, lE
5112	Gx	13 21.9	+ 38 44 s	CVn	3.9	12p	F, L, iR, vglbM
5102	Gx	13 22.0	− 36 38 s	Cen	9.3	9.7	vB, pS, R, svmbM
4230 I	Gx	13 22.1	+ 26 44 u	Com	1.1	15p	F, S, R, N
5110	Gx	13 22.5	− 13 05 r	Vir			eF, pS, R, in line with 2 pB st
885 I	Gx	13 22.6	+ 21 19 m	Com	0.8	15p	vF, pS, R
4229 I		13 22.6	− 2 24 d	Vir			eF, eS, R, susp
5111	Gx	13 22.8	− 12 58 r	Vir		13p	cF, cS, iR, glbM
5115	Gx	13 22.9	+ 13 57 r	Vir		15p	eeF, S, R, * nf, D* f 24^s
5116	Gx	13 22.9	+ 26 59 s	Com	2.2	14p	pF, pS, pmE, glbM, r
5144	Gx	13 22.9	+ 70 31 s	UMi	1.4	13p	◯ ?, cB, S, R, g, slbM
884 I		13 22.9	− 12 44 d	Vir			vF, pS, R
5117	Gx	13 23.0	+ 28 19 s	CVn	2.3	14p	vF, L, △ 2 st 11 np
4234 I	Gx	13 23.1	+ 27 07 m	Com	0.6	15p	F, cS, R, N, r
5108	Gx	13 23.2	− 32 20 r	Cen		15p	eeF, p of 2
5123	Gx	13 23.2	+ 43 04 r	CVn		13p	pF, S, R, gmbM
4231 I	Gx	13 23.2	− 26 18 c	Hya	1.6		pL, vmE
4232 I	Gx	13 23.4	− 26 07 c	Hya	1.1		bM, mag 14
5118	Gx	13 23.5	+ 6 23 r	Vir		14p	vF, S, R, gbM
4236 I		13 23.6	+ 6 14 d	Vir			eeF, pS, mE, v diffic
5127	Gx	13 23.8	+ 31 34 s	CVn	2.6	14p	pB, pL, R, gmbM, ⁑ p
5119	Gx	13 23.9	− 12 17 r	Vir		14p	pB, S, lE
5125	Gx	13 23.9	+ 9 42 r	Vir		13p	pF, S, R, gbM
886 I		13 23.9	− 4 24 d	Vir			vF, vS, bMN, v diffic
4235 I		13 23.9	− 12 45 d	Vir			eF, vS, R
5114	Gx	13 24.0	− 32 21 r	Cen		14p	F, lE, psbM, f of 2
5131	Gx	13 24.0	+ 30 59 r	CVn		14p	F, pS, lE, N = *15
4233 I		13 24.0	− 30 19 d	Cen			eeF, pS, R, 4 st sf
4238 I		13 24.0	+ 30 56 d	CVn			F, vS, dif, 5131 np
5122	Gx	13 24.1	− 10 39 r	Vir		14p	vF, S, R
5129	Gx	13 24.1	+ 13 59 r	Vir		13p	pB, vS, R, gmbM, ⁑ f
887 I		13 24.2	− 12 28 d	Vir			vF, vS, nearly bet 2 st
5130	Gx	13 24.3	− 10 13 r	Vir		14p	vF, vS, gbM
5132	Gx	13 24.4	+ 14 05 r	Vir		14p	vF, r
4239 I		13 24.4	+ 30 57 d	CVn			F, cS, dif
4237 I	Gx	13 24.5	− 21 08 c	Vir	2.1		vF, S, lbM, r
4240 I		13 24.5	+ 30 59 d	CVn			F, vS, dif
4242 I		13 24.7	+ 31 01 d	CVn			F, S, R, N
5121	Gx	13 24.8	− 37 41 s	Cen	2.3	12p	cB, S, R, psmbM, r
5124	Gx	13 24.8	− 30 19 r	Cen		13p	vF, S, vlE
5136	Gx	13 24.8	+ 13 44 r	Vir		14p	eF, vS, R, psbM
5137	Gx	13 24.8	+ 14 04 r	Vir		15p	eeF, pL, v diffic
4241 I	Gx	13 24.8	+ 26 44 m	Com	0.5	15p	F, S, iF, *12.5 att
5126	Gx	13 24.9	− 30 20 r	Cen		14p	vF, vS
5133	Gx	13 24.9	− 4 02 r	Vir		15p	vF, vS, irrR, bM
5141	Gx	13 24.9	+ 36 23 s	CVn	1.7	12.8	cF, cS, R, vsmbM *, *12 sp, sp of 2
5142	Gx	13 25.0	+ 36 24 s	CVn	1.1	13.3	F, cS, R, vsmbM *, nf of 2
5143	Gx	13 25.0	+ 36 26 r	CVn		15p	vF
4244 I	Gx	13 25.0	+ 26 27 z	Com		16p	F, S, R, gbM
5145	Gx	13 25.2	+ 43 15 s	CVn	2.3	13p	pB, vS, vlE, glbM
5134	Gx	13 25.3	− 21 08 s	Vir	2.8	12p	F, pS, lE, vgbM

NGC	Type	α_{2000}	δ_{2000}	Const.	Size	Mag.	Description
		h m	o ′		′		
5128	Gx	13 25.5	− 43 01 s	Cen	18.2	7.0	!!, vB, vL, vmE 122°, bifid
5135	Gx	13 25.7	− 29 50 s	Hya	2.4	13p	pB, S, E
888 I		13 25.8	+ 13 45 d	Vir			eeF, pS, R
4243 I		13 25.9	− 27 38 d	Hya			bM, mag 14
5120	OC	13 26.1	− 63 25 o	Cen	3	13p	Cl, eRi, mC, st 12...16
5149	Gx	13 26.1	+ 35 56 r	CVn		14p	cF, pS, E, bM, sp of 2
4245 I		13 26.1	− 26 40 d	Hya			neb 0′.3 p IC 4246
4246 I		13 26.1	− 26 40 d	Hya			neb 0′.3 f IC 4245
5140	Gx	13 26.3	− 33 53 m	Cen	0.5	13p	vF, S, R, glbM
5147	Gx	13 26.3	+ 2 06 s	Vir	1.8	11.8	pB, pL, vlE, vsmbM *12
4250 I	Gx	13 26.3	+ 26 29 z	Com		15p	F, S, dif
5154	Gx	13 26.4	+ 36 00 r	CVn		15p	vF, pL, R, nf of 2
5146	Gx	13 26.5	− 12 19 r	Vir		14p	vF, vS, stellar
5148	Gx	13 26.6	+ 2 19 v	Vir	1.1		eF, S
5151	Gx	13 26.6	+ 16 52 r	Com		15p	vF, S, R, *8 nf 4′
889 I	Gx	13 26.6	+ 11 52 z	Vir		15p	F, vS, R, N = 14m
4247 I	Gx	13 26.7	− 30 22 m	Cen	1.2	15p	S, E, mag 14
5139	Gb	13 26.8	− 47 29 s	Cen	36.3	3.7	!!!, ⊕, ω Cen
4248 I		13 26.8	− 29 54 d	Hya			F, spir, *13 in M
5163	Gx	13 26.9	+ 52 45 r	UMa		15p	cF, stellar
4256 I		13 27.0	+ 31 03 d	CVn			vF, S, R
5164	Gx	13 27.2	+ 55 29 s	UMa	1.2	15p	cF, S, iR
4249 I	Gx	13 27.2	− 27 56 m	Hya	0.4	14p	vF, bM, mag 13, nr B*
5138	OC	13 27.3	− 59 01 s	Cen	8	7.6	Cl, Ri, lC, st 11
4257 I		13 27.3	+ 46 52 d	CVn			eF, S, R, dif
5157	Gx	13 27.4	+ 32 01 r	CVn		14p	F, pS, vlE, bM, p of 2
4251 I		13 27.4	− 29 28 d	Hya			vF, bM, mag 14, 5150 sf
4252 I	Gx	13 27.5	− 27 19 c	Hya	1.5		bM, mag 13.5
4253 I	Gx	13 27.5	− 27 52 c	Hya	1.4		bM; spir?
5150	Gx	13 27.6	− 29 34 s	Hya	1.4	13p	cF, S, R, pslbM, * f 2′
5158	Gx	13 27.7	+ 17 46 r	Com		14p	vF, R
4254 I		13 27.8	− 27 14 d	Hya			bM, dif, mag 14.5
5152	Gx	13 27.9	− 29 37 r	Hya		14p	vF, S, R, p of Dneb
4258 I		13 27.9	+ 28 23 d	CVn			F, S, gbMN
5153	Gx	13 28.0	− 29 37 r	Hya		14p	pF, S, f of Dneb
4255 I	Gx	13 28.0	− 27 22 m	Hya	0.3	15p	bM, mag 13.5
5169	Gx	13 28.2	+ 46 40 s	CVn	2.4	14p	vF, pS, R
5159	Gx	13 28.3	+ 2 59 r	Vir		15p	eF, S, lE
5160	D*	13 28.3	+ 5 59 r	Vir			pF (vF D* with F* close?)
5166	Gx	13 28.3	+ 32 01 r	CVn		14p	pF, pL, lE, lbM, f of 2
5173	Gx	13 28.4	+ 46 36 s	CVn	1.3	13p	F, vS, R, stellar
890 I		13 28.4	− 16 05 d	Vir			vF, sbM *13.5, r
5165	Gx	13 28.6	+ 11 23 r	Vir		14p	F, vS, R, *13 sf
5167	Gx	13 28.6	+ 12 42 r	Vir		14p	vF, sev vF st close
4263 I	Gx	13 28.6	+ 46 56 v	CVn	2.0		eF, pL, mE, mbM
5156	Gx	13 28.7	− 48 55 s	Cen	2.1	13p	pB, cS, iE, glbM, r
5162	Gx	13 29.1	+ 11 16 r	Vir		15p	vF, pL, lE, F* nr nf
4266 I		13 29.1	+ 37 37 d	CVn			F, S, R, N
5161	Gx	13 29.2	− 33 10 s	Cen	5.4	12p	pF, L, vmE, pgbM, rr
5201	Gx	13 29.2	+ 53 04 r	UMa		14p	pF, cS, R, vglbM
4268 I		13 29.2	+ 37 40 d	CVn			F, S, R, N
5171	Gx	13 29.3	+ 11 44 r	Vir		14p	pB, L
5172	Gx	13 29.3	+ 17 03 s	Com	3.3	11.9	F, pL, R, gbM
5174	Gx	13 29.3	+ 11 00 r	Vir		13p	vF, pL, D with 5175
5175	Gx	13 29.3	+ 11 00 r	Vir		13p	vF, pL, D with 5174

NGC	Type	α_{2000}	δ_{2000}	Const.	Size	Mag.	Description
		h m	o '		'		
5176	Gx	13 29.3	+ 11 47 r	Vir		15p	no description
5177	Gx	13 29.3	+ 11 48 r	Vir		15p	no description
5178	Gx	13 29.4	+ 11 37 r	Vir		15p	vF
5179	Gx	13 29.4	+ 11 45 r	Vir		15p	vF, * in centre
5180	Gx	13 29.4	+ 16 49 r	Com		14p	vF, S, R, am 3 st, *7 nf
4269 I	Gx	13 29.4	+ 37 39 m	CVn	0.3	15p	F, S, N
4271 I	Gx	13 29.4	+ 37 26 m	CVn	0.7	15p	F, S, R, gbM, r
4259 I		13 29.5	− 30 08 d	Hya			bM, mag 14
4260 I		13 29.5	− 28 17 d	Hya			bM, mag 14.5
5155	−	13 29.6	− 63 25 r	Cen			Cl, vRi
5181	Gx	13 29.6	+ 13 18 r	Vir		14p	vF, S, R
5204	Gx	13 29.6	+ 58 25 s	UMa	4.8	11.3	pB, cL, iR, gmbM, r
5170	Gx	13 29.8	− 17 58 s	Vir	8.1	12p	cF, L, mE 129°, pgbM
5187	Gx	13 29.9	+ 31 07 r	CVn		14p	vF, vS, R, glbM
5194	Gx	13 29.9	+ 47 12 s	CVn	11.0	8.4	!!!, great spiral neb M51
5205	Gx	13 29.9	+ 62 31 s	UMa	3.4	13p	vF, pS, R, bet 2 vF st
4261 I		13 29.9	− 28 02 d	Hya			bM, mag 14
5185	Gx	13 30.0	+ 13 25 r	Vir		14p	vF, S, iR
5186	Gx	13 30.0	+ 12 10 r	Vir		15p	no description
5195	Gx	13 30.0	+ 47 16 s	CVn	5.4	9.6	B, pS, lE, vgbM, inv in M51
891 I	Gx	13 30.0	+ 0 18 m	Vir	0.3	15p	F, S, R, N = 13m
5183	Gx	13 30.1	− 1 44 r	Vir		13p	F, cS, lE, gbM, p of 2
5184	Gx	13 30.2	− 1 41 r	Vir		13p	pF, pL, iR, bM, f of 2
5198	Gx	13 30.2	+ 46 40 s	CVn	2.1	13p	pF, pS, R, mbM
4262 I		13 30.3	− 28 17 d	Hya			bM, wisps extend 0'.1
4264 I	Gx	13 30.3	− 27 56 c	Hya	1.8		bM, mag 14.5
4277 I		13 30.3	+ 47 19 d	CVn			eF, S, vmE, nf M51
4265 I		13 30.4	− 25 46 d	Hya			bM, mag 14
4278 I	Gx	13 30.4	+ 47 15 v	CVn			eF, vS, R, bM, f M51
5190	Gx	13 30.6	+ 18 08 r	Com		13p	cF, S, R, bM, ** f
5199	Gx	13 30.6	+ 34 49 r	CVn		15p	vF, vS, lE
4267 I	Gx	13 30.6	− 26 16 m	Hya	1.2	15p	wisp, 0'.7 long
5182	Gx	13 30.7	− 28 08 r	Hya		13p	vF, pL, vlE, *7 nf 10'
5191	Gx	13 30.7	+ 11 12 r	Vir		15p	eF, *9 f 57ˢ
4270 I	Gx	13 30.8	− 25 20 m	Hya	0.8	14p	bM, mag 14
5192	Gx	13 30.9	− 1 47 r	Vir		15p	vF
5168	OC	13 31.2	− 60 56 s	Cen	4	9.1	Cl, vF, S, vRi, st 15
4272 I		13 31.2	− 29 58 d	Hya			bM, D(?), mag 14
5188	Gx	13 31.3	− 34 47 s	Cen		13p	F, pL, vlE, vglbM
4282 I		13 31.3	+ 47 11 d	CVn			eF, S, R, dif
5196	Gx	13 31.4	− 1 37 r	Vir		15p	vF
4273 I		13 31.4	− 28 54 d	Hya			bM, mag 13
4274 I	Pl	13 31.4	− 25 59 x	Hya			○ , stellar
5197	Gx	13 31.5	− 1 42 r	Vir		15p	vF
4284 I		13 31.5	+ 46 47 d	CVn			eF, vS, R
5200	D*	13 31.7	− 0 02 F	Vir			*12 in F neb
4275 I		13 31.7	− 29 44 d	Hya			bM, mag 12.5
892 I	Gx	13 31.8	− 2 43 u	Vir	1.3	14p	pB, iF, bM, r
893 I	Gx	13 31.8	− 2 36 u	Vir	1.2	15p	F, vS, dif
4285 I		13 31.8	+ 46 49 d	CVn			eF, vS, lE
5193	Gx	13 31.9	− 33 14 s	Cen	1.8	13p	pB, S, R, g, psbM
5202	Gx	13 32.1	− 1 42 r	Vir		15p	vF
5216	Gx	13 32.1	+ 62 42 s	UMa	3.0	14p	pB, S, vlE
894 I	Gx	13 32.1	+ 17 03 m	Com	1.0	15p	pF, vS, R, lbM
5203	Gx	13 32.2	− 8 48 r	Vir		14p	vF, cS, R, gbM, r

NGC	Type	α_{2000}	δ_{2000}	Const.	Size	Mag.	Description
		h m	° ′		′		
5207	Gx	13 32.2	+ 13 54 r	Vir		14p	F, S, cE, *11 att np
5218	Gx	13 32.2	+ 62 46 s	UMa	2.1	12.3	pB, pL, R, gbM
4276 I		13 32.2	− 28 10 d	Hya			bM, wisps 0′.2 each side
4283 I	Gx	13 32.2	+ 28 24 z	CVn		15p	F, S, R, *14 att
895 I		13 32.3	+ 35 40 d	CVn			vF, pLR, sbM, D?
5208	Gx	13 32.5	+ 7 19 r	Vir		14p	F, vS, R, psbM, p of 2
4279 I	Gx	13 32.5	− 27 08 c	Hya	1.6		bM; wisps 0′.3 l?
4280 I		13 32.5	− 24 13 d	Hya			eF, pS, R, * nf, vF* n
5212	Gx	13 32.6	+ 7 18 r	Vir		15p	eF
4281 I		13 32.6	− 27 10 d	Hya			bM, mag 13.5
5209	Gx	13 32.7	+ 7 20 r	Vir		14p	F, vS, R, stellar, f of 2
4287 I	Gx	13 32.7	+ 25 26 z	Com		15p	F, S, R, gbM; another vnr?
5214	Gx	13 32.8	+ 41 52 r	CVn		14p	vF, S, R, lbM
5210	Gx	13 32.9	+ 7 10 r	Vir		14p	F, S, R, psbMN
5211	Gx	13 33.2	− 1 02 r	Vir		14p	pB, S, R, psmbM
5225	Gx	13 33.3	+ 51 30 r	CVn		14p	cF, pS, iR, lbM
5189	Pl	13 33.5	− 65 59 s	Mus	2.6	10p	!, B, pL, cE, bM curved axis, 4 st inv
5206	Gx	13 33.7	− 48 09 r	Cen			F, pL, R, vgbM
4286 I		13 33.7	− 27 38 d	Hya			bM, mag 14
897 I	Gx	13 33.9	+ 17 43 u	Com	1.0	15p	vF, s of 5217
5217	Gx	13 34.1	+ 17 51 r	Com		14p	vF, S, R, bM
5229	Gx	13 34.1	+ 47 55 s	CVn	3.3	14p	eF, L, mE, v diffic
896 I	Gx	13 34.1	+ 4 52 u	Vir	1.0	15p	vF, vS, dif, lbM
898 I	Gx	13 34.2	+ 13 17 z	Vir		15p	vF, vS, dif
5223	Gx	13 34.4	+ 34 42 s	CVn	1.8	14p	F, cS, R, *10 p, p of 2
5228	Gx	13 34.5	+ 34 46 r	CVn		14p	vF, vS, R, f of 2
4288 I	Gx	13 34.6	− 27 19 m	Hya	0.6	15p	bM, mag 14
5213	Gx	13 34.7	+ 4 07 r	Vir		15p	vF, S, lE
5238	Gx	13 34.7	+ 51 37 s	CVn	2.0	13p	cF, pL, R, vlbM
900 I	Gx	13 34.7	+ 9 21 v	Vir	1.7		F, S, R, gbM
5221	Gx	13 34.9	+ 13 49 r	Vir		14p	vF, S, vlE, 1st of 3
5222	Gx	13 34.9	+ 13 44 r	Vir		14p	cF, S, R, bM, 2nd of 3
899 I	Gx	13 34.9	− 8 05 n	Vir	0.3	15p	F, vS, R, sbM N
4289 I	Gx	13 34.9	− 27 08 m	Hya	0.3	15p	bM, mag 14
5215	Gx	13 35.0	− 33 30 r	Cen		15p	eF, eS, * s and * p
5226	Gx	13 35.0	+ 13 54 r	Vir			eF, pS, 5221 sp
5233	Gx	13 35.1	+ 34 40 r	CVn		15p	F, S, R, vS* nr
5224	Gx	13 35.2	+ 6 28 r	Vir		15p	vF, S, *9 nf inv?
5227	Gx	13 35.3	+ 1 25 s	Vir	1.9	15p	vF, S, R
4290 I	Gx	13 35.3	− 28 01 c	Hya	2.3		annular, F, pL, stell N
4297 I	Gx	13 35.3	+ 26 26 u	Com	1.1	15p	F, S, R, dif
5262	Gx	13 35.4	+ 75 02 r	UMi		15p	eF, S
4300 I	Gx	13 35.4	+ 33 25 m	CVn	0.2	16p	F, vS, dif
5230	Gx	13 35.5	+ 13 40 s	Vir	2.2	13p	F, L, E, vgbM, 3rd of 3
4301 I	Gx	13 35.6	+ 33 22 m	CVn	0.8	15p	F, S, dif, N
4302 I	Gx	13 35.6	+ 33 29 u	CVn	1.3	16p	vF, cS, dif
901 I	Gx	13 35.7	+ 13 20 u	Vir	1.3	16p	pF, eS, R
5231	Gx	13 35.8	+ 2 59 r	Vir		14p	F, S, bM
4292 I		13 35.8	− 27 41 d	Hya			bM, mag 13.5
5220	Gx	13 35.9	− 33 28 r	Cen			vF, S, R, *10 f
5240	Gx	13 35.9	+ 35 34 r	CVn		14p	vF, pL, R, lbM
5232	Gx	13 36.0	− 8 30 r	Vir		13p	F, vS
5250	Gx	13 36.0	+ 51 14 r	UMa		14p	pB, S, R, vgbM
902 I	Gx	13 36.0	+ 49 58 u	UMa	2.2	15p	eeF, S, mE, v diffic
4293 I	Gx	13 36.0	− 25 53 c	Hya	1.8		bM, mag 13

NGC	Type	α_{2000}	δ_{2000}	Const.	Size	Mag.	Description
		h m	° '		'		
4304 I	Gx	13 36.0	+ 33 26 u	CVn	1.3	15p	pB, pS, R, gbM, r
4305 I	Gx	13 36.0	+ 33 28 m	CVn	0.3	14p	pB, cS, lE ns, bMN
5235	Gx	13 36.1	+ 6 34 r	Vir		15p	vF, pS, vlE, *9 sp
5243	Gx	13 36.2	+ 38 21 s	CVn	1.7	14p	cF, pL, E 65°, biN?
4306 I	Gx	13 36.3	+ 33 25 m	CVn	0.4	15p	F, vS, gbM, *13 nr
5239	Gx	13 36.5	+ 7 22 r	Boo		14p	vF, pL, R, er
4294 I		13 36.5	− 28 47 d	Hya			bM, mag 14
4295 I		13 36.5	− 29 06 d	Hya			S, lE, mag 14
4307 I	Gx	13 36.5	+ 27 15 m	Boo	0.5	15p	F, S, E pf, *11 p 6ˢ
5241	Gx	13 36.6	− 8 24 r	Vir		15p	pF, eS, vF* close
4296 I	Gx	13 36.6	− 33 58 s	Cen		10.6	pF, pS, R
4298 I	Gx	13 36.7	− 26 34 m	Hya	1.4	14p	bM; spiral?
4299 I	Gx	13 36.8	− 34 04 s	Cen		12.7	eeF, eS, F* att
4308 I		13 36.8	+ 32 43 d	CVn			F, S, dif, vlbM
5236	Gx	13 37.0	− 29 52 s	Hya	11.2	7.6	!! vB, vL, E 55°, esbMN, 3-br spir; = M83
4291 I		13 37.0	− 62 03 d	Cen			pS, R, bM
5242	−	13 37.1	+ 2 46 r	Vir			eF, eL
5255	Gx	13 37.3	+ 57 06 r	UMa		15p	vF, vS
4303 I	Gx	13 37.3	− 28 38 m	Hya	0.4	15p	bM, mag 13.5
5234		13 37.5	− 49 50 c	Cen	1.2		eeF, S, lE
5245	Gx	13 37.5	+ 3 53 r	Vir			vF, vS
5246	Gx	13 37.5	+ 4 05 r	Vir		15p	vF, vS
5248	Gx	13 37.5	+ 8 53 s	Boo	6.5	10.2	B, L, E 150°, psbMrN
5251	Gx	13 37.5	+ 27 25 r	Boo		14p	vF, S, vlE
5237	Gx	13 37.6	− 42 52 r	Cen			F, pL, cE, vglbM
5249	Gx	13 37.6	+ 15 58 r	Boo		14p	vF, S, R, bM
5247	Gx	13 38.1	− 17 53 s	Vir	5.4	10.5	!! cF, vL, vg, psmbMLN, 2-branched spiral
5252	Gx	13 38.3	+ 4 31 r	Vir		14p	vF, S, R, bM
5256	Gx	13 38.3	+ 48 17 s	UMa	1.4	14p	eF, vS, R, gbM
903 I	Nb	13 38.4	− 0 14 x	Vir	0.3		pB, lE ns, gbM N = 13m
4313 I		13 38.4	+ 26 45 d	Boo			F, vS, R, stell
4314 I		13 38.4	+ 26 44 d	Boo			F, vS, N, stell
5244	Gx	13 38.6	− 45 53 r	Cen			vF, S, R, vglbM, *13 att
5295	Gx	13 38.6	+ 79 27 r	Cam		15p	vF, vS, R
904 I	Gx	13 38.6	+ 0 32 u	Vir	1.1	15p	F, vS, dif
5219	Gx	13 38.7	− 45 51 c	Cen			vF, S, R, * n, nr; = 5244
4309 I		13 38.7	− 29 41 d	Hya			bM, mag 14
4310 I	Gx	13 38.9	− 25 51 c	Hya	2.3		vF, bM, wisps 0'.3 l
5259	Gx	13 39.3	+ 30 59 r	CVn		15p	vF, S, iR
907 I		13 39.5	+ 50 43 d	UMa			eF, pS, R
5254	Gx	13 39.6	− 11 30 s	Vir	3.2	13p	pB, L, pmE, glbM
5253	Gx	13 39.9	− 31 39 s	Cen	4.0	10.6	B, pL, E 45°±, psmbM
5257	Gx	13 39.9	+ 0 50 s	Vir	1.9	14p	vF, S, R, bM, p of Dneb
5258	Gx	13 40.0	+ 0 50 s	Vir	1.8	14p	F, S, iR, f of Dneb
5263	Gx	13 40.0	+ 28 24 r	CVn		14p	cF, S, mE 0°±, *9 sp
4315 I	Gx	13 40.0	− 25 28 c	Hya	1.6		wisp 1'.3 l
5265	Gx	13 40.1	+ 36 51 r	CVn		15p	F, cS, vlE, er
905 I	Gx	13 40.1	+ 23 10 m	Boo	0.8	15p	F, vS, R, lbM, stellar
906 I	Gx	13 40.1	+ 23 22 m	Boo	0.8	16p	eF, S, bM
4311 I		13 40.1	− 51 03 d	Cen			vF; spiral?
5261	Gx	13 40.3	+ 5 03 r	Vir		15p	vF, R, am pB st
4316 I	Gx	13 40.3	− 28 54 c	Hya	2.2		bM, mag 14.5
5260	Gx	13 40.4	− 23 51 s	Hya	1.9	13p	eF, pL, 3 st f in a line
4312 I	Gx	13 40.5	− 51 04 c	Cen	1.6		eeF, bM
5267	Gx	13 40.6	+ 38 46 r	CVn		14p	F, S, R, gbM, S* np

NGC	Type	α_{2000}	δ_{2000}	Const.	Size	Mag.	Description
		h m	° ′		′		
909 I	Gx	13 40.8	+ 24 29 z	Boo		15p	no descr
5283	Gx	13 41.1	+ 67 40 s	Dra	1.3	14p	F, S, stell
910 I	Gx	13 41.1	+ 23 17 m	Boo	0.5	15p	F, S, bM, r
908 I	Gx	13 41.2	− 4 19 m	Vir	0.8	15p	eF, pS, *13.5 close
911 I	Gx	13 41.4	+ 23 15 m	Boo	0.4	16p	eF, eS, R, lbM
912 I	Gx	13 41.4	+ 23 15 m	Boo	0.6	16p	eF, eS, R, lbM
913 I	Gx	13 41.5	+ 23 10 u	Boo	1.0	16p	vF, vS, R, dif
5264	Gx	13 41.6	− 29 55 s	Hya	1.8	13p	vF, pL, R, vlbM
5271	Gx	13 41.6	+ 30 07 r	CVn		15p	vF, vS, R, gvlbM
5278	Gx	13 41.6	+ 55 40 s	UMa	1.4	14p	pF, R, vS neb 40″ f, * n
5279	Gx	13 41.7	+ 55 40 s	UMa	1.3	14p	F, vS, f of 2
914 I	Gx	13 41.7	+ 23 12 m	Boo	0.6	15p	vF, vS, R, dif
4317 I		13 41.8	+ 27 06 d	Boo			F, S, R, N, r
5268	*?	13 42.1	− 13 52 F	Vir			a nebula
5273	Gx	13 42.1	+ 35 39 s	CVn	3.1	11.6	cB, pL, R, g, psmbM
5272	Gb	13 42.2	+ 28 23 s	CVn	16.2	6.4	!!, ⊕ , eB, vL, vsmbM, st 11...; = M3
5270	Gx	13 42.3	+ 4 14 r	Vir		14p	eF, S, bet 2 st
5274	Gx	13 42.3	+ 29 50 r	CVn		15p	vF, vS, R, bM
5275	Gx	13 42.3	+ 29 49 r	CVn		15p	F, S, R, gmbM
5276	Gx	13 42.4	+ 35 38 s	CVn	1.1	15p	F, S
5277	Gx	13 42.6	+ 29 57 r	CVn		15p	eF, S, R, bM
916 I	Gx	13 42.6	+ 24 28 m	Boo	0.5	15p	N = 13m
917 I		13 42.7	+ 55 38 d	UMa			S
5280	Gx	13 42.8	+ 29 51 r	CVn		15p	F, vS, R, bM
918 I		13 42.8	+ 55 36 d	UMa			vF, vS
919 I		13 42.9	+ 55 35 d	UMa			cB, R, bM
5266	Gx	13 43.0	− 48 11 s	Cen	3.2	12p	B, pL, vlE, vglbM, 3 st nr
921 I		13 43.2	+ 55 40 d	UMa			vS, R, bM
5282	Gx	13 43.3	+ 30 04 r	CVn		15p	F, S, R, gbM *14
922 I	Nb	13 43.3	+ 55 36 x	UMa	0.1		vS, R, bM
923 I		13 43.3	+ 55 37 d	UMa			vS
4318 I	Gx	13 43.3	− 28 57 m	Hya	0.8	15p	bM, mag 14
925 I		13 43.4	+ 55 36 d	UMa			vS
4319 I	Gx	13 43.4	− 29 48 c	Hya	1.6		cL, E, bM, mag 13.5
915 I		13 43.5	− 17 20 d	Vir			eF, vS, diffic
926 I		13 43.5	+ 55 39 d	UMa			vS, R, bM
928 I	Nb	13 43.7	+ 55 37 x	UMa	0.1		F, vS, R, gbM
929 I		13 43.7	+ 55 39 d	UMa			vS, R, bM
4322 I	Gx	13 43.7	+ 25 23 z	Boo		15p	F, S, R, N, r
930 I		13 43.8	+ 55 41 d	UMa			F, vS, R, gbM
931 I	Nb	13 43.8	+ 55 37 x	UMa	0.1		F, vS, R, gbM
932 I		13 43.8	+ 55 38 d	UMa			vS, R
934 I		13 44.0	+ 55 37 d	UMa			F, vS, R
935 I		13 44.0	+ 55 36 d	UMa			F, vS, R, gbM
936 I		13 44.0	+ 55 37 d	UMa			F, vS, R
4320 I	Gx	13 44.1	− 27 15 m	Hya	0.6	14p	bM, mag 13.5
4321 I	Gx	13 44.4	− 30 08 m	Cen	0.5	15p	bM, mag 15
5285	Gx	13 44.5	+ 2 05 r	Vir		15p	eF, vS, R, gvlbM
937 I		13 44.5	+ 55 39 d	UMa			vS
938 I		13 44.6	+ 55 37 d	UMa			vS
5269	−	13 44.8	− 62 55 r	Cen			Cl, P, L, iF, st 12
5287	Gx	13 44.9	+ 29 48 r	CVn		16p	F, S, irr, r?
5289	Gx	13 45.1	+ 41 30 s	CVn	1.9	14p	vF, vS, lE 90°±, sbM
4323 I		13 45.1	− 28 39 d	Hya			cS, wisp, mE
5294	Gx	13 45.2	+ 55 17 r	UMa		15p	eF, 2 st att or inv

NGC	Type	α_{2000}	δ_{2000}	Const.	Size	Mag.	Description
		h m	° ′		′		
5290	Gx	13 45.3	+ 41 43 s	CVn	3.7	13p	cB, pL, E 90° ±, bMN
933 I	Gx	13 45.3	+ 23 13 u	Boo	1.3	15p	vF, vS, R, N = 13m, stellar
4324 I	Gx	13 45.4	− 30 13 m	Cen	0.4	15p	bM, mag 13.5
5323	Gx	13 45.5	+ 76 51 r	UMi		14p	vF, pS, lE 0° ±
920 I	Gx	13 45.5	− 12 34 m	Vir	0.4	15p	F, vS, R, bM N, r
924 I		13 45.6	− 12 27 d	Vir			F, S, dif, 86 Vir nf
927 I		13 45.9	− 12 28 d	Vir			F, S, dif, 86 Vir nf
5314	Gx	13 46.2	+ 70 21 r	UMi		14p	vF, eS, stellar, eF ∗ v close
5296	Gx	13 46.3	+ 43 51 s	CVn	1.2	15p	R, bM, is sp 5297
5286	Gb	13 46.4	− 51 22 s	Cen	9.1	7.6	⊕ , vB, pL, R, rrr, st 15
5297	Gx	13 46.4	+ 43 52 s	CVn	5.6	12p	cB, L, pmE 142°, gbM
5301	Gx	13 46.4	+ 46 06 s	CVn	4.4	13p	cF, L, vmE
5281	OC	13 46.6	− 62 54 s	Cen	5	5.9	Cl, B, S, pC, iR, st 10...12
5284	−	13 46.6	− 59 11 r	Cen			Cl, L, vRi, st 7...16
5293	Gx	13 46.9	+ 16 16 s	Boo	1.9	14p	eF, vL, r
5308	Gx	13 47.0	+ 60 58 s	UMa	3.5	11.3	B, pL, mE 57°, psbMBEN
4330 I	Gx	13 47.2	− 28 20 c	Hya	1.4		pL, E, mag 13.5
5291	Gx	13 47.4	− 30 25 s	Cen	1.4		vF, R, vlbM, ∗ p
942 I	Gx	13 47.6	+ 56 36 m	UMa	0.3	15p	eF, pS, R
4325 I	Gx	13 47.6	− 29 26 m	Hya	0.8	16p	R, ○ ?, mag 14
5292	Gx	13 47.7	− 30 57 s	Cen	1.6	14p	pF, S, R, 2 st nr
939 I	Gx	13 47.7	+ 3 24 m	Vir	1.0	15p	pB, vS, bM
5303	Gx	13 47.8	+ 38 18 s	CVn	1.1	13p	pF, cS, lE, F ∗ inv
5305	Gx	13 47.9	+ 37 50 r	CVn		14p	eF, S, R
940 I	Gx	13 47.9	+ 3 27 z	Vir		15p	vF, vS, dif
945 I	Gx	13 48.0	+ 72 03 m	UMi	0.5	16p	eeF, S, R, 2 st nf
5298	Gx	13 48.2	− 30 27 s	Cen	1.4	14p	F, S, R, gbM
5300	Gx	13 48.3	+ 3 57 s	Vir	3.9	12p	vF, vL, lE, vgbM
4326 I	Gx	13 48.4	− 29 37 m	Hya	0.6	15p	R, ○ ?, mag 14
941 I	Gx	13 48.5	+ 24 00 z	Boo		15p	F, eS, gbM, r
5288	OC	13 48.7	− 64 41 s	Cir	4	12p	Cl, S, C, iR, st 14
4327 I	Gx	13 48.7	− 30 13 c	Cen	1.1		bM, mag 12.5
5302	Gx	13 48.8	− 30 31 s	Cen	1.7	12.2	F, S, R, gbM
5311	Gx	13 49.0	+ 40 00 r	CVn		13p	cF, cS, R, sbM, p of 2
5306	Gx	13 49.1	− 7 12 r	Vir		14p	vF, vS, R, r
5340	Gx	13 49.1	+ 72 39 r	UMi		15p	eF, S, R
4328 I		13 49.1	− 29 57 d	Hya			R, lbM, mag 14
4329 I	Gx	13 49.1	− 30 18 s	Cen	3.2	11.5	F, cS, bM
5322	Gx	13 49.3	+ 60 12 s	UMa	5.5	10.0	vB, pL, iR, psmbM
4331 I		13 49.4	+ 25 09 d	Boo			pF, S, R, dif
5313	Gx	13 49.7	+ 39 59 s	CVn	1.9	13p	pB, pS, vlE, glbM, f of 2
4335 I		13 49.7	+ 33 40 d	CVn			vF, stell, neb(?); ∗13 nnf 2′.5
5310	∗	13 49.8	+ 0 04 F	Vir			∗12 in F neb
5312	Gx	13 49.8	+ 33 38 r	CVn		15p	vF, R, stellar, 1st of 4
4334 I	Pl	13 49.8	+ 29 40 x	CVn	0.1		F, vS, R, N
4332 I	Gx	13 49.9	+ 25 11 m	Boo	0.8	15p	F, S, R, gbM
5304	Gx	13 50.0	− 30 35 s	Cen	1.0	15p	eF, pS, lE, vF ∗ at 160°, dist 0′.7
5309	−	13 50.0	− 15 45 r	Vir			vF, pS, R, bet ∗ and D ∗
5344	Gx	13 50.0	+ 73 58 r	UMi		15p	vF, S, R
954 I	Gx	13 50.0	+ 71 10 v	UMi	1.3		eeF, S, R, B ∗ f
5320	Gx	13 50.3	+ 41 22 s	CVn	3.5	13p	cF, pL, R, gbM
5299	Ast	13 50.4	− 59 56 A	Cen	30		Cl, vL, vRi
5318	Gx	13 50.5	+ 33 43 r	CVn		13p	F, S, R, psbM, 2nd of 4
5319	Gx	13 50.5	+ 33 43 r	CVn		15p	vF, R, n of 5318, 3rd of 4
943 I	Gx	13 50.5	+ 3 11 m	Vir	0.6	15p	pF, iF, lbM, F ∗ close

NGC	Type	α_{2000}	δ_{2000}	Const.	Size	Mag.	Description
		h m	o /		/		
5321	Gx	13 50.7	+ 33 39 r	CVn		15p	eF, pL, R, svmbM $*$, 4th of 4
4336 I	Gx	13 50.7	+ 39 42 u	CVn	1.6	15p	eF, pL, dif, lbM, r
5326	Gx	13 50.8	+ 39 34 s	CVn	2.5	13p	cF, S, vlE, sbM
5325	Gx	13 51.0	+ 38 17 r	CVn		15p	eeF, pS, R, v diffic, 2 B st nr
5307	Pl	13 51.1	− 51 12 s	Cen	0.2	12p	◯, or vF, es, Dneb
5317	−	13 51.2	+ 5 00 r	Vir			vF, vL, R, vgbM
5342	Gx	13 51.4	+ 59 53 r	UMa		14p	eF, vS
944 I	Gx	13 51.5	+ 14 05 u	Boo	1.7	15p	vS, pS, mE, 3 st f
951 I	Gx	13 51.7	+ 51 00 u	UMa	1.4	14p	eeF, pS, R, 2 st nr sp
5324	Gx	13 52.1	− 6 03 s	Vir	2.4	12p	cF, L, iR, bM
5327	Gx	13 52.1	− 2 12 r	Vir		14p	F, pS, R, 2 st p
5332	Gx	13 52.1	+ 16 59 r	Boo		14p	vF, S, R
5336	Gx	13 52.1	+ 43 15 r	CVn		13p	cF, pL, R, psbM
946 I	Gx	13 52.1	+ 14 06 u	Boo	1.0	14p	eF, vS, R, $*$ close f
5329	Gx	13 52.2	+ 2 20 r	Vir		14p	F, vS, R, psbM
949 I	Gx	13 52.2	+ 22 31 u	Boo	1.2	15p	pF
4337 I	Gx	13 52.2	+ 14 16 z	Boo		15p	eeF, pL, R, v diffic, 3rd of 4
5331	Gx	13 52.4	+ 2 06 r	Vir		14p	vF, S, E 0°, rr
5385	−	13 52.4	+ 76 11 r	UMi			Cl, P, S
948 I	Gx	13 52.4	+ 14 05 u	Boo	1.2	14p	eF, S, R
950 I	Gx	13 52.4	+ 14 29 u	Boo	1.4	15p	F, es, R, lbM
5337	Gx	13 52.5	+ 39 42 r	CVn		13p	vF, S, iR, $*$7 p
5341	Gx	13 52.6	+ 37 50 r	CVn		14p	lE, bM, sp 5351
947 I	Gx	13 52.7	+ 0 48 u	Vir	1.7	14p	pB, vS, R, sbMN = 12m
4338 I		13 52.7	− 1 08 x	Vir			eF, vL, cE ns, F$*$ nr each end; = 5334
5328	Gx	13 52.9	− 28 29 s	Hya	1.7	11.8	pB, S, R, slbM
5334	Gx	13 52.9	− 1 07 s	Vir	4.4	12p	cF, vL, R, lbM, r; = IC 4338
5330	Gx	13 53.0	− 28 28 s	Hya		15p	eeF, S, R, v diffic, nf 5328
5335	Gx	13 53.0	+ 2 50 r	Vir		14p	F, iR
5346	Gx	13 53.2	+ 39 35 r	CVn		15p	eF, pL, irrR, glbM, r?
5349	Gx	13 53.2	+ 37 54 r	CVn		15p	bM, sp 5351
5347	Gx	13 53.3	+ 33 29 s	CVn	1.9	12.6	pF, cL, R, lbM
5350	Gx	13 53.4	+ 40 22 s	CVn	3.2	11.4	cF, pL, bM, $*$7 p, 1st of 4
5338	Gx	13 53.5	+ 5 13 r	Vir		14p	vF, E pf, 4′ f D$*$
5351	Gx	13 53.5	+ 37 55 s	CVn	3.1	12.1	cF, L, lE 90°, vgbM
5353	Gx	13 53.5	+ 40 17 s	CVn	2.8	11.1	pB, S, R, 2nd of 4
5354	Gx	13 53.5	+ 40 18 s	CVn	2.3	11.5	pF, S, R, 3rd of 4
4339 I		13 53.5	+ 37 32 d	CVn			F, S, R, r
5352	Gx	13 53.6	+ 36 09 r	CVn		14p	cF, S, R, lbM, $*$ nf 90″
4340 I	Gx	13 53.6	+ 37 23 m	CVn	0.7	14p	F, S, R, gbM
4341 I		13 53.6	+ 37 32 d	CVn			F, S, R, r, $*$12 nr
952 I	Gx	13 53.7	+ 3 22 u	Vir	1.4	15p	F, E pf, F$*$ inv
5339	Gx	13 53.8	− 7 56 s	Vir	2.1	12p	vF, pS, R
5355	Gx	13 53.8	+ 40 21 r	CVn		14p	vF, pS, 4th of 4
5315	Pl	13 53.9	− 66 31 s	Cir	0.1	13p	◯, stellar = 10.5 mag
5316	OC	13 53.9	− 61 52 s	Cen	14	6.0	Cl, pL, pC, st 11
5343	Gx	13 54.0	− 7 34 r	Vir		14p	vF, S, R, lbM
5358	Gx	13 54.1	+ 40 17 r	CVn		14p	vF, vS, R, 2 vF st inv
5370	Gx	13 54.1	+ 60 41 r	UMa		14p	F, S
5348	Gx	13 54.2	+ 5 14 s	Vir	3.6	14p	vF, mE ns
5345	Gx	13 54.3	− 1 25 r	Vir		14p	F, S, R, bM
4342 I	Gx	13 54.4	+ 25 07 m	Boo	0.8	15p	F, S, R, lbM, r
5333	Gx	13 54.5	− 48 31 t	Cen	1.9		vF, vS, R, $*$8 f
5368	Gx	13 54.5	+ 54 20 s	UMa	1.1	14p	F, cS, R, stellar, $*$16 nf
5452	Gx	13 54.5	+ 78 13 s	UMi	2.3	13p	vF, pL, iR, vgvlbM

NGC	Type	α_{2000}	δ_{2000}	Const.	Size	Mag.	Description
		h m	° ′		′		
5361	Gx	13 54.7	+ 38 27 r	CVn		14p	eF, cS, E
5372	Gx	13 54.7	+ 58 41 r	UMa		13p	cF, S, E; ⚹ inv?
956 I	Gx	13 54.7	+ 20 43 z	Boo		16p	eF, vS, ∗14 n
5362	Gx	13 54.9	+ 41 19 s	CVn	2.4	13p	pB, pL, E
5356	Gx	13 55.0	+ 5 20 s	Vir	3.2	14p	F, pL, vmE 17°, r
953 I		13 55.0	− 30 21 d	Cen			vF, eS, gbM
4343 I	Gx	13 55.0	+ 25 06 m	Boo	0.7	16p	F, S, R, N, r
4344 I		13 55.2	+ 25 02 d	Boo			F, vS, N, stell
4345 I		13 55.2	+ 25 04 d	Boo			cF, vS, R, N, stell
5376	Gx	13 55.3	+ 59 30 s	UMa	2.1	13p	cB, pL, vlE, vgmbM
5379	Gx	13 55.6	+ 59 45 s	UMa	2.2	14p	pB, pS, E, mbM
5360	Gx	13 55.7	+ 4 59 s	Vir	2.0	14p	vF, vS, lE
5371	Gx	13 55.7	+ 40 28 s	CVn	4.4	10.8	pB, L, R, bMFN
955 I		13 55.7	− 30 16 d	Cen			vF, vS, gbM
4346 I		13 55.7	+ 25 09 d	Boo			F, S, R, gbMN
4348 I	Gx	13 55.7	+ 25 11 z	Boo		16p	F, S, R, N
958 I	?	13 55.8	+ 5 02 z	Vir			eeF, pS, iR
961 I	Gx	13 55.8	+ 25 50 z	Boo		15p	vF, S, dif
4349 I		13 55.8	+ 25 09 d	Boo			F, S, bM
5357	Gx	13 56.0	− 30 20 s	Cen		14p	pF, S, R, glbM, bet 2 st 10
959 I	Gx	13 56.0	+ 13 30 u	Boo	1.8	14p	eeF, S, R
960 I	Gx	13 56.0	+ 17 31 m	Boo	0.8	15p	F, pL, lbM, dif
5363	Gx	13 56.1	+ 5 15 s	Vir	4.2	10.2	B, pL, R, psbM, ∗8 nf
5389	Gx	13 56.1	+ 59 44 s	UMa	4.1	13p	pB, pL, E, mbMN
957 I		13 56.1	− 30 14 d	Cen			vF, S, gbM
5364	Gx	13 56.2	+ 5 01 s	Vir	7.1	10.4	cF, L, R, gbM
5377	Gx	13 56.3	+ 47 14 s	CVn	4.6	11.2	B, L, mE 42°, smbMN
5366	Gx	13 56.4	− 0 14 r	Vir		14p	S, R, ∗9 dist 2′
5369	Gx	13 56.8	− 5 29 r	Vir			vF, vS, R
5375	Gx	13 56.8	+ 29 10 s	CVn	3.5	12p	pB, pL, R, lbM
5378	Gx	13 56.8	+ 37 48 s	CVn	2.7	14p	pB, lE, vglbM
5380	Gx	13 56.9	+ 37 37 s	CVn	2.1	13p	F, cS, R, smbM
5391	Gx	13 57.0	+ 46 17 r	CVn		16p	F, vS, ∗ close
5415	Gx	13 57.0	+ 70 46 r	UMi		15p	eF, vS, R, 2 F st nr
5383	Gx	13 57.1	+ 41 51 s	CVn	3.5	11.4	cB, cL, R, gbM
4353 I		13 57.1	+ 37 46 d	CVn			eF, vF st & neb?, ∗8.4 nf 3′
5373	Gx	13 57.2	+ 5 16 r	Vir		15p	vF, vS, stell
4350 I	Gx	13 57.2	− 25 15 c	Hya	1.9		eeF, eS, F∗ close s
5390	−	13 57.3	+ 40 26 r	CVn			F, L, vgbM, ∗9 nf; = 5371?
962 I		13 57.3	+ 12 03 d	Boo			pF, vS, R, bM
5412	Gx	13 57.4	+ 73 36 r	UMi		14p	pF, S, R, D∗ p
963 I	Gx	13 57.4	+ 17 25 m	Boo	0.7	15p	eF, vS, R
5374	Gx	13 57.5	+ 6 06 s	Vir	1.9	14p	cF, pL, R, vgbM, ∗11 np
4347 I		13 57.6	− 40 01 d	Cen			∗9 in eeF neb
5367	Nb	13 57.7	− 39 59 s	Cen	4		!, vB, vL, vl, vsmbM ⚹
964 I	Gx	13 57.7	+ 17 31 m	Boo	0.3	15p	eF, eS, R
965 I	Gx	13 57.8	+ 17 31 m	Boo	0.8	15p	vF, vS, R, vSN
5365	Gx	13 57.9	− 43 57 s	Cen	3.1	12p	pB, cS, R, pgbM, am st
5413	Gx	13 57.9	+ 64 56 r	Dra		14p	pF, pS, R, pslbM, ∗7 p 37ˢ
4351 I	Gx	13 57.9	− 29 19 s	Hya	5.6	12p	S, lE
5384	Gx	13 58.1	+ 6 32 r	Vir		14p	F, vS, stell
4355 I	Gx	13 58.1	+ 28 25 m	CVn	0.4	15p	F, S, R, glbM
5382	Gx	13 58.2	+ 6 16 r	Vir		14p	vF, vS, r, stellar
5386	Gx	13 58.2	+ 6 21 r	Vir		13p	vF, vS, biN, r, stellar
5402	Gx	13 58.2	+ 59 49 r	UMa		14p	vF, vS, R

NGC	Type	α_{2000}	δ_{2000}	Const.	Size	Mag.	Description
		h m	° ′		′		
966 I	Gx	13 58.2	+ 5 24 u	Vir	1.6	15p	F, S, R, gbM, r
5387	Gx	13 58.4	+ 6 04 s	Vir	1.8	15p	vF ray, 2′ l
967 I	Gx	13 58.4	+ 14 27 m	Boo	0.7	15p	pF, vS, R, *14 nr
4352 I	Gx	13 58.4	− 34 31 c	Cen	1.9		sev eF st in eeF neb, 2 st 8 n
5394	Gx	13 58.6	+ 37 27 s	CVn	1.9	13.0	cF, S, np of 2
5395	Gx	13 58.6	+ 37 25 s	CVn	3.1	11.6	cF, cL, E 15°, lbM, sf of 2
4354 I		13 58.6	− 12 35 d	Vir			eF, vS, eE 110°
4356 I		13 58.7	+ 37 30 d	CVn			F, vS, stell N = *15
5388	−	13 58.9	− 14 09 r	Vir			F, S, R, vgbM
5396	−	13 59.0	+ 29 07 r	CVn			vF, S, iR, sbM *
5392		13 59.4	− 3 12 d	Vir			vF, cS, R, gbM
5399	Gx	13 59.5	+ 34 47 r	CVn		14p	eF, vS, pmE 90°
5401	Gx	13 59.7	+ 36 15 r	CVn		14p	cF, cS, E
5359	OC	13 59.8	− 70 24 A	Cir			Cl, vL, lRi, lC, st 11
5403	Gx	13 59.9	+ 38 11 s	CVn	3.2	15p	vF, pL, iF
5406	Gx	14 00.3	+ 38 55 s	CVn	2.1	13p	F, pS, R, lbM
5393	Gx	14 00.5	− 28 50 r	Hya		15p	vF, S, R, glbM
5381	OC	14 00.6	− 59 34 s	Cen	14		Cl, Ri, vC, pL, st 11...12
5400	Gx	14 00.6	− 2 51 r	Vir		14p	vF, cS
968 I		14 00.6	− 2 57 d	Vir			vF, vS, stellar
5410	Gx	14 00.7	+ 41 00 r	CVn		14p	pF, pS, bM
5422	Gx	14 00.7	+ 55 10 s	UMa	3.9	13p	pB, S, pmE 45°±, vsvmbMN
4357 I	Gx	14 00.7	+ 31 54 u	CVn	1.2	15p	F, S, R, gvlbM
5425	Gx	14 00.8	+ 48 27 r	UMa		14p	eF, S, mE 290°, B* 4′ n
5430	Gx	14 00.8	+ 59 20 s	UMa	2.4	13p	pB, S, iE, mbM
5407	Gx	14 00.9	+ 39 09 r	CVn		14p	vF, vS, R, bM, in Cl
5404	D*	14 01.1	+ 0 05 F	Vir			*12 in neb
5405	Gx	14 01.1	+ 7 43 r	Boo		14p	vF, iF, bM
5397	Gx	14 01.2	− 33 57 r	Cen			vF, S, R, gbM
5398	Gx	14 01.4	− 33 04 s	Cen	2.9	13p	pB, pL, R, vgbM
5409	Gx	14 01.7	+ 9 30 r	Boo		14p	eF, R, 5416 f 26^s
5421	Gx	14 01.7	+ 33 50 r	CVn		14p	F, irrR, 2 vF st inv
969 I		14 01.8	− 4 11 d	Vir			vF, vS, R, N = 14m
5411	Gx	14 01.9	+ 8 57 r	Boo		14p	vvF
5414	Gx	14 02.0	+ 9 57 r	Boo		14p	S, F* in centre, *10-11 nf
5439	Gx	14 02.0	+ 46 19 r	CVn		14p	vF, pL, cE, bet 2 st
5416	Gx	14 02.1	+ 9 27 r	Boo		13p	eF, vS, E, r
5417	Gx	14 02.1	+ 8 03 r	Boo		14p	cF, S, R, psbM, * p
5418	Gx	14 02.2	+ 7 42 r	Boo		14p	vF, R, bM
5443	Gx	14 02.2	+ 55 49 s	UMa	2.8	13p	pF, L, E
5433	Gx	14 02.5	+ 32 31 s	CVn	1.7	14p	vF, cS, lE 0°, bM
5447	Kt	14 02.5	+ 54 17 r	UMa			pB, S, R, gmbM, conn with M101
5449	Kt	14 02.5	+ 54 19 A	UMa			vF, pL, gvlbM, conn with M101
5450	Kt	14 02.5	+ 54 14 A	UMa			F, pS, iR, glbM, conn with M101
970 I	Gx	14 02.5	+ 14 33 u	Boo	1.2	15p	pB, vS, R
5423	Gx	14 02.7	+ 9 21 r	Boo		14p	vF, R, * in centre
5451	Kt	14 02.7	+ 54 22 A	UMa			vF, pL, iR, vlbM, conn with M101
5448	Gx	14 02.8	+ 49 10 s	UMa	4.2	12p	pB, cL, vmE 90°±, smbMN
5469	Gx	14 02.8	+ 9 20 r	Boo		15p	vF, pS, R
5424	Gx	14 02.9	+ 9 26 r	Boo		14p	vF, R, * in centre
5420	Gx	14 03.0	− 14 37 d	Vir		13p	F, pS, mE, com
5431	Gx	14 03.0	+ 9 23 r	Boo		15p	vF
5440	Gx	14 03.0	+ 34 46 s	CVn	3.3	13p	pF, cS, lE, bM, *11 sp
5453	Kt	14 03.0	+ 54 18 A	UMa			F, pL, lE, vlbM, conn w M101
5455	Kt	14 03.0	+ 54 12 r	UMa			pB, pS, R, psbM, conn w M101

NGC	Type	α_{2000}	δ_{2000}	Const.	Size	Mag.	Description
		h m	o /		/		
5441	Gx	14 03.2	+ 34 41 r	CVn		15p	vF, S
5457	Gx	14 03.2	+ 54 21 s	UMa	26.9	7.7	pB, vL, iR, g, vsmbMBSN; = M101
5458	–	14 03.2	+ 54 16 r	UMa			vF, pL, R, vlbM, conn w M101
5408	Pl	14 03.3	– 41 23 s	Cen			eF, E bet 2 vS st
5434	Gx	14 03.3	+ 9 27 r	Boo		14p	vF, L
5426	Gx	14 03.4	– 6 04 s	Vir	2.9	12.2	pF, cL, R, gmbM, sp of 2
5427	Gx	14 03.4	– 6 02 s	Vir	2.5	11.4	pF, cL, R, nf of 2
5428	*	14 03.4	– 6 02 F	Vir			1st of 2 nr 5427
5429	*	14 03.4	– 6 02 F	Vir			2nd of 2, in line with 5426-7
5444	Gx	14 03.4	+ 35 08 s	CVn	2.7	13p	pB, pL, ivlE, vsmbM
5445	Gx	14 03.5	+ 35 02 r	CVn		14p	F, *13 p
4358 I	Gx	14 03.5	– 10 09 m	Vir	1.2	15p	pL, mE 120°; spir neb f (IC 971)
5432	*	14 03.6	– 5 57 F	Vir			vF
5436	Gx	14 03.6	+ 9 35 r	Boo		15p	1st of 3 vF in a line, 2'-3' dist
5419	Gx	14 03.7	– 33 59 s	Cen		12p	pB, pL, R, gpmbM
5437	Gx	14 03.7	+ 9 31 r	Boo		15p	2nd of 3
5438	Gx	14 03.7	+ 9 37 r	Boo		14p	3rd of 3, nf *8.6
5461	Kt	14 03.7	+ 54 19 r	UMa			B, pS, R, psbM, conn with M101
5435	*	14 03.8	– 5 54 F	Vir			vF, *10-11 close f
971 I		14 03.8	– 10 08 D	Vir			fine spiral, pL, mbM
4365 I	Gx	14 03.8	+ 9 31 m	Boo	0.8	15p	*13 in vF, S neb (perhaps 5438)
5462	Kt	14 03.9	+ 54 22 r	UMa			pB, pL, iR, gbM, conn with M101
4360 I		14 04.1	– 11 24 d	Vir			eF, eS, E 35°
4361 I	Gx	14 04.1	– 9 46 m	Vir	0.6	15p	eF, vS, cE 150°
4369 I		14 04.1	+ 33 19 d	CVn			vF, S, R, dif
4363 I		14 04.2	– 9 38 d	Vir			eF, vS, cE 150°
4370 I		14 04.2	+ 33 21 d	CVn			F, S, iF, gbM, *14 nr
4371 I		14 04.2	+ 33 18 d	CVn			F, S, R, vlbM
4364 I	Gx	14 04.3	– 10 00 m	Vir	0.6	15p	eF, vS, R
972 I	Pl	14 04.4	– 17 15 s	Vir	0.7	15p	F, vS, R, r
5471	Kt	14 04.6	+ 54 24 r	UMa			F, S, R, *12-13 p
5454	Gx	14 04.7	+ 14 23 r	Boo		14p	pF, S
5473	Gx	14 04.7	+ 54 54 s	UMa	2.6	11.4	pB, S, R, gbM
4368 I		14 04.7	– 9 57 d	Vir			F, S, R, bM
5442	Gx	14 04.9	– 9 43 r	Vir		14p	vF, vS, iR
5456	Gx	14 04.9	+ 11 53 r	Boo		14p	F, pS
4333 I	Gx	14 05.	– 84 16 c	Oct	1.7		eF, vS, eE 40°, susp
5474	Gx	14 05.0	+ 53 40 s	UMa	4.5	10.9	pB, L, bM
5446	Gx	14 05.1	+ 9 37 r	Boo			eF, eS
5475	Gx	14 05.2	+ 55 45 s	UMa	2.2	13p	pB, S, pmE, bM
4366 I	Gx	14 05.2	– 33 46 c	Cen	1.8		vF, vS, cE 170°
5459		14 05.3	+ 13 08 D	Boo			F, S, lE, pB* sp
4359 I		14 05.4	– 45 16 d	Cen			eF, vS, E 170°, bet 2 F st
4362 I	Gx	14 05.4	– 41 49 c	Cen	1.7		vF, S, vE 175°
5466	Gb	14 05.5	+ 28 32 s	Boo	11.0	9.1	Cl, L, vRi, vmC, st 11...
5477	Gx	14 05.6	+ 54 28 s	UMa	1.7	13.8	vF, pL
4367 I	Gx	14 05.6	– 39 12 c	Cen	1.8		eeF, pS, R, bet 2 st
4372 I		14 05.7	– 10 53 d	Vir			eF, eS, E 75°
4373 I	Gx	14 05.7	+ 25 14 z	Boo		15p	F, S, R, N, r
5479	Gx	14 05.9	+ 65 41 r	UMi		15p	eF, vS, R, nearly bet 2 st
5463	Gx	14 06.1	+ 9 22 r	Boo		14p	eF, S, lE
5465	Gx	14 06.4	– 5 32 h	Vir	0.8	15p	eF, vS, sp 5468
5470	Gx	14 06.4	+ 6 02 r	Vir		14p	F, mE, vglbM
5480	Gx	14 06.4	+ 50 43 s	UMa	1.8	13p	F, pS, vgbM, np of 2
5467	*	14 06.5	– 5 29 r	Vir			eF, vS, sp 5468

NGC	Type	α_{2000}	δ_{2000}	Const.	Size	Mag.	Description
		h m	o ′		′		
973 I	*	14 06.5	− 5 29 F	Vir			stellar 13.5m
5468	Gx	14 06.6	− 5 27 s	Vir	2.5	12p	F, L, R, vgbM, *9 sf 4′
974 I	*	14 06.6	− 5 31 F	Vir			neb object 1′.8 sff of 5465
5481	Gx	14 06.7	+ 50 43 s	Boo	1.7	13p	F, vS, smbM, stellar, sf of 2
5484	Gx	14 06.8	+ 55 02 s	UMa		16p	vF, S, R, 4′ from 5485
5472	Gx	14 06.9	− 5 28 s	Vir	1.4	15p	pF, vS, bet 2 vF st
5464	Gx	14 07.1	− 30 01 s	Hya	1.0	13p	pF, S, R, pslbM
5485	Gx	14 07.2	+ 55 00 s	UMa	2.6	11.5	cB, R, vgbM, f of 2
975 I		14 07.2	+ 15 21 d	Boo			vF, vS, R
5486	Gx	14 07.4	+ 55 06 s	UMa	1.7	14p	F, pL
4374 I	Gx	14 07.5	− 27 01 c	Hya	1.6		eeF, pS, R
5460	OC	14 07.6	− 48 19 s	Cen	25	5.6	Cl, vL, vlC, st 8...
5488	Gx	14 08.0	− 33 18 A	Cen			F, R, *8 s nr; = IC 4375
4375 I	Gx	14 08.1	− 33 19 c	Cen	3.0		eF, eS, ee 15°, stell N, * sp; = 5488
5476	Gx	14 08.2	− 6 05 r	Vir		14p	F, pS, iR
5478	Gx	14 08.2	− 1 42 r	Vir		14p	vF, vS
5482	Gx	14 08.4	+ 8 56 r	Boo		14p	eF, S
976 I	Gx	14 08.7	− 1 09 u	Vir	1.5	14p	eF, vS, R, eF, * att s
977 I	Gx	14 08.7	− 3 00 k	Vir	0.6	15p	vF, S, dif
978 I	Gx	14 09.0	− 2 58 k	Vir	0.8	15p	vF, S, R, bMN
979 I		14 09.3	+ 14 51 d	Boo			eeF, pS, R, v diffic
5503	Gx	14 09.4	+ 60 25 r	UMa		16p	eeF, vS, R, v diffic, 2 st nr
5502	−	14 09.6	+ 60 26 r	UMa			eeF, pS, R, v diffic, bet 2 st
5487	Gx	14 09.7	+ 8 05 r	Boo		14p	eF (place uncertain)
5547	Gx	14 09.8	+ 78 36 r	UMi		14p	eF, vS, E 0°±
5490	Gx	14 10.0	+ 17 33 s	Boo	2.6	13p	cF, cS, R, sbMF $^{*}_{*}$
982 I	Gx	14 10.0	+ 17 42 v	Boo	1.5		vS, R, N = 11m
4380 I	Gx	14 10.0	+ 37 33 m	Boo	0.5	14p	F, S, R, dif
983 I	Gx	14 10.1	+ 17 44 v	Boo	5.5		eS, R, N = 11m
984 I	Gx	14 10.1	+ 18 22 u	Boo	1.9	14p	pB, S, gbM
5500	Gx	14 10.2	+ 48 33 r	Boo		14p	cF, cS, iR
5483	Gx	14 10.4	− 43 19 s	Cen	3.1	12p	pF, vL, R, vgbM
5497	Gx	14 10.4	+ 38 53 r	Boo		15p	eF, S, R, lbM
980 I		14 10.4	− 7 21 d	Vir			F, S, R, N = 13m, r
5492	Gx	14 10.5	+ 19 37 s	Boo	1.8	14p	pB, vS, E
981 I	Gx	14 10.5	− 4 10 n	Vir	0.6	15p	F, S, gbM
4376 I	*.*	14 10.8	− 30 49 x	Cen			F, S, eE 40°
4404 I		14 10.8	+ 78 38 d	UMi			eF
5491	Gx	14 10.9	+ 6 22 r	Vir		14p	pB, pS, R, gbM, r
5499	Gx	14 10.9	+ 35 54 r	Boo		14p	F, S, R, gbM, r?
5498	Gx	14 11.0	+ 25 42 r	Boo		15p	F, S, R, lbM, r?
4381 I		14 11.0	+ 25 29 d	Boo			F, cS, R, biN
4382 I		14 11.1	+ 25 30 d	Boo			F, S, R, gbM, 5498 n 11′
986 I		14 11.4	+ 1 20 d	Vir			F, S, N = 13.5, r
5493	Gx	14 11.5	− 5 03 s	Vir	2.0	11.5	pB, vS, R, psmbM *, *18 inv
985 I	Gx	14 11.5	− 3 14 m	Vir	0.5	15p	eF, eS
987 I	Gx	14 11.5	+ 19 11 m	Boo	1.2	15p	eF, vS, stellar, v diffic
5496	Gx	14 11.6	− 1 09 s	Vir	4.4	13p	pB, vL, E ns
4384 I	Gx	14 11.9	+ 27 07 u	Boo	1.1	15p	F, S, R, bMN, r
5489	Gx	14 12.0	− 46 05 t	Cen	1.4		vF, S, R, bM
4378 I		14 12.1	− 34 16 d	Cen			vF, vS, E 150°
4379 I		14 12.1	− 34 17 d	Cen			vF, vS, E 90°
4383 I		14 12.2	+ 15 51 d	Boo			1′.7 np 5504 (no descr)
5504	Gx	14 12.3	+ 15 50 r	Boo		14p	vF, vlE, vlbM
5509	Gx	14 12.3	+ 24 39 r	Boo			vF, S, R, stellar Nucl

NGC	Type	α_{2000}	δ_{2000}	Const.	Size	Mag.	Description
		h m	° ′		′		
5520	Gx	14 12.3	+ 50 22 r	Boo		13p	F, S, lE, stellar
5494	Gx	14 12.4	− 30 39 s	Cen	2.2	13p	pB, L, R, gbM, rr
5495	Gx	14 12.4	− 27 07 r	Hya		13p	vF, S, R, bM, *10 nf
5501	Gx	14 12.4	+ 1 16 r	Vir		15p	vF, S, rr
5508	Gx	14 12.4	+ 24 39 r	Boo		15p	eF, eS, R, lbM
5505	Gx	14 12.5	+ 13 18 r	Boo		14p	vF, pS, bet * and D*
5515	Gx	14 12.5	+ 39 18 r	Boo		13p	vF, S, vlE
5512	Gx	14 12.6	+ 30 51 r	Boo		15p	vF, vS, R, sbMN, r?
5517	Gx	14 13.0	+ 35 42 r	Boo		15p	F, eS, R, bMN
5511	Gx	14 13.1	+ 8 37 r	Boo		15p	vF, S, *10 p
5506	Gx	14 13.2	− 3 13 s	Vir	2.9	13p	pB, L, E 20°±, lbM
5513	Gx	14 13.2	+ 20 26 r	Boo		14p	pB, pL, iR
5507	Gx	14 13.3	− 3 09 s	Vir	2.0	13p	cF, S, R, stellar
5510	Gx	14 13.6	− 17 59 r	Vir		14p	vF, S, R, gbM
5514	Gx	14 13.6	+ 7 40 r	Boo		14p	F, pS, R, lbM, *16 nf
5518	Gx	14 13.9	+ 20 51 r	Boo		15p	F, vS, R, gbM
5526	Gx	14 13.9	+ 57 46 r	UMa		14p	vF, S, E, r
5519		14 14.4	+ 7 26 D	Boo			vF, pL, *10 p
5524	Gx	14 14.5	+ 36 24 r	Boo		15p	vF
988 I	Gx	14 14.5	+ 3 11 z	Vir		15p	F, vS, R
4385 I		14 14.7	− 42 18 d	Cen			vS, R, lbM
5522	Gx	14 14.8	+ 15 09 r	Boo		14p	vF, vS, E
5523	Gx	14 14.8	+ 25 19 s	Boo	4.5	13p	F, pL, pmE 90°, *10 np
5540	Gx	14 14.8	+ 60 00 r	UMa		15p	eF, vS, R, stellar
989 I	Gx	14 14.8	+ 3 07 u	Vir	1.3	14p	F, vS, R, bM
4386 I	Gx	14 15.0	− 43 58 c	Cen	3.1		F, vS, R
4387 I	Gx	14 15.0	− 44 00 c	Cen	1.3		F, vS, R
5527	Gx	14 15.4	+ 36 11 r	Boo		16p	eeF
5521	Gx	14 15.5	+ 4 24 r	Vir		14p	F, S, R, bM
5525	Gx	14 15.6	+ 14 17 r	Boo		14p	pF, pS, iR, bM
5529	Gx	14 15.6	+ 36 13 s	Boo	5.9	13p	cF, pL, vmE 110°, vgvmbM
990 I	Gx	14 15.7	+ 39 47 m	Boo	0.6	15p	vF, S, dif
5516	Gx	14 15.8	− 48 07 r	Cen			pF, S, R, psbM, S$_*^*$ nf
4392 I		14 15.9	− 13 07 d	Vir			eF, vS, mE 80°, F* sf, susp
4388 I	Gx	14 16.0	− 31 46 m	Cen	0.8	15p	vF, vS, R, sbM
5533	Gx	14 16.1	+ 35 21 s	Boo	3.2	11.8	pB, R, vsmbM, 2 or 3 st inv
5528	Gx	14 16.2	+ 8 17 r	Boo		15p	eeF, pS, R, 2 vF st nr
5536	Gx	14 16.3	+ 39 30 r	Boo		14p	cF, vS, R, sp of 2
4391 I	Gx	14 16.3	− 31 41 m	Cen	0.5	15p	vF, vS, R
5541	Gx	14 16.4	+ 39 35 r	Boo		13p	cF, S, R, gbM, nf of 2
4394 I		14 16.5	+ 39 42 d	Boo			eF, S, R
995 I	Gx	14 16.6	+ 57 48 u	UMa	1.4	14p	eeF, S, lE, v diffic
5531	Gx	14 16.7	+ 10 53 r	Boo		14p	F, S, R, 5532 f 10^s
4389 I		14 16.8	− 40 33 d	Cen			vF, vS, R, dif
5532	Gx	14 16.9	+ 10 48 s	Boo	1.9	12.0	vF, vS, R, gbM, r
5544	Gx	14 17.0	+ 36 34 s	Boo	1.1	13p	F, pS, E 80°, Dneb or biN with 5545
996 I		14 17.0	+ 57 39 d	UMa			eeF, S, mE, v diffic
4377 I	Gx	14 17.0	− 75 39 c	Aps	2.6		eeF, vS, mE 180°, vmbM
4390 I	Gx	14 17.0	− 44 59 c	Cen	1.7		eF, vS, mE 5°, stell N
5545	Gx	14 17.1	+ 36 35 s	Boo	1.3	13p	E, lbM, Dneb or biN with 5544
4395 I	Gx	14 17.2	+ 26 51 u	Boo	1.5	15p	F, S, R, N, stell
5561	Gx	14 17.4	+ 58 44 r	UMa		15p	eF, pS, R, F* close p
5537	Gx	14 17.5	+ 7 03 r	Vir		15p	eeF, S, lE
4396 I		14 17.5	+ 28 48 d	Boo			F, S, dif
5535	Gx	14 17.6	+ 8 11 r	Boo		15p	eF, S, iR

NGC	Type	α_{2000}	δ_{2000}	Const.	Size	Mag.	Description
		h m	° ′		′		
5538	Gx	14 17.6	+ 7 29 r	Boo		15p	eF, S, E
5539	Gx	14 17.6	+ 8 11 r	Boo		15p	F, pL, iF, gbM
5534	Gx	14 17.7	− 7 25 s	Vir	1.4	14p	pF, st inv, *12 np
991 I	Gx	14 17.7	− 13 53 m	Vir	1.4	13p	F, S
5542	Gx	14 17.8	+ 7 33 r	Boo		15p	vF, vS
4393 I	Gx	14 17.8	− 31 21 c	Cen	2.3		cF, S, eE 75°
4397 I	Gx	14 17.9	+ 26 25 u	Boo	1.1	14p	F, cS, R, bM, r
5543	Gx	14 18.0	+ 7 39 r	Boo		15p	eF, vS
5548	Gx	14 18.0	+ 25 08 s	Boo	1.9	12.5	cF, pS, R, vsvmbM *
5546	Gx	14 18.1	+ 7 34 r	Boo		14p	pB, cS, gbM
993 I		14 18.1	+ 11 16 d	Boo			vF, iF, diffic
4398 I	Gx	14 18.2	+ 28 51 m	Boo	0.5	15p	F, S, R, gbM, r
992 I	Gx	14 18.3	+ 0 53 u	Vir	1.6	15p	F, pS, R, *10.5 nf
994 I	Gx	14 18.3	+ 11 11 u	Boo	1.4	15p	pB, vS, R
1005 I		14 18.3	+ 71 36 d	UMi			F, S, R, bM
4399 I	Gx	14 18.3	+ 26 23 u	Boo	1.2	15p	F, cS, R, N, r
4403 I	Gx	14 18.3	+ 31 39 u	Boo	1.4	15p	F, S, R, gbM, *14 n
5550	Gx	14 18.4	+ 12 52 r	Boo		14p	vF, cS, pmE
5553	Gx	14 18.4	+ 26 17 r	Boo		15p	vF, S, lE
5557	Gx	14 18.4	+ 36 30 s	Boo	2.4	11.1	cB, S, R, vsbM *
5530	Gx	14 18.5	− 43 24 s	Lup	4.1	12p	!, vF, pmE, esvmbM *12
5549	Gx	14 18.5	+ 7 22 r	Vir		14p	vF, vS, R
5551	Gx	14 18.9	+ 5 26 r	Vir		15p	3 st in neby
5552	Gx	14 18.9	+ 7 02 r	Vir		15p	vF, S
5555	Gx	14 19.0	− 19 08 r	Vir		15p	vF, S, iR, gbMN
5559	Gx	14 19.1	+ 24 48 r	Boo		15p	vF, S, vlE, bM
5554	Gx	14 19.2	+ 7 01 r	Vir		15p	eF, S
5567	Gx	14 19.3	+ 35 08 r	Boo		15p	pF, R
5568	Gx	14 19.4	+ 35 05 r	Boo		15p	vF, S, v dif
5570	Gx	14 19.4	+ 7 26 r	Boo			F, S, iR
5607	Gx	14 19.4	+ 71 35 s	UMi	1.1	14p	pF, cS, iR, bM, er
4401 I	Gx	14 19.4	− 4 31 m	Vir	1.0	15p	vF, S, mE 200°, nr IC 997
4405 I	Gx	14 19.4	+ 26 16 m	Boo	0.9	15p	F, S, dif
5572	Gx	14 19.5	+ 36 08 r	Boo		15p	eF, vS, bM
5571	−	14 19.6	+ 35 09 r	Boo			S Cl of F st in neb; = 5579?
999 I	Gx	14 19.6	+ 17 52 u	Boo	0.8	14p	F, vS, R, N = 14m, stellar
5558	−	14 19.7	+ 7 02 r	Vir			eF, S, lE, np of 2
1000 I	Gx	14 19.7	+ 17 51 u	Boo	0.8	14p	F, vS, R, N = 14m, stellar
5585	Gx	14 19.8	+ 56 44 s	UMa	5.5	10.9	pF, L, iR, vgmbM, r
997 I	Gx	14 19.9	− 4 27 m	Vir	1.0	14p	pF, S, R, * n
5560	Gx	14 20.1	+ 4 00 s	Vir	3.9	12.4	pF, cL, E, gbM
5562	Gx	14 20.1	+ 10 15 r	Boo		14p	vF, S, vF* 3sf
5563	Gx	14 20.1	+ 7 03 r	Vir		15p	eF, S, lE
5564	−	14 20.2	+ 7 01 r	Vir			eF, S; probably = 5563
5565	−	14 20.2	+ 7 00 r	Vir			eF, S, v diffic; probably = 5563
998 I		14 20.2	− 4 28 d	Vir			eeF, S, R, v diffic
5566	Gx	14 20.3	+ 3 56 s	Vir	6.5	10.5	B, pL, R, psbM, r, *12 f 1′.5
5569	Gx	14 20.5	+ 3 59 s	Vir	1.9	15p	eF, pL, R
5579	Gx	14 20.5	+ 35 11 r	Boo		14p	vF, cL, p of 2
5556	Gx	14 20.6	− 29 15 s	Hya	3.1	12p	eF, L, S* inv
5573	Gx	14 20.6	+ 6 54 r	Vir		15p	vF, S, lE
5580	?	14 20.7	+ 35 13 A	Boo			pB, S, f of 2
5582	Gx	14 20.7	+ 39 42 r	Boo		13p	pB, pS, R, bMFN, * sp
1001 I		14 20.7	+ 5 08 d	Vir			eF, S, dif
1002 I		14 20.7	+ 5 11 d	Vir			eF, vS, lbM

NGC	Type	α_{2000}	δ_{2000}		Const.	Size	Mag.	Description
		h m	° ′			′		
5640	Gx	14 20.8	+ 80 06	r	Cam		15p	eF, S, lE
5574	Gx	14 20.9	+ 3 14	s	Vir	1.6	12.4	pF, pS, lE, p of 2
5575	Gx	14 20.9	+ 6 12	r	Vir		14p	F, vS, or neb*
1003 I		14 20.9	+ 5 27	d	Vir			eF, vS, vS * att, diffi
1004 I		14 20.9	+ 17 39	d	Boo			pF, sbM
5576	Gx	14 21.1	+ 3 16	s	Vir	3.2	10.9	B, S, R, vsmbM, f of 2
5581	Gx	14 21.1	+ 23 29	r	Boo		15p	vF* in vF, vS, R neby
5577	Gx	14 21.2	+ 3 26	s	Vir	3.4	13p	pF, pL, vmE 53°
5578	−	14 21.2	+ 6 12	r	Vir			vF, vS, lE, mbMN
4402 I	Gx	14 21.2	− 46 18	c	Lup	3.4		L, eE 125°, pointed ends
4408 I	Gx	14 21.2	+ 29 59	u	Boo	1.0	15p	F, S, R, gbM
5588	D*	14 21.5	+ 35 07	r	Boo			vF, R, gbM
5589	Gx	14 21.5	+ 35 15	r	Boo		14p	vF, S, R, np of 2
4409 I	Gx	14 21.5	+ 31 35	m	Boo	0.7	15p	F, S, R, *13.5 close
5583	Gx	14 21.7	+ 13 13	r	Boo		14p	vF, pS, R, pB* nr
5590	Gx	14 21.7	+ 35 11	r	Boo		13p	cF, S, R, bM *, sf of 2
5586	−	14 22.1	+ 13 10	r	Boo			eF, vS, R
5587	Gx	14 22.2	+ 13 55	s	Boo	2.9	14p	F, cS, vlE, *8 sf
5602	Gx	14 22.3	+ 50 31	r	Boo		13p	pF, pS, lE, mbM
4400 I		14 22.3	− 60 35	d	Cen			F, S, E
4410 I	Gx	14 22.3	+ 17 23	m	Boo	0.6	16p	vF, vS, R
5584	Gx	14 22.4	− 0 23	s	Vir	3.3	12p	F, L, mE, dif, glbM
4406 I	Pl	14 22.4	− 44 09	s	Lup	0.5	11p	○ , stellar, 10 mag, E 80°
5596	Gx	14 22.5	+ 37 07	s	Boo	1.5	15p	eF, S, R, stellar
5598	Gx	14 22.5	+ 40 19	r	Boo		14p	F, vS, R, bM
5620	Gx	14 22.5	+ 69 34	r	UMi		15p	eF, vS
5591	Gx	14 22.6	+ 13 43	r	Boo		14p	eF, S, R, pB* nr sf
5601	Gx	14 22.9	+ 40 18	r	Boo		15p	vF, bet 5598 and 5603
1006 I	Gx	14 23.0	+ 23 47	m	Boo	1.0	15p	F
4413 I	Gx	14 23.0	+ 37 32	m	Boo	0.2	16p	F, S, R
5603	Gx	14 23.1	+ 40 22	r	Boo		14p	cF, pS, R, gbM
5594	Gx	14 23.2	+ 26 15	r	Boo		15p	eF, vS, stellar; = IC 4412
4412 I		14 23.2	+ 26 16	x	Boo			F, S, R, dif; = 5594
5608	Gx	14 23.3	+ 41 46	s	Boo	2.7	13p	F, pL, lE, vglbM
4407 I		14 23.6	− 5 59	F	Vir			no description
5599	Gx	14 23.7	+ 6 34	r	Vir		14p	F, S, lE
5600	Gx	14 23.8	+ 14 38	s	Boo	1.4	12.7	pB, pS, gbM
4414 I	Gx	14 23.8	+ 28 19	m	Boo	0.5	15p	pB, cS, gbMN, r
5592	Gx	14 23.9	− 28 41	s	Hya	1.7	13p	F, S, E, gvlbM, r
5609	Gx	14 23.9	+ 34 50	r	Boo			eeF
5613	Gx	14 24.1	+ 34 54	s	Boo	1.1	16p	eF, pS, dif, 2′ n of 5614
5614	Gx	14 24.1	+ 34 52	s	Boo	2.7	11.7	pB, S, R, smbM
5595	Gx	14 24.2	− 16 43	s	Lib	2.0	12p	F, pL, R, vgbM, p of 2
5611	Gx	14 24.2	+ 33 01	r	Boo		13p	F, S, R, bM
5615	Gx	14 24.2	+ 34 52	r	Boo		15p	close n of 5614 (vF*?)
5616	Gx	14 24.2	+ 36 26	r	Boo		15p	vF, S, cE, vgbM, er
5610	Gx	14 24.3	+ 24 36	r	Boo		14p	vF, S, pmE 0° ±, *9 f
4415 I		14 24.4	+ 16 38	d	Boo			vF, vS, R, lbM
4416 I	Gx	14 24.4	+ 29 37	m	Boo	0.3	16p	F, S, R, N
5597	Gx	14 24.5	− 16 46	s	Lib	2.0	12.1	vF, L, vlE, vglbM, f of 2
1007 I	Gx	14 24.6	+ 4 32	z	Vir		15p	vF, vS, R, lbM, *10.5 nr
5604	Gx	14 24.7	− 3 13	r	Vir		14p	F, pS, R, vgbM*, r
4417 I	Gx	14 24.9	+ 17 02	m	Boo	0.2	15p	vF, vS, R, lbM
1008 I		14 25.0	+ 28 20	d	Boo			pF
4411 I		14 25.0	− 35 01	d	Cen			F, S, eE 45°

NGC	Type	α_{2000}	δ_{2000}	Const.	Size	Mag.	Description
		h m	° ′		′		
5605	Gx	14 25.1	− 13 10 *s*	Lib	1.8	13*p*	vF, pL, R, vgbM
4418 I		14 25.3	+ 25 31 *d*	Boo			pB, S, R, gbMN
4420 I	Gx	14 25.6	+ 25 22 *m*	Boo	0.7	15*p*	F, S, E 220°, N
5593	OC	14 25.8	− 54 49 *r*	Lup			Cl, vlRi, vlC, st 10
4419 I		14 25.8	+ 16 38 *d*	Boo			F, vS, R, lbM
4422 I	Gx	14 26.0	+ 30 28 *m*	Boo	0.2	15*p*	F, cS, r
5622	Gx	14 26.2	+ 48 33 *r*	Boo		14*p*	vF, pS, vlE, vglbM
1009 I	Gx	14 26.3	+ 12 21 *z*	Boo		15*p*	vF, S, dif
4423 I	Gx	14 26.3	+ 26 15 *u*	Boo	1.1	15*p*	vF, S, R, dif
5624	Gx	14 26.6	+ 51 36 *r*	Boo		14*p*	eF, S, lE
5631	Gx	14 26.6	+ 56 35 *s*	UMa	2.2	13*p*	B, S, R, psbMN
4425 I	Gx	14 26.7	+ 27 12 *z*	Boo		15*p*	F, S, R, dif
5625	Gx	14 27.0	+ 39 57 *r*	Boo		15*p*	vF, S, R, gbM
4427 I	Gx	14 27.0	+ 26 51 *m*	Boo	0.7	15*p*	F, cS, dif, r
4431 I	Gx	14 27.1	+ 30 57 *u*	Boo	1.3	15*p*	F, cS, R gbM, r
5618	Gx	14 27.2	− 2 16 *s*	Vir	1.8	15*p*	eF, S
5623	Gx	14 27.2	+ 33 14 *r*	Boo		13*p*	cF, S, R, vsmbM, r
1012 I		14 27.2	+ 30 59 *d*	Boo			no description
5619	Gx	14 27.3	+ 4 48 *s*	Vir	2.5	14*p*	vF, S, R, vgbM
1010 I	Gx	14 27.3	+ 1 02 *u*	Vir	2.3	15*p*	F, S, dif
4426 I	Gx	14 27.3	+ 16 50 *m*	Boo	0.4	16*p*	F, vS, R, lbM
4428 I		14 27.4	+ 16 12 *d*	Boo			F, eS, R, lbM
4437 I		14 27.4	+ 41 29 *d*	Boo			no descr, *8 nf
5633	Gx	14 27.5	+ 46 09 *s*	Boo	2.3	12.3	cB, pS, R, pglbM
4424 I	Gx	14 27.5	+ 4 49 *m*	Vir	0.8	15*p*	eF, S, stellar
4435 I	Gx	14 27.5	+ 37 29 *m*	Boo	0.5	14*p*	F, R, sbM *13.5
5630	Gx	14 27.6	+ 41 16 *s*	Boo	2.5	14*p*	F, S, E 90°±, gbM
5671		14 27.7	+ 69 38 *D*	UMi			vF, pL, R, bM
4429 I	Gx	14 27.7	+ 16 53 *m*	Boo	0.6	15*p*	F, vS, R
5606	OC	14 27.8	− 59 38 *s*	Cen	3	7.7	Cl, S, pC, st L & S
5621	−	14 27.8	+ 8 15 *r*	Boo			eeF, L, r
1013 I		14 27.8	+ 25 50 *D*	Boo			eF, vS
4433 I		14 27.8	+ 16 12 *d*	Boo			F, vS, R, mbM
4434 I		14 27.9	+ 16 13 *d*	Boo			F, vS, R, lbM
4436 I	Gx	14 27.9	+ 26 29 *m*	Boo	0.8	15*p*	pB, S, R, gbM, r
1011 I	Gx	14 28.1	+ 1 00 *m*	Vir	0.4	15*p*	F, vS, R, N = 14m
1017 I	Gx	14 28.1	+ 25 52 *u*	Boo	1.1	15*p*	pF, vS, sbM, stellar
1019 I	Gx	14 28.1	+ 25 56 *m*	Boo	0.4	15*p*	F, vS, R, stellar, * 13 nr
4421 I		14 28.1	− 37 35 *d*	Cen			eef, vS, R, F* f
4470 I	OC	14 28.1	+ 78 54 *x*	UMi			Cl, eF, S; neb?
5629	Gx	14 28.3	+ 25 50 *r*	Boo		14*p*	pF, S, R, gbM
5632	Gx	14 28.3	− 0 12 *r*	Vir			neb, *11 f 150*s*
1014 I	Gx	14 28.3	+ 13 47 *s*	Boo	2.8	13*p*	F, pL, R, vgbM
1015 I	Gx	14 28.3	+ 15 25 *m*	Boo	0.6	15*p*	vF, iF
1018 I	Gx	14 28.3	+ 25 51 *u*	Boo	2.3	14*p*	eF, eS, v diffic
5628	Gx	14 28.4	+ 17 55 *r*	Boo		14*p*	pF, S, R, gbMN = 14m
5627	Gx	14 28.5	+ 11 22 *r*	Boo		14*p*	vF, vS, R, *9 sp
5635	Gx	14 28.5	+ 27 25 *s*	Boo	2.6	14*p*	F, S, E, sbM
4438 I	Gx	14 28.6	+ 17 21 *m*	Boo	0.4	16*p*	F, vS, R, dif
4439 I	Gx	14 28.7	+ 17 02 *z*	Boo		16*p*	F, S, R, mbM
5639	Gx	14 28.8	+ 30 24 *r*	Boo		14*p*	vF, R, *7 p, *11 s
1016 I		14 28.8	+ 4 50 *d*	Vir			vF, vS, R, f 5619
1020 I	Gx	14 28.8	+ 26 02 *u*	Boo	1.2	15*p*	F, stellar, vF* close
4442 I	Gx	14 28.8	+ 28 57 *m*	Boo	1.0	15*p*	F, S, R, N
5637	Gx	14 28.9	+ 23 11 *r*	Boo		14*p*	vF, S, R, vgbM

NGC	Type	α_{2000}	δ_{2000}	Const.	Size	Mag.	Description
		h m	o ′		′		
4440 I	Gx	14 29.0	+ 17 20 m	Boo	0.6	16p	bM, mag 15
4446 I	Gx	14 29.0	+ 37 28 m	Boo	0.8	15p	F, cS, R, dif
5642	Gx	14 29.2	+ 30 01 r	Boo		14p	cF, S, * inv, *12 nf
1021 I	Gx	14 29.2	+ 20 40 u	Boo	1.2	15p	F, S, iR
5641	Gx	14 29.3	+ 28 49 s	Boo	2.7	13p	pB, pS, lE, mbM, r?
4443 I		14 29.3	+ 16 11 d	Boo			vS, vlE, lbM
4430 I		14 29.4	− 33 37 d	Cen			cF, cS, indistinct
5646	Gx	14 29.5	+ 35 26 r	Boo		15p	eF, E sp nf, 45″ l
5634	Gb	14 29.6	− 5 59 s	Vir	4.9	9.6	⊕ , vB, cL, R, gbM, rrr st 19, *8 sf
4447 I		14 29.6	+ 30 49 d	Boo			F, S, R, gbMN, r
5626	Gx	14 29.7	− 29 46 r	Hya		15p	eF, S, R
5636	Gx	14 29.7	+ 3 16 s	Vir	1.9	15p	eF, cL, R, np of 2
5638	Gx	14 29.7	+ 3 14 s	Vir	2.6	11.3	cB, pL, R, sf of 2
5712	Gx	14 29.7	+ 78 51 r	UMi		15p	vF, S, R, S Cl p
5617	OC	14 29.8	− 60 43 s	Cen	10	6.3	Cl, L, pRi, pCM, st 8...
5660	Gx	14 29.8	+ 49 37 s	Boo	2.8	11.8	pB, L, iR, vgbM
1027 I		14 29.8	+ 53 57 D	Boo			eeF, pS, R, *13 sp 0′.7
4432 I		14 29.8	− 39 32 d	Cen			vF, vS, mE 85°
5654	Gx	14 29.9	+ 36 21 r	Boo		14p	F, S, E?, ⁎ inv?
1022 I	Gx	14 30.0	+ 3 46 u	Vir	1.2	15p	vF, E ns
5653	Gx	14 30.2	+ 31 13 s	Boo	1.8	12.2	pF, pS, R, bM
5644	Gx	14 30.4	+ 11 55 r	Boo		14p	pB, pS, R, gmbM
5656	Gx	14 30.4	+ 35 19 s	Boo	2.1	13p	pF, pL, R, mbM, r
5667	Gx	14 30.4	+ 59 29 s	Dra	1.8	13p	pB, pS, E 0°
5647	Gx	14 30.6	+ 11 52 r	Boo		15p	F, S, R, vlbM
5648	Gx	14 30.6	+ 14 00 r	Boo		14p	vF, S, no Nucl; = 5649
5649	Gx	14 30.6	+ 14 00 D	Boo		14p	eF, vS, np of 2
5645	Gx	14 30.7	+ 7 17 s	Vir	2.6	12.3	cF, pL, iR, gbM
5657	Gx	14 30.7	+ 29 10 r	Boo		14p	F, S, irr, sev vF st inv, r?
5650	Gx	14 30.8	+ 6 00 h	Vir	0.2	15p	vF, pS, R
5652	Gx	14 30.9	+ 5 58 r	Vir		14p	pB, pL, vlE, bM
5655	Gx	14 31.0	+ 13 59 r	Boo			eeF, sf of 2
5659	Gx	14 31.1	+ 25 21 r	Boo		15p	eF
1026 I	*	14 31.2	+ 31 13 z	Boo			pB
5651	−	14 31.3	− 0 56 r	Vir			neb, R
4449 I		14 31.3	+ 15 15 d	Boo			vF, vS, R, dif
1024 I	Gx	14 31.4	+ 3 00 u	Vir	1.6	14p	pB, vS, E ns
4441 I		14 31.4	− 43 31 d	Lup			pF, pS, R
5673	Gx	14 31.5	+ 49 58 s	Boo	2.6	14p	F, S, cE, *15 np
1025 I	Gx	14 31.5	+ 7 04 z	Vir		15p	eF, sbM
4444 I	Gx	14 31.7	− 43 25 s	Lup	1.9	12p	vF, vS, * M, spir or annular
5661	Gx	14 31.9	+ 6 14 r	Vir		14p	vF, pS, iE
4445 I		14 31.9	− 46 02 d	Lup			F, cS, E 160°
5678	Gx	14 32.1	+ 57 55 s	Dra	3.2	12p	B, L, lE 0°, vgmbM
4450 I	Gx	14 32.1	+ 28 33 u	Boo	1.2	15p	F, cS, dif, *10.5 nf
5658	Gx	14 32.4	+ 0 16 r	Vir		14p	neb, F, E
5665	Gx	14 32.4	+ 8 05 s	Boo	2.1	13p	pB, pL, R, gbM, r
1023 I		14 32.4	− 35 48 d	Cen			neb
4452 I	Gx	14 32.4	+ 27 26 z	Boo		15p	F, S, R, gbM, r
1028 I		14 32.5	+ 41 51 d	Boo			pB, S, R, F* close nf
1029 I	Gx	14 32.5	+ 49 54 v	Boo	3.0		vF, S, lE, mbM
5672	Gx	14 32.6	+ 31 40 s	Boo	1.0	13.6	vF, vL, iR, lbM, ⁎ p
5675	Gx	14 32.6	+ 36 17 r	Boo		14p	F, pS, E, bM
5643	Gx	14 32.7	− 44 10 s	Lup	4.6	11p	pB, L, R, vglbM, st inv
5669	Gx	14 32.7	+ 9 53 s	Boo	4.1	12p	F, L, R, lbM, r

NGC	Type	α_{2000}	δ_{2000}	Const.	Size	Mag.	Description
		h m	° ′		′		
5676	Gx	14 32.8	+ 49 28 s	Boo	3.9	10.9	B, L, E 45°±, pgbM, r
5666	Gx	14 33.1	+ 10 29 r	Boo		13p	vF, vS, R, stellar
4454 I		14 33.3	+ 17 43 d	Boo			F, eS, R, lbM
5668	Gx	14 33.4	+ 4 27 s	Vir	3.3	11.5	F, pS, vlE, *14 inv
5664		14 33.7	− 14 35 D	Lib			pF, S, E, gbM
1030 I		14 33.7	+ 31 42 d	Boo			pF
5674	Gx	14 33.8	+ 5 26 r	Vir		13p	cF, pS, R, gbM
5663	Gx	14 33.9	− 16 34 r	Lib		15p	eF, vS, R, glbM
5612	Gx	14 34.1	− 78 24 s	Aps	2.0	13p	vF, E, gbM, r
4456 I		14 34.1	+ 16 11 d	Boo			F, S, R, dif
5677	Gx	14 34.2	+ 25 27 r	Boo		15p	vF, vS, R, r, 3 st 9, 10 np
4453 I	Gx	14 34.5	− 27 31 c	Hya	2.0		pB, eS, R, F* close
4455 I		14 34.5	− 14 38 d	Lib			eF, cS, cE 30°
4457 I		14 34.5	+ 18 13 d	Boo			F, vS, R, lbM
4459 I	Gx	14 34.5	+ 30 58 m	Boo	0.5	15p	F, pL, E ns, glbM, r
1031 I		14 34.6	+ 48 02 d	Boo			eeF, S, R
4451 I	Gx	14 34.6	− 36 17 c	Cen	1.9		vF, vS, R, * n 0′.5
4460 I	Gx	14 34.6	+ 30 17 m	Boo	0.7		F, S, dif, glbM
1032 I		14 34.7	+ 47 57 d	Boo			eeF, vS, R
5682	Gx	14 34.8	+ 48 40 s	Boo	2.0	14.0	F, pS, E
1033 I		14 34.8	+ 47 56 d	Boo			eeF, S, R
5683	Gx	14 34.9	+ 48 40 v	Boo	0.7	14.8	F, vS, lE
5687	Gx	14 34.9	+ 54 29 s	Boo	2.6	11.8	pF, S, iF, r, *10 f
5679	Gx	14 35.0	+ 5 20 r	Vir		14p	vF, S, R, *12 att
4461 I		14 35.0	+ 26 31 d	Boo			F, vS, R, N, r
4462 I		14 35.0	+ 26 32 d	Boo			F, S, R
5662	OC	14 35.2	− 56 33 s	Cen	12	5.5	Cl, L, pRi, lC, st 9...
5689	Gx	14 35.5	+ 48 45 s	Boo	3.7	11.9	cB, pL, E 87°, psmbM
5670	Gx	14 35.7	− 45 57 t	Lup	2.0		vF, S, cE, bet 2 st
5681	Gx	14 35.7	+ 8 18 r	Boo		14p	F, S
5680	Gx	14 35.8	− 0 03 r	Vir		15p	vF, vS
5684	Gx	14 35.8	+ 36 32 r	Boo		14p	F, cS, R, bM, p of 2
4463 I	Gx	14 35.8	+ 16 02 z	Boo		15p	F, vS, R
4465 I		14 35.9	+ 15 34 d	Boo			vF, vS, lE 180°
5686	Gx	14 36.0	+ 36 29 r	Boo		15p	vF, S, R, f of 2
5685	Gx	14 36.2	+ 29 54 r	Boo		15p	vF, vS, R, gbMN = 15m
5693	Gx	14 36.2	+ 48 35 s	Boo	1.9	15p	F, pL, *13 att s
4471 I		14 36.4	+ 41 40 x	Boo			no description; = 5697
5697	Gx	14 36.6	+ 41 41 r	Boo		14p	F, vS, R, bM, 4 B st p; = IC 4471
4466 I		14 36.7	+ 18 20 d	Boo			F, vS, lE
4467 I	Gx	14 36.8	+ 18 21 z	Boo		15p	F, vS, R, lbM
5696	Gx	14 37.0	+ 41 49 r	Boo		14p	cF, cS, R, lbM, r
5700	Gx	14 37.1	+ 48 33 r	Boo		15p	eF, S, r, *11 sp 4′
5698	Gx	14 37.2	+ 38 28 r	Boo		14p	cF, cS, lE, in △ of st
1034 I	Gx	14 37.2	+ 14 40 z	Boo		16p	vF, lbM
4458 I		14 37.2	− 39 28 d	Cen			eF, eS, E 100°
5695	Gx	14 37.3	+ 36 34 r	Boo		14p	pB, cS, R, bM, r
4469 I	Gx	14 37.3	+ 18 15 u	Boo	1.6	16p	F, pL, eE 110°
5707	Gx	14 37.5	+ 51 34 s	Boo	2.8	13p	B, pS, R
5690	Gx	14 37.7	+ 2 17 s	Vir	3.5	13p	vF, mE 138°, F* att sf, *7 p 4′
1046 I	Gx	14 37.8	+ 69 00 m	UMi	0.8	15p	eF, S, R, D* f
4464 I	Gx	14 37.8	− 36 53 c	Cen	1.6		vF, S, R, N, wisp at 45°
5691	Gx	14 37.9	− 0 24 s	Vir	2.0	13p	pB, pS, lE, gbM
5704	−	14 37.9	+ 40 31 r	Boo			F, cS, lE 0°±
4473 I	Gx	14 37.9	+ 15 50 m	Boo	0.5	15p	vS, com, 170°

NGC	Type	α_{2000}	δ_{2000}	Const.	Size	Mag.	Description
		h m	° ′		′		
1035 I	Gx	14 38.1	+ 9 20 m	Boo	0.7	15p	pF, vS, R, S, * nr
5714	Gx	14 38.2	+46 38 s	Boo	3.0	14p	vF, pS, E pf, D* n, 1st of 6
5692	Gx	14 38.3	+ 3 24 s	Vir	0.9	13p	pB, vS, R, gbM
5699	—	14 38.3	+29 30 r	Boo			eF, vS; = 5706?
5708	Gx	14 38.3	+40 28 r	Boo		14p	F, pL, E 0°±, gbM
1036 I	Gx	14 38.3	+18 07 z	Boo		16p	pF, S
5720	Gx	14 38.4	+50 52 r	Boo		14p	eeF, pS, R, bet 2 st
1037 I	Gx	14 38.4	+18 10 m	Boo	0.8	15p	F, vS, R, stellar
4468 I	Gx	14 38.4	− 22 22 c	Lib	2.3		F, pL, cE 160°, cbM
4474 I		14 38.4	+23 26 d	Boo			F, vS, R, N
4475 I	Gx	14 38.4	+23 20 z	Boo		15p	F, vS, N, stell
5703	—	14 38.5	+29 30 r	Boo			vF, vS, iR; = 5709?
4477 I	Gx	14 38.5	+28 27 z	Boo		15p	F, vS, dif, *12 p 2ˢ, 15″ n
5706	Gx	14 38.6	+30 29 r	Boo		15p	vF, vS, R, vlbM
5717	Gx	14 38.6	+46 41 r	Boo		15p	vF, S, R, D* nr, 2nd of 6
4479 I	Gx	14 38.7	+28 30 u	Boo	1.5	15p	F, cS, N, dif
5702	Gx	14 38.8	+20 31 r	Boo		14p	vF, vS
5709	Gx	14 38.8	+30 27 r	Boo		14p	vF, S, iF, E pf
5721	Gx	14 38.9	+46 41 r	Boo		15p	vF, S, R; forms trapez with 5722-4
5723	Gx	14 38.9	+46 41 r	Boo		15p	vF, S, R
5722	Gx	14 39.0	+46 40 r	Boo		15p	vF, S, R, psbM
5724	Gx	14 39.1	+46 44 r	Boo		17p	vF, S, R; F neb connecting 5721-4?
5701	Gx	14 39.2	+ 5 22 s	Vir	4.7	12p	cB, pS, R, mbM, *11 p 15ˢ
4478 I	Gx	14 39.2	+15 53 z	Boo		15p	bM, mag 15
5710	Gx	14 39.3	+20 03 r	Boo		14p	vF, S, vgbM, ⁑ f, p of 2
5711	Gx	14 39.4	+20 00 r	Boo		15p	eF, vS, ⁑ att, f of 2
1038 I	Gx	14 39.4	+11 55 z	Boo		15p	F, vS, stellar, *10 f 8ˢ
5688	Gx	14 39.5	− 45 02 t	Lup	3.9		F, S, vgbM, am st
5694	Gb	14 39.6	− 26 32 s	Hya	3.6	10.2	cB, cS, R, psbM, r, *9.5 sp
1049 I		14 39.6	+62 02 D	Dra			eeF, pS, R
5705	Gx	14 39.8	− 0 43 s	Vir	2.8	14p	eF, L, lE, eF dif neby around
4480 I	Gx	14 39.8	+18 29 m	Boo	0.5	15p	F, S, R, dif, * in M
4476 I		14 39.9	− 16 14 d	Lib			neb, *7 nf 5′
5731	Gx	14 40.0	+42 46 r	Boo		14p	vF, eS, lE
4481 I		14 40.1	+16 08 d	Boo			eF, vS, R, dif
4482 I	Gx	14 40.1	+18 57 z	Boo		15p	F, S, R
5713	Gx	14 40.2	− 0 17 s	Vir	2.8	11.4	cB, pL, R, psmbM, r
4472 I	Gx	14 40.2	− 44 19 c	Lup	1.8		L, eE 180°, bet 2 st ns, doubtful
5730		14 40.3	+42 45 D	Boo			vF, cS, E 90°±
1040 I	Gx	14 40.3	+ 9 28 z	Boo		15p	eF, vS
4483 I	Gx	14 40.3	+16 41 u	Boo	1.6	15p	E 200°, lbM
5727	Gx	14 40.5	+33 59 s	Boo	2.3	14p	eF, pL, R, dif
1039 I	Gx	14 40.5	+ 3 25 z	Vir		16p	vF, vS, lbM
4448 I	Gx	14 40.5	− 78 49 c	Aps	1.0		!! F, vS, annul, * in M
4485 I		14 40.5	+28 40 d	Boo			F, S, dif
5732	Gx	14 40.6	+38 39 r	Boo		14p	vF, S, R, lbM
1041 I		14 40.6	+ 3 21 d	Vir			pB, vS, R, N = 12m
1042 I		14 40.6	+ 3 26 d	Vir			vF, vS, R, bM, close D with 5718
1043 I		14 40.7	+ 3 21 d	Vir			vF, vS, R, bM
1045 I		14 40.7	+42 45 d	Boo			eeF, pS, R, nearly bet 2 st
5718	Gx	14 40.8	+ 3 28 r	Vir		14p	vF, S, R, vglbM, *8-9 nf
5719	Gx	14 40.9	− 0 19 s	Vir	3.4	14p	pF, S, lE, bM
5716	Gx	14 41.1	− 17 29 s	Lib	1.9	13p	vF, pL, R
5725	Gx	14 41.1	+ 2 10 r	Vir		14p	vF, S, disc, *15 s 95″
1044 I	Gx	14 41.5	+ 9 26 m	Boo	1.0	15p	F, vS, R, gbM

NGC	Type	α_{2000}	δ_{2000}	Const.	Size	Mag.	Description
		h m	° ′		′		
4486 I	Gx	14 41.9	+ 18 33 m	Boo	0.7	16p	vF, vS, R, dif
5729	Gx	14 42.0	− 9 03 s	Lib	3.0	13p	F, pL, E, r
4487 I		14 42.0	+ 18 37 d	Boo			F, eS, R, lbM
5728	Gx	14 42.4	− 17 15 s	Lib	2.8	11.3	pF, pL, pmE 45°±, mbM, *10 s
5735	Gx	14 42.4	+ 28 44 r	Boo		14p	vF, L, iR, lbM
1047 I	Gx	14 42.4	+ 19 10 m	Boo	0.6	16p	vF, S, v, dif
5739	Gx	14 42.5	+ 41 50 s	Boo	2.2	13p	pB, S, R, smbM, r, * nr
4492 I		14 42.6	+ 37 25 d	Boo			F, vS, R, N, stell
5733	Gx	14 42.8	− 0 21 s	Vir	1.3	15p	vF, S, mE
4488 I		14 42.8	+ 18 36 d	Boo			vF, eS, R, lbM
5726		14 42.9	− 18 26 D	Lib			F, S, R, gbM, *10.5 np 3′
1048 I	Gx	14 42.9	+ 4 53 s	Vir	2.5	14p	pB, pL, E pf, r
5737	Gx	14 43.2	+ 18 53 r	Boo		14p	vF, cS, R, vglbM
4489 I		14 43.2	+ 18 31 d	Boo			vF, eS, R, lbM
5715	OC	14 43.4	− 57 33 s	Cir	6	10p	Cl, L, pRi, CM, st 11...13
5736	Gx	14 43.5	+ 11 13 r	Boo		15p	eeF, S, lE, v diffic
5744	Gx	14 43.9	− 18 29 A	Lib			eF, vS, neb?
5751	Gx	14 43.9	+ 53 25 r	Boo		14p	F, S, vlE, △ 2 st 10-11
4496 I	Gx	14 43.9	+ 33 23 m	Boo	0.3	15p	F, S, R, N
5738	Gx	14 44.0	+ 1 37 r	Vir		14p	F, S, bM
1050 I	Gx	14 44.1	+ 18 01 z	Boo		15p	vF, S, R, dif
1051 I	Gx	14 44.2	+ 19 01 z	Boo		15p	F, vS, stellar
1052 I	Gx	14 44.2	+ 20 37 u	Boo	1.1	15p	neb *12
4495 I	Gx	14 44.2	+ 23 33 z	Boo		16p	vF, vS, R
4497 I	Gx	14 44.3	+ 28 32 m	Boo	0.6	15p	F, S, R, N, r, *12.5 f 5^s
5740	Gx	14 44.4	+ 1 41 s	Vir	3.1	11.9	pB, L, iR, gbM, r
5747	Gx	14 44.4	+ 12 09 r	Boo		14p	eF, S; = IC 4493
4493 I		14 44.4	+ 12 07 z	Boo			eF, S, R, dif, rM; = 5747
4491 I		14 44.5	− 13 44 d	Lib			F, S, eE 0°
4494 I	Gx	14 44.5	+ 15 30 m	Boo	1.0	15p	vF, vS, R, dif
4500 I	Gx	14 44.6	+ 37 29 m	Boo	0.3	15p	F, S, R, gbM
5746	Gx	14 44.9	+ 1 57 s	Vir	7.9	10.6	B, L, vmE 170°, bmBN
5748	Gx	14 45.0	+ 21 55 r	Boo		15p	eF, vS
4498 I	Gx	14 45.0	+ 26 17 m	Boo	0.4	15p	F, S, R, gbM
5734	Gx	14 45.1	− 20 52 r	Lib		14p	vF, S, lE, glbM
5743	Gx	14 45.1	− 20 54 r	Lib		13p	F, S, mE, smbMN
5745	Gx	14 45.1	− 13 56 r	Lib		14p	vF, S, E, pslbM
5752	Gx	14 45.3	+ 38 43 r	Boo		14p	F, 1′ p 5754
4502 I		14 45.3	+ 37 18 d	Boo			F, S, dif r, *14 vnr
5753	Gx	14 45.4	+ 38 43 r	Boo		15p	F, bM, np 5754
5754	Gx	14 45.4	+ 38 47 r	Boo		14p	cF, cS, R, bM
4490 I		14 45.4	− 36 10 d	Cen			oval, around 2 st 9.5 & 10
5755	Gx	14 45.5	+ 38 46 r	Boo		15p	F, 2′ nf 5754
1053 I	Gx	14 45.6	+ 16 57 m	Boo	0.5	15p	eF, vS, v dif, *4 p 28^s
5742	Gx	14 45.8	− 11 48 r	Lib		14p	F, pS, pmE, gbMN
1056 I	Gx	14 45.8	+ 50 25 u	Boo	2.0	14p	eeF, L, R, 3 pB st sf
1057 I		14 46.0	+ 50 22 d	Boo			eF, pS, R, bet 3 st
5741	Gx	14 46.1	− 11 54 r	Lib		15p	vF, vS, R, sbMN
5750	Gx	14 46.2	− 0 13 s	Vir	2.9	11.6	pF, pS, vlE, r
1054 I	Gx	14 46.5	+ 1 16 u	Vir	1.2	15p	vF, vS, sbMN = 14m
4504 I	Gx	14 46.5	+ 31 42 z	Boo		15p	F, S, R, N, r
4503 I	Gx	14 46.6	+ 16 06 m	Boo	0.8	15p	F, vS, R
4505 I		14 46.6	+ 33 24 d	Boo			F, S, R, N
4506 I		14 46.7	+ 33 24 d	Boo			vF, vS, N
5758	Gx	14 47.1	+ 13 40 r	Boo		15p	eF, pS, R, *9 f 22^s

NGC	Type	α_{2000}	δ_{2000}	Const.	Size	Mag.	Description
		h m	° ′		′		
5759	Gx	14 47.3	+ 13 28 r	Boo		15p	eF, S, R
1055 I	Gx	14 47.4	− 13 44 v	Lib	2.6		F, pL, E ns
4501 I	Gx	14 47.5	− 22 25 m	Lib	0.9	14p	vF, S, indistinct
5756	Gx	14 47.6	− 14 51 s	Lib	2.0	13p	pB, pL, pmE, gpmbM
5760	Gx	14 47.7	+ 18 31 r	Boo		14p	vF, vS, cE 90°, vglbM
4484 I	Gx	14 47.7	− 73 18 c	Aps	2.5		eF, eE 140°, susp
4507 I	Gx	14 47.7	+ 18 27 m	Boo	0.8	16p	vF, eS, R
5757	Gx	14 47.8	− 19 05 s	Lib	2.1	13p	vF, S, iR, lbM
4508 I	Gx	14 47.8	+ 31 47 z	Boo		15p	F, S, R, sbM *14
4509 I	Gx	14 48.4	+ 31 48 u	Boo	1.0	15p	F, cS, iF, r
5762	Gx	14 48.7	+ 12 28 r	Boo		14p	vF, S, R, p of 2
5749	OC	14 48.9	− 54 31 s	Lup	8	9p	Cl, pL, pRi, lC, st 10...11
5763	Gx	14 49.0	+ 12 29 r	Boo		15p	eeF, pS, v diffic, f of 2
5761	Gx	14 49.1	− 20 22 r	Lib		14p	vF, S, R, glbMN
1058 I	Gx	14 49.1	+ 17 02 u	Boo	1.6	15p	F, E ns, mbMN = 14m
1065 I	Gx	14 49.3	+ 63 16 s	Dra	1.3	13.4	vF, pS, R
5767	Gx	14 49.7	+ 47 23 r	Boo		15p	eF, pS, R, * nr
4512 I		14 49.9	+ 27 42 d	Boo			vF, S, R
1059 I	Gx	14 50.7	− 0 52 z	Lib		16p	F, S, lbm, r
4510 I		14 50.7	− 20 44 d	Lib			vF, vS, iR, susp
5765	Gx	14 50.8	+ 5 07 r	Vir		14p	Dneb, both eF
4514 I		14 50.9	+ 27 37 d	Boo			F, S, R, N, *13 vnr
1069 I		14 51.0	+ 54 23 d	Boo			pF, vS, R, no st nr
4515 I		14 51.1	+ 37 36 d	Boo			F, S, R, gbM, r
1061 I		14 51.2	+ 18 45 d	Boo			eF, eS, diffic
5777	Gx	14 51.3	+ 58 58 s	Dra	3.3	14p	vF, vS, lE
1062 I	Gx	14 51.3	+ 18 41 m	Boo	0.3	15p	pF, iF, diffic
5772	Gx	14 51.7	+ 40 36 s	Boo	2.3	14p	pB, pL, lE, pslbM, *8 np
1060 I	Gx	14 51.9	− 7 13 m	Lib	1.0	14p	no descr
1074 I	Gx	14 52.0	+ 51 17 u	Boo	1.0	15p	eeF, S, R
5768	Gx	14 52.1	− 2 32 s	Lib	2.0	13p	F, R, bMFN, S* s
4511 I		14 52.1	− 40 30 d	Cen			cS, R, lbM, dif
5771	Gx	14 52.2	+ 29 51 r	Boo		14p	vF, S, R, pgbM
5779	Gx	14 52.2	+ 55 54 r	Dra		15p	vF, pS, lE, lbM
1063 I		14 52.2	+ 4 41 d	Vir			pF, stellar
1064 I		14 52.2	+ 4 40 d	Vir			vF, vS, R, lbM
4513 I		14 52.3	− 20 44 d	Lib			F, S, vE 80°
5773	Gx	14 52.5	+ 29 48 r	Boo		14p	vF, S, R, pgbM
5769	Gx	14 52.6	+ 7 56 r	Boo		15p	vF
1066 I	Gx	14 53.0	+ 3 18 u	Vir	1.6	14p	F, vS, R
1067 I	Gx	14 53.1	+ 3 20 v	Vir	2.3		F, vS, R, bM
5766	Gx	14 53.2	− 21 22 r	Lib		14p	eF, pS, R, gbM
5788	Gx	14 53.2	+ 52 03 r	Boo		15p	eeF, S, R, v diffic, sf of 2
5770	Gx	14 53.4	+ 3 57 r	Vir		13p	cF, S, vlE, bM, biN
5783	Gx	14 53.5	+ 52 05 s	Boo	3.0	13p	pB, pS, iR, F* inv
1068 I	Gx	14 53.5	+ 3 04 m	Vir	0.2	15p	F, pL, dif
5764	OC	14 53.6	− 52 41 s	Lup	2	13p	Cl, vF, vS, vC
5774	Gx	14 53.7	+ 3 35 s	Vir	3.2	12.2	pF, pL, R, np of 2
5808		14 53.8	+ 73 01 D	UMi			vF, S, iR, bet 2 st
5785	−	14 53.9	+ 52 09 r	Boo			vF, pS, F* close f, np of 2
1070 I	Gx	14 53.9	+ 3 29 z	Vir		15p	vF, S, R, diffic
4516 I		14 53.9	+ 16 23 d	Boo			vF, pS, R
5775	Gx	14 54.0	+ 3 33 s	Vir	4.3	11.4	F, pS, vmE 148°, gvlbM
5819	Gx	14 54.0	+ 73 08 r	UMi		14p	F, pL, △ 2 st
5784	Gx	14 54.2	+ 42 33 r	Boo		13p	pB, S, R, smbM, stellar

NGC	Type	α_{2000}	δ_{2000}	Const.	Size	Mag.	Description
		h m	° ′		′		
1071 I	Gx	14 54.2	+ 4 45 u	Vir	1.2	14p	vF, S, R, bM
1072 I	Gx	14 54.2	+ 4 51 m	Vir	0.5	15p	vF, vS, R, vlbM, 2nd of 3
1073 I	Gx	14 54.2	+ 4 48 z	Vir		15p	vF, S, R, S∗ s, 3rd of 3
5780	Gx	14 54.4	+ 28 57 r	Boo		14p	vF, S, R, ∗ nr sp
5778	Gx	14 54.5	+ 18 38 r	Boo		15p	eeF, pS, R, pB∗ close f, diffic
4517 I	Gx	14 54.5	+ 23 38 z	Boo		15p	F, S, N dif
5776	Gx	14 54.6	+ 2 58 r	Vir		14p	vF, pL, vlbM, ∗8-9 sp
1075 I	Gx	14 54.8	+ 18 06 u	Boo	1.3	15p	eeF, pS, R, v diffic
4519 I	Gx	14 54.8	+ 37 25 m	Boo	0.6	15p	F, S, dif, ∗14 sp
1076 I	Gx	14 55.0	+ 18 02 v	Boo	1.2		ef, pS, R, bM, ∗ sp
4520 I	Gx	14 55.1	+ 33 43 m	Boo	0.4	15p	F, vS, R, N, r
5787	Gx	14 55.3	+ 42 30 s	Boo	1.2	14p	F, cS, R, pslbM
1083 I	Gx	14 55.6	+ 68 24 m	UMi	0.7	16p	eeF, S, R
5794	Gx	14 55.7	+ 49 44 r	Boo		14p	pF, S, vsbM ∗13, 1st of 4
5804	Gx	14 55.7	+ 49 39 r	Boo			vF, vS, vsmbM, ∗6 nr
5807	Gx	14 55.7	+ 63 55 r	Dra		15p	vF, vS, r
5782		14 55.9	+ 11 53 D	Boo			eF, vS, E, ∗ nr sf
5805	Gx	14 55.9	+ 49 43 r	Boo			S
5795	Gx	14 56.3	+ 49 23 r	Boo		14p	vF, pS, lE, pB∗ close to p end
5797	Gx	14 56.3	+ 49 42 r	Boo		13p	F, S, vsbM ∗13, 2nd of 4
1078 I		14 56.5	+ 9 21 d	Boo			pF, vS, R, lbM
5781	Gx	14 56.6	− 17 15 r	Lib		14p	F, S, R, bM, ∗16 sp
5789	Gx	14 56.6	+ 30 13 r	Boo		14p	eF, pS, iF
1079 I		14 56.6	+ 9 22 d	Boo			F, vS, R, gbM
1077 I	Gx	14 57.4	− 19 13 c	Lib	2.0		vF, vS, R, gbMN
5790	Gx	14 57.5	+ 8 17 r	Boo		15p	eF, vS, iF, lbM
5798	Gx	14 57.7	+ 29 58 r	Boo		13p	F, S, R, vgbM, ∗ nf
4518 I	Gx	14 57.7	− 43 08 c	Lup	1.4		eS, R; also one pL, eE 100°
5832	Gx	14 57.8	+ 71 41 s	UMi	4.0	12p	pB, cL, iR, bp, r
1080 I	Gx	14 58.1	− 6 42 m	Lib	0.4	14p	vF, vS, R, lbM
5792	Gx	14 58.4	− 1 05 s	Lib	7.2	12p	pB, pL, R, mbM, ∗8-9 np 1′
5820	Gx	14 58.7	+ 53 53 s	Boo	2.5	11.9	B, E 90°±, sbM, B D∗ f 8′
5791	Gx	14 58.8	− 19 16 s	Lib	2.4	13p	pF, S, R, stellar
5818	Gx	14 58.8	+ 49 49 r	Boo		15p	vF, pS, R, eF∗ inv, bet 2 st
5821	Gx	14 58.9	+ 53 55 r	Boo		15p	vF, S
1081 I	Gx	14 58.9	− 19 14 c	Lib	1.6		eF, pL, E 175°
1082 I	Gx	14 58.9	+ 7 00 z	Vir		15p	pF, S, R
5786	Gx	14 59.0	− 42 01 r	Cen			F, mE, B∗ sf
5793	Gx	14 59.4	− 16 42 s	Lib	1.8	13.2	eF, pS, E, bMN
5796	Gx	14 59.4	− 16 37 s	Lib	1.9	13p	F, pS∗ in centre
5836	Gx	14 59.5	+ 73 53 r	UMi		15p	eF, vS, lE, 2 st inv
5817	Gx	14 59.6	− 16 11 r	Lib		15p	vF, pS
4521 I	Gx	14 59.6	+ 25 35 m	Boo	0.5	15p	F, cS, E pf, gbM
5826	−	14 59.8	+ 55 31 r	Dra			vF, pL, E
5806	Gx	15 00.0	+ 1 54 s	Vir	3.1	11.6	cB, cL, E 165°±, sbMN
4499 I	Gb	15 00.3	− 82 13 s	Aps	7.6	10.6	Cl, vF, 4′ diam; 3 F st in neb?
5801	Gx	15 00.4	− 13 54 r	Lib			vF, vS, sbM, 1st of 3
5802	Gx	15 00.5	− 13 55 r	Lib			vF, vS, sbM, 2nd and brightest
5811	Gx	15 00.5	+ 1 37 s	Vir	1.0	15p	vF, S, iR
5815	Gx	15 00.5	− 16 50 r	Lib		14p	eF, pS, E 10°, D∗ inv
5828	Gx	15 00.6	+ 49 59 r	Boo		14p	eF, pS, R, bet 2 dist st
5809	Gx	15 00.9	− 14 10 r	Lib		14p	vF, S, E, glbM
5803		15 01.0	− 13 54 D	Lib			vF, vS, sbM, 3rd of 3
5812	Gx	15 01.0	− 7 27 s	Lib	2.4	11.2	cB, S, R, svmbM
5813	Gx	15 01.2	+ 1 42 s	Vir	3.6	10.7	B, pS, R, psmbM

NGC	Type	α_{2000}	δ_{2000}	Const.	Size	Mag.	Description
		h m	o ′		′		
1084 I	Gx	15 01.3	− 7 27 m	Lib	0.4	14p	eF, S, R, dif
5814	Gx	15 01.4	+ 1 37 r	Vir		14p	vF, vS, R
4528 I	Gx	15 01.4	+ 49 07 m	Boo	0.7	15p	eF, pS, dif, r
5830	Gx	15 01.7	+ 47 52 r	Boo		15p	vF, S, R, B∗ nr f
5827	Gx	15 01.8	+ 25 58 s	Boo	1.4	14p	pB, pL, R, bM
5800	−	15 02.0	− 51 55 r	Lup			Cl, pL, pRi, lC
5825	−	15 02.0	+ 18 42 r	Boo			eeF, pS, lE, pB∗ close f
5816	−	15 02.1	− 16 08 r	Lib			F, pS, gbMN, stellar
4524 I	Gx	15 02.1	+ 25 35 z	Boo		16p	F, S, iF, gbM, r
5835	Gx	15 02.3	+ 48 52 r	Boo		15p	vF, pS, R
4525 I	Gx	15 02.4	+ 25 38 z	Boo		16p	vF, cS, dif
5810	Gx	15 02.6	− 17 53 r	Lib		14p	eF, vS, lE 230°, bet 2 vF st
4526 I		15 02.6	+ 23 22 d	Boo			vF, vS, N
5829	Gx	15 02.7	+ 23 20 s	Boo	1.9	15p	vF, vL, irrR, bM
1085 I	Gx	15 02.7	+ 17 14 m	Boo	1.2	15p	pB, vS, lE ns
1086 I		15 03.4	+ 17 05 d	Boo			F, iR, bMN
1090 I	Gx	15 03.7	+ 42 41 v	Boo	0.4		eF, neb?
4530 I	Gx	15 03.8	+ 26 05 u	Boo	1.0	15p	F, S, dif, ∗13.5 nf
5824	Gb	15 04.0	− 33 04 s	Lup	6.2	9.0	pB, S, stell, N
5834		15 04.0	− 33 04 D	Lup			eeF? B, stellar; = 5824
5831	Gx	15 04.1	+ 1 13 s	Vir	2.2	11.5	pB, S, mbM
5840	−	15 04.3	+ 29 30 r	Boo			eeF, pS, lE, v diffic
4531 I	Gx	15 04.4	+ 23 24 z	Boo		16p	F, vS, R, N
4533 I	Gx	15 04.4	+ 27 48 u	Boo	1.0	15p	F, S, iF, ∗10.5 f
4532 I		15 04.5	+ 23 13 d	Boo			vF, N, stellar
5837	Gx	15 04.7	+ 12 38 r	Boo		14p	vF, S, R, D∗ np
5842	Gx	15 04.8	+ 21 04 r	Boo		15p	eF, vS, R, lbM
5822	OC	15 05.2	− 54 21 s	Lup	40	7p	Cl, vL, Ri, lC, st 9...12
4523 I	Gx	15 05.2	− 43 31 c	Lup	2.0		bM, mag 14
5838	Gx	15 05.4	+ 2 06 s	Vir	4.2	10.8	pB, pS
5799	Gx	15 05.5	− 72 26 r	Aps			eF, S, R, bM
5839	Gx	15 05.5	+ 1 38 s	Vir	1.4	14p	pF, pS
5841	−	15 05.6	+ 1 59 r	Vir			F, S, E
5823	OC	15 05.7	− 55 36 s	Cir	10	7.9	Cl, cL, Ri, lCM, st 13...14
4527 I	Gx	15 05.7	− 42 27 c	Lup	1.5		cS, E 225°, bM
5853	Gx	15 05.8	+ 39 31 r	Boo		15p	pF, pS, R, mbM, r?
5845	Gx	15 06.0	+ 1 38 s	Vir	0.9	12.3	vF, R
5862	Gx	15 06.0	+ 55 34 r	Dra		15p	eF, pS, R, v diffic
5847	Gx	15 06.3	+ 6 23 r	Vir		15p	eF, S, iR
1100 I	Gx	15 06.3	+ 63 00 u	Dra	1.0	14p	vF, pS, lE, bet 2 st
5846	Gx	15 06.4	+ 1 36 s	Vir	3.4	10.2	vB, pL, R, psbMN, F∗ inv s, rr
5867	−	15 06.4	+ 55 44 r	Dra			eF, vS, stellar
1098 I	∗	15 06.4	+ 55 36 z	Dra			vF (only a ∗13?)
4529 I	Gx	15 06.4	− 43 14 c	Lup	0.6		bM, mag 14
5866	Gx	15 06.5	+ 55 46 s	Dra	5.2	10.0	vB, cL, pmE 146°, gbM
5860	Gx	15 06.6	+ 42 38 s	Boo	1.0	14p	F, S, R, psbM
5870	Gx	15 06.6	+ 55 28 r	Dra		15p	eF, pS, lE, v diffic, ∗ f
5848	Gx	15 06.7	+ 2 00 r	Vir		15p	eF, S, close D∗ sf 7′
1087 I		15 06.7	+ 3 46 d	Vir			vF, vS
1088 I		15 06.7	+ 3 46 d	Vir			eeF, vS
5849	Gx	15 06.9	− 14 36 r	Lib		15p	∗13 in vF neb, 3 st p 1ˢ, ∗8 f 10ˢ, 15′ s
5851	Gx	15 06.9	+ 12 52 r	Boo		15p	eF, vS, np of 2
1099 I	Gx	15 06.9	+ 56 31 v	Dra	1.4		eeF, pS, R, bet 2 F st
5852	Gx	15 07.0	+ 12 51 r	Boo		14p	eF, vS, sf of 2
5850	Gx	15 07.1	+ 1 33 s	Vir	4.3	11.0	cF, S, lE, psbM

NGC	Type	α_{2000}		δ_{2000}		Const.	Size	Mag.	Description
		h m		° ′			′		
5856	–	15 07.3	+ 18 27	r	Boo			neb *6 (??)
1089 I	Gx	15 07.4	+ 7 08	z	Vir		15p	eF, vS, R
5843	Gx	15 07.5	– 36 20	c	Lup	2.0		vF, S, lE, vlbM, r
5857	Gx	15 07.5	+ 19 36	s	Boo	1.4	13.1	cF, cS, E, p of Dneb
1092 I	Gx	15 07.5	+ 9 23	z	Boo		15p	vF, vS, R
5859	Gx	15 07.6	+ 19 35	s	Boo	3.0	12.4	pF, pS, E, f of Dneb
1093 I	Gx	15 07.7	+ 14 33	u	Boo	1.0	15p	pB, vS, R, lbM
1094 I	Gx	15 07.7	+ 14 38	m	Boo	0.5	15p	pB, vS, R, biN
5854	Gx	15 07.8	+ 2 34	s	Vir	2.7	11.8	pB, S, vlE, lbM, am st
5855	Gx	15 07.9	+ 3 58	r	Vir		15p	eF, S, R, 2 st nf
5874	Gx	15 07.9	+ 54 45	s	Boo	2.5	14p	vF, pL, R, in △ of 3 B st
1091 I	Gx	15 08.2	– 11 09	v	Lib	1.4		vF, S, dif
4534 I		15 08.2	+ 23 42	d	Boo			pB, S, E ns, N
1095 I		15 08.5	+ 14 01	d	Boo			eeF, S, lE
1096 I	Gx	15 08.5	+ 19 11	u	Boo	1.1	15p	vF, S, dif
1097 I	Gx	15 08.5	+ 19 11	u	Boo	1.1	15p	vF, vS, R, lbM
4535 I		15 08.7	+ 37 34	d	Boo			F, S, dif, *14 sp
5858	Gx	15 08.8	– 11 13	s	Lib	1.4	14p	F, S, stell N, 5861 sf
5881		15 09.1	+ 62 57	d	Dra			pF, cS, R, vgbM (place?)
5875	Gx	15 09.2	+ 52 32	s	Boo	2.6	13p	pB, pL, lE
5861	Gx	15 09.3	– 11 19	s	Lib	3.0	12p	F, L, E, r
5876	Gx	15 09.5	+ 54 30	s	Boo	2.6	14p	F, S, R, mbM
5864	Gx	15 09.6	+ 3 03	s	Vir	2.8	13p	pF, cS, ilE, gbM, *14 f
5879	Gx	15 09.8	+ 57 00	s	Dra	4.4	11.5	cB, S, E, mbMRN, r
5865	Gx	15 09.9	+ 0 31	A	Vir		15p	eF, 5869 s 3′
5868		15 09.9	+ 0 31	A	Vir			eF, 5869 s 3′; = 5865
5869		15 09.9	+ 0 28	F	Vir		13p	pF, S, E, psbM
5871	*	15 10.1	+ 0 31	F	Vir			eF, forms trapez with 3 neb p
5844		15 10.7	– 64 41	r	TrA			pB, pL, R, vgvlbM
5863	Gx	15 10.8	– 18 27	r	Lib		14p	*12 in eF neb, S, R
1101 I		15 10.9	+ 5 46	D	Vir			eF, vS, *13 f 1ˢ.5, *13 p 2ˢ
5872	Gx	15 11.0	– 11 30	r	Lib		14p	vF, S, R, vmbM, *13 nf 0′.5
1102 I	Gx	15 11.1	+ 4 18	u	Vir	1.2	15p	eeF, vS, F* sf, v diffic
1114 I		15 11.3	+ 75 27	d	UMi			vF; only a *13?
5909	Gx	15 11.5	+ 75 22	A	UMi		14p	vF, vS
4522 I	Gx	15 11.5	– 75 52	c	Aps	2.9		vF, vS, cbM, st inv
1103 I		15 11.6	+ 19 12	d	Ser			vF, S
5894	Gx	15 11.7	+ 59 49	s	Dra	3.3	13p	pF, pS, E 0°±
5912	Gx	15 11.7	+ 75 22	A	UMi		14p	vF, vS
5833	Gx	15 11.8	– 72 52	r	Aps			F, cS, lE, glbM, am st
1110 I	Gx	15 12.1	+ 67 22	u	UMi	1.3	15p	eeF, S, mE
5886	Gx	15 12.7	+ 41 13	r	Boo		15p	F, vS, R, bM
5873	Pl	15 12.8	– 38 08	s	Lup	0.1	13p	◯ , stellar = 9.5 mag
5877	*⃰*	15 12.8	– 4 56	F	Lib			vF, S, *12 att n
1104 I	*	15 12.8	– 5 05	F	Lib			vF
5888	Gx	15 13.1	+ 41 16	s	Boo	1.5	14p	cF, vS, R, bM, r
5884		15 13.2	+ 31 52	D	Boo			only 2 F st (pos 170°, dist 7″)
4536 I	Gx	15 13.2	– 18 08	c	Lib	2.6		vF, L, R, F* att np, F* nr sf
5889	Gx	15 13.3	+ 41 20	s	Boo	0.9	16p	eeF, glbM
1105 I		15 13.3	+ 4 16	d	Ser			eeF, S, lE, F* np
5893	Gx	15 13.6	+ 41 58	s	Boo	1.4	14p	F, S, R, r, 3 st nr
5892	Gx	15 13.7	– 15 30	r	Lib		13p	eF, L, gbM
5878	Gx	15 13.8	– 14 16	s	Lib	3.5	11.5	pB, pL, pmE 0°, psmbM, * inv
5895	Gx	15 13.8	+ 41 59	r	Boo		15p	vF, S, E ns, apparently conn with 5896
5896	Gx	15 13.8	+ 41 59	r	Boo		15p	vF, vS, R

NGC	Type	α_{2000}	δ_{2000}	Const.	Size	Mag.	Description
		h m	o ′		′		
1106 I	Gx	15 14.0	+ 4 43 z	Ser		15p	vF, vS, R, gbM
1107 I	Gx	15 14.2	+ 4 43 z	Ser		15p	F, vS, R, gbM
5902	Gx	15 14.4	+ 50 21 r	Boo		15p	vF, vS, stellar
1111 I		15 14.4	+ 54 32 d	Boo			pB, S, R, 2 st nr
5887	Gx	15 14.8	+ 1 08 r	Ser		15p	pF, pS, gbM
5899	Gx	15 15.0	+ 42 03 s	Boo	3.0	11.8	cB, pL, pmE, smbMN
5880	Gx	15 15.1	− 14 34 F	Lib		15p	eF, vS, R, bM, in field with 5883
5885	Gx	15 15.1	− 10 05 s	Lib	3.5	11.7	F, cL, R, vgbM
5900	Gx	15 15.1	+ 42 13 s	Boo	1.6	15p	vF, S, vlE, gbM
5901	*	15 15.1	+ 42 12 r	Boo			close n of 5900, eF, S
5883	Gx	15 15.2	− 14 37 D	Lib			vF, pS, stellar N
5905	Gx	15 15.4	+ 55 31 s	Dra	4.2	12p	pF, pS, iR
5906	Gx	15 15.8	+ 56 20 h	Dra	0.5	14p	a ray, vmE, par to 5907 and close p it
5907	Gx	15 15.9	+ 56 19 s	Dra	12.3	10.4	cB, vL, vmE 155°, vg, psbMN
5891	Gx	15 16.3	− 11 31 r	Lib		14p	vF, pS, lE, gbM, *11 f
5908	Gx	15 16.7	+ 55 25 s	Dra	3.2	11.9	pF, pS, R
5882	Pl	15 16.8	− 45 39 s	Lup	0.1	11p	◯ , vS, R, quite sharp
1108 I		15 16.8	− 45 39 d	Lup			stellar, gaseous spectrum
1109 I	Gx	15 17.1	+ 5 15 z	Ser		15p	eeF, pS, R, * nf, v diffic
5897	Gb	15 17.4	− 21 01 s	Lib	12.6	8.6	⊕ , pF, L, viR, vgbM, rrr
4537 I	Gx	15 17.5	+ 2 02 z	Ser		16p	eF, vS, R, bM
5890	Gx	15 17.9	− 17 35 r	Lib		14p	vF, vS, E 235°
1112 I	Gx	15 17.9	+ 7 13 z	Ser		15p	eeF, pS, R
5898	Gx	15 18.2	− 24 06 s	Lib	1.7	11.5	F, S, R, gbM
1113 I	Gx	15 18.3	+ 12 29 m	Ser	0.6	15p	eF, *12 nr
4539 I	Gx	15 18.5	+ 32 24 m	CrB	0.4	15p	F, S, R, vlbM
5903	Gx	15 18.6	− 24 04 s	Lib	2.0	11.5	cF, S, R, gpmbM
5904	Gb	15 18.6	+ 2 05 s	Ser	17.4	5.8	!!, ⊕ , vB, L, eCM, st 11...15; = M5
5914	Gx	15 18.7	+ 41 52 r	Boo		15p	F, vS, R, F st inv
5910	Gx	15 19.3	+ 20 55 r	Ser		15p	vF, S, er
5918	Gx	15 19.3	+ 45 54 r	Boo		14p	cF, L, pmE, glbM, *̣ s
4540 I		15 20.1	+ 1 47 d	Ser			vF, pS, mE, B* nr
5911	Gx	15 20.4	+ 3 32 r	Ser		14p	vF, vS, 2 S st inv
5913	Gx	15 20.9	− 2 35 r	Ser		14p	vF, pL, vlE, r
5922	Gx	15 21.2	+ 41 40 h	Boo	0.5	15p	eF, S
5923	Gx	15 21.2	+ 41 43 s	Boo	2.0	15p	vF, pL, vlE, vgbM
4538 I	Gx	15 21.2	− 23 39 c	Lib	2.6		eeF, vL
5917	Gx	15 21.4	− 7 22 r	Lib		14p	eF, vS, psbM
5919	Gx	15 21.5	+ 7 44 r	Ser		15p	eeF, pS, lE, np of 2
5915	Gx	15 21.6	− 13 06 s	Lib	1.6	12p	B, S, R, glbM, p of 2
5916	Gx	15 21.6	− 13 10 s	Lib	2.9	14p	F, S, lE, glbM, f of 2
5920	Gx	15 21.8	+ 7 42 s	Ser	1.4	13.6	eeF, pS, lE, sf of 2
5921	Gx	15 21.9	+ 5 04 s	Ser	4.9	10.8	cB, cL, iR, vsbM *12, am st
5924	Gx	15 21.9	+ 31 14 r	CrB		15p	neb*, vF, S, F* close s
1116 I	Gx	15 21.9	+ 8 26 m	Ser	1.2	15p	eeF, S, R
4542 I		15 22.1	+ 33 10 d	Boo			F, S, R, N, *12 sp
1115 I	*	15 22.4	− 4 28 F	Lib			only a D*, 12.5 & 13.5, dist 5″
5926	Gx	15 23.4	+ 12 42 r	Ser		15p	F, vS, 2 st nr
1117 I		15 24.4	+ 15 27 d	Ser			F, vS, R, lbM
4543 I	Pl	15 24.6	+ 13 29 z	Ser			eF, pS, vF* nr np
5939	Gx	15 24.8	+ 68 45 r	UMi		13p	pB, pS, lE
1118 I	Gx	15 25.1	+ 13 26 m	Ser	0.8	15p	pB, vS, R, S* nr
1119 I	Gx	15 25.7	− 3 39 m	Ser	0.5	15p	F, pS, R, *11.5 nf
5928	Gx	15 25.9	+ 18 05 r	Ser		14p	pB, cS, R, psbM, *7 n
5929	Gx	15 26.1	+ 41 40 s	Boo	1.1	13p	vF, vS, sp of Dneb

NGC	Type	α_{2000}	δ_{2000}	Const.	Size	Mag.	Description
		h m	° ′		′		
5930	Gx	15 26.1	+ 41 41 s	Boo	2.0	13p	pF, pS, R, nf of Dneb
1120 I		15 26.2	+ 18 52 d	Ser			eF, eS, vF, * att
5932	Gx	15 26.8	+ 48 37 r	Boo		15p	vF, pS, R, np of 2
5933	Gx	15 27.0	+ 48 37 r	Boo		15p	eeF, vS, R, sf of 2
4546 I	Gx	15 27.0	+ 28 51 m	CrB	0.6	15p	F, vS, R, *13 att
4547 I	Gx	15 27.3	+ 28 48 z	CrB		15p	F, S, R, N, r
4548 I		15 27.4	+ 28 51 d	CrB			vF, S, iF, r
5925	OC	15 27.7	− 54 31 s	Nor	15	8p	Cl, vL, vRi, lC, st 11...14
1121 I	Gx	15 27.8	+ 6 49 z	Ser		16p	eeF, eS, stellar, vF* close
5927	Gb	15 28.0	− 50 40 s	Lup	12.0	8.3	⊕, cB, L, R, vgbM, rrr, st 15
5949	Gx	15 28.0	+ 64 46 s	Dra	2.4	13p	F, S, lE 45°±, vglbM
5934	Gx	15 28.2	+ 42 55 r	Boo		14p	F, S, irr, lE ns, 2 S st inv
5935	Gx	15 28.3	+ 42 56 r	Boo		15p	*13-14 seems slightly nebs
1123 I		15 28.9	+ 42 53 d	Boo			vF, eS, stellar
4549 I	Gx	15 29.2	+ 32 50 m	Boo	0.5	15p	F, cS, E pf
4544 I		15 29.4	− 50 35 d	Nor			◯, stellar
5931	Gx	15 29.5	+ 7 35 r	Ser		15p	ef, pL, R
1122 I	Gx	15 29.5	+ 7 35 m	Ser	0.2	15p	vF, pS, mbM, *11 p 1′
1139 I	Gx	15 29.6	+ 82 36 z	UMi		16p	eeF, S, lE, v diffic
5943	Gx	15 29.8	+ 42 47 r	Boo		14p	vF, pS, dif
5945	Gx	15 29.8	+ 42 55 r	Boo		14p	pF, pL, gmbM, S* att np
4541 I	Gx	15 29.9	− 70 35 c	Aps	2.0		eF, vS, mE 150°, susp
5936	Gx	15 30.0	+ 12 59 s	Ser	1.5	12.4	F, pL, iR, vgbM, r
1124 I		15 30.0	+ 23 38 D	Ser			pB, cS, E 250°, N
5947	Gx	15 30.7	+ 42 43 r	Boo		15p	vF, S, dif
1143 I	Gx	15 30.7	+ 82 28 v	UMi	1.8		pF, vS, R, * nr
5937	Gx	15 30.8	− 2 49 r	Ser		13p	pB, pS, R, vgbM, 3 st f
5940	Gx	15 31.2	+ 7 28 r	Ser		14p	eF, pS, R, F* p, 1st of 4
5941	Gx	15 31.5	+ 7 20 r	Ser		15p	eeF, S, R, 2nd of 4
5950	Gx	15 31.5	+ 40 26 r	Boo		15p	vF, S, R, S* np
5942	Gx	15 31.6	+ 7 18 r	Ser		15p	eeF, S, R, 3rd of 4
5944	Gx	15 31.7	+ 7 19 r	Ser		15p	eeF, S, R, 4th of 4
1129 I	Gx	15 32.0	+ 68 15 u	UMi	1.2	14p	vF, pS, iR, D* nf
5948	−	15 32.9	+ 3 59 r	Ser			F* in vF neby, vF* close
1125 I	Gx	15 33.1	− 1 38 u	Ser	1.7	14p	F, pL, R, dif
5963	Gx	15 33.5	+ 56 35 s	Dra	3.5	12p	pF, pS, iF
5951	Gx	15 33.7	+ 15 00 s	Ser	3.5	13p	F, pS, E 150°±
4551 I		15 33.9	+ 6 01 z	Ser			eeF, L, R, v dif; = 5964
5965	Gx	15 34.0	+ 56 42 s	Dra	5.4	13p	cF, cL, lE
5953	Gx	15 34.5	+ 15 12 s	Ser	2.0	13p	pB, cS, p of Dneb
5954	Gx	15 34.6	+ 15 12 s	Ser	1.3	14p	pB, cS, f of Dneb
4557 I	Gx	15 34.6	+ 39 44 z	Boo		16p	F, vS, N
5958	Gx	15 34.7	+ 28 40 r	CrB		13p	pF, pL, iR, bM, r
5952	Gx	15 34.8	+ 4 57 r	Ser		15p	eF, vS, alm stell; = IC 1126
4550 I		15 34.8	− 50 39 d	Nor			B, pS, lE
5969	Gx	15 34.9	+ 56 28 r	Dra		15p	eS, R, stellar
5956	Gx	15 35.0	+ 11 45 r	Ser		13p	F, S, R, *16 close f
1126 I		15 35.0	+ 5 00 z	Ser			*13, nebulous?; = 5952
4552 I		15 35.0	+ 4 42 d	Ser			eF, pS, R
4553 I	Gx	15 35.0	+ 23 29 s	Ser	2.0	14p	F, S, R, gbM
5955	Gx	15 35.1	+ 5 04 r	Ser		15p	eF, vS, stellar
4554 I		15 35.1	+ 23 28 d	Ser			vF, vS, N, stell
5961	Gx	15 35.2	+ 30 51 s	CrB	0.8	14p	pF, S, E pf
5957	Gx	15 35.4	+ 12 03 s	Ser	3.0	13p	pB, pL, com, lbM
5946	Gb	15 35.5	− 50 40 s	Nor	7.1	9.6	⊕, cB, pL, R, vglbM, rrr, st 16

NGC	Type	α_{2000}	δ_{2000}	Const.	Size	Mag.	Description
		h m	o ′		′		
4556 I	Gx	15 35.5	+ 25 19 m	Ser	0.4	15p	F, S, R, N
5971	Gx	15 35.6	+ 56 29 r	Dra		15p	eeF, vS, R, lbM
5966	Gx	15 35.8	+ 39 47 r	Boo		14p	vF, S, R, gbM, 2 st 8 f
4558 I		15 35.8	+ 25 21 d	Ser			vF, vS
4560 I		15 35.8	+ 39 51 d	Boo			vF, vS; 5966 sf
1127 I		15 35.9	+ 23 29 d	Ser			pF
4559 I		15 35.9	+ 25 21 d	Ser			F, vS, R, N
4562 I	Gx	15 36.0	+ 43 29 v	Boo	1.5		pB, S, R, mbM, F∗ or neb 1′ nf
4563 I	Gx	15 36.0	+ 39 50 m	Boo	0.7	14p	vF, vS, N
5960	Gx	15 36.2	+ 5 40 r	Ser		15p	vF, S, neb∗
5938	Gx	15 36.4	− 66 52 c	TrA	2.8		F, S, am st
5962	Gx	15 36.5	+ 16 37 s	Ser	2.8	11.4	pF, pL, ilE, gbM
4564 I		15 36.6	+ 43 31 d	Boo			pF, R, gbM
4565 I	Gx	15 36.6	+ 43 25 u	Boo	1.0	15p	F, R, gbM
4566 I	Gx	15 36.7	+ 43 33 v	Boo	2.0		pF, R, gbM
5976	Gx	15 36.8	+ 59 23 v	Dra	1.0	14.8	eeF, S, R
4561 I	Gx	15 36.9	+ 25 25 m	Ser	0.3	15p	F, vS, R, N
5959	Gx	15 37.4	− 16 37 r	Lib		14p	vF, pS, vlE, bMN
4567 I		15 37.5	+ 43 16 d	Boo			pF, R, gbM
5964	Gx	15 37.6	+ 5 59 s	Ser	4.2	13p	eF, vL, R, vgbM, r; = IC 4551?
1130 I	Gx	15 37.8	+ 17 15 m	Ser	0.6	15p	vF (another 2′ sp?), ∗8.7 f
5981	Gx	15 37.9	+ 59 23 s	Dra	2.8	13.0	F, mE
1128 I		15 37.9	− 1 33 d	Ser			pF, pS, R
5970	Gx	15 38.5	+ 12 11 s	Ser	3.0	11.4	pF, pL, R, rr
5982	Gx	15 38.7	+ 59 21 s	Dra	2.9	11.1	cB, S, R, psbM, r
5972	Gx	15 38.8	+ 17 02 r	Ser		15p	F, pS, irrR
1131 I	Gx	15 38.9	+ 12 05 v	Ser	1.0		pF, vS, R, stellar, 5970 np
5974	Gx	15 39.0	+ 31 45 s	CrB	0.5	14p	vF, vS, R, bM
5985	Gx	15 39.6	+ 59 20 s	Dra	5.5	11.0	pB, cL, iE, r
5968	Gx	15 39.9	− 30 33 s	Lup	2.2	13p	vF, L, R, gbM, r
5987	Gx	15 39.9	+ 58 05 s	Dra	4.7	13p	pF, cS
5975	Gx	15 40.0	+ 21 28 r	Ser		14p	vF, vS, irrR, sev vF st inv
1132 I	Gx	15 40.0	+ 20 40 m	Ser	1.1	14p	no descr
4568 I	Gx	15 40.1	+ 28 09 z	CrB		15p	F, S, R, N
5973	Gx	15 40.2	− 8 37 r	Lib			F, S, iR
5977	Gx	15 40.4	+ 17 07 r	Ser		15p	eF, S, R, lbM
4569 I	Gx	15 40.8	+ 28 17 m	CrB	0.5	15p	pB, D ∗13 in S neb
1133 I	Gx	15 41.2	+ 15 34 u	Ser	1.3	15p	pB, pL, iF
4570 I	Gx	15 41.3	+ 28 14 u	CrB	1.0	15p	F, cS, R
5980	Gx	15 41.4	+ 15 47 s	Ser	2.1	13p	F, pS, E 0°
5989	Gx	15 41.5	+ 59 45 r	Dra		13p	vF, vS
4545 I	Gx	15 41.5	− 81 38 c	Aps	2.0		eeF, eS, mE 145°, bet 2 vF st, susp
4572 I	Gx	15 41.9	+ 28 07 m	CrB	0.9	15p	pB, cS, gbM, dif, r
4574 I	Gx	15 42.0	+ 28 15 z	CrB		16p	pF, S, R
4573 I	Gx	15 42.2	+ 23 48 z	Ser		16p	F, vS, dif, r
4575 I		15 42.3	+ 23 48 d	Ser			F, S, dif, r, ∗15 att
5978	Gx	15 42.4	− 13 14 r	Lib		14p	eF, vS, sbMN, am st
4576 I	Gx	15 42.6	+ 23 41 z	Ser		15p	F, vS, R, N, ∗14 np
5983	Gx	15 42.7	+ 8 14 r	Ser		15p	eF, eS, R, vlbM
4577 I		15 42.7	+ 23 47 d	Ser			F, S, R, gbM, r
4579 I		15 42.8	+ 23 46 d	Ser			F, S, R, gbM, r
5984	Gx	15 42.9	+ 14 14 s	Ser	3.0	13p	pB, S, E 135°±, bM
4580 I	Gx	15 43.2	+ 28 22 z	CrB		15p	F, S, R
4581 I	Gx	15 44.0	+ 28 17 z	CrB		15p	F, S, iF, ∗12.5 nr
5992	Gx	15 44.4	+ 41 05 s	Boo	1.1	14p	vF, vS, R, bM, sp of 2

NGC	Type	α_{2000}	δ_{2000}	Const.	Size	Mag.	Description
		h m	° ′		′		
5993	Gx	15 44.5	+ 41 07 r	Boo		14p	cF, vS, R, bM, nf of 2
5988	Gx	15 44.6	+ 10 17 r	Ser		15p	eeF, pS, R, F* nr n
1134 I	Gx	15 44.9	+ 16 58 m	Ser	0.4	15p	vF, vS, dif
5991	Gx	15 45.3	+ 24 37 r	Ser		14p	pF, S, R, mbM
1135 I	Gx	15 45.6	+ 17 42 m	Ser	0.6	15p	vF, vS, R
4582 I	Gx	15 45.7	+ 28 06 u	CrB	1.4	15p	F, S, E pf, gbM, *12.5 f 6ˢ.5
5986	Gb	15 46.1	− 37 47 s	Lup	9.8	7.1	!, ⊕, vB, L, R, vgbM, st 13...15
1145 I		15 46.2	+ 72 27 d	UMi			eeF, pS, R, 6011 nr
5990	Gx	15 46.4	+ 2 24 r	Ser		13p	vF, vS, R, gbM
4583 I	Gx	15 46.4	+ 23 49 m	Ser	0.8	15p	F, vS, E, N, r
6011	Gx	15 46.6	+ 72 09 r	UMi		14p	vF, S, E 90°±, vS* f
5994	Gx	15 46.8	+ 17 51 r	Ser		15p	S, sp 5996
5996	Gx	15 46.9	+ 17 52 r	Ser		13p	pF, cS, R, r, bet 2 D st
5997	Gx	15 47.4	+ 8 19 r	Ser		15p	eF, eeS, stell
1136 I	Gx	15 47.6	− 1 33 z	Ser		15p	F, eS, stellar
5979	Pl	15 47.7	− 61 13 s	TrA	0.1		!, ○, pF, vS, R, r? am 150 st
6001	Gx	15 47.7	+ 28 38 r	CrB		14p	vF, S, R
6002	Gx	15 47.7	+ 28 37 m	CrB	0.2	17p	neb 100″ s of 6001
5967	Gx	15 48.1	− 75 40 s	Aps	2.9	12p	F, pL, R, vgbM
1138 I	Gx	15 48.2	+ 26 12 u	CrB	1.0	15p	vF, S, iF, lbM, r
4555 I	Gx	15 48.3	− 78 11 c	Aps	1.9		vF, vS, eE 55°, bM
5995	Gx	15 48.4	− 13 47 r	Lib		14p	eF, S, R, vS* p
1146 I	Gx	15 48.5	+ 69 23 m	Dra	0.9	14p	vF, pS, R, 2 st nr, sp of 2
1137 I		15 48.9	+ 8 35 d	Ser			vF, S, R, *9 close np
4571 I	Gx	15 48.9	− 67 19 c	TrA	1.4		cF, cS, mE 155°
1140 I		15 49.1	+ 19 04 d	Ser			vF (S Cl?), *9.5 close
6003	Gx	15 49.3	+ 19 01 r	Ser		14p	F, vS, S* inv
5998	−	15 49.4	− 28 36 r	Sco			Cl, pL, pRi, st vS
1142 I		15 49.4	+ 18 09 d	Ser			vF, dif
1141 I		15 49.6	+ 12 24 d	Ser			vF, vS, R
6000	Gx	15 49.9	− 29 24 t	Sco	1.9		vF, S, R, sbM
1147 I	Gx	15 50.1	+ 69 33 m	Dra	0.4	15p	eeF, S, R, nf of 2
6004	Gx	15 50.3	+ 18 56 r	Ser		13p	vF, pL, lE, lbM
1144 I	Gx	15 51.3	+ 43 25 m	Her	0.6	15p	eeF, vS, R, * sf
6015	Gx	15 51.4	+ 62 19 s	Dra	5.4	11.2	B, mE
5999	OC	15 52.2	− 56 28 s	Nor	5	9p	Cl, L, pRi, st 12...14
6019	Gx	15 52.3	+ 64 51 r	Dra		15p	eeF, S, R, v diffic
1154 I	Gx	15 52.5	+ 70 23 u	UMi	1.8	15p	vF, pS, R
6008	Gx	15 52.9	+ 21 08 r	Ser		14p	vF, R, pL, bM
6013	Gx	15 52.9	+ 40 39 r	Her		14p	eF, vS, iR, lbM
6006	Gx	15 53.0	+ 12 02 r	Ser		15p	vF, S
6024	Gx	15 53.2	+ 64 56 r	Dra		15p	pF, pS, R, bM, * close
4578 I	Gx	15 53.2	− 74 50 c	Aps	2.1		eF, eS, cE 140°, bet 2 vF st
6007	Gx	15 53.4	+ 11 57 s	Ser	1.9	14p	F, pL
6009	Gx	15 53.5	+ 12 05 r	Ser		15p	F, vS, stell
6012	Gx	15 54.2	+ 14 35 s	Ser	2.3	13p	F, bet 2 B st
6010	Gx	15 54.4	+ 0 32 r	Ser		13p	pF, S, E 90°±, gbM, r
4586 I		15 54.9	+ 6 01 x	Ser			eF, S, R, bet *8 f & curve of st p; = 6014
1164 I		15 55.1	+ 70 35 d	UMi			*13 with neb?
6068	Gx	15 55.4	+ 79 00 s	UMi	1.2	13p	vF, vS, lE 0°, r
6005	OC	15 55.8	− 57 26 s	Nor	3	10.7	Cl, pS, pRi, mC, st 16
6014	Gx	15 55.8	+ 5 57 r	Ser		14p	pB, pL, E; = IC 4586
6016	Gx	15 55.9	+ 26 59 r	CrB		15p	vF, S, E
1152 I	Gx	15 56.7	+ 48 05 m	Her	1.0	14p	vF, S, R, sp of 2
1153 I		15 56.8	+ 48 10 d	Her			pF, pS, R, bM, * nf, nf of 2

NGC	Type	α_{2000}	δ_{2000}	Const.	Size	Mag.	Description
		h m	° ′		′		
1148 I		15 56.9	+ 22 25 x	Ser			neb *; = 6020
6017	Gx	15 57.2	+ 6 00 r	Ser		14p	!, vF, vS, R, disc g, smbM
6020	Gx	15 57.2	+ 22 24 s	Ser	1.7	12.6	eF, eS, iR, lbM; = IC 1148?
6018	Gx	15 57.5	+ 15 51 s	Ser	1.8	15p	vF, S, lE, p of 2
6021	Gx	15 57.5	+ 15 56 s	Ser	2.1	14p	eF, vS, lE, f of 2
6048	Gx	15 57.6	+ 70 42 s	UMi	2.5	14p	F, R, bM
6022	Gx	15 57.8	+ 16 16 s	Ser	0.8	15p	eF, eS
6023	Gx	15 57.8	+ 16 18 s	Ser	1.4	15p	F, S, R, bM
1149 I		15 58.0	+ 12 05 d	Ser			eeF, pS, R, am 4 st, v diffic
1150 I		15 58.3	+ 15 52 d	Ser			2 S st in F neby
1151 I	Gx	15 58.5	+ 17 27 x	Ser		13p	vF, pL, dif
6027	Gx	15 59.2	+ 20 45 s	Ser	2.2	12.4	eF, vF* inv, 2 vF st nr
1187 I	Gx	15 59.3	+ 70 34 m	UMi	0.3	16p	*13 with neb
4587 I	Gx	15 59.9	+ 25 57 z	CrB		15p	eF, eS, T CBr sp
4584 I	Gx	16 00.2	− 66 23 c	TrA	1.7		eF, S, iF
4585 I	Gx	16 00.3	− 66 19 c	TrA	2.0		eF, S, iF
1155 I	Gx	16 00.6	+ 15 42 v	Ser	1.3		vF, S, diffic
1156 I	Gx	16 00.6	+ 19 44 x	Her		15p	eeF, pS, lE, 2 st nr
1157 I	Gx	16 01.0	+ 15 31 m	Ser	0.6	16p	vF, vS
1159 I		16 01.0	+ 15 25 d	Ser			vF, eS, R
6071	Gx	16 01.1	+ 70 37 r	UMi		15p	eF, vS
1160 I		16 01.1	+ 15 29 d	Ser			vF, vS, R
1161 I	Gx	16 01.3	+ 15 39 m	Her	0.6	15p	F, vS, R, vSN
1162 I	Gx	16 01.3	+ 17 41 x	Her		15p	vF, vS, R, diffic (another susp)
6026	Pl	16 01.4	− 34 32 s	Lup	0.8		F, S, R, gpmbM, △ of st np
6028	Gx	16 01.4	+ 19 21 s	Her	1.7	13.2	vF, pS, no Nucl
1158 I	Gx	16 01.5	+ 1 43 s	Ser	2.9	13p	eeF, pL, iR
1163 I	Gx	16 01.5	+ 15 30 m	Ser	0.2	15p	F, R, vSN
6030	Gx	16 01.8	+ 17 58 r	Her		14p	pF, vS, R, bM
6029	Gx	16 02.0	+ 12 34 r	Ser		15p	vF, vS
1165 I		16 02.1	+ 15 42 d	Her			vF, S, diffic
1166 I	Gx	16 02.1	+ 26 20 z	CrB		15p	vF, vS, vF, * nf
6038	Gx	16 02.6	+ 37 21 r	CrB		14p	vF, S, R, *10 sf
6032	Gx	16 03.0	+ 20 58 s	Her	1.8	15p	vF, pL, lE, vlbM, np of 2
6034	Gx	16 03.4	+ 17 12 r	Her		15p	eeF, vS, R, v diffic
6035	Gx	16 03.4	+ 20 54 s	Her	1.2	14p	vF, pL, lE, sf of 2
6025	OC	16 03.7	− 60 30 s	TrA	12	5.1	Cl, B, vL, pRi, lC, st 7...
1167 I	Gx	16 03.9	+ 14 57 m	Ser	0.5		F, vS, R
1168 I	Gx	16 04.0	+ 14 54 m	Ser	0.5	16p	pF, vS, iF, D?, 3 F st n
1169 I	Gx	16 04.2	+ 13 45 u	Ser	1.0	14p	eF, vS, stellar
6033	Gx	16 04.4	− 2 08 r	Ser		15p	vF neb*
6036	Gx	16 04.4	+ 3 52 r	Ser		14p	vF, vS, R, stell
6037	Gx	16 04.4	+ 3 48 r	Ser		15p	vF, S
6039	*	16 04.4	+ 17 42 A	Her			eeF, vS, R, sp of 3 in line
6040	Gx	16 04.4	+ 17 45 s	Her	1.6	15p	vF, eS, F* close
6058	Pl	16 04.4	+ 40 41 s	Her	0.4	13p	pF, vS, R, stellar
6079		16 04.5	+ 69 38 D	Dra			vF, vS
1170 I	Gx	16 04.5	+ 17 43 x	Her	0.3		vF, vS, vSFN, 6041 f
1200 I	Gx	16 04.5	+ 69 42 u	UMi	1.4	14p	pF, pS, lE, *12 nr; = IC 1204?
6041	Gx	16 04.6	+ 17 43 s	Her	1.6	13.7	F, S
6042	Gx	16 04.6	+ 17 42 r	Her		15p	vF, vS
6043	Gx	16 04.9	+ 17 47 r	Her		15p	eeF, pS, lE, "4th of 10"
6046	−	16 04.9	+ 19 21 r	Her			eF, pL, partly verified
6051	Gx	16 04.9	+ 23 56 s	Ser	1.9	13.0	F, S, R, gbMN, *10 sf; = IC 4588
1171 I	*	16 04.9	+ 17 59 x	Her			neb *?

NGC	Type	α_{2000}	δ_{2000}	Const.	Size	Mag.	Description
		h m	o ′		′		
1172 I	Gx	16 04.9	+ 17 52 z	Her		15p	vF, S, stellar N
4588 I	Gx	16 04.9	+ 23 56 u	Ser	2.1	15p	vF, vS, R, stell, 5051 p
6044	Gx	16 05.0	+ 17 52 v	Her	0.5	16p	eeF, vS, R, vF∗ close p
6045	Gx	16 05.1	+ 17 45 v	Her	1.3	14.2	eeF, vS, R, v diffic
6047	Gx	16 05.1	+ 17 43 s	Her	1.3	13.6	eF, R, pS, F∗ close n
6052	Gx	16 05.2	+ 20 32 s	Her	1.0	13.0	F, pL, iR; = 6064?
1173 I	Gx	16 05.2	+ 17 25 v	Her	1.3		pF, S, iF, gbM, r
1175 I	?	16 05.3	+ 18 08 z	Her			neb object, 6055 f 2′
1177 I	Gx	16 05.3	+ 18 19 z	Her			vF, ∗9.5 4′ s
6050	Gx	16 05.4	+ 17 46 s	Her		15p	eeF, S, R, v diffic
6053	∗	16 05.4	+ 18 08 A	Her			eeF, S, R, v diffic; = IC 1180
6054	Gx	16 05.4	+ 17 47 r	Her		15p	eeF, pS, lE, F∗ sp; = IC 1179
1174 I	Gx	16 05.4	+ 15 02 u	Ser	1.0	14p	pF, S, bMN = 12m
1176 I	Gx	16 05.4	+ 17 58 z	Her		15p	eeF, pS, iR, 2 st nr s
1179 I	Gx	16 05.4	+ 17 45 z	Her	0.6	16p	eeF, pS, R; = 6054?
1180 I	?	16 05.4	+ 18 07 z	Her			F∗ with neb?, 6055 f
6055	Gx	16 05.5	+ 18 10 s	Her	1.5	15p	eeF, pS, R, v diffic
6056	Gx	16 05.5	+ 17 58 s	Her		15p	eeF, v diffic
1178 I	Gx	16 05.5	+ 17 36 v	Her	1.4		eeF, pS, bet 2 st
6057	Gx	16 05.6	+ 18 10 r	Her		15p	eeF, eS, R
1181 I	Gx	16 05.6	+ 17 35 v	Her	1.1		eeF, S, R, "12th of 12"
1182 I	Gx	16 05.6	+ 17 48 v	Her	0.6	16p	vF, S, dif, lbM
1183 I	Gx	16 05.6	+ 17 46 v	Her	0.9	14.3	vF, vS, stellar, ∗11 sp 1′
6049	−	16 05.7	+ 8 06 r	Ser			∗7 in photosphere
1184 I	Gx	16 05.7	+ 17 47 z	Her	0.1	16p	∗13 with neb?
1185 I	Gx	16 05.7	+ 17 43 s	Her	0.8	13.9	∗13 with S neb
1186 I	Gx	16 05.7	+ 17 22 v	Her	0.8		F, S, dif
1201 I	Gx	16 05.8	+ 69 37 u	Dra	1.1	16p	eeF, pS, iR, v diffic
6060	Gx	16 05.9	+ 21 30 s	Her	2.2	14p	eF, E, sbM
1188 I	Gx	16 06.1	+ 17 27 z	Her	0.5		vF, S, dif
1189 I	Gx	16 06.2	+ 18 11 v	Her	0.6		eeF, pS, iR, bet 2 st
6061	Gx	16 06.3	+ 18 15 s	Her	1.4	15p	eeF, S, R, 4 B st s
6062	Gx	16 06.3	+ 19 47 r	Her		14p	eF, R, vlbM, r
1190 I	?	16 06.3	+ 18 14 z	Her			eeF, S, R, 6061 nr
1191 I	Gx	16 06.5	+ 18 16 z	Her	0.5		eeF, S, lE
1193 I	Gx	16 06.5	+ 17 43 z	Her	0.4		F, S, r
6094	Gx	16 06.6	+ 72 30 r	UMi		14p	vF, vS, lE
1192 I	Gx	16 06.6	+ 17 46 z	Her	0.7		vF, S, iF, dif
1194 I	Gx	16 06.7	+ 17 46 v	Her	0.5	14.3	eF, vS, dif
1195 I	Gx	16 06.7	+ 17 12 v	Her	0.6		vF, S, dif
6064	−	16 07.0	+ 20 33 r	Her			vF, vS, r, pB∗ sf; = 6052?
1204 I		16 07.1	+ 69 56 D	UMi			vF, S, stell N, ∗11 f 3′
6063	Gx	16 07.2	+ 7 58 r	Ser		14p	F, pL, R, vlbM
6059		16 07.4	− 6 25 D	Oph			vF, S, R
4589 I	∗	16 07.4	− 6 23 F	Oph			∗13, in eF neb?
6065	Gx	16 07.5	+ 13 52 r	Ser		15p	eeF, vS, R, sp of 2
6031	OC	16 07.6	− 54 04 s	Nor	2	8.5	Cl, S, mC, st 11...14
6066	Gx	16 07.7	+ 13 56 r	Ser		15p	eeF, vS, R, 2 pB st nr, nf of 2
6069	Gx	16 07.7	+ 38 55 r	CrB		15p	vF∗ in vF, vS, R neb
6091	Gx	16 07.8	+ 69 55 r	UMi		14p	vF, vS, R, ∗ n
1196 I	Gx	16 08.0	+ 10 47 u	Ser	1.1	15p	eeF, nr p ∗ of 3 in line
1197 I	Gx	16 08.3	+ 7 32 u	Ser	2.8	15p	L, mE, ∗ att nf
4590 I	Gx	16 08.3	+ 28 29 m	CrB	0.3	16p	F, S, gbM, dif
1198 I	Gx	16 08.6	+ 12 20 m	Ser	0.6	15p	F, vS, R, N = 13m
6070	Gx	16 10.0	+ 0 43 s	Ser	3.6	11.7	F, L, pmE, vgbM, r

NGC	Type	α_{2000}		δ_{2000}		Const.	Size	Mag.	Description
		h	m	o	/		/		
6073	Gx	16	10.1	+ 16	42	r	Her		14p	vF, S, r
1199 I	Gx	16	10.6	+ 10	02	u	Ser	1.3	15p	eeF, S, E, *9.5 f 9ˢ
6088	Gx	16	10.7	+ 57	28	r	Dra		14p	vF, vS, lE
6076	Gx	16	11.1	+ 26	52	r	CrB		15p	vF, S, E
6077	Gx	16	11.1	+ 26	56	r	CrB		15p	F, sbM
6095	Gx	16	11.1	+ 61	16	r	Dra		14p	eF, pS, R, in line with 2 st
4594 I		16	11.3	+ 23	40	d	Her			F, S, R, N, r
6074	Gx	16	11.4	+ 14	15	r	Her		15p	eF, vS, R, bM
6075	Gx	16	11.4	+ 23	57	r	Her		15p	F, vS, R, * or st inv; rr?
6090	Gx	16	11.7	+ 52	27	s	Dra	1.9	14p	vF, S, R
4593 I	Pl	16	11.7	+ 12	04	x	Her	2.0	11p	◯ , stellar
4592 I	Nb	16	12.0	− 19	28	s	Sco	150		vL, E, inv ν^2 Sco
6078	Gx	16	12.1	+ 14	12	r	Her		14p	eF, vS, R, bM
4591 I		16	12.3	− 27	56	d	Sco			*5.6 in F neb
6085	Gx	16	12.5	+ 29	22	r	CrB		14p	F, S
6086	Gx	16	12.6	+ 29	29	s	CrB	2.0	15p	F, vS, stellar N
6089	Gx	16	12.7	+ 33	02	r	CrB		15p	vF, S, R, bM
6092	Gx	16	12.7	+ 27	58	r	CrB		15p	vF, stellar N
6072	Pl	16	13.0	− 36	14	s	Sco	1.2	14p	pF, R, vgvlbM, r
6081	Gx	16	13.0	+ 9	52	r	Her		14p	vF, S, R, bM; = IC 1202
1202 I	Gx	16	13.0	+ 9	52	u	Her	1.7	14p	eF, pS, R
6080	Gx	16	13.1	+ 2	10	r	Ser		14p	pB, pS, R, mbM, with *12.5 20″ nf (nebs?)
6067	OC	16	13.2	− 54	13	s	Nor	13	5.6	Cl, vB, vL, vRi, lC, st 10...
6083	Gx	16	13.3	+ 14	10	r	Her		15p	eF, vS, diffic
6084	Gx	16	14.2	+ 17	45	r	Her		15p	eeF, pS, R, v diffic
6097	Gx	16	14.3	+ 35	06	r	CrB		15p	neb *13
1205 I	Gx	16	14.3	+ 9	31	m	Her	0.6	15p	F, S, lE, * p
1210 I	Gx	16	14.5	+ 62	33	u	Dra	1.6	14p	vF, vS, lE, r
6096	Gx	16	14.7	+ 26	34	r	CrB		15p	vF, vS, R, bM
1203 I		16	15.3	− 22	20	d	Sco			no descr
1206 I	Gx	16	15.3	+ 11	18	u	Her	1.1	15p	eF, S, R
6111		16	15.5	+ 62	44	D	Dra			vF, pS, lE, D* nr s
1212 I	Gx	16	15.5	+ 64	14	z	Dra		15p	eeF, pS, R, 3 st n in line
6082	−	16	15.6	− 34	15	r	Sco			eF, S, E, lbM; nonexistent?
6098	Gx	16	15.6	+ 19	27	r	Her		14p	eF, vS, R, *8 f 41ˢ, np of 2
6099	Gx	16	15.6	+ 19	27	r	Her		14p	eF, vS, R, sf of 2
6102	Gx	16	15.6	+ 28	09	r	CrB		15p	vF, S, R
1215 I	Gx	16	15.6	+ 68	25	u	Dra	1.3	14p	vF, S, R, 1st of 3
6103	Gx	16	15.7	+ 31	57	r	CrB		14p	vF, S, R, vglbM
1208 I	Gx	16	15.7	+ 36	32	z	CrB		15p	vF, *7 105″ n
1216 I	Gx	16	16.0	+ 68	22	u	Dra	1.1	15p	eeF, pS, R, 2nd of 3
1217 I		16	16.1	+ 69	41	d	Dra			eeF, S, R, v diffic
4596 I	Gx	16	16.1	− 22	38	c	Sco	1.9		F, S, mE 40°, mbMN, prob spir
1214 I	Gx	16	16.2	+ 65	58	u	Dra	1.1	15p	eF, S, R
6104	Gx	16	16.5	+ 35	42	r	CrB		14p	vF, S, iR
1211 I	Gx	16	16.8	+ 53	01	u	Dra	1.2	14p	pB, vS, R, bM
1218 I	Gx	16	16.8	+ 68	13	m	Dra	0.9	15p	vF, vS, lE
6093	Gb	16	17.0	− 22	59	s	Sco	8.9	7.2	!! ⊕ , vB, L, vmbM (var*), rrr, st 14; = M80
6100	Gx	16	17.0	+ 0	48	r	Ser		14p	eeF, vS, eeF* close p
6105	Gx	16	17.0	+ 34	52	r	CrB		15p	F, S, R, gvlbM
6107	Gx	16	17.2	+ 34	53	r	CrB		14p	F, vS
6123	Gx	16	17.2	+ 61	56	r	Dra		14p	pF, vS, E, * nr
6108	Gx	16	17.3	+ 35	07	r	CrB		15p	eF, vS, R, lbM
6110	Gx	16	17.6	+ 35	05	r	CrB		15p	eF, vS, R, gbM
6109	Gx	16	17.7	+ 35	00	s	CrB	1.3	15p	F, S, R, gbM

NGC	Type	α_{2000}	δ_{2000}	Const.	Size	Mag.	Description
		h m	° ′		′		
4597 I		16 17.8	− 34 22 d	Sco			bM, mag 14
6112	Gx	16 17.9	+ 35 06 r	CrB		15p	vF, vS, R, bM
4598 I		16 18.2	− 31 27 d	Sco			neb streak of F st, 1′ ns
6114	Gx	16 18.3	+ 35 10 r	CrB		15p	eF, S, R, glbM
4600 I		16 18.3	− 22 47 d	Sco			eF, eS, R
1209 I	Nb	16 18.7	+ 15 34 x	Her	0.3		pF, vS, R, bM, r
6106	Gx	16 18.8	+ 7 25 s	Her	2.6	12.2	F, pL, lE, vgbM, r
6116	Gx	16 18.8	+ 35 09 r	CrB		15p	vF, vS, R, gbM
6087	OC	16 18.9	− 57 54 s	Nor	12	5.4	Cl, B, L, lC, st 7...10
6125	−	16 18.9	+ 57 36 r	Dra			pF, pS, lE; = 6130?
6135	−	16 19.0	+ 64 54 r	Dra			vF, vS, mE, 2 st nr
6128	Gx	16 19.1	+ 57 59 u	Dra	1.4	13p	pF, pS, R, bM
6113	Gx	16 19.2	+ 14 07 r	Her		15p	vF, S, R
6127	Gx	16 19.2	+ 57 58 r	Dra		13p	pF, vS, R
6117	Gx	16 19.3	+ 37 05 r	CrB		14p	vF, S, R
4599 I		16 19.3	− 42 16 d	Sco			◯, 15 mag
1207 I		16 19.4	− 29 39 d	Sco			no descr
6130	Gx	16 19.5	+ 57 37 r	Dra		14p	pF, pL, R, B∗ nr p
6119	Gx	16 19.7	+ 37 48 r	CrB		15p	vF, eS, R
6120	Gx	16 19.8	+ 37 47 s	CrB	0.6	14p	vF, vS, R, D∗ nf
4601 I	Nb	16 20.0	− 20 02 s	Sco	20		2 st 8 in eL, dif neb, lE npsf
6133	−	16 20.1	+ 56 40 r	Dra			eeF, S, cE, v diffic
6122	Gx	16 20.2	+ 37 48 r	CrB		15p	vF, R, no N
4595 I	Gx	16 20.7	− 70 09 c	TrA	2.5		F, S, eE 55°
6136	Gx	16 20.8	+ 55 57 r	Dra		15p	eeF, S, R, v diffic
6140	Gx	16 20.9	+ 65 23 s	Dra	6.2	12p	cF, pL, iR
6126	Gx	16 21.4	+ 36 23 r	CrB		14p	F, vS, R, bMSN
6143	Gx	16 21.7	+ 55 05 s	Dra	1.2	14p	pB, iR, vgvlbM
6118	Gx	16 21.8	− 2 17 s	Ser	4.7	12p	vF, cL, cE 45°±, r
6129	Gx	16 21.8	+ 37 59 r	CrB		14p	eF, vS, R, lbM
6131	Gx	16 22.0	+ 38 56 r	CrB		14p	vF, pL, iR, dif
1213 I		16 22.0	− 1 31 d	Ser			F, vS, R
6138	?	16 22.9	+ 40 56 A	Her			vF, vS, R, bM
6137	Gx	16 23.1	+ 37 55 s	CrB	2.2	14p	F, S, iR, bM
6141	?	16 23.1	+ 40 48 A	Her			vF, pS, no Nucl
6142	Gx	16 23.4	+ 37 16 r	CrB		15p	eF, S, bM
4602 I		16 23.4	+ 12 45 d	Her			eeF, lE, e diffic, F∗ f
6121	Gb	16 23.6	− 26 32 s	Sco	26.3	5.9	Cl, 8 or 10 B st line, with 5 st, rrr; = M4
6132	Gx	16 23.7	+ 11 48 r	Her		15p	eF, vS, vlbM
1219 I	Gx	16 24.4	+ 19 28 u	Her	1.4	15p	F, S, E pF, lbM
6115	OC	16 24.6	− 51 58 o	Nor	3	11p	Cl, eL, eRi
6145	Gx	16 25.0	+ 40 56 r	Her		15p	F, R, bM
6147	Gx	16 25.1	+ 40 55 A	Her		16p	eF, one of 3
6146	Gx	16 25.2	+ 40 53 r	Her		14p	cF, vS, R, bM
6124	OC	16 25.6	− 40 40 s	Sco	29	5.8	Cl, B, L, pRi, lCM, st 9...11
6154	Gx	16 25.6	+ 49 50 s	Her	2.4	14p	vF, S, R, lbM, er
4603 I	Nb	16 25.6	− 24 28 s	Oph	20		eF, vL, dif, st inv
4604 I	Nb	16 25.6	− 23 26 s	Oph	60		ρ Oph in eL neb
6157	Gx	16 25.7	+ 55 22 r	Dra		15p	eeF, pS, R, v diffic
6101	Gb	16 25.8	− 72 12 s	Aps	10.7	9.3	⊕, pF, L, iR, vgbM, rr, st 14
6150	Gx	16 25.8	+ 40 30 r	Her		15p	vF, vS, R
6155	Gx	16 26.1	+ 48 22 r	Her		13p	F, pS, iF, gbM
6170	−	16 27.0	+ 59 35 r	Dra			eeF, vS, R, v diffic; = 6176?
6148	Gx	16 27.1	+ 24 05 r	Her			vF, S, with st
6144	Gb	16 27.3	− 26 02 s	Sco	9.3	9.1	Cl, cL, mC, gbM, rrr

NGC	Type	α_{2000}	δ_{2000}	Const.	Size	Mag.	Description
		h m	o ′		′		
6149	Gx	16 27.4	+ 19 36 r	Her		15p	vF, pS, R, pB* nr s
6159	Gx	16 27.4	+ 42 41 r	Her		15p	vF, S, iR, lbM
6176	Gx	16 27.5	+ 59 35 r	Dra		15p	eF, eS, v diffic
6134	OC	16 27.7	− 49 09 s	Nor	7	7.2	Cl, cL, pRi, lCM, st 13...15
6139	Gb	16 27.7	− 38 51 s	Sco	5.5	9.2	B, pL, R, psbM, rr
6158	Gx	16 27.7	+ 39 23 s	Her		16p	F, S, iF
6160	Gx	16 27.7	+ 40 55 s	Her	2.1	15p	cF, pL, R, gbM, r
6161	Gx	16 28.3	+ 32 49 r	Her		15p	vF, S, lbM
6162	Gx	16 28.4	+ 32 52 r	Her		15p	F, S, lbM
6163	Gx	16 28.4	+ 32 52 r	Her		15p	vF, S, lbM
6166	Gx	16 28.6	+ 39 33 s	Her	2.4	12.0	pF, S, vlE, vgmbM
1220 I		16 29.2	+ 8 27 d	Her			eeF, pS, E
6182	Gx	16 29.5	+ 55 31 r	Dra		14p	vF, vS, iR
6174	Gx	16 29.7	+ 40 51 r	Her		15p	vF
6173	Gx	16 29.8	+ 40 49 s	Her	2.2	14p	cF, vS, R, bM
6175	Gx	16 29.9	+ 40 39 r	Her		15p	vF, vS, R
4605 I	Nb	16 30.2	− 25 06 s	Sco	30		*7 in eF, vL neb
4607 I		16 30.3	+ 24 34 d	Her			F, cS, dif
6180	Gx	16 30.5	+ 40 34 r	Her		15p	eF, vS, R, mbM
6177	Gx	16 30.6	+ 35 04 r	Her		15p	vF, pL, iE, rr, * nr
6179	Gx	16 30.7	+ 35 07 r	Her		15p	vF, S, bMN, 4′ nf 6177
6168	Gx	16 31.4	+ 20 12 r	Her		14p	eeF, mE, F* at p end, v diffic
6153	Pl	16 31.5	− 40 15 s	Sco	0.4	12p	◯ , stellar
6184	Gx	16 31.5	+ 40 35 r	Her		15p	eF, vS, R, vlbM
6187	Gx	16 31.6	+ 57 43 r	Dra		15p	vF, vS, lbM
6189	Gx	16 31.6	+ 59 39 r	Dra		13p	vF, pS, lE
4606 I		16 31.6	− 26 03 d	Sco			neb; F* p 4ˢ.5, 0′.5 n
6190	Gx	16 32.0	+ 58 27 r	Dra		13p	vF, pS, R, F* nr
6191	−	16 32.0	+ 58 48 r	Dra			pF, pL, E, 2 st p
6172	−	16 32.1	− 1 29 r	Oph			vF, eS, R, bM
6181	Gx	16 32.3	+ 19 50 s	Her	2.6	11.9	pB, pL, vlE, pgmbM
6171	Gb	16 32.5	− 13 03 s	Oph	10.0	8.1	⊕ , L, vRi, vmC, R, rrr; = M107
6252	Gx	16 32.5	+ 82 36 r	UMi		15p	vF, vS, f of 2
6217	Gx	16 32.6	+ 78 12 s	UMi	3.1	11.2	B, cL, lE, slbM
6251	Gx	16 32.6	+ 82 33 r	UMi		14p	cF, S, bM, p of 2
6152	OC	16 32.7	− 52 37 s	Nor	30	8p	Cl, L, lC, st L
4609 I	Gx	16 33.0	+ 22 46 m	Her	0.7	15p	F, vS, R, gbMN
6185	Gx	16 33.2	+ 35 20 r	Her		14p	F, S, R, gbM, *11 np
4610 I		16 33.6	+ 39 16 d	Her			F, eS, R, gbM
4611 I		16 33.7	+ 39 20 d	Her			F, vS, iF
4612 I		16 33.8	+ 39 16 d	Her			F, eS, R, gbM
6164	Pl	16 34.0	− 48 06 r	Nor			eF (strongly susp), D* f nr
6165	Pl	16 34.0	− 48 06 r	Nor			F, cS, lE, vglbM, D* p
6169	OC	16 34.1	− 44 03 s	Nor	7	7p	Cl, μ Nor inv
6167	OC	16 34.4	− 49 36 s	Nor	8	6.7	Cl, L, lC, iF
6186	Gx	16 34.4	+ 21 33 s	Her	1.8	14p	eF, vS, E
1221 I	Gx	16 34.7	+ 46 24 u	Her	1.3	15p	eeF, pS, E, p of 2
6156	Gx	16 34.8	− 60 36 r	TrA			pF, pL, vlE, gbM
1222 I	Gx	16 35.1	+ 46 13 v	Her	1.9		eeF, pL, R, f of 2
1223 I		16 35.4	+ 49 16 d	Her			eeF, pS, R, bet 2 dist F st
6198	Gx	16 35.5	+ 57 31 r	Dra		15p	vF, vS, R, 2 st f
6178	OC	16 35.7	− 45 38 s	Sco	4	7.2	Cl, B, S, st pL
6202	−	16 36.2	+ 61 57 r	Dra			eeF, pS, * f
6195	Gx	16 36.5	+ 39 02 s	Her	1.8	15p	vF, S, R, gbM, bet 2 st
6194	Gx	16 36.6	+ 36 11 r	Her		14p	vF, vS, sbM *12

NGC	Type	α_{2000}	δ_{2000}	Const.	Size	Mag.	Description
		h m	° ′		′		
1225 I	Gx	16 36.9	+ 67 38 u	Dra	1.5	15p	eeF, vS, 2 or 3 F st inv, ∗ p
4613 I	Gx	16 37.3	+ 35 59 z	Her			eF, dif; = 6196?
6196	Gx	16 37.4	+ 36 06 A	Her		14p	vF, vS, stellar
6197	Gx	16 37.5	+ 36 02 A	Her		15p	eF, E, stellar
4614 I	Gx	16 37.8	+ 36 07 z	Her			eF, stellar
4615 I	Gx	16 37.9	+ 36 04 s	Her	1.7	12.8	∗13 in S neb
4616 I	Gx	16 38.0	+ 36 00 z	Her			eF, S, dif, r; ∗12 sf 2′
6151		16 38.3	− 73 15 r	Aps			vF, vS ∗9 nr
6199	∗	16 39.0	+ 36 06 A	Her			eF
6214	Gx	16 39.5	+ 66 01 r	Dra		14p	eF, vS, R
6206	Gx	16 40.1	+ 58 38 r	Dra		14p	pF, eS, R, stell, 3 vF st nr; = IC 1227
1227 I	?	16 40.1	+ 58 37 z	Dra			vF, S, R, stellar N; = 6206
6201	Gx	16 40.2	+ 23 45 r	Her		15p	eF, vS
6192	OC	16 40.3	− 43 22 s	Sco	8	9p	Cl, pL, pRi, iR, st 11...14
6203	Gx	16 40.4	+ 23 46 r	Her		15p	eF, vS
6188	Nb	16 40.5	− 48 47 s	Ara	20		! F, vL, viE, B∗ inv
1226 I	Gx	16 41.1	+ 46 00 z	Her		15p	eF, S, R, forms arc with 4 st
6193	OC	16 41.3	− 48 46 s	Ara	15	5.2	Cl, vL, lRi, lC, rrr, F neb inv
6211	Gx	16 41.5	+ 57 47 s	Dra	2.0	14p	vF, pS, R, sp of 2
6213	Gx	16 41.5	+ 57 50 r	Dra		15p	eF, vS, R, nf of 2
6183	Gx	16 41.6	− 69 23 r	TrA			vF, eS, R, gbM
6205	Gb	16 41.7	+ 36 28 s	Her	16.6	5.9	!! ⊕, eB, vRi, vgeCM, st 11...; = M13
1228 I	Gx	16 42.0	+ 65 34 u	Dra	1.6	14p	vF, pS∗ n, 4 st in curve s
4617 I	Gx	16 42.1	+ 36 41 z	Her			S, E 29°, bM
1224 I	Gx	16 42.9	+ 19 15 m	Her	0.7	15p	vF, vS, R, stellar
6207	Gx	16 43.1	+ 36 50 s	Her	3.0	11.6	pB, pL, E 45°±, vgmbM
6223	Gx	16 43.1	+ 61 34 s	Dra	3.4	13p	F, S, R, mbM
6212	Gx	16 43.3	+ 39 48 r	Her		15p	eF
6232	Gx	16 43.3	+ 70 38 r	Dra		13p	pF, pL, lE
6226	Gx	16 43.5	+ 61 58 r	Dra		14p	F, S, △ with 2 st 12 & 14
6200	OC	16 44.2	− 47 29 s	Ara	12	7.4	Cl (in Milky Way)
4619 I	Gx	16 44.2	+ 17 46 z	Her		15p	F, R
6210	Pl	16 44.5	+ 23 49 s	Her	0.2	9p	○, vB, vS, R, disc & border (Nucl variable?)
6236	Gx	16 44.5	+ 70 48 s	Dra	3.0	12p	F, pL
1229 I	Gx	16 45.0	+ 51 17 u	Dra	1.0	15p	eeF, pS, v diffic, np of 2
1230 I		16 45.3	+ 51 13 d	Her			eeF, L, R, v diffic, sf of 2
6245	Gx	16 45.5	+ 70 48 r	Dra			vF, pL, R
6219	Gx	16 46.3	+ 9 02 r	Her		15p	F, S
6248	Gx	16 46.4	+ 70 22 s	Dra	3.3	13p	eeF, pL, R, v diffic
6204	OC	16 46.5	− 47 01 s	Ara	5	8.2	Cl, pRi, eiCM, st 11...12
6237	Gx	16 46.5	+ 70 23 r	Dra			eF, S, E
1231 I	Gx	16 46.9	+ 58 27 u	Dra	2.4	14p	eeF, L, R, pB∗ sp
4608 I	Gx	16 46.9	− 77 29 c	Aps	1.2		vF, vS, cE 85°, bM
6229	Gb	16 47.0	+ 47 32 s	Her	4.5	9.4	⊕, vB, L, R, disc & F border, r
6218	Gb	16 47.2	− 1 57 s	Oph	14.5	6.6	!! ⊕, vB, vL, iR, gmbM, rrr, st 10...; = M12
6220	Gx	16 47.2	− 0 17 r	Oph		15p	eeF, pS, iR, 3 F st s
6238	Gx	16 47.2	+ 62 08 r	Dra		14p	eeF, eS, eF∗ close, v diffic
6228	Gx	16 48.0	+ 26 12 r	Her		15p	vF, S
6244	Gx	16 48.1	+ 62 11 r	Dra		14p	vF, vS, R, bet 2 st, nf of 2
6224	Gx	16 48.2	+ 6 18 r	Her		15p	eeF, vS, lE, pB∗ nr n, n of 2
6247	Gx	16 48.2	+ 62 58 r	Dra		13p	F, pS, iF
6225	Gx	16 48.3	+ 6 13 r	Her		15p	eF, vS, lE, F st inv, s of 2
1233 I		16 48.4	+ 63 09 d	Dra			eF, vS, vE, bet 2 st (= 6247?)
4620 I		16 48.5	+ 18 17 d	Her			vF, R
1232 I		16 49.1	+ 46 05 d	Her			eeF, S, iR, B∗ sf

NGC	Type	α_{2000}	δ_{2000}	Const.	Size	Mag.	Description
		h m	o ′		′		
6216	OC	16 49.4	− 44 44 s	Sco	4	10p	Cl, pS, pRi, pC, st 12...15
6208	OC	16 49.5	− 53 49 s	Ara	16	7.2	Cl, L, Ri, lCM, st 9...12
6246	Gx	16 49.9	+ 55 33 s	Dra	1.7	14.1	eF, S, R
6233	Gx	16 50.1	+ 23 34 r	Her		15p	pF, S, R, gbM
6239	Gx	16 50.1	+ 42 44 s	Her	2.8	12.3	vF, E, biN np sf
6241	Gx	16 50.1	+ 45 24 r	Her		15p	eF, pS
6230	Gx	16 50.6	+ 4 35 r	Her		15p	eeF, pS, R, v diffic
6222	OC	16 50.7	− 44 45 r	Sco		10p	Cl, vL, vRi, lbM, st 12...13
4621 I	Gx	16 50.8	+ 8 48 u	Her	1.1	15p	vF, vS
6215	Gx	16 51.1	− 58 59 s	Ara	2.0	12p	pF, R, vglbM, *4 p 79^s
4623 I	Gx	16 51.2	+ 22 31 m	Her	0.6	15p	F, S, R, gbM
4624 I	Gx	16 51.5	+ 17 27 z	Her		16p	vF, R
6227	−	16 51.6	− 41 13 r	Sco			Cl, eL, eRi (Milky Way)
6260	Gx	16 51.8	+ 63 43 r	Dra		15p	eF, pS, R, sev st nr sf
6234	Gx	16 51.9	+ 4 23 r	Oph		15p	F, S, R
1235 I	Gx	16 52.1	+ 63 07 z	Dra		15p	vF, dif, pS, *8 nf 3′
4622 I	?	16 52.1	− 16 14 z	Oph			cF, S, iF, D
6258	Gx	16 52.3	+ 60 33 r	Dra		14p	eF, vS, R, B* & D* p
6243	Gx	16 52.4	+ 23 21 r	Her		15p	vF, vS, iF, dif
6221	Gx	16 52.8	− 59 13 s	Ara	3.2	11p	⊕, pB, cL, R, glbM, rr
1234 I		16 52.9	+ 56 54 d	Dra			vF, sev st in neb?
4625 I		16 52.9	+ 2 26 z	Oph			neb, *10 close nf; = 6240?
6240	Gx	16 53.0	+ 2 24 s	Oph	2.2	15p	vF, pL, lE, dif; = IC 4625
6235	Gb	16 53.4	− 22 11 s	Oph	5.0	10.2	pB, cL, iR, rrr, st 14...16
4626 I	*	16 53.4	+ 2 19 F	Oph			eF
6262	−	16 53.6	+ 56 56 r	Dra			eeF, pS, R, v diffic
6231	C+N	16 54.0	− 41 48 s	Sco	15	2.6	Cl, B, cL, pRi, st 10...13
4627 I		16 54.1	− 7 38 d	Oph			eF, eS, dif, *12 s 12″
6255	Gx	16 54.8	+ 36 30 s	Her	3.5	14p	eF, cL, E 90°
6209	Gx	16 55.1	− 72 32 r	Aps			vF, pL, vgvlbM
4630 I	Gx	16 55.1	+ 26 39 u	Her	1.3	15p	F, S, R, stell N
6242	OC	16 55.6	− 39 30 s	Sco	9	6.4	Cl, B, L, Ri, st 8...11
6275	Gx	16 55.6	+ 63 15 s	Dra		15p	eeF, S, lE, v diffic
6257	Gx	16 56.0	+ 39 39 r	Her		15p	vF (vS D*?), F D* nf
4629 I		16 56.2	− 16 43 d	Oph			vF, vS, eE 75°, susp
1237 I	Gx	16 56.3	+ 55 02 v	Dra	2.1		eF, pL, lE, * nr p
6261	Gx	16 56.5	+ 28 00 r	Her		15p	eF, eS, iF
6263	Gx	16 56.7	+ 27 50 r	Her		15p	vF, vS, R
4628 I	Nb	16 57.0	− 40 20 s	Sco	90		F, eL, E pf, dif
6254	Gb	16 57.1	− 4 06 s	Oph	15.1	6.6	! ⊕, B, vL, R, gvmbM, rrr, st 10...15; = M10
6264	Gx	16 57.3	+ 27 52 r	Her		15p	eF, vS
6265	Gx	16 57.5	+ 27 51 r	Her		15p	eF, vS
6288	Gx	16 57.5	+ 68 27 r	Dra		15p	eF, vS, R, sp of 2
6249	OC	16 57.6	− 44 47 s	Sco	6	8.2	Cl, pRi, vlC, iF, st L & S
6289	Gx	16 57.8	+ 68 31 r	Dra		15p	eF, pL, mE, nf of 2
4618 I	Gx	16 57.9	− 77 00 c	Aps	1.9		!! eF, eS, 2-branch spiral
6250	OC	16 58.0	− 45 48 s	Ara	8	5.9	Cl, L, lRi, lC, st 8...12
6269	Gx	16 58.0	+ 27 52 r	Her		14p	F, S, R
6267	Gx	16 58.2	+ 22 59 r	Her		14p	vF, pL, R, lbM
6285	Gx	16 58.4	+ 58 59 s	Dra	1.3	15p	eeF, S, R, v diffic, np of 2
1236 I	Gx	16 58.5	+ 20 02 v	Her	1.2		eF, pS, vlE, vF* close p
4632 I		16 58.5	+ 22 55 d	Her			eF; neb?
6286	Gx	16 58.6	+ 58 58 s	Dra	1.5	14p	eF, pS, R
6270	Gx	16 58.7	+ 27 38 r	Her		15p	eF, S, R
6271	Gx	16 58.8	+ 27 59 r	Her		15p	vF, R

NGC	Type	α_{2000}	δ_{2000}	Const.	Size	Mag.	Description
		h m	° ′		′		
6272	Gx	16 58.9	+ 27 56 r	Her		15p	vF
6279	Gx	16 59.0	+ 47 14 r	Her		15p	vF, pS, lE, coarse D∗ np
4636 I		16 59.0	+ 47 11 d	Her			vF, fainter than 6279
6253	OC	16 59.1	− 52 43 s	Ara	5	10p	Cl, S, triangular, st 13
6274	Gx	16 59.4	+ 29 57 r	Her		14p	eF, vS
6283	Gx	16 59.4	+ 49 56 r	Her		13p	vF, cS, iR
6256	Gb	16 59.5	− 37 07 s	Sco			⊕, vF, vL, iR, vgbM, rrr
6276	Gx	17 00.3	+ 23 07 r	Her			eF
1238 I		17 00.6	+ 23 05 d	Her			eF
6259	OC	17 00.7	− 44 40 s	Sco	10	8.0	! Cl, B, vL, vRi, st 11...
6277	Gx	17 00.8	+ 23 03 r	Her		15p	eF
6282	Gx	17 00.8	+ 29 50 r	Her		15p	vF, S, R
1239 I	Gx	17 00.8	+ 23 01 u	Her	2.1	14p	eF, eF stell N; = 6276?
6278	Gx	17 00.9	+ 23 01 r	Her		14p	vF, stellar
6290	Gx	17 00.9	+ 59 00 r	Dra		14p	eF, pS, R, ∗ close f
6291	Gx	17 00.9	+ 58 58 r	Dra		15p	eeF, eS, R
1240 I		17 01.0	+ 61 03 d	Dra			susp neb, 3′ nf ∗8.7
6266	Gb	17 01.2	− 30 07 s	Oph	14.1	6.6	! ⊕, vB, L, gmbM, rrr, st 14...16; = M62
4638 I		17 01.2	+ 33 34 d	Her			no descr, ∗9 sf 2′.5
1241 I	Gx	17 01.4	+ 63 42 u	Dra	1.7	14p	eF, pS, R
4634 I	Pl	17 01.6	− 21 50 s	Oph	0.2	11p	◯, stellar
6280	Gx	17 01.9	+ 6 40 r	Oph		15p	pB, S, lE
6268	OC	17 02.4	− 39 44 s	Sco	6	10p	Cl, B, pL, cRi, st 10...
6273	Gb	17 02.6	− 26 16 s	Oph	13.5	7.2	⊕, vB, L, R, vCM, rrr, st 16; = M19
4639 I		17 02.9	+ 22 54 d	Her			vF, vS, R
6292	Gx	17 03.0	+ 61 03 r	Dra		14p	eF, E, v diffic, F st nr
6295	Gx	17 03.1	+ 60 20 r	Dra		15p	eF, S, mE, F∗ nr
6298		17 03.4	+ 62 02 d	Dra			vF, eS, R, bet 2 st, f of 2
6331	Gx	17 03.5	+ 78 38 r	UMi		15p	eF, S
6297	Gx	17 03.6	+ 62 02 r	Dra		14p	pB, pS, R, bet 2 st, p of 2
6284	Gb	17 04.5	− 24 46 s	Oph	5.6	9.0	⊕, B, L, R, CM, rrr, st 16...
6281	C+N	17 04.8	− 37 54 s	Sco	60	5.4	Cl, L, pRi, lC, st 9...11
6299	Gx	17 05.0	+ 62 27 r	Dra		15p	vF, vS, R
6303		17 05.1	+ 68 21 D	Dra			eF, pL, mE, nearly bet 2 st
6287	Gb	17 05.2	− 22 42 s	Oph	5.1	9.2	⊕, cB, L, R, gmpCM, rrr, st 16
4637 I	Pl	17 05.2	− 40 53 s	Sco	0.3	14p	◯, stellar
6324	Gx	17 05.4	+ 75 25 r	UMi		13p	vF, S, E, S∗ s
6306	Gx	17 07.6	+ 60 44 s	Dra	1.2	14p	vF, vS, lE
6307	Gx	17 07.7	+ 60 45 s	Dra	1.6	14p	vF, vS, lE, ∗13 nr n
6310	Gx	17 08.0	+ 61 00 s	Dra	2.1	14p	F, pL, lE
4643 I		17 08.5	+ 42 20 x	Her			F, ∗12 inv; = 6301
6301	Gx	17 08.6	+ 42 20 r	Her		14p	F, stellar; = IC 4643
6296	Gx	17 08.7	+ 3 54 s	Oph	1.1	14p	pB
1242 I	Gx	17 08.7	+ 4 02 u	Oph	1.0	15p	vS, R, vlbM
6317	Gx	17 09.3	+ 62 53 r	Dra		16p	eeF, S, R, F∗ nr, sp of 2
6319	Gx	17 09.6	+ 62 59 r	Dra		14p	vF, vS, R, lbM, nf of 2
1251 I	Gx	17 10.1	+ 72 24 u	Dra	1.7	14p	eeF, pS, R, sp of 2, 6340 nr
6293	Gb	17 10.2	− 26 35 s	Oph	7.9	8.2	⊕, vB, L, R, psbM, rrr, st 16
6294	−	17 10.3	− 26 34 r	Oph			only a D∗ 13, 13.5, dist 8″
6313	Gx	17 10.4	+ 48 19 r	Her		15p	eeF, vS, lE, bet 2 F st
6340	Gx	17 10.4	+ 72 18 s	Dra	3.4	11.0	cF, pL, R, vgmbM
6311	Gx	17 10.6	+ 41 39 r	Her		15p	pB, vS, R
1243 I	?	17 10.6	+ 10 47 x	Oph			only 5 st 12-14 in line ns, 45″ long
1244 I	Gx	17 10.6	+ 36 17 u	Her	1.2	15p	vF, pS, R, bet 2 st
6312	Gx	17 10.8	+ 42 17 r	Her		15p	eF, irrR, dif, vS∗ inv

NGC	Type	α_{2000}	δ_{2000}	Const.	Size	Mag.	Description
		h m	o '		'		
4631 I		17 11.0	− 77 36 d	Aps			eF, eeS, ann?, susp
1254 I	Gx	17 11.5	+ 72 24 v	Dra	1.9	13.9	eeF, pS, R, nf of 2, v diffic
1248 I	Gx	17 11.8	+ 60 00 v	Dra	1.5		eeF, pS, R, bet 2 st p & f
4642 I	Pl	17 11.8	− 55 24 s	Ara	0.4	13p	○ , stellar
6308	Gx	17 12.0	+ 23 23 s	Her	1.3	14p	vF, S, R, sbM
6314	Gx	17 12.6	+ 23 16 s	Her	1.8	13.1	F, vS, R, bM
1245 I	Gx	17 12.6	+ 38 02 u	Her	1.7	15p	eF, S, R, bM, F* close s
6315	Gx	17 12.8	+ 23 13 s	Her	0.9	13.3	eF, S
6320	Gx	17 12.9	+ 40 16 r	Her		15p	eF, *13 p 0^s.5
6323	Gx	17 13.3	+ 43 46 r	Her		15p	eF, vS, diffic
6302	Pl	17 13.7	− 37 06 s	Sco	0.8	13p	pB, E pf, ○
4633 I	Gx	17 13.8	− 77 32 c	Aps	3.7		vF, cL, cbM; spir?
6327	Gx	17 14.0	+ 43 38 r	Her		15p	eF, vS, diffic
6309	Pl	17 14.1	− 12 55 s	Oph	1.1	11p	close Dneb, 160°, both B, eS
6329	Gx	17 14.3	+ 43 41 r	Her		14p	vF, vS, R, bM
1246 I		17 14.3	+ 20 14 d	Her			neb *13? *10 n 1'
1250 I		17 14.4	+ 57 25 d	Dra			pF, S, cE
6304	Gb	17 14.5	− 29 28 s	Oph	6.8	8.4	⊕ , B, cL, R, lbM, rrr, st 16
6321	Gx	17 14.5	+ 20 18 r	Her		14p	eF, iR, pS, vlbM
4645 I	Gx	17 14.6	+ 43 07 z	Her		16p	eF, pS, *13.5 f 80''
1249 I	Gx	17 14.9	+ 35 31 z	Her		15p	eeF, pS, R, v diffic, 4 st s
6332	Gx	17 15.0	+ 43 39 r	Her		14p	vF, oval, ibM
6338	Gx	17 15.3	+ 57 25 r	Dra		14p	F, S, R, vglbM
6345	Gx	17 15.3	+ 57 21 r	Dra		15p	eeF, vS, R, 2nd of 3
6346	Gx	17 15.3	+ 57 19 r	Dra		15p	eeF, S, R, 3rd of 3
4635 I	Gx	17 15.7	− 77 29 c	Aps	3.1		vF, eS, cbM
6330	Gx	17 15.8	+ 29 23 r	Her		15p	eF, S, R
1252 I		17 15.8	+ 57 23 d	Dra			vF, pS, *12.5 v close
4649 I		17 15.8	+ 57 23 d	Dra			eF, pS, v dif, *12.5 f 0'.5
4650 I		17 15.9	+ 57 20 d	Dra			eF, st and neb
4648 I	OC	17 16.0	+ 45 52 z	Her			Cl, vS, neb, vF D* inv
6336	Gx	17 16.3	+ 43 48 r	Her		14p	vF, vS, R, bM
1247 I	*	17 16.4	− 12 47 F	Oph			stellar, *9.8 sp 0'.7; D* 12-12 is 30^{s}p
6316	Gb	17 16.6	− 28 08 s	Oph	4.9	9.0	⊕ , cB, pS, R, gvmbM, rrr, st 16
6300	Gx	17 17.0	− 62 49 s	Ara	5.4	11p	F, vL, vlE, am st, 2 st inv
6339	Gx	17 17.1	+ 40 51 s	Her	3.4	13p	vF, L, iR, sp of 2
6341	Gb	17 17.1	+ 43 08 s	Her	11.2	6.5	⊕ , vB, vL, eCM, rrr, st S; = M92
6344	Gx	17 17.2	+ 42 27 r	Her			F, S, R, *12 nf, nr
6343	Gx	17 17.3	+ 41 03 r	Her		14p	vF, S, lE, nf of 2
6318	OC	17 17.8	− 39 27 s	Sco	4	12p	Cl, pL, Ri, R, gbM, st 12...14
6359	Gx	17 17.9	+ 61 47 s	Dra	1.2	12.6	pB, S, R, bMN = *12
6325	Gb	17 18.0	− 23 46 s	Oph	4.3	10.7	pF, L, R, rr
6305	Gx	17 18.1	− 59 09 t	Ara			vF, vS, R, glbM
6348	Gx	17 18.4	+ 41 39 r	Her		15p	eF, vS, iR, lbM
6322	OC	17 18.5	− 42 57 s	Sco	10	6.0	Cl, vL, pRi, lC (place of * nf)
6361	Gx	17 18.6	+ 60 37 s	Dra	2.4	14p	vF, pS, mE, nearly bet 2 st
6350	Gx	17 18.7	+ 41 41 r	Her		14p	pF, pS, gbM
6358	Gx	17 19.0	+ 52 37 r	Dra		15p	eF, S, R, D* nr np
6349	Gx	17 19.1	+ 36 03 r	Her		15p	vF, eS, R, lbM, p of 2
6333	Gb	17 19.2	− 18 31 s	Oph	9.3	7.9	⊕ , B, L, R, eCM, rrr, st 14; = M9
6351	Gx	17 19.2	+ 36 02 r	Her		16p	vF, vS, fainter than 6349
1253 I		17 19.8	+ 18 40 d	Her			F
6347	Gx	17 19.9	+ 16 40 r	Her		14p	eF, iR, dif
6334	Nb	17 20.5	− 35 43 s	Sco	40		cF, vL, icE, vglbf, *8 inv
6335	−	17 20.5	− 30 08 r	Sco			dif neb in patches

NGC	Type	α_{2000}	δ_{2000}	Const.	Size	Mag.	Description
		h m	° ′		′		
6326	Pl	17 20.8	− 51 45 s	Ara	0.2	12p	!!! ○ , pB, vS, R
6342	Gb	17 21.2	− 19 35 s	Oph	3.0	9.9	cB, pS, lE, er
6353	−	17 21.2	+ 15 42 r	Her			pB, pS, 3 S st inv, *10 nf 1′
4660 I	Gx	17 21.6	+ 75 51 v	UMi	1.5		pL, E ns, *9.2 sp 30″
6337	Pl	17 22.3	− 38 29 s	Sco	0.8		!!! ◎, eF, S, am st
6363	Gx	17 22.7	+ 41 08 r	Her		14p	vF, S, R, gbM
6365	Gx	17 22.7	+ 62 11 r	Dra		14p	eeF, pL, iR, eF st inv, * sf
1255 I	Gx	17 23.1	+ 12 41 u	Oph	1.1	14p	vF, pS, R, forms trap with 3 st
6370	Gx	17 23.3	+ 57 00 r	Dra		14p	vF, vS, R, B* nr n
1261 I		17 23.5	+ 71 17 d	Dra			eeF, pS, R
6356	Gb	17 23.6	− 17 49 s	Oph	7.2	8.4	⊕ , vB, cL, vgvmbM, rrr, st 20
6328	Gx	17 23.7	− 64 59 A	Ara			eF pair of st only, one hazy
1256 I	Gx	17 23.8	+ 26 28 u	Her	1.7	14p	F, S, gbM
4640 I	Gx	17 23.9	− 80 04 c	Aps	1.5		vF, eS, cbM
4646 I	Gx	17 23.9	− 60 00 c	Ara	2.6		F, pL, spir
6355	Gb	17 24.0	− 26 21 s	Oph	5.0	9.6	cF, L, R, gbM, rrr
4641 I	Gx	17 24.2	− 80 09 c	Aps	1.6		eF, vS, bM
6373	Gx	17 24.3	+ 59 01 r	Dra		14p	eeF, pL, v diffic
6364	Gx	17 24.5	+ 29 24 r	Her		14p	pF, vS, R, bM *13
6354	Ast	17 24.6	− 38 32 r	Sco			eF, S
6357	Nb	17 24.6	− 34 10 s	Sco	50		F, L, E, vglbM, D* inv
4644 I	Gx	17 24.6	− 73 56 c	Aps	2.1		eF, vS, mE 135°
4651 I	OC	17 24.7	− 49 57 s	Ara	12	6.9	Cl, pC
6367	Gx	17 25.2	+ 37 46 r	Her		15p	vF* in vF, vS, R neb
6360	−	17 25.4	− 30 00 r	Oph			neb in patches (Milky Way)
6376	Gx	17 25.4	+ 58 50 r	Dra		14p	eeF, eS, R, v diffic
6377	Gx	17 25.4	+ 58 50 r	Dra		14p	eF, eS, R, lbM
6352	Gb	17 25.5	− 48 25 s	Ara	7.1	8.2	Cl (not neb), pF, L
4647 I	Gx	17 26.0	− 80 12 c	Aps	1.7		bM
6395	Gx	17 26.4	+ 71 06 s	Dra	2.6	13p	vF, pL, lE, D* n
4652 I	Gx	17 26.4	− 59 44 c	Ara	1.7		F, ○ , 15 mag
6368	Gx	17 27.1	+ 11 33 s	Oph	4.0	13p	F, S, E
1257 I		17 27.1	− 7 06 d	Oph			F, pL, lbM
4653 I	Gx	17 27.1	− 60 53 c	Ara	1.6		eeF, eS, bM, eF, * vnr, susp
6371	Gx	17 27.2	+ 26 30 r	Her		15p	vF, S, R, np of 2
6381	Gx	17 27.3	+ 60 01 s	Dra	1.5	14p	vF, pL, E
1258 I	Gx	17 27.3	+ 58 31 v	Dra	1.2		pB, pS, R, 1st of 3
1259 I	Gx	17 27.4	+ 58 33 v	Dra	1.5		pB, pS, R, 2nd of 3
1260 I		17 27.4	+ 58 29 d	Dra			eeF, S, R, 3rd of 3
6372	Gx	17 27.5	+ 26 28 s	Her	1.9	14p	vF, pS, iF, sf of 2
6366	Gb	17 27.7	− 5 05 s	Oph	8.3	10.0	F, L, vlbM
6382	Gx	17 27.8	+ 56 52 r	Dra		15p	pF, pS, R
6385	Gx	17 28.0	+ 57 33 r	Dra		14p	eF, S, R, B* s
6387	Gx	17 28.4	+ 57 34 r	Dra		15p	eF, S, R
6390	Gx	17 28.5	+ 60 06 r	Dra		14p	eeF, mE, v diffic
6386	Gx	17 28.9	+ 52 44 r	Dra		15p	vF, pS, R, bet 2 st
6391	Gx	17 28.9	+ 58 52 r	Dra		15p	eF, vS, R, nearly bet 2 st
6369	Pl	17 29.3	− 23 46 s	Oph	1.1	13p	!! ◎, pB, S, R
6375	Gx	17 29.3	+ 16 12 r	Her		14p	F, vS, R
6412	Gx	17 29.6	+ 75 42 s	Dra	2.3	11.8	⊕ , cL, R, vgbM, rr
6394	Gx	17 30.1	+ 59 32 r	Dra		16p	eF, pS, R, n of 2
6393	Gx	17 30.3	+ 59 39 r	Dra		15p	eF, pS, R, s of 2
6378	Gx	17 30.6	+ 6 17 r	Oph		15p	v difficult
6379	Gx	17 30.6	+ 16 17 s	Her	1.3	15p	vF, pL
6414	Gx	17 30.6	+ 74 23 r	Dra		15p	eeF, pS, R, v diffic, bet 2 st

NGC	Type	α_{2000}	δ_{2000}	Const.	Size	Mag.	Description
		h m	° ′		′		
6399	Gx	17 31.8	+ 59 38 r	Dra		15p	eF, vS, R
6362	Gb	17 31.9	− 67 03 s	Ara	10.7	8.3	⊕, cB, L, vgmbM, rrr, st 14...17
6374	OC	17 32.3	− 32 36 s	Sco	3	9.0	Cl, S, P, B∗ inv
6384	Gx	17 32.4	+ 7 04 s	Oph	6.0	10.6	pB, S, vlE
6389	Gx	17 32.7	+ 16 24 s	Her	3.1	14p	F, S, iF, er
4657 I	?	17 32.7	− 17 31 x	Oph			vF, ∗11 np 2′
1262 I	Gx	17 33.0	+ 43 45 u	Her	1.5	15p	eF, pS, R, 1st of 3
1263 I	Gx	17 33.1	+ 43 49 u	Her	1.7	15p	eF, pS., R, 2nd of 3
1264 I	Gx	17 33.3	+ 43 38 u	Her	1.4	16p	eF, pS, R, 3rd of 3
4659 I		17 34.2	− 17 56 d	Oph			pF, S, ∗8 f 21^s, 3′ n
4655 I		17 34.6	− 60 43 d	Ara			eF, eS, mE 170°
6383	C+N	17 34.8	− 32 34 s	Sco	80	5.5	Cl, st 13, ∗6-7 in M
6410	∗	17 35.2	+ 60 49 r	Dra			eeF, S, R, nearly bet 2 st, sp of 2
6380	Gb	17 35.4	− 39 04 s	Sco	3.9		eF, pS, lE, ∗9 att
6411	Gx	17 35.6	+ 60 48 r	Dra		13p	vS, gbM
6419	Gx	17 35.9	+ 68 08 r	Dra		15p	eeF, eS, R, v diffic
6420	Gx	17 36.1	+ 68 01 r	Dra		15p	eeF, eS, R, v diffic
6424	Gx	17 36.2	+ 69 59 r	Dra		15p	vF, pS, R
6388	Gb	17 36.3	− 44 44 s	Sco	8.7	6.9	⊕, vB, L, R, pg, psvmbM, rrr, st 17...
6422	Gx	17 36.3	+ 68 02 r	Dra		15p	eF, pS, R, nearly bet 2 st
6409	Gx	17 36.6	+ 50 46 r	Dra		15p	vF, S, R
6423	Gx	17 36.7	+ 68 09 r	Dra		15p	eeF, vS, R, ∗ close f
1265 I	Gx	17 36.7	+ 42 05 u	Her	2.1	14p	eeF, S, lE
6434	Gx	17 36.8	+ 72 05 r	Dra		13p	vF, vS, R, stellar, ∗8 s
4654 I	Gx	17 37.1	− 74 23 c	Aps	1.7		eF, eS, R, vmbM
4658 I		17 37.2	− 59 35 d	Ara			F, ○, 15 mag
6402	Gb	17 37.6	− 3 15 s	Oph	11.7	7.6	! ⊕, B, vL, R, eRi, vgmbM, rrr, st 15; = M14
4656 I	Gx	17 37.7	− 63 44 c	Ara	2.2		eeF, vS, eE 90°, cbM
6396	OC	17 38.1	− 35 00 s	Sco	3	8.5	Cl, pL, lRi, lC
6418	Gx	17 38.1	+ 58 43 r	Dra		14p	eF, pS, R
6406	−	17 38.3	+ 18 50 r	Her			vF, eS, stellar
6401	Gb	17 38.6	− 23 55 s	Oph	5.6	9.5	pB, pL, R, ∗12 f inv
6461	Gx	17 38.7	+ 73 30 r	Dra		15p	eF, pS, R, 5 st nr
1267 I	Gx	17 38.7	+ 59 23 v	Dra	1.7		eeF, pS, R, v diffic
6408	Gx	17 38.8	+ 18 52 r	Her		14p	F, S, iR, gbM
6404	OC	17 39.6	− 33 15 s	Sco	5	11p	Cl, F, L, pRi, lC, st 13...15
6405	OC	17 40.1	− 32 13 s	Sco	15	4.2	Cl, L, iR, lC, st 7, 10...; = M6
6435	Gx	17 40.1	+ 62 37 r	Dra		15p	eeF, vS, R, vF D∗ nr f
6397	Gb	17 40.7	− 53 40 s	Ara	25.7	5.7	⊕, B, vL, Ri, st 13
6413	−	17 40.7	+ 12 37 r	Oph			vF, vS, smbM
6400	OC	17 40.8	− 36 57 s	Sco	8	9p	Cl, pL, pRi, iR, st 9...10
6436	Gx	17 41.2	+ 60 27 r	Dra		15p	eeF, pS, R, ∗∗ nr
6417	Gx	17 41.7	+ 23 40 r	Her		14p	pF, S, vlbM
6456	Gx	17 42.4	+ 67 34 r	Dra		15p	eeF, eS, R, v diffic, bet 2 st
6398	Gx	17 42.7	− 61 41 A	Pav			eF hazy ∗ only, p of 2
6457	Gx	17 42.8	+ 66 28 r	Dra		14p	F, vS, R, bM
6403	Gx	17 43.2	− 61 41 A	Pav			eF hazy ∗ only, f of 2
6392	Gx	17 43.5	− 69 47 c	Aps	1.5		cF, S, R, glbM, ∗13 sp
6463	Gx	17 43.5	+ 67 35 r	Dra		15p	eeF, S, R, v diffic, 2nd of 6
6427	Gx	17 43.6	+ 25 29 r	Her		14p	vF, vS, stellar
6449	Gx	17 43.7	+ 56 47 r	Dra		14p	vF, pS, R
6428	−	17 43.9	+ 25 32 r	Her			vF, S, stellar
6477	Gx	17 43.9	+ 67 37 r	Dra			eeF, eS, R, v diffic, ∗ nr
6429	Gx	17 44.0	+ 25 21 r	Her		14p	F, S, stellar
6433	Gx	17 44.0	+ 36 46 r	Her		14p	vF, S, pmE, bM

NGC	Type	α_{2000}	δ_{2000}	Const.	Size	Mag.	Description
		h m	° ′		′		
6470	Gx	17 44.1	+ 67 34 r	Dra		15p	eeF, vS, R, v diffic, 3rd of 6
6471	Gx	17 44.1	+ 67 34 r	Dra		15p	eeF, eS, R, ∗ nr, 4th of 6
6472	Gx	17 44.2	+ 67 36 r	Dra		15p	eeF, eS, R, v diffic, 5th of 6
6431	−	17 44.3	+ 25 30 r	Her			vF, vS, R
6448	−	17 44.3	+ 53 32 r	Dra			vF, pS, R, lbM
6415	−	17 44.4	− 35 01 r	Sco			nebs portion of Milky Way
6416	OC	17 44.4	− 32 21 s	Sco	18	5.7	Cl, vL, Ri, lC
6430	Ast	17 44.6	+ 18 09 r	Her			vF, S, mE
6443	Gx	17 44.6	+ 48 05 r	Her		15p	eF, pS, lE
6462	Gx	17 44.7	+ 61 53 r	Dra		14p	F, eS, R, ◯ ?
6426	Gb	17 44.9	+ 3 00 s	Oph	3.2	11.2	vF, cL, E, vlbM
6454	Gx	17 44.9	+ 55 42 s	Dra	1.4	15p	vF, pS, R, lbM
6407	Gx	17 45.0	− 60 44 c	Pav	1.9		eF, S, R, 3 st nr
4663 I	Pl	17 45.5	− 44 54 s	Sco	0.2	13p	◯ , stell
1266 I		17 45.6	− 46 06 d	Ara			stellar (gaseous spectrum)
6421	−	17 45.8	− 33 42 r	Sco			Cl, vL, pRi, st 8...12
6464	Gx	17 45.8	+ 60 53 r	Dra		15p	eeF, pS, R, s of 4 st
4666 I	Gx	17 45.8	+ 55 46 m	Dra	0.6	16p	eF∗, slightly nebs
6459	Gx	17 45.9	+ 55 45 r	Dra		16p	eF, eS, R, r
6446	Gx	17 46.1	+ 35 33 r	Her		15p	eF, vS, iR
6447	Gx	17 46.3	+ 35 33 r	Her		14p	vF, S, R
4665 I	OC	17 46.3	+ 5 43 s	Oph	41	4.2	Cl, co
4667 I		17 46.3	+ 55 53 d	Dra			2 stell neb susp
6425	OC	17 46.9	− 31 32 s	Sco	8	7.2	Cl, pS, lRi, lC, st 10...12
6442	Gx	17 46.9	+ 20 45 r	Her		14p	pF, S, iR, gbM
6474	−	17 46.9	+ 57 20 r	Dra			eF, pS, R, n of 3, 3 st nr
4668 I		17 46.9	+ 57 24 d	Dra			eF, ∗ 3′ n
6473	Gx	17 47.0	+ 57 20 r	Dra		15p	eeF, S, R, s of 2
4662 I	Gx	17 47.1	− 64 38 s	Pav	2.2	11.4	F, pS, lE
4669 I	Gx	17 47.2	+ 61 26 x	Dra			eF, S; eF st inv?
6432		17 47.4	− 24 53 D	Sgr			only 4 st 12-13
6450	−	17 47.5	+ 18 35 r	Her			vF, vS, B∗ f 2′; nonexistent?
1270 I	∗	17 47.8	+ 62 13 x	Dra			eeF, S, R, v diffic, 6488 f
6452	Gx	17 48.0	+ 20 51 r	Her		15p	eeF, S
6466	Gx	17 48.2	+ 51 26 r	Dra		15p	eF, vS, R, bet 2 st
6439	Pl	17 48.3	− 16 29 s	Sgr	0.1	14p	◯ , stellar = 13m
6479	Gx	17 48.3	+ 54 10 r	Dra		14p	eF, pS, R, 3 st n
6478	Gx	17 48.6	+ 51 09 s	Dra	1.9	14p	pB, S, vmE, spindle
6440	Gb	17 48.9	− 20 22 s	Sgr	5.4	9.7	pB, pL, R, bM
4664 I	Gx	17 49.0	− 63 15 c	Pav	1.7		eF, vS, cE, cbM
6437	−	17 49.1	− 35 26 r	Sco			Cl, F, eL, vS st + neb
6445	Pl	17 49.2	− 20 01 s	Sgr	0.6	13p	pB, pS, R, gbM, r, ∗15 np
6458	Gx	17 49.2	+ 20 49 r	Her		15p	eF, vS, stellar
6488	Gx	17 49.3	+ 62 14 r	Dra		14p	pF, pS, E
6503	Gx	17 49.4	+ 70 09 s	Dra	6.2	10.2	B or pB, L, mE, ∗9 f 4′
6444	OC	17 49.5	− 34 49 s	Sco	12		Cl, vL, vRi, st 12...13
6460	Gx	17 49.6	+ 20 46 r	Her		14p	vF, pL, iR
6508	Gx	17 49.9	+ 72 02 r	Dra		14p	vF, S, 3 st nr
6489	Gx	17 50.0	+ 60 06 r	Dra		15p	eeF, pL, lE, bet 2 st
6491	Gx	17 50.1	+ 61 32 r	Dra		14p	pF, eS, vF∗ att, np of 2
6441	Gb	17 50.2	− 37 03 s	Sco	7.8	7.4	⊕ , vB, pL, R, vgmbM, rrr, st 18
6493	Gx	17 50.4	+ 61 33 v	Dra	1.4		F, eS, R, ◯ ?, F∗ vnr, sf of 2
6451	OC	17 50.7	− 30 13 s	Sco	8	8p	Cl, pL, pRi, bifid, st 12...
6467	Gx	17 50.7	+ 17 32 s	Her	2.7	15p	vF, vS, lE
6468	Gx	17 50.7	+ 17 32 u	Her	2.3	14p	vF, S, R

NGC	Type	α_{2000}	δ_{2000}		Const.	Size	Mag.	Description
		h m	° ′			′		
1268 I		17 50.7	+ 17 13	D	Her			eeF, pS, R, v diffic
6453	Gb	17 50.9	− 34 36	s	Sco	3.5	9.9	cL, iR, pmbM, r
6498	−	17 51.0	+ 59 29	r	Dra			pF, pS, R, F∗ vnr, sf of 2
4661 I	Gx	17 51.0	− 74 02	c	Aps	2.5		eF, vS, R, cbM
6497	Gx	17 51.2	+ 59 30	r	Dra		14p	eF, pS, lE, ∗ close n, np of 2
6505	Gx	17 51.3	+ 65 33	r	Dra		15p	eeF, vS, R
6484	Gx	17 51.7	+ 24 30	r	Her		13p	eF, vS, R, mbM
6482	Gx	17 51.8	+ 23 04	s	Her	2.3	11.3	! vF, S, R, vsvmbMvSRN
6485	Gx	17 51.8	+ 31 28	r	Her		14p	vF, vS, R
6455	−	17 52.0	− 35 23	r	Sco			Cl, rr, st eS + neb
1269 I	Gx	17 52.1	+ 21 34	v	Her	1.9		eeF, pL, R, 2 F st; ∗10 sp 4′
6486	Gx	17 52.6	+ 29 50	r	Her		15p	vS∗ slightly nebs
6487	Gx	17 52.7	+ 29 51	r	Her		14p	F, S, R, gbM
6481	D∗	17 52.8	+ 4 10	r	Oph			vS, bM
6465		17 52.9	− 25 24	D	Sgr			only 2 F D st
6469	OC	17 52.9	− 22 21	s	Sgr	12	8p	Cl, pRi (in Milky Way)
6476	−	17 53.8	− 29 08	r	Sgr			neb or nebs part of Milky Way
6475	OC	17 53.9	− 34 49	s	Sco	80	3.3	Cl, vB, pRi, lC, st 7...12; = M7
6510		17 54.0	+ 60 48	D	Dra			eeF, pS, lE, v diffic
6538	Gx	17 54.2	+ 73 25	r	Dra		14p	eF, vS, lE, bet 2 eF st
6490	Gx	17 54.5	+ 18 23	r	Her		14p	vF, vS, stellar
6480	−	17 54.6	− 30 26	r	Sco			neb or nebs part of Milky Way
6511		17 54.7	+ 60 48	D	Dra			F, pL, bM
6495	Gx	17 54.8	+ 18 20	r	Her		14p	F, S, R
6512	Gx	17 54.8	+ 62 39	r	Dra		15p	vF, R, 1st of 3
4670 I	Nb	17 55.1	− 21 48	x	Sgr	5		stellar, 12.5 mag
4671 I		17 55.1	− 10 17	d	Ser			spiral? (edge of plate)
6516	Gx	17 55.2	+ 62 40	r	Dra		15p	vF, vS, 2nd of 3
6499	D∗	17 55.3	+ 18 23	r	Her			S D∗ in neb
6521	Gx	17 55.8	+ 62 37	r	Dra		14p	F, pL, 3rd of 3
6500	Gx	17 56.0	+ 18 20	s	Her	2.5	13p	vF, vS, sp of 2
6504	Gx	17 56.0	+ 33 12	s	Her	2.5	13p	F, vmE, sbM
6534	Gx	17 56.0	+ 64 19	r	Dra		15p	eeF, pS, R
6501	Gx	17 56.1	+ 18 22	s	Her	2.0	12.3	vF, vS, nf of 2
6494	OC	17 56.8	− 19 01	s	Sgr	27	5.5	Cl, B, vL, pRi, lC, st 10...; = M23
6536	Gx	17 57.3	+ 64 56	r	Dra		14p	vF, pL, R
6515	Gx	17 57.4	+ 50 44	r	Dra		14p	vF, vS, R, 2 B st nr
4677 I	Gx	17 58.3	+ 66 38	m	Dra	1.0	15p	vF, S; 6543 f 16^s.5
6543	Pl	17 58.6	+ 66 38	s	Dra	5.8	9p	◯ , vB, pS, sbMvSN
6496	Gb	17 59.0	− 44 16	s	Sco	6.9	9.2	neb + Cl, pL, mE, gvlbM
6532	Gx	17 59.1	+ 56 13	r	Dra		15p	eeF, pS, R
6524	Gx	17 59.2	+ 45 55	r	Her		14p	pF, pS, lE
6509	Gx	17 59.4	+ 6 17	s	Oph	2.3	13p	vF, pL, irrR, lbM
6483	Gx	17 59.5	− 63 40	r	Pav			F, S, E, bM, bet 2 st 10
6513	Gx	17 59.5	+ 24 54	r	Her		14p	vF, vS, stellar
6507	OC	17 59.6	− 17 24	s	Sgr	7	10p	Cl, pS, lRi, lC
6518	Gx	17 59.7	+ 28 52	r	Her		15p	2 vF, close st in vF, vS neb
6542	Gx	17 59.7	+ 61 22	s	Dra	1.5	14p	eF, S, mE, 2 st sp
6506	−	17 59.8	− 24 39	r	Sgr			Cl, Ri, eL, vlC
6552	Gx	18 00.1	+ 66 36	r	Dra		14p	F, pS, iR
6517	Gb	18 01.8	− 8 58	s	Oph	4.3	10.3	pB, pL, R, rr
6527	Gx	18 01.8	+ 19 44	r	Her		15p	eeF, vS, R
6525	−	18 02.1	+ 11 03	r	Oph			Cl, P, st L
6514	C+N	18 02.3	− 23 02	s	Sgr	29	6.3	!!! vB, vL, trifid, D∗ inv; = M20
4672 I		18 02.4	− 62 50	d	Pav			eeF, eS, vE 45°, cbM

NGC	Type	α_{2000}	δ_{2000}	Const.	Size	Mag.	Description
		h m	o ′		′		
6526	Nb	18 02.6	− 23 35 s	Sgr	40		F, L, cE
6492	Gx	18 02.8	− 66 25 r	Pav			pF, S, pmE 90°, *12 att f
4676 I	Gx	18 02.8	+ 11 49 z	Oph		16p	eF, vS
4675 I		18 03.2	− 9 15 d	Oph			doubtful, not seen a second time
4673 I	Pl	18 03.3	− 27 06 s	Sgr	0.3		◯ , 13 mag, *13 nf 33″
6519	−	18 03.4	− 29 48 r	Sgr			vF, np 6522
6520	OC	18 03.4	− 27 54 s	Sgr	6	8p	Cl, pS, Ri, lC, st 9...13
6522	Gb	18 03.6	− 30 02 s	Sgr	5.6	8.6	⊕ , B, pL, R, gvmbM, rrr, st 16
6523	Nb	18 03.8	− 24 23 s	Sgr	90	5.8	!!! vB, eL, eiF, with L Cl; = M8
6535	Gb	18 03.8	− 0 18 s	Ser	3.6	10.6	pF, L, diam 1′ or 2′
6502	Gx	18 04.2	− 65 25 c	Pav	1.2		vF, vS, f * of D* inv
6531	OC	18 04.6	− 22 30 s	Sgr	13	5.9	Cl, pRi, lC, st 9...12; = M21
6528	Gb	18 04.8	− 30 03 s	Sgr	3.7	9.5	⊕ , pF, cS, R, gbM, rrr, st 16
6530	OC	18 04.8	− 24 20 s	Sgr	15	4.6	Cl, B, L, pRi, f M8
6539	Gb	18 04.8	− 7 35 s	Ser	6.9	9.6	no description
6562	Gx	18 04.9	+ 56 15 r	Dra		14p	F, pS, R, bM, bet 2 st
1272 I	OC	18 04.9	+ 25 05 x	Her			S Cl
1273 I	OC	18 05.0	+ 25 07 x	Her			vF, S Cl with neb? *10 f 3′
6533	−	18 05.1	− 24 53 r	Sgr			eL, eiF, st f
6547	Gx	18 05.1	+ 25 13 r	Her		14p	F, vS, E, mbM
6537	Pl	18 05.2	− 19 51 s	Sgr	0.2	13p	◯ , B, S, stellar
6560	Gx	18 05.3	+ 46 52 s	Her	1.3	14p	eeF, pS, iR
6529	−	18 05.5	− 36 18 r	Sgr			Cl in Milky Way
1271 I		18 05.5	− 24 27 D	Sgr			eF, vL, B* inv, part of 6523
6549	Gx	18 05.8	+ 18 32 r	Her		15p	vF, pL, iR, near 6548
6548	Gx	18 06.0	+ 18 35 D	Her		13p	cF, S, lE, r; = 6550
6550	Gx	18 06.0	+ 18 35 D	Her		13p	vF, pS, R, sev F st inv, near 6549
6540	OC	18 06.3	− 27 49 s	Sgr	1	15p	pF, S, iE, er or Cl
6566	Gx	18 07.0	+ 52 16 r	Dra		15p	eF, vS, R, *16 nr
6546	OC	18 07.2	− 23 20 s	Sgr	13	8.0	Cl, vL, vRi
6544	Gb	18 07.3	− 25 00 s	Sgr	8.9	8.3	cF, pL, iR, r
6555	Gx	18 07.8	+ 17 36 s	Her	2.1	12p	F, L, R, vglbM
6541	Gb	18 08.0	− 43 42 s	CrA	13.1	6.6	⊕ , B, R, eC, gbM, rrr, st 15...16
4678 I		18 08.0	− 23 52 d	Sgr			B, S, E
4688 I	Gx	18 08.1	+ 11 42 u	Oph	1.6	15p	vF, pS, dif, *12 close f
4674 I	Gx	18 08.2	− 62 24 c	Pav	1.5		eF, vS, eE 80°, cbM stell N
4681 I		18 08.3	− 23 24 d	Sgr			S neb or neb*
4683 I		18 08.7	− 26 14 d	Sgr			vF, eeL
4691 I	Gx	18 08.7	+ 11 50 z	Oph		15p	F, S, iF, 1 or 2 F st inv
6598	Gx	18 08.8	+ 69 04 r	Dra		14p	eF, pS, R
6551	−	18 09.0	− 29 33 r	Sgr			vF, vS, R, rr
6554	−	18 09.1	− 18 26 r	Sgr			Cl, pRi, vlC, st L & S
6564	−	18 09.1	+ 17 24 r	Her			eF, vS
4684 I	Nb	18 09.1	− 23 25 s	Sgr	3		S neb or neb*
4693 I		18 09.2	+ 17 20 d	Her			eF, S, bM, sev eF st inv
6553	Gb	18 09.3	− 25 54 s	Sgr	8.1	8.3	⊕ , F, L, lE, vglbM, rr, st 20
4685 I	Nb	18 09.3	− 23 59 s	Sgr	10		*7.5 in L, dif neb
1274 I	Nb	18 09.5	− 23 44 s	Sgr	9		3 st 8.5 to 9m in pL neb
6592	Gx	18 09.9	+ 61 25 r	Dra		15p	vF, vS, R
6556		18 10.0	− 27 31 D	Sgr			F, vL, cE, lbM, rr; no nebulosity?
6559	Nb	18 10.0	− 24 06 s	Sgr	8		vF, vL, lE, ⚹ inv
1275 I	Nb	18 10.0	− 23 50 s	Sgr	10		2 st 8 & 8.5 in pL neb
6594	Gx	18 10.2	+ 61 07 r	Dra		15p	vF, vS, R
1277 I	OC	18 10.2	+ 31 00 x	Her			S Cl
6558	Gb	18 10.3	− 31 46 s	Sgr	3.7		⊕ , pB, pL, R, glbM, rrr, st 16

NGC	Type	α_{2000}	δ_{2000}	Const.	Size	Mag.	Description
		h m	° ′		′		
6561	—	18 10.5	− 16 48 r	Sgr			Cl, L, lC, st cL
1278 I		18 10.5	+ 31 09 d	Her			vF, vS, sev st susp
4690 I		18 10.5	− 19 49 d	Sgr			*9.5 in neb, E spnf
1276 I	Gb	18 10.7	− 7 12 s	Ser	7.1		eeF, vL, v diffic, D* close p
6575	Gx	18 10.8	+ 31 05 r	Her		14p	pB, S, R
6571	Gx	18 10.9	+ 21 14 r	Her		15p	eF, vS, stell
6582	Gx	18 11.0	+ 49 53 r	Her		15p	eeF, pS, R
6570	Gx	18 11.1	+ 14 06 s	Oph	1.8	13p	pF, pL, R
1279 I		18 11.1	+ 36 02 d	Her			eeF, pS, R, v diffic
6597	Gx	18 11.3	+ 61 10 r	Dra		15p	vF, vS, R, B* nr
4679 I	Gx	18 11.4	− 56 15 c	Tel	1.9		cF, S, R, vmbM; susp
1281 I	?	18 11.6	+ 36 01 x	Her			= IC 1279
6576	Gx	18 11.8	+ 21 25 r	Her		15p	eF, vS
6565	Pl	18 11.9	− 28 11 s	Sgr	0.2	13p	○, stellar
6574	Gx	18 11.9	+ 14 59 s	Her	1.4	12.0	pB, S, R
6601	Gx	18 11.9	+ 61 26 r	Dra		15p	eF, pS, R
6563	Pl	18 12.0	− 33 52 s	Sgr	0.8	14p	○, F, L, cE, hazy border
6572	Pl	18 12.1	+ 6 51 s	Oph	0.1	9p	○, vB, vS, R, l hazy
6577	Gx	18 12.1	+ 21 28 r	Her		14p	vF, S
1280 I	Gx	18 12.2	+ 25 40 m	Her	0.4	15p	*13, nebulous?
6545	Gx	18 12.3	− 63 46 A	Pav			eeF, eeS, R
6579		18 12.3	+ 21 26 D	Her			F, p of Dneb
6607	Gx	18 12.3	+ 61 19 r	Dra		15p	eF, pS, R, v diffic
6580		18 12.4	+ 21 26 D	Her			F, f of Dneb
6585	Gx	18 12.4	+ 39 37 r	Her		13p	eeF, S, eE, bet sev B st
4697 I	Gx	18 12.5	+ 25 26 u	Her	1.6	15p	F, S, iF, r
6581	Gx	18 12.6	+ 25 25 r	Her		15p	eF, dif, bet 2 F st
6608	Gx	18 12.6	+ 61 19 r	Dra		15p	vF, eS, R, vF* nr
6609	Gx	18 12.6	+ 61 19 r	Dra		15p	vF, pS, lE, F* nr
6568	OC	18 12.8	− 21 36 s	Sgr	13	9p	Cl, vL, lC
6621	Gx	18 12.9	+ 68 22 s	Dra	2.5	13.1	pF, pS, R, lbM, s of 2
6622	Gx	18 13.0	+ 68 20 r	Dra		13p	pF, pS, R, lbM, n of 2
4680 I	Gx	18 13.5	− 64 29 c	Pav	1.7		eF, vS, eE 85°, cbM
6569	Gb	18 13.6	− 31 50 s	Sgr	5.8	8.7	⊕, cB, L, R, rrr, st 15...
4686 I	Gx	18 13.6	− 57 44 c	Pav	0.5		bM, mag 14
6567	Pl	18 13.7	− 19 05 s	Sgr	0.1	12p	○, stell, 11 mag, in a Cl
6586	Gx	18 13.7	+ 21 05 r	Her		14p	eF, S, R
4687 I	Gx	18 13.7	− 57 44 c	Pav	1.5		bM mag 14
4689 I	Gx	18 13.7	− 57 45 c	Pav	0.9		bM, mag 14
4708 I	Gx	18 13.7	+ 61 09 z	Dra		15p	eF, eS, v diffic, 6617 nr
6573	—	18 13.8	− 22 10 r	Sgr			Cl, st vS
6587	Gx	18 13.9	+ 18 50 s	Her	2.3	12.1	F, vS, R, stell
6591	Gx	18 14.0	+ 21 02 r	Her			eeF, vS, stell
6617	Gx	18 14.1	+ 61 19 r	Dra		15p	eeF, pL, R, v diffic
1282 I	?	18 14.1	+ 21 06 x	Her			vF, 2 or 3 st susp
6593	Gx	18 14.2	+ 22 17 r	Her		15p	vF, vS, R, lbM
6606	Gx	18 14.7	+ 43 16 r	Lyr		14p	vF, S, R, gbM, vF* inv
4692 I	Gx	18 14.8	− 58 42 c	Pav	1.7		F, S, iF, susp
4694 I	Gx	18 15.4	− 58 13 c	Pav	2.1		F, S, eE 20°, lbM
6599	Gx	18 15.6	+ 24 56 r	Her		13p	pF, vS, R, gbM, S* att f
6600	—	18 15.7	+ 25 02 r	Her			F, vS, stell; = 6602
6583	OC	18 15.8	− 22 08 s	Sgr	3	10p	Cl, pRi, pC, cE, st 13...
1285 I	OC	18 16.1	+ 25 06 x	Her			S Cl
6612	Gx	18 16.2	+ 36 05 r	Lyr		15p	eeF, eS, R, v diffic
1286 I	Gx	18 16.2	+ 55 34 u	Dra	1.5	15p	eF, pS, R, 2 st nr

NGC	Type	α_{2000}	δ_{2000}		Const.	Size	Mag.	Description
		h m	° ′			′		
6578	Pl	18 16.3	− 20 27	s	Sgr	0.2	13p	◯ , stellar = 13 mag
4682 I	Gx	18 16.4	− 71 35	c	Pav	2.5		vF, cS, cE 140°, stell N
4701 I	Nb	18 16.5	− 16 44	s	Sgr	60		eL, conn with cloud IC 4715
6602	Gx	18 16.6	+ 25 02	r	Her		14p	Cl, vS, st F, 30″, nebulous?
6589		18 16.9	− 19 46	D	Sgr	5		D∗ in centre of eF, pL neby
6590	C+N	18 17.0	− 19 53	s	Sgr	4		D∗ in centre of pF, pL, R neby; = 6595
6595	OC	18 17.0	− 19 53	s	Sgr	11	7p	F, pL, cE, *⁎ inv; = IC 4700
6605	OC	18 17.1	− 14 58	s	Ser		6p	Cl, lRi, lC, st 10...12
4700 I		18 17.1	− 19 52	x	Sgr			∗9.4 in dense neb; = 6595
6610	−	18 17.2	+ 15 00	r	Her			F, S, E, mbM, r
1283 I	Nb	18 17.3	− 19 44	d	Sgr			∗9.3 nebulous
4695 I		18 17.4	− 58 55	d	Pav			eF, vS, R, bM, sev st nr; susp
6596	OC	18 17.5	− 16 40	s	Sgr			Cl, lC
1284 I	Nb	18 17.7	− 19 40	x	Sgr	10		∗7.6 in neb, 15′ diam
6616	Gx	18 17.8	+ 22 15	r	Her		15p	vF, eS, mE, 2 st 9-10 nr, one p 2ˢ, 0′.6 s
6604	C+N	18 18.1	− 12 14	s	Ser	60	6.5	Cl, lRi, lC
6603	OC	18 18.4	− 18 25	s	Sgr	5	11p	!, Cl, vRi, vmC, R, st 15 (Milky Way)
4699 I	Pl	18 18.5	− 45 59	s	Tel	0.2	12p	◯ , stellar
6584	Gb	18 18.6	− 52 13	s	Tel	7.9	9.2	⊕ , cB, cL, R, gmbM, rrr, st 15
6615	Gx	18 18.6	+ 13 16	s	Oph	1.2	15p	vF, vS
6611	C+N	18 18.8	− 13 47	s	Ser	35	6.0	Cl, at least 100 st L & S; = M16
6619	Gx	18 18.8	+ 23 40	r	Her		14p	F, S, E
4703 I	OC	18 18.9	− 13 47	x	Ser			B, eL, Cl M16 inv
6623	Gx	18 19.5	+ 23 43	r	Her		14p	pF, S, R, bM
4706 I		18 19.6	− 16 01	d	Sgr			∗9.2 in S neb, conn with M17
6643	Gx	18 19.8	+ 74 34	s	Dra	3.9	11.1	pB, pL, E 50°, 2 st p
6613	OC	18 19.9	− 17 08	s	Sgr	9	6.9	Cl, P, vlC; = M18
4707 I		18 20.1	− 16 01	d	Sgr			∗9.4 in S neb, conn with M17
4696 I	Gx	18 20.3	− 64 44	c	Pav	2.4		neb, susp
6618	C+N	18 20.8	− 16 11	s	Sgr	46	6.0	!!!, B, eL, eiF, 2 hooked; = M17
4698 I		18 21.0	− 63 22	d	Pav			eF, vS, eE 45°, stell N
6557	Gx	18 21.4	− 76 34	A	Oct			vF, vS, R, glbM
6588		18 21.5	− 63 48	D	Pav			sev vF st (no neb)
6636	Gx	18 22.0	+ 66 38	r	Dra		14p	eeF, pS, R, 3 st nr
6628	Gx	18 22.2	+ 23 29	r	Her		15p	vF, S, lE, bM
6627	Gx	18 22.7	+ 15 42	s	Her	1.5	13.2	vF, pL
6620	Pl	18 22.9	− 26 49	s	Sgr	0.1	15p	◯ , stellar
4702 I	Gx	18 23.1	− 59 14	c	Pav	1.6		eF, eS, ∗ in disc, ring susp
6625	OC	18 23.2	− 12 03	s	Sct		9p	Cl, lC, lRi, st 11...12
6624	Gb	18 23.7	− 30 22	s	Sgr	5.9	8.3	⊕ , vB, pL, R, rrr, st 16
6654	Gx	18 24.1	+ 73 11	s	Dra	3.0	11.6	∗12-13 in pB, pL neby
6651	Gx	18 24.3	+ 71 36	s	Dra	1.8	14p	eeF, pS, lE, v diffic
4709 I		18 24.3	− 56 12	d	Tel			eF, vS, vE 0°, stell N; susp
6626	Gb	18 24.5	− 24 52	s	Sgr	11.2	6.9	!, ⊕ , vB, L, R, geCM, rrr, st 14...16; = M28
6632	Gx	18 25.0	+ 27 32	s	Her	3.1	13p	F, S, R, gbM
6614	Gx	18 25.2	− 63 14	r	Pav			vF, S, R, gvlbM, ∗9 p
6650	Gx	18 25.4	+ 68 00	r	Dra		15p	vF, vS, R
6648	−	18 25.6	+ 64 59	r	Dra			S, pmE, *⁎ inv
6629	Pl	18 25.7	− 23 12	s	Sgr	0.3	12p	plan or ⊕ , pB, eeS, R
6438	Gx	18 26.	− 85 25	s	Oct	2.6	13p	pB, R, vgbM
4715 I	C+N	18 26.2	− 18 26	F	Sgr	30		eeL cloud of st and neb
4733 I		18 26.5	+ 64 58	d	Dra			vF, stellar
6631	OC	18 27.2	− 12 02	s	Sct	5	12p	Cl, pL, pRi, st 12...15
6635	Gx	18 27.6	+ 14 49	s	Her	1.3	15p	vF, S, R
6633	OC	18 27.7	+ 6 34	s	Oph	27	4.6	Cl, lC, st L

NGC	Type	α_{2000}	δ_{2000}	Const.	Size	Mag.	Description
		h m	o ′		′		
4704 I	Gx	18 27.9	− 71 37 c	Pav	3.2		cB, bM
6640	Gx	18 28.1	+ 34 18 r	Lyr		14p	vF, S, R, vlbM
4711 I		18 28.1	− 64 57 d	Pav			eF, eS, eE 125°, stell N
4705 I	Gx	18 28.2	− 71 42 c	Pav	2.7		eF, eS, R
4710 I	Gx	18 28.7	− 66 59 s	Pav	4.2	12p	vF, vS, R, bM
6641	Gx	18 28.8	+ 22 54 r	Her		14p	vF, vS, R, bM
1288 I	Gx	18 29.4	+ 39 43 u	Lyr	1.3	14p	v F, S, lE, 3 st nr
6646	Gx	18 29.6	+ 39 52 r	Lyr		13p	F, S, iF
1289 I		18 29.8	+ 40 00 d	Lyr			eeF, pS, lE, 3 st nr
6634	−	18 29.9	− 33 25 r	Sgr			neb, without stars
4713 I	Gx	18 30.0	− 67 13 c	Pav	1.2		vF
6639	OC	18 30.1	− 13 12 r	Sct			Cl (in Milky Way)
6667	Gx	18 30.7	+ 67 59 s	Dra	2.6	12p	vF, pL, lE, vF D∗ nr
6638	Gb	18 30.9	− 25 30 s	Sgr	5.0	9.2	⊕, B, S, R, rr
4714 I	Gx	18 30.9	− 66 39 c	Pav	1.1		vF
4712 I	Gx	18 31.1	− 71 42 c	Pav	2.1		vF, vS, R, bM
1287 I	Nb	18 31.3	− 10 50 s	Sct	44		∗5.5 in L, E neb
6637	Gb	18 31.4	− 32 21 s	Sgr	7.1	7.7	⊕, B, L, R, rrr, st 14...16; = M69
6647	OC	18 31.5	− 17 21 s	Sgr		8p	Cl, L, Ri, lC, st vS
4725 I	OC	18 31.6	− 19 15 s	Sgr	32	4.6	Cl, pC; = M25
6642	Gb	18 31.9	− 23 29 s	Sgr	4.5	8.8	⊕, pB, pL, iR, gpmbM rrr, st 16
4762 I	OC	18 32.5	+ 67 50 z	Dra			vF, eS, Cl or ∗ with neb
6630	Gx	18 32.6	− 63 17 A	Pav			pF, S, R, gbM
6644	Pl	18 32.6	− 25 08 s	Sgr	0.1	12p	◯, stellar
6645	OC	18 32.6	− 16 54 s	Sgr	10	9p	Cl, pL, vRi, pC, st 11...15
4716 I		18 32.7	− 56 58 d	Pav			eeF, eS, lE 90°, susp
6657	Gx	18 33.0	+ 34 02 r	Lyr		14p	vF, vS, sbM
6676	Gx	18 33.2	+ 66 57 r	Dra		15p	eeF, pS, lE, lbM, v diffic
6678	−	18 33.2	+ 67 51 r	Dra			pF, pS, R; nonexistent?
4719 I	Gx	18 33.2	− 56 44 c	Tel	1.3		eF, vS, 2 patches, susp
6668		18 33.3	+ 67 08 D	Dra			pB, pS, mE; = 6677?
4717 I	Gx	18 33.3	− 57 58 c	Pav	1.5		F, S, eE 95°, stell N
6649	OC	18 33.5	− 10 24 s	Sct	6	8.9	Cl, P, lC, pS, st 9-10, 12...13
6663	Gx	18 33.5	+ 40 03 r	Lyr		15p	eeF, pS, R, v diffic
6670	Gx	18 33.5	+ 59 53 r	Dra		15p	eeF, S, mE, v diffic
4720 I	Gx	18 33.5	− 58 24 c	Pav	2.5		cF, S, eE 165°, cbM
4763 I		18 33.5	+ 67 08 d	Dra			vF, neb∗?; 6677 nr
6677	Gx	18 33.6	+ 67 08 r	Dra		13p	vF, vS, bet ∗ v close & vF D∗
6679	Gx	18 33.6	+ 67 08 r	Dra		13p	eF, neb D∗ 12.5, dist 5″
6672	Gx	18 33.8	+ 42 48 r	Lyr		15p	2 close st, n one nebs
4718 I	Gx	18 33.8	− 60 08 c	Pav	2.1		cB, S, E 125°, B, stell N
6658	Gx	18 33.9	+ 22 53 s	Her	1.9	12.9	F, vS, lE
6659	−	18 33.9	+ 23 34 r	Her			Cl, P, lC
1291 I	Gx	18 33.9	+ 49 16 s	Dra	2.4	14p	eF, vS, R, F, 2 st 12 nf and np
4732 I	Pl	18 33.9	− 22 39 s	Sgr	0.1	13p	◯, stellar
6662	Gx	18 34.0	+ 32 03 r	Lyr		15p	F∗ in vF, vS, lE neby
6665	Gx	18 34.5	+ 30 42 r	Lyr		14p	vF, vS
4721 I	Gx	18 34.5	− 58 30 s	Pav	4.1	13p	F, cL, E 150°
4722 I	Gx	18 34.5	− 57 48 c	Pav	1.6		F, vS, 2-branch spir
6660		18 34.6	+ 22 55 D	Her			pB, pS, R, mbM, bet 2 st; = 6661
6661	Gx	18 34.6	+ 22 55 s	Her	2.0	11.9	F, vS, R, gbM
6655	−	18 34.8	− 5 59 r	Sct			pF, vS, E
6690	Gx	18 34.8	+ 70 32 s	Dra	3.8	13p	pF, L, R, bet 2 st
6689	Gx	18 34.9	+ 70 32 t	Dra	3.9	12p	vF, pS, ∗8 f, 7′ dist
6666		18 35.3	+ 33 35 D	Lyr			eF, S, R, v diffic

NGC	Type	α_{2000}	δ_{2000}	Const.	Size	Mag.	Description
		h m	° ′		′		
6652	Gb	18 35.8	− 32 59 s	Sgr	3.5	8.9	B, S, lE, rrr, st 15
4723 I	Pl	18 35.8	− 63 22 x	Pav	0.2	15p	vF, vS, R
6656	Gb	18 36.4	− 23 54 s	Sgr	24.0	5.1	!!, ⊕, vB, vL, R, vRi, vmC, st 11...15; M22
6664	OC	18 36.7	− 8 13 s	Sct	16	7.8	Cl, L, pRi, vlC
4726 I		18 36.9	− 62 51 d	Pav			eF, vS, R, eF∗ 0′.5 nf
6687	Gx	18 37.2	+ 59 37 r	Dra		15p	eF, pL, R, bet 2 st
6671	Gx	18 37.4	+ 26 24 r	Lyr		14p	vF, vS, R, mbM
6675	Gx	18 37.4	+ 40 04 r	Lyr		13p	vF, E, 45″
4727 I	Gx	18 37.9	− 62 42 c	Pav	1.4		vF, eS, R
4728 I	Gx	18 37.9	− 62 32 c	Pav	2.0		eF, S, cE 170°, stell N
6669	Gx	18 38.0	+ 22 04 r	Her			eF, pL
4734 I	Gx	18 38.4	− 57 29 c	Pav	1.4		vF, vS, lE 130°
1290 I		18 38.5	− 24 07 D	Sgr			Cl of half dozen st 12...
6674	Gx	18 38.6	+ 25 23 s	Her	4.2	12.1	F, pS, iR, bM
4724 I		18 38.6	− 70 07 d	Pav			eF, eS, cE 170°
4736 I	Gx	18 38.6	− 57 54 c	Pav	1.5		eF, eS, R
4731 I	Gx	18 38.7	− 62 57 c	Pav	1.5		vF, vS, eE 88°, stell N
4730 I	Gx	18 38.8	− 63 21 c	Pav	1.8		eeF, eS, eE 0°, ∗9 s 2′
4756 I	OC	18 39.0	+ 5 27 s	Ser	52	5p	Cl, C
6691	Gx	18 39.3	+ 55 38 s	Dra	1.7	14p	vF, pL, R, pB∗ s nr
4735 I		18 39.7	− 62 57 d	Pav			eF, vS, bM
6680	Gx	18 39.8	+ 22 18 r	Her		15p	eF, S, close to a S∗
6685		18 39.9	+ 39 59 D	Lyr			eeF, vS, R, v diffic, sp of 2
4737 I		18 39.9	− 62 36 d	Pav			eF, vS, cE 10°, bet 2 F st
4772 I	Gx	18 39.9	+ 40 00 u	Lyr	1.1	15p	eF, eS; 6685 f 2^s, 2′.7 s
6696	Gx	18 40.0	+ 59 19 r	Dra		16p	eeF, pL, v diffic
4729 I	Gx	18 40.0	− 67 26 c	Pav	1.4		vF, S, R, stell N
6686	Gx	18 40.1	+ 40 08 r	Lyr		15p	eeF, eS, R, v diffic, nf of 2
4738 I		18 40.4	− 61 54 d	Pav			eeF, eS, eF∗ sf 0′.5
6688	Gx	18 40.7	+ 36 16 r	Lyr		14p	F, pS, R, bM
4739 I		18 40.8	− 61 54 d	Pav			eeF, eS, eF∗ inv
4743 I		18 41.3	− 61 46 d	Pav			vF, bM
6682	−	18 41.6	− 4 46 r	Sct			Cl, L, Ri, st 10...18
6693	∗	18 41.6	+ 36 55 r	Lyr			vF
4741 I		18 41.6	− 63 57 d	Pav			vF, vS, lE 20°, stell N, 4 F st inv
6692	Gx	18 41.7	+ 34 49 r	Lyr		14p	vF, vS, irrE, sev vF st inv
1293 I		18 41.7	+ 56 19 D	Dra			3 st 14, of which the f one is nebs
4744 I		18 41.8	− 63 14 d	Pav			eeF, eS, R, eF∗ inv
4768 I	OC	18 41.8	− 5 31 x	Sct			Cl, D, st sc
4742 I	Gx	18 41.9	− 63 52 c	Pav	1.3		cF, vS, R, bM, F∗ inv
6683	OC	18 42.2	− 6 17 s	Sct	11	10p	Cl, vRi, vlC (in Milky Way)
4745 I	Gx	18 42.6	− 64 57 c	Pav	2.2		eF, vS, vF∗ p 0′.4
6695	Gx	18 42.7	+ 40 24 r	Lyr		14p	vF, S, irrE ns, vlbM
4748 I		18 42.7	− 64 05 d	Pav			eF, vS, R, F∗ sf 1′
4749 I		18 42.9	− 63 13 d	Pav			eeF, eS, 3 F st nr
4740 I	Gx	18 43.0	− 68 22 c	Pav	1.1		eeF, vS, R, lbM, 2 eF st nr
4750 I		18 43.0	− 62 58 d	Pav			eeF, eS, R, ∗11 np 0′.5
6681	Gb	18 43.2	− 32 18 s	Sgr	7.8	8.1	⊕, B, pL, R, gbM, st 14...17; = M70
6701	Gx	18 43.2	+ 60 40 s	Dra	1.8	13p	pB, pS, mE, F∗ close f
4751 I		18 43.2	− 62 07 d	Pav			vF, vS, R, bM
4753 I		18 43.5	− 62 06 d	Pav			vF, vS, R, bM
4752 I		18 43.8	− 64 05 d	Pav			eF, vS, R, vF∗ sf 1′
4757 I	Gx	18 43.9	− 57 10 c	Pav	1.6		eF, eS, cE 50°
4761 I	Gx	18 43.9	− 52 51 c	Tel	1.7		vF, bM, doubtful
4754 I	Gx	18 44.0	− 61 59 c	Pav	1.4		eF, pS, R, stell N; ring?

NGC	Type	α_{2000}	δ_{2000}	Const.	Size	Mag.	Description
		h m	o ′		′		
6653	Gx	18 44.6	− 73 16 c	Pav	1.8		vF, S, lE, glbM
1292 I		18 44.8	− 27 49 d	Sgr			stellar, gaseous spectrum, *9.6 sf
4755 I		18 45.0	− 63 41 d	Pav			vF, vS, eE 90°, stell N
6673	Gx	18 45.1	− 62 17 r	Pav			pF, S, R, psbM, r
6694	OC	18 45.2	− 9 24 s	Sct	15	8.0	Cl, cL, pRi, pC, st 12...15; = M26
6697	Gx	18 45.2	+ 25 31 r	Her		14p	F, vS, stell
4759 I	Gx	18 45.7	− 63 05 c	Pav	1.2		eF, eS, R
4760 I		18 45.7	− 62 57 d	Pav			eF, vS, R, F* np 1′
4776 I	Pl	18 45.8	− 33 21 s	Sgr	0.1	12p	◯, stellar
6714	−	18 45.9	+ 66 44 r	Dra			eeF, pS, v diffic, sev B st n
4746 I		18 45.9	− 72 40 d	Pav			eF, eS
4747 I		18 45.9	− 72 37 d	Pav			vF, eS, cE 75°
6700	Gx	18 46.0	+ 32 17 r	Lyr		14p	eF, lE, dif, iR
4758 I		18 46.4	− 65 45 d	Pav			vF, S, R
6702	Gx	18 47.0	+ 45 42 s	Lyr	2.1	12.2	pF, S, lE
4764 I		18 47.0	− 63 29 d	Pav			eeF, eS, bM
6703	Gx	18 47.3	+ 45 33 s	Lyr	2.6	11.4	B, S, R, mbM
4765 I	Gx	18 47.3	− 63 20 c	Pav	3.6		vF, S, R, bM
4766 I		18 47.5	− 63 17 d	Pav			eF, eS, bM
4767 I		18 47.7	− 63 24 c	Pav	1.3		eF, eS, mE 25°, cbM
4769 I	Gx	18 47.7	− 63 10 c	Pav	2.1		eF, vS, mE 170°, cbM
4770 I		18 48.1	− 63 23 d	Pav			eeF, eS, bM
4777 I		18 48.1	− 53 08 d	Tel			vF, ◯, lE
6698	−	18 48.2	− 25 55 r	Sgr			suspected Cl, cL, st vF
4774 I	Gx	18 48.2	− 57 56 c	Pav	1.1		eF, S, iF, mbM
4771 I		18 48.3	− 63 15 d	Pav			eF, eS, R, bM
4775 I	Gx	18 48.4	− 57 11 c	Pav	1.4		eF, eS, mE 15°, susp
6684	Gx	18 49.0	− 65 11 s	Pav	3.7	10.5	vB, pL, R, vg, psvmbM *7 p
6711	Gx	18 49.0	+ 47 39 s	Dra	1.3	14p	vF, pS, R, lbM
4791 I		18 49.0	+ 19 20 d	Her			neb; *6 f 2′
1294 I		18 49.9	+ 40 15 d	Lyr			eeF, S, iR, v diffic, F* close nf
4778 I	Gx	18 50.0	− 61 43 c	Pav	1.5		cF, vS, cE 35°
4780 I		18 50.0	− 59 14 d	Pav			eF, vS, lE 120°
4779 I		18 50.5	− 63 00 d	Pav			eeF, eS, eF* p 0′.3
6710	Gx	18 50.6	+ 26 50 s	Lyr	2.0	12.8	vF, S, R, bM
6713	Gx	18 50.7	+ 33 57 r	Lyr		14p	vF, S, R, bM
6704	OC	18 50.9	− 5 12 s	Sct	6	9.2	Cl, B, 60 st 13
4782 I	Gx	18 50.9	− 55 29 c	Tel	1.6		eeF, eS, susp
6705	OC	18 51.1	− 6 16 s	Sct	14	5.8	!, Cl, vB, L, iR, Ri, *9, st 11...; = M11
4773 I	Gx	18 51.3	− 69 55 c	Pav	1.6		eF, dif
6709	OC	18 51.5	+ 10 21 s	Aql	13	6.7	Cl, pRi, lC, iF
4783 I		18 51.5	− 58 48 d	Pav			eF, vS
4781 I		18 51.7	− 62 47 d	Pav			3 eeF st in neb
6699	Gx	18 52.1	− 57 19 s	Pav	1.9	13p	pF, pS, lE 90°, pslbM
4786 I		18 52.7	− 56 42 d	Tel			eeF, eS, mE 0°
4784 I		18 52.9	− 63 25 d	Pav			cF, S, R, bM
4785 I	Gx	18 52.9	− 59 15 c	Pav	2.9		eF, vS, iF, stell N
6712	Gb	18 53.1	− 8 42 s	Sct	7.2	8.2	⊕, pB, vL, irr, vglbM, rrr
1296 I	Gx	18 53.3	+ 33 04 u	Lyr	1.3	15p	eF, pS, iR, 4′ np M57
6720	Pl	18 53.6	+ 33 02 s	Lyr	2.5	9.0	!!!, ⊙, B, pL, cE (in Lyra); = M57
6716	OC	18 54.6	− 19 53 s	Sgr	7	6.9	Cl, pRi, st 9...13
1295 I	Pl	18 54.6	− 8 50 s	Sct	1.4	15p	pB, pL, gbM
4788 I		18 54.7	− 63 26 d	Pav			eeF, eS, eE 35°
6715	Gb	18 55.1	− 30 29 s	Sgr	9.1	7.7	⊕, vB, L, R, g, smbM, rrr, st 15; = M54
6717	Gb	18 55.1	− 22 42 s	Sgr	3.9		F, S, rr, Cl + neb

NGC	Type	α_{2000}	δ_{2000}	Const.	Size	Mag.	Description
		h m	o ʹ		ʹ		
4802 I		18 55.1	− 22 42 d	Sgr			neb *13, 15ʺ nf 6717
6747	Gx	18 55.3	+ 72 47 r	Dra		15p	eeF, v diffic, pB st sf
6707	Gx	18 55.4	− 53 49 v	Tel			F, S, vlE, gbM
6708	Gx	18 55.6	− 53 43 v	Tel			pF, S, R, gpmbM, last of group
4792 I		18 55.7	− 56 25 d	Tel			eeF, eS, mE 160°, bet 2 st, susp
4787 I	Gx	18 56.1	− 68 41 c	Pav	1.4		eF, dif
4789 I	Gx	18 56.3	− 68 34 c	Pav	1.4		eF, eS, R
6732	Gx	18 56.4	+ 52 22 r	Dra		14p	pB, vS, R, F* n
4796 I	Gx	18 56.5	− 54 13 c	Tel	1.6		14m, bM, near edge of plate
4797 I	Gx	18 56.5	− 54 18 s	Tel	2.8	11.3	14m, bM, near edge of plate
4790 I		18 56.6	− 64 56 d	Pav			cB, S, R, bM
6706	Gx	18 56.9	− 63 10 c	Pav	1.5		vF, vS, eE 120°, stell N
4793 I		18 56.9	− 61 23 d	Pav			eF, vS, cE 130°
6724	−	18 57.0	+ 10 22 r	Aql			Cl
6731	−	18 57.0	+ 43 04 r	Lyr			vF
4794 I		18 57.1	− 62 05 d	Pav			F, S, R, bM
4795 I		18 57.2	− 61 36 d	Pav			eeF, eS, eE 40°
4798 I	Gx	18 58.3	− 62 07 c	Pav	1.9		F, S, R, bM
4800 I	Gx	18 58.7	− 63 08 c	Pav	1.7		vF, S, stell N, oval ring, 2 wisps
4799 I		18 58.9	− 63 55 d	Pav			vF, S, R, stell N, ring, 2 wisps
6742	Pl	18 59.3	+ 48 28 s	Dra	0.5	15p	vF, stellar
6723	Gb	18 59.6	− 36 38 s	Sgr	11.0	7.3	⊕ , vL, vlE, vgbM, rrr, st 14...16
4801 I	Gx	18 59.6	− 64 40 c	Pav	1.7		cF, S, R, bM
6728	−	19 00.0	− 8 57 r	Aql			Cl, vL, P
4803 I		19 00.6	− 62 04 d	Pav			eeF, eS, R
6750	Gx	19 00.7	+ 59 10 r	Dra		13p	vF, vS, R
6721	Gx	19 00.8	− 57 47 s	Pav	1.9	12.0	pF, cS, R, vmbM
6735	OC	19 00.8	− 0 28 F	Aql			Cl, vL, P, st 12...
6740	Gx	19 00.8	+ 28 45 r	Lyr		15p	eeF, S
4804 I	Gx	19 01.1	− 61 50 c	Pav	1.5		eeF, eS, cE
4808 I	Gx	19 01.1	− 45 19 c	CrA	2.0		vF, cL, cE 45°, lbM, susp
4812 I	Nb	19 01.1	− 37 04 d	CrA			*7 inv in eL neb
6738	OC	19 01.4	+ 11 36 s	Aql	15	8p	Cl, P, lC
6743	?	19 01.4	+ 29 16 A	Lyr			Cl, pL, P, st 11...12
6718	Gx	19 01.5	− 66 07 c	Pav	1.5		vF, S, R, glbM, *9 sp
4806 I	Gx	19 01.5	− 57 32 c	Pav	2.1		eeF, eS, eE 10°, 2 st vnr, susp
6745	Gx	19 01.6	+ 40 45 r	Lyr		13p	vF, lE ns
6726	Nb	19 01.7	− 36 53 s	CrA	2		*6-7 in F, pL, neb
6725	Gx	19 01.8	− 53 56 A	Tel			eF, eS, stell N, with straight wisp at 40°
6727	Nb	19 01.8	− 36 54 r	CrA			*8 in F, pL neb
4816 I		19 01.8	− 13 09 d	Sgr			○ , stellar
6729	Nb	19 01.9	− 36 57 s	CrA	1		var* (11...) with neb!!
4805 I		19 02.0	− 63 03 d	Pav			eF, vS, eE 25°, bM
6737	−	19 02.2	− 18 32 r	Sgr			Cl, pL, pRi, R, st 12...15
4807 I	Gx	19 02.3	− 56 56 c	Pav	0.9		vF, vS, lE, ○ ?, susp
6741	Pl	19 02.6	− 0 27 s	Aql	0.1	11p	○ , stellar
4810 I	Gx	19 03.0	− 56 10 c	Tel	3.0		eF, S, eE 140°, lbM, susp
6719	Gx	19 03.1	− 68 35 c	Pav	1.6		vF, pL, R, vgvlbM
6722	Gx	19 03.7	− 64 54 c	Pav	2.9		pF, S, E, glbM, 2 st 8 p
6748	−	19 03.8	+ 21 36 r	Vul			pB, vS, bM
4809 I		19 04.0	− 62 10 d	Pav			eF, vS, lE 20°
4814 I		19 05.0	− 58 44 d	Pav			eeF, cS, cE 100°, susp
6749	Gb	19 05.1	+ 1 47 s	Aql	6.3	11.1	Cl, L, lC, st L & S
6757	Gx	19 05.1	+ 55 43 r	Dra		14p	pF, mE, 3 F st inv
6762	Gx	19 05.6	+ 63 56 r	Dra		14p	eF, mE; = 6763

NGC	Type	α_{2000}	δ_{2000}	Const.	Size	Mag.	Description
		h m	o $'$		$'$		
6763	Gx	19 05.6	+ 63 56 D	Dra		14p	eF, vS, cE, F* nr
4811 I		19 05.8	− 67 07 d	Pav			eeF, eS, R, alm stell
4813 I		19 05.8	− 66 31 d	Pav			vF, S, R
6751	Pl	19 05.9	− 6 00 s	Aql	0.3	13p	pB, S
4818 I	Gx	19 06.0	− 55 08 c	Tel	1.6		eF, eS, cE 90°
6733	Gx	19 06.2	− 62 12 c	Pav	1.7		eeF, vglbM, v difficult
4817 I	Gx	19 06.2	− 56 10 c	Tel	1.5		eF, vS, cE 0°
4815 I		19 06.7	− 61 41 d	Pav			cF, vS, R, bM
6759	Gx	19 06.9	+ 50 19 r	Dra		15p	vF, S, R, vF D* close sp
4819 I	Gx	19 07.1	− 59 28 c	Pav	2.7		vF, S, eE 130°
6734	Gx	19 07.2	− 65 28 c	Pav	1.4		vF, S, R, glbM, p of 2
6736	Gx	19 07.5	− 65 26 c	Pav	1.2		eF, S, R, glbM, f of 2
6730	Gx	19 07.6	− 68 55 c	Pav	1.5		vF, S, R, pmbM, *7-8 nf
6739	Gx	19 07.8	− 61 22 c	Pav	2.2		cF, vS, cE, psbM, 3 st p
6755	OC	19 07.8	+ 4 14 s	Aql	15	7.5	Cl, vL, vRi, pC, st 12...14
6764	Gx	19 08.3	+ 50 56 s	Cyg	2.5	13p	pF, pL, mE, sev vF st inv
6756	OC	19 08.7	+ 4 41 s	Aql	4	11p	Cl, S, Ri, lC, st 11...12
4820 I	Gx	19 09.2	− 63 28 c	Pav	1.4		eeF, eS
4821 I	Gx	19 09.5	− 55 01 c	Tel	1.8		vF, vS, eE 10°
6744	Gx	19 09.8	− 63 51 s	Pav	15.5	9p	cB, cL, R, vg, svmbM, r
6766	−	19 09.9	+ 46 15 r	Lyr			◯ , stellar
6746	Gx	19 10.4	− 61 58 c	Pav	1.4		eF, cS, R, glbM
6752	Gb	19 10.9	− 59 59 s	Pav	20.4	5.4	⊕ , B, vL, iR, rrr, st 11...16
6786	Gx	19 10.9	+ 73 24 r	Dra		13p	F, S, R, 2 st nf
6765	Pl	19 11.1	+ 30 33 s	Lyr	0.6		F, S, E
6760	Gb	19 11.2	+ 1 02 s	Aql	6.6	9.1	pB, pL, vglbM
6753	Gx	19 11.4	− 57 03 s	Pav	2.5	12p	pB, pL, R, gbM
6754	Gx	19 11.4	− 50 39 s	Tel	2.2	13p	pF, pL, mE 63°, vglbM
6767	−	19 11.6	+ 37 43 r	Lyr			vF, S, R, stellar, S* nr n
4823 I		19 12.2	− 64 00 d	Pav			vF, vS
4826 I	Gx	19 12.3	− 57 12 c	Pav	1.7		eF, eeS, R
4829 I	Gx	19 12.6	− 56 32 c	Tel	2.0		eeF, eS, mE 20°
4824 I	Gx	19 13.2	− 62 05 c	Pav	2.5		eF, eS, Dneb
4827 I	Gx	19 13.3	− 60 52 c	Pav	2.5		F, cS, eE 170°, stell N
4828 I		19 13.6	− 62 04 d	Pav			vF, vS, cE 60°
4830 I	Gx	19 13.8	− 59 18 c	Pav	1.7		eF, eS, R, lbM
6758	Gx	19 13.9	− 56 19 s	Tel	2.1	13p	pB, S, R
4832 I	Gx	19 14.1	− 56 37 c	Tel	2.0		vF, vS, eE 145°, stell N
6772	Pl	19 14.6	− 2 42 s	Aql	1.0	14p	vF, L, R, vvlbM, r
4831 I	Gx	19 14.7	− 62 16 c	Pav	3.3		! cF, vS, eE 150°, 2-br spir
4822 I		19 14.9	− 72 26 d	Pav			F, S, R
6773	−	19 15.0	+ 4 53 r	Aql			Cl, P, lC
6761	Gx	19 15.3	− 50 40 v	Tel	2.2		vF, pS, iR
4837 I	Gx	19 15.3	− 54 40 s	Tel	2.8	12p	F, cS, R, bM
4835 I		19 15.5	− 58 14 d	Pav			eF, eS, cE 0°
4833 I		19 15.6	− 62 20 d	Pav			eeF, eS, R, bM
4839 I	Gx	19 15.6	− 54 38 c	Tel	2.4		F, neb*
4840 I	Gx	19 15.9	− 56 13 c	Tel	1.1		cF, vS
6787	Gx	19 16.3	+ 60 25 r	Dra		15p	eeF, pS, 4 st sf, e diffic
4836 I	Gx	19 16.3	− 60 12 c	Pav	1.1		F, cL, iF, 2 st inv
6768	Gx	19 16.5	− 40 11 r	CrA			vF, S, R, pslbM
4834 I		19 16.5	− 64 01 d	Pav			eF, vS, lE 140°
4846 I	Pl	19 16.5	− 9 03 s	Aql		13p	◯ , stellar
6774	OC	19 16.6	− 16 16 r	Sgr			Cl, vL, lC
6779	Gb	19 16.6	+ 30 11 s	Lyr	7.1	8.3	⊕ , B, L, iR, gvmCM, rrr, st 11...14; = M56

NGC	Type	α_{2000}	δ_{2000}		Const.	Size	Mag.	Description
		h m	° ′			′		
6783	Gx	19 16.6	+ 46 01	r	Cyg		15p	eF, diffic
6789	Gx	19 16.7	+ 64 00	r	Dra		13p	eeF, pL, R, v diffic
6775	Ast	19 16.8	− 0 55	F	Aql			Cl, P, lC, st 10...11
4838 I		19 16.8	− 61 37	d	Pav			cF, S, eE 45°
4825 I		19 17.3	− 72 45	d	Pav			eF, eS, R
1297 I	Pl	19 17.4	− 39 37	s	CrA	0.1		stellar (gaseous spectrum)
6769	Gx	19 18.4	− 60 31	s	Pav	2.5	11.8	vF, S, R, lbM, 1st of 3
6778	Pl	19 18.4	− 1 36	s	Aql	0.3	13p	S, E, ill-defined disc
6781	Pl	19 18.4	+ 6 33	s	Aql	1.8	12p	◯ , F, L, R, vsbM disc, S∗ nf
1298 I	OC	19 18.5	− 1 37	x	Aql			vS Cl, 6778 p 3′
6770	Gx	19 18.7	− 60 31	s	Pav	2.5	12.0	eF, vS, 2nd of 3
6771	Gx	19 18.7	− 60 33	s	Pav	2.6	12.5	eF, S, 3rd of 3
4844 I	Gx	19 19.0	− 56 02	c	Tel	1.6		vF, vS
4843 I		19 19.3	− 59 18	d	Pav			eF, eS, cE 90°
4842 I	Gx	19 19.5	− 60 39	s	Pav	2.4	12.3	vF, vS, R
4845 I	Gx	19 20.4	− 60 23	c	Pav	1.7		cF, bM, ∗11 sp 0′.4
4850 I		19 20.4	− 0 08	d	Aql			◯ , stellar
6791	OC	19 20.7	+ 37 51	s	Lyr	16	9.5	vF
4841 I		19 20.8	− 72 13	d	Pav			eF, S, R, cbM
6785		19 20.9	− 1 06	D	Aql			eS, stellar
6792	Gx	19 21.0	+ 43 08	r	Lyr		13p	F, E 26°, glbM, ∗9.5 sf
6796	Gx	19 21.5	+ 61 09	s	Dra	2.1	14p	vF, pS, mE ns
1299 I	OC	19 22.6	+ 20 45	x	Vul			S Cl of vF st
4848 I		19 22.8	− 56 47	d	Pav			eF, eS, R
6780	Gx	19 22.9	− 55 47	s	Tel	1.9	13p	vF, L, R, vglbM
6790	Pl	19 23.2	+ 1 31	s	Aql	0.1	10p	◯ , B, eS, stell = 9.5 mag
6793	OC	19 23.2	+ 22 11	r	Vul			Cl, P, lC
4847 I		19 23.5	− 65 31	d	Pav			vF, eS, R, ∗8.9 sf 4′
6782	Gx	19 24.0	− 59 55	s	Pav	2.7	13p	cF, cS, R, lbM, ∗9 s
6798	Gx	19 24.0	+ 53 38	r	Cyg		14p	F, vS, R, ∗ vnr
1300 I	?	19 24.1	+ 52 39	x	Cyg			= 6798
6776	Gx	19 25.4	− 63 52	s	Pav	1.9	12.0	pB, S, R, pgbM
4849 I		19 25.4	− 62 54	d	Pav			vF, vS
4851 I	Gx	19 25.5	− 57 40	c	Pav	1.6		vF, vS, eE 15°, vmbM, susp
6795	−	19 26.1	+ 3 31	r	Aql			Cl, Ri, bet 2 st 9
4852 I	Gx	19 26.4	− 60 20	c	Pav	1.7		cF, bM
4867 I	Gx	19 26.5	+ 50 07	u	Cyg	1.0	14p	S; 2 st 7 nf 3′ (= IC 1301?)
6784	Gx	19 26.6	− 65 37	c	Pav	0.8		eeeF, pS, am S st
1301 I	Gx	19 26.6	+ 49 45	v	Cyg	1.4		eeF, vS, R, 3 st f; = IC 4867?
6777		19 26.8	− 71 30	D	Pav			2 st 8 or 9 mag nr (no neb)
6788		19 26.9	− 54 57	D	Tel			pB, S, mE, pslbM
6800	OC	19 27.2	+ 25 08	s	Vul			Cl, vL, pRi, vlC, st 10...
4854 I		19 27.4	− 59 18	d	Pav			vF, cS, R
4855 I		19 27.5	− 59 18	d	Pav			eF, vS, R, susp
4856 I	Gx	19 27.5	− 54 55	c	Tel	1.0		eF, eS, Dneb, susp
6801		19 27.7	+ 54 22	r	Cyg		15p	eF, pS, R, F∗ s nr
6794	Gx	19 27.9	− 38 53	r	Sgr			eF, pS, R, vgvlbM
4863 I		19 28.3	− 36 12	d	Sgr			close D∗, nebulous?
4857 I	Gx	19 28.6	− 58 46	c	Pav	1.8		vF, cS, R; = IC 4858
4858 I	Gx	19 28.6	− 58 46	c	Pav	1.8		eeF, eS, prob spir; susp
6797	−	19 28.9	− 25 40	r	Sgr			neb with ∗9 att f; nonexistent?
4861 I		19 29.2	− 57 34	d	Pav			vF, eS, cE 25°, susp
6802	OC	19 30.6	+ 20 16	s	Vul	3	8.8	Cl, L, vC, E 0°, st 14...18
4859 I		19 30.8	− 66 19	d	Pav			eF, S, cbM, alm stell N
1302 I	Gx	19 30.9	+ 35 47	s	Cyg	1.0	13.3	vF, undefined

NGC	Type	α_{2000}	δ_{2000}	Const.	Size	Mag.	Description
		h m	o ′		′		
4853 I		19 30.9	− 71 04 d	Pav			eeF, eS, lE 170°
4865 I		19 30.9	− 46 42 d	Tel			F, perh stell N; *9.5 att sf
6803	Pl	19 31.3	+ 10 03 s	Aql	0.1	11p	◯ , stellar
1303 I	Gx	19 31.5	+ 35 53 v	Cyg	1.5	14.2	vF, S, with S Cl
4860 I	Gx	19 31.5	− 67 22 c	Pav	1.1		eF, S, R
6804	Pl	19 31.6	+ 9 13 s	Aql	1.1	12p	cB, S, iR, rrr
4862 I	Gx	19 31.7	− 67 19 c	Pav	1.4		eF, S, cbM, lE 0°
6799	Gx	19 32.3	− 55 54 c	Tel	1.5		eF, vS, R, lbM, 3 vS st nr
4868 I		19 33.5	− 45 54 d	Tel			eS, lE, mag 9.4
6807	Pl	19 34.6	+ 5 41 s	Aql		14p	◯ , stellar
4866 I	Gx	19 34.6	− 61 09 c	Pav	1.6		cF, S, R, bM
4873 I		19 34.9	− 46 08 d	Tel			F, S, R, F* M
1304 I		19 35.5	+ 41 02 d	Cyg			F neby
4871 I	Gx	19 35.7	− 57 31 c	Pav	3.2		vF, S, eE 15°
4872 I	Gx	19 35.7	− 57 31 c	Pav	3.2		vF, S, eE 5°; = IC 4871
4869 I	Gx	19 36.0	− 61 02 c	Pav	2.3		F, S, R, bM, F* sp 1′
4874 I	Gx	19 36.4	− 47 16 c	Tel	1.4		F, S, R, F* M
6805	Gx	19 36.8	− 37 33 c	Sgr	1.2		eF, R, vgbM
6806	Gx	19 37.2	− 42 19 v	Sgr			eF, vS, *14 att
6817	Gx	19 37.4	+ 62 22 r	Dra		15p	eeF, pS, lE
4870 I	Gx	19 37.6	− 65 49 c	Pav	1.5		vF, S, F* inv
4875 I	Gx	19 37.7	− 52 04 c	Tel	1.3		F, S, R, lbM
4876 I	Gx	19 37.7	− 52 51 c	Tel	1.2		F, S, R, lbM
4877 I	Gx	19 37.9	− 51 59 c	Tel	1.1		F, S, R, lbM
6811	OC	19 38.2	+ 46 34 s	Cyg	13	6.8	Cl, L, pRi, lC, st 11..14
4878 I		19 38.8	− 58 13 d	Pav			eF, eS, mE 40°
1305 I		19 39.3	+ 20 13 d	Vul			vF, *9.5 at sf end
4879 I		19 39.7	− 52 22 d	Tel			F, S, R, lbM
6809	Gb	19 40.0	− 30 58 s	Sgr	19.0	7.0	⊕ , pB, L, R, vRi, vgbM, st 12...15; = M55
4864 I	Gx	19 40.1	− 77 33 c	Oct	1.6		eF, vS, eE 70°, vF* sp 1′
6813	Nb	19 40.4	+ 27 18 s	Vul	3		* in vF, S neb
4881 I	Gx	19 40.4	− 55 51 c	Tel	1.5		eF, vS, R
4882 I	Gx	19 40.4	− 55 12 c	Tel	1.2		eF, eS, R
4880 I	Gx	19 40.5	− 56 25 c	Tel	1.5		eF, vS, R
6815	OC	19 40.9	+ 26 51 r	Vul			Cl, vL, pRi, lC, st 10...15
6819	OC	19 41.3	+ 40 11 s	Cyg	5	7.3	Cl, vL, vRi, st 11...15
6825	Gx	19 41.7	+ 64 05 r	Dra		15p	eF, vS, v diffic, F* nr
1306 I	?	19 41.7	+ 37 39 x	Cyg			neb group of F st
4883 I	Gx	19 42.0	− 55 33 c	Tel	1.3		vF, vS, mE 170°
6814	Gx	19 42.7	− 10 19 s	Aql	3.2	11.2	pF, pL, R, bM, r
4884 I		19 42.7	− 58 07 d	Pav			eF, eS, cE 170°
1307 I	?	19 42.8	+ 27 30 x	Vul			F, vL, E ns, st inv
6820	Nb	19 43.1	+ 23 17 s	Vul	40		F, S, R, bM
6823	OC	19 43.1	+ 23 18 s	Vul	12	7.1	Cl, cRi, E, st 11...12
4886 I	Gx	19 43.1	− 51 48 c	Tel	1.5		F, S, R, mbM
6810	Gx	19 43.6	− 58 40 s	Pav	3.8	12p	cF, S, eE 170°, stell N
6824	Gx	19 43.7	+ 56 07 s	Cyg	2.1	11.9	pB, iF, bM
6808	Gx	19 43.9	− 70 39 s	Pav	1.7	13p	pB, E, biN, *8 f
4885 I	Gx	19 43.9	− 60 39 c	Pav	2.0		vF, eS, eE 85°, stell N
6816		19 44.0	− 28 33 D	Sgr			eF, pS, R, vlbM, *14 at pos 20°, dist 30″
6818	Pl	19 44.0	− 14 09 s	Sgr	0.3	10p	◯ , B, vS, R
6821	Gx	19 44.4	− 6 50 s	Aql	1.1	14p	F, pL, R
6826	Pl	19 44.8	+ 50 31 s	Cyg	2.3	10p	◯ , B, pL, R, *11 M
6822	Gx	19 44.9	− 14 48 s	Sgr	10.2	9p	vF, vS, E, dif; = IC 4895
4888 I	Gx	19 44.9	− 54 27 c	Tel	1.3		F, vS, R, lbM

NGC	Type	α_{2000}	δ_{2000}	Const.	Size	Mag.	Description
		h m	° ′		′		
4895 I	Gx	19 45.0	− 14 48 m	Sgr	10.0	8p	group of neb, 25′ diam; = 6822
1308 I		19 45.1	− 14 43 d	Sgr			eF, eS, lE, gbM, 6822 p 12ˢ
4889 I	Gx	19 45.3	− 54 20 s	Tel	2.6	12p	bM, mag 10
4891 I	Gx	19 45.3	− 54 21 c	Tel	2.8		cB, S, R, bM; = IC 4889
6812	Gx	19 45.4	− 55 21 c	Tel	2.1		pB, pS, pmE, glbM
4890 I	Gx	19 45.6	− 56 33 c	Tel	1.3		eeF, eS, R, F∗ s 1′
4894 I	Gx	19 47.0	− 51 51 c	Tel	0.9		bM, mag 15
6829	Gx	19 47.1	+ 59 55 r	Dra		15p	eF, pS, R, pB∗ close s, p of 2
4898 I		19 47.8	− 33 19 d	Sgr			eeF, eS, e dif, sev F st nr
6831	Gx	19 47.9	+ 59 54 r	Dra		14p	eF, S, R, f of 2
6832	−	19 48.1	+ 59 25 r	Dra			Cl, vL, lC, st 7...
4887 I		19 48.3	− 69 35 d	Pav			cB, S, R, bM
6827	OC	19 48.9	+ 21 13 r	Vul			vF, E, dif, sev st inv
4896 I		19 49.1	− 58 59 d	Pav			eeF, eS, R, bet 2 eF st
4897 I	Gx	19 49.3	− 51 52 c	Tel	1.1		bM, mag 16
4892 I	Gx	19 49.5	− 70 14 c	Pav	1.6		eF, S, eE 10°
6833	Pl	19 49.7	+ 48 58 s	Cyg	< 0.1	14p	◯ , stellar
4900 I		19 50.3	− 51 20 d	Tel			bM, mag 15
6828	−	19 50.4	+ 7 55 r	Aql			Cl, P, lC
4893 I		19 50.6	− 72 31 d	Pav			eF, vS, R, bM
6830	OC	19 51.0	+ 23 04 s	Vul	12	7.9	Cl, L, pRi, pC, st 11...12
6834	OC	19 52.2	+ 29 25 s	Cyg	5	7.8	Cl, P, lC, st 11...12
6837	OC	19 53.5	+ 11 41 A	Aql			Cl, S, P
6838	Gb	19 53.8	+ 18 47 s	Sge	7.2	8.3	Cl, vL, vRi, pmC, st 11...16; = M71
4899 I		19 54.4	− 70 36 d	Pav			eeF, eS, vF∗ sp 1′
4901 I	Gx	19 54.4	− 58 43 c	Pav	5.0		cF, S, vlE 135°
4902 I		19 54.4	− 56 23 d	Tel			eeF, eS, cE 0°; susp
6835	Gx	19 54.5	− 12 34 s	Sgr	2.7	12.5	F, pL, mE
6839	−	19 54.5	+ 17 54 r	Sge			Cl, vS, vC
6836	Gx	19 54.7	− 12 41 s	Sgr	1.2	13p	vF, pL, R, dif, ∗13.5 att f
6842	Pl	19 55.0	+ 29 17 s	Vul	0.8	14p	F, pL, vlE
6840	OC	19 55.3	+ 12 06 A	Aql			Cl, P, lC
6843	OC	19 56.1	+ 12 09 A	Aql			Cl, S, P
4905 I		19 56.1	− 61 13 d	Pav			eeF, eS, mE 130°, nr 2 eF st
4907 I		19 56.2	− 52 27 d	Tel			bM, mag 16
6846	OC	19 56.5	+ 30 21 r	Cyg		14p	eF, vS, 3 st inv
4909 I	Gx	19 56.7	− 50 03 c	Tel	2.1		bM, mag 15
4906 I	Gx	19 56.8	− 60 28 c	Pav	1.7		F, S, R, bM, 4 st around
4913 I	Gx	19 56.8	− 37 20 c	Sgr	1.9		eeF, pS, e diffic, 3 st 10 s 8′
4908 I		19 56.9	− 55 47 d	Tel			eF, eS, R, susp
6847	−	19 57.0	+ 29 20 r	Vul			neb, r
4911 I		19 57.7	− 51 58 d	Tel			bM, mag 16
4841 I	Gx	19 57.8	− 31 49 c	Sgr	1.5		vF, S, R, psbM
4910 I		19 57.8	− 56 52 d	Pav			eF, eS, cE 130°, am st; susp
4914 I		19 58.1	− 50 07 d	Tel			F, vS, R
4903 I		19 58.2	− 70 27 d	Pav			eF, vS, bet 2 F st
4916 I	Gx	19 58.3	− 50 16 c	Tel	1.3		F, S, R, F∗ M
4904 I		19 58.5	− 70 11 d	Pav			vF, S, R
4915 I	Gx	19 58.5	− 52 38 c	Tel	1.4		bM, mag 15
4917 I	Gx	19 58.9	− 52 16 c	Tel	1.2		bM, mag 16
6856	−	19 59.3	+ 56 08 r	Cyg			Cl, pS, pmC, iR, st 12...16
4918 I		19 59.3	− 52 17 d	Tel			bM, mag 16
4922 I		19 59.5	− 40 22 d	Sgr			vF, vS, R; susp
6853	Pl	19 59.6	+ 22 43 s	Vul	15.2	8.1	!!!, vB, vL, biN, iE (Dumbbell); = M27
4924 I		19 59.9	− 41 33 d	Sgr			dif (defect?)

NGC	Type	α_{2000}	δ_{2000}	Const.	Size	Mag.	Description
		h m	o ′		′		
4920 I		20 00.1	− 53 23 d	Tel			vF, vLE, lbM
4919 I	Gx	20 00.2	− 55 22 c	Tel	1.6		eeF, eS, R, * f 1′; susp
4926 I		20 00.2	− 38 35 d	Sgr			eeF, S, lE, v diffic, p of 2
6852	Pl	20 00.6	+ 1 43 s	Aql	0.5		F neb, am st
6869	Gx	20 00.7	+ 66 13 s	Dra	1.7	13p	pB, pS, R
4931 I	Gx	20 00.8	− 38 35 c	Sgr	2.6		eeF, pS, R, *8 f 20^s, f of 2
6845	Gx	20 00.9	− 47 05 r	Tel			vF, S, vlE, glbM
4923 I	Gx	20 01.0	− 52 38 c	Tel	1.3		bM, mag 14
4925 I		20 01.2	− 52 51 d	Tel			F, S, vME 170°
6849		20 01.3	− 40 13 d	Sgr			pB, S, R, vS* np
4927 I	Gx	20 01.8	− 53 55 c	Tel	1.3		F, S, E 170°
6857	Pl	20 01.9	+ 33 31 r	Cyg			F, am Milky Way st
4932 I		20 02.3	− 52 50 d	Tel			bM, mag 15
4930 I		20 02.4	− 54 18 d	Tel			cB, S, mE 45°, susp
6844	Gx	20 02.8	− 65 14 c	Pav	1.6		eF, vS, R, psbM, *11 np
6848	Gx	20 02.8	− 56 05 c	Tel	2.5		cF, cL, R, vglbM, 2 st f
6858	−	20 03.1	+ 11 16 r	Aql			Cl, cL, E, pRi, st 13...
1309 I	Gx	20 03.1	− 17 14 c	Sgr	2.0		F, vS, R, r
4921 I		20 03.3	− 67 50 d	Pav			vF, S, R; cbM
6850	Gx	20 03.5	− 54 51 v	Tel			vF, S, R, bM
4933 I	Gx	20 03.5	− 54 59 c	Tel	2.5		eF, eS, 2-branch spir
6851	Gx	20 03.6	− 48 17 s	Tel	1.8	13p	pF, S, vlE, psbM
6866	OC	20 03.7	+ 44 00 s	Cyg	7	7.6	Cl, L, vRi, cC
6859	*′*	20 03.9	+ 0 26 F	Aql			vS Cl, *10 p 1^s, s 1′ 29″
4935 I	Gx	20 04.6	− 57 36 c	Pav	1.5		vF, vS, mE 5°, * 1′ sp; susp
4954 I	Nb	20 04.8	+ 29 15 s	Vul	25		D neb*, iF, *11 close
4955 I		20 04.9	+ 29 11 d	Vul			fine neb *12
6863	Ast	20 05.1	− 3 34 F	Aql			Cl, S, vmC, st 19
4937 I	Gx	20 05.3	− 56 15 c	Tel	2.0		eF, vS, eE 0°, N; susp
6854	Gx	20 05.7	− 54 23 s	Tel	2.3	13p	F, S, vlE, glbM
4940 I		20 05.7	− 44 42 d	Sgr			F, S, E 100°
6871	OC	20 05.9	+ 35 47 s	Cyg	20	5.2	Cl, st L and S, ⚹ inv
4936 I	Gx	20 05.9	− 61 26 c	Pav	1.6		eF, vS, eE 20°, 2 F st np
6865	Gx	20 06.0	− 9 02 r	Aql			F, S, E
4946 I		20 06.0	− 44 02 d	Sgr			eF, S, R
6864	Gb	20 06.1	− 21 55 s	Sgr	6.0	8.6	⊕, B, pL, R, vmbMBN, rr; = M75
4938 I	Gx	20 06.2	− 60 13 c	Pav	1.9		! vF, pS, annul, stell N, vF* sf
4943 I	Gx	20 06.5	− 48 22 c	Tel	2.2		eeF, pS, R, F* n, v diffic
4948 I		20 06.5	− 43 37 d	Sgr			vF, pS, R, 2 st f, * np
4929 I	Gx	20 06.7	− 71 41 c	Pav	1.3		F, S, cE 15°
6855	Gx	20 06.8	− 56 24 r	Tel			pF, S, R
4912 I	Gx	20 06.8	− 77 21 c	Oct	1.0		eF, vS, F* np 1′; susp
4942 I	Gx	20 06.8	− 52 37 c	Tel	1.3		F, vS, R
4941 I	Gx	20 07.0	− 53 39 c	Tel	1.2		F, S, R, lbM, v dif
4944 I	Gx	20 07.1	− 54 27 c	Tel	1.9		bM, mag 14
4934 I		20 07.2	− 69 28 d	Pav			vF, vS, cE 15°, lbM; susp
4939 I		20 07.2	− 60 44 d	Pav			eeF, eS, cE 150°, F* s 2′
6861	Gx	20 07.3	− 48 22 s	Tel	2.7	11.1	B, S, cE, gpmbM
4949 I	Gx	20 07.3	− 48 22 c	Tel	3.0		B, vS, cE; = 6861
4947 I	Gx	20 07.5	− 53 08 c	Tel	1.2		bM, mag 15
6874	−	20 07.8	+ 38 14 r	Cyg			Cl, P, lC
6873	D*	20 08.3	+ 21 06 r	Sge			Cl, lC, st 10...13, ⚹ inv
4950 I	Gx	20 08.4	− 56 10 c	Tel	1.3		eF, vS, eE 35°, lbM
4952 I	Gx	20 08.6	− 55 27 c	Tel	1.3		F, vS, cE 10°
6860	Gx	20 08.8	− 61 06 c	Pav	1.6		F, pS, gbM

NGC	Type	α_{2000}	δ_{2000}	Const.	Size	Mag.	Description
		h m	° ′		′		
6862	Gx	20 08.9	− 56 24 c	Tel	1.9		F, S, lE, glbM
4951 I	Gx	20 09.5	− 61 51 c	Pav	2.8		vF, vS, eE 170°, vmbM
4957 I	Gx	20 09.6	− 55 43 c	Tel	1.0		bM, mag 14
6868	Gx	20 09.9	− 48 23 s	Tel	2.7	12p	vB, S, R, pgvmbM
1310 I		20 10.0	+ 34 58 d	Cyg			F neby
4953 I		20 10.1	− 62 48 d	Pav			eF, eS, cE 60°, bet 2 eF st
6870	Gx	20 10.2	− 48 17 s	Tel	2.5	12.2	cF, cS, E 90°, gbM
4928 I		20 10.2	− 77 18 d	Oct			eF, vS, eE 25°, eF∗ n 1′; susp
1311 I	C+N	20 10.3	+ 41 13 s	Cyg	60	13p	eF, within circle of st
6867	Gx	20 10.4	− 54 47 r	Tel			eeF, L, pmE
6884	Pl	20 10.4	+ 46 28 s	Cyg	0.1	13p	◯ , stellar
6879	Pl	20 10.5	+ 16 55 s	Sge	0.1	13p	◯ , stellar = 10m
6881	Pl	20 10.8	+ 37 25 s	Cyg	0.1	14p	◯ , stellar
4959 I		20 11.0	− 53 06 d	Tel			hazy star
6883	OC	20 11.3	+ 35 51 s	Cyg	15	8p	Cl, pRi, ∗ inv
4945 I	Gx	20 11.3	− 71 01 c	Pav	1.0		F, S, E 5°, cbM
4956 I	Gx	20 11.5	− 45 36 c	Tel	1.9		vF, pS, R
4961 I	Gx	20 11.5	− 53 08 c	Tel	1.4		F, pS, mE 90°, dif
6882	OC	20 11.7	+ 26 33 s	Vul	18	8.1	Cl, P, lC
4977 I		20 11.9	− 21 38 d	Cap			stellar, close to ∗13
6885	OC	20 12.0	+ 26 29 s	Vul	7	6p	Cl, vB, vL, Ri, lC, st 6...11
6888	Nb	20 12.0	+ 38 21 s	Cyg	20		F, vL, vmE, ∗ att
4963 I	Gx	20 12.1	− 55 15 c	Tel	2.0		vF, vS, R
4966 I		20 12.3	− 53 36 d	Tel			F, vS, E 40°
4965 I	Gx	20 12.5	− 56 50 c	Pav	1.5		bM, mag 15
6886	Pl	20 12.7	+ 19 59 s	Sge	0.1	12p	◯ , stellar = 10m
4969 I	Gx	20 12.9	− 53 55 c	Tel	1.0		F, vS, R
6875	Gx	20 13.2	− 46 09 s	Tel	2.5	13p	F, vS, R, vgmbM, ∗7 sp 3′
6878	Gx	20 13.9	− 44 31 s	Sgr	1.7	13.4	vF, pL, R, glbM
4975 I	Gx	20 14.0	− 52 43 c	Tel	1.3		bM, mag 15
4968 I		20 14.6	− 64 47 d	Pav			vF, S, B∗ sf 3′
4973 I		20 14.6	− 58 22 d	Pav			eeF, vS, R
4978 I		20 14.6	− 54 26 d	Tel			bM, mag 15
4979 I	Gx	20 14.7	− 53 28 c	Tel	1.3		vF, S, R, dif
6891	Pl	20 15.2	+ 12 42 s	Del	1.2	12p	◯ , stellar = 9.5m
4974 I		20 15.3	− 61 52 d	Pav			eF, eS, R, bM, ∗ sp 1′
4960 I	Gx	20 15.4	− 70 32 c	Pav	1.0		eF, eS, bM
4958 I		20 15.5	− 72 42 d	Pav			eF, bM
4976 I		20 15.5	− 61 53 d	Pav			eF, eS, R, bM, ∗ 3′ np
4980 I	Gx	20 15.5	− 57 55 c	Pav	1.6		vF, S, lE 130°, ∗ 2′ s
4962 I		20 15.9	− 71 00 d	Pav			F, S, eE 160°, vmbM
4983 I	Gx	20 16.1	− 52 05 c	Tel	1.1		vF, cS, R, lbM, dif
4984 I		20 16.3	− 52 43 d	Tel			vF, S, R, dif, 6887 f
6894	Pl	20 16.4	+ 30 34 s	Cyg	0.7	14p	!!, ⊚, F, S, vvlE
6895	−	20 16.4	+ 50 14 r	Cyg			Cl, pRi, lC
4967 I	Gx	20 16.4	− 70 34 c	Pav	0.6		vF, bM
4996 I	OC	20 16.5	+ 37 38 s	Cyg	6	7.3	Cl, st 8...13
6892	−	20 16.8	+ 18 02 r	Sge			eF neb∗ (eS Cl?); = IC 1312?
1312 I		20 16.8	+ 18 01 x	Sge			eF, pL, dif; = 6892
6872	Gx	20 16.9	− 70 46 s	Pav	4.7	11.6	F, pS, lE, glbM, ∗9 p 10^s.5, 1st of 4
4970 I	Gx	20 16.9	− 70 45 s	Pav	0.8	13.9	bM, nr 6872
4971 I		20 17.0	− 70 38 d	Pav			eF, vS
6887	Gx	20 17.2	− 52 47 s	Tel	4.1	12p	pF, cL, pmE, glbM
4986 I	Gx	20 17.2	− 55 02 c	Tel	2.0		eeF, S, cE 0°, bet 2 F st
4987 I	Gx	20 17.3	− 52 17 c	Tel	1.4		F, vS, R, lbM

NGC	Type	α_{2000}	δ_{2000}	Const.	Size	Mag.	Description
		h m	° ′		′		
1315 I		20 17.4	+ 30 41 d	Cyg			*13 with eF neb?
4964 I	Gx	20 17.4	− 73 53 c	Pav	1.3		F, S, cbM
1314 I		20 17.7	+ 25 11 d	Vul			F, pL, partly resolved
4972 I	Gx	20 17.7	− 70 55 c	Pav	1.0		eF, vS, eE 15°
6896	−	20 18.0	+ 30 39 r	Cyg			Cl (+ neb?), S, st vS
6876	Gx	20 18.3	− 70 52 s	Pav	2.4	13p	pB, S, R, eS* sf, 2nd of 4
6890	Gx	20 18.3	− 44 48 s	Sgr	1.5	12.5	pF, S, R, vglbM
4991 I	Gx	20 18.4	− 41 03 c	Sgr	2.5		vF, cS, R
6877	Gx	20 18.6	− 70 51 s	Pav	1.4	12.7	vF, vS, R, 3rd of 4
1313 I	Gx	20 18.7	− 16 57 c	Cap	2.6		F, vS, R, *13 close
6889	Gx	20 18.9	− 53 57 c	Tel	1.9		vF, L, lE
6880	Gx	20 19.5	− 70 52 s	Pav	2.1		F, S, R, r, vS* att, 4th of 4
4989 I		20 19.5	− 58 33 d	Pav			cS, mE 175°, spir, F* M
6911	Gx	20 19.6	+ 66 45 r	Dra		15p	eF, L, lbM, pB* nr
4981 I	Gx	20 19.7	− 70 51 c	Pav	0.7		eF, eS, * nr
4994 I	Gx	20 19.7	− 53 27 c	Tel	2.0		bM, mag 15
4995 I	Gx	20 20.0	− 52 37 c	Tel	1.7		bM, mag 14
4997 I	Pl	20 20.2	+ 16 45 s	Sge	< 0.1	12p	◯ , stellar
4982 I		20 20.4	− 71 00 d	Pav			vF, bM
4985 I		20 20.7	− 70 59 d	Pav			vF, bM
6893	Gx	20 20.8	− 48 14 s	Tel	2.8	13p	pF, S, R, sbM *12
6897	Gx	20 21.0	− 12 16 r	Cap		15p	vF, S
6898	Gx	20 21.2	− 12 21 r	Cap		14p	F, S, iR
4990 I		20 21.5	− 66 54 d	Pav			eF, eS, cE 15°, bM, susp
6900	Gx	20 21.6	− 2 34 r	Aql		14p	vF, S, R
6904	−	20 21.8	+ 25 45 r	Vul			Cl, S, vlC, st 10...11
4988 I		20 21.8	− 69 23 d	Pav			hazy patch, st?; susp
4993 I		20 22.0	− 67 00 d	Pav			eF, vS, R, bM, susp
1318 I		20 22.2	+ 40 15 d	Cyg	240		γ Cyg, surr by L patches of F neby
4998 I	Gx	20 22.2	− 38 18 c	Sgr	1.7		eF, pS, R, bet 2 st 8.5 sp, nf
5018 I	Gx	20 22.2	− 38 18 c	Sgr	1.7		eF, pS, R, bet 2 st 8.5 sp, nf; = IC 4998
6901	Gx	20 22.3	+ 6 27 r	Aql		15p	eF; = IC 5000, IC 1316
6905	Pl	20 22.4	+ 20 07 s	Del	1.7	12p	!!, ◯ , B, pS, R, 4 S st nr
1316 I		20 22.4	+ 6 32 x	Aql			eF, neb, suspected; = IC 5000
5000 I	Gx	20 22.4	+ 6 26 v	Aql	1.5		pS, eF st inv
6910	OC	20 23.1	+ 40 47 s	Cyg	8	7.4	Cl, pB, pS, P, pC, st 10...12
1317 I	Gx	20 23.3	+ 0 40 s	Aql	0.9	13.4	plan = *12, diam 10″-15″
6916	Gx	20 23.5	+ 58 22 r	Cyg		15p	eeF, pS, F* close p, v diffic
4992 I	Gx	20 23.5	− 71 34 c	Pav	2.0		vF, S, eE 65°, *9 nf 2′
6903	Gx	20 23.6	− 19 19 r	Cap		13p	Cl, E, bM *17, *10 att n
6906	Gx	20 23.6	+ 6 27 s	Aql	1.8	12.7	pF, pL, R
5006 I	Gx	20 23.7	+ 6 27 m	Aql	1.6	12p	*14 in F, vS, R neb
6913	OC	20 23.9	+ 38 32 s	Cyg	7	6.6	Cl, P, lC, st L and S; = M29
4999 I	Gx	20 23.9	− 26 01 c	Cap	1.9		vF, pL, R, am st
6899	Gx	20 24.4	− 50 26 c	Tel	1.9		F, S, R, glbM, am st
6902	Gx	20 24.5	− 43 39 s	Sgr	2.2	13p	F, cS, R, bM
6914	Nb	20 24.7	+ 42 29 s	Cyg	13		vF, vL, iR, dif, 2 st att p
6907	Gx	20 25.1	− 24 49 s	Cap	3.4	11.3	cF, cL, vlE, vglbM, r, 3 st p
6908	−	20 25.2	− 24 48 r	Cap			eF, vS, lE, 6907 p
5003 I		20 25.2	− 29 52 d	Sgr			vF, cS, R, 2 st sf in line
5005 I	Gx	20 25.3	− 25 50 c	Cap	2.3		pS, R, vgbM, F* close np
5004 I		20 25.4	− 30 52 d	Sgr			eF, pS, lE, 2 st s
5007 I		20 25.6	− 29 42 d	Sgr			eeF, cL, R
1319 I	Gx	20 26.0	− 18 31 m	Cap	0.6	14p	pF, vS, R, r
5001 I	Gx	20 26.3	− 54 47 c	Tel	1.3		bM, mag 15

NGC	Type	α_{2000}	δ_{2000}	Const.	Size	Mag.	Description
		h m	° ′		′		
1320 I	Gx	20 26.4	+ 2 55 u	Del	1.0	14p	pF, S, R, gbM, r
5002 I	Gx	20 26.7	− 54 48 c	Tel	1.6		bM, mag 13
6912	Gx	20 26.9	− 18 38 s	Cap	1.6	14p	vF, 2 st 14-15 np, *8 f
6917	Gx	20 27.4	+ 8 06 r	Del		14p	vF, S, att to a S*
6909	Gx	20 27.7	− 47 02 s	Tel	2.3	13p	pB, pL, gbM, 2 st 10 nr
6915	Gx	20 27.8	− 3 05 v	Aql	1.2		pB, S, R
1321 I	Gx	20 28.2	− 18 18 m	Cap	0.6	15p	F, S, iF, r
6921	Gx	20 28.5	+ 25 43 s	Vul	1.1	15p	F, S, E
5011 I	Gx	20 28.6	− 36 02 c	Mic	2.2		pB, vS, vmE
5013 I	Gx	20 28.6	− 36 02 c	Mic	2.2		eS, vmE ns; = IC 5011
5015 I		20 28.6	− 31 42 d	Mic			pB, pS, R, nearly bet 2 st
5012 I	Gx	20 29.5	− 56 45 c	Pav	1.4		pS, E 225°, lbM
6922	Gx	20 29.9	− 2 11 r	Aql		14p	vF, pL, R
1322 I		20 30.1	− 15 13 d	Cap			F, vS, R
1323 I	D*	20 30.5	− 15 11 F	Cap			vS, neb *
5020 I	Gx	20 30.6	− 33 29 s	Mic		13p	pF, pS, iE
6918	Gx	20 30.8	− 47 28 c	Ind	1.0		vF, *12 att sp
5019 I	Gx	20 30.8	− 36 05 c	Mic	2.0		vF, cS, R
5010 I		20 31.0	− 65 55 d	Pav			vF, vS, cE 20°, mbM
6939	OC	20 31.4	+ 60 38 s	Cep	8	7.8	Cl, pL, eRi, pCM, st 11...16
6919	Gx	20 31.6	− 44 13 r	Mic			eF, pS, R, vgvlbM
6923	Gx	20 31.7	− 30 50 s	Mic	2.5	12.1	pF, cS, R, gbM, bet 2 st
5017 I	Gx	20 32.1	− 57 35 c	Ind	1.3		bM, mag 14.5
1324 I		20 32.2	− 9 04 D	Cap			eeF, S, R, *8 s
6927	Gx	20 32.6	+ 9 55 v	Del	0.6	14.5	eF, lE
5009 I		20 32.6	− 72 10 d	Pav			vF, vS, bM
5008 I	Gx	20 32.7	− 72 42 c	Pav	1.2		eF, vS, lE 90°, lbM
6928	Gx	20 32.8	+ 9 56 s	Del	2.2	12.6	pB, pL, mE
1325 I		20 32.8	+ 9 53 x	Del			vF, S, sev F st inv; = 6928
6930	Gx	20 33.0	+ 9 52 s	Del	1.4	13.1	F, mE
1326 I		20 33.0	+ 9 54 x	Del			eeF, S, mE, pF* s; = 6930
6926	Gx	20 33.1	− 2 01 s	Aql	2.1	12.4	vF, pL, E 176°, p of 2
6924	Gx	20 33.2	− 25 30 r	Cap		14p	vF, pS, R, sbMN
6929	Gx	20 33.4	− 2 02 s	Aql	0.9	13.5	vF, vS, sf of 2
5021 I		20 33.5	− 54 31 d	Ind			vS, R disc, mag 14
6931	Gx	20 33.6	− 11 23 r	Cap		14p	eF, pS, E 120°, gbM
6933	D*	20 33.6	+ 7 23 r	Del			pB, vS, 6934 f
6934	Gb	20 34.2	+ 7 24 s	Del	5.9	8.9	⊕ , B, L, R, rrr, st 16..., *9 p
6925	Gx	20 34.3	− 31 59 s	Mic	4.1	11.3	cB, L, mE 6°, pslbM
6940	OC	20 34.6	+ 28 18 s	Vul	31	6.3	Cl, vB, vL, vRi, cC, st pL
6938	−	20 34.8	+ 22 15 r	Vul			Cl, vL, P, vlC
6946	Gx	20 34.8	+ 60 09 s	Cep	11.0	8.9	vF, vL, vg, vsbM, rr
6949	Gx	20 35.1	+ 64 48 r	Cep		15p	eF, pS, iR
5014 I		20 35.3	− 73 28 d	Pav			F, S, bM, bet 2 F st
5016 I		20 35.6	− 72 55 d	Pav			eeF, eS, *11 sp 1′
1327 I	Gx	20 35.7	+ 0 01 z	Aql		15p	vF, *8 1′ f
6936		20 35.9	− 25 17 D	Cap			vF, vS, R, slbM
6941	Gb	20 36.3	− 4 38 r	Aql		13p	eF, lE, lbM
6986		20 36.6	− 18 38 D	Cap			vF, vS, R, glbMN
6952	Gx	20 37.0	+ 66 06 D	Cep			pB, oval, dif, *15 close f; = 6951
6951	Gx	20 37.2	+ 66 06 s	Cep	3.8	11.1	pB, pL, lE
6953		20 37.7	+ 65 46 D	Cep			vS group of 4 st (no neb)
5023 I		20 38.1	− 67 11 d	Pav			F, S, cE 130°
6935	Gx	20 38.4	− 52 06 s	Ind	2.0	13p	pB, cL, R, glbM, r, p of 2
6944	Gx	20 38.4	+ 7 00 s	Del	1.7	13.3	pF, S, R

NGC	Type	α_{2000}	δ_{2000}	Const.	Size	Mag.	Description
		h m	° '		'		
6937	Gx	20 38.8	− 52 09 s	Ind	3.0		vF, cS, R, slbM, f of 2
6945	Gx	20 38.9	− 5 01 r	Aqr		13p	pF, vS, R, mbM
5024 I		20 40.1	− 71 06 d	Pav			eF, S, mE 15°
5029 I	?	20 40.3	− 29 50 x	Mic			eeF, eS, mE, F∗ sf, np of 2
5030 I		20 40.6	− 29 51 d	Mic			eeF, vS, mE, v dif, sf of 2
6942	Gx	20 40.8	− 54 19 s	Ind	2.6	13p	pB, pL, R, pslbM
5022 I	Gx	20 41.1	− 76 27 c	Oct	1.2		eF, S, R, cbM, susp
5027 I		20 41.1	− 55 29 d	Ind			R, mag 15
6950	−	20 41.2	+ 16 38 r	Del			Cl, P, vlC
6947	Gx	20 41.3	− 32 29 c	Mic	2.0		vF, L, R, gbM
1328 I	Gx	20 42.0	− 19 38 m	Cap	0.8	15p	F, S, vF∗ close
6932	Gx	20 42.1	− 73 37 c	Pav	2.0		F, S, R, gbM, 5 st p
5039 I	Gx	20 43.2	− 29 51 s	Mic	2.5	12.6	vF, pS, vmE, sp of 2
5046 I	Gx	20 43.2	− 29 51 c	Mic	1.9		eF, pS, mE, 2 vF st sf, sp of 2; = IC 5039
5028 I	Gx	20 43.4	− 65 39 c	Pav	1.4		vF, dif, ∗10 s 2′, susp
6948	Gx	20 43.5	− 53 21 c	Ind	2.5		vF, pS, cE, lbM
5041 I	Gx	20 43.6	− 29 42 c	Mic	3.0		eeF, pS, mE, v diffic, nf of 2
5047 I	Gx	20 43.6	− 29 42 c	Mic	3.0		eeF, pS, mE, v diffic, nf of 2; = IC 5041
1329 I		20 43.7	+ 15 35 d	Del			eeF, pL, R, bet 4 st, v diffic
5034 I	Gx	20 43.7	− 57 02 c	Ind	1.6		bM, mag 14.5
5033 I		20 43.8	− 57 19 d	Ind			vS, R, lbM, mag 15
6920	Gx	20 43.9	− 80 00 c	Oct	1.8		pB, cS, R, psmbM
6956	Gx	20 44.0	+ 12 31 s	Del	2.1	14p	vF, S, stell, ∗ att
6954	Gx	20 44.1	+ 3 13 s	Del	1.1	13.2	F, S, vlE
5035 I		20 44.3	− 57 08 d	Ind			vS, R, lbM, mag 15
6955	Gx	20 44.4	+ 2 35 r	Del		15p	eF, pL, R
6943	Gx	20 44.5	− 68 45 s	Pav	4.1	12p	pF, L, mE, vglbM vS∗
5036 I		20 44.7	− 57 37 d	Ind			F, pS, mE 125°
6957	Gx	20 44.9	+ 2 34 r	Del		15p	vF, S, R
5025 I	Gx	20 45.0	− 76 59 c	Oct	1.3		vF, vS, cE 125°, bM, susp
5031 I	?	20 45.3	− 67 32 x	Pav			eF, eS, R, susp
5050 I	Gx	20 45.3	− 5 39 m	Aqr	1.0	14p	F, cS, dif, vS E N
5032 I		20 45.4	− 67 32 d	Pav			eF, eS, R, susp
5037 I		20 45.6	− 58 26 d	Ind			F, pS, mE 170°
6960	Nb	20 45.7	+ 30 43 s	Cyg	70		!! pB, cL, eiF, 52 Cyg inv
1330 I	Gx	20 46.3	− 14 02 m	Aqr	0.8	15p	F, vS, dif
5043 I		20 46.7	− 56 59 d	Ind			F, S, E 210°
5038 I		20 46.9	− 65 01 d	Pav			vF, vS, R, alm stell
6959	Gx	20 47.1	+ 0 27 r	Aqr		14p	vF
6961	Gx	20 47.2	+ 0 23 r	Aqr		15p	eF, vS
5057 I	∗	20 47.2	+ 0 19 x	Aqr			cF, neb∗ or eS neb
6962	Gx	20 47.3	+ 0 19 s	Aqr	3.0	12.0	cF, S, R, bM
6963	Gx	20 47.3	+ 0 29 s	Aqr	0.7	14.1	neb ∗13
6964	Gx	20 47.4	+ 0 18 s	Aqr	1.9	12.7	F, vS, R, bM, ∗14 sf 0′.5
6965		20 47.4	+ 0 30 A	Aqr			vF, vS; = 6963
6966	D∗	20 47.4	+ 0 22 F	Aqr			eF, vS
5049 I	Gx	20 47.4	− 38 25 c	Mic	1.2		eeF, pS, R
5058 I	∗	20 47.4	+ 0 29 x	Aqr			eF, distinct from 6963
6967	Gx	20 47.6	+ 0 25 r	Aqr		14p	eF, vS, ∗10 50″ f
5061 I	∗∗	20 47.6	+ 0 20 x	Aqr			eF, vS Cl; neb?
5042 I		20 47.8	− 65 05 d	Pav			vF, vS, R, alm stell
5067 I		20 47.8	+ 44 22 d	Cyg			F
1331 I	Gx	20 47.9	− 9 59 m	Aqr	1.8	14p	F, S, bM, r
5062 I	D∗	20 48.2	− 8 22 F	Aqr			∗13.5 with eF st & neb, ∗13 p 1′
6968	Gx	20 48.4	− 8 20 r	Aqr		14p	F, S, R, gbM, F∗ inv

NGC	Type	α_{2000}	δ_{2000}	Const.	Size	Mag.	Description
		h m	° ′		′		
6969	Gx	20 48.4	+ 7 45 r	Del		15p	F, pL, E
5026 I	Gx	20 48.5	− 78 04 c	Oct	2.5		eF, vS, mE 70°, lbM, susp
6958	Gx	20 48.6	− 38 00 s	Mic	2.4	12p	B, cS, R, pgmbM, 4 st p
5056 I		20 49.0	− 39 11 d	Mic			F, cL, eE 150°
6971	Gx	20 49.4	+ 6 00 r	Del		15p	vF, S, R
6972	Gx	20 50.0	+ 9 54 s	Del	1.4	14p	F, S, R
5044 I		20 50.6	− 71 57 d	Pav			eF, eS, R
5045 I		20 50.7	− 71 58 d	Pav			eF, eS, R
6974	Nb	20 50.8	+ 31 52 r	Cyg			neb*, neby cE pf
5068 I	Nb	20 50.8	+ 42 31 s	Cyg	80		vF
5070 I	Nb	20 50.8	+ 44 21 s	Cyg	80		F, dif
6979	Nb	20 51.0	+ 32 09 r	Cyg			vF, S, iE, sev F st f nr
5059 I		20 51.3	− 57 41 d	Ind			vF, S, R, dif
5048 I		20 51.6	− 71 48 d	Pav			eF, vS
5065 I	Gx	20 51.8	− 29 51 c	Mic	1.2		vF, pS, R
1332 I	Gx	20 51.9	− 13 43 m	Aqr	0.8	15p	F, vS, R
5063 I	Gx	20 52.0	− 57 05 s	Ind	1.9	12.0	bM, mag 13
6970	Gx	20 52.1	− 48 48 s	Ind	1.2	12.7	pB, S, lE, gbM
6973	*	20 52.1	− 5 53 F	Aqr			vF, S, r
5052 I	Gx	20 52.1	− 69 12 s	Pav	5.8	12p	F, L, eE 140°, 4′ l
1334 I	Gx	20 52.2	− 16 17 m	Cap	1.1	15p	F, S
1333 I		20 52.3	− 16 15 d	Cap			vF, vS, sbM
5040 I		20 52.3	− 76 40 d	Oct			cB, S, R, susp
5051 I		20 52.3	− 71 47 d	Pav			eF, vS
6975	Gx	20 52.4	− 5 46 D	Aqr			vF, S; = 6976
6976	Gx	20 52.4	− 5 46 r	Aqr		14p	eF, iR
6977	Gx	20 52.5	− 5 44 r	Aqr		14p	vF, S, iR
6978	Gx	20 52.6	− 5 43 s	Aqr	1.9	14p	vF
5064 I	Gx	20 52.6	− 57 14 c	Ind	1.6		bM, mag 14
6980	*	20 52.8	− 5 49 F	Aqr			vF, S, r
5055 I		20 52.9	− 68 27 d	Pav			vF, bM, susp
1335 I		20 53.1	− 16 20 d	Cap			F, S, stellar
6981	Gb	20 53.5	− 12 32 s	Aqr	5.9	9.4	⊕, pB, pL, R, gmCM, rrr; = M72
5053 I	Gx	20 53.6	− 71 08 c	Pav	1.9		cF, vS, bM, *11 n 2′
5054 I	Gx	20 53.7	− 71 01 c	Pav	1.8		cF, vS, bet 2 F st
6989	−	20 54.1	+ 45 17 r	Cyg			Cl, cL, st pS
5060 I		20 54.6	− 71 38 d	Pav			eF, eS, bet 2 F st
1336 I	Gx	20 55.1	− 18 04 m	Cap	0.6	15p	vF, S, dif, F* f
6988	Gx	20 55.8	+ 10 32 r	Del		15p	eF, pL, R
5076 I	Nb	20 55.9	+ 47 25 s	Cyg	9		vF, vL, lE ns, st inv
6985	−	20 56.0	− 11 05 r	Aqr			eF, vS, iR
1340 I	Nb	20 56.2	+ 31 04 s	Cyg	25		possibly conn with 6995
6992	Nb	20 56.4	+ 31 43 s	Cyg	60		!!, eF, eL, eE, eiF, bifurcated
6996	OC	20 56.4	+ 45 28 A	Cyg			Cl, P, lC
6997	OC	20 56.5	+ 44 38 o	Cyg	15	10p	Cl, P, lC, st L
6991	OC	20 56.6	+ 47 25 r	Cyg			Cl, L, P, vlC
6983	Gx	20 56.8	− 43 58 r	Mic			eF, cS, R
1337 I		20 56.9	− 16 35 d	Cap			F, vS, R, gbM
1338 I		20 57.0	− 16 30 d	Cap			vF, vS, dif
6995	Nb	20 57.1	+ 31 13 s	Cyg	12		F, eL, neb & st in groups
5066 I		20 57.1	− 73 09 d	Pav			vF, vS, bM
6982	Gx	20 57.4	− 51 51 v	Ind			vF, S, E, p of 2
6984	Gx	20 57.9	− 51 52 s	Ind	1.7	13p	F, pL, vlE, vgbM, f of 2
1339 I	Gx	20 57.9	− 17 57 c	Cap	1.9		F, S, gbM, r
6987	Gx	20 58.0	− 48 37 r	Ind			pF, S, vlE, gpmbM, B* p 1′

NGC	Type	α_{2000}	δ_{2000}	Const.	Size	Mag.	Description
		h m	° ′		′		
7000	Nb	20 58.8	+ 44 20 s	Cyg	120		F, eeL, dif nebulosity
6994	OC	20 59.0	− 12 38 s	Aqr	3	9p	Cl, eP, vlC, no neb; = M73
6993	−	20 59.5	− 25 41 r	Cap			vF, vS, R, sbMN
6990	Gx	20 59.9	− 55 34 c	Ind	1.1		eeF, vS, vmE 0°, *13 att, n
5069 I		21 00.0	− 71 48 d	Pav			eF, S, R
1341 I	Gx	21 00.4	− 13 58 m	Aqr	0.5	15p	F, vS, R, lbM
1342 I		21 00.4	− 14 30 d	Aqr			vF, vS, E pf, lbM
7023	C+N	21 00.5	+ 68 10 s	Cep	18	7p	*7 in eF, eL, neby
7008	Pl	21 00.6	+ 54 33 s	Cyg	1.4	13p	cB, L, E 45°±, r, $\overset{*}{*}$ att
7003	Gx	21 00.8	+ 17 48 r	Del		14p	vF, vS, lE, *15 close f
5074 I		21 00.9	− 63 08 d	Pav			R, ◯, mag 14
7001	Gx	21 01.2	− 0 11 D	Aqr		14p	pB, S, E 0°
1343 I		21 01.2	− 15 24 d	Cap			pB, vS, R, mbM
1344 I	Gx	21 01.3	− 13 22 m	Aqr	0.6	15p	pB, pL, iF, sbM
5071 I	Gx	21 01.3	− 72 39 c	Pav	3.5		cB, S, eE 20°, stell N
1345 I		21 01.4	− 13 24 d	Aqr			vF, S, R, vlbM
7006	Gb	21 01.5	+ 16 11 s	Del	2.8	10.6	B, pL, R, gbM
6998	Gx	21 01.6	− 28 01 r	Mic			eeF, vS
1346 I		21 01.7	− 13 52 d	Aqr			pB, vS, R, gbM
1347 I	Gx	21 01.7	− 13 19 v	Aqr	1.3		pB, R
1348 I		21 01.7	− 13 21 d	Aqr			F, vS, R, bM
1349 I		21 01.8	− 13 16 d	Aqr			vF, vS, R, lbM
7011	−	21 01.9	+ 47 19 r	Cyg			Cl, no description
1351 I		21 01.9	− 13 12 d	Aqr			F, vS, R, lbM
1352 I		21 01.9	− 13 23 d	Aqr			pB
1353 I		21 01.9	− 13 16 d	Aqr			vF, vS, R
6999	Gx	21 02.0	− 28 04 c	Mic	0.9		eeF, vS
7005	OC	21 02.0	− 12 53 F	Aqr			Cl, S, P
1350 I	Gx	21 02.0	− 13 51 m	Aqr	0.6	15p	F, S, iF, lbM, r
1354 I		21 02.0	− 13 45 d	Aqr			F, vS, R, bM
1355 I		21 02.0	− 13 10 d	Aqr			F, vS, R, bM
5072 I		21 02.0	− 72 59 d	Pav			eF, eS, R
5080 I	Gx	21 02.5	+ 19 13 z	Del		16p	F, vS, R, stell N
5078 I	Gx	21 02.6	− 16 49 c	Cap	4.0		eE, nr 2nd * of 3; susp
1356 I		21 02.9	− 15 48 d	Cap			F, R, sbM
5081 I		21 03.0	+ 19 12 d	Del			vF, vS, R, stell N
5073 I	Gx	21 03.3	− 72 41 c	Pav	1.2		eF, S, R
7002	Gx	21 03.6	− 49 01 r	Ind			cF, cS, R, bM
7013	Gx	21 03.6	+ 29 54 s	Cyg	4.9	12p	pB, cS, R, psbM, pB* np
5083 I	Gx	21 03.8	+ 11 46 z	Equ		15p	eeF, vS, v diffic; *8 f 13^s
7004	Gx	21 03.9	− 49 07 r	Ind			eF, R, lbM, *11 f
7009	Pl	21 04.2	− 11 22 s	Aqr	1.7	8p	!!!, ◯, vB, S, elliptic
5075 I		21 04.5	− 71 51 d	Pav			vF, S, cbM
7010	Gx	21 04.7	− 12 20 r	Aqr		14p	eF, S, R, lbM; = IC 5082
5082 I		21 04.7	− 12 21 x	Aqr			eF, S; = 7010
7007	Gx	21 05.5	− 52 33 s	Ind	1.9	13p	pB, S, R, psbM, am st
5079 I	OC	21 05.5	− 56 15 x	Ind			F, S, E; vS Cl or ◎? (RA ±)
7015	Gx	21 05.7	+ 11 25 s	Equ	2.0	13p	vF, pS, glbM
1357 I		21 05.9	− 10 43 d	Aqr			vF, vS, iF, vlbM
7024	−	21 06.0	+ 41 30 r	Cyg			Cl, P, lC, st 10...
7026	Pl	21 06.3	+ 47 51 s	Cyg	0.4	13p	pB, biN, ◯
7019	Gx	21 06.4	− 24 25 c	Cap	0.7		vF, vS, R, sbMN
1358 I		21 06.5	− 16 12 d	Cap			vF, vS
7012	Gx	21 06.8	− 44 49 c	Mic	3.2		F, pL, E, vgvlbM, * p
7027	Pl	21 07.1	+ 42 14 s	Cyg	0.3	10p	◯, stellar = 8.5m

NGC	Type	α_{2000}	δ_{2000}	Const.	Size	Mag.	Description
		h m	° ′		′		
7031	OC	21 07.3	+ 50 50 s	Cyg	5	9.1	Cl of triple st, lC
7016	Gx	21 07.4	− 25 30 r	Cap		15p	vF, eS, R, bMN, 1st of 3
7017	Gx	21 07.5	− 25 30 r	Cap		15p	eF, vS, R, bMN, 2nd of 3
7018	Gx	21 07.6	− 25 28 r	Cap		14p	vF, vS, vlE, glbM, 3 of 3
7014	Gx	21 07.9	− 47 11 s	Ind	1.9	12.3	pF, S, R, bM, 2 st 12 n
7025	Gx	21 07.9	+ 16 20 r	Del		14p	vF, vS, R, stell
7028	−	21 08.3	+ 18 29 r	Del			vF, S, vlE
5086 I	Gx	21 08.5	− 29 46 c	Mic	2.0		eeF, pS, R, F∗ f
1359 I	Gx	21 08.7	+ 12 27 u	Del	1.1	15p	eeF, eS, stellar, eF∗ att
5077 I		21 09.0	− 73 39 d	Pav			eF, eS, ∗10 np 2′
5084 I	Gx	21 09.2	− 63 17 c	Pav	1.6		F, pS, eE 155°, cbM
5088 I	Gx	21 09.4	− 22 53 c	Cap	1.8		eF, vS, diffic
7022	Gx	21 09.5	− 49 18 r	Ind			eeF, S, R, B∗∗∗ sf
7033	Gx	21 09.6	+ 15 07 r	Peg		15p	vF, S, R
7034	Gx	21 09.7	+ 15 09 r	Peg		15p	vF, vS, R
7036	−	21 10.2	+ 15 27 r	Peg			Cl, lC
1363 I	?	21 10.6	+ 46 51 x	Cyg			F, ∗9.4 at s end
7037	−	21 10.7	+ 33 43 r	Cyg			Cl, pRi, iF, st 11...15
7035	Gx	21 10.8	− 23 08 c	Cap	1.2		eF, S, iR
1360 I	Gx	21 10.8	+ 5 04 x	Equ			F, dif
5089 I		21 11.0	− 3 51 d	Aqr			eF, vS, bM, F∗ 30″ sp
7030	Gx	21 11.2	− 20 30 r	Cap			vF, vS, iR, bMN
7039	OC	21 11.2	+ 45 39 s	Cyg	25	7.6	Cl, vL, pRi, E, st 10...
7021		21 11.3	− 64 02 c	Pav			pF, cS, R, psbM, ∗7-8 p; = 7020
7020	Gx	21 11.4	− 64 03 s	Pav	4.3	12p	pB, cS, lE, pgbM
1361 I	Gx	21 11.5	+ 5 03 u	Equ	1.1	15p	vF, vS, dif
5090 I	Gx	21 11.6	− 2 02 u	Aqr	1.1	14p	vF, S, R, sbM
1362 I	Gx	21 11.8	+ 2 20 z	Aqr		16p	vF, vS, R, ∗14 nf
7029	Gx	21 11.9	− 49 17 s	Ind	1.4	11.8	B, cS, R, pgmbM
1369 I	OC	21 12.1	+ 47 44 s	Cyg	4	6.8	S neb Cl of st 13m
7044	OC	21 12.9	+ 42 29 r	Cyg		11p	Cl, vF, pL, vRi, vC st 15...18
7040	Gx	21 13.2	+ 8 51 r	Equ		15p	eF, vL, mE ns
1364 I	Gx	21 13.3	+ 2 47 m	Equ	0.3	15p	pB, pS, R, sbM
5085 I		21 13.4	− 74 06 d	Pav			vF, vS, R
7042	Gx	21 13.8	+ 13 33 s	Peg	2.2	13p	vF, S, R
1365 I	Gx	21 13.9	+ 2 35 m	Equ	0.2	15p	eF, pS, R (another p?)
7043	Gx	21 14.1	+ 13 36 r	Peg		15p	vF, S, R
1366 I	Gx	21 14.1	+ 1 45 z	Aqr		16p	F, S, iR, bet 2 st 11 & 13
7048	Pl	21 14.2	+ 46 16 s	Cyg	1.0	11p	pF, pL, dif, iR, vlbM
1367 I	Gx	21 14.2	+ 2 59 z	Equ		15p	vF, vS, R, F, ∗ nr
1368 I		21 14.3	+ 2 10 D	Aqr			eeF, S, mE 225°, v diffic
5087 I	Gx	21 14.3	− 73 46 c	Pav	1.4		vF, vS, ∗11 np 3′
7045	D∗	21 14.8	+ 4 31 A	Equ			not a neb; only 2 F close st
7046	Gx	21 14.9	+ 2 50 s	Equ	2.0	14p	eF, pL, R, lbM
5097 I	∗∗∗	21 15.0	+ 4 27 x	Equ			eF, stell, 3′ sf 7045
5098 I	D∗	21 15.0	+ 4 29 x	Equ			eF, 2′.5 sff 7045
7050	−	21 15.1	+ 36 12 r	Cyg			Cl, no description
7038	Gx	21 15.2	− 47 13 s	Ind	3.0	12p	pB, pL, lE, gbM
1370 I	Gx	21 15.2	+ 2 12 z	Aqr		15p	vF, 2 F st inv
7032	Gx	21 15.4	− 68 17 c	Pav	1.1		vF, cS, R, glbM
5092 I	Gx	21 16.2	− 64 28 c	Pav	2.9		pL, E, mbM
7041	Gx	21 16.5	− 48 22 s	Ind	3.9	11.1	B, cS, cE, psmbM, ∗10 f
7047	Gx	21 16.5	− 0 50 r	Aqr		14p	eF, vS, biN pf
5095 I		21 17.3	− 59 56 d	Pav			pL, E
5091 I		21 17.7	− 70 39 d	Pav			eF, vS, R

NGC	Type	α_{2000}	δ_{2000}	Const.	Size	Mag.	Description
		h m	o ′		′		
5094 I	Gx	21 17.8	− 66 26 c	Pav	1.4		vF, vS, R, * np 0′.5
5096 I	Gx	21 18.4	− 63 46 c	Pav	3.0		F, pL, eE 145°, stell N
7052	Gx	21 18.6	+ 26 27 s	Vul	2.8	14p	F, S, vlE, r
5093 I		21 18.8	− 70 38 d	Pav			eeF, vS, R, susp
7049	Gx	21 19.0	− 48 34 s	Ind	2.8	10.7	vB, pS, E, mbM
7055	−	21 19.4	+ 57 35 r	Cep			Cl, F, pS, P
7051	Gx	21 19.8	− 8 47 r	Aqr		14p	vF, R, gbM, * nr
1371 I	Gx	21 20.3	− 4 53 m	Aqr	0.8	15p	F, S, dif, gbM, r
1372 I		21 20.3	− 5 37 d	Aqr			vF, vS, R, dif, *14 sf
1373 I	Gx	21 20.6	+ 1 05 m	Aqr	0.3	15p	F, vS, R, sbM, 2 others south
7054	−	21 20.7	+ 39 10 r	Cyg			vF, vS, R, F* inv
7058	−	21 21.0	+ 50 48 r	Cyg			Cl, P, lC
1374 I	Gx	21 21.0	+ 1 43 z	Aqr		16p	vF, vS, lbM
1375 I	Gx	21 21.0	+ 4 00 z	Equ		15p	F, S, 2 F st inv
7053	Gx	21 21.1	+ 23 04 r	Peg		14p	pB, S, vlE
5104 I	Gx	21 21.5	+ 21 14 u	Peg	1.8	14p	F, vS, E ns, dif, *14 nr
5100 I	Gx	21 21.7	− 65 56 c	Pav	1.7		F, S, cE 110°
5099 I		21 21.9	− 71 00 d	Pav			vF, S, lE 10°
5101 I	Gx	21 21.9	− 65 50 c	Pav	1.4		cF, S, * in neb
7056	Gx	21 22.2	+ 18 39 r	Peg		14p	pF, S, R
1378 I		21 23.0	+ 55 27 d	Cep			F, dif, F st inv
7062	OC	21 23.2	+ 46 23 s	Cyg	7	8.3	Cl, pS, pRi, pC, st 13...
7067	OC	21 24.2	+ 48 01 s	Cyg	3	9.7	Cl, P, neb?
7063	OC	21 24.4	+ 36 30 s	Cyg	8	7.0	Cl, P, st 10...
5105 I	Gx	21 24.4	− 40 37 s	Mic	2.5	11.5	vF, vS, R, st n & s
1376 I		21 24.7	− 5 45 d	Aqr			no descr
7057	Gx	21 25.0	− 42 29 r	Mic			eF, vS, R, p of 2
1377 I	Gx	21 25.4	+ 4 19 m	Equ	0.6	14p	pB, S, R
7060	Gx	21 25.9	− 42 24 r	Mic			vF, pS, R, f of 2
1379 I	Gx	21 26.0	+ 3 06 z	Equ		16p	vF, bM, stellar
7066	Gx	21 26.2	+ 14 10 r	Peg		15p	eeF, close sf of M of 3 F st
7076	Nb	21 26.3	+ 62 53 s	Cep	2		vF, er
5102 I		21 26.3	− 73 19 d	Pav			eF, eS, bM
7071	−	21 26.5	+ 47 57 r	Cyg			Cl, S, C, cE; = 7067?
7068	Gx	21 26.6	+ 12 13 r	Peg		15p	vF, close to a S*
7065	Gx	21 26.7	− 7 00 s	Aqr	1.4		vF, sbM
1382 I		21 26.9	+ 18 39 d	Peg			pF, pS, iF
1380 I	Gx	21 27.1	+ 2 43 z	Peg		15p	pB, S
7059	Gx	21 27.4	− 60 01 s	Pav	3.2	13p	B, pL, lC, gpmbM
7061	Gx	21 27.4	− 49 04 c	Ind	1.5		eeF, vS, R
1381 I	Gx	21 27.6	− 1 11 m	Aqr	0.5	15p	F, vS, R, bM
1383 I	Gx	21 27.7	− 1 05 z	Aqr		16p	F, vS, R, stellar
1384 I	Gx	21 27.8	− 1 22 m	Aqr	0.6	14p	vF, vS, R
7069	Gx	21 28.1	− 1 38 r	Aqr		15p	vF, S, R, stell
5111 I	Gx	21 28.2	+ 2 29 m	Aqr	0.8	15p	F, S, iF
5107 I		21 28.3	− 65 44 d	Pav			eF, vS, cE 10°
5106 I	Gx	21 28.6	− 70 50 c	Pav	1.3		F, S, R, bM
1385 I	Gx	21 28.9	− 1 04 m	Aqr	0.4	15p	pB, vS, R
7064	Gx	21 29.0	− 52 46 s	Ind	4.1	13p	eF, pL, vmE 91°, * s
5103 I	Gx	21 29.2	− 74 04 c	Pav	1.4		eF, vS, R
7082	OC	21 29.4	+ 47 05 s	Cyg	25	7.2	Cl, L, cRi, lC, st 10...13
7073	Gx	21 29.5	− 11 28 r	Cap		14p	vF, vS, iR
7074	Gx	21 29.5	+ 6 42 r	Peg			vF, S, E
5112 I	OC	21 29.5	+ 6 47 x	Peg			Cl, eF, eS
1386 I	Gx	21 29.6	− 21 12 c	Cap	2.1		F, biN, or neb D*

NGC	Type	α_{2000}	δ_{2000}	Const.	Size	Mag.	Description
		h m	° '		'		
1387 I	Gx	21 29.6	− 1 21 m	Aqr	0.4	15p	pB, vS, iF
5113 I	OC	21 29.7	+ 6 49 x	Peg			Cl, eF, S; nebs?
7077	Gx	21 29.9	+ 2 25 s	Aqr	0.8	14p	F
1388 I	Gx	21 29.9	− 0 38 m	Aqr	0.4	15p	eF, vS, 2 st nf
7078	Gb	21 30.0	+ 12 10 s	Peg	12.3	6.4	!, ⊕, vB, vL, iR, vsmbM, rrr, st vS; = M15
7080	Gx	21 30.0	+ 26 43 s	Vul	2.0	14p	vF, S, vlE
7070	Gx	21 30.5	− 43 06 s	Gru	2.1	12.3	F, cL, lE, gvlbM, p of 2
7086	OC	21 30.5	+ 51 35 s	Cyg	9	8.4	Cl, cL, vRi, pC, st 11...16
5115 I		21 30.5	+ 11 47 d	Peg			eeF, vS, F∗ f
7072	Gx	21 30.6	− 43 09 s	Gru	0.8	13.9	F, S, R, vglbM, f of 2
5110 I		21 30.6	− 59 59 d	Ind			vF, vlE
7081	Gx	21 31.4	+ 2 30 r	Aqr		13p	F, S, R, mbM, ∗14 s
7075	Gx	21 31.5	− 38 36 r	Gru			cF, cS, R, pgbM
7084	−	21 31.8	+ 17 25 r	Peg			Cl, lC
1389 I		21 32.1	− 18 01 d	Cap			F, vS, R, gbM
7092	OC	21 32.2	+ 48 26 s	Cyg	32	4.6	Cl, vL, vP, vlC, st 7...10; = M39
7085	Gx	21 32.3	+ 6 36 r	Peg		15p	eF, S, E
7079	Gx	21 32.5	− 44 05 s	Gru	2.8	11.6	B, R, cS, psbM
1390 I	Gx	21 32.5	− 1 52 z	Aqr		15p	F, vS, R, bM
5117 I	Pl	21 32.5	+ 44 35 s	Cyg	0.1	13p	◯, stellar
5108 I	Gx	21 32.9	− 72 40 c	Ind	1.4		eF, vS, cbM
7088	−	21 33.4	− 0 23 r	Aqr			eF, eL, dif, E pf, n of M2
7089	Gb	21 33.5	− 0 49 s	Aqr	12.9	6.5	!!, ⊕, B, vL, gpmbM, rrr, st eS; = M2
5109 I		21 33.9	− 74 06 d	Ind			vF, bM
5119 I	Gx	21 34.0	+ 21 49 u	Peg	1.0	15p	F, vS, dif, ∗15 att, ∗13 n
7091	Gx	21 34.1	− 36 38 r	Gru			eF, pL, vgbM, ∗6 f 40ˢ
5114 I	Gx	21 34.1	− 36 39 c	Gru	2.0		eF, pS, R, 2 st f 30ˢ; = 7091
7087	Gx	21 34.6	− 40 49 r	Gru			cF, S, R, gbM
7093	−	21 34.8	+ 46 01 r	Cyg			Cl, P, lC
1391 I	Gx	21 35.1	− 0 30 z	Aqr		16p	vF, S, dif
1392 I	Gx	21 35.6	+ 35 24 u	Cyg	1.7	13p	pB, vmbM∗
7083	Gx	21 35.7	− 63 54 s	Ind	4.5	12p	pF, cL, vlE, vgpmbM, r
7090	Gx	21 36.5	− 54 33 s	Ind	7.1	11p	pB, pL, vmE 127°, g, pslbM
7094	Pl	21 36.9	+ 12 47 s	Peg	1.6		∗ in eeF neby, v diffic
5116 I		21 37.1	− 70 59 d	Ind			cF, S, R, stell N
5120 I	Gx	21 38.8	− 64 21 c	Ind	2.1		F, alm R
1396 I	C+N	21 39.1	+ 57 30 s	Cep	170	3.5	neb part of Milky Way
7100	Gx	21 39.5	+ 8 53 r	Peg		14p	vF, r
7101	?	21 39.6	+ 8 54 D	Peg			F, vS, R, stell; = 7100?
7102	Gx	21 39.7	+ 6 17 s	Peg	1.9	13.1	F, pL, R; = IC 5127
5122 I		21 39.8	− 22 24 d	Cap			eF, vS; 7103-04, IC 1393 nr
5127 I		21 39.8	+ 6 14 x	Peg			eF, pL, sev eF st & neb; = 7102
7103	Gx	21 39.9	− 22 28 r	Cap		15p	vF, vS, R, gbM, 1st of 2
5124 I		21 39.9	− 22 26 d	Cap			eeF, S, diffic; another susp 1' s
7104	Gx	21 40.1	− 22 25 r	Cap		15p	vF, vS, iR, gbMN, 2nd of 2
5126 I		21 40.1	− 5 22 d	Aqr			vF, vS, R, bet 2 st 14
7095	Gx	21 40.2	− 42 32 c	Gru	1.6		F, pL, R, vglbM, ∗13 inv; = 7097
1393 I		21 40.2	− 22 25 d	Cap			eF, vS, R, dif
1394 I	Gx	21 40.2	+ 14 38 m	Peg	0.8	15p	eF, S, R
7097	Gx	21 40.3	− 42 32 s	Gru	2.5	12p	B, S, vlE, mbM
5118 I		21 40.3	− 71 23 d	Ind			vF, S, cE 35°, ∗10 sp 2'
7099	Gb	21 40.4	− 23 11 s	Cap	11.0	7.5	!, ⊕, B, L, lE, gpmbM, st 12...16; = M30
7105	−	21 40.5	− 10 20 r	Cap			F, vS, E 130°, smbMN, ∗ np; nonexistent?
7096	Gx	21 41.3	− 63 54 s	Ind	2.7	13p	vF, S, R, vS∗ nf
7129	C+N	21 41.3	+ 66 06 s	Cep	8	12p	!, cF, pL, gbM ∗∗

NGC	Type	α_{2000}	δ_{2000}	Const.	Size	Mag.	Description
		h m	o ′		′		
5121 I	Gx	21 41.3	− 63 55 c	Ind	1.7		◯ , stellar, 13 mag; = 7096
7114	−	21 41.7	+ 42 50 r	Cyg			nebulous var *; ◯ ?
1395 I	Gx	21 41.7	+ 4 07 z	Peg		15p	vF, vS, iF, lbM
7111	Gx	21 41.8	− 6 43 r	Aqr		15p	eF, eS, R, bM
5125 I	Gx	21 41.8	− 52 46 c	Ind	1.4		F, eS, R, bM
7109	Gx	21 41.9	− 34 27 r	PsA			eF, vS, am st
7110	Gx	21 42.2	− 34 10 r	PsA			F, S, R, bM
7112	Gx	21 42.3	+ 12 30 r	Peg		15p	eeF, S, R, pB* close p
5132 I		21 42.3	+ 66 08 d	Cep			1st of 2 st 13m in vF neb
7107	Gx	21 42.4	− 44 48 s	Gru	1.9	13p	vF, cL, R, vglbM
7108	Gx	21 42.4	− 6 47 r	Aqr			vF, S, R, stell
7113	Gx	21 42.4	+ 12 35 r	Peg		15p	vF, S, stell
5133 I		21 42.4	+ 66 09 d	Cep			2nd of 2 st 13m in vF neb
7106	Gx	21 42.6	− 52 42 c	Ind	1.8		eF, cS, lE, vglbM
7116	Gx	21 42.6	+ 28 57 r	Cyg		14p	vF, pL, mE
7133	Nb	21 42.6	+ 66 03 r	Cep			vF, pL
5128 I		21 42.7	− 39 00 d	Gru			eeF, vS, R, dif, st sp
5134 I		21 43.0	+ 66 06 d	Cep			*9.5 in neb; 7129 close
7115	Gx	21 43.6	− 25 21 r	PsA		14p	vF, pS, mE 90°, com, 2 st inv
7127	OC	21 43.9	+ 54 37 s	Cyg	3		Cl, S, P, lC
7128	OC	21 44.0	+ 53 43 s	Cyg	3	9.7	Cl, S, pRi, has a ruby *9.5
1397 I		21 44.0	− 4 53 d	Aqr			F, vS, stellar
1400 I		21 44.2	+ 52 57 d	Cyg			F, dif, partly resolved
7120	Gx	21 44.4	− 6 33 r	Aqr		15p	vF, S, vlE
1402 I		21 44.8	+ 53 16 d	Cyg			F, partly res, st 14m
5123 I	Gx	21 44.8	− 72 25 c	Ind	1.9		cF, vS, cE 15°, *12 p 1′
7121	Gx	21 44.9	− 3 37 r	Aqr		14p	vF, vS, R, vlbM
7117	Gx	21 45.7	− 48 24 r	Gru			F, S, R, glbM, p of 2
7122	D*	21 45.7	− 8 49 F	Cap			nebulous * 10-11 or vS Cl
7139	Pl	21 45.9	+ 63 39 s	Cep	1.3		vF, cS, R, r
7142	OC	21 45.9	+ 65 48 s	Cep	4	9.3	Cl, cL, cRi, pC, st 11...14
1398 I	Gx	21 45.9	+ 9 28 m	Peg	0.8	15p	vF, vS, bM
7118	Gx	21 46.1	− 48 21 r	Gru			F, S, R, glbM, f of 2
1399 I	Gx	21 46.1	+ 4 24 z	Peg		16p	vF, vS, stellar
7119	Gx	21 46.3	− 46 31 s	Gru	1.1	14p	F, S, R, gbM
7098	Gx	21 46.8	− 75 07 v	Oct	4.4		pF, R, g, psmbM, am st
1401 I	Gx	21 46.9	+ 1 42 v	Aqr	2.2		pB, pS, r
7132	Gx	21 47.2	+ 10 14 r	Peg		14p	vF, pL, lE, bet 2 st
5131 I	Gx	21 47.4	− 34 53 s	PsA	1.6	12.4	vF, vS, R
7131	Gx	21 47.7	− 13 11 r	Cap		14p	vF, S, vlE, vgbM
5129 I		21 47.8	− 65 23 d	Ind			no descr
7124	Gx	21 48.1	− 50 34 s	Ind	2.7	13p	pB, L, pmE, vgbM
7137	Gx	21 48.2	+ 22 10 s	Peg	1.5	12.4	F, pS, R, vglbM, r
7130	Gx	21 48.3	− 34 57 A	PsA			pB, S, R, glbM; = IC 5135
5135 I	Gx	21 48.3	− 34 57 s	PsA	1.3	12.3	vF, pL, R; = 7130
5136 I		21 48.8	− 33 39 d	PsA			eeF, S, R
7134	Ast	21 48.9	− 12 59 D	Cap			only 3 or 4 vF st (no neb)
7143	D*	21 48.9	+ 29 57 r	Cyg			vF; D*? (inv in neb?)
7138	Gx	21 49.0	+ 12 30 r	Peg		15p	vF, vS, stell
7125	Gx	21 49.3	− 60 43 s	Ind	3.2	13p	eF, pL, R, sp of 2
7126	Gx	21 49.3	− 60 37 s	Ind	2.3	13p	pB, pS, lE, gbM, nf of 2
7136	D*	21 49.7	− 11 47 F	Cap			stellar, nebulosity doubtful
7135	Gx	21 49.8	− 34 53 s	PsA	2.8	11.7	pB, pL, R, vgbM, *14 att p
7150	Ast	21 50.4	+ 49 45 A	Cyg			neb, no description
5130 I	Gx	21 50.4	− 74 00 c	Ind	2.4		vF, vS

NGC	Type	α_{2000}	δ_{2000}	Const.	Size	Mag.	Description
		h m	° ′		′		
5139 I	Gx	21 50.4	− 31 00 c	PsA	2.2		vF, S, lE
1403 I		21 50.5	− 2 43 d	Aqr			eF, S, F, * att, v diffic
7123	Gx	21 50.8	− 70 20 c	Ind	3.5		pB, S, R, vgbM, *9 f
1405 I	Gx	21 50.8	+ 2 01 u	Aqr	1.0	15p	pB, vS, R, bM
1404 I		21 50.9	− 9 16 d	Cap			F, vS, R, sbM *13
1406 I	Gx	21 51.0	+ 1 59 z	Aqr		15p	F, vS, R, stellar
5137 I		21 51.6	− 65 35 d	Ind			eF, S, R, stell N, spir?; susp
7146	Gx	21 51.8	+ 3 01 r	Peg		15p	F, R
7147	Gx	21 52.0	+ 3 04 r	Peg		15p	F, S, lE
7148	D*	21 52.1	+ 3 20 F	Peg			vF, vS, R
7141	Gx	21 52.2	− 55 34 v	Ind			F, L, R, gpsmbM
7149	Gx	21 52.2	+ 3 18 r	Peg		14p	vF, vS, R
7140	Gx	21 52.3	− 55 34 c	Ind			pF, cS, R, bM; = 7141
1407 I	Gx	21 52.3	+ 3 26 z	Peg		15p	F, S, r
7144	Gx	21 52.7	− 48 15 s	Gru	3.5	10.7	vB, pS, R, mbMN
1408 I	Gx	21 53.2	− 13 21 m	Cap	0.6	15p	F, vS, R, bM
7145	Gx	21 53.3	− 47 53 s	Gru	2.5	11.2	B, S, R, in △ of st 13
1409 I		21 53.3	− 7 30 d	Aqr			eF, S, iF
5141 I	Gx	21 53.3	− 59 30 c	Ind	1.8		○ , stell, 15 mag
5146 I	C+N	21 53.4	+ 47 16 s	Cyg	12	7.2	pB, vL, iF, *9.5 in M
5138 I		21 53.5	− 68 57 d	Ind			eF, eS, R, susp
7160	OC	21 53.7	+ 62 36 s	Cep	7	6.1	Cl, P, vlC
7152	Gx	21 53.9	− 29 16 r	PsA		14p	eeF, vS
5144 I		21 53.9	+ 15 06 d	Peg			F, S, sev F st close f
5145 I		21 54.2	+ 15 13 d	Peg			no descr
5140 I	Gx	21 54.3	− 67 20 c	Ind	1.9		eF, vS, mE 135°
7153	Gx	21 54.4	− 29 02 r	PsA		14p	eF, S, E or has eF* nr
7156	Gx	21 54.6	+ 2 57 s	Peg	1.7	13.0	F, pL, R, bM, r
7151	Gx	21 55.0	− 50 40 r	Ind			vF, pL, lE, vgbM, r
5142 I	Gx	21 55.3	− 65 31 c	Ind	1.4		eF, vS, R, bet 2 st, susp
7154	Gx	21 55.4	− 34 49 v	PsA	1.3		B, pL, iR, glbM, r
1410 I		21 56.0	− 2 53 d	Aqr			pF, vSN
1411 I	Gx	21 56.1	− 1 31 u	Aqr	0.9	14p	F, vS, R, vlbM
7155	Gx	21 56.2	− 49 32 s	Ind	1.9	13p	pB, S, lE, mbM
5143 I		21 56.3	− 49 03 d	Gru			eeF, pS, R
7159	Gx	21 56.4	+ 13 34 r	Peg		15p	eeF, eS, R, vF* sf inv
7164	Gx	21 56.6	+ 1 22 r	Aqr			eF, R, 4 vF st n
7157	Gx	21 56.8	− 25 23 r	PsA		14p	vF, vS, R, sbMN, B D* p 8ˢ
7161	D*	21 57.0	+ 2 57 F	Peg			Cl, vS, st 19, bet 2 st 16
7158	**	21 57.4	− 11 36 F	Cap			vF neb*, *9.5 nf 3′
1412 I	Gx	21 58.3	− 17 11 c	Cap	1.6		F, vS; D stell neb?
1414 I		21 58.3	+ 8 24 d	Peg			vF, vS, R, 2 F st s
1413 I		21 58.5	− 3 06 d	Aqr			F, S, stellar
1415 I	*	21 58.7	+ 1 21 F	Aqr			eF, *9.5 sf 8′
5149 I		21 58.7	− 27 23 d	PsA			eF, S, R, *6.5 f 63ˢon par
7175	−	21 58.8	+ 54 49 r	Cyg			Cl, vL, pRi, lC
1416 I		21 58.8	+ 1 27 D	Aqr			eF, trace of neby
5151 I	Gx	21 58.9	+ 3 45 z	Peg		15p	F, vS, R, gbMN, r
5150 I		21 59.2	− 39 25 d	Gru			pB, pL, annular
7163	Gx	21 59.3	− 31 53 s	PsA	1.8	13.4	F, pL, vlE, vglbM
5147 I	Gx	21 59.4	− 65 27 c	Ind	1.4		eF, eS, R, F* f 2′
7165	Gx	21 59.5	− 16 31 r	Aqr		14p	eF, bM *13
5148 I	Pl	21 59.5	− 39 23 s	Gru	2.0		vF, L, lE, * att
7162	Gx	21 59.8	− 43 19 s	Gru	2.8	13p	cF, cL, cE, glbM
1417 I	Gx	22 00.4	− 13 09 v	Aqr	1.4		pB, pL, part more condensed

NGC	Type	α_{2000}	δ_{2000}	Const.	Size	Mag.	Description
		h m	° ′		′		
5153 I	?	22 00.4	+ 17 51 x	Peg			eF, st?; *9.5 sf 1′.4
7167	Gx	22 00.5	− 24 38 r	Aqr		13p	F, pS, R, vglbM, *10 f
7166	Gx	22 00.7	− 43 25 s	Gru	2.4	11.8	cB, S, vlE, smbMN
7177	Gx	22 00.7	+ 17 44 s	Peg	3.3	11.2	pB, pS, R, bMN, r, * sp
7171	Gx	22 01.0	− 13 16 s	Aqr	2.8	12.3	vF, cL, E 124°, vgbM
7186		22 01.0	+ 35 06 D	Peg			vF, am 5 or 6 st
7170		22 01.4	− 5 27 D	Aqr			vF, pS, iR, bMN, D* p 36^s
7181	Gx	22 01.8	− 1 58 r	Aqr		15p	eF, vS, stellar
7182	Gx	22 01.9	− 2 12 r	Aqr		15p	eF, vS, stellar
7172	Gx	22 02.0	− 31 52 s	PsA	2.2	11.9	pB, pL, lE, gbM, 1st of 4
7173	Gx	22 02.0	− 31 58 s	PsA	1.3	12.1	cB, cS, R, sbM*, 2nd of 4
1418 I	Gx	22 02.0	+ 4 21 m	Peg	0.8	14p	vF, S
7168	Gx	22 02.1	− 51 45 s	Ind	2.0	13p	pB, S, R, psbM
7174	Gx	22 02.1	− 31 59 s	PsA	1.3	12.6	cF, S, R, p of Dneb, 3rd of 4
7176	Gx	22 02.1	− 31 59 s	PsA	1.3	11.9	B, pL, R, f of Dneb, 4th of 4
5155 I	*	22 02.1	+ 0 30 F	Aqr			eF, S, smbM, *13 f 1′.5
7180	Gx	22 02.3	− 20 33 s	Aqr	1.8	12.5	vF, S, R, lbM, p of 2
7183	Gx	22 02.4	− 18 56 r	Aqr		14p	vF, pL, E 90°, lbM
7178	Gx	22 02.5	− 35 49 r	PsA			eF, S, R, *8 s 2′
1420 I	Gx	22 02.6	+ 19 45 s	Peg	1.6	14p	eeF, pS, R, bet 2 F st
7184	Gx	22 02.7	− 20 49 s	Aqr	5.8	12p	pB, pL, mE 64°, bet 3 st, er
7187	Gx	22 02.7	− 32 48 c	PsA	1.7		pF, pS, R, lbM
5159 I	*	22 02.7	+ 0 21 x	Aqr			eF, vS, stell, *11.5 nff 1′.5
7169	Gx	22 02.8	− 47 42 c	Gru	1.0		eF, S, R, *8 np
7197	Gx	22 02.9	+ 41 03 r	Lac		14p	F, cS, cE, vglbM, er
5152 I	Gx	22 02.9	− 51 17 s	Ind	4.5	12p	F, cL, cE 150°, cbM
1419 I		22 03.0	− 9 55 d	Aqr			eF, slbM
1422 I	Gx	22 03.0	+ 2 37 z	Peg		16p	vF, eS, lbM, bet 2 st 13.5
7185	Gx	22 03.1	− 20 28 r	Aqr		14p	vF, pL, iR, vglbM, f of 2
7190	Gx	22 03.1	+ 11 12 r	Peg		15p	eF, vS, iR, lbM
1421 I	Gx	22 03.1	− 9 57 m	Aqr	0.3	15p	neb *14
1423 I	Gx	22 03.2	+ 4 18 u	Peg	1.1	15p	F, vS, R, gvlbM
1424 I	Gx	22 03.2	+ 11 13 u	Peg	1.0	15p	eF, vS, 1′ f 7190
5160 I	Gx	22 03.2	+ 10 56 u	Peg	1.1	15p	F, vS, R
7189	Gx	22 03.3	+ 0 34 r	Aqr		14p	F, S, lE
1427 I		22 03.3	+ 15 07 d	Peg			vF, vS
5156 I	Gx	22 03.3	− 33 50 s	PsA		13p	pF, pS, R
7195	Gx	22 03.4	+ 12 39 r	Peg		15p	eeF, R, v diffic
1425 I	Gx	22 03.4	+ 2 37 z	Peg		15p	F, lE pf, r, D?
5157 I	Gx	22 03.4	− 34 56 c	PsA	2.1		pB, pS, R, 3 st in line nf
7188	Gx	22 03.5	− 20 20 r	Aqr		14p	eF, pS, E, lbM
7194	Gx	22 03.5	+ 12 37 r	Peg		14p	vF, vS, R, lbM
7193	−	22 03.6	+ 10 49 r	Peg			Cl, lRi, lC, st 9…10
1426 I		22 03.9	− 9 55 d	Aqr			F, S, iF, lbM
1428 I	Gx	22 04.4	+ 2 38 z	Peg		16p	vF, S, R, *14 nr
5154 I		22 04.6	− 66 07 d	Ind			vF, bM
7179	Gx	22 04.8	− 64 03 v	Ind	1.8		cF, pS, vgbM
7209	OC	22 05.2	+ 46 30 s	Lac	25	6.7	Cl, L, cRi, pC, st 9…12
7198	Gx	22 05.3	− 0 39 r	Aqr		15p	eF, vS, stellar
7206	Gx	22 05.6	+ 16 47 r	Peg		15p	F, S, lE, bM
5161 I		22 05.6	+ 9 34 d	Peg			F, R, stell, r
7207	Gx	22 05.7	+ 16 45 r	Peg			vF, S
5163 I		22 05.8	+ 27 05 d	Peg			eF, 2 st 13 nr
7196	Gx	22 06.0	− 50 07 s	Ind	1.9	11.5	cB, S, R, am st
5164 I		22 06.0	+ 27 03 d	Peg			eF, stell

NGC	Type	α_{2000}	δ_{2000}	Const.	Size	Mag.	Description
		h m	° ′		′		
5166 I		22 06.1	+ 27 04 d	Peg			eF, stell N, or vS Cl
7211	Gx	22 06.2	− 8 07 r	Aqr			eF, S, stellar
7210	−	22 06.3	+ 27 06 r	Peg			eF, R, bM, vF D∗ np
5158 I	Gx	22 06.4	− 67 31 c	Ind	1.1		eeF, eS, bM
7201	Gx	22 06.5	− 31 16 s	PsA	1.7	14p	F, R, gbM, 1st of 4
7202	Gx	22 06.7	− 31 12 m	PsA	1.3	13p	eF, S, stellar, 2nd of 4
7203	Gx	22 06.7	− 31 10 s	PsA	1.9	13p	cF, R, stellar, 3rd of 4
7192	Gx	22 06.8	− 64 19 s	Ind	2.5	12p	pB, S, R, pmbM
7191	Gx	22 06.9	− 64 38 v	Ind			vF, S, lE, vgbM
7204	Gx	22 06.9	− 31 03 s	PsA		14p	pB, L, lE, gbM, 4th of 4
1429 I		22 06.9	+ 10 06 d	Peg			neb susp close to ∗11
7212	Gx	22 07.0	+ 10 14 r	Peg		15p	eF, vS, lE
7200	Gx	22 07.2	− 50 00 v	Ind	1.6		pF, S, R, smbM
5167 I	∗	22 07.5	− 8 08 F	Aqr			vF, neb?
1431 I		22 07.7	− 13 30 F	Aqr			eF, v diffic, F∗ np
7217	Gx	22 07.9	+ 31 22 s	Peg	3.7	10.2	B, pL, gbM, er
5162 I		22 08.1	− 52 43 d	Ind			eF, eS, vE 95°
7208	Gx	22 08.4	− 29 06 r	PsA		14p	vF, vS, R, almost ◯
7199	Gx	22 08.5	− 64 42 v	Ind	1.3		vF, S, R, pslbM, ∗11 p 3′
7205	Gx	22 08.5	− 57 25 s	Ind	4.3	11p	pB, L, cE, gpslbM
1430 I		22 08.5	− 13 34 d	Aqr			F, S, vlbM, diffic
7215	Gx	22 08.6	+ 0 30 r	Aqr		15p	vF, S, E
5168 I	Gx	22 08.8	− 27 51 c	PsA	1.3		eeF, vS, mE, 2 F st
7214	Gx	22 09.1	− 27 49 s	PsA	1.9	12.4	⊕, pL, iR, rr
7213	Gx	22 09.3	− 47 10 s	Gru	1.9	10.5	vB, pS, R, gbM
5172 I	Gx	22 09.9	+ 12 49 z	Peg		16p	vF, vS, stell, ∗14 att
1432 I		22 10.1	+ 3 41 d	Peg			vF, vS, sbM ∗14, ∗13.5 nr
5165 I	Gx	22 10.1	− 64 35 c	Tuc	1.4		eF, eS
7218	Gx	22 10.2	− 16 40 s	Aqr	2.5	12.1	pB, lE, r
7223	Gx	22 10.2	+ 41 00 r	Lac		13p	eF, pS, lE, r, am 3 st
5169 I	Gx	22 10.2	− 36 05 c	PsA	2.2		eF, eS, stell N, spir or oval
7226	OC	22 10.5	+ 55 25 s	Cep	2	9.6	pB, L, in cluster
1434 I	OC	22 10.5	+ 52 50 s	Lac	8	9p	fine Cl, 6 branches, st 12-15m
5171 I	Gx	22 10.9	− 46 05 c	Gru	2.8		no descr
7222	Gx	22 11.0	+ 2 05 r	Aqr		15p	vF, S
5180 I	Gx	22 11.1	+ 38 55 u	Lac	1.1	15p	vF, S, sbM
7221	Gx	22 11.3	− 30 37 s	PsA	2.2	12p	F, S, R, gbM, r, 2 vS st nr
7220	Gx	22 11.5	− 22 58 r	Aqr		15p	eF, vS, vlE, gbM, ∗10 n 3′
7227	Gx	22 11.5	+ 38 42 r	Lac		15p	vF, vS, R, lbM, np of 2
7224	Gx	22 11.6	+ 25 50 r	Peg		14p	F, S, R
5177 I	Gx	22 11.6	+ 11 48 u	Peg	1.6	15p	F, S, E ns, glbM
7228	Gx	22 11.8	+ 38 41 r	Lac		15p	F, vS, R, lbM, sf of 2
7234	−	22 12.1	+ 56 58 r	Cep			Cl, S, P, lC
1433 I	Gx	22 12.2	− 12 46 m	Aqr	0.4	15p	F, S, E pf, bM
7231	Gx	22 12.4	+ 45 19 r	Lac		14p	eF, S, er
5170 I	Gx	22 12.5	− 47 13 c	Gru	1.8		no descr
5178 I	Gx	22 12.5	− 22 57 c	Aqr	1.4		eF, vS, 7220 p 63ˢ
7216	Gx	22 12.6	− 68 40 c	Ind	1.4		pF, S, R, gbM
7235	OC	22 12.6	+ 57 17 s	Cep	4	7.7	Cl, pC, has a ruby ∗10
5174 I	Gx	22 12.7	− 38 10 c	Gru	0.8		eF, eS, cE 150°
5175 I		22 12.7	− 38 08 d	Gru			eF, eS, R, bM
7219	Gx	22 13.1	− 64 51 s	Tuc	2.4	13p	pB, S, R, 2 st nr
7225	Gx	22 13.2	− 26 09 r	PsA		13p	pF, S, lE, bM
5181 I	Gx	22 13.4	− 46 02 s	Gru	2.8	11.7	no descr
1435 I	Gx	22 13.5	− 22 06 m	Aqr	0.9	14p	F, S

NGC	Type	α_{2000}	δ_{2000}	Const.	Size	Mag.	Description
		h m	o ′		′		
1436 I	Gx	22 13.9	− 10 11 m	Aqr	0.2	15p	eF, vS, R, vSN
7229	Gx	22 14.0	− 29 25 s	PsA	1.8	12p	F, pL, R, vglbM
7230	Gx	22 14.3	− 17 04 r	Aqr		14p	vF, S, R, bM
7236	Gx	22 14.7	+ 13 51 s	Peg	1.0	13.5	vF, S, stellar
7237	Gx	22 14.8	+ 13 50 s	Peg	1.0	13.7	vF, S, stellar
5173 I	Gx	22 14.8	− 69 22 c	Ind	1.6		eF, S, mE 75°
7239	Gx	22 14.9	− 5 05 r	Aqr			eF, vS
5176 I	Gx	22 14.9	− 66 51 c	Tuc	4.7		vF, S, eE 30°, * n
5191 I	Gx	22 15.0	+ 37 18 x	Lac	0.8		one of 6 neb incl 7240, 7242, & IC 5195
5192 I	Gx	22 15.2	+ 37 16 x	Lac	0.2		another of group of 6
7238	−	22 15.3	+ 22 30 r	Peg			pF, S, R, mbM, 4 st p
7243	OC	22 15.3	+ 49 53 s	Lac	21	6.4	Cl, L, P, lC, st vL
7245	OC	22 15.3	+ 54 20 s	Lac	5	9.2	Cl, C, st eS
1441 I	Gx	22 15.3	+ 37 18 v	Lac	0.9		eF, S, S stellar N
7240	Gx	22 15.4	+ 37 17 s	Lac	0.8	13.8	eF, eS, * att n, p of 2; = IC 1441
5183 I		22 15.4	− 35 50 d	PsA			pB, cS, F* att sf
7232	Gx	22 15.7	− 45 51 s	Gru	3.0	13p	pB, S, pmE, psbM, p of 2
7242	Gx	22 15.7	+ 37 18 s	Lac	2.6	12.0	vF, S, lbM, f of 2
1437 I	Gx	22 15.7	+ 2 03 u	Aqr	1.1	15p	pB, vS, R, mbM
5193 I	Gx	22 15.7	+ 37 15 x	Lac			another of group of 6
5195 I	Gx	22 15.7	+ 37 18 x	Lac			eF, S, 0′.5 s of 7242
7233	Gx	22 15.8	− 45 51 s	Gru	2.2		F, vS, R, *8 f, f of 2
7241	Gx	22 15.8	+ 19 14 s	Peg	3.5	14p	pF, lE, *10 att s
5179 I	Gx	22 16.1	− 36 50 s	Gru	2.3	11.9	vF, L, R, * nr s; B* sp
5182 I		22 16.1	− 65 27 d	Tuc			eF, eS, bM
5184 I	Gx	22 16.1	− 36 51 c	Gru	2.6		pF, pS, lE, bet 2 st ns; = IC 5179
5189 I	*	22 16.2	− 5 00 F	Aqr			eF*; nebs?
7244	Gx	22 16.4	+ 16 28 v	Peg	0.7	14.4	eF, eS, R, bM
1438 I	Gx	22 16.5	− 21 26 c	Aqr	2.4		F, biN
1440 I	Gx	22 16.5	− 16 00 m	Aqr	0.6	15p	F, S, stellar
1442 I	OC	22 16.5	+ 54 03 s	Lac		9.1	Cl of neb stars
1439 I	Gx	22 16.7	− 21 29 c	Aqr	1.8		vF, S, vlbM
7248	Gx	22 16.9	+ 40 30 s	Lac	2.1	14p	vF, vS, mbM
5194 I	Gx	22 17.1	− 15 57 x	Aqr	0.2		eF (not found again)
7246	Gx	22 17.5	− 15 32 r	Aqr		15p	vF, S, vlE, vgbM, *13 n
5198 I		22 17.7	− 15 40 d	Aqr			eF, pL, R, bM, r
7247	Gx	22 17.8	− 23 43 r	Aqr		13p	pF, vS, R, lbM, B D* p 13ˢ
5185 I		22 17.8	− 65 51 d	Tuc			eF, vS, bM
7250	Gx	22 18.3	+ 40 35 r	Lac		13p	vF, S, mE 165°±
5187 I		22 18.3	− 59 37 d	Tuc			vS, R, disc, mag 14.5
5188 I	Gx	22 18.4	− 59 38 c	Tuc	1.5		F, cS, R, cbM
5186 I	Gx	22 18.8	− 36 48 c	Gru	1.5		eeF, S, R, F* nr p
5190 I	Gx	22 19.0	− 59 53 c	Tuc	1.6		vF, 2-br spir, *15 in M
1443 I	Gx	22 19.1	− 20 56 c	Aqr	1.7		pB, S, iF, mbM
7253	Gx	22 19.4	+ 29 24 r	Peg		14p	vF, pE
5199 I	Gx	22 19.5	− 37 32 c	Gru	1.6		eF, eS, cE 160°
5197 I	Gx	22 19.8	− 60 08 c	Tuc	1.3		bM, mag 15
5196 I		22 20.2	− 65 24 d	Tuc			eF, eeS, eE 105°, stell N
7251	Gx	22 20.4	− 15 46 r	Aqr		13p	F, pS, R, gpmbM
7261	OC	22 20.4	+ 58 05 s	Cep	6	8.4	Cl, L, pRi, lC
7249	Gx	22 20.5	− 55 08 c	Gru	1.1		eeF, R, doubtful object
7252	Gx	22 20.7	− 24 41 s	Aqr	2.2	12.1	F, S, R, er
5204 I		22 20.7	− 14 24 d	Aqr			vF, vmE
5201 I	Gx	22 21.4	− 46 04 s	Gru	8.5	11p	no descr
7263	Gx	22 21.8	+ 36 21 v	Lac	0.8		F, S, R

NGC	Type	α_{2000}	δ_{2000}	Const.	Size	Mag.	Description
		h m	o ′		′		
7255	−	22 21.9	− 15 33 r	Aqr			eF, L, mE 30°, sbMN
7254		22 22.0	− 21 44 D	Aqr			vF, vS, R, *11 p 4′.5; = 7256
7257	−	22 22.2	− 4 01 r	Aqr			F, vS, lE
7264	Gx	22 22.2	+ 36 24 r	Lac		14p	vF, pS, mE
1444 I	Gx	22 22.3	+ 5 08 u	Peg	1.1	16p	F, S, iF, mbM, vF* close
5200 I		22 22.3	− 65 45 d	Tuc			eeF, eS, R, F* np 1′
7265	Gx	22 22.4	+ 36 14 r	Lac		13p	F, vS, R, mbM
5210 I	Gx	22 22.5	− 18 52 c	Aqr	1.6		eeF, vS, R, p of 2
5203 I	Gx	22 22.6	− 59 46 c	Tuc	1.6		bM, mag 15
7256	Gx	22 22.7	− 21 44 r	Aqr		14p	3 F st in F neb
7260	Gx	22 22.7	− 4 07 r	Aqr		14p	eF, pS, iR
5211 I		22 22.7	− 18 53 d	Aqr			eF, S, f of 2
5205 I		22 22.8	− 59 48 d	Tuc			bM, mag 16
5202 I	Gx	22 22.9	− 65 48 c	Tuc	1.4		! eF, vS, stell N, spir
7258	Gx	22 23.0	− 28 22 r	PsA		14p	vF, S, E, glbM; biN?
7259	Gx	22 23.1	− 28 59 v	PsA			eF, pL, R, vlbM
5209 I		22 23.1	− 37 59 d	Gru			F, eS, R, 2 st np
7262	Gx	22 23.4	− 32 20 r	PsA			eF, S, R, lbM
5207 I	Gx	22 23.5	− 60 34 c	Tuc	1.6		bM, mag 16
5212 I	Gx	22 23.5	− 38 02 c	Gru	1.4		eF, eS, cE 40°
7270	Gx	22 23.6	+ 32 24 r	Peg		15p	vF, S, E
5214 I		22 23.7	− 27 28 d	PsA			eF, pS, R, *8 p
7271	Gx	22 23.8	+ 32 22 r	Peg		15p	vF, S, vlE
5217 I	Pl	22 23.9	+ 50 58 s	Lac	0.1	13p	⃝ , stellar
7266	Gx	22 24.1	− 4 04 r	Aqr		15p	F, vS, R, alm stellar
7273	Gx	22 24.1	+ 36 13 r	Lac		15p	F, vS, R, mbM
7275	Gx	22 24.1	+ 32 27 r	Peg		15p	eF, S, mE
5206 I	Gx	22 24.1	− 66 51 c	Tuc	1.2		eF, vS, R, stell N
7274	Gx	22 24.2	+ 36 08 s	Lac	1.8	14p	pF, vS, mbM
7276	Gx	22 24.2	+ 36 06 r	Lac		15p	vF, vS, mbM
7267	Gx	22 24.3	− 33 41 r	PsA			cB, pS, vlE, glbM, B** sp
7272	Gx	22 24.5	+ 16 36 r	Peg		15p	vF, S, iR
5208 I	Gx	22 24.6	− 65 14 c	Tuc	1.3		eeF, eS, eE 65°, stell N
7281	OC	22 24.7	+ 57 50 s	Cep			Cl, L, pRi, lC, st 10...16
5216 I		22 24.7	− 18 05 d	Aqr			vF, S, R, N
5213 I		22 25.0	− 60 29 d	Tuc			bM, mag 16
1445 I	Gx	22 25.5	− 17 15 c	Aqr	2.1		pF, vS, gbMN
7268	Gx	22 25.7	− 31 12 c	PsA	1.8		F, cS, vlE, p of 2
7269	Gx	22 25.8	− 13 09 r	Aqr		14p	eF, pS, R, glbM
7282	Gx	22 26.0	+ 40 19 r	Lac		15p	eF, pL, dif, bet 3 st
7277	Gx	22 26.4	− 31 10 r	PsA		14p	F, cS, vlE, f of 2
7280	Gx	22 26.5	+ 16 09 s	Peg	2.4	13p	F, cS, R, gbM S*, 3 st n, nf
5215 I		22 27.0	− 65 56 d	Tuc			eF, vS, R, * 2′ nf; susp
7279	Gx	22 27.1	− 35 08 r	PsA			vF, pS, R, vgvlbM
7286	Gx	22 28.0	+ 29 07 r	Peg		13p	vF, S, R, am st
5218 I	Gx	22 28.1	− 60 24 c	Tuc	1.4		F, pS, E 195°
7296	OC	22 28.2	+ 52 17 s	Lac	4	10p	Cl, iR, lC, st vS
5220 I		22 28.2	− 59 43 d	Tuc			F, pS, E 105°
7288	Gx	22 28.3	− 2 51 r	Aqr		14p	vF, eS, stellar
7278	Gx	22 28.4	− 60 10 c	Tuc	0.9		eeF, lE, vgvlbM, 3 st sf
7290	Gx	22 28.4	+ 17 09 s	Peg	1.8	14p	pB, S, pmE
7292	Gx	22 28.4	+ 30 18 s	Peg	2.1	13p	eF, S, oval, F* inv
7295	−	22 28.4	+ 52 50 r	Lac			Cl, P, lC, st 12...13
7291	Gx	22 28.5	+ 16 47 r	Peg		15p	eF, eS, R, smbM
7283	Gx	22 28.6	+ 17 30 r	Peg		15p	vF, vS, R

NGC	Type	α_{2000}	δ_{2000}	Const.	Size	Mag.	Description
		h m	o '		'		
7284	Gx	22 28.6	− 24 51 r	Aqr		13p	cF, cS, lE, r
7285	Gx	22 28.7	− 24 51 r	Aqr		13p	neb* at pos 60°, dist 40'', from 7284
5219 I		22 28.7	− 65 52 d	Tuc			eF, eS, cE 15°, susp
7287	Gx	22 28.8	− 22 12 c	Aqr	0.7		eF, slightly nebs D*
5221 I		22 28.9	− 65 53 d	Tuc			eF, bM, susp
1446 I		22 29.1	− 1 12 d	Aqr			vF, stellar
7289	Gx	22 29.2	− 35 27 r	PsA			vF, S, R, gbM
7293	Pl	22 29.6	− 20 48 s	Aqr	12.8		! pF, vL, E or biN
5223 I	Gx	22 29.8	+ 7 58 u	Peg	1.1	16p	F, vS, dif, r
5222 I	Gx	22 29.9	− 65 40 c	Tuc	1.7		! eF, pS, stell N, susp
1447 I		22 30.0	− 5 09 D	Aqr			eeF, pS, R, *9.0 n 3'
7301	Gx	22 30.4	− 17 34 r	Aqr		14p	vF, pS, lE, lbM
5224 I	Gx	22 30.5	− 46 00 c	Gru	1.4		no descr
7298	Gx	22 30.8	− 14 11 s	Aqr	1.5	14p	vF, pL, iR
7297	Gx	22 30.9	− 37 49 r	Gru			eF, S, R, p of 2
7300	Gx	22 31.0	− 14 00 s	Aqr	2.2	12.9	vF, pL, E 150°, vglbM
5239 I	Gx	22 31.1	− 38 02 c	Gru	1.6		vF, pS, R
7299	Gx	22 31.4	− 37 49 r	Gru			eF, S, R, f of 2
7304	−	22 31.5	+ 30 58 r	Peg			vF, pS, vlbM, nf 7303(?)
5225 I		22 31.5	− 25 22 d	PsA			eeF, pS, R, bet 2 st
7303	Gx	22 31.6	+ 30 58 r	Peg		13p	vF, S, R, gvlbM
5226 I		22 31.7	− 24 40 d	Aqr			eeF, pL, R
7294	Gx	22 32.2	− 25 23 r	PsA		14p	vF, vS, R
7305	Gx	22 32.2	+ 11 43 r	Peg		15p	eF, S, R, 4 F st around
7302	Gx	22 32.4	− 14 07 s	Aqr	1.9	12.1	F, pS, R, vsbMSN; = IC 5228
5228 I	Gx	22 32.4	− 14 08 t	Aqr	1.9	13p	pB, pS, R, B* s; = 7302
7306	Gx	22 33.5	− 27 14 r	PsA		13p	vF, S, lE, *11 p
7307	Gx	22 33.8	− 40 57 s	Gru	4.2	13p	F, pL, pmE
5231 I	Gx	22 34.0	+ 23 21 m	Peg	0.4	15p	F, S, R, gbMN
5227 I	Gx	22 34.1	− 64 42 c	Tuc	1.5		F, S, stell N
7311	Gx	22 34.2	+ 5 35 r	Peg		13p	pF, S, R, psbM, r
7309	Gx	22 34.3	− 10 21 s	Aqr	2.1	12.5	vF, pL, R, glbM, r
7308	Gx	22 34.5	− 12 56 r	Aqr		14p	pB, vS, R; = IC 1448
1448 I	Gx	22 34.6	− 12 56 m	Aqr	1.0	14p	vF, vS, diffic
7310	Gx	22 34.7	− 22 29 r	Aqr		14p	vF, pS, R, bMN
7312	Gx	22 34.7	+ 5 49 r	Peg		14p	F, S
5229 I		22 34.8	− 61 23 d	Tuc			bM, mag 15
1449 I		22 35.1	− 8 47 d	Aqr			F, S, iF, bM, r
7315	Gx	22 35.4	+ 34 50 r	Peg		14p	vF, eS, R, bM
7313	Gx	22 35.5	− 26 06 v	PsA			eF, E
5230 I		22 35.6	− 61 32 d	Tuc			eF, eS, cE 35°, cbM
7314	Gx	22 35.8	− 26 03 s	PsA	4.6	10.9	cF, L, mE 0°, vlbM
7316	Gx	22 35.9	+ 20 19 s	Peg	1.3	14p	F, S, R, *8 sp
7317	Gx	22 35.9	+ 33 57 r	Peg	1.0	13.6	vF, vS
7318	Gx	22 36.0	+ 33 58 s	Peg	1.9	13.1	eF, eS
7319	Gx	22 36.1	+ 33 59 s	Peg	1.7	13.1	eF, eS
7320	Gx	22 36.1	+ 33 57 s	Peg	2.2	12.7	F, vS
7321	Gx	22 36.4	+ 21 38 r	Peg		14p	F, S, iR, vgvlbM
5233 I	Gx	22 36.6	+ 25 46 u	Peg	1.1	15p	F, vS, dif, *12.5 v close
7323	Gx	22 36.8	+ 19 09 r	Peg		14p	pF, pL, iR
7325	D*	22 36.8	+ 34 22 A	Peg			F, vS, 7331 f
7326	D*	22 36.8	+ 34 25 A	Peg			eF, eS, 7331 f
7327	*	22 36.8	+ 34 29 r	Peg			eF, eS, np 7331
7330	Gx	22 36.9	+ 38 33 r	Lac		13p	pB, S, lE, bM
7324	Gx	22 37.0	+ 19 09 r	Peg		15p	vF, vS, neb*

NGC	Type	α_{2000}	δ_{2000}	Const.	Size	Mag.	Description
		h m	° ′		′		
7331	Gx	22 37.1	+ 34 25 s	Peg	10.7	9.5	B, pL, pmE 163°, smbM
7333	Gx	22 37.2	+ 34 26 h	Peg	0.1	15p	vF, vS, p 7335
7336	Gx	22 37.2	+ 34 29 r	Peg		15p	eF, vS
7335	Gx	22 37.3	+ 34 27 s	Peg	1.7	15p	vF, vS
7332	Gx	22 37.4	+ 23 48 s	Peg	4.2	11.0	cB, S, mE 156°, smbMN, p of 2
7337	Gx	22 37.4	+ 34 22 v	Peg	1.3		eF, S, stellar
7328	Gx	22 37.5	+ 10 32 r	Peg		14p	eF, pS, lE 90°, vglbM
7338	Gx	22 37.5	+ 34 25 h	Peg	0.2	14p	eF, eS, sf 7335
7340	Gx	22 37.6	+ 34 26 r	Peg		15p	vF, vS
7322	Gx	22 37.7	− 37 13 r	Gru			vF, S, vlE, gbM
7334	Gx	22 37.8	− 37 14 c	Gru			eeF; = 7322
7339	Gx	22 37.8	+ 23 47 s	Peg	3.0	12.1	F, pS, mE 89°, vglbM, f of 2
5232 I		22 37.8	− 68 52 d	Ind			eF, eeS, bM
1450 I	*	22 38.0	+ 34 33 x	Peg			vF, eS, stellar
7342	Gx	22 38.1	+ 35 31 r	Peg		15p	eF, vS
7343	Gx	22 38.6	+ 34 04 s	Peg	1.2	13.4	eF, vS, R, lbM, S* inv
7345	Gx	22 38.6	+ 35 33 r	Peg		15p	eF, vS
7341	Gx	22 39.2	− 22 41 r	Aqr		13p	pF, pS, E, lbM
7346	Gx	22 39.5	+ 11 05 r	Peg		15p	eF, vS, stellar
7353	Gx	22 39.5	+ 11 47 r	Peg		15p	eF
7344	Gx	22 39.7	− 4 10 r	Aqr		14p	pF, vS, R
7352	−	22 39.7	+ 57 24 r	Cep			Cl, vL, pRi, vlC
7347	Gx	22 39.9	+ 11 02 r	Peg		14p	eF, pL, E
5234 I		22 40.2	− 65 48 d	Tuc			eF, eeS, cE 165°, cbM
7354	Pl	22 40.4	+ 61 17 s	Cep	0.3	13p	○ , B, S, R, pgvlbM
7329	Gx	22 40.5	− 66 28 s	Tuc	4.2	12p	pB, pS, mE 90°
7348	Gx	22 40.6	+ 11 54 s	Peg	1.3	15p	vF, pL, iR
7350	*	22 41.0	+ 11 58 r	Peg			vF
5242 I	Gx	22 41.2	+ 23 24 u	Peg	1.0	15p	F, S, R, gbM, *13 nf
7351	Gx	22 41.3	− 4 27 r	Aqr		13p	pF, pS, mE 180°, bM, r
5235 I		22 41.4	− 66 34 d	Tuc			eeF, bM
5243 I	Gx	22 41.4	+ 23 23 v	Peg	0.7		F, cS, iF, dif
7349		22 41.5	− 22 54 d	Aqr			eF, vS, E 175°, biN, bn
5236 I		22 41.5	− 66 36 d	Tuc			eF, eeS, cE 60°, bM
5238 I		22 41.5	− 60 45 d	Tuc			F, vS, vlE
5241 I	Gx	22 41.5	+ 2 38 u	Aqr	1.0	15p	pB, cS, R, gbM, r
5240 I	Gx	22 41.9	− 44 48 s	Gru	3.2	12p	pF, pL, R, F* sf
7356	Gx	22 42.1	+ 30 43 r	Peg		15p	eF, pS, R, glbM, * att
7361	Gx	22 42.3	− 30 03 s	PsA	3.5	12.5	F, pL, vmE 0°, vgvlbM
5237 I	Gx	22 42.3	− 30 03 c	PsA	4.0		eeF, eS, eE, *8 np; = 7361
7357	Gx	22 42.4	+ 30 11 r	Peg		15p	vF, vS, vF* inv
1454 I	Pl	22 42.6	+ 80 27 s	Cep	0.6	15p	vF, S, *7 4′ f
7363	Gx	22 43.3	+ 34 00 s	Peg	1.1	15p	pF, pL, E, D* f
7355	−	22 43.4	− 37 52 r	Gru			eeF, S, R, D* f 40ˢ
7360	Gx	22 43.6	+ 4 09 r	Peg		14p	eF, vS
7362	Gx	22 43.9	+ 8 43 r	Peg		15p	vF, S, R, lbM
5244 I	Gx	22 44.2	− 64 03 c	Tuc	3.3		eF, pS, eE 0°, stell N
7366	Gx	22 44.3	+ 10 46 r	Peg		15p	eF, S, stellar
7369	Gx	22 44.3	+ 34 21 r	Peg		15p	pF, bet 2 F st
7364	Gx	22 44.5	− 0 07 r	Aqr		14p	F, S, R, psbM
7367	Gx	22 44.7	+ 3 41 r	Peg		15p	vF, pS, lE
5248 I		22 44.7	− 0 21 d	Aqr			susp (13.5 mag)
7359		22 44.8	− 23 41 D	Aqr			pF, vS, pmE, bMN
7365	Gx	22 45.0	− 19 59 r	Aqr		14p	vF, eS, R, gbMN, *11 nf 4′
5245 I		22 45.1	− 65 20 d	Tuc			eF, eS, R, F* np 0′.5

NGC	Type	α_{2000}	δ_{2000}	Const.	Size	Mag.	Description
		h m	o ′		′		
5251 I	*	22 45.1	+ 11 09 x	Peg			eF
5253 I	Gx	22 45.4	+ 21 49 u	Peg	1.0	15p	F, S, E ns, *13.5 nr
7370	Gx	22 45.5	+ 11 03 r	Peg			eF, vS
7368	Gx	22 45.6	− 39 20 v	Gru	3.2		F, cS, lE, glbM
7358	Gx	22 45.7	− 65 07 r	Tuc			F, S, R, bM, stell N with wisps 175°
7372	Gx	22 45.7	+ 11 08 r	Peg		14p	F, S, iR
5255 I		22 45.8	+ 36 14 d	Lac			F, S, R, gbM
1452 I		22 45.9	+ 16 51 d	Peg			vF, vS, quite stellar
7374	Gx	22 46.0	+ 10 51 r	Peg		15p	vF, pL, R
5254 I		22 46.0	+ 21 07 d	Peg			F, vS, R, r, *14 att sf, 7375 f
7371	Gx	22 46.1	− 11 00 s	Aqr	2.1	12.1	vF, pL, R, lbM
1451 I	Gx	22 46.2	− 10 22 m	Aqr	0.4	15p	vF, S, dif, vS, excent N
7373	Gx	22 46.5	+ 3 13 r	Peg		15p	F, vS, bM, stellar
7375	Gx	22 46.6	+ 21 05 r	Peg		15p	eF, vS, R
5246 I		22 46.6	− 64 54 d	Tuc			eF, eS
1453 I	Gx	22 46.8	− 13 27 m	Aqr	0.6	15p	pB, pL, R
5247 I		22 46.9	− 65 17 d	Tuc			vF, vS, mE 125°, mbM
7380	C+N	22 47.0	+ 58 06 s	Cep	25	7.2	Cl, pL, pRi, lC, st 9...13
5249 I	Gx	22 47.1	− 64 50 c	Tuc	3.7		eF, vS, eE 15°, vlbM
5250 I	Gx	22 47.3	− 65 03 c	Tuc	3.8		cB, S, R, F* f 0′.5
7376	Gx	22 47.4	+ 3 40 r	Peg		15p	eF, vS, R
7379	Gx	22 47.4	+ 40 14 r	Lac		14p	eF, S, R, lbM
7377	Gx	22 47.8	− 22 19 s	Aqr	2.2	11.6	pB, S, vlE, vgmbM, *12 p
7378	Gx	22 47.9	− 11 49 r	Aqr		13p	vF, pL
5252 I	Gx	22 48.1	− 68 54 c	Ind	1.2		F, S, R, cbM
7383	Gx	22 49.6	+ 11 36 s	Peg	1.0	13.9	vF, vS, R, 7385 nf
7384	Gx	22 49.7	+ 11 33 r	Peg			eF, 5′ nf 7383
5256 I	Gx	22 49.8	− 68 42 c	Ind	1.1		vF, vS, cE 25°, cbM
7385	Gx	22 49.9	+ 11 36 s	Peg	1.6	12.3	cF, S, R, glbM, *11 np
7381	Gx	22 50.0	− 19 43 r	Aqr		15p	eF, vS, R, gbM
7386	Gx	22 50.0	+ 11 42 s	Peg	2.1	12.5	cF, S, R, pgbM, f of 2
7388	Gx	22 50.2	+ 11 44 r	Peg			vF, *11 f 2′.5
7382	Gx	22 50.3	− 36 51 r	Gru			eF, vS, R, *12 att np
7387	Gx	22 50.3	+ 11 38 s	Peg	0.7	14.0	eF, vS, R, 2 st 11 s
7389	Gx	22 50.3	+ 11 35 s	Peg	1.3	13.4	vF, R
7390	Gx	22 50.3	+ 11 32 r	Peg		15p	eF, s of 7389
7394	−	22 50.6	+ 52 10 r	Lac			Cl, vP
7391	Gx	22 50.7	− 1 31 r	Aqr		13p	cF, cS, R, sbM *13, * np
7395	Gx	22 51.2	+ 37 05 r	Lac		15p	eF, vS, R, bM
5258 I	Gx	22 51.5	+ 23 02 m	Peg	0.4	14p	F, vS, R, mbM, r
7393	Gx	22 51.7	− 5 33 s	Aqr	2.0	14p	vF, pL, lE, vgbM, r
7392	Gx	22 51.8	− 20 36 s	Aqr	2.0	11.9	pB, pS, lE 120°, mbM
5257 I		22 52.3	− 67 26 d	Ind			eF, eeS, stell N
7396	Gx	22 52.5	+ 1 06 r	Psc		14p	pF, pS, R, gbM
7399	Gx	22 52.7	− 9 16 r	Aqr		14p	eF, pL
7405	Gx	22 52.8	+ 12 35 r	Peg			eF, S, R
5259 I		22 52.8	+ 36 43 d	Lac			neb; D *9.5 f 2′
7397	Gx	22 52.9	+ 1 08 r	Psc		15p	eF, vS
7398	Gx	22 52.9	+ 1 13 r	Psc		15p	vF, pL
7402	Gx	22 53.0	+ 1 10 r	Psc		14p	eF, vS
7401	Gx	22 53.1	+ 1 10 r	Psc			eF, vS
7403	*	22 53.1	+ 1 29 F	Psc			* slightly nebs? (prob not)
7407	Gx	22 53.3	+ 32 08 r	Peg		14p	eF, vS
7409	Gx	22 53.7	+ 20 12 r	Peg		15p	eF
1455 I	Gx	22 53.9	+ 1 23 u	Psc	1.0	15p	F, pS, R, 2 st 11 nr

NGC	Type	α_{2000}	δ_{2000}	Const.	Size	Mag.	Description
		h m	° ′		′		
7406	Gx	22 54.0	− 6 36 r	Aqr		15p	F, S, lE
7400	Gx	22 54.3	− 45 21 c	Gru	2.5		pF, lE, glbM, vS* inv
7404	Gx	22 54.3	− 39 19 r	Gru			vF, S, R
7419	OC	22 54.3	+ 60 50 s	Cep	2	13p	Cl, pRi, cC
5260 I	Gx	22 54.3	− 39 19 c	Gru	1.5		eeF, pS, R, *9 sp, v diffic; = 7404
5261 I	Gx	22 54.4	− 20 22 c	Aqr	1.7		eeF, pL, R, v diffic, *9 p 22^s
7411	Gx	22 54.5	+ 20 14 r	Peg		15p	vF, vS
7415	Gx	22 54.8	+ 20 15 r	Peg		15p	eF
7410	Gx	22 55.0	− 39 40 s	Gru	5.5	10.4	cB, L, vmE 43°, mbM
7413	Gx	22 55.1	+ 13 13 v	Peg		14.1	eeF, pS, R, v diffic, s of 2
5262 I		22 55.2	− 33 50 d	PsA			eeF, pS, R, v diffic
7414	Gx	22 55.3	+ 13 15 r	Peg			eeF, S, R, v diffic, n of 2
7423	OC	22 55.3	+ 57 08 o	Cep	6	15p	vF, pL, iF, er
1456 I		22 55.3	− 12 43 d	Aqr			vF, vS
1457 I	*	22 55.4	− 5 33 x	Aqr			eF, *10 sf 1′
7420	Gx	22 55.6	+ 29 48 r	Peg		15p	vF, S
7416	Gx	22 55.7	− 5 30 s	Aqr	3.4	12.3	F, pL, pmE, vgbM
7412	Gx	22 55.8	− 42 39 s	Gru	4.0	11.4	eF, vL, *7 nf
7408	Gx	22 55.9	− 63 42 v	Tuc			pB, pS, R, vglbM
7429	OC	22 55.9	+ 59 59 s	Cep			Cl, P, pC, st 9...11
7426	Gx	22 56.1	+ 36 21 r	Lac		13p	vF, cS, R, stellar, D* p
7422	Gx	22 56.2	+ 3 56 r	Psc		14p	vF, pS, vlE
5268 I		22 56.2	+ 36 36 d	Lac			B, S
7418	Gx	22 56.6	− 37 02 s	Gru	3.3	11.4	cB, vL, vlE, vglbM
1458 I	Gx	22 56.8	− 7 23 m	Aqr	1.2	14p	vF, pL, dif
7421	Gx	22 56.9	− 37 21 s	Gru	2.2	12.0	cB, L, vlE, gpmbM, rr
5264 I	Gx	22 56.9	− 36 33 c	Gru	2.7		vF, S, vmE, sp of 2
1460 I	Gx	22 57.1	+ 4 41 v	Psc	0.4	14.4	pB, vS, mbM
7427	Gx	22 57.2	+ 8 30 r	Peg		15p	F, S, *9 sf 4′
1459 I	Gx	22 57.2	− 36 28 s	Gru		10.0	F, pS, com, N = 12m
5265 I	Gx	22 57.2	− 36 28 c	Gru	6.0		B, cL, R, bet 2 st pf, nf of 2; = IC 1459
5267 I	Gx	22 57.2	− 43 24 s	Gru	5.0	10.5	pB, S, R, mbM
7424	Gx	22 57.3	− 41 04 s	Gru	7.6	11p	F, cL, vlE, vgmbM
7425	Gx	22 57.3	− 10 57 r	Aqr		15p	eF, vlE, *10 p 4′
7428	Gx	22 57.3	− 1 02 s	Psc	2.6	14p	F, vS, R, bM
7430	Gx	22 57.5	+ 8 48 r	Peg		15p	eF, vS
7438	−	22 57.6	+ 54 21 r	Cas			Cl, vL, E
5269 I	Gx	22 57.7	− 36 02 s	PsA	2.5	13p	vF, pS, R, np of 2
7417	Gx	22 57.8	− 65 02 v	Tuc			pB, cS, R, gpmbM
7431	Gx	22 57.8	+ 26 10 r	Peg		15p	eF, vS
7435	Gx	22 57.9	+ 26 08 r	Peg		15p	eF, s of 7436
5270 I	Gx	22 57.9	− 35 51 c	PsA	3.2		vF, pS, mE, sf of 2
7432	Gx	22 58.0	+ 13 08 r	Peg		15p	eF, S, R
7433	Gx	22 58.0	+ 26 09 r	Peg		14p	eF, vS, p 7436
7436	Gx	22 58.0	+ 26 09 r	Peg		14p	F, pS, F* att p, gbM
5271 I	Gx	22 58.0	− 33 45 s	PsA		13p	pF, pS, mE 145°, cbM
7437	Gx	22 58.2	+ 14 18 s	Peg	1.9	13p	eeF, L, R, F* nr nf, v diffic
5263 I	Gx	22 58.2	− 69 03 c	Ind	1.2		cF, S, R, * in neb
5266 I	OC	22 58.3	− 65 08 c	Tuc	1.5		eF, vS, eE, stell N
7434	Gx	22 58.4	− 1 11 r	Psc		15p	vF, vS, R, stellar
7440	Gx	22 58.5	+ 35 48 s	And	1.9	15p	eF, S, iR
5274 I	Gx	22 58.5	+ 18 55 u	Peg	1.1	15p	F, cS, R, gbMN
1461 I	Gx	22 58.6	+ 15 10 v	Peg			eeF, vS, R
1462 I		22 58.6	+ 8 24 d	Peg			vF, eS; only a *?
5275 I		22 58.6	+ 18 52 d	Peg			pF, vS, dif

NGC	Type	α_{2000}	δ_{2000}		Const.	Size	Mag.	Description
		h m	o ′			′		
7439		22 58.7	+ 29 10	D	Peg			long patch of F neby
5276 I	Gx	22 58.7	+ 18 49	z	Peg		15p	F, S, E 135°, gbM, r, bet 2 F st
1463 I	D*	22 59.3	− 10 32	F	Aqr			only a F D*, dist 20″, in a trapez of st 10
7442	Gx	22 59.4	+ 15 33	s	Peg	1.2	14p	pF, R, bet 2 st 16, *13 nf
7441	Gx	22 59.5	− 7 04	r	Aqr		15p	vF, pS, iR, *10 p; (decl?)
7445	Gx	22 59.5	+ 39 06	r	And		15p	eF, vS
5273 I	Gx	22 59.5	− 37 42	s	Gru	2.9	11.5	vF, cL, lE, 4 st p
7446	Gx	22 59.6	+ 39 04	r	And		15p	eF, vS, R, r
5272 I		22 59.6	− 65 11	d	Tuc			eF, vS, R
7449	Gx	22 59.7	+ 39 08	r	And		15p	vF, S, R, vS* in centre
7443	Gx	23 00.1	− 12 48	s	Aqr	1.8	14p	F, vS, vlE, smbM, er, n of 2
7444	Gx	23 00.1	− 12 50	s	Aqr	2.0	14p	F, vS, vlE, smbM, er, s of 2
7448	Gx	23 00.1	+ 15 59	s	Peg	2.7	11.7	pB, L, E 173°, vgbM, *11 f 2′.5
7447		23 00.4	− 10 32	D	Aqr			nonexistent; only a F*′* np place
7451		23 00.4	+ 8 25	D	Peg			pF, pL, *10-11 sp 2′
7455	Gx	23 00.6	+ 7 17	v	Psc			eF, pS, cE, *10 nf 2′
5278 I		23 00.6	− 8 08	d	Aqr			eF (not verified)
7450	Gx	23 00.9	− 12 56	r	Aqr		13p	vF, S
7457	Gx	23 01.0	+ 30 09	s	Peg	4.4	10.8	cB, cL, lE, gmbM, r, 2 S st n
7452	Gx	23 01.1	+ 6 45	r	Psc		15p	eeF, pL, R, v diffic
7454	Gx	23 01.1	+ 16 23	s	Peg	2.0	14p	F, cS, lE, lbM, *11 p 1′
7453	*′*	23 01.4	− 6 21	A	Aqr			B, vS, *11 close np
7458	Gx	23 01.5	+ 1 45	r	Psc		14p	cF, cS, psbM
7459	−	23 01.7	+ 6 44	r	Psc			eeF, pL, R, * nr
7461	Gx	23 01.7	+ 15 35	r	Peg		14p	vF, vS, alm stellar
7460	Gx	23 01.8	+ 2 16	s	Psc	1.3	14p	eF, pL, R
7463	Gx	23 01.9	+ 15 59	s	Peg	3.0	13p	vF, S, lE, p of 2
7464	Gx	23 01.9	+ 15 58	s	Peg	0.7	14p	vF, vS, E, sf 7463
5277 I		23 01.9	− 65 12	d	Tuc			vF, S, R, almost a *; susp
7465	Gx	23 02.0	+ 15 58	s	Peg	1.6	13p	vF, vS, f of 2
7466	Gx	23 02.0	+ 27 03	r	Peg		14p	eF, eS, bM; = IC 5281
7456	Gx	23 02.1	− 39 35	s	Gru	5.9	12p	vF, L, mE 34°, vglbM
7467	Gx	23 02.3	+ 15 33	r	Peg		15p	eF, vS
5281 I		23 02.4	+ 27 02	d	Peg			eF, stell, *13 sff 2′.5
5282 I	Gx	23 02.7	+ 21 53	u	Peg	1.5	15p	F, cS, iF, vlbM
7462	Gx	23 02.8	− 40 50	s	Gru	3.7	13p	cF, pS, vmE 5°±, *11 np
1465 I	OC	23 02.9	+ 16 35	x	Peg			vF; vS Cl?
7468	Gx	23 03.0	+ 16 36	s	Peg	1.1	14p	eF, vS
5279 I	Gx	23 03.0	− 69 13	c	Ind	1.8		vF, vS, cE 40°, stell N
1464 I		23 03.2	− 9 00	d	Aqr			F, r, D?
7469	Gx	23 03.3	+ 8 52	s	Peg	1.8	11.9	vF, vS, vsmbM *12
5283 I	Gx	23 03.3	+ 8 54	s	Peg	0.9	13.8	F, S, R, 7469 p 2ˢ, 1′ s
1466 I		23 03.7	− 2 46	d	Psc			pB, vS, iF
5280 I	Gx	23 03.8	− 65 13	c	Tuc	1.7		eF, vS, eE 5°, stell N, bet 2 st; susp
7471	−	23 03.9	− 22 55	r	Aqr			eF, vS, lE 85°, sbM, 3 st 10 p 20ˢ
7473	Gx	23 03.9	+ 30 10	r	Peg		15p	vF, S, R
7474	Gx	23 04.0	+ 20 02	r	Peg		15p	eF, vS
7475	Gx	23 04.1	+ 20 03	r	Peg		15p	vF, S
7478	Gx	23 04.9	+ 2 35	r	Psc			eF, E
7479	Gx	23 04.9	+ 12 19	s	Peg	4.1	11.0	pB, cL, mE 12°, bet 2 st
1467 I	Gx	23 04.9	− 3 13	m	Psc	0.7	15p	F, S, biN
7470	Gx	23 05.2	− 50 07	c	Gru	1.5		eF, pL, R, glbM, *11 np
7476	Gx	23 05.2	− 43 07	r	Gru			F, S, R, △ with 2 st 7
1468 I	Gx	23 05.2	− 3 11	m	Psc	0.6	15p	vF, vS, iF, sbM
1470 I	Nb	23 05.2	+ 60 15	s	Cep	15		vF, vS, stellar N north edge

NGC	Type	α_{2000}	δ_{2000}	Const.	Size	Mag.	Description
		h m	° ′		′		
7480	Gx	23 05.3	+ 2 32 r	Psc		15p	vF, vS, vlE, vgbM
7472		23 05.7	+ 3 04 D	Psc			F neb*; = 7482
7477		23 05.7	+ 3 04 D	Psc			F, S, bM *15, *17 att n; = 7482
7482	Gx	23 05.7	+ 3 03 r	Psc		14p	F, vS, stellar
7481	−	23 05.8	− 19 57 r	Aqr			vF, vS, R, gbM
7483	Gx	23 05.9	+ 3 32 r	Psc		14p	vF, S, E, psbM
7485	Gx	23 06.1	+ 34 06 r	Peg		14p	vF, S, R, bM, *10 p
7486	Gx	23 06.2	+ 34 04 r	Peg			vF, vS, 2′ f 7485
1469 I		23 06.5	− 13 32 d	Aqr			F, S, R, F* f
5284 I	Gx	23 06.8	+ 19 07 v	Peg	1.3		F, cS, R, N
7487	Gx	23 06.9	+ 28 11 r	Peg		15p	vF, S, R
5285 I	Gx	23 06.9	+ 22 56 v	Peg	1.9		F, vS, R, *9.4 s 1′.5
7484	Gx	23 07.1	− 36 16 r	Scl			pB, S, R, lbM, *8-9 att s
7489	Gx	23 07.4	+ 23 00 r	Peg		14p	F, S, R
7490	Gx	23 07.4	+ 32 22 r	Peg		13p	vF, vS, iR, lbM
7488	Gx	23 07.9	+ 0 56 r	Psc		15p	vF, vS, stellar
7491	Gx	23 08.1	− 5 58 r	Aqr		14p	vF, S, R, vlbM
7492	Gb	23 08.4	− 15 37 s	Aqr	6.2	11.5	eF, L, Cl of eF st
7493	*	23 08.6	+ 0 54 F	Psc			vF, stellar
1471 I	Gx	23 08.7	− 12 39 m	Aqr	0.7	14p	pB, S, R, bM
7494	Gx	23 08.9	− 24 22 r	Aqr		15p	eF, vS, stellar
7495	Gx	23 09.0	+ 12 04 s	Peg	2.1	15p	eF, S, lE, *9 nf nr
7497	Gx	23 09.1	+ 18 11 s	Peg	5.0	13p	vF, L, pmE 45°, lbM
1472 I	Gx	23 09.2	+ 17 14 m	Peg	0.9	15p	F, vS, bM, 2 st f
5287 I	Gx	23 09.4	+ 0 45 u	Psc	1.1	15p	F, vS, R, vlbM
7496	Gx	23 09.8	− 43 26 s	Gru	3.5	11.1	pB, cL, lE, vgbM *13
7498	Gx	23 09.8	− 24 25 r	Aqr		15p	vF, S, iR
5286 I		23 09.8	− 68 16 d	Ind			eeF, eS, mE 130°, 2 st s, susp
7499	Gx	23 10.4	+ 7 35 s	Psc	1.4	13.8	vF, vS, stellar
7501	Gx	23 10.5	+ 7 35 s	Psc	0.8	13.8	eF
7500	Gx	23 10.6	+ 11 01 r	Peg		15p	eF, vS, R
7504	*	23 10.6	+ 14 24 r	Peg			vF, S, stellar
7503	Gx	23 10.7	+ 7 34 s	Psc	0.9	13.8	vF, S, stellar
7502	D*	23 10.8	− 21 46 r	Aqr			eF, vS, E 290°; F D*?
5289 I		23 10.9	− 32 33 d	Scl			S Cl, st eF, in neb
1473 I	Gx	23 11.1	+ 29 38 u	Peg	2.1	14p	F, pS, gbM
7505	Gx	23 11.2	+ 13 37 r	Peg		15p	eeF, eS, lE, bet a B & 2 F st
7510	OC	23 11.5	+ 60 34 s	Cep	4	7.9	Cl, pRi, pC, fan-sh, st pB
5288 I	Gx	23 11.7	− 68 06 c	Ind	1.8		eF, eS, alm *, susp
7506	Gx	23 11.8	− 2 10 r	Psc		14p	cF, vS, R, sbM *15
7508	Gx	23 11.9	+ 12 58 r	Peg		15p	eF, bM*, *11 np 2′
7507	Gx	23 12.1	− 28 32 s	Scl	2.6	10.4	pB, cS, R, psvmbM, *10 np
7512	Gx	23 12.3	+ 31 08 r	Peg		14p	F, S, R, vS* in centre
7509	Gx	23 12.4	+ 14 37 r	Peg		15p	vF, S, R, bet 2 st
7514	Gx	23 12.4	+ 34 53 r	Peg		13p	eF, pL, iR
7511	Gx	23 12.5	+ 13 43 r	Peg		15p	eeF, S, R, v diffic, sev st nf
7519		23 12.7	+ 10 47 D	Peg			vF, pL
7516	Gx	23 12.8	+ 20 14 r	Peg		14p	F, vS, stellar
1474 I	Gx	23 12.8	+ 5 47 u	Psc	1.1	15p	F, R, pS, gbM
7515	Gx	23 12.9	+ 12 41 r	Peg		14p	F, cS, R, vglbM, r
5290 I	Gx	23 12.9	− 23 28 c	Aqr	1.8		vF, S, stell N
7518	Gx	23 13.1	+ 6 19 s	Psc	1.5	14p	vF, S, R
7513	Gx	23 13.2	− 28 22 s	Scl	3.2	11.8	vF, pL, E, gbM
7517	Gx	23 13.3	− 2 07 r	Psc		15p	vF, vS, stellar
7538	Nb	23 13.5	+ 61 31 s	Cep	10		vF, L, 2 pB st inv

NGC	Type	α_{2000}	δ_{2000}	Const.	Size	Mag.	Description
		h m	o '		'		
7527	Gx	23 13.6	+ 24 54 *r*	Peg		14*p*	vF, vS, stellar
7520	–	23 13.7	– 23 48 *r*	Aqr			F, pS, bet 2 st; nonexistent?
7521	Gx	23 13.7	– 1 44 *r*	Psc		15*p*	vF, pS, psbM
7523	Gx	23 13.7	+ 14 00 *r*	Peg		15*p*	eeF, E
7525	Gx	23 13.7	+ 14 01 *s*	Peg		15*p*	eF, vS, vlE, gbM
5291 I	Gx	23 13.7	+ 9 13 *z*	Peg		16*p*	F, vS, R, N, stell
7522	–	23 13.8	– 22 54 *r*	Aqr			eF, vS, iR, *10 nff 3'; nonexistent?
7524	Gx	23 13.8	– 1 45 *r*	Psc			eF, vS
5292 I	Gx	23 13.8	+ 13 41 *z*	Peg		15*p*	vF, S, slbM
7526	Ast	23 13.9	– 9 12 *F*	Aqr			eF, vS
1475 I		23 14.0	– 28 25 *d*	Scl			neb *
7529	Gx	23 14.1	+ 8 58 *r*	Peg		14*p*	vF
7528	Gx	23 14.3	+ 10 13 *r*	Peg			F, S
7530	Gx	23 14.3	– 2 45 *r*	Psc		15*p*	eF, vS, alm stellar
7535	Gx	23 14.3	+ 13 35 *r*	Peg		15*p*	eeF, pS, R, v diffic, n of 2
7536	Gx	23 14.3	+ 13 26 *r*	Peg		15*p*	eeF, pS, R, am 6 st, s of 2
7532	Gx	23 14.4	– 2 42 *s*	Psc	1.8	15*p*	vF, vS, lE
7533	Gx	23 14.4	– 2 01 *r*	Psc		15*p*	F, S, R
7539	Gx	23 14.4	+ 23 40 *r*	Peg		13*p*	F, S, R, psbM
7534	Gx	23 14.5	– 2 39 *r*	Psc		14*p*	eF, vS, lE
7540	Gx	23 14.5	+ 15 56 *r*	Peg		15*p*	F, vS, stellar
7537	Gx	23 14.6	+ 4 30 *s*	Psc	2.3	13.2	vF, cS, R, bM, sp of 2
7543	Gx	23 14.6	+ 28 19 *r*	Peg		14*p*	vF, S, R, lbM
7551	Gx	23 14.6	+ 15 55 *r*	Peg			neb* 13m
7541	Gx	23 14.7	+ 4 32 *s*	Psc	3.5	11.7	B, L, mE 97°, mbM, nf of 2
5293 I	Gx	23 14.7	+ 25 08 *z*	Peg		16*p*	F, S, like D* in neb
7531	Gx	23 14.8	– 43 36 *s*	Gru	3.5	11.3	pB, S, lE, pgbM
7542	Gx	23 14.8	+ 10 39 *r*	Peg		15*p*	eF, eS, stellar
7544	Gx	23 15.0	– 2 12 *r*	Psc			eF, vS
7547	Gx	23 15.0	+ 18 58 *s*	Peg	1.3	15*p*	vF, S, iR
7548	Gx	23 15.1	+ 25 16 *r*	Peg		14*p*	vF, vS, *16 p 11^s
7546	Gx	23 15.2	– 2 18 *r*	Psc		14*p*	eF, S, lE
7549	Gx	23 15.3	+ 19 02 *s*	Peg	2.9	14*p*	pF, pS, R, *10-11 p
7550	Gx	23 15.3	+ 18 57 *s*	Peg	1.7	14*p*	cF, S, R
7553	Gx	23 15.3	+ 19 01 *r*	Peg			vF, vS, R
1476 I	OC	23 15.3	+ 30 33 *x*	Peg			S Cl?
7545	Gx	23 15.5	– 38 32 *r*	Gru			F, S, vlE, vgvlbM, *10 att
5295 I	Gx	23 15.5	+ 25 07 *z*	Peg		16*p*	F, vS, R, N
7555	–	23 15.6	+ 12 35 *r*	Peg			F, R, bM, place very rough
7558	Gx	23 15.6	+ 18 55 *r*	Peg		16*p*	eeF, neb* 13m
7564	Gx	23 15.6	+ 7 17 *v*	Psc			vF, eS, stellar N
7554	Gx	23 15.7	– 2 23 *r*	Psc			eF, eS, alm stell, 7556 f
7557	Gx	23 15.7	+ 6 41 *r*	Psc		15*p*	vF, vS, p of 2
5296 I	Gx	23 15.7	+ 25 06 *u*	Peg	1.0	15*p*	F, S, R, *15 att
7556	Gx	23 15.9	– 2 20 *r*	Psc		14*p*	cF, pL, R, B$^*_*$ f
7559	Gx	23 15.9	+ 13 17 *r*	Peg		14*p*	F, cS, R, bM *16, np of 2
7560	D*	23 16.0	+ 4 30 *r*	Psc			F, vS, iR, sp of 2
7561		23 16.0	+ 4 31 *D*	Psc			eF, stellar, nf of 2
7562	Gx	23 16.0	+ 6 41 *s*	Psc	2.3	11.5	cB, pS, iR, psbM
7563	Gx	23 16.0	+ 13 11 *r*	Peg		14*p*	pF, cS, R, sbM *16, sf of 2
5297 I	Gx	23 16.0	+ 25 01 *z*	Peg		16*p*	F, S, R, N
5298 I	Gx	23 16.1	+ 25 33 *m*	Peg	0.6	15*p*	vF, vS, dif
7552	Gx	23 16.2	– 42 35 *s*	Gru	3.5	10.7	B, S, mE 90°±, vsbM *13
7567	Gx	23 16.2	+ 15 52 *r*	Peg		15*p*	eeF, vS, E
5294 I	Gx	23 16.2	– 42 35 *c*	Gru	3.2		pB, pS, R, *8 p; = 7552

NGC	Type	α_{2000}	δ_{2000}	Const.	Size	Mag.	Description
		h m	° ′		′		
7565	*	23 16.3	− 0 03 r	Psc			vF
7568	Gx	23 16.3	+ 24 29 r	Peg		14p	eF, pL, iR, sev st inv
7573	Gx	23 16.3	− 22 10 r	Aqr		14p	eF, S, iR, b np, *10 p 4′
5299 I		23 16.3	+ 20 51 d	Peg			F, eS, *13 close s
7566		23 16.6	− 2 21 D	Psc			vF, pS, E, er, 3 F st inv
5300 I	Gx	23 16.6	+ 20 49 z	Peg		16p	F, S, R, neb *15
7569	−	23 16.8	+ 10 55 r	Peg			vF, S, R, 3 F st sf
7570	Gx	23 16.8	+ 13 29 r	Peg		14p	eF, eS
7572	Gx	23 16.8	+ 18 29 r	Peg		15p	eeF, alm stellar
7574	−	23 16.8	+ 24 00 r	Peg			pF, S, E, rr
7571		23 17.2	+ 18 59 D	Peg			vF, cE, sev knots or gr of neb
7578	Gx	23 17.2	+ 18 41 s	Peg	1.6	14p	vF, am vS st
7596	Gx	23 17.2	− 6 55 r	Aqr			vF, pS, lE 0°, lbMN
1477 I	Gx	23 17.2	− 6 56 m	Aqr	0.6	15p	F, S, r
7575	*	23 17.3	+ 6 39 r	Psc			F, S, vlE
7576	Gx	23 17.4	− 4 44 s	Aqr	1.5	13.0	F, S, smbM
7577	Gx	23 17.4	+ 7 22 r	Psc			*13.5 in vF neb
7580	Gx	23 17.6	+ 14 00 s	Peg	0.9	15p	vF, pS, R, F* sp
7579	Gx	23 17.7	+ 9 25 r	Peg		15p	eF, vS, stellar
7586	Gx	23 17.7	+ 8 15 r	Peg		15p	eF, vS, alm stellar
7581	−	23 17.8	+ 4 40 r	Psc			vF, mE, *12-13 close f; = 7541?
7588	Gx	23 17.8	+ 18 45 r	Peg		15p	eF, eS
7583	Gx	23 17.9	+ 7 24 r	Psc		15p	vF, vS
7604	Gx	23 17.9	+ 7 26 r	Psc		15p	eF, vS, bM
5303 I	D*	23 17.9	+ 0 16 F	Psc			vF, S, sbM (D* in M?)
7584	Gx	23 18.0	+ 9 25 r	Peg		15p	eF, vS, stellar
7585	Gx	23 18.0	− 4 39 s	Aqr	2.3	11.7	pB, pS, iR, gbM
7587	Gx	23 18.0	+ 9 41 s	Peg	1.4	15p	vF, vS, lE, gbM
7593	Gx	23 18.0	+ 11 21 r	Peg		14p	F, S, R
5305 I	Gx	23 18.0	+ 10 16 m	Peg	0.4	15p	pF, vS, 7594 nr
5306 I		23 18.1	+ 10 15 d	Peg			vF, S
1478 I	Gx	23 18.2	+ 10 18 u	Peg	1.7	15p	vF, S, dif
5304 I		23 18.2	− 10 18 d	Aqr			eF, S, R, 3 or 4 F st sp
5307 I	Gx	23 18.2	+ 10 13 m	Peg	0.6	16p	vF, vS
7594	Gx	23 18.3	+ 10 13 r	Peg		16p	pF, R, 3 st p; = IC 5307
7582	Gx	23 18.4	− 42 22 s	Gru	4.6	10.6	pB, L, pmE, gbM
7589	Gx	23 18.4	+ 0 16 r	Psc		15p	eF, vS
7591	Gx	23 18.4	+ 6 34 r	Psc		14p	pF, S, R, vgbM
7592	Gx	23 18.4	− 4 25 s	Aqr	1.4	14p	eF, vS
7595	Gx	23 18.5	+ 9 54 r	Peg			F, stellar
7597	Gx	23 18.5	+ 18 41 v	Peg	1.3		eF, vS, gbM
7598	Gx	23 18.5	+ 18 44 r	Peg		15p	eF, eS, stellar
1479 I	Gx	23 18.7	− 10 25 m	Aqr	0.8	14p	pF, S, R, stellar
7601	Gx	23 18.8	+ 9 14 s	Peg	1.5	15p	pB, dif
7602	Gx	23 18.8	+ 18 42 v	Peg	0.6		eF, eS, stellar
5301 I		23 18.8	− 69 34 d	Ind			eeF, eS, vF, * f 1′, susp
7590	Gx	23 18.9	− 42 14 s	Gru	2.7	11.6	pB, pL, pmE, gbM, p of 2
7600	Gx	23 18.9	− 7 35 s	Aqr	2.4	13p	cF, S, R, psmbM
7605	−	23 18.9	+ 7 25 r	Psc			vF, S, R, glbM; = 7583?
7603	Gx	23 19.0	+ 0 15 s	Psc	1.7	14p	F, vS, stellar
7607	−	23 19.0	+ 11 21 r	Peg			vF, S, R, *16 nf 0′.5 (nebs?)
1480 I	OC	23 19.0	+ 11 19 z	Peg			vS Cl, nebs?
7606	Gx	23 19.1	− 8 29 s	Aqr	5.8	10.8	pF, cL, pmE 0°±
5309 I		23 19.2	+ 7 59 d	Psc			F, S, fan-shaped, * att s
7599	Gx	23 19.3	− 42 15 s	Gru	4.4	11.4	F, pL, pmE, gbM, f of 2

NGC	Type	α_{2000}	δ_{2000}	Const.	Size	Mag.	Description
		h m	o $'$		$'$		
7608	Gx	23 19.3	+ 8 20 r	Peg		15p	vF, pS, lE, lbM
5308 I	Gx	23 19.3	− 42 16 t	Gru	4.9	12p	eeF, S, cE, f 7599
1481 I	Gx	23 19.4	+ 5 54 u	Psc	0.9	14p	vF, vS, R
7609	Gx	23 19.5	+ 9 29 s	Peg	1.5	15p	vF, vS, gbM
7616	Gx	23 19.5	+10 09 r	Peg			pF, dif
7610	Gx	23 19.6	+10 10 s	Peg	3.0	15p	F, S, dif
7611	Gx	23 19.6	+ 8 04 s	Psc	1.5	12.6	F, S, R, △ with 2 st 19 n
5302 I	Gx	23 19.6	− 64 34 c	Tuc	1.3		vF, vS, 2 st nr, susp
7612	Gx	23 19.8	+ 8 33 r	Peg		14p	pB, vS, R, bM
7618	Gx	23 19.8	+42 51 r	And		14p	F, S, R, gbM
7613	Gx	23 19.9	+ 0 24 r	Psc			vF
7615	Gx	23 19.9	+ 8 24 s	Peg	1.2	16p	eF, cS
7614	−	23 20.0	+ 0 13 r	Psc			vF, nf of 2
7620	Gx	23 20.1	+24 13 s	Peg	1.3	14p	F, S, vlE
7617	Gx	23 20.2	+ 8 10 s	Psc	1.0	13.8	eF, vS
7619	Gx	23 20.2	+ 8 12 s	Peg	2.9	11.1	cB, pS, R, psbM
7621	Gx	23 20.4	+ 8 20 r	Peg		15p	eF, vS, stellar
7624	Gx	23 20.4	+27 19 s	Peg	1.1	13.4	vF, lE or iR, dif, vlbM
7623	Gx	23 20.5	+ 8 24 s	Peg	1.9	12.4	F, vS, R, psbM
7625	Gx	23 20.5	+17 14 s	Peg	1.8	12.1	pB, cS, R, smbM
5311 I	*	23 20.6	+17 16 x	Peg			eF, susp, 2$'$.5 nff 7625
7626	Gx	23 20.7	+ 8 13 s	Peg	2.5	11.2	cB, pS, R, psbM
7635	Nb	23 20.7	+61 12 s	Cas	15		vF, *8 inv l excentric
7628	Gx	23 20.8	+25 53 r	Peg		14p	vF, S, R, bM
1482 I	Gx	23 20.8	+ 1 44 m	Psc	0.3	14p	pB, vS, R
5310 I		23 20.8	− 22 09 d	Aqr			eF, eS, alm stell, *9.5 n 5$'$
5312 I		23 21.0	+19 19 d	Peg			F, S, R, gbM, r
5314 I	Gx	23 21.1	+19 17 m	Peg	0.5	15p	F, S, R, gbM, r
5315 I	Gx	23 21.3	+25 22 u	Peg	1.0	15p	F, vS, like neb D* 15
7629	Gx	23 21.4	+ 1 23 r	Psc		15p	vF, vS, stellar
7630	Gx	23 21.4	+11 24 r	Peg		15p	F, S
7631	Gx	23 21.4	+ 8 13 s	Peg	1.9	14p	vF, vS
7622	?	23 21.6	− 62 07 A	Tuc			cF, eS, am 5 st (doubtful)
7634	Gx	23 21.6	+ 8 52 s	Peg	1.5	14p	F, S, F$^*_*$ att
5316 I		23 21.9	+21 13 d	Peg			vF, vS, R, N, stell
5313 I	Gx	23 22.0	− 42 29 c	Gru	2.5		eeF, pL, R, *10 sp; = 7632
7632	Gx	23 22.1	− 42 30 v	Gru			F, S, R, lbM
7640	Gx	23 22.1	+40 51 s	And	10.7	10.9	cF, L, mE 164°, vlbM, r
7636	Gx	23 22.3	− 29 18 r	Scl		15p	eF, S, sbM
1483 I	Gx	23 22.4	+11 18 m	Peg	0.6	15p	F, S, lbM
7627		23 22.5	+11 54 D	Peg			vF, S, mE, 2 st n; = 7641
7638	Gx	23 22.5	+11 18 r	Peg		15p	1st of 2 neb, F, S
7641	Gx	23 22.6	+11 53 r	Peg		15p	vF, S, iR, dif, lbM
1484 I		23 22.7	+11 23 d	Peg			vF, vS
1485 I	Gx	23 22.7	+11 21 m	Peg	0.3	15p	vF, vS, R, vSN
7639	Gx	23 22.8	+11 21 r	Peg		15p	2nd of 2 neb, F, S
7642	Gx	23 22.9	+ 1 26 r	Psc		14p	vF, vS, bM
7643	Gx	23 22.9	+11 59 r	Peg		15p	F, pS, iR, dif, lbM
7633	Gx	23 23.1	− 67 39 c	Ind	2.1		F, vS, E 90°, psbM
5317 I	Gx	23 23.4	+21 09 z	Peg		15p	F, S, R, gbMN, r
7645	Gx	23 23.7	− 29 23 r	Scl		14p	vF, S, R, glbM
7648	Gx	23 23.8	+ 9 39 s	Peg	1.9	14p	vF, pS, lE, bM; = IC 1486
1486 I	Gx	23 23.8	+ 9 39 u	Peg	1.6	13p	vF, S
7646	Gx	23 24.0	− 11 52 r	Aqr			vF, vS, E 260°(neb?), *9 n 3$'$.6
5318 I	Gx	23 24.0	− 11 53 m	Aqr	0.9	14p	vF, vS, *9.5 p 1^s

NGC	Type	α_{2000}	δ_{2000}	Const.	Size	Mag.	Description
		h m	° ′		′		
7647	Gx	23 24.1	+ 16 47 r	Peg		15p	eF, cL(?), p a row of st
7654	OC	23 24.2	+ 61 35 s	Cas	13	6.9	Cl, L, Ri, mCM, R, st 9...13; = M52
7649	Gx	23 24.3	+ 14 38 s	Peg	1.6	13.7	vF, pL, R
7667	Gx	23 24.3	− 0 07 r	Psc		14p	vF
7644	Gx	23 24.5	+ 13 58 r	Peg			vF, pS, lE
7651	Gx	23 24.5	+ 13 58 r	Peg		15p	eF, S, R
7656	Gx	23 24.5	− 19 05 r	Aqr		14p	vF, vS, R, bMN
1487 I		23 24.6	+ 14 38 D	Peg			eeF, pS, iR, F∗ nf, ∗7 p 15ˢand 9′ s
1488 I		23 24.8	+ 15 20 d	Peg			eF, vS, E ns, v diffic, 7653 s
5319 I		23 24.8	+ 14 00 d	Peg			eF, eS, ∗9.5 f, 7651 nr
7653	Gx	23 24.9	+ 15 16 r	Peg		14p	vF, pS, R, gbM; = IC 1488
7650	Gx	23 25.3	− 57 48 r	Tuc			pF, pS, R, glbM, np of 2
7652	Gx	23 25.6	− 57 54 r	Tuc			eF, S, R, sf of 2
7660	Gx	23 25.7	+ 27 01 r	Peg		14p	F, vS, psmbM, ∗10 p
7662	Pl	23 25.9	+ 42 33 s	And	2.2	9p	!!! ○ or ◎, vB, pS, R, blue, variable Nucl
7659	Gx	23 26.0	+ 14 12 r	Peg		15p	vF, vS, R, psbM
5321 I	Gx	23 26.3	− 17 58 m	Aqr	1.0	14p	eF, vS, R, ∗10 np 1′
7637	Gx	23 26.5	− 81 55 c	Oct	2.5		vF, pL, R, vlbM, ∗ nr
7658	Gx	23 26.5	− 39 14 r	Gru			D, both eF, S, R, 4 st p
1489 I	Gx	23 26.5	− 12 31 m	Aqr	0.4	14p	F, vS, vS, ∗9 south
7664	Gx	23 26.6	+ 25 04 r	Peg		13p	vF, ∗ s, 2 st 11-12 p
7655	Gx	23 26.7	− 68 02 A	Ind			group of st (not a neb), ∗10 p
7657	Gx	23 26.7	− 57 49 r	Tuc			eF, R
7663	Gx	23 26.7	− 4 56 r	Aqr			vF
7661	Gx	23 27.2	− 65 16 c	Tuc	1.9		eF, cL, R, vgvlbM
7665	Gx	23 27.2	− 9 24 r	Aqr		13p	eF, S, stellar
7668	−	23 27.2	− 0 11 r	Psc			vF, near 7667
7669	−	23 27.2	− 0 11 r	Psc			vF, near 7667
7670	−	23 27.2	− 0 11 r	Psc			vF, near 7667
7671	Gx	23 27.3	+ 12 28 s	Peg	1.7	12.7	pB, S, R, vsmbM, ∗9 p
7666	−	23 27.4	− 4 11 r	Aqr			vF
5320 I		23 27.4	− 67 45 d	Ind			bM, mag 14
7672	Gx	23 27.5	+ 12 23 s	Peg	1.0	15p	vF, S, 5′ s of 7671
5322 I		23 27.5	− 67 45 d	Tuc			bM, mag 14
5323 I	Gx	23 27.6	− 67 49 c	Tuc	1.6		F, S, bM
7673	Gx	23 27.7	+ 23 35 s	Peg	1.7	12.7	F, S, R
7674	Gx	23 27.9	+ 8 47 s	Peg	1.2	14p	F, cS, gbM, p of 2
7675	Gx	23 28.0	+ 8 46 s	Peg	0.7	15p	vF, S, R, gbM, f of 2
7677	Gx	23 28.1	+ 23 32 s	Peg	1.9	14p	eF, vS, stell
5324 I	Gx	23 28.3	− 67 49 c	Tuc	1.3		F, S, bM
7678	Gx	23 28.5	+ 22 25 s	Peg	2.3	12.2	vF, pL, vlE, lbM, am 4 st
7680	Gx	23 28.5	+ 32 24 r	Peg		13p	vF, S, R, lbM, r
7681	Gx	23 28.6	+ 17 16 r	Peg		15p	vF, S, iR, r, ⁎ f
5325 I	Gx	23 28.7	− 41 19 s	Phe	2.5	12p	F, S, R, gbM, ∗ sp 1′
7679	Gx	23 28.8	+ 3 31 s	Psc	1.9	12.7	pB, S, R, mbMN, stell
1497 I		23 28.8	+ 11 59 D	Peg			eF, suspected
7676	Gx	23 28.9	− 59 43 r	Tuc			B, S, lE, vsvmbM ∗11
1490 I		23 29.0	− 4 08 d	Aqr			eF, pS, R, vF∗ close n
7682	Gx	23 29.1	+ 3 32 s	Psc	1.2	13.4	eF, ∗14 p 13ˢ.7, ln
7683	Gx	23 29.1	+ 11 26 r	Peg		14p	F, ∗13 n
1491 I	Gx	23 29.4	− 16 18 m	Aqr	0.5	15p	F, S, R
5326 I	Gx	23 29.5	− 28 48 m	Scl	0.8	14p	eeF, S, mE, ∗8 p
7686	OC	23 30.2	+ 49 08 s	And	15	5.6	Cl, P, lC, st 7...11
5327 I		23 30.3	− 13 35 d	Aqr			pF, pS, ∗11 f 1′
7684	Gx	23 30.5	+ 0 04 r	Psc		15p	F, vS, stell

NGC	Type	α_{2000}	δ_{2000}	Const.	Size	Mag.	Description
		h m	° ′			′	
1493 I		23 30.5	+ 14 27 d	Peg			F, vS, sbM, another susp 7^{s}p, 1′ n
7685	Gx	23 30.6	+ 3 54 s	Psc	2.1	15p	eF, cL, R, gbM, $^*_*$ nr
1492 I	Gx	23 30.7	− 3 02 m	Psc	0.8	14p	eF, S, R, sp of 2
1496 I		23 30.7	− 2 57 d	Psc			eeF, pS, R, nf of 2
1494 I		23 30.8	− 12 44 d	Aqr			F, R, lbM
1495 I	Gx	23 30.8	− 13 30 m	Aqr	1.0	13p	F, S, lbM
7687	Gx	23 30.9	+ 3 32 r	Psc		15p	vF, vS, *11 f 1^s, n 85″
7688	Gx	23 31.2	+ 21 24 r	Peg		15p	F, vS, dif, *11 201°, 80″
1498 I	Gx	23 32.0	− 5 00 m	Aqr	1.4	14p	eeF, pS, R, *9.5 p 36^s, 3′ s
1499 I	D*	23 32.0	− 13 27 F	Aqr			pB, pL, iF
7691	Gx	23 32.6	+ 15 50 r	Peg		14p	eF, pL, △ with 2 st 10
7689	Gx	23 32.7	− 54 05 s	Phe	2.8	12p	pF, L, R, vgbM
7692	Gx	23 32.8	− 5 36 r	Aqr		15p	neb, *9 f 18^s, 73″ s
7690	Gx	23 32.9	− 51 41 s	Phe	2.8	13p	cB, S, lE, psbM, *8 f
5328 I	Gx	23 33.2	− 45 02 s	Phe	2.5	12p	vF, S, R, bet 2 st
7693	Gx	23 33.3	− 1 17 r	Psc		14p	S neb or neb* 14
7695	−	23 33.3	− 2 43 r	Psc			eF, stell (nr 7694)
1500 I	Gx	23 33.3	+ 4 34 z	Psc		15p	F, vS, E ns, lbM
5329 I	Gx	23 33.3	+ 21 14 u	Peg	1.8	16p	vF, S, E 250°
7694	Gx	23 33.4	− 2 42 r	Psc		14p	eF, pL, stellar
5330 I		23 33.5	− 2 52 d	Psc			vF, S, bM, others nr
5331 I	Gx	23 33.5	+ 21 08 u	Peg	1.1	15p	F, S, fan, gbM
7696	Gx	23 33.9	+ 4 53 r	Psc		15p	F, S, lE
7698	Gx	23 34.0	+ 24 56 r	Peg		14p	vF, eS, R, bMSN
7708	−	23 34.3	+ 72 55 r	Cep			Cl, L, P, lC, st 8, 10...15
7699	Gx	23 34.4	− 2 54 r	Psc			eF, vS
5332 I	Gx	23 34.5	− 36 06 s	Scl	6.6	10.6	eeF, vL, bet 2 st, D* p 45^s
7700	Gx	23 34.6	− 2 57 r	Psc		14p	vF, eS, stellar
7701	Gx	23 34.6	− 2 51 r	Psc		14p	vF, S, R, mbM, *11 sp
5334 I	Gx	23 34.7	− 4 31 m	Aqr	1.5	14p	neb *10.5 (close D*?)
7707	Gx	23 34.8	+ 44 18 r	And		15p	eF, S, R, *9-10 p vnr
1501 I	Gx	23 34.8	− 3 08 m	Psc	1.0	14p	vF, S, dif
7697	Gx	23 34.9	− 65 24 A	Tuc			eeF, pL (certain)
7703	Gx	23 34.9	+ 16 04 r	Peg		15p	vF, vS, gbM, *14 nf 1′
5333 I	Gx	23 34.9	− 65 24 c	Tuc	1.5		cB, S, dif, susp; = 7697
7704	Gx	23 35.2	+ 4 54 r	Psc		15p	eF, *12 p, sp of 2
7705	Gx	23 35.2	+ 4 48 r	Psc		15p	eF
7706	Gx	23 35.3	+ 4 59 r	Psc		14p	vF, pS, *18 close s, nf of 2
7702	Gx	23 35.4	− 56 00 s	Phe	1.9	12.2	B, cS, E, g, sbM, *8-9 p
7709	Gx	23 35.4	− 16 42 r	Aqr		13p	pF, S, R, lbM
7711	Gx	23 35.7	+ 15 18 r	Peg		14p	F, S, R, psbM, stellar
7710	Gx	23 35.8	− 2 53 r	Psc		15p	pF, vS, stellar
5335 I	Gx	23 35.8	− 67 24 c	Tuc	1.3		F, S, susp
7712	Gx	23 35.9	+ 23 36 r	Peg		13p	vF
7714	Gx	23 36.2	+ 2 09 s	Psc	2.1	13p	pB, S, R, psbM, *12 sp, *6 sf
1502 I	Gx	23 36.2	+ 75 40 u	Cep	1.3	15p	vF, S, vF* close
5336 I		23 36.3	+ 21 05 d	Peg			F, S, E ns, vlbM
7715	Gx	23 36.4	+ 2 09 s	Psc	2.6	15p	eF, pL, R
5337 I	Gx	23 36.4	+ 21 09 v	Peg	0.9		F, S, R, gbMN
7713	Gx	23 36.5	− 37 56 s	Scl	4.3	12p	pB, L, E, vgbM
7716	Gx	23 36.5	+ 0 18 s	Psc	2.3	12.2	F, pL, lE, gbM, *10 s
5338 I	Gx	23 36.5	+ 21 09 s	Peg	1.1	13.8	F, S, lE ns, gbMN
7717	Gx	23 37.7	− 15 07 r	Aqr		13p	vF, S
7719	Gx	23 38.0	− 22 58 r	Aqr			eF, vS, R
7718	Gx	23 38.1	+ 25 41 r	Peg		15p	vF, S, R

NGC	Type	α_{2000}	δ_{2000}	Const.	Size	Mag.	Description
		h m	o /		/		
5339 I	Gx	23 38.1	− 68 27 c	Tuc	1.2		bM
5341 I	Gx	23 38.4	+ 26 59 x	Peg			eF, eS, 7720 nr
7720	Gx	23 38.5	+ 27 02 s	Peg	1.9	12.6	F, S, lE, bM, am st
1503 I	Gx	23 38.5	+ 4 49 u	Psc	1.0	14p	F, S, R, gbM
5340 I		23 38.6	− 4 52 d	Aqr			eF, *13 n 1'.5
5342 I	Gx	23 38.6	+ 27 01 v	Peg	0.4		eF, eS, others nr
7726	Gx	23 38.7	+ 27 00 r	Peg		15p	eeF, pS, R, v diffic
7721	Gx	23 38.8	− 6 31 s	Aqr	3.4	11.8	pF, cL, E 12°±, vgbM
7722	Gx	23 38.8	+ 15 57 r	Peg		13p	pB, pL, R, mbM
7723	Gx	23 38.9	− 12 58 s	Aqr	3.6	11.1	cB, cL, E, gmbM, r
7724	Gx	23 39.1	− 12 14 r	Aqr		13p	eF, pL, iR
7725	Gx	23 39.3	− 4 32 F	Aqr		14p	eeF
5344 I		23 39.3	− 4 58 d	Aqr			vF, L, others nr
5343 I	Gx	23 39.4	− 22 31 m	Aqr	0.6	14p	eF, pS, *7.5 sf 19ˢ
5345 I	Gx	23 39.6	− 22 25 m	Aqr	0.5	14p	vF, vS, R, 6' n of IC 5343
7727	Gx	23 39.9	− 12 18 s	Aqr	4.2	10.7	pB, pL, iR, mbM
7728	Gx	23 40.0	+ 27 08 r	Peg		14p	vF, vS, lE, *10 sp
7729	Gx	23 40.6	+ 29 11 r	Peg		14p	vF, S, iE, F* inv s
5346 I	Gx	23 41.0	+ 24 57 z	Peg		16p	F, cS, R, gvlbM
1504 I	Gx	23 41.3	+ 4 02 u	Psc	1.9	14p	F, pL, E pf, gbM
7730	−	23 41.4	− 20 14 r	Aqr			pB, pL, E; nonexistent?
5347 I	Gx	23 41.5	+ 24 53 z	Peg		16p	vF, vS, R, sbM *15
7731	Gx	23 41.6	+ 3 45 s	Psc	1.7	14p	F, S
1505 I		23 41.6	− 3 34 D	Aqr			eeF, pS, R, 3 st f, diffic
7732	Gx	23 41.7	+ 3 44 s	Psc	2.0	15p	vF, pL
7735	Gx	23 42.3	+ 26 13 r	Peg		15p	vF, S, vlE, *13 nf, vnr
7736	Gx	23 42.4	− 19 27 r	Aqr		14p	eF, eS, gbM, bet 2 st 12
7733	Gx	23 42.6	− 65 57 c	Tuc	1.4		eF, S, R, p of 2
7734	Gx	23 42.7	− 65 57 c	Tuc	1.6		eF, cS, R, f of 2
7737	Gx	23 42.8	+ 27 03 r	Peg		15p	vF, S, mbMN
7740	Gx	23 43.3	+ 27 21 r	Peg		15p	vF, S, lbM, stellar
7739	−	23 43.6	+ 0 28 r	Psc			s of 2, vnr
7741	Gx	23 43.9	+ 26 05 s	Peg	4.0	11.4	cF, cL, iR, D* 10-12 np 2'
7738	Gx	23 44.1	+ 0 31 s	Psc	2.2	14p	vF, n of 2
7742	Gx	23 44.3	+ 10 46 s	Peg	2.0	11.5	cB, cS, gmbM, *12 f 72''
7743	Gx	23 44.4	+ 9 56 s	Peg	3.1	11.2	pF, S, R, *14 sf
7745	Gx	23 44.8	+ 25 53 r	Peg			eF
1506 I	Gx	23 44.8	+ 4 44 m	Psc	0.6	15p	vF, gbM
7744	Gx	23 45.0	− 42 55 s	Phe	2.3	13p	cB, S, vlE, svmbM *14
7748	−	23 45.0	+ 69 45 r	Cep			vL neby, surrounds *7
5348 I	Gx	23 45.0	− 42 55 c	Phe	1.9		eF, eS, R; = 7744
7746	Gx	23 45.4	− 1 41 r	Psc		14p	eF, pS, R, * nr s
7747	Gx	23 45.6	+ 27 22 r	Peg		14p	vF, vS, iR
1507 I	Gx	23 45.6	+ 1 42 u	Psc	1.4	15p	pB, iF, mbM
7749	Gx	23 45.9	− 29 33 r	Scl		14p	vF, S, R, gmbM, *12 f
1508 I	Gx	23 45.9	+ 12 04 v	Peg	2.0		F, pL, E ns
5349 I	Gx	23 46.3	− 28 00 m	Scl	0.6	15p	vF, vS, vmE 200°; neb D*?
7750	Gx	23 46.7	+ 3 47 s	Psc	1.8	14p	cF, pL, vlE 0°, lbM, *11 sf
7751	Gx	23 47.0	+ 6 51 r	Psc		14p	F, S, R, gbM, er
7752	Gx	23 47.0	+ 29 27 s	Peg	0.7	14p	F, S, lE, p 7753
7753	Gx	23 47.1	+ 29 29 s	Peg	3.4	13p	cF, cL, vlE, vglbM, r
1509 I	Gx	23 47.2	− 15 17 m	Aqr	1.3	15p	F, S, E ns, gbM
5350 I	Gx	23 47.2	− 27 58 m	Scl	0.3	15p	eeF, eS, R, *9 nr f
5355 I	Gx	23 47.2	+ 32 48 u	And	1.1	14p	F, pL, E ns, gbM
5351 I		23 47.3	− 2 18 d	Psc			cF, vS, bM, *10 sf 5'' ±

NGC	Type	α_{2000}	δ_{2000}	Const.	Size	Mag.	Description
		h m	o ′		′		
5352 I		23 47.4	− 2 16 d	Psc			pF, pS, gbM
5357 I		23 47.4	− 2 18 d	Psc			pB, R, mbM
5353 I	Gx	23 47.5	− 28 07 c	Scl	1.6		eF, S, R, *6 f
5354 I		23 47.5	− 28 08 d	Scl			eeF, S, R
5356 I	Gx	23 47.5	− 2 19 m	Psc	0.3	15p	pF, R, mbM
5358 I	Gx	23 47.7	− 28 08 c	Scl	2.6		eF, pS, biN 20″
5359 I	Gx	23 47.7	− 2 17 m	Psc	1.0	15p	F, pS, gbM, *9.5 p 2′
7755	Gx	23 47.9	− 30 31 s	Scl	3.7	12p	B, cL, R, psmbM
5360 I		23 47.9	− 37 04 d	Scl			eeF, cS, R
7756	*	23 48.5	+ 4 07 A	Psc			neb, 5′ sp 7757
7757	Gx	23 48.8	+ 4 10 s	Psc	2.6	14p	vF, cL, vlE, vglbM, 2 st 13 n
7758	Gx	23 48.9	− 22 03 r	Aqr			eF, vS, iR, sbM, D* 10 nf 50ˢ
7759	Gx	23 48.9	− 16 32 r	Aqr		14p	vF, S, R, lbM, B* n
7754	Gx	23 49.2	− 16 35 r	Aqr		15p	eF, vS
7760	Gx	23 49.3	+ 30 58 r	Peg		15p	cB, vS, R, psbM, *12 att
7761		23 49.6	− 13 23 D	Aqr		14p	F, vS, R, gbM, *10 p 8′; nonexistent?
7762	OC	23 49.8	+ 68 02 s	Cep	11	10p	Cl, pRi, pC, st 11...15
7763	Gx	23 50.3	− 16 37 r	Aqr			eF, vS, R, F* f
1510 I	Gx	23 50.7	+ 2 07 m	Psc	0.6	15p	F, S, R, biN
7765	Gx	23 50.8	+ 27 10 r	Peg		15p	vvF, 100″ np 7768
7764	Gx	23 50.9	− 40 44 s	Phe	1.5	12.3	B, pL, R, gbM
7766	Gx	23 50.9	+ 27 07 r	Peg		15p	vF, S, 85″ s of 7768
7767	Gx	23 50.9	+ 27 05 r	Peg		14p	vF, S, lE, * p 19″; = IC 1511
7768	Gx	23 50.9	+ 27 10 s	Peg	1.7	14p	vF, S, E, * inv, * p vnr
1511 I		23 51.0	+ 27 05 x	Peg			eF, susp close to *12.5; = 7767
1512 I		23 51.0	+ 27 03 d	Peg			*13, nebulous?
7769	Gx	23 51.1	+ 20 09 s	Peg	1.8	12.1	pF, pS, R, mbM
7770	Gx	23 51.4	+ 20 06 s	Peg	1.0	15p	vF, vS, iR, s of 2
7771	Gx	23 51.4	+ 20 07 s	Peg	2.7	12.3	pB, pL, E 84°, bM, n of 2
5361 I	Gx	23 51.4	− 13 23 m	Aqr	0.4	14p	vF, vS, bM, stellar
5362 I	Gx	23 51.6	− 28 22 c	Scl	1.5		eeF, pS, *8 sf
7772	OC	23 51.8	+ 16 15 r	Peg			Cl of sc st 10m
7774	Gx	23 52.2	+ 11 28 r	Peg		14p	eF, S, R, in centre of 3 st
5363 I		23 52.2	− 28 38 d	Scl			vF, eS, R, 3 st in line p
7773	Gx	23 52.3	+ 31 16 r	Peg		14p	pF, cS, R, *13 nf nr
7775	Gx	23 52.5	+ 28 46 r	Peg		14p	vF, pS, lE, glbM
7776		23 52.7	− 13 23 D	Aqr			eF, vS, lE, gbM; nonexistent?
7777	Gx	23 53.3	+ 28 17 r	Peg		14p	vF, vS, R, bM
7778	Gx	23 53.3	+ 7 52 r	Psc		14p	cF, S, R, psbM, stellar, 1st of 4
7779	Gx	23 53.4	+ 7 52 s	Psc	1.6	14p	pF, S, R, psbM, stellar, 2nd of 4
1513 I	Gx	23 53.5	+ 11 20 u	Peg	1.0	15p	F, vS, E pf, gbM
7780	Gx	23 53.6	+ 8 07 s	Psc	1.2	15p	vF, vS, R, lbM, F* inv
7781	Gx	23 53.8	+ 7 51 r	Psc		15p	F, S, R, 3rd of 4
7782	Gx	23 53.9	+ 7 58 s	Psc	2.4	13p	pF, pL, lE, glbM, 4th of 4
7783	Gx	23 54.2	+ 0 23 s	Psc	1.9	14p	F, S, lE
1514 I	Gx	23 54.2	− 13 35 m	Aqr	0.8	15p	vF, S, excent N
7784	Gx	23 55.3	+ 21 45 r	Peg		15p	vF, eS, lbM, r?, p of 2
7785	Gx	23 55.3	+ 5 55 s	Psc	2.3	11.6	pB, pS, iR, psbM, r, *8 p 4′.5
7786	Gx	23 55.4	+ 21 35 r	Peg		14p	pF, pS, lE, vF st inv, f of 2
7787	Gx	23 56.2	+ 0 33 r	Psc		15p	vF, S, R
1515 I	Gx	23 56.2	− 0 59 v	Psc	1.2		eeF, pS, *9.5 inv, bet 2 st
5364 I		23 56.2	− 29 04 d	Scl			vF, pS, R, *8 sf
1516 I	Gx	23 56.3	− 0 55 v	Psc	1.6		vF, pS, R, B* sf, nf of 2
1517 I	Gx	23 56.4	− 0 17 z	Psc		15p	eeF, vS, R, 3 st p
7788	OC	23 56.7	+ 61 24 s	Cas	9	9p	Cl, S, pRi, vC, st 10, 13...

NGC	Type	α_{2000}	δ_{2000}	Const.	Size	Mag.	Description
		h m	° ′		′		
7789	OC	23 57.0	+ 56 44 s	Cas	16	6.7	Cl, vL, vRi, vmC, st 11...18
1518 I		23 57.1	+ 12 28 d	Peg			vF, vS, R
1519 I		23 57.1	+ 12 28 d	Peg			F, vS, lbM, stellar
5365 I		23 57.6	− 37 01 d	Scl			pB, cS, vmE, * sf
5366 I	?	23 57.7	+ 52 47 x	Cas			eL, mE (30′ by 10′)
7793	Gx	23 57.8	− 32 35 s	Scl	9.1	9.1	like a comet
7791	D*	23 58.0	+ 10 45 r	Peg			vF, vS; F*?
1520 I	Gx	23 58.0	− 14 02 m	Cet	0.5	14p	vF, pL, R
7792	Gx	23 58.1	+ 16 29 r	Peg		15p	eF, eS, bM
7790	OC	23 58.4	+ 61 13 s	Cas	17	8.5	Cl, pRi, pC
7794	Gx	23 58.6	+ 10 42 r	Peg		14p	vF, pS, iR
7795	−	23 58.7	+ 60 00 r	Cas			Cl, vL, P, lC, st 7, 10...
5367 I		23 58.7	+ 22 26 d	Peg			F, lE 120°, gbMN, r
7796	Gx	23 59.0	− 55 27 s	Phe	2.3	12p	pB, cS, R, gmbM
7797	Gx	23 59.0	+ 3 38 r	Psc		15p	eF, pS, iR, lbM
1521 I		23 59.0	− 7 09 d	Cet			vF, S, iF
1522 I	Gx	23 59.1	+ 1 43 x	Psc		15p	F, S, E ns
1523 I		23 59.1	+ 6 52 d	Psc			vF, *4 3′ f
1524 I	Gx	23 59.3	− 4 09 v	Psc	1.9		no description
5368 I		23 59.3	+ 6 52 d	Psc			eF, vS, lbM, 3′ p or f from ω Psc
7798	Gx	23 59.4	+ 20 45 s	Peg	1.5	13p	pF, S, R, sbM, *10 sp
1525 I	Gx	23 59.4	+ 46 54 v	And	2.1		eF, pS
7799	Gx	23 59.5	+ 31 17 r	Peg			vF, vS, *16 close p
7800	Gx	23 59.6	+ 14 49 s	Peg	2.6	13p	F, pS, E 39°
7807	Gx	23 59.6	− 18 51 c	Cet	1.0		eF, pS, iF
5369 I		23 59.8	+ 32 41 d	And			F, S, R, N

Right Ascensions of NGC Objects

NGC	α_{2000}	NGC	α_{2000}	NGC	α_{2000}	NGC	α_{2000}	NGC	α_{2000}
	h m		h m		h m		h m		h m
1	0 07.3	89	0 21.3	177	0 37.5	265	0 47.6	353	1 02.6
2	0 07.3	90	0 21.9	178	0 39.1	266	0 49.8	354	1 03.3
3	0 07.3	91	0 21.8	179	0 37.8	267	0 48.0	355	1 03.2
4	0 07.4	92	0 21.5	180	0 38.0	268	0 50.2	356	1 03.3
5	0 07.8	93	0 22.0	181	0 38.2	269	0 48.5	357	1 03.4
6	0 08.3	94	0 22.2	182	0 38.2	270	0 50.7	358	1 05.2
7	0 08.4	95	0 22.2	183	0 38.3	271	0 50.8	359	1 04.4
8	0 08.8	96	0 22.3	184	0 38.5	272	0 51.4	360	1 02.9
9	0 08.9	97	0 22.4	185	0 39.0	273	0 50.8	361	1 02.2
10	0 08.6	98	0 22.8	186	0 38.5	274	0 51.0	362	1 03.2
11	0 08.7	99	0 24.0	187	0 39.6	275	0 51.1	363	1 06.1
12	0 08.7	100	0 24.0	188	0 44.	276	0 52.1	364	1 04.6
13	0 08.8	101	0 23.9	189	0 39.6	277	0 51.5	365	1 04.1
14	0 08.8	102	0 24.4	190	0 38.9	278	0 52.1	366	1 06.4
15	0 09.1	103	0 25.3	191	0 39.0	279	0 52.3	367	1 04.9
16	0 09.1	104	0 24.1	192	0 39.3	280	0 52.5	368	1 04.4
17	0 11.0	105	0 25.3	193	0 39.3	281	0 52.8	369	1 05.1
18	0 09.4	106	0 24.7	194	0 39.3	282	0 52.8	370	1 06.6
19	0 09.4	107	0 25.6	195	0 39.6	283	0 53.3	371	1 03.3
20	0 09.5	108	0 25.9	196	0 39.3	284	0 53.6	372	1 06.7
21	0 10.7	109	0 26.2	197	0 39.4	285	0 53.7	373	1 07.0
22	0 09.8	110	0 27.4	198	0 39.4	286	0 53.6	374	1 07.1
23	0 09.9	111	0 26.7	199	0 39.6	287	0 53.6	375	1 07.1
24	0 09.9	112	0 26.7	200	0 39.6	288	0 52.8	376	1 03.9
25	0 09.9	113	0 27.0	201	0 39.7	289	0 52.7	377	1 06.3
26	0 10.4	114	0 27.1	202	0 39.7	290	0 51.3	378	1 06.2
27	0 10.5	115	0 26.8	203	0 39.7	291	0 53.6	379	1 07.3
28	0 10.3	116	0 27.2	204	0 39.8	292	0 52.8	380	1 07.3
29	0 10.8	117	0 27.2	205	0 40.4	293	0 54.3	381	1 08.3
30	0 10.8	118	0 27.3	206	0 40.6	294	0 52.1	382	1 07.4
31	0 10.5	119	0 27.1	207	0 40.0	295	0 55.2	383	1 07.4
32	0 10.9	120	0 27.5	208	0 40.4	296	0 55.4	384	1 07.4
33	0 10.9	121	0 26.8	209	0 39.1	297	0 55.0	385	1 07.4
34	0 11.1	122	0 27.7	210	0 40.6	298	0 55.0	386	1 07.5
35	0 11.2	123	0 27.8	211	0 41.0	299	0 54.0	387	1 07.5
36	0 11.4	124	0 27.9	212	0 40.1	300	0 54.9	388	1 07.8
37	0 11.3	125	0 28.8	213	0 41.2	301	0 56.3	389	1 08.5
38	0 11.9	126	0 29.1	214	0 41.5	302	0 56.4	390	1 08.1
39	0 12.3	127	0 29.2	215	0 40.8	303	0 54.8	391	1 07.5
40	0 13.0	128	0 29.2	216	0 41.4	304	0 56.1	392	1 08.4
41	0 12.8	129	0 29.9	217	0 41.5	305	0 56.0	393	1 08.6
42	0 12.9	130	0 29.3	218	0 41.8	306	0 54.9	394	1 08.4
43	0 13.0	131	0 29.6	219	0 42.3	307	0 56.6	395	1 05.3
44	0 13.1	132	0 30.2	220	0 40.5	308	0 56.4	396	1 08.0
45	0 14.1	133	0 31.2	221	0 42.7	309	0 56.7	397	1 08.5
46	0 14.1	134	0 30.4	222	0 40.6	310	0 56.9	398	1 08.8
47	0 14.5	135	0 31.8	223	0 42.7	311	0 57.6	399	1 09.0
48	0 14.0	136	0 31.5	224	0 42.7	312	0 56.3	400	1 09.0
49	0 14.3	137	0 31.1	225	0 43.4	313	0 57.8	401	1 09.1
50	0 14.7	138	0 31.0	226	0 42.8	314	0 56.9	402	1 09.2
51	0 14.6	139	0 31.0	227	0 42.6	315	0 57.8	403	1 09.2
52	0 14.6	140	0 31.3	228	0 42.8	316	0 57.8	404	1 09.4
53	0 14.7	141	0 31.4	229	0 43.0	317	0 57.6	405	1 08.3
54	0 15.1	142	0 31.3	230	0 42.4	318	0 58.1	406	1 07.4
55	0 14.9	143	0 31.4	231	0 41.0	319	0 57.0	407	1 10.6
56	0 15.4	144	0 31.4	232	0 42.7	320	0 58.8	408	1 10.9
57	0 15.4	145	0 31.7	233	0 43.4	321	0 57.4	409	1 09.5
58	0 14.5	146	0 33.1	234	0 43.4	322	0 57.2	410	1 11.0
59	0 15.5	147	0 33.2	235	0 42.8	323	0 56.7	411	1 07.9
60	0 16.0	148	0 34.3	236	0 43.5	324	0 58.6	412	1 10.3
61	0 16.5	149	0 33.7	237	0 43.5	325	0 57.9	413	1 09.5
62	0 17.1	150	0 34.3	238	0 43.4	326	0 58.4	414	1 11.3
63	0 17.7	151	0 34.0	239	0 44.6	327	0 57.9	415	1 10.2
64	0 17.5	152	0 32.8	240	0 45.1	328	0 57.0	416	1 08.1
65	0 19.1	153	0 34.0	241	0 43.4	329	0 58.0	417	1 11.1
66	0 19.2	154	0 34.1	242	0 43.6	330	0 56.2	418	1 10.6
67	0 18.2	155	0 34.7	243	0 45.9	331	0 58.6	419	1 08.3
68	0 18.3	156	0 34.6	244	0 45.8	332	0 58.8	420	1 12.1
69	0 18.3	157	0 34.8	245	0 46.1	333	0 58.8	421	1 12.1
70	0 18.4	158	0 34.9	246	0 47.0	334	0 58.8	422	1 08.9
71	0 18.4	159	0 34.6	247	0 47.1	335	0 59.3	423	1 11.4
72	0 18.5	160	0 36.1	248	0 45.4	336	0 58.8	424	1 11.5
73	0 18.8	161	0 35.5	249	0 45.4	337	0 59.8	425	1 13.0
74	0 18.9	162	0 36.1	250	0 47.3	338	1 00.6	426	1 12.9
75	0 19.5	163	0 36.0	251	0 47.8	339	0 57.7	427	1 12.5
76	0 19.6	164	0 36.5	252	0 48.0	340	1 00.6	428	1 12.9
77	0 20.0	165	0 36.5	253	0 47.6	341	1 00.8	429	1 13.0
78	0 20.4	166	0 35.8	254	0 47.5	342	1 00.8	430	1 13.1
79	0 21.0	167	0 35.3	255	0 47.8	343	1 00.8	431	1 14.2
80	0 21.2	168	0 36.7	256	0 45.9	344	1 01.6	432	1 11.8
81	0 21.2	169	0 36.9	257	0 48.1	345	1 01.4	433	1 15.3
82	0 21.4	170	0 36.7	258	0 48.2	346	0 59.1	434	1 12.2
83	0 21.4	171	0 37.4	259	0 48.1	347	1 01.4	435	1 14.0
84	0 21.5	172	0 37.3	260	0 48.6	348	1 00.8	436	1 15.6
85	0 21.4	173	0 37.2	261	0 46.5	349	1 01.9	437	1 14.4
86	0 21.5	174	0 36.9	262	0 48.8	350	1 02.0	438	1 13.4
87	0 21.2	175	0 37.4	263	0 48.9	351	1 02.1	439	1 13.8
88	0 21.3	176	0 35.8	264	0 48.3	352	1 02.1	440	1 12.9

Right Ascensions of NGC Objects

NGC	α_{2000}	NGC	α_{2000}	NGC	α_{2000}	NGC	α_{2000}	NGC	α_{2000}
	h m		h m		h m		h m		h m
441	1 14.0	529	1 25.7	617	1 33.9	705	1 52.8	793	2 02.9
442	1 14.6	530	1 24.7	618	1 36.3	706	1 51.8	794	2 02.5
443	1 15.1	531	1 26.3	619	1 34.8	707	1 51.2	795	1 59.8
444	1 15.9	532	1 25.3	620	1 37.0	708	1 52.8	796	1 56.7
445	1 14.9	533	1 25.5	621	1 36.7	709	1 52.9	797	2 03.4
446	1 14.9	534	1 24.6	622	1 36.0	710	1 53.0	798	2 03.4
447	1 15.6	535	1 25.5	623	1 35.0	711	1 52.5	799	2 02.3
448	1 15.3	536	1 26.4	624	1 35.7	712	1 53.2	800	2 02.3
449	1 16.1	537	1 26.3	625	1 35.1	713	1 55.1	801	2 03.7
450	1 15.5	538	1 25.4	626	1 35.2	714	1 53.6	802	1 59.1
451	1 16.2	539	1 25.3	627	1 37.1	715	1 53.2	803	2 03.8
452	1 16.3	540	1 27.1	628	1 36.7	716	1 52.9	804	2 03.9
453	1 16.3	541	1 25.7	629	1 40.3	717	1 54.0	805	2 04.4
454	1 14.4	542	1 26.5	630	1 35.6	718	1 53.2	806	2 03.6
455	1 16.0	543	1 25.8	631	1 36.8	719	1 53.7	807	2 04.8
456	1 14.4	544	1 25.1	632	1 37.3	720	1 53.0	808	2 04.0
457	1 19.1	545	1 26.0	633	1 36.4	721	1 54.8	809	2 04.4
458	1 14.9	546	1 25.1	634	1 38.2	722	1 54.8	810	2 05.3
459	1 18.0	547	1 26.0	635	1 38.3	723	1 53.9	811	2 04.7
460	1 14.8	548	1 26.0	636	1 39.1	724	1 53.8	812	2 06.8
461	1 17.3	549	1 25.5	637	1 42.9	725	1 52.6	813	2 01.6
462	1 18.1	550	1 26.7	638	1 39.6	726	1 55.6	814	2 02.9
463	1 18.9	551	1 27.6	639	1 38.9	727	1 53.7	815	2 02.9
464	1 19.0	552	1 27.8	640	1 39.3	728	1 55.1	816	2 08.0
465	1 15.5	553	1 27.8	641	1 38.7	729	1 54.0	817	2 08.4
466	1 17.2	554	1 27.2	642	1 39.0	730	1 55.3	818	2 08.7
467	1 19.2	555	1 27.2	643	1 35.1	731	1 54.9	819	2 08.5
468	1 19.8	556	1 27.2	644	1 38.9	732	1 56.5	820	2 08.4
469	1 19.4	557	1 26.5	645	1 40.2	733	1 56.4	821	2 08.4
470	1 19.7	558	1 27.3	646	1 37.4	734	1 54.8	822	2 06.6
471	1 19.9	559	1 29.5	647	1 39.8	735	1 56.6	823	2 07.3
472	1 20.5	560	1 27.4	648	1 38.7	736	1 56.7	824	2 06.8
473	1 19.9	561	1 28.2	649	1 40.0	737	1 56.7	825	2 08.5
474	1 20.1	562	1 28.4	650	1 42.3	738	1 56.9	826	2 09.4
475	1 20.0	563	1 27.1	651	1 42.3	739	1 57.0	827	2 08.8
476	1 20.2	564	1 27.8	652	1 40.7	740	1 56.9	828	2 10.2
477	1 21.3	565	1 28.2	653	1 42.4	741	1 56.4	829	2 08.7
478	1 20.2	566	1 29.0	654	1 44.1	742	1 56.5	830	2 09.0
479	1 21.3	567	1 26.9	655	1 42.0	743	1 58.7	831	2 09.5
480	1 20.9	568	1 27.9	656	1 42.4	744	1 58.4	832	2 10.1
481	1 21.0	569	1 29.1	657	1 43.7	745	1 54.2	833	2 09.3
482	1 20.3	570	1 29.0	658	1 42.2	746	1 57.9	834	2 11.0
483	1 22.0	571	1 29.9	659	1 44.2	747	1 56.2	835	2 09.4
484	1 19.6	572	1 28.6	660	1 43.0	748	1 56.4	836	2 10.5
485	1 21.4	573	1 30.9	661	1 44.2	749	1 55.6	837	2 10.4
486	1 22.1	574	1 29.0	662	1 44.5	750	1 57.5	838	2 09.6
487	1 21.8	575	1 30.8	663	1 46.0	751	1 57.6	839	2 09.7
488	1 21.8	576	1 28.9	664	1 43.8	752	1 57.8	840	2 10.2
489	1 21.8	577	1 30.7	665	1 44.8	753	1 57.7	841	2 11.3
490	1 22.1	578	1 30.5	666	1 46.0	754	1 54.4	842	2 09.8
491	1 21.4	579	1 31.7	667	1 45.1	755	1 56.4	843	2 11.1
492	1 22.2	580	1 30.7	668	1 46.3	756	1 54.5	844	2 10.2
493	1 22.2	581	1 33.2	669	1 47.2	757	1 56.4	845	2 12.3
494	1 23.0	582	1 31.9	670	1 47.4	758	1 56.0	846	2 12.2
495	1 22.9	583	1 29.7	671	1 46.9	759	1 57.8	847	2 12.2
496	1 23.3	584	1 31.3	672	1 47.9	760	1 57.8	848	2 10.3
497	1 22.4	585	1 31.7	673	1 48.4	761	1 57.8	849	2 10.2
498	1 23.3	586	1 31.6	674	1 49.2	762	1 57.1	850	2 11.2
499	1 23.2	587	1 32.5	675	1 49.0	763	1 57.4	851	2 11.2
500	1 22.7	588	1 32.7	676	1 49.0	764	1 57.2	852	2 08.9
501	1 23.4	589	1 32.6	677	1 49.1	765	1 58.8	853	2 11.8
502	1 22.8	590	1 33.6	678	1 49.4	766	1 58.7	854	2 11.6
503	1 23.5	591	1 33.5	679	1 49.7	767	1 58.9	855	2 14.0
504	1 23.5	592	1 33.2	680	1 49.8	768	1 58.7	856	2 13.6
505	1 22.9	593	1 32.3	681	1 49.2	769	1 59.5	857	2 12.6
506	1 23.6	594	1 33.0	682	1 49.0	770	1 59.2	858	2 12.5
507	1 23.7	595	1 33.5	683	1 49.6	771	2 03.4	859	2 13.9
508	1 23.7	596	1 32.9	684	1 50.2	772	1 59.3	860	2 15.1
509	1 23.4	597	1 32.2	685	1 47.8	773	1 59.0	861	2 15.8
510	1 23.7	598	1 33.9	686	1 49.0	774	1 59.4	862	2 13.0
511	1 23.5	599	1 32.8	687	1 50.6	775	1 58.5	863	2 14.6
512	1 24.0	600	1 33.1	688	1 50.8	776	1 59.9	864	2 15.5
513	1 23.8	601	1 33.3	689	1 49.9	777	2 00.2	865	2 16.1
514	1 24.1	602	1 29.6	690	1 47.8	778	2 00.3	866	2 14.6
515	1 24.6	603	1 34.4	691	1 50.7	779	1 59.7	867	2 15.9
516	1 24.1	604	1 34.5	692	1 48.7	780	2 00.5	868	2 16.0
517	1 24.7	605	1 35.1	693	1 50.5	781	2 00.1	869	2 19.0
518	1 24.3	606	1 34.9	694	1 51.0	782	1 57.8	870	2 17.2
519	1 24.5	607	1 34.3	695	1 51.2	783	2 01.1	871	2 17.2
520	1 24.6	608	1 35.4	696	1 49.4	784	2 01.3	872	2 15.4
521	1 24.6	609	1 37.2	697	1 51.3	785	2 01.8	873	2 16.6
522	1 24.8	610	1 34.3	698	1 49.6	786	2 01.5	874	2 16.1
523	1 25.3	611	1 34.3	699	1 50.6	787	2 01.0	875	2 17.1
524	1 24.8	612	1 34.0	700	1 52.2	788	2 01.1	876	2 17.9
525	1 24.8	613	1 34.3	701	1 51.1	789	2 02.5	877	2 18.0
526	1 23.9	614	1 35.8	702	1 51.3	790	2 01.5	878	2 17.8
527	1 24.0	615	1 35.1	703	1 52.8	791	2 01.7	879	2 16.3
528	1 25.5	616	1 36.0	704	1 52.7	792	2 02.3	880	2 18.4

NGC	α_{2000}		NGC	α_{2000}		NGC	α_{2000}		NGC	α_{2000}		NGC	α_{2000}	
	h	m		h	m		h	m		h	m		h	m
881	2	18.7	969	2	34.1	1057	2	43.0	1145	2	54.6	1233	3	12.5
882	2	19.7	970	2	34.2	1058	2	43.5	1146	2	57.5	1234	3	09.6
883	2	19.0	971	2	34.2	1059	2	42.6	1147	2	55.3	1235	3	12.8
884	2	22.4	972	2	34.2	1060	2	43.2	1148	2	57.1	1236	3	11.6
885	2	14.6	973	2	34.3	1061	2	43.2	1149	2	57.4	1237	3	10.7
886	2	23.5	974	2	34.4	1062	2	43.7	1150	2	57.1	1238	3	10.9
887	2	19.6	975	2	33.2	1063	2	42.2	1151	2	57.1	1239	3	11.0
888	2	17.5	976	2	34.0	1064	2	42.2	1152	2	57.6	1240	3	12.9
889	2	19.1	977	2	33.0	1065	2	42.1	1153	2	58.1	1241	3	11.3
890	2	22.0	978	2	34.8	1066	2	43.8	1154	2	58.1	1242	3	11.3
891	2	22.6	979	2	31.5	1067	2	43.8	1155	2	58.2	1243	3	11.4
892	2	20.7	980	2	35.5	1068	2	42.7	1156	2	59.7	1244	3	06.5
893	2	20.0	981	2	32.9	1069	2	42.8	1157	2	58.2	1245	3	14.7
894	2	21.6	982	2	35.4	1070	2	43.3	1158	2	57.3	1246	3	07.0
895	2	21.6	983	2	35.0	1071	2	43.0	1159	3	00.7	1247	3	12.2
896	2	24.8	984	2	34.7	1072	2	43.5	1160	3	01.2	1248	3	12.8
897	2	21.1	985	2	34.6	1073	2	43.7	1161	3	01.2	1249	3	10.1
898	2	23.3	986	2	33.6	1074	2	43.7	1162	2	58.9	1250	3	15.4
899	2	21.9	987	2	36.8	1075	2	43.7	1163	3	00.3	1251	3	14.1
900	2	23.5	988	2	35.4	1076	2	43.7	1164	3	01.9	1252	3	10.5
901	2	23.6	989	2	33.8	1077	2	46.1	1165	2	58.7	1253	3	14.1
902	2	22.4	990	2	36.4	1078	2	44.2	1166	3	00.6	1254	3	14.4
903	2	23.8	991	2	35.5	1079	2	43.7	1167	3	01.7	1255	3	13.5
904	2	24.0	992	2	37.2	1080	2	45.2	1168	3	00.8	1256	3	13.9
905	2	22.6	993	2	36.7	1081	2	45.2	1169	3	03.6	1257	3	16.4
906	2	25.2	994	2	36.7	1082	2	45.7	1170	3	02.5	1258	3	13.9
907	2	23.0	995	2	38.5	1083	2	45.8	1171	3	04.0	1259	3	17.0
908	2	23.1	996	2	38.7	1084	2	46.0	1172	3	01.6	1260	3	17.5
909	2	25.4	997	2	37.2	1085	2	46.4	1173	3	04.2	1261	3	12.3
910	2	25.4	998	2	37.2	1086	2	47.9	1174	3	05.5	1262	3	15.7
911	2	25.8	999	2	38.8	1087	2	46.4	1175	3	04.5	1263	3	15.8
912	2	25.8	1000	2	38.9	1088	2	47.0	1176	3	04.5	1264	3	17.9
913	2	25.8	1001	2	39.2	1089	2	46.4	1177	3	04.6	1265	3	18.3
914	2	26.1	1002	2	38.9	1090	2	46.6	1178	3	04.6	1266	3	16.0
915	2	25.7	1003	2	39.3	1091	2	45.4	1179	3	02.6	1267	3	18.7
916	2	25.7	1004	2	37.6	1092	2	45.7	1180	2	57.1	1268	3	18.8
917	2	26.1	1005	2	39.5	1093	2	48.2	1181	2	57.0	1269	3	17.3
918	2	25.9	1006	2	37.4	1094	2	47.5	1182	3	03.5	1270	3	19.0
919	2	26.2	1007	2	37.8	1095	2	47.6	1183	3	04.7	1271	3	19.2
920	2	27.8	1008	2	37.9	1096	2	43.8	1184	3	16.6	1272	3	19.3
921	2	26.6	1009	2	38.3	1097	2	46.3	1185	3	03.0	1273	3	19.4
922	2	25.1	1010	2	37.5	1098	2	44.9	1186	3	05.5	1274	3	19.7
923	2	27.6	1011	2	37.6	1099	2	45.3	1187	3	02.6	1275	3	19.8
924	2	26.8	1012	2	39.3	1100	2	45.6	1188	3	03.7	1276	3	19.9
925	2	27.3	1013	2	37.8	1101	2	48.3	1189	3	03.4	1277	3	19.8
926	2	26.1	1014	2	37.8	1102	2	47.1	1190	3	03.5	1278	3	19.9
927	2	26.6	1015	2	38.1	1103	2	48.0	1191	3	03.6	1279	3	20.1
928	2	27.7	1016	2	38.3	1104	2	48.6	1192	3	03.7	1280	3	18.0
929	2	27.3	1017	2	37.8	1105	2	52.4	1193	3	05.8	1281	3	20.1
930	2	27.9	1018	2	38.0	1106	2	50.6	1194	3	03.8	1282	3	20.2
931	2	28.3	1019	2	38.4	1107	2	49.3	1195	3	03.4	1283	3	20.3
932	2	27.9	1020	2	38.7	1108	2	48.6	1196	3	03.5	1284	3	17.6
933	2	29.2	1021	2	38.8	1109	2	49.1	1197	3	06.2	1285	3	17.8
934	2	27.6	1022	2	38.5	1110	2	49.3	1198	3	06.2	1286	3	17.8
935	2	28.2	1023	2	40.4	1111	2	49.7	1199	3	06.3	1287	3	18.6
936	2	27.6	1024	2	39.2	1112	2	50.0	1200	3	03.8	1288	3	17.2
937	2	29.5	1025	2	36.3	1113	2	50.2	1201	3	04.1	1289	3	18.9
938	2	28.5	1026	2	39.3	1114	2	49.2	1202	3	04.9	1290	3	19.4
939	2	26.4	1027	2	42.7	1115	2	50.5	1203	3	05.2	1291	3	17.3
940	2	29.4	1028	2	39.5	1116	2	50.6	1204	3	04.6	1292	3	18.2
941	2	28.5	1029	2	39.5	1117	2	51.3	1205	3	02.4	1293	3	21.6
942	2	29.2	1030	2	39.9	1118	2	50.0	1206	3	06.1	1294	3	21.7
943	2	29.2	1031	2	36.6	1119	2	48.3	1207	3	08.2	1295	3	20.1
944	2	26.7	1032	2	39.4	1120	2	49.2	1208	3	06.2	1296	3	18.9
945	2	28.6	1033	2	40.1	1121	2	50.8	1209	3	06.0	1297	3	19.2
946	2	30.7	1034	2	38.2	1122	2	52.8	1210	3	06.8	1298	3	20.2
947	2	28.5	1035	2	39.5	1123	2	52.8	1211	3	06.9	1299	3	20.1
948	2	28.8	1036	2	40.5	1124	2	51.6	1212	3	08.6	1300	3	19.7
949	2	30.8	1037	2	38.0	1125	2	51.8	1213	3	09.2	1301	3	20.5
950	2	29.2	1038	2	40.1	1126	2	52.4	1214	3	06.9	1302	3	19.9
951	2	28.8	1039	2	42.0	1127	2	52.9	1215	3	07.1	1303	3	20.7
952	2	31.3	1040	2	42.2	1128	2	52.6	1216	3	07.3	1304	3	21.0
953	2	31.2	1041	2	40.3	1129	2	54.5	1217	3	06.2	1305	3	21.4
954	2	28.9	1042	2	40.4	1130	2	54.4	1218	3	08.4	1306	3	21.0
955	2	30.6	1043	2	40.7	1131	2	54.6	1219	3	08.5	1307	3	22.2
956	2	32.4	1044	2	41.1	1132	2	52.9	1220	3	11.7	1308	3	22.5
957	2	33.6	1045	2	40.4	1133	2	52.7	1221	3	08.1	1309	3	22.1
958	2	30.7	1046	2	41.2	1134	2	53.6	1222	3	08.9	1310	3	21.0
959	2	32.3	1047	2	40.5	1135	2	50.8	1223	3	08.3	1311	3	20.1
960	2	31.6	1048	2	40.6	1136	2	50.9	1224	3	11.3	1312	3	23.7
961	2	31.2	1049	2	39.7	1137	2	54.0	1225	3	08.8	1313	3	18.3
962	2	32.8	1050	2	42.5	1138	2	56.5	1226	3	11.1	1314	3	22.6
963	2	30.5	1051	2	41.1	1139	2	52.9	1227	3	11.2	1315	3	23.1
964	2	31.1	1052	2	41.1	1140	2	54.6	1228	3	08.2	1316	3	22.7
965	2	32.5	1053	2	43.2	1141	2	55.2	1229	3	08.2	1317	3	22.8
966	2	31.8	1054	2	42.2	1142	2	55.2	1230	3	08.3	1318	3	22.8
967	2	32.2	1055	2	41.8	1143	2	55.1	1231	3	09.6	1319	3	23.9
968	2	34.1	1056	2	42.9	1144	2	55.2	1232	3	09.8	1320	3	24.8

NGC	α_{2000}	NGC	α_{2000}	NGC	α_{2000}	NGC	α_{2000}	NGC	α_{2000}
	h m		h m		h m		h m		h m
1321	3 24.9	1409	3 41.2	1497	4 02.1	1585	4 27.5	1673	4 42.4
1322	3 25.0	1410	3 41.2	1498	4 00.5	1586	4 30.7	1674	4 52.4
1323	3 25.0	1411	3 38.8	1499	4 00.7	1587	4 30.7	1675	4 52.4
1324	3 25.0	1412	3 40.6	1500	3 58.2	1588	4 30.8	1676	4 43.7
1325	3 24.4	1413	3 40.3	1501	4 07.0	1589	4 30.8	1677	4 50.8
1326	3 23.9	1414	3 41.5	1502	4 07.7	1590	4 31.2	1678	4 51.7
1327	3 24.7	1415	3 41.0	1503	3 56.5	1591	4 29.4	1679	4 50.0
1328	3 25.6	1416	3 41.0	1504	4 02.5	1592	4 29.6	1680	4 48.6
1329	3 25.9	1417	3 42.0	1505	4 02.7	1593	4 31.9	1681	4 51.7
1330	3 29.3	1418	3 42.3	1506	4 00.4	1594	4 30.8	1682	4 52.3
1331	3 26.5	1419	3 40.6	1507	4 04.5	1595	4 28.4	1683	4 52.3
1332	3 26.3	1420	3 42.7	1508	4 05.8	1596	4 27.6	1684	4 52.5
1333	3 29.3	1421	3 42.5	1509	4 04.0	1597	4 31.2	1685	4 52.6
1334	3 30.1	1422	3 41.5	1510	4 03.5	1598	4 28.6	1686	4 52.8
1335	3 30.4	1423	3 42.6	1511	3 59.5	1599	4 31.6	1687	4 51.3
1336	3 26.6	1424	3 43.2	1512	4 03.9	1600	4 31.7	1688	4 48.4
1337	3 28.1	1425	3 42.2	1513	4 10.0	1601	4 31.8	1689	4 53.6
1338	3 29.0	1426	3 42.8	1514	4 09.2	1602	4 27.9	1690	4 54.3
1339	3 28.1	1427	3 42.3	1515	4 04.1	1603	4 31.7	1691	4 54.6
1340	3 28.3	1428	3 42.4	1516	4 08.1	1604	4 31.9	1692	4 55.4
1341	3 28.0	1429	3 44.0	1517	4 09.3	1605	4 35.0	1693	4 47.5
1342	3 31.6	1430	3 43.4	1518	4 06.8	1606	4 32.1	1694	4 55.2
1343	3 37.8	1431	3 44.6	1519	4 08.1	1607	4 32.0	1695	4 47.6
1344	3 28.3	1432	3 45.8	1520	3 57.5	1608	4 31.9	1696	4 48.0
1345	3 29.4	1433	3 42.0	1521	4 08.3	1609	4 32.6	1697	4 48.6
1346	3 30.1	1434	3 44.4	1522	4 06.1	1610	4 34.1	1698	4 49.4
1347	3 29.7	1435	3 46.1	1523	4 06.2	1611	4 33.0	1699	4 57.0
1348	3 33.8	1436	3 43.6	1524	4 10.3	1612	4 33.1	1700	4 56.9
1349	3 31.4	1437	3 43.6	1525	4 10.3	1613	4 33.3	1701	4 55.8
1350	3 31.1	1438	3 45.4	1526	4 05.2	1614	4 34.0	1702	4 49.3
1351	3 30.5	1439	3 44.8	1527	4 08.4	1615	4 36.0	1703	4 52.8
1352	3 31.5	1440	3 45.0	1528	4 15.4	1616	4 32.7	1704	4 49.7
1353	3 32.1	1441	3 45.7	1529	4 07.2	1617	4 31.7	1705	4 54.2
1354	3 32.4	1442	3 45.0	1530	4 23.4	1618	4 36.1	1706	4 52.5
1355	3 33.4	1443	3 45.7	1531	4 12.0	1619	4 36.2	1707	4 58.9
1356	3 30.7	1444	3 49.4	1532	4 12.1	1620	4 36.6	1708	5 02.6
1357	3 33.2	1445	3 44.9	1533	4 09.9	1621	4 36.3	1709	4 58.8
1358	3 33.7	1446	3 46.0	1534	4 08.8	1622	4 36.6	1710	4 57.3
1359	3 33.8	1447	3 45.8	1535	4 14.2	1623	4 34.9	1711	4 50.5
1360	3 33.3	1448	3 44.5	1536	4 11.0	1624	4 40.4	1712	4 51.3
1361	3 34.2	1449	3 46.0	1537	4 13.7	1625	4 37.1	1713	4 58.9
1362	3 33.8	1450	3 45.6	1538	4 14.7	1626	4 37.2	1714	4 52.1
1363	3 34.8	1451	3 46.1	1539	4 19.0	1627	4 37.5	1715	4 52.1
1364	3 35.0	1452	3 45.4	1540	4 15.2	1628	4 37.5	1716	4 58.4
1365	3 33.6	1453	3 46.4	1541	4 17.0	1629	4 29.3	1717	4 59.2
1366	3 33.9	1454	3 45.9	1542	4 17.2	1630	4 37.3	1718	4 52.2
1367	3 34.7	1455	3 45.4	1543	4 12.8	1631	4 38.4	1719	4 59.6
1368	3 35.0	1456	3 48.2	1544	5 03.	1632	4 37.9	1720	4 59.3
1369	3 34.1	1457	3 44.5	1545	4 20.9	1633	4 40.0	1721	4 59.2
1370	3 35.2	1458	3 47.0	1546	4 14.6	1634	4 40.0	1722	4 52.2
1371	3 35.0	1459	3 47.0	1547	4 17.2	1635	4 40.1	1723	4 59.4
1372	3 37.0	1460	3 46.1	1548	4 21.0	1636	4 40.7	1724	5 03.5
1373	3 35.1	1461	3 48.5	1549	4 15.7	1637	4 41.5	1725	4 59.3
1374	3 35.3	1462	3 50.3	1550	4 19.6	1638	4 41.6	1726	4 59.7
1375	3 35.2	1463	3 46.2	1551	4 19.6	1639	4 40.9	1727	4 52.2
1376	3 37.1	1464	3 51.4	1552	4 20.3	1640	4 42.2	1728	4 59.4
1377	3 36.7	1465	3 53.6	1553	4 16.2	1641	4 36.1	1729	5 00.1
1378	3 35.9	1466	3 44.5	1554	4 21.8	1642	4 42.9	1730	4 59.6
1379	3 36.1	1467	3 51.9	1555	4 22.9	1643	4 43.6	1731	4 53.4
1380	3 36.5	1468	3 52.2	1556	4 17.7	1644	4 38.0	1732	4 52.9
1381	3 36.6	1469	4 00.5	1557	4 13.3	1645	4 44.0	1733	4 53.9
1382	3 37.1	1470	3 52.2	1558	4 19.3	1646	4 44.3	1734	4 53.3
1383	3 37.6	1471	3 53.1	1559	4 17.6	1647	4 46.0	1735	4 53.9
1384	3 39.2	1472	3 53.7	1560	4 32.8	1648	4 44.5	1736	4 53.1
1385	3 37.5	1473	3 47.4	1561	4 23.0	1649	4 38.1	1737	4 54.3
1386	3 36.9	1474	3 54.2	1562	4 21.7	1650	4 45.1	1738	5 01.7
1387	3 37.0	1475	3 54.1	1563	4 22.9	1651	4 37.5	1739	5 01.7
1388	3 38.3	1476	3 52.1	1564	4 22.9	1652	4 38.1	1740	5 01.9
1389	3 37.2	1477	3 54.0	1565	4 23.4	1653	4 45.8	1741	5 01.6
1390	3 37.9	1478	3 54.1	1566	4 20.0	1654	4 45.8	1742	5 01.7
1391	3 38.5	1479	3 54.4	1567	4 21.1	1655	4 46.2	1743	4 54.0
1392	3 36.8	1480	3 54.5	1568	4 24.4	1656	4 45.8	1744	5 00.0
1393	3 38.6	1481	3 54.4	1569	4 30.8	1657	4 46.2	1745	4 54.3
1394	3 39.1	1482	3 54.7	1570	4 22.1	1658	4 44.0	1746	5 03.6
1395	3 38.5	1483	3 52.7	1571	4 22.2	1659	4 46.5	1747	4 54.9
1396	3 38.1	1484	3 54.2	1572	4 22.6	1660	4 44.2	1748	4 54.4
1397	3 39.6	1485	4 05.1	1573	4 35.0	1661	4 47.2	1749	4 54.4
1398	3 38.9	1486	3 56.3	1574	4 22.0	1662	4 48.5	1750	5 03.9
1399	3 38.5	1487	3 55.8	1575	4 26.3	1663	4 48.6	1751	4 54.2
1400	3 39.5	1488	3 58.1	1576	4 26.2	1664	4 51.1	1752	5 02.1
1401	3 39.4	1489	3 57.6	1577	4 26.3	1665	4 48.2	1753	5 02.4
1402	3 39.4	1490	3 53.5	1578	4 23.8	1666	4 48.5	1754	4 54.4
1403	3 39.3	1491	4 03.4	1579	4 30.2	1667	4 48.6	1755	4 55.0
1404	3 38.9	1492	3 58.1	1580	4 28.2	1668	4 46.1	1756	4 54.6
1405	3 40.2	1493	3 57.5	1581	4 24.7	1669	4 43.0	1757	5 02.6
1406	3 39.4	1494	3 57.7	1582	4 32.0	1670	4 49.9	1758	5 04.4
1407	3 40.2	1495	3 58.4	1583	4 28.3	1671	4 50.3	1759	5 00.8
1408	3 39.4	1496	4 04.4	1584	4 28.1	1672	4 45.7	1760	4 56.5

Right Ascensions of NGC Objects

NGC	α_{2000}	NGC	α_{2000}	NGC	α_{2000}	NGC	α_{2000}	NGC	α_{2000}
	h m		h m		h m		h m		h m
1761	4 56.4	1849	5 09.2	1937	5 22.3	2025	5 33.1	2113	5 45.5
1762	5 03.6	1850	5 08.5	1938	5 21.4	2026	5 43.1	2114	5 45.8
1763	4 56.8	1851	5 14.1	1939	5 21.4	2027	5 35.1	2115	5 51.3
1764	4 56.2	1852	5 09.0	1940	5 22.6	2028	5 33.7	2116	5 46.9
1765	4 58.4	1853	5 12.3	1941	5 23.1	2029	5 35.4	2117	5 47.3
1766	4 55.8	1854	5 09.1	1942	5 24.7	2030	5 35.4	2118	5 47.2
1767	4 56.3	1855	5 09.4	1943	5 22.7	2031	5 33.7	2119	5 57.4
1768	4 56.7	1856	5 09.4	1944	5 21.9	2032	5 35.3	2120	5 50.6
1769	4 57.7	1857	5 20.2	1945	5 25.4	2033	5 34.5	2121	5 48.0
1770	4 57.0	1858	5 09.7	1946	5 25.1	2034	5 35.7	2122	5 48.7
1771	4 58.9	1859	5 11.4	1947	5 26.8	2035	5 35.3	2123	5 51.7
1772	4 56.7	1860	5 10.4	1948	5 25.5	2036	5 34.4	2124	5 57.9
1773	4 58.3	1861	5 10.1	1949	5 25.1	2037	5 34.7	2125	5 50.7
1774	4 57.8	1862	5 12.2	1950	5 24.5	2038	5 34.5	2126	6 03.0
1775	4 56.8	1863	5 11.4	1951	5 25.9	2039	5 44.1	2127	5 51.1
1776	4 58.4	1864	5 12.5	1952	5 34.5	2040	5 36.1	2128	6 04.7
1777	4 55.8	1865	5 12.2	1953	5 25.4	2041	5 36.4	2129	6 01.0
1778	5 08.1	1866	5 13.5	1954	5 32.8	2042	5 35.8	2130	5 52.1
1779	5 05.3	1867	5 13.5	1955	5 26.1	2043	5 36.2	2131	5 58.7
1780	5 06.4	1868	5 14.5	1956	5 19.7	2044	5 35.9	2132	5 55.2
1781	5 07.9	1869	5 13.8	1957	5 32.9	2045	5 45.0	2133	5 51.4
1782	4 57.6	1870	5 13.0	1958	5 25.5	2046	5 35.3	2134	5 50.1
1783	4 58.9	1871	5 13.7	1959	5 25.8	2047	5 35.6	2135	5 53.1
1784	5 05.4	1872	5 13.0	1960	5 36.1	2048	5 35.2	2136	5 52.8
1785	4 58.6	1873	5 13.7	1961	5 42.1	2049	5 43.4	2137	5 53.2
1786	4 59.1	1874	5 13.2	1962	5 26.5	2050	5 36.5	2138	5 54.5
1787	4 59.1	1875	5 21.8	1963	5 33.3	2051	5 36.2	2139	6 01.1
1788	5 06.9	1876	5 13.2	1964	5 33.4	2052	5 37.3	2140	5 54.0
1789	4 57.8	1877	5 13.2	1965	5 26.5	2053	5 37.3	2141	6 03.1
1790	5 11.3	1878	5 12.6	1966	5 26.8	2054	5 45.2	2142	6 01.9
1791	4 59.0	1879	5 19.8	1967	5 26.5	2055	5 37.0	2143	6 03.0
1792	5 05.2	1880	5 13.6	1968	5 27.2	2056	5 36.5	2144	5 41.0
1793	4 59.4	1881	5 13.2	1969	5 26.5	2057	5 36.7	2145	5 54.5
1794	5 07.9	1882	5 15.2	1970	5 26.5	2058	5 36.6	2146	6 18.7
1795	4 59.5	1883	5 25.9	1971	5 26.7	2059	5 36.7	2147	5 56.0
1796	5 02.7	1884	5 15.9	1972	5 26.7	2060	5 37.6	2148	5 58.7
1797	5 07.7	1885	5 15.0	1973	5 35.1	2061	5 43.9	2149	6 03.5
1798	5 11.6	1886	5 21.8	1974	5 27.9	2062	5 40.0	2150	5 55.9
1799	5 07.7	1887	5 15.8	1975	5 35.4	2063	5 46.8	2151	5 56.3
1800	5 06.4	1888	5 22.5	1976	5 35.4	2064	5 46.3	2152	6 00.9
1801	5 00.5	1889	5 22.5	1977	5 35.5	2065	5 37.3	2153	5 57.5
1802	5 10.2	1890	5 13.9	1978	5 28.6	2066	5 37.5	2154	5 57.5
1803	5 05.4	1891	5 21.3	1979	5 33.8	2067	5 46.5	2155	5 58.4
1804	5 00.9	1892	5 17.1	1980	5 35.4	2068	5 46.7	2156	5 57.6
1805	5 02.2	1893	5 22.7	1981	5 35.2	2069	5 38.5	2157	5 57.3
1806	5 01.9	1894	5 15.7	1982	5 35.6	2070	5 38.6	2158	6 07.5
1807	5 10.7	1895	5 16.9	1983	5 27.5	2071	5 47.2	2159	5 57.9
1808	5 07.7	1896	5 25.4	1984	5 27.5	2072	5 38.1	2160	5 58.0
1809	5 02.0	1897	5 17.4	1985	5 37.7	2073	5 45.9	2161	5 55.6
1810	5 03.1	1898	5 16.7	1986	5 27.5	2074	5 38.9	2162	6 00.5
1811	5 08.7	1899	5 17.8	1987	5 27.2	2075	5 38.2	2163	6 07.8
1812	5 08.9	1900	5 19.0	1988	5 37.5	2076	5 46.8	2164	5 58.7
1813	5 02.6	1901	5 17.8	1989	5 34.4	2077	5 39.6	2165	6 11.1
1814	5 03.8	1902	5 18.1	1990	5 36.2	2078	5 39.6	2166	5 59.3
1815	5 02.3	1903	5 17.2	1991	5 29.0	2079	5 39.6	2167	6 06.9
1816	5 03.8	1904	5 24.5	1992	5 34.5	2080	5 39.7	2168	6 08.9
1817	5 12.1	1905	5 18.2	1993	5 35.5	2081	5 40.1	2169	6 08.4
1818	5 04.2	1906	5 24.8	1994	5 28.2	2082	5 41.8	2170	6 07.5
1819	5 11.7	1907	5 28.0	1995	5 32.5	2083	5 39.9	2171	5 58.6
1820	5 03.8	1908	5 26.0	1996	5 38.2	2084	5 39.9	2172	5 59.9
1821	5 11.7	1909	5 25.9	1997	5 30.5	2085	5 40.2	2173	5 58.1
1822	5 05.0	1910	5 18.1	1998	5 33.3	2086	5 40.4	2174	6 09.7
1823	5 03.5	1911	5 19.2	1999	5 36.5	2087	5 44.3	2175	6 09.8
1824	5 06.9	1912	5 28.7	2000	5 27.4	2088	5 40.8	2176	6 01.4
1825	5 04.1	1913	5 18.4	2001	5 29.1	2089	5 47.8	2177	6 01.0
1826	5 05.4	1914	5 17.6	2002	5 30.2	2090	5 47.0	2178	6 02.8
1827	5 10.1	1915	5 19.6	2003	5 30.7	2091	5 40.9	2179	6 08.0
1828	5 04.1	1916	5 17.5	2004	5 30.6	2092	5 41.5	2180	6 09.6
1829	5 04.7	1917	5 19.0	2005	5 30.0	2093	5 41.5	2181	6 02.6
1830	5 04.5	1918	5 19.1	2006	5 31.2	2094	5 42.1	2182	6 09.5
1831	5 06.1	1919	5 20.0	2007	5 35.0	2095	5 42.7	2183	6 10.8
1832	5 12.1	1920	5 20.6	2008	5 35.1	2096	5 42.2	2184	6 10.9
1833	5 04.3	1921	5 19.3	2009	5 30.8	2097	5 44.1	2185	6 11.1
1834	5 05.3	1922	5 19.7	2010	5 30.6	2098	5 42.5	2186	6 12.2
1835	5 05.2	1923	5 21.0	2011	5 32.1	2099	5 52.4	2187	6 03.9
1836	5 05.9	1924	5 27.9	2012	5 22.6	2100	5 42.0	2188	6 10.1
1837	5 04.7	1925	5 21.8	2013	5 44.4	2101	5 46.4	2189	6 12.3
1838	5 05.9	1926	5 20.5	2014	5 32.2	2102	5 42.2	2190	6 00.8
1839	5 05.9	1927	5 28.7	2015	5 31.9	2103	5 41.6	2191	6 08.4
1840	5 06.4	1928	5 20.8	2016	5 31.5	2104	5 47.1	2192	6 15.2
1841	4 45.	1929	5 21.6	2017	5 39.4	2105	5 44.2	2193	6 06.2
1842	5 07.1	1930	5 25.9	2018	5 30.6	2106	5 50.7	2194	6 13.8
1843	5 14.1	1931	5 31.4	2019	5 31.7	2107	5 43.2	2195	6 14.4
1844	5 07.2	1932	5 22.4	2020	5 33.1	2108	5 43.8	2196	6 12.2
1845	5 06.3	1933	5 22.2	2021	5 33.4	2109	5 44.4	2197	6 05.9
1846	5 07.6	1934	5 21.8	2022	5 42.1	2110	5 52.2	2198	6 13.9
1847	5 06.9	1935	5 21.9	2023	5 41.6	2111	5 44.7	2199	6 04.7
1848	5 07.3	1936	5 22.1	2024	5 41.9	2112	5 53.9	2200	6 13.4

Right Ascensions of NGC Objects

NGC	α_{2000}	NGC	α_{2000}	NGC	α_{2000}	NGC	α_{2000}	NGC	α_{2000}
	h m		h m		h m		h m		h m
2201	6 13.4	2289	6 50.7	2377	7 24.9	2465	7 57.7	2553	8 17.7
2202	6 16.9	2290	6 51.0	2378	7 27.4	2466	7 45.2	2554	8 17.9
2203	6 04.7	2291	6 51.0	2379	7 27.4	2467	7 52.6	2555	8 18.0
2204	6 15.7	2292	6 47.6	2380	7 23.9	2468	7 58.0	2556	8 19.2
2205	6 10.6	2293	6 47.7	2381	7 20.0	2469	7 58.1	2557	8 19.2
2206	6 16.0	2294	6 51.2	2382	7 23.9	2470	7 54.3	2558	8 19.4
2207	6 16.4	2295	6 47.3	2383	7 24.8	2471	7 58.3	2559	8 17.1
2208	6 22.5	2296	6 48.6	2384	7 25.1	2472	7 58.6	2560	8 19.9
2209	6 08.7	2297	6 44.4	2385	7 28.4	2473	7 58.4	2561	8 19.6
2210	6 11.5	2298	6 49.0	2386	7 28.6	2474	7 57.9	2562	8 20.4
2211	6 18.4	2299	6 51.1	2387	7 29.0	2475	7 58.0	2563	8 20.6
2212	6 18.5	2300	7 32.	2388	7 28.8	2476	7 56.7	2564	8 18.6
2213	6 10.7	2301	6 51.8	2389	7 29.1	2477	7 52.3	2565	8 19.8
2214	6 12.8	2302	6 51.9	2390	7 29.0	2478	7 54.7	2566	8 18.7
2215	6 21.0	2303	6 56.2	2391	7 29.2	2479	7 55.1	2567	8 18.6
2216	6 21.6	2304	6 55.0	2392	7 29.2	2480	7 57.2	2568	8 18.0
2217	6 21.7	2305	6 48.6	2393	7 30.0	2481	7 57.3	2569	8 21.5
2218	6 24.7	2306	6 54.6	2394	7 28.6	2482	7 54.9	2570	8 21.5
2219	6 23.4	2307	6 48.8	2395	7 27.1	2483	7 55.9	2571	8 18.9
2220	6 21.8	2308	6 58.6	2396	7 28.1	2484	7 58.5	2572	8 21.4
2221	6 20.2	2309	6 56.2	2397	7 21.3	2485	7 56.7	2573	1 42.
2222	6 20.3	2310	6 54.0	2398	7 30.3	2486	7 57.9	2574	8 20.8
2223	6 24.6	2311	6 57.8	2399	7 29.9	2487	7 58.3	2575	8 22.8
2224	6 27.6	2312	6 58.8	2400	7 30.0	2488	8 01.8	2576	8 22.9
2225	6 26.6	2313	6 58.0	2401	7 29.4	2489	7 56.2	2577	8 22.7
2226	6 26.7	2314	7 10.5	2402	7 30.8	2490	7 59.2	2578	8 21.4
2227	6 25.9	2315	7 02.5	2403	7 36.9	2491	7 58.4	2579	8 21.1
2228	6 21.2	2316	6 59.7	2404	7 37.1	2492	7 59.4	2580	8 21.6
2229	6 21.3	2317	6 58.8	2405	7 32.2	2493	8 00.4	2581	8 24.5
2230	6 21.4	2318	6 59.5	2406	7 31.9	2494	7 59.2	2582	8 25.3
2231	6 20.4	2319	7 01.1	2407	7 31.9	2495	8 00.6	2583	8 23.2
2232	6 26.6	2320	7 05.6	2408	7 40.5	2496	7 58.6	2584	8 23.2
2233	6 21.7	2321	7 05.9	2409	7 31.6	2497	8 02.3	2585	8 23.4
2234	6 29.3	2322	7 05.9	2410	7 35.0	2498	7 59.6	2586	8 24.4
2235	6 22.3	2323	7 03.2	2411	7 34.6	2499	7 58.8	2587	8 23.5
2236	6 29.7	2324	7 04.2	2412	7 34.4	2500	8 01.9	2588	8 23.2
2237	6 30.3	2325	7 02.7	2413	7 33.3	2501	7 58.6	2589	8 24.5
2238	6 30.6	2326	7 08.4	2414	7 33.3	2502	7 55.9	2590	8 25.1
2239	6 31.0	2327	7 04.3	2415	7 36.9	2503	8 00.6	2591	8 37.4
2240	6 32.9	2328	7 02.5	2416	7 35.7	2504	7 59.8	2592	8 27.1
2241	6 22.7	2329	7 09.2	2417	7 30.1	2505	8 04.0	2593	8 26.8
2242	6 34.0	2330	7 09.5	2418	7 36.5	2506	8 00.2	2594	8 27.3
2243	6 29.8	2331	7 07.2	2419	7 38.1	2507	8 01.6	2595	8 27.7
2244	6 32.4	2332	7 09.5	2420	7 38.5	2508	8 02.0	2596	8 27.4
2245	6 32.7	2333	7 08.4	2421	7 36.3	2509	8 00.7	2597	8 30.0
2246	6 32.4	2334	7 09.9	2422	7 36.6	2510	8 02.2	2598	8 30.0
2247	6 33.2	2335	7 06.6	2423	7 37.1	2511	8 02.3	2599	8 32.2
2248	6 34.6	2336	7 27.1	2424	7 40.7	2512	8 03.1	2600	8 34.8
2249	6 25.9	2337	7 10.2	2425	7 38.3	2513	8 02.5	2601	8 25.5
2250	6 32.8	2338	7 07.7	2426	7 43.2	2514	8 02.8	2602	8 35.2
2251	6 34.7	2339	7 08.3	2427	7 36.5	2515	8 03.4	2603	8 35.5
2252	6 35.0	2340	7 11.0	2428	7 39.2	2516	7 58.3	2604	8 33.3
2253	6 42.4	2341	7 09.3	2429	7 43.7	2517	8 02.8	2605	8 35.4
2254	6 36.0	2342	7 09.4	2430	7 39.4	2518	8 07.3	2606	8 35.7
2255	6 34.0	2343	7 08.3	2431	7 45.3	2519	8 08.0	2607	8 33.9
2256	6 47.2	2344	7 12.5	2432	7 40.9	2520	8 02.5	2608	8 35.3
2257	6 30.4	2345	7 08.3	2433	7 43.0	2521	8 08.8	2609	8 29.5
2258	6 47.8	2346	7 09.4	2434	7 34.9	2522	8 06.1	2610	8 33.4
2259	6 38.6	2347	7 16.1	2435	7 44.2	2523	8 15.0	2611	8 35.5
2260	6 38.1	2348	7 03.1	2436	7 46.1	2524	8 08.1	2612	8 33.8
2261	6 39.2	2349	7 10.0	2437	7 41.8	2525	8 05.6	2613	8 33.4
2262	6 38.4	2350	7 13.2	2438	7 41.8	2526	8 06.9	2614	8 42.8
2263	6 38.4	2351	7 13.5	2439	7 40.8	2527	8 05.3	2615	8 34.6
2264	6 41.1	2352	7 13.6	2440	7 41.9	2528	8 07.4	2616	8 35.6
2265	6 41.5	2353	7 14.6	2441	7 52.2	2529	8 07.8	2617	8 35.7
2266	6 43.2	2354	7 14.3	2442	7 36.4	2530	8 07.9	2618	8 36.2
2267	6 40.8	2355	7 16.9	2443	7 36.3	2531	8 08.0	2619	8 37.6
2268	7 14.	2356	7 17.1	2444	7 46.9	2532	8 10.2	2620	8 37.5
2269	6 43.9	2357	7 17.6	2445	7 46.9	2533	8 07.0	2621	8 37.7
2270	6 43.9	2358	7 16.8	2446	7 48.7	2534	8 12.9	2622	8 38.3
2271	6 42.8	2359	7 18.6	2447	7 44.6	2535	8 11.2	2623	8 38.4
2272	6 42.7	2360	7 17.8	2448	7 44.6	2536	8 11.3	2624	8 38.1
2273	6 50.1	2361	7 18.4	2449	7 47.3	2537	8 13.2	2625	8 38.4
2274	6 47.2	2362	7 18.8	2450	7 47.5	2538	8 11.4	2626	8 35.6
2275	6 47.2	2363	7 28.7	2451	7 45.4	2539	8 10.7	2627	8 37.3
2276	7 27.	2364	7 20.8	2452	7 47.4	2540	8 12.8	2628	8 40.5
2277	6 47.8	2365	7 22.5	2453	7 47.8	2541	8 14.7	2629	8 47.2
2278	6 48.3	2366	7 28.9	2454	7 50.5	2542	8 11.3	2630	8 45.4
2279	6 48.4	2367	7 20.1	2455	7 49.0	2543	8 13.0	2631	8 47.1
2280	6 44.8	2368	7 21.0	2456	7 54.1	2544	8 21.7	2632	8 40.1
2281	6 49.3	2369	7 16.6	2457	7 54.7	2545	8 14.2	2633	8 48.1
2282	6 46.9	2370	7 25.0	2458	7 55.4	2546	8 12.4	2634	8 48.4
2283	6 45.9	2371	7 25.6	2459	7 52.0	2547	8 10.7	2635	8 38.5
2284	6 49.1	2372	7 25.6	2460	7 56.9	2548	8 13.8	2636	8 48.4
2285	6 49.4	2373	7 26.5	2461	7 56.0	2549	8 19.0	2637	8 41.1
2286	6 47.6	2374	7 24.0	2462	7 56.7	2550	8 24.6	2638	8 42.4
2287	6 47.0	2375	7 27.1	2463	7 57.1	2551	8 24.8	2639	8 43.6
2288	6 50.7	2376	7 26.6	2464	7 57.2	2552	8 19.3	2640	8 37.4

Right Ascensions of NGC Objects

NGC	α_{2000}	NGC	α_{2000}	NGC	α_{2000}	NGC	α_{2000}	NGC	α_{2000}
	h m		h m		h m		h m		h m
2641	8 48.1	2729	9 01.5	2817	9 17.3	2905	9 32.2	2993	9 45.8
2642	8 40.7	2730	9 02.3	2818	9 16.0	2906	9 32.2	2994	9 47.2
2643	8 41.7	2731	9 02.1	2819	9 18.2	2907	9 31.6	2995	9 44.1
2644	8 41.5	2732	9 13.4	2820	9 21.8	2908	9 43.5	2996	9 46.5
2645	8 38.9	2733	9 02.1	2821	9 16.8	2909	9 44.0	2997	9 45.6
2646	8 50.4	2734	9 03.0	2822	9 14.0	2910	9 30.4	2998	9 48.7
2647	8 42.6	2735	9 02.6	2823	9 19.3	2911	9 33.8	2999	9 45.2
2648	8 42.7	2736	9 00.4	2824	9 19.0	2912	9 33.7	3000	9 49.1
2649	8 44.1	2737	9 03.9	2825	9 19.4	2913	9 34.0	3001	9 46.3
2650	8 50.0	2738	9 03.9	2826	9 19.4	2914	9 34.0	3002	9 49.0
2651	8 44.0	2739	9 06.0	2827	9 19.2	2915	9 26.2	3003	9 48.6
2652	8 43.3	2740	9 06.1	2828	9 19.5	2916	9 35.0	3004	9 49.2
2653	8 55.6	2741	9 04.0	2829	9 19.5	2917	9 34.5	3005	9 49.2
2654	8 49.2	2742	9 07.6	2830	9 19.7	2918	9 35.8	3006	9 49.3
2655	8 55.6	2743	9 05.0	2831	9 19.7	2919	9 34.8	3007	9 47.6
2656	8 47.8	2744	9 04.7	2832	9 19.8	2920	9 34.3	3008	9 49.6
2657	8 45.4	2745	9 04.6	2833	9 19.9	2921	9 34.7	3009	9 50.2
2658	8 43.4	2746	9 06.0	2834	9 20.0	2922	9 36.8	3010	9 50.6
2659	8 42.6	2747	9 05.3	2835	9 17.9	2923	9 36.0	3011	9 49.7
2660	8 42.2	2748	9 13.7	2836	9 13.7	2924	9 35.2	3012	9 49.8
2661	8 46.0	2749	9 05.4	2837	9 18.4	2925	9 33.7	3013	9 50.1
2662	8 45.7	2750	9 05.7	2838	9 20.7	2926	9 37.5	3014	9 49.2
2663	8 45.1	2751	9 05.5	2839	9 20.6	2927	9 37.2	3015	9 49.4
2664	8 47.2	2752	9 05.7	2840	9 20.8	2928	9 37.3	3016	9 49.7
2665	8 46.0	2753	9 07.2	2841	9 22.0	2929	9 37.4	3017	9 49.1
2666	8 50.0	2754	9 05.0	2842	9 15.6	2930	9 37.5	3018	9 49.7
2667	8 48.3	2755	9 07.9	2843	9 20.4	2931	9 37.6	3019	9 50.0
2668	8 49.4	2756	9 09.0	2844	9 21.8	2932	9 35.3	3020	9 50.1
2669	8 44.9	2757	9 05.5	2845	9 18.6	2933	9 38.0	3021	9 51.0
2670	8 45.5	2758	9 05.4	2846	9 19.9	2934	9 38.0	3022	9 49.8
2671	8 46.2	2759	9 08.6	2847	9 20.1	2935	9 36.7	3023	9 49.9
2672	8 49.3	2760	9 15.7	2848	9 20.2	2936	9 37.7	3024	9 50.5
2673	8 49.4	2761	9 07.5	2849	9 19.3	2937	9 37.7	3025	9 49.5
2674	8 48.2	2762	9 09.8	2850	9 21.0	2938	9 38.3	3026	9 50.9
2675	8 51.9	2763	9 06.8	2851	9 20.6	2939	9 38.1	3027	9 55.7
2676	8 51.5	2764	9 08.3	2852	9 23.2	2940	9 38.1	3028	9 49.9
2677	8 50.0	2765	9 07.6	2853	9 23.3	2941	9 38.4	3029	9 48.7
2678	8 50.2	2766	9 08.8	2854	9 24.0	2942	9 39.1	3030	9 50.2
2679	8 51.5	2767	9 10.1	2855	9 21.5	2943	9 38.6	3031	9 55.6
2680	8 51.5	2768	9 11.6	2856	9 24.2	2944	9 39.3	3032	9 52.1
2681	8 53.5	2769	9 10.4	2857	9 24.5	2945	9 37.6	3033	9 48.8
2682	8 50.4	2770	9 09.6	2858	9 22.9	2946	9 39.1	3034	9 55.8
2683	8 52.7	2771	9 10.5	2859	9 24.3	2947	9 38.4	3035	9 51.8
2684	8 54.8	2772	9 07.7	2860	9 24.9	2948	9 38.9	3036	9 49.3
2685	8 55.6	2773	9 09.6	2861	9 23.6	2949	9 40.0	3037	9 51.4
2686	8 54.9	2774	9 10.6	2862	9 24.9	2950	9 42.6	3038	9 51.3
2687	8 55.0	2775	9 10.9	2863	9 23.6	2951	9 39.7	3039	9 52.5
2688	8 55.3	2776	9 12.2	2864	9 24.2	2952	9 39.3	3040	9 53.0
2689	8 55.2	2777	9 10.7	2865	9 23.5	2953	9 40.4	3041	9 53.1
2690	8 52.7	2778	9 12.3	2866	9 22.0	2954	9 40.5	3042	9 53.4
2691	8 54.8	2779	9 12.3	2867	9 21.4	2955	9 41.3	3043	9 56.2
2692	8 57.0	2780	9 12.7	2868	9 23.4	2956	9 39.3	3044	9 53.7
2693	8 57.0	2781	9 11.5	2869	9 23.6	2957	9 47.9	3045	9 53.2
2694	8 57.0	2782	9 14.1	2870	9 27.8	2958	9 40.6	3046	9 53.3
2695	8 54.5	2783	9 13.6	2871	9 25.7	2959	9 45.1	3047	9 54.6
2696	8 54.4	2784	9 12.3	2872	9 25.7	2960	9 40.6	3048	9 55.0
2697	8 55.1	2785	9 15.2	2873	9 25.9	2961	9 45.4	3049	9 54.8
2698	8 55.6	2786	9 14.0	2874	9 25.8	2962	9 40.9	3050	9 54.3
2699	8 55.9	2787	9 19.3	2875	9 25.8	2963	9 47.8	3051	9 53.8
2700	8 55.7	2788	9 09.0	2876	9 25.2	2964	9 42.9	3052	9 54.5
2701	8 59.1	2789	9 15.0	2877	9 25.8	2965	9 43.2	3053	9 55.6
2702	8 55.9	2790	9 15.0	2878	9 25.8	2966	9 42.2	3054	9 54.5
2703	8 55.9	2791	9 15.0	2879	9 25.4	2967	9 42.1	3055	9 55.3
2704	8 56.9	2792	9 12.4	2880	9 29.6	2968	9 43.2	3056	9 54.5
2705	8 56.0	2793	9 16.8	2881	9 25.9	2969	9 41.8	3057	10 05.6
2706	8 56.3	2794	9 16.0	2882	9 26.5	2970	9 43.5	3058	9 53.5
2707	8 56.2	2795	9 16.1	2883	9 25.2	2971	9 43.7	3059	9 50.2
2708	8 56.1	2796	9 16.7	2884	9 26.4	2972	9 40.3	3060	9 56.4
2709	8 56.3	2797	9 16.4	2885	9 29.6	2973	9 38.0	3061	9 56.2
2710	8 59.8	2798	9 17.4	2886	9 26.5	2974	9 42.6	3062	9 56.6
2711	8 57.3	2799	9 17.5	2887	9 23.3	2975	9 41.2	3063	10 01.6
2712	8 59.5	2800	9 18.6	2888	9 26.3	2976	9 47.3	3064	9 55.6
2713	8 57.3	2801	9 16.7	2889	9 27.2	2977	9 43.8	3065	10 01.9
2714	8 53.5	2802	9 16.7	2890	9 26.6	2978	9 43.3	3066	10 02.2
2715	9 08.1	2803	9 16.7	2891	9 26.8	2979	9 43.1	3067	9 58.4
2716	8 57.3	2804	9 16.8	2892	9 32.9	2980	9 43.2	3068	9 58.5
2717	8 57.0	2805	9 20.3	2893	9 30.3	2981	9 45.0	3069	9 57.9
2718	8 58.9	2806	9 17.0	2894	9 29.4	2982	9 42.4	3070	9 58.0
2719	9 00.3	2807	9 17.0	2895	9 32.4	2983	9 43.7	3071	9 58.9
2720	8 59.2	2808	9 12.0	2896	9 30.3	2984	9 43.6	3072	9 57.6
2721	8 58.9	2809	9 17.1	2897	9 29.8	2985	9 50.4	3073	10 00.9
2722	8 58.8	2810	9 22.1	2898	9 29.8	2986	9 44.3	3074	9 59.7
2723	9 00.2	2811	9 16.2	2899	9 27.0	2987	9 45.6	3075	9 59.0
2724	9 01.0	2812	9 17.6	2900	9 30.3	2988	9 46.8	3076	9 57.7
2725	9 01.1	2813	9 17.7	2901	9 32.4	2989	9 45.4	3077	10 03.3
2726	9 04.9	2814	9 21.2	2902	9 30.9	2990	9 46.3	3078	9 58.4
2727	9 01.1	2815	9 16.3	2903	9 32.2	2991	9 46.8	3079	10 02.0
2728	9 01.8	2816	9 21.1	2904	9 30.2	2992	9 45.7	3080	9 59.9

Right Ascensions of NGC Objects

NGC	α_{2000}	NGC	α_{2000}	NGC	α_{2000}	NGC	α_{2000}	NGC	α_{2000}
	h m		h m		h m		h m		h m
3081	9 59.5	3169	10 14.2	3257	10 28.8	3345	10 43.6	3433	10 52.1
3082	9 58.9	3170	10 16.1	3258	10 28.9	3346	10 43.7	3434	10 52.0
3083	9 59.9	3171	10 15.6	3259	10 32.6	3347	10 42.8	3435	10 54.8
3084	9 59.0	3172	11 50.	3260	10 29.1	3348	10 47.2	3436	10 42.4
3085	9 59.6	3173	10 14.5	3261	10 29.0	3349	10 43.8	3437	10 52.6
3086	10 00.2	3174	10 20.8	3262	10 29.2	3350	10 44.4	3438	10 52.4
3087	9 59.2	3175	10 14.7	3263	10 29.3	3351	10 44.0	3439	10 52.4
3088	10 01.1	3176	10 15.3	3264	10 32.4	3352	10 44.3	3440	10 53.9
3089	9 59.6	3177	10 16.6	3265	10 31.1	3353	10 45.4	3441	10 52.5
3090	10 00.6	3178	10 16.1	3266	10 33.3	3354	10 43.1	3442	10 53.1
3091	10 00.2	3179	10 18.0	3267	10 29.8	3355	10 43.5	3443	10 53.0
3092	10 00.9	3180	10 18.1	3268	10 30.0	3356	10 44.2	3444	10 53.0
3093	10 01.0	3181	10 18.2	3269	10 30.0	3357	10 44.4	3445	10 54.6
3094	10 01.5	3182	10 19.5	3270	10 31.5	3358	10 43.6	3446	10 52.1
3095	10 00.1	3183	10 21.8	3271	10 30.5	3359	10 46.6	3447	10 53.4
3096	10 00.7	3184	10 18.3	3272	10 32.2	3360	10 44.3	3448	10 54.7
3097	10 04.3	3185	10 17.6	3273	10 30.5	3361	10 44.4	3449	10 52.9
3098	10 02.3	3186	10 17.6	3274	10 32.3	3362	10 44.8	3450	10 48.1
3099	10 02.7	3187	10 17.8	3275	10 30.9	3363	10 45.3	3451	10 54.4
3100	10 00.7	3188	10 19.7	3276	10 31.1	3364	10 48.5	3452	10 54.1
3101	10 01.7	3189	10 18.2	3277	10 32.9	3365	10 46.3	3453	10 53.7
3102	10 04.6	3190	10 18.1	3278	10 31.6	3366	10 35.2	3454	10 54.5
3103	10 00.7	3191	10 19.1	3279	10 34.6	3367	10 46.6	3455	10 54.5
3104	10 03.9	3192	10 19.0	3280	10 32.6	3368	10 46.8	3456	10 54.1
3105	10 00.8	3193	10 18.4	3281	10 31.9	3369	10 46.7	3457	10 54.7
3106	10 03.9	3194	10 23.0	3282	10 32.3	3370	10 47.1	3458	10 56.0
3107	10 03.3	3195	10 09.5	3283	10 32.9	3371	10 47.0	3459	10 54.7
3108	10 02.6	3196	10 18.8	3284	10 36.0	3372	10 43.8	3460	10 54.8
3109	10 03.1	3197	10 14.4	3285	10 33.6	3373	10 47.2	3461	10 54.9
3110	10 04.1	3198	10 19.9	3286	10 36.3	3374	10 47.9	3462	10 55.3
3111	10 06.2	3199	10 17.1	3287	10 34.8	3375	10 47.0	3463	10 55.1
3112	10 04.0	3200	10 18.6	3288	10 36.4	3376	10 47.4	3464	10 54.7
3113	10 04.4	3201	10 17.6	3289	10 34.2	3377	10 47.7	3465	10 59.3
3114	10 02.7	3202	10 20.5	3290	10 35.1	3378	10 46.6	3466	10 56.3
3115	10 05.2	3203	10 19.6	3291	10 36.1	3379	10 47.8	3467	10 56.7
3116	10 06.6	3204	10 20.2	3292	10 35.6	3380	10 48.2	3468	10 57.4
3117	10 06.2	3205	10 20.8	3293	10 35.8	3381	10 48.4	3469	10 56.9
3118	10 07.3	3206	10 21.8	3294	10 36.3	3382	10 48.5	3470	10 58.7
3119	10 06.6	3207	10 21.0	3295	10 32.7	3383	10 47.3	3471	10 59.1
3120	10 05.4	3208	10 19.7	3296	10 32.7	3384	10 48.3	3472	10 57.3
3121	10 06.8	3209	10 20.6	3297	10 35.4	3385	10 48.2	3473	10 58.0
3122	10 06.5	3210	10 27.2	3298	10 37.2	3386	10 48.2	3474	10 58.1
3123	10 07.0	3211	10 17.8	3299	10 36.4	3387	10 48.2	3475	10 58.3
3124	10 06.7	3212	10 28.1	3300	10 36.6	3388	10 48.3	3476	10 58.1
3125	10 06.6	3213	10 21.3	3301	10 36.9	3389	10 48.5	3477	10 58.2
3126	10 08.2	3214	10 23.1	3302	10 35.8	3390	10 48.1	3478	10 59.5
3127	10 06.3	3215	10 29.0	3303	10 37.1	3391	10 48.9	3479	10 58.9
3128	10 05.9	3216	10 21.7	3304	10 37.6	3392	10 51.0	3480	10 58.9
3129	10 08.4	3217	10 21.4	3305	10 36.3	3393	10 48.3	3481	10 59.5
3130	10 08.2	3218	10 26.5	3306	10 37.2	3394	10 50.6	3482	10 58.6
3131	10 08.7	3219	10 22.7	3307	10 36.3	3395	10 49.8	3483	10 59.0
3132	10 07.0	3220	10 23.7	3308	10 36.4	3396	10 49.9	3484	11 03.0
3133	10 07.2	3221	10 22.3	3309	10 36.6	3397	10 54.2	3485	11 00.0
3134	10 09.5	3222	10 22.6	3310	10 38.7	3398	10 51.5	3486	11 00.4
3135	10 10.9	3223	10 21.6	3311	10 36.7	3399	10 49.4	3487	11 00.7
3136	10 05.8	3224	10 21.6	3312	10 37.0	3400	10 50.8	3488	11 01.4
3137	10 09.2	3225	10 25.1	3313	10 37.5	3401	10 50.4	3489	11 00.3
3138	10 09.1	3226	10 23.4	3314	10 37.2	3402	10 50.0	3490	10 59.9
3139	10 10.1	3227	10 23.5	3315	10 37.3	3403	10 53.9	3491	11 00.6
3140	10 09.5	3228	10 21.8	3316	10 37.6	3404	10 50.3	3492	11 00.9
3141	10 09.3	3229	10 23.4	3317	10 37.4	3405	10 49.7	3493	11 01.5
3142	10 10.1	3230	10 23.7	3318	10 37.3	3406	10 51.8	3494	11 01.2
3143	10 10.2	3231	10 26.7	3319	10 39.2	3407	10 52.3	3495	11 01.3
3144	10 15.5	3232	10 24.3	3320	10 39.6	3408	10 52.2	3496	10 59.8
3145	10 10.2	3233	10 22.0	3321	10 38.8	3409	10 50.2	3497	11 01.4
3146	10 11.2	3234	10 24.9	3322	10 38.8	3410	10 51.9	3498	11 01.9
3147	10 16.9	3235	10 24.9	3323	10 39.7	3411	10 50.3	3499	11 03.2
3148	10 13.4	3236	10 26.8	3324	10 37.3	3412	10 50.9	3500	11 01.7
3149	10 03.8	3237	10 25.8	3325	10 39.3	3413	10 51.3	3501	11 02.9
3150	10 13.4	3238	10 26.7	3326	10 39.5	3414	10 51.3	3502	11 02.1
3151	10 13.5	3239	10 25.1	3327	10 40.0	3415	10 51.7	3503	11 01.3
3152	10 13.6	3240	10 24.5	3328	10 39.7	3416	10 51.7	3504	11 03.2
3153	10 12.9	3241	10 24.3	3329	10 44.7	3417	10 51.0	3505	11 02.7
3154	10 13.1	3242	10 24.8	3330	10 38.6	3418	10 51.3	3506	11 03.2
3155	10 17.6	3243	10 26.4	3331	10 39.0	3419	10 51.3	3507	11 03.5
3156	10 12.7	3244	10 25.5	3332	10 40.4	3420	10 50.1	3508	11 02.9
3157	10 11.8	3245	10 27.3	3333	10 39.9	3421	10 50.8	3509	11 04.4
3158	10 13.8	3246	10 26.7	3334	10 41.4	3422	10 51.1	3510	11 03.7
3159	10 13.9	3247	10 25.9	3335	10 39.6	3423	10 51.2	3511	11 03.4
3160	10 13.9	3248	10 27.8	3336	10 40.3	3424	10 51.8	3512	11 04.0
3161	10 14.0	3249	10 26.3	3337	10 41.8	3425	10 51.4	3513	11 03.8
3162	10 13.5	3250	10 26.5	3338	10 42.1	3426	10 51.6	3514	11 03.9
3163	10 14.1	3251	10 29.3	3339	10 42.2	3427	10 51.4	3515	11 04.6
3164	10 15.2	3252	10 34.4	3340	10 42.3	3428	10 51.4	3516	11 06.8
3165	10 13.5	3253	10 28.5	3341	10 42.6	3429	10 50.9	3517	11 05.6
3166	10 13.8	3254	10 29.3	3342	10 42.7	3430	10 52.2	3518	11 04.3
3167	10 14.6	3255	10 26.5	3343	10 46.1	3431	10 51.2	3519	11 04.0
3168	10 16.4	3256	10 27.8	3344	10 43.5	3432	10 52.5	3520	11 05.5

NGC	α_{2000}	NGC	α_{2000}	NGC	α_{2000}	NGC	α_{2000}	NGC	α_{2000}
	h m		h m		h m		h m		h m
3521	11 05.8	3609	11 17.8	3697	11 28.7	3785	11 39.5	3873	11 45.7
3522	11 06.6	3610	11 18.4	3698	11 29.0	3786	11 39.7	3874	11 45.8
3523	11 02.8	3611	11 17.5	3699	11 28.0	3787	11 39.7	3875	11 45.8
3524	11 06.5	3612	11 18.2	3700	11 29.5	3788	11 39.7	3876	11 45.4
3525	11 06.4	3613	11 18.6	3701	11 29.4	3789	11 38.1	3877	11 46.1
3526	11 07.0	3614	11 18.3	3702	11 30.2	3790	11 39.8	3878	11 46.2
3527	11 07.3	3615	11 18.0	3703	11 29.6	3791	11 39.8	3879	11 46.9
3528	11 07.3	3616	11 18.2	3704	11 30.0	3792	11 39.8	3880	11 46.3
3529	11 07.3	3617	11 17.8	3705	11 30.1	3793	11 39.4	3881	11 46.5
3530	11 08.7	3618	11 18.5	3706	11 29.7	3794	11 39.6	3882	11 46.1
3531	11 06.9	3619	11 19.4	3707	11 30.1	3795	11 40.1	3883	11 46.8
3532	11 06.4	3620	11 16.1	3708	11 30.7	3796	11 40.6	3884	11 46.2
3533	11 07.2	3621	11 18.3	3709	11 30.7	3797	11 40.1	3885	11 46.8
3534	11 08.7	3622	11 20.2	3710	11 31.0	3798	11 40.2	3886	11 47.1
3535	11 08.5	3623	11 18.9	3711	11 29.4	3799	11 40.2	3887	11 47.1
3536	11 08.8	3624	11 18.8	3712	11 31.1	3800	11 40.2	3888	11 47.6
3537	11 08.6	3625	11 20.5	3713	11 31.6	3801	11 40.3	3889	11 47.9
3538	11 11.5	3626	11 20.1	3714	11 31.8	3802	11 40.3	3890	11 49.4
3539	11 09.1	3627	11 20.2	3715	11 31.5	3803	11 40.3	3891	11 48.0
3540	11 09.3	3628	11 20.3	3716	11 31.7	3804	11 40.9	3892	11 48.0
3541	11 08.8	3629	11 20.5	3717	11 31.5	3805	11 40.8	3893	11 48.6
3542	11 10.0	3630	11 20.3	3718	11 32.6	3806	11 40.8	3894	11 48.8
3543	11 10.8	3631	11 21.0	3719	11 32.2	3807	11 40.8	3895	11 49.1
3544	11 11.5	3632	11 20.5	3720	11 32.4	3808	11 40.7	3896	11 48.9
3545	11 10.2	3633	11 20.4	3721	11 34.4	3809	11 41.3	3897	11 49.0
3546	11 09.8	3634	11 20.6	3722	11 34.5	3810	11 41.0	3898	11 49.2
3547	11 09.9	3635	11 20.6	3723	11 32.4	3811	11 41.3	3899	11 49.2
3548	11 10.4	3636	11 20.4	3724	11 34.5	3812	11 41.1	3900	11 49.2
3549	11 10.9	3637	11 20.7	3725	11 33.7	3813	11 41.3	3901	11 43.0
3550	11 10.6	3638	11 20.3	3726	11 33.3	3814	11 41.5	3902	11 49.3
3551	11 09.6	3639	11 21.5	3727	11 33.7	3815	11 41.7	3903	11 49.1
3552	11 10.6	3640	11 21.1	3728	11 33.2	3816	11 41.8	3904	11 49.2
3553	11 10.6	3641	11 21.2	3729	11 33.8	3817	11 41.9	3905	11 49.1
3554	11 10.7	3642	11 22.3	3730	11 34.7	3818	11 42.0	3906	11 49.7
3555	11 09.7	3643	11 21.4	3731	11 34.2	3819	11 42.1	3907	11 49.5
3556	11 11.5	3644	11 21.5	3732	11 34.2	3820	11 42.1	3908	11 49.9
3557	11 10.0	3645	11 21.6	3733	11 35.0	3821	11 42.2	3909	11 49.6
3558	11 10.9	3646	11 21.7	3734	11 34.7	3822	11 42.2	3910	11 50.0
3559	11 10.7	3647	11 21.6	3735	11 36.0	3823	11 42.2	3911	11 49.4
3560	11 10.7	3648	11 22.6	3736	11 35.6	3824	11 42.8	3912	11 50.1
3561	11 11.2	3649	11 22.2	3737	11 35.6	3825	11 42.4	3913	11 50.6
3562	11 12.9	3650	11 22.6	3738	11 35.8	3826	11 42.4	3914	11 50.6
3563	11 11.4	3651	11 22.4	3739	11 35.6	3827	11 42.6	3915	11 50.6
3564	11 10.6	3652	11 22.6	3740	11 36.2	3828	11 42.9	3916	11 50.8
3565	11 09.9	3653	11 22.5	3741	11 36.0	3829	11 43.5	3917	11 50.8
3566	11 09.9	3654	11 24.1	3742	11 35.4	3830	11 43.2	3918	11 50.3
3567	11 11.3	3655	11 22.9	3743	11 35.8	3831	11 43.2	3919	11 50.6
3568	11 10.8	3656	11 23.6	3744	11 35.8	3832	11 43.5	3920	11 50.1
3569	11 12.1	3657	11 23.8	3745	11 37.7	3833	11 43.5	3921	11 51.1
3570	11 12.1	3658	11 24.0	3746	11 37.7	3834	11 43.6	3922	11 51.2
3571	11 11.5	3659	11 23.8	3747	11 37.5	3835	11 44.1	3923	11 51.0
3572	11 10.4	3660	11 23.6	3748	11 37.8	3836	11 43.5	3924	11 52.6
3573	11 11.3	3661	11 23.7	3749	11 35.8	3837	11 43.9	3925	11 51.3
3574	11 12.2	3662	11 23.8	3750	11 37.9	3838	11 44.2	3926	11 51.5
3575	11 13.1	3663	11 24.0	3751	11 37.9	3839	11 43.9	3927	11 51.6
3576	11 11.8	3664	11 24.4	3752	11 37.6	3840	11 43.8	3928	11 51.8
3577	11 13.8	3665	11 24.7	3753	11 37.9	3841	11 44.0	3929	11 51.7
3578	11 12.8	3666	11 24.4	3754	11 37.9	3842	11 44.0	3930	11 51.8
3579	11 11.9	3667	11 24.3	3755	11 36.6	3843	11 43.9	3931	11 51.2
3580	11 12.1	3668	11 25.5	3756	11 36.8	3844	11 44.0	3932	11 52.5
3581	11 12.1	3669	11 25.4	3757	11 37.1	3845	11 44.1	3933	11 52.0
3582	11 12.3	3670	11 24.7	3758	11 36.4	3846	11 44.5	3934	11 52.2
3583	11 12.4	3671	11 25.8	3759	11 36.9	3847	11 44.2	3935	11 52.4
3584	11 12.4	3672	11 25.0	3760	10 36.9	3848	11 43.7	3936	11 52.3
3585	11 13.3	3673	11 25.2	3761	11 36.8	3849	11 44.2	3937	11 52.7
3586	11 12.6	3674	11 26.4	3762	11 37.5	3850	11 45.6	3938	11 52.8
3587	11 14.0	3675	11 26.1	3763	11 36.4	3851	11 44.3	3939	11 53.2
3588	11 14.0	3676	11 25.6	3764	11 36.9	3852	11 44.4	3940	11 52.7
3589	11 15.2	3677	11 26.3	3765	11 37.1	3853	11 44.4	3941	11 52.9
3590	11 12.9	3678	11 26.2	3766	11 36.1	3854	11 44.5	3942	11 51.4
3591	11 14.1	3679	11 26.2	3767	11 37.3	3855	11 44.3	3943	11 52.9
3592	11 14.4	3680	11 26.2	3768	11 37.2	3856	11 44.4	3944	11 53.1
3593	11 14.6	3681	11 26.5	3769	11 37.7	3857	11 44.8	3945	11 53.2
3594	11 16.1	3682	11 27.7	3770	11 38.0	3858	11 44.9	3946	11 53.4
3595	11 15.4	3683	11 27.5	3771	11 38.4	3859	11 44.9	3947	11 53.4
3596	11 15.1	3684	11 27.2	3772	11 37.8	3860	11 44.6	3948	11 53.4
3597	11 14.6	3685	11 26.2	3773	11 38.2	3861	11 44.8	3949	11 53.7
3598	11 15.2	3686	11 27.7	3774	11 38.6	3862	11 45.1	3950	11 53.7
3599	11 15.4	3687	11 28.0	3775	11 38.3	3863	11 45.1	3951	11 53.7
3600	11 15.8	3688	11 27.8	3776	11 38.3	3864	11 45.2	3952	11 53.7
3601	11 15.8	3689	11 27.8	3777	11 36.1	3865	11 44.9	3953	11 53.8
3602	11 15.8	3690	11 28.5	3778	11 38.4	3866	11 45.3	3954	11 53.7
3603	11 15.1	3691	11 28.2	3779	11 38.9	3867	11 45.4	3955	11 54.0
3604	11 16.3	3692	11 28.4	3780	11 39.4	3868	11 45.4	3956	11 54.0
3605	11 16.2	3693	11 28.2	3781	11 39.0	3869	11 45.8	3957	11 54.0
3606	11 16.2	3694	11 28.9	3782	11 39.3	3870	11 45.9	3958	11 54.6
3607	11 16.9	3695	11 29.2	3783	11 39.0	3871	11 46.2	3959	11 54.6
3608	11 17.0	3696	11 28.8	3784	11 39.4	3872	11 45.8	3960	11 50.9

NGC	α_{2000}	NGC	α_{2000}	NGC	α_{2000}	NGC	α_{2000}	NGC	α_{2000}
	h m		h m		h m		h m		h m
3961	11 55.0	4049	12 03.0	4137	12 09.3	4225	12 16.7	4313	12 22.6
3962	11 54.7	4050	12 02.9	4138	12 09.5	4226	12 16.4	4314	12 22.6
3963	11 55.0	4051	12 03.2	4139	12 09.6	4227	12 16.5	4315	12 22.7
3964	11 54.8	4052	12 01.9	4140	12 09.7	4228	12 16.6	4316	12 22.8
3965	11 55.1	4053	12 03.2	4141	12 09.7	4229	12 16.7	4317	12 22.6
3966	11 55.7	4054	12 03.2	4142	12 09.5	4230	12 17.3	4318	12 22.7
3967	11 55.2	4055	12 03.7	4143	12 09.6	4231	12 16.8	4319	12 21.7
3968	11 55.5	4056	12 04.0	4144	12 10.0	4232	12 16.8	4320	12 23.1
3969	11 55.1	4057	12 05.3	4145	12 10.0	4233	12 17.1	4321	12 22.9
3970	11 55.3	4058	12 03.8	4146	12 10.3	4234	12 17.2	4322	12 23.0
3971	11 55.6	4059	12 03.9	4147	12 10.1	4235	12 17.2	4323	12 22.9
3972	11 55.8	4060	12 04.1	4148	12 10.1	4236	12 16.7	4324	12 23.1
3973	11 55.6	4061	12 04.1	4149	12 10.4	4237	12 17.2	4325	12 23.2
3974	11 55.7	4062	12 04.1	4150	12 10.6	4238	12 16.9	4326	12 23.2
3975	11 55.9	4063	12 04.1	4151	12 10.5	4239	12 17.3	4327	12 23.2
3976	11 56.0	4064	12 04.2	4152	12 10.6	4240	12 17.4	4328	12 23.3
3977	11 56.1	4065	12 04.2	4153	12 10.8	4241	12 17.4	4329	12 23.4
3978	11 56.2	4066	12 04.2	4154	12 10.7	4242	12 17.5	4330	12 23.3
3979	11 56.1	4067	12 04.2	4155	12 10.8	4243	12 17.6	4331	12 22.4
3980	11 56.1	4068	12 04.0	4156	12 10.8	4244	12 17.5	4332	12 22.8
3981	11 56.1	4069	12 04.2	4157	12 11.1	4245	12 17.6	4333	12 23.4
3982	11 56.5	4070	12 04.2	4158	12 11.2	4246	12 18.0	4334	12 23.4
3983	11 56.4	4071	12 04.2	4159	12 10.7	4247	12 18.0	4335	12 23.0
3984	11 57.8	4072	12 04.3	4160	12 11.6	4248	12 17.8	4336	12 23.6
3985	11 56.7	4073	12 04.5	4161	12 11.4	4249	12 18.0	4337	12 23.9
3986	11 56.7	4074	12 04.6	4162	12 11.9	4250	12 17.4	4338	12 23.1
3987	11 57.4	4075	12 04.7	4163	12 12.2	4251	12 18.1	4339	12 23.6
3988	11 57.4	4076	12 04.6	4164	12 12.1	4252	12 18.5	4340	12 23.6
3989	11 57.4	4077	12 04.7	4165	12 12.2	4253	12 18.4	4341	12 24.0
3990	11 57.6	4078	12 04.8	4166	12 12.2	4254	12 18.8	4342	12 23.6
3991	11 57.6	4079	12 04.8	4167	12 12.2	4255	12 19.0	4343	12 23.7
3992	11 57.6	4080	12 05.0	4168	12 12.3	4256	12 18.7	4344	12 23.6
3993	11 57.6	4081	12 04.6	4169	12 12.2	4257	12 19.1	4345	12 22.7
3994	11 57.6	4082	12 05.3	4170	12 12.3	4258	12 19.0	4346	12 23.5
3995	11 57.7	4083	12 05.3	4171	12 12.3	4259	12 19.4	4347	12 23.9
3996	11 57.8	4084	12 05.3	4172	12 12.2	4260	12 19.4	4348	12 23.9
3997	11 57.8	4085	12 05.4	4173	12 12.3	4261	12 19.4	4349	12 24.5
3998	11 57.9	4086	12 05.5	4174	12 12.4	4262	12 19.5	4350	12 24.0
3999	11 58.4	4087	12 05.6	4175	12 12.5	4263	12 19.7	4351	12 24.0
4000	11 58.0	4088	12 05.6	4176	12 12.7	4264	12 19.6	4352	12 24.1
4001	11 58.1	4089	12 05.6	4177	12 12.8	4265	12 19.7	4353	12 24.0
4002	11 58.0	4090	12 05.5	4178	12 12.8	4266	12 19.7	4354	12 24.1
4003	11 58.0	4091	12 05.7	4179	12 12.9	4267	12 19.8	4355	12 24.2
4004	11 58.1	4092	12 05.9	4180	12 13.1	4268	12 19.8	4356	12 24.3
4005	11 58.2	4093	12 05.9	4181	12 13.4	4269	12 19.8	4357	12 24.0
4006	11 58.2	4094	12 05.9	4182	12 13.4	4270	12 19.8	4358	12 24.0
4007	11 58.2	4095	12 06.0	4183	12 13.3	4271	12 19.6	4359	12 24.2
4008	11 58.3	4096	12 06.0	4184	12 13.6	4272	12 19.8	4360	12 24.3
4009	11 58.4	4097	12 06.1	4185	12 13.4	4273	12 19.9	4361	12 24.5
4010	11 58.6	4098	12 06.1	4186	12 14.1	4274	12 19.8	4362	12 24.2
4011	11 58.4	4099	12 06.1	4187	12 13.4	4275	12 19.9	4363	12 23.5
4012	11 58.5	4100	12 06.2	4188	12 14.2	4276	12 20.2	4364	12 24.0
4013	11 58.5	4101	12 06.2	4189	12 13.8	4277	12 20.1	4365	12 24.5
4014	11 58.6	4102	12 06.4	4190	12 13.7	4278	12 20.1	4366	12 25.0
4015	11 58.7	4103	12 06.7	4191	12 13.9	4279	12 20.4	4367	12 24.6
4016	11 58.4	4104	12 06.6	4192	12 13.8	4280	12 20.4	4368	12 24.7
4017	11 58.7	4105	12 06.7	4193	12 13.9	4281	12 20.4	4369	12 24.6
4018	11 58.7	4106	12 06.8	4194	12 14.2	4282	12 20.4	4370	12 24.9
4019	11 58.9	4107	12 06.7	4195	12 14.2	4283	12 20.3	4371	12 24.9
4020	11 58.9	4108	12 06.8	4196	12 14.4	4284	12 20.2	4372	12 25.8
4021	11 59.0	4109	12 06.9	4197	12 14.6	4285	12 20.7	4373	12 25.3
4022	11 59.0	4110	12 07.1	4198	12 14.3	4286	12 20.7	4374	12 25.1
4023	11 59.1	4111	12 07.1	4199	12 14.8	4287	12 20.8	4375	12 25.0
4024	11 58.5	4112	12 07.1	4200	12 14.8	4288	12 20.6	4376	12 25.3
4025	11 59.2	4113	12 07.2	4201	12 14.7	4289	12 21.0	4377	12 25.2
4026	11 59.4	4114	12 07.2	4202	12 18.2	4290	12 20.8	4378	12 25.3
4027	11 59.5	4115	12 07.2	4203	12 15.1	4291	12 20.3	4379	12 25.2
4028	11 59.9	4116	12 07.6	4204	12 15.2	4292	12 21.3	4380	12 25.4
4029	12 00.1	4117	12 07.8	4205	12 14.8	4293	12 21.2	4381	12 25.1
4030	12 00.4	4118	12 07.9	4206	12 15.3	4294	12 21.3	4382	12 25.4
4031	12 00.5	4119	12 07.9	4207	12 15.5	4295	12 21.2	4383	12 25.4
4032	12 00.6	4120	12 08.5	4208	12 15.4	4296	12 21.5	4384	12 25.2
4033	12 00.6	4121	12 07.9	4209	12 15.5	4297	12 21.5	4385	12 25.7
4034	12 01.5	4122	12 07.2	4210	12 15.3	4298	12 21.5	4386	12 24.5
4035	12 00.5	4123	12 08.2	4211	12 15.6	4299	12 21.7	4387	12 25.7
4036	12 01.4	4124	12 08.2	4212	12 15.7	4300	12 21.7	4388	12 25.8
4037	12 01.4	4125	12 08.1	4213	12 15.7	4301	12 21.6	4389	12 25.6
4038	12 01.9	4126	12 08.7	4214	12 15.6	4302	12 21.7	4390	12 25.8
4039	12 01.9	4127	12 08.4	4215	12 15.9	4303	12 21.9	4391	12 25.3
4040	12 02.2	4128	12 08.5	4216	12 15.9	4304	12 22.2	4392	12 25.2
4041	12 02.2	4129	12 08.9	4217	12 15.8	4305	12 22.1	4393	12 25.8
4042	12 02.4	4130	12 08.9	4218	12 15.8	4306	12 22.1	4394	12 25.9
4043	12 02.4	4131	12 08.7	4219	12 16.4	4307	12 22.1	4395	12 25.8
4044	12 02.5	4132	12 09.0	4220	12 16.2	4308	12 21.9	4396	12 26.0
4045	12 02.7	4133	12 08.6	4221	12 16.6	4309	12 22.2	4397	12 26.0
4046	12 02.8	4134	12 09.2	4222	12 16.4	4310	12 22.4	4398	12 26.1
4047	12 02.9	4135	12 09.2	4223	12 16.5	4311	12 22.4	4399	12 25.9
4048	12 02.9	4136	12 09.3	4224	12 16.6	4312	12 22.5	4400	12 25.9

NGC	α_{2000}	NGC	α_{2000}	NGC	α_{2000}	NGC	α_{2000}	NGC	α_{2000}
	h m		h m		h m		h m		h m
4401	12 25.9	4489	12 30.8	4577	12 37.5	4665	12 45.1	4753	12 52.4
4402	12 26.1	4490	12 30.6	4578	12 37.5	4666	12 45.1	4754	12 52.3
4403	12 26.3	4491	12 31.0	4579	12 37.7	4667	12 45.3	4755	12 53.6
4404	12 26.4	4492	12 31.0	4580	12 37.8	4668	12 45.5	4756	12 52.9
4405	12 26.1	4493	12 31.2	4581	12 38.2	4669	12 44.8	4757	12 52.8
4406	12 26.2	4494	12 31.4	4582	12 38.2	4670	12 45.3	4758	12 52.7
4407	12 26.3	4495	12 31.3	4583	12 38.0	4671	12 45.8	4759	12 53.1
4408	12 26.2	4496	12 31.6	4584	12 38.3	4672	12 46.3	4760	12 53.1
4409	12 26.5	4497	12 31.5	4585	12 38.1	4673	12 45.6	4761	12 53.1
4410	12 26.5	4498	12 31.7	4586	12 38.5	4674	12 46.1	4762	12 52.9
4411	12 26.5	4499	12 32.1	4587	12 38.6	4675	12 45.6	4763	12 53.4
4412	12 26.6	4500	12 31.4	4588	12 38.8	4676	12 46.1	4764	12 53.2
4413	12 26.5	4501	12 32.0	4589	12 37.4	4677	12 47.0	4765	12 53.2
4414	12 26.4	4502	12 32.1	4590	12 39.5	4678	12 46.7	4766	12 53.1
4415	12 26.6	4503	12 32.1	4591	12 39.3	4679	12 47.5	4767	12 53.9
4416	12 26.8	4504	12 32.3	4592	12 39.3	4680	12 46.9	4768	12 53.3
4417	12 26.8	4505	12 32.3	4593	12 39.7	4681	12 47.5	4769	12 53.3
4418	12 26.9	4506	12 32.2	4594	12 40.0	4682	12 47.3	4770	12 53.5
4419	12 26.9	4507	12 35.6	4595	12 39.9	4683	12 47.7	4771	12 53.4
4420	12 27.0	4508	12 32.4	4596	12 39.9	4684	12 47.3	4772	12 53.5
4421	12 27.0	4509	12 33.1	4597	12 40.2	4685	12 47.1	4773	12 53.6
4422	12 27.1	4510	12 31.7	4598	12 40.3	4686	12 46.7	4774	12 53.2
4423	12 27.1	4511	12 32.2	4599	12 40.5	4687	12 47.4	4775	12 53.8
4424	12 27.2	4512	12 32.6	4600	12 40.4	4688	12 47.8	4776	12 54.1
4425	12 27.2	4513	12 31.9	4601	12 40.8	4689	12 47.8	4777	12 54.0
4426	12 27.2	4514	12 32.5	4602	12 40.6	4690	12 47.9	4778	12 54.1
4427	12 27.2	4515	12 33.0	4603	12 40.9	4691	12 48.2	4779	12 53.8
4428	12 27.5	4516	12 33.1	4604	12 40.7	4692	12 47.9	4780	12 54.1
4429	12 27.4	4517	12 32.8	4605	12 40.0	4693	12 47.1	4781	12 54.4
4430	12 27.4	4518	12 33.2	4606	12 41.0	4694	12 48.2	4782	12 54.6
4431	12 27.5	4519	12 33.5	4607	12 41.2	4695	12 47.5	4783	12 54.6
4432	12 27.6	4520	12 33.8	4608	12 41.2	4696	12 48.8	4784	12 54.6
4433	12 27.6	4521	12 32.8	4609	12 42.3	4697	12 48.6	4785	12 53.5
4434	12 27.5	4522	12 33.7	4610	12 41.4	4698	12 48.4	4786	12 54.5
4435	12 27.7	4523	12 33.8	4611	12 41.5	4699	12 49.0	4787	12 54.1
4436	12 27.7	4524	12 33.8	4612	12 41.5	4700	12 49.1	4788	12 54.2
4437	12 32.8	4525	12 33.8	4613	12 41.4	4701	12 49.2	4789	12 54.3
4438	12 27.8	4526	12 34.0	4614	12 41.4	4702	12 49.0	4790	12 54.9
4439	12 28.4	4527	12 34.1	4615	12 41.5	4703	12 49.3	4791	12 54.8
4440	12 27.9	4528	12 34.1	4616	12 42.3	4704	12 48.8	4792	12 55.1
4441	12 27.3	4529	12 31.8	4617	12 41.1	4705	12 49.4	4793	12 54.6
4442	12 28.1	4530	12 33.8	4618	12 41.5	4706	12 49.9	4794	12 55.2
4443	12 28.1	4531	12 34.3	4619	12 41.7	4707	12 48.4	4795	12 55.0
4444	12 28.6	4532	12 34.3	4620	12 42.0	4708	12 49.7	4796	12 55.1
4445	12 28.3	4533	12 34.4	4621	12 42.0	4709	12 50.1	4797	12 54.9
4446	12 28.2	4534	12 34.1	4622	12 42.6	4710	12 49.6	4798	12 55.0
4447	12 28.3	4535	12 34.3	4623	12 42.2	4711	12 48.9	4799	12 55.3
4448	12 28.2	4536	12 34.5	4624	12 42.3	4712	12 49.6	4800	12 54.6
4449	12 28.2	4537	12 35.2	4625	12 41.9	4713	12 50.0	4801	12 54.6
4450	12 28.5	4538	12 34.7	4626	12 42.4	4714	12 50.3	4802	12 55.8
4451	12 28.7	4539	12 34.6	4627	12 42.4	4715	12 49.8	4803	12 55.7
4452	12 28.7	4540	12 34.8	4628	12 42.4	4716	12 50.5	4804	12 55.9
4453	12 28.7	4541	12 35.2	4629	12 42.6	4717	12 50.6	4805	12 55.4
4454	12 28.8	4542	12 34.8	4630	12 42.5	4718	12 50.5	4806	12 56.2
4455	12 28.7	4543	12 35.4	4631	12 42.1	4719	12 50.1	4807	12 55.5
4456	12 27.8	4544	12 35.6	4632	12 42.5	4720	12 50.7	4808	12 55.8
4457	12 29.0	4545	12 34.6	4633	12 42.6	4721	12 50.2	4809	12 54.8
4458	12 29.0	4546	12 35.5	4634	12 42.7	4722	12 51.5	4810	12 54.8
4459	12 29.0	4547	12 34.8	4635	12 42.6	4723	12 51.1	4811	12 56.9
4460	12 28.8	4548	12 35.4	4636	12 42.8	4724	12 50.9	4812	12 56.9
4461	12 29.0	4549	12 34.8	4637	12 42.9	4725	12 50.4	4813	12 56.6
4462	12 29.3	4550	12 35.5	4638	12 42.8	4726	12 51.5	4814	12 55.4
4463	12 30.0	4551	12 35.6	4639	12 42.9	4727	12 51.0	4815	12 58.0
4464	12 29.4	4552	12 35.7	4640	12 43.1	4728	12 50.5	4816	12 56.2
4465	12 29.4	4553	12 36.1	4641	12 43.2	4729	12 51.8	4817	12 56.2
4466	12 29.5	4554	12 35.7	4642	12 43.3	4730	12 52.0	4818	12 56.8
4467	12 29.5	4555	12 35.7	4643	12 43.3	4731	12 51.0	4819	12 56.5
4468	12 29.5	4556	12 35.8	4644	12 42.7	4732	12 50.1	4820	12 57.0
4469	12 29.5	4557	12 36.1	4645	12 44.2	4733	12 51.1	4821	12 56.5
4470	12 29.6	4558	12 35.8	4646	12 42.9	4734	12 51.2	4822	12 57.0
4471	12 29.7	4559	12 36.0	4647	12 43.5	4735	12 51.0	4823	12 57.4
4472	12 29.8	4560	12 36.1	4648	12 41.8	4736	12 50.9	4824	12 56.6
4473	12 29.8	4561	12 36.1	4649	12 43.7	4737	12 50.9	4825	12 57.2
4474	12 29.9	4562	12 35.6	4650	12 44.3	4738	12 51.1	4826	12 56.7
4475	12 29.8	4563	12 35.9	4651	12 43.7	4739	12 51.6	4827	12 56.7
4476	12 30.0	4564	12 36.4	4652	12 43.9	4740	12 51.5	4828	12 56.7
4477	12 30.0	4565	12 36.3	4653	12 43.9	4741	12 50.9	4829	12 57.3
4478	12 30.3	4566	12 35.9	4654	12 44.0	4742	12 51.8	4830	12 57.4
4479	12 30.3	4567	12 36.5	4655	12 43.6	4743	12 52.3	4831	12 57.6
4480	12 30.4	4568	12 36.6	4656	12 44.0	4744	12 52.4	4832	12 57.8
4481	12 29.8	4569	12 36.8	4657	12 44.2	4745	12 51.3	4833	12 59.6
4482	12 30.2	4570	12 36.9	4658	12 44.6	4746	12 51.9	4834	12 56.4
4483	12 30.7	4571	12 36.9	4659	12 44.5	4747	12 51.8	4835	12 58.1
4484	12 28.9	4572	12 35.9	4660	12 44.5	4748	12 52.2	4836	12 57.5
4485	12 30.5	4573	12 37.7	4661	12 45.2	4749	12 51.2	4837	12 56.9
4486	12 30.8	4574	12 37.7	4662	12 44.5	4750	12 50.1	4838	12 57.9
4487	12 31.1	4575	12 37.9	4663	12 44.8	4751	12 52.9	4839	12 57.4
4488	12 30.9	4576	12 37.6	4664	12 45.1	4752	12 52.3	4840	12 57.5

NGC	α_{2000}	NGC	α_{2000}	NGC	α_{2000}	NGC	α_{2000}	NGC	α_{2000}
	h m		h m		h m		h m		h m
4841	12 57.5	4929	13 02.7	5017	13 12.9	5105	13 21.8	5193	13 31.9
4842	12 57.6	4930	13 04.1	5018	13 13.0	5106	13 21.7	5194	13 29.9
4843	12 58.0	4931	13 03.0	5019	13 12.8	5107	13 21.4	5195	13 30.0
4844	12 58.1	4932	13 02.6	5020	13 12.6	5108	13 23.2	5196	13 31.4
4845	12 58.0	4933	13 03.9	5021	13 12.1	5109	13 20.9	5197	13 31.5
4846	12 57.9	4934	13 03.3	5022	13 13.5	5110	13 22.5	5198	13 30.2
4847	12 58.5	4935	13 03.3	5023	13 12.2	5111	13 22.8	5199	13 30.6
4848	12 58.1	4936	13 04.3	5024	13 12.9	5112	13 21.9	5200	13 31.7
4849	12 58.2	4937	13 04.7	5025	13 12.8	5113	13 21.4	5201	13 29.2
4850	12 58.4	4938	13 03.0	5026	13 14.2	5114	13 24.0	5202	13 32.1
4851	12 58.3	4939	13 04.2	5027	13 13.4	5115	13 22.9	5203	13 32.2
4852	13 00.1	4940	13 04.9	5028	13 13.8	5116	13 22.9	5204	13 29.6
4853	12 58.6	4941	13 04.2	5029	13 12.6	5117	13 23.0	5205	13 29.9
4854	12 58.8	4942	13 04.3	5030	13 13.9	5118	13 23.5	5206	13 33.7
4855	12 59.3	4943	13 03.8	5031	13 14.1	5119	13 23.9	5207	13 32.2
4856	12 59.3	4944	13 03.8	5032	13 13.4	5120	13 26.1	5208	13 32.5
4857	12 57.2	4945	13 05.4	5033	13 13.4	5121	13 24.8	5209	13 32.7
4858	12 59.0	4946	13 05.4	5034	13 12.2	5122	13 24.1	5210	13 32.9
4859	12 59.0	4947	13 05.4	5035	13 14.8	5123	13 23.2	5211	13 33.2
4860	12 59.1	4948	13 04.9	5036	13 14.7	5124	13 24.8	5212	13 32.6
4861	12 59.0	4949	13 04.2	5037	13 15.0	5125	13 23.9	5213	13 34.7
4862	12 59.4	4950	13 05.5	5038	13 15.1	5126	13 24.9	5214	13 32.8
4863	12 59.6	4951	13 05.1	5039	13 14.9	5127	13 23.8	5215	13 35.0
4864	12 59.2	4952	13 05.0	5040	13 13.6	5128	13 25.5	5216	13 32.1
4865	12 59.3	4953	13 06.1	5041	13 14.6	5129	13 24.1	5217	13 34.1
4866	12 59.5	4954	13 02.2	5042	13 15.5	5130	13 24.3	5218	13 32.2
4867	12 59.3	4955	13 06.1	5043	13 16.7	5131	13 24.0	5219	13 38.7
4868	12 59.1	4956	13 05.1	5044	13 15.4	5132	13 24.4	5220	13 35.9
4869	12 59.4	4957	13 05.2	5045	13 17.0	5133	13 24.9	5221	13 34.9
4870	12 59.3	4958	13 05.8	5046	13 15.8	5134	13 25.3	5222	13 34.9
4871	12 59.5	4959	13 05.7	5047	13 15.8	5135	13 25.7	5223	13 34.4
4872	12 59.6	4960	13 05.8	5048	13 16.1	5136	13 24.8	5224	13 35.2
4873	12 59.6	4961	13 05.8	5049	13 16.0	5137	13 24.8	5225	13 33.3
4874	12 59.6	4962	13 05.9	5050	13 15.8	5138	13 27.3	5226	13 35.0
4875	12 59.6	4963	13 05.8	5051	13 16.3	5139	13 26.8	5227	13 35.3
4876	12 59.7	4964	13 05.4	5052	13 15.6	5140	13 26.3	5228	13 34.5
4877	13 00.4	4965	13 07.2	5053	13 16.4	5141	13 24.9	5229	13 34.1
4878	13 00.3	4966	13 06.3	5054	13 17.0	5142	13 25.0	5230	13 35.5
4879	13 00.5	4967	13 05.7	5055	13 15.8	5143	13 25.0	5231	13 35.8
4880	13 00.2	4968	13 07.1	5056	13 16.2	5144	13 22.9	5232	13 36.0
4881	13 00.0	4969	13 07.0	5057	13 16.5	5145	13 25.2	5233	13 35.1
4882	13 00.0	4970	13 07.5	5058	13 16.8	5146	13 26.5	5234	13 37.5
4883	12 59.9	4971	13 06.9	5059	13 17.0	5147	13 26.3	5235	13 36.1
4884	13 00.0	4972	13 04.2	5060	13 17.3	5148	13 26.6	5236	13 37.0
4885	13 00.5	4973	13 05.5	5061	13 18.1	5149	13 26.1	5237	13 37.6
4886	13 00.0	4974	13 05.9	5062	13 18.4	5150	13 27.6	5238	13 34.7
4887	13 00.6	4975	13 08.0	5063	13 18.4	5151	13 26.6	5239	13 36.5
4888	13 01.1	4976	13 08.6	5064	13 19.0	5152	13 27.9	5240	13 35.9
4889	13 00.1	4977	13 06.2	5065	13 17.6	5153	13 28.0	5241	13 36.6
4890	13 00.6	4978	13 07.8	5066	13 18.4	5154	13 26.4	5242	13 37.1
4891	13 00.8	4979	13 07.6	5067	13 18.4	5155	13 29.6	5243	13 36.2
4892	13 00.0	4980	13 09.2	5068	13 18.9	5156	13 28.7	5244	13 38.6
4893	13 00.1	4981	13 08.8	5069	13 18.7	5157	13 27.4	5245	13 37.5
4894	13 00.3	4982	13 08.8	5070	13 19.2	5158	13 27.7	5246	13 37.5
4895	13 00.3	4983	13 08.4	5071	13 18.7	5159	13 28.3	5247	13 38.1
4896	13 00.5	4984	13 09.0	5072	13 19.1	5160	13 28.3	5248	13 37.5
4897	13 00.9	4985	13 08.1	5073	13 19.4	5161	13 29.2	5249	13 37.6
4898	13 00.3	4986	13 08.4	5074	13 18.4	5162	13 29.1	5250	13 36.0
4899	13 00.9	4987	13 08.0	5075	13 19.2	5163	13 26.9	5251	13 37.5
4900	13 00.6	4988	13 09.8	5076	13 19.4	5164	13 27.2	5252	13 38.3
4901	12 59.9	4989	13 09.4	5077	13 19.5	5165	13 28.6	5253	13 39.9
4902	13 01.0	4990	13 09.4	5078	13 19.8	5166	13 28.3	5254	13 39.6
4903	13 01.4	4991	13 09.3	5079	13 19.6	5167	13 28.6	5255	13 37.3
4904	13 01.0	4992	13 09.0	5080	13 19.4	5168	13 31.2	5256	13 38.3
4905	13 01.5	4993	13 09.7	5081	13 19.2	5169	13 28.2	5257	13 39.9
4906	13 00.7	4994	13 09.8	5082	13 20.9	5170	13 29.8	5258	13 40.0
4907	13 00.8	4995	13 09.7	5083	13 19.0	5171	13 29.3	5259	13 39.3
4908	13 00.9	4996	13 09.6	5084	13 20.3	5172	13 29.3	5260	13 40.4
4909	13 02.0	4997	13 10.0	5085	13 20.3	5173	13 28.4	5261	13 40.3
4910	13 01.4	4998	13 08.2	5086	13 21.2	5174	13 29.3	5262	13 35.4
4911	13 00.9	4999	13 09.6	5087	13 20.4	5175	13 29.3	5263	13 40.0
4912	13 00.8	5000	13 09.8	5088	13 20.3	5176	13 29.3	5264	13 41.6
4913	13 00.8	5001	13 09.6	5089	13 19.6	5177	13 29.3	5265	13 40.1
4914	13 00.7	5002	13 10.7	5090	13 21.1	5178	13 29.4	5266	13 43.0
4915	13 01.5	5003	13 08.6	5091	13 21.2	5179	13 29.4	5267	13 40.6
4916	13 00.7	5004	13 11.1	5092	13 19.9	5180	13 29.4	5268	13 42.1
4917	13 00.9	5005	13 10.9	5093	13 19.6	5181	13 29.6	5269	13 44.8
4918	13 01.8	5006	13 11.8	5094	13 20.7	5182	13 30.7	5270	13 42.3
4919	13 01.3	5007	13 09.3	5095	13 20.6	5183	13 30.1	5271	13 41.6
4920	13 01.9	5008	13 11.3	5096	13 20.2	5184	13 30.2	5272	13 42.2
4921	13 01.4	5009	13 10.8	5097	13 20.9	5185	13 30.0	5273	13 42.1
4922	13 01.4	5010	13 12.5	5098	13 20.2	5186	13 30.0	5274	13 42.3
4923	13 01.5	5011	13 12.9	5099	13 21.3	5187	13 29.9	5275	13 42.3
4924	13 02.2	5012	13 11.6	5100	13 21.1	5188	13 31.3	5276	13 42.4
4925	13 02.1	5013	13 12.2	5101	13 21.4	5189	13 33.5	5277	13 42.6
4926	13 01.9	5014	13 11.5	5102	13 22.0	5190	13 30.6	5278	13 41.6
4927	13 02.0	5015	13 12.4	5103	13 20.5	5191	13 30.7	5279	13 41.7
4928	13 03.0	5016	13 12.1	5104	13 21.4	5192	13 30.9	5280	13 42.8

NGC	α_{2000}		NGC	α_{2000}		NGC	α_{2000}		NGC	α_{2000}		NGC	α_{2000}	
	h	m		h	m		h	m		h	m		h	m
5281	13	46.6	5369	13	56.8	5457	14	03.2	5545	14	17.1	5633	14	27.5
5282	13	43.3	5370	13	54.1	5458	14	03.2	5546	14	18.1	5634	14	29.6
5283	13	41.1	5371	13	55.7	5459	14	05.3	5547	14	09.8	5635	14	28.5
5284	13	46.6	5372	13	54.7	5460	14	07.6	5548	14	18.0	5636	14	29.7
5285	13	44.5	5373	13	57.2	5461	14	03.7	5549	14	18.5	5637	14	28.9
5286	13	46.4	5374	13	57.5	5462	14	03.9	5550	14	18.4	5638	14	29.7
5287	13	44.9	5375	13	56.8	5463	14	06.1	5551	14	18.9	5639	14	28.8
5288	13	48.7	5376	13	55.3	5464	14	07.1	5552	14	18.9	5640	14	20.8
5289	13	45.1	5377	13	56.3	5465	14	06.4	5553	14	18.4	5641	14	29.3
5290	13	45.3	5378	13	56.8	5466	14	05.5	5554	14	19.2	5642	14	29.2
5291	13	47.4	5379	13	55.6	5467	14	06.5	5555	14	19.0	5643	14	32.7
5292	13	47.7	5380	13	56.9	5468	14	06.6	5556	14	20.6	5644	14	30.4
5293	13	46.3	5381	14	00.6	5469	14	02.8	5557	14	18.4	5645	14	30.7
5294	13	45.2	5382	13	58.2	5470	14	06.4	5558	14	19.7	5646	14	29.5
5295	13	38.6	5383	13	57.1	5471	14	04.6	5559	14	19.1	5647	14	30.6
5296	13	46.3	5384	13	58.1	5472	14	06.9	5560	14	20.1	5648	14	30.6
5297	13	46.4	5385	13	52.4	5473	14	04.7	5561	14	17.4	5649	14	30.6
5298	13	48.3	5386	13	58.2	5474	14	05.0	5562	14	20.1	5650	14	30.8
5299	13	50.4	5387	13	58.4	5475	14	05.2	5563	14	20.1	5651	14	31.3
5300	13	48.3	5388	13	58.9	5476	14	08.2	5564	14	20.2	5652	14	30.9
5301	13	46.4	5389	13	56.1	5477	14	05.6	5565	14	20.2	5653	14	30.2
5302	13	48.8	5390	13	57.3	5478	14	08.2	5566	14	20.3	5654	14	29.9
5303	13	47.8	5391	13	57.0	5479	14	05.9	5567	14	19.3	5655	14	31.0
5304	13	50.0	5392	13	59.4	5480	14	06.4	5568	14	19.4	5656	14	30.4
5305	13	47.9	5393	14	00.5	5481	14	06.7	5569	14	20.5	5657	14	30.7
5306	13	49.1	5394	13	58.6	5482	14	08.4	5570	14	19.4	5658	14	32.4
5307	13	51.1	5395	13	58.6	5483	14	10.4	5571	14	19.6	5659	14	31.1
5308	13	47.0	5396	13	59.0	5484	14	06.8	5572	14	19.5	5660	14	29.8
5309	13	50.0	5397	14	01.2	5485	14	07.2	5573	14	20.6	5661	14	31.9
5310	13	49.8	5398	14	01.4	5486	14	07.4	5574	14	20.9	5662	14	35.2
5311	13	49.0	5399	13	59.5	5487	14	09.7	5575	14	20.9	5663	14	33.9
5312	13	49.8	5400	14	00.6	5488	14	08.0	5576	14	21.1	5664	14	33.7
5313	13	49.7	5401	13	59.7	5489	14	12.0	5577	14	21.2	5665	14	32.4
5314	13	46.2	5402	13	58.2	5490	14	10.0	5578	14	21.2	5666	14	33.1
5315	13	53.9	5403	13	59.9	5491	14	10.9	5579	14	20.5	5667	14	30.4
5316	13	53.9	5404	14	01.1	5492	14	10.5	5580	14	20.7	5668	14	33.4
5317	13	51.2	5405	14	01.1	5493	14	11.5	5581	14	21.1	5669	14	32.7
5318	13	50.5	5406	14	00.3	5494	14	12.4	5582	14	20.7	5670	14	35.7
5319	13	50.5	5407	14	00.9	5495	14	12.4	5583	14	21.7	5671	14	27.7
5320	13	50.3	5408	14	03.3	5496	14	11.6	5584	14	22.4	5672	14	32.6
5321	13	50.7	5409	14	01.7	5497	14	10.4	5585	14	19.8	5673	14	31.5
5322	13	49.3	5410	14	00.7	5498	14	11.0	5586	14	22.1	5674	14	33.8
5323	13	45.5	5411	14	01.9	5499	14	10.9	5587	14	22.2	5675	14	32.6
5324	13	52.1	5412	13	57.4	5500	14	10.2	5588	14	21.5	5676	14	32.8
5325	13	51.0	5413	13	57.9	5501	14	12.4	5589	14	21.5	5677	14	34.2
5326	13	50.8	5414	14	02.0	5502	14	09.6	5590	14	21.7	5678	14	32.1
5327	13	52.1	5415	13	57.0	5503	14	09.4	5591	14	22.6	5679	14	35.0
5328	13	52.9	5416	14	02.1	5504	14	12.3	5592	14	23.9	5680	14	35.8
5329	13	52.2	5417	14	02.1	5505	14	12.5	5593	14	25.8	5681	14	35.7
5330	13	53.0	5418	14	02.2	5506	14	13.2	5594	14	23.2	5682	14	34.8
5331	13	52.4	5419	14	03.7	5507	14	13.3	5595	14	24.2	5683	14	34.9
5332	13	52.1	5420	14	03.0	5508	14	12.4	5596	14	22.5	5684	14	35.8
5333	13	54.5	5421	14	01.7	5509	14	12.3	5597	14	24.5	5685	14	36.2
5334	13	52.9	5422	14	00.7	5510	14	13.6	5598	14	22.5	5686	14	36.0
5335	13	53.0	5423	14	02.7	5511	14	13.1	5599	14	23.7	5687	14	34.9
5336	13	52.1	5424	14	02.9	5512	14	12.6	5600	14	23.8	5688	14	39.5
5337	13	52.5	5425	14	00.8	5513	14	13.2	5601	14	22.9	5689	14	35.5
5338	13	53.8	5426	14	03.4	5514	14	13.6	5602	14	22.3	5690	14	37.7
5339	13	53.8	5427	14	03.4	5515	14	12.5	5603	14	23.1	5691	14	37.9
5340	13	49.1	5428	14	03.4	5516	14	15.8	5604	14	24.7	5692	14	38.3
5341	13	52.6	5429	14	03.4	5517	14	13.0	5605	14	25.1	5693	14	36.2
5342	13	51.4	5430	14	00.8	5518	14	13.9	5606	14	27.8	5694	14	39.6
5343	13	54.0	5431	14	03.0	5519	14	14.4	5607	14	19.4	5695	14	37.3
5344	13	50.0	5432	14	03.6	5520	14	12.3	5608	14	23.3	5696	14	37.0
5345	13	54.3	5433	14	02.5	5521	14	15.5	5609	14	23.9	5697	14	36.6
5346	13	53.2	5434	14	03.3	5522	14	14.8	5610	14	24.3	5698	14	37.2
5347	13	53.3	5435	14	03.8	5523	14	14.8	5611	14	24.2	5699	14	38.3
5348	13	54.2	5436	14	03.6	5524	14	14.5	5612	14	34.1	5700	14	37.1
5349	13	53.2	5437	14	03.7	5525	14	15.6	5613	14	24.1	5701	14	39.2
5350	13	53.4	5438	14	03.7	5526	14	13.9	5614	14	24.1	5702	14	38.8
5351	13	53.5	5439	14	02.0	5527	14	15.4	5615	14	24.2	5703	14	38.5
5352	13	53.6	5440	14	03.0	5528	14	16.2	5616	14	24.2	5704	14	37.9
5353	13	53.5	5441	14	03.2	5529	14	15.6	5617	14	29.8	5705	14	39.8
5354	13	53.5	5442	14	04.9	5530	14	18.5	5618	14	27.2	5706	14	38.6
5355	13	53.8	5443	14	02.2	5531	14	16.7	5619	14	27.3	5707	14	37.5
5356	13	55.0	5444	14	03.4	5532	14	16.9	5620	14	22.5	5708	14	38.3
5357	13	56.0	5445	14	03.5	5533	14	16.1	5621	14	27.8	5709	14	38.8
5358	13	54.1	5446	14	05.1	5534	14	17.7	5622	14	26.2	5710	14	39.3
5359	13	59.8	5447	14	02.5	5535	14	17.6	5623	14	27.2	5711	14	39.4
5360	13	55.7	5448	14	02.8	5536	14	16.3	5624	14	26.6	5712	14	29.7
5361	13	54.7	5449	14	02.5	5537	14	17.5	5625	14	27.0	5713	14	40.2
5362	13	54.9	5450	14	02.5	5538	14	17.6	5626	14	29.7	5714	14	38.2
5363	13	56.1	5451	14	02.7	5539	14	17.6	5627	14	28.5	5715	14	43.4
5364	13	56.2	5452	13	54.5	5540	14	14.8	5628	14	28.4	5716	14	41.1
5365	13	57.9	5453	14	03.0	5541	14	16.4	5629	14	28.3	5717	14	38.6
5366	13	56.4	5454	14	04.7	5542	14	17.8	5630	14	27.6	5718	14	40.8
5367	13	57.7	5455	14	03.0	5543	14	18.0	5631	14	26.6	5719	14	40.9
5368	13	54.5	5456	14	04.9	5544	14	17.0	5632	14	28.3	5720	14	38.4

Right Ascensions of NGC Objects

NGC	α_{2000}	NGC	α_{2000}	NGC	α_{2000}	NGC	α_{2000}	NGC	α_{2000}
	h m		h m		h m		h m		h m
5721	14 38.9	5809	15 00.9	5897	15 17.4	5985	15 39.6	6073	16 10.1
5722	14 39.0	5810	15 02.6	5898	15 18.2	5986	15 46.1	6074	16 11.4
5723	14 38.9	5811	15 00.5	5899	15 15.0	5987	15 39.9	6075	16 11.4
5724	14 39.1	5812	15 01.0	5900	15 15.1	5988	15 44.6	6076	16 11.1
5725	14 41.1	5813	15 01.2	5901	15 15.1	5989	15 41.5	6077	16 11.1
5726	14 42.9	5814	15 01.4	5902	15 14.4	5990	15 46.4	6078	16 12.1
5727	14 40.5	5815	15 00.5	5903	15 18.6	5991	15 45.3	6079	16 04.5
5728	14 42.4	5816	15 02.1	5904	15 18.6	5992	15 44.4	6080	16 13.1
5729	14 42.0	5817	14 59.6	5905	15 15.4	5993	15 44.5	6081	16 13.0
5730	14 40.3	5818	14 58.8	5906	15 15.8	5994	15 46.8	6082	16 15.6
5731	14 40.0	5819	14 54.0	5907	15 15.9	5995	15 48.4	6083	16 13.3
5732	14 40.6	5820	14 58.7	5908	15 16.7	5996	15 46.9	6084	16 14.2
5733	14 42.8	5821	14 58.9	5909	15 11.5	5997	15 47.4	6085	16 12.5
5734	14 45.1	5822	15 05.2	5910	15 19.3	5998	15 49.4	6086	16 12.6
5735	14 42.4	5823	15 05.7	5911	15 20.4	5999	15 52.2	6087	16 18.9
5736	14 43.5	5824	15 04.0	5912	15 11.7	6000	15 49.9	6088	16 10.7
5737	14 43.2	5825	15 02.0	5913	15 20.9	6001	15 47.7	6089	16 12.7
5738	14 44.0	5826	14 59.8	5914	15 18.7	6002	15 47.7	6090	16 11.7
5739	14 42.5	5827	15 01.8	5915	15 21.6	6003	15 49.3	6091	16 07.8
5740	14 44.4	5828	15 00.6	5916	15 21.6	6004	15 50.3	6092	16 12.7
5741	14 46.1	5829	15 02.7	5917	15 21.4	6005	15 55.8	6093	16 17.0
5742	14 45.8	5830	15 01.7	5918	15 19.3	6006	15 53.0	6094	16 06.6
5743	14 45.1	5831	15 04.1	5919	15 21.5	6007	15 53.4	6095	16 11.1
5744	14 43.9	5832	14 57.8	5920	15 21.8	6008	15 52.9	6096	16 14.7
5745	14 45.1	5833	15 11.8	5921	15 21.9	6009	15 53.5	6097	16 14.3
5746	14 44.9	5834	15 04.0	5922	15 21.2	6010	15 54.4	6098	16 15.6
5747	14 44.4	5835	15 02.3	5923	15 21.2	6011	15 46.6	6099	16 15.6
5748	14 45.0	5836	14 59.5	5924	15 21.9	6012	15 54.2	6100	16 17.0
5749	14 48.9	5837	15 04.7	5925	15 27.7	6013	15 52.9	6101	16 25.8
5750	14 46.2	5838	15 05.4	5926	15 23.4	6014	15 55.8	6102	16 15.6
5751	14 43.9	5839	15 05.5	5927	15 28.0	6015	15 51.4	6103	16 15.7
5752	14 45.3	5840	15 04.3	5928	15 25.9	6016	15 55.9	6104	16 16.5
5753	14 45.4	5841	15 05.6	5929	15 26.1	6017	15 57.2	6105	16 17.0
5754	14 45.4	5842	15 04.8	5930	15 26.1	6018	15 57.5	6106	16 18.8
5755	14 45.5	5843	15 07.5	5931	15 29.5	6019	15 52.3	6107	16 17.2
5756	14 47.6	5844	15 10.7	5932	15 26.8	6020	15 57.2	6108	16 17.3
5757	14 47.8	5845	15 06.0	5933	15 27.0	6021	15 57.5	6109	16 17.7
5758	14 47.1	5846	15 06.4	5934	15 28.2	6022	15 57.8	6110	16 17.6
5759	14 47.3	5847	15 06.3	5935	15 28.3	6023	15 57.8	6111	16 15.5
5760	14 47.7	5848	15 06.9	5936	15 30.0	6024	15 53.2	6112	16 17.9
5761	14 49.1	5849	15 06.9	5937	15 30.8	6025	16 03.7	6113	16 19.2
5762	14 48.7	5850	15 07.1	5938	15 36.4	6026	16 01.4	6114	16 18.3
5763	14 49.0	5851	15 06.9	5939	15 24.8	6027	15 59.2	6115	16 24.6
5764	14 53.6	5852	15 07.0	5940	15 31.2	6028	16 01.4	6116	16 18.8
5765	14 50.8	5853	15 05.8	5941	15 31.5	6029	16 02.0	6117	16 19.3
5766	14 53.2	5854	15 07.8	5942	15 31.6	6030	16 01.8	6118	16 21.8
5767	14 49.7	5855	15 07.9	5943	15 29.8	6031	16 07.6	6119	16 19.7
5768	14 52.1	5856	15 07.3	5944	15 31.7	6032	16 03.0	6120	16 19.8
5769	14 52.6	5857	15 07.5	5945	15 29.8	6033	16 04.4	6121	16 23.6
5770	14 53.4	5858	15 08.8	5946	15 35.5	6034	16 03.4	6122	16 20.2
5771	14 52.2	5859	15 07.6	5947	15 30.7	6035	16 03.4	6123	16 17.2
5772	14 51.7	5860	15 06.6	5948	15 32.9	6036	16 04.4	6124	16 25.6
5773	14 52.5	5861	15 09.3	5949	15 28.0	6037	16 04.4	6125	16 18.9
5774	14 53.7	5862	15 06.0	5950	15 31.5	6038	16 02.6	6126	16 21.4
5775	14 54.0	5863	15 10.8	5951	15 33.7	6039	16 04.4	6127	16 19.2
5776	14 54.6	5864	15 09.6	5952	15 34.8	6040	16 04.4	6128	16 19.1
5777	14 51.3	5865	15 09.9	5953	15 34.5	6041	16 04.6	6129	16 21.8
5778	14 54.5	5866	15 06.5	5954	15 34.6	6042	16 04.6	6130	16 19.5
5779	14 52.2	5867	15 06.4	5955	15 35.1	6043	16 04.9	6131	16 22.0
5780	14 54.4	5868	15 09.9	5956	15 35.0	6044	16 05.0	6132	16 23.7
5781	14 56.6	5869	15 09.9	5957	15 35.4	6045	16 05.1	6133	16 20.1
5782	14 55.9	5870	15 06.6	5958	15 34.7	6046	16 04.9	6134	16 27.7
5783	14 53.5	5871	15 10.1	5959	15 37.4	6047	16 05.1	6135	16 19.0
5784	14 54.2	5872	15 11.0	5960	15 36.2	6048	15 57.6	6136	16 20.8
5785	14 53.9	5873	15 12.8	5961	15 35.2	6049	16 05.7	6137	16 23.1
5786	14 59.0	5874	15 07.9	5962	15 36.5	6050	16 05.4	6138	16 22.9
5787	14 55.3	5875	15 09.2	5963	15 33.5	6051	16 04.9	6139	16 27.7
5788	14 53.2	5876	15 09.5	5964	15 37.6	6052	16 05.2	6140	16 20.9
5789	14 56.6	5877	15 12.8	5965	15 34.0	6053	16 05.4	6141	16 23.1
5790	14 57.5	5878	15 13.8	5966	15 35.8	6054	16 05.4	6142	16 23.7
5791	14 58.8	5879	15 09.8	5967	15 48.1	6055	16 05.5	6143	16 21.7
5792	14 58.4	5880	15 15.1	5968	15 39.9	6056	16 05.5	6144	16 27.3
5793	14 59.4	5881	15 09.1	5969	15 34.9	6057	16 05.6	6145	16 25.0
5794	14 55.7	5882	15 16.8	5970	15 38.5	6058	16 04.4	6146	16 25.2
5795	14 56.3	5883	15 15.2	5971	15 35.6	6059	16 07.4	6147	16 25.1
5796	14 59.4	5884	15 13.2	5972	15 38.8	6060	16 05.9	6148	16 27.1
5797	14 56.3	5885	15 15.1	5973	15 40.2	6061	16 06.3	6149	16 27.4
5798	14 57.7	5886	15 12.7	5974	15 39.0	6062	16 06.3	6150	16 25.8
5799	15 05.5	5887	15 14.8	5975	15 40.0	6063	16 07.2	6151	16 38.3
5800	15 02.0	5888	15 13.1	5976	15 36.8	6064	16 07.0	6152	16 32.7
5801	15 00.4	5889	15 13.5	5977	15 40.4	6065	16 07.5	6153	16 31.5
5802	15 00.5	5890	15 17.9	5978	15 42.4	6066	16 07.7	6154	16 25.6
5803	15 01.0	5891	15 16.3	5979	15 47.7	6067	16 13.2	6155	16 26.1
5804	14 55.7	5892	15 13.7	5980	15 41.4	6068	15 55.4	6156	16 34.8
5805	14 55.9	5893	15 13.6	5981	15 37.9	6069	16 07.7	6157	16 25.7
5806	15 00.0	5894	15 11.7	5982	15 38.7	6070	16 10.0	6158	16 27.7
5807	14 55.7	5895	15 13.8	5983	15 42.7	6071	16 01.1	6159	16 27.4
5808	14 53.8	5896	15 13.8	5984	15 42.9	6072	16 13.0	6160	16 27.7

Right Ascensions of NGC Objects

NGC	α_{2000}	NGC	α_{2000}	NGC	α_{2000}	NGC	α_{2000}	NGC	α_{2000}
	h m		h m		h m		h m		h m
6161	16 28.3	6249	16 57.6	6337	17 22.3	6425	17 46.9	6513	17 59.5
6162	16 28.4	6250	16 58.0	6338	17 15.3	6426	17 44.9	6514	18 02.3
6163	16 28.4	6251	16 32.6	6339	17 17.1	6427	17 43.6	6515	17 57.4
6164	16 34.0	6252	16 32.5	6340	17 10.4	6428	17 43.9	6516	17 55.2
6165	16 34.0	6253	16 59.1	6341	17 17.1	6429	17 44.0	6517	18 01.8
6166	16 28.6	6254	16 57.1	6342	17 21.2	6430	17 44.6	6518	17 59.7
6167	16 34.4	6255	16 54.8	6343	17 17.3	6431	17 44.3	6519	18 03.4
6168	16 31.4	6256	16 59.5	6344	17 17.2	6432	17 47.4	6520	18 03.4
6169	16 34.1	6257	16 56.0	6345	17 15.3	6433	17 44.0	6521	17 55.8
6170	16 27.0	6258	16 52.3	6346	17 15.3	6434	17 36.8	6522	18 03.6
6171	16 32.5	6259	17 00.7	6347	17 19.9	6435	17 40.1	6523	18 03.8
6172	16 32.1	6260	16 51.8	6348	17 18.4	6436	17 41.2	6524	17 59.2
6173	16 29.8	6261	16 56.5	6349	17 19.1	6437	17 49.1	6525	18 02.1
6174	16 29.7	6262	16 53.6	6350	17 18.7	6438	18 26.	6526	18 02.6
6175	16 29.9	6263	16 56.7	6351	17 19.2	6439	17 48.3	6527	18 01.8
6176	16 27.5	6264	16 57.5	6352	17 25.5	6440	17 48.9	6528	18 04.8
6177	16 30.6	6265	16 57.5	6353	17 21.2	6441	17 50.2	6529	18 05.5
6178	16 35.7	6266	17 01.2	6354	17 24.6	6442	17 46.9	6530	18 04.8
6179	16 30.7	6267	16 58.2	6355	17 24.0	6443	17 44.6	6531	18 04.6
6180	16 30.5	6268	17 02.4	6356	17 23.6	6444	17 49.5	6532	17 59.1
6181	16 32.3	6269	16 58.0	6357	17 24.6	6445	17 49.2	6533	18 05.1
6182	16 29.5	6270	16 58.7	6358	17 19.0	6446	17 46.1	6534	17 56.0
6183	16 41.6	6271	16 58.8	6359	17 17.9	6447	17 46.3	6535	18 03.8
6184	16 31.5	6272	16 58.9	6360	17 25.4	6448	17 44.3	6536	17 57.3
6185	16 33.2	6273	17 02.6	6361	17 18.6	6449	17 43.7	6537	18 05.2
6186	16 34.4	6274	16 59.4	6362	17 31.9	6450	17 47.5	6538	17 54.2
6187	16 31.6	6275	16 55.6	6363	17 22.7	6451	17 50.7	6539	18 04.8
6188	16 40.5	6276	17 00.3	6364	17 24.5	6452	17 48.0	6540	18 06.3
6189	16 31.6	6277	17 00.8	6365	17 22.7	6453	17 50.9	6541	18 08.0
6190	16 32.0	6278	17 00.9	6366	17 27.7	6454	17 44.9	6542	17 59.7
6191	16 32.0	6279	16 59.0	6367	17 25.2	6455	17 42.0	6543	17 58.6
6192	16 40.3	6280	17 01.9	6368	17 27.1	6456	17 42.4	6544	18 07.3
6193	16 41.3	6281	17 04.8	6369	17 29.3	6457	17 42.8	6545	18 12.3
6194	16 36.6	6282	17 00.8	6370	17 23.3	6458	17 49.2	6546	18 07.2
6195	16 36.5	6283	16 59.4	6371	17 27.2	6459	17 45.9	6547	18 05.1
6196	16 37.4	6284	17 04.5	6372	17 27.5	6460	17 49.6	6548	18 06.0
6197	16 37.5	6285	16 58.4	6373	17 24.3	6461	17 38.7	6549	18 05.8
6198	16 35.5	6286	16 58.6	6374	17 32.3	6462	17 44.7	6550	18 06.0
6199	16 39.0	6287	17 05.2	6375	17 29.3	6463	17 43.5	6551	18 09.0
6200	16 44.2	6288	16 57.5	6376	17 25.4	6464	17 45.8	6552	18 00.1
6201	16 40.2	6289	16 57.8	6377	17 25.4	6465	17 52.9	6553	18 09.3
6202	16 36.2	6290	17 00.9	6378	17 30.6	6466	17 48.2	6554	18 09.1
6203	16 40.4	6291	17 00.9	6379	17 30.6	6467	17 50.7	6555	18 07.8
6204	16 46.5	6292	17 03.0	6380	17 35.4	6468	17 50.7	6556	18 10.0
6205	16 41.7	6293	17 10.2	6381	17 27.3	6469	17 52.9	6557	18 21.4
6206	16 40.1	6294	17 10.3	6382	17 27.8	6470	17 44.1	6558	18 10.3
6207	16 43.1	6295	17 03.1	6383	17 34.8	6471	17 44.1	6559	18 10.0
6208	16 49.5	6296	17 08.7	6384	17 32.4	6472	17 44.2	6560	18 05.3
6209	16 55.1	6297	17 03.6	6385	17 28.0	6473	17 47.0	6561	18 10.5
6210	16 44.5	6298	17 03.4	6386	17 28.9	6474	17 46.9	6562	18 04.9
6211	16 41.5	6299	17 05.0	6387	17 28.4	6475	17 53.9	6563	18 12.0
6212	16 43.3	6300	17 17.0	6388	17 36.3	6476	17 53.8	6564	18 09.1
6213	16 41.5	6301	17 08.6	6389	17 32.7	6477	17 43.9	6565	18 11.9
6214	16 39.5	6302	17 13.7	6390	17 28.5	6478	17 48.6	6566	18 07.0
6215	16 51.1	6303	17 05.1	6391	17 28.9	6479	17 48.3	6567	18 13.7
6216	16 49.4	6304	17 14.5	6392	17 43.5	6480	17 54.6	6568	18 12.8
6217	16 32.6	6305	17 18.1	6393	17 30.3	6481	17 52.8	6569	18 13.6
6218	16 47.2	6306	17 07.6	6394	17 30.1	6482	17 51.8	6570	18 11.1
6219	16 46.3	6307	17 07.7	6395	17 26.4	6483	17 59.5	6571	18 10.9
6220	16 47.2	6308	17 12.0	6396	17 38.1	6484	17 51.7	6572	18 12.1
6221	16 52.8	6309	17 14.1	6397	17 40.7	6485	17 51.8	6573	18 13.8
6222	16 50.7	6310	17 08.0	6398	17 42.7	6486	17 52.6	6574	18 11.9
6223	16 43.1	6311	17 10.6	6399	17 31.8	6487	17 52.7	6575	18 10.8
6224	16 48.2	6312	17 10.8	6400	17 40.8	6488	17 49.3	6576	18 11.8
6225	16 43.5	6313	17 10.4	6401	17 38.6	6489	17 50.0	6577	18 12.1
6226	16 43.5	6314	17 12.6	6402	17 37.6	6490	17 54.5	6578	18 16.3
6227	16 51.6	6315	17 12.8	6403	17 43.2	6491	17 50.1	6579	18 12.3
6228	16 48.0	6316	17 16.6	6404	17 39.6	6492	18 02.8	6580	18 12.4
6229	16 47.0	6317	17 09.3	6405	17 40.1	6493	17 50.4	6581	18 12.6
6230	16 50.6	6318	17 17.8	6406	17 38.3	6494	17 56.8	6582	18 11.0
6231	16 54.0	6319	17 09.6	6407	17 45.0	6495	17 54.8	6583	18 15.8
6232	16 43.3	6320	17 12.9	6408	17 38.8	6496	17 59.0	6584	18 18.6
6233	16 50.1	6321	17 14.5	6409	17 36.6	6497	17 51.2	6585	18 12.4
6234	16 51.9	6322	17 18.5	6410	17 35.2	6498	17 51.0	6586	18 13.7
6235	16 53.4	6323	17 13.3	6411	17 35.6	6499	17 55.3	6587	18 13.9
6236	16 44.5	6324	17 05.4	6412	17 29.6	6500	17 56.0	6588	18 21.5
6237	16 46.5	6325	17 18.0	6413	17 40.7	6501	17 56.1	6589	18 16.9
6238	16 47.2	6326	17 20.8	6414	17 30.6	6502	18 04.2	6590	18 17.0
6239	16 50.1	6327	17 14.0	6415	17 44.4	6503	17 49.4	6591	18 14.0
6240	16 53.0	6328	17 23.7	6416	17 44.4	6504	17 56.0	6592	18 09.9
6241	16 56.1	6329	17 14.3	6417	17 41.7	6505	17 51.3	6593	18 14.2
6242	16 55.6	6330	17 15.8	6418	17 38.1	6506	17 59.8	6594	18 10.2
6243	16 56.2	6331	17 03.5	6419	17 35.9	6507	17 59.6	6595	18 17.0
6244	16 48.1	6332	17 15.0	6420	17 36.1	6508	17 49.9	6596	18 17.5
6245	16 45.5	6333	17 19.2	6421	17 36.3	6509	17 59.4	6597	18 11.3
6246	16 49.9	6334	17 20.5	6422	17 36.3	6510	17 54.0	6598	18 08.8
6247	16 48.2	6335	17 20.5	6423	17 36.7	6511	17 54.7	6599	18 15.6
6248	16 46.4	6336	17 16.3	6424	17 36.2	6512	17 54.8	6600	18 15.7

Right Ascensions of NGC Objects

NGC	α_{2000}	NGC	α_{2000}	NGC	α_{2000}	NGC	α_{2000}	NGC	α_{2000}
	h m		h m		h m		h m		h m
6601	18 11.9	6689	18 34.9	6777	19 26.8	6865	20 06.0	6953	20 37.7
6602	18 16.6	6690	18 34.8	6778	19 18.4	6866	20 03.7	6954	20 44.1
6603	18 18.4	6691	18 39.3	6779	19 16.6	6867	20 10.4	6955	20 44.4
6604	18 18.1	6692	18 41.7	6780	19 22.9	6868	20 09.9	6956	20 44.0
6605	18 17.1	6693	18 41.6	6781	19 18.4	6869	20 00.7	6957	20 44.9
6606	18 14.7	6694	18 45.2	6782	19 24.0	6870	20 10.2	6958	20 48.6
6607	18 12.3	6695	18 42.7	6783	19 16.6	6871	20 05.9	6959	20 47.1
6608	18 12.6	6696	18 40.0	6784	19 26.6	6872	20 16.9	6960	20 45.7
6609	18 12.6	6697	18 45.2	6785	19 20.9	6873	20 08.3	6961	20 47.2
6610	18 17.2	6698	18 48.2	6786	19 10.9	6874	20 07.8	6962	20 47.3
6611	18 18.8	6699	18 52.1	6787	19 16.3	6875	20 13.2	6963	20 47.3
6612	18 16.2	6700	18 46.0	6788	19 26.9	6876	20 18.3	6964	20 47.4
6613	18 19.9	6701	18 43.2	6789	19 16.7	6877	20 18.6	6965	20 47.4
6614	18 25.2	6702	18 47.0	6790	19 23.2	6878	20 13.9	6966	20 47.4
6615	18 18.6	6703	18 47.0	6791	19 20.7	6879	20 10.5	6967	20 47.6
6616	18 17.8	6704	18 50.9	6792	19 21.0	6880	20 19.5	6968	20 48.4
6617	18 14.1	6705	18 51.1	6793	19 23.2	6881	20 10.8	6969	20 48.4
6618	18 20.8	6706	18 56.9	6794	19 27.9	6882	20 11.7	6970	20 52.1
6619	18 18.8	6707	18 55.4	6795	19 26.1	6883	20 11.3	6971	20 49.4
6620	18 22.9	6708	18 55.6	6796	19 21.5	6884	20 10.4	6972	20 50.0
6621	18 12.9	6709	18 51.5	6797	19 28.9	6885	20 12.0	6973	20 52.1
6622	18 13.0	6710	18 49.0	6798	19 24.0	6886	20 12.7	6974	20 50.8
6623	18 19.5	6711	18 49.0	6799	19 32.3	6887	20 17.2	6975	20 52.4
6624	18 23.7	6712	18 53.1	6800	19 27.2	6888	20 12.0	6976	20 52.4
6625	18 23.2	6713	18 50.7	6801	19 27.7	6889	20 18.9	6977	20 52.5
6626	18 24.5	6714	18 45.9	6802	19 30.6	6890	20 18.3	6978	20 52.6
6627	18 22.7	6715	18 55.1	6803	19 31.3	6891	20 15.2	6979	20 51.0
6628	18 22.2	6716	18 54.6	6804	19 31.6	6892	20 16.8	6980	20 52.8
6629	18 25.7	6717	18 55.1	6805	19 36.8	6893	20 20.8	6981	20 53.5
6630	18 32.6	6718	19 01.5	6806	19 37.2	6894	20 16.4	6982	20 57.4
6631	18 27.2	6719	19 03.1	6807	19 34.6	6895	20 16.4	6983	20 56.8
6632	18 25.0	6720	18 53.6	6808	19 43.9	6896	20 18.0	6984	20 57.9
6633	18 27.7	6721	19 00.8	6809	19 40.0	6897	20 21.0	6985	20 56.0
6634	18 29.9	6722	19 03.7	6810	19 43.6	6898	20 21.2	6986	20 36.6
6635	18 27.6	6723	18 59.6	6811	19 38.2	6899	20 24.4	6987	20 58.0
6636	18 22.0	6724	18 57.0	6812	19 45.4	6900	20 21.6	6988	20 55.8
6637	18 31.4	6725	19 01.8	6813	19 40.4	6901	20 22.3	6989	20 54.1
6638	18 30.9	6726	19 01.7	6814	19 42.7	6902	20 24.5	6990	20 59.9
6639	18 30.1	6727	19 01.8	6815	19 40.9	6903	20 23.6	6991	20 56.6
6640	18 28.1	6728	19 00.0	6816	19 44.0	6904	20 21.8	6992	20 56.4
6641	18 28.8	6729	19 01.9	6817	19 37.4	6905	20 22.4	6993	20 59.5
6642	18 31.9	6730	19 07.6	6818	19 44.0	6906	20 23.6	6994	20 59.0
6643	18 19.8	6731	18 57.0	6819	19 41.3	6907	20 25.1	6995	20 57.1
6644	18 32.6	6732	18 56.4	6820	19 43.1	6908	20 25.2	6996	20 56.4
6645	18 32.6	6733	19 06.2	6821	19 44.4	6909	20 27.7	6997	20 56.5
6646	18 29.6	6734	19 07.2	6822	19 44.9	6910	20 23.1	6998	21 01.6
6647	18 31.5	6735	19 00.8	6823	19 43.1	6911	20 19.6	6999	21 02.0
6648	18 25.6	6736	19 07.5	6824	19 43.7	6912	20 26.9	7000	20 58.8
6649	18 33.5	6737	19 02.2	6825	19 41.7	6913	20 23.9	7001	21 01.2
6650	18 25.4	6738	19 01.4	6826	19 44.8	6914	20 24.7	7002	21 03.6
6651	18 24.3	6739	19 07.8	6827	19 48.9	6915	20 27.8	7003	21 00.8
6652	18 35.8	6740	19 00.8	6828	19 50.4	6916	20 23.5	7004	21 03.9
6653	18 44.6	6741	19 02.6	6829	19 47.1	6917	20 27.4	7005	21 02.0
6654	18 24.1	6742	18 59.3	6830	19 51.0	6918	20 30.8	7006	21 01.5
6655	18 34.8	6743	19 01.4	6831	19 47.9	6919	20 31.6	7007	21 05.5
6656	18 36.4	6744	19 09.8	6832	19 48.1	6920	20 43.9	7008	21 00.6
6657	18 33.0	6745	19 01.6	6833	19 49.7	6921	20 28.5	7009	21 04.2
6658	18 33.9	6746	19 10.4	6834	19 52.2	6922	20 29.9	7010	21 04.7
6659	18 33.9	6747	18 55.3	6835	19 54.5	6923	20 31.7	7011	21 01.9
6660	18 34.6	6748	19 03.8	6836	19 54.7	6924	20 33.2	7012	21 06.8
6661	18 34.6	6749	19 05.1	6837	19 53.5	6925	20 34.3	7013	21 03.6
6662	18 34.0	6750	19 00.7	6838	19 53.8	6926	20 33.1	7014	21 07.9
6663	18 33.5	6751	19 05.9	6839	19 54.5	6927	20 32.6	7015	21 05.7
6664	18 36.7	6752	19 10.9	6840	19 55.3	6928	20 32.8	7016	21 07.4
6665	18 34.5	6753	19 11.4	6841	19 57.8	6929	20 33.4	7017	21 07.5
6666	18 35.3	6754	19 11.4	6842	19 55.0	6930	20 33.0	7018	21 07.6
6667	18 30.7	6755	19 07.8	6843	19 56.1	6931	20 33.6	7019	21 06.4
6668	18 33.3	6756	19 08.7	6844	20 02.8	6932	20 42.1	7020	21 11.4
6669	18 38.0	6757	19 05.1	6845	20 00.9	6933	20 33.6	7021	21 11.3
6670	18 33.5	6758	19 13.9	6846	19 56.5	6934	20 34.2	7022	21 09.5
6671	18 37.4	6759	19 06.9	6847	19 57.0	6935	20 38.4	7023	21 00.5
6672	18 33.8	6760	19 11.2	6848	20 02.8	6936	20 35.9	7024	21 06.0
6673	18 45.1	6761	19 15.3	6849	20 01.3	6937	20 38.8	7025	21 07.9
6674	18 38.6	6762	19 05.6	6850	20 03.5	6938	20 34.8	7026	21 06.3
6675	18 37.4	6763	19 05.6	6851	20 03.6	6939	20 31.4	7027	21 07.1
6676	18 33.2	6764	19 08.3	6852	20 00.6	6940	20 34.6	7028	21 08.3
6677	18 33.6	6765	19 11.1	6853	19 59.6	6941	20 36.3	7029	21 11.9
6678	18 33.2	6766	19 09.9	6854	20 05.7	6942	20 40.8	7030	21 11.2
6679	18 33.6	6767	19 11.6	6855	20 06.8	6943	20 44.5	7031	21 07.3
6680	18 39.8	6768	19 16.5	6856	19 59.3	6944	20 38.4	7032	21 15.4
6681	18 43.2	6769	19 18.4	6857	20 01.9	6945	20 38.9	7033	21 09.6
6682	18 41.6	6770	19 18.7	6858	20 03.1	6946	20 34.8	7034	21 09.7
6683	18 42.2	6771	19 18.7	6859	20 03.9	6947	20 41.3	7035	21 10.8
6684	18 49.0	6772	19 14.6	6860	20 08.8	6948	20 43.5	7036	21 10.2
6685	18 39.9	6773	19 15.0	6861	20 07.3	6949	20 35.1	7037	21 10.7
6686	18 40.1	6774	19 16.6	6862	20 08.9	6950	20 41.2	7038	21 15.2
6687	18 37.2	6775	19 16.8	6863	20 05.1	6951	20 37.2	7039	21 11.2
6688	18 40.7	6776	19 25.4	6864	20 06.1	6952	20 37.0	7040	21 13.2

NGC	α_{2000}		NGC	α_{2000}		NGC	α_{2000}		NGC	α_{2000}		NGC	α_{2000}	
	h	m		h	m		h	m		h	m		h	m
7041	21	16.5	7129	21	41.3	7217	22	07.9	7305	22	32.2	7393	22	51.7
7042	21	13.8	7130	21	48.3	7218	22	10.2	7306	22	33.5	7394	22	50.6
7043	21	14.1	7131	21	47.7	7219	22	13.1	7307	22	33.8	7395	22	51.2
7044	21	12.9	7132	21	47.2	7220	22	11.5	7308	22	34.5	7396	22	52.5
7045	21	14.8	7133	21	42.6	7221	22	11.3	7309	22	34.3	7397	22	52.9
7046	21	14.9	7134	21	48.9	7222	22	11.0	7310	22	34.7	7398	22	52.9
7047	21	16.5	7135	21	49.8	7223	22	10.2	7311	22	34.2	7399	22	52.7
7048	21	14.2	7136	21	49.7	7224	22	11.6	7312	22	34.7	7400	22	54.3
7049	21	19.0	7137	21	48.2	7225	22	13.2	7313	22	35.5	7401	22	53.1
7050	21	15.1	7138	21	49.0	7226	22	10.5	7314	22	35.8	7402	22	53.0
7051	21	19.8	7139	21	45.9	7227	22	11.5	7315	22	35.4	7403	22	53.1
7052	21	18.6	7140	21	52.3	7228	22	11.8	7316	22	35.9	7404	22	54.3
7053	21	21.1	7141	21	52.2	7229	22	14.0	7317	22	35.9	7405	22	52.8
7054	21	20.7	7142	21	45.9	7230	22	14.3	7318	22	36.0	7406	22	54.0
7055	21	19.4	7143	21	52.2	7231	22	12.4	7319	22	36.1	7407	22	53.3
7056	21	22.2	7144	21	52.7	7232	22	15.7	7320	22	36.1	7408	22	55.9
7057	21	25.0	7145	21	53.3	7233	22	15.8	7321	22	36.4	7409	22	53.7
7058	21	21.0	7146	21	51.8	7234	22	12.1	7322	22	37.7	7410	22	55.0
7059	21	27.4	7147	21	52.0	7235	22	12.6	7323	22	36.8	7411	22	54.5
7060	21	25.9	7148	21	52.1	7236	22	14.7	7324	22	37.0	7412	22	55.8
7061	21	27.4	7149	21	52.2	7237	22	14.8	7325	22	36.8	7413	22	55.1
7062	21	23.2	7150	21	50.4	7238	22	15.3	7326	22	36.8	7414	22	55.3
7063	21	24.4	7151	21	55.0	7239	22	14.9	7327	22	36.8	7415	22	54.8
7064	21	29.0	7152	21	53.9	7240	22	15.4	7328	22	37.5	7416	22	55.7
7065	21	26.7	7153	21	54.4	7241	22	15.8	7329	22	40.5	7417	22	57.8
7066	21	26.2	7154	21	55.4	7242	22	15.7	7330	22	36.9	7418	22	56.6
7067	21	24.2	7155	21	56.2	7243	22	15.3	7331	22	37.1	7419	22	54.3
7068	21	26.6	7156	21	54.6	7244	22	16.4	7332	22	37.4	7420	22	55.6
7069	21	28.1	7157	21	56.8	7245	22	15.3	7333	22	37.2	7421	22	56.9
7070	21	30.5	7158	21	57.4	7246	22	17.5	7334	22	37.8	7422	22	56.2
7071	21	26.5	7159	21	56.4	7247	22	17.8	7335	22	37.3	7423	22	55.3
7072	21	30.6	7160	21	53.7	7248	22	16.9	7336	22	37.2	7424	22	57.3
7073	21	29.5	7161	21	57.0	7249	22	20.5	7337	22	37.4	7425	22	57.3
7074	21	29.5	7162	21	59.8	7250	22	18.3	7338	22	37.5	7426	22	56.1
7075	21	31.5	7163	21	59.5	7251	22	20.4	7339	22	37.8	7427	22	57.2
7076	21	26.3	7164	21	56.6	7252	22	20.7	7340	22	37.6	7428	22	57.3
7077	21	29.9	7165	21	59.5	7253	22	19.4	7341	22	39.2	7429	22	55.9
7078	21	30.0	7166	22	00.7	7254	22	22.0	7342	22	38.1	7430	22	57.5
7079	21	32.5	7167	22	00.5	7255	22	21.9	7343	22	38.6	7431	22	57.8
7080	21	30.0	7168	22	02.1	7256	22	22.7	7344	22	39.7	7432	22	58.0
7081	21	31.4	7169	22	02.8	7257	22	22.2	7345	22	38.6	7433	22	58.0
7082	21	29.4	7170	22	01.4	7258	22	23.0	7346	22	39.5	7434	22	58.4
7083	21	35.7	7171	22	01.0	7259	22	23.1	7347	22	39.9	7435	22	57.9
7084	21	31.8	7172	22	02.0	7260	22	22.7	7348	22	40.6	7436	22	58.0
7085	21	32.3	7173	22	02.0	7261	22	20.4	7349	22	41.5	7437	22	58.2
7086	21	30.5	7174	22	02.1	7262	22	23.4	7350	22	41.0	7438	22	57.6
7087	21	34.6	7175	21	58.8	7263	22	21.8	7351	22	41.3	7439	22	58.7
7088	21	33.4	7176	22	02.1	7264	22	22.2	7352	22	39.7	7440	22	58.5
7089	21	33.5	7177	22	00.7	7265	22	22.4	7353	22	39.5	7441	22	59.5
7090	21	36.5	7178	22	02.5	7266	22	24.1	7354	22	40.4	7442	22	59.4
7091	21	34.1	7179	22	04.8	7267	22	24.3	7355	22	43.4	7443	23	00.1
7092	21	32.2	7180	22	02.3	7268	22	25.7	7356	22	42.1	7444	22	59.5
7093	21	34.8	7181	22	01.8	7269	22	25.8	7357	22	42.4	7445	22	59.5
7094	21	36.9	7182	22	01.9	7270	22	23.6	7358	22	45.7	7446	22	59.6
7095	21	40.2	7183	22	02.4	7271	22	23.8	7359	22	44.8	7447	23	00.4
7096	21	41.3	7184	22	02.7	7272	22	24.5	7360	22	43.6	7448	23	00.1
7097	21	40.3	7185	22	03.1	7273	22	24.1	7361	22	42.3	7449	22	59.7
7098	21	46.8	7186	22	01.0	7274	22	24.2	7362	22	43.9	7450	23	00.9
7099	21	40.4	7187	22	02.7	7275	22	24.1	7363	22	43.3	7451	23	00.4
7100	21	39.5	7188	22	03.5	7276	22	24.2	7364	22	44.5	7452	23	01.1
7101	21	39.6	7189	22	03.3	7277	22	26.4	7365	22	45.0	7453	23	01.4
7102	21	39.9	7190	22	03.1	7278	22	28.4	7366	22	44.3	7454	23	01.1
7103	21	39.9	7191	22	06.9	7279	22	27.1	7367	22	44.7	7455	23	00.6
7104	21	40.1	7192	22	06.8	7280	22	26.5	7368	22	45.6	7456	23	02.1
7105	21	40.5	7193	22	03.6	7281	22	24.7	7369	22	44.3	7457	23	01.0
7106	21	42.6	7194	22	03.5	7282	22	26.0	7370	22	45.5	7458	23	01.5
7107	21	42.4	7195	22	03.4	7283	22	28.6	7371	22	46.1	7459	23	01.7
7108	21	42.4	7196	22	06.0	7284	22	28.6	7372	22	45.7	7460	23	01.8
7109	21	42.4	7197	22	02.9	7285	22	28.7	7373	22	46.5	7461	23	01.7
7110	21	42.2	7198	22	05.3	7286	22	28.0	7374	22	46.0	7462	23	02.8
7111	21	41.8	7199	22	08.5	7287	22	28.8	7375	22	46.8	7463	23	01.9
7112	21	42.3	7200	22	07.2	7288	22	28.3	7376	22	47.4	7464	23	01.9
7113	21	42.4	7201	22	06.5	7289	22	29.2	7377	22	47.8	7465	23	02.0
7114	21	41.7	7202	22	06.7	7290	22	28.4	7378	22	47.9	7466	23	02.0
7115	21	43.6	7203	22	06.7	7291	22	28.5	7379	22	47.4	7467	23	02.3
7116	21	42.6	7204	22	06.9	7292	22	28.4	7380	22	47.0	7468	23	03.0
7117	21	45.7	7205	22	08.5	7293	22	29.6	7381	22	50.0	7469	23	03.3
7118	21	46.1	7206	22	05.6	7294	22	32.2	7382	22	50.5	7470	23	05.2
7119	21	46.3	7207	22	05.7	7295	22	28.4	7383	22	49.6	7471	23	03.9
7120	21	44.4	7208	22	08.4	7296	22	28.2	7384	22	49.7	7472	23	05.7
7121	21	44.9	7209	22	05.2	7297	22	30.9	7385	22	49.9	7473	23	03.9
7122	21	45.7	7210	22	06.3	7298	22	30.8	7386	22	50.0	7474	23	04.0
7123	21	50.8	7211	22	06.2	7299	22	31.4	7387	22	50.3	7475	23	04.1
7124	21	48.1	7212	22	07.0	7300	22	31.0	7388	22	50.2	7476	23	05.2
7125	21	49.3	7213	22	09.3	7301	22	30.4	7389	22	50.3	7477	23	05.7
7126	21	49.3	7214	22	09.1	7302	22	32.4	7390	22	50.3	7478	23	04.9
7127	21	43.9	7215	22	08.6	7303	22	31.6	7391	22	50.7	7479	23	04.9
7128	21	44.0	7216	22	12.6	7304	22	31.5	7392	22	51.8	7480	23	05.3

Right Ascensions of NGC Objects

NGC	α_{2000}	NGC	α_{2000}	NGC	α_{2000}	NGC	α_{2000}	NGC	α_{2000}
	h m		h m		h m		h m		h m
7481	23 05.8	7553	23 15.3	7625	23 20.5	7697	23 34.9	7769	23 51.1
7482	23 05.7	7554	23 15.7	7626	23 20.7	7698	23 34.0	7770	23 51.4
7483	23 05.9	7555	23 15.6	7627	23 22.5	7699	23 34.4	7771	23 51.4
7484	23 07.1	7556	23 15.9	7628	23 20.8	7700	23 34.6	7772	23 51.8
7485	23 06.1	7557	23 15.7	7629	23 21.4	7701	23 34.6	7773	23 52.3
7486	23 06.2	7558	23 15.6	7630	23 21.4	7702	23 35.4	7774	23 52.2
7487	23 06.9	7559	23 15.9	7631	23 21.4	7703	23 34.9	7775	23 52.5
7488	23 07.9	7560	23 16.0	7632	23 22.1	7704	23 35.2	7776	23 52.7
7489	23 07.4	7561	23 16.0	7633	23 23.1	7705	23 35.2	7777	23 53.3
7490	23 07.4	7562	23 16.0	7634	23 21.6	7706	23 35.3	7778	23 53.3
7491	23 08.1	7563	23 16.0	7635	23 20.7	7707	23 34.8	7779	23 53.4
7492	23 08.4	7564	23 15.6	7636	23 22.3	7708	23 34.3	7780	23 53.6
7493	23 08.6	7565	23 16.3	7637	23 26.5	7709	23 35.4	7781	23 53.8
7494	23 08.9	7566	23 16.6	7638	23 22.5	7710	23 35.8	7782	23 53.9
7495	23 09.0	7567	23 16.2	7639	23 22.8	7711	23 35.7	7783	23 54.2
7496	23 09.8	7568	23 16.3	7640	23 22.1	7712	23 35.9	7784	23 55.3
7497	23 09.1	7569	23 16.8	7641	23 22.6	7713	23 36.5	7785	23 55.3
7498	23 09.8	7570	23 16.8	7642	23 22.9	7714	23 36.2	7786	23 55.4
7499	23 10.4	7571	23 17.2	7643	23 22.9	7715	23 36.4	7787	23 56.2
7500	23 10.6	7572	23 16.8	7644	23 24.5	7716	23 36.5	7788	23 56.7
7501	23 10.5	7573	23 16.3	7645	23 23.7	7717	23 37.7	7789	23 57.0
7502	23 10.8	7574	23 16.8	7646	23 24.0	7718	23 38.1	7790	23 58.4
7503	23 10.7	7575	23 17.3	7647	23 24.1	7719	23 38.0	7791	23 58.0
7504	23 10.6	7576	23 17.4	7648	23 23.8	7720	23 38.5	7792	23 58.1
7505	23 11.2	7577	23 17.4	7649	23 24.3	7721	23 38.8	7793	23 57.8
7506	23 11.8	7578	23 17.2	7650	23 25.3	7722	23 38.8	7794	23 58.6
7507	23 12.1	7579	23 17.7	7651	23 24.5	7723	23 38.9	7795	23 58.7
7508	23 11.9	7580	23 17.6	7652	23 25.6	7724	23 39.1	7796	23 59.0
7509	23 12.4	7581	23 17.8	7653	23 24.9	7725	23 39.3	7797	23 59.0
7510	23 11.5	7582	23 18.4	7654	23 24.2	7726	23 38.7	7798	23 59.4
7511	23 12.5	7583	23 17.9	7655	23 26.7	7727	23 39.9	7799	23 59.5
7512	23 12.3	7584	23 18.0	7656	23 24.5	7728	23 40.0	7800	23 59.6
7513	23 13.2	7585	23 18.0	7657	23 26.7	7729	23 40.6	7801	0 00.4
7514	23 12.4	7586	23 17.7	7658	23 26.5	7730	23 41.4	7802	0 01.1
7515	23 12.9	7587	23 17.9	7659	23 26.0	7731	23 41.6	7803	0 01.4
7516	23 12.8	7588	23 17.8	7660	23 25.7	7732	23 41.7	7804	0 01.3
7517	23 13.3	7589	23 18.4	7661	23 27.2	7733	23 42.6	7805	0 01.4
7518	23 13.1	7590	23 18.9	7662	23 25.9	7734	23 42.7	7806	0 01.5
7519	23 12.7	7591	23 18.4	7663	23 26.7	7735	23 42.3	7807	23 59.6
7520	23 13.7	7592	23 18.4	7664	23 26.6	7736	23 42.4	7808	0 03.5
7521	23 13.7	7593	23 18.0	7665	23 27.2	7737	23 42.8	7809	0 02.2
7522	23 13.8	7594	23 18.3	7666	23 27.4	7738	23 44.1	7810	0 02.4
7523	23 13.7	7595	23 18.5	7667	23 24.3	7739	23 43.6	7811	0 02.5
7524	23 13.8	7596	23 17.2	7668	23 27.2	7740	23 43.3	7812	0 02.9
7525	23 13.7	7597	23 18.5	7669	23 27.2	7741	23 43.9	7813	0 03.2
7526	23 13.9	7598	23 18.5	7670	23 27.2	7742	23 44.3	7814	0 03.3
7527	23 13.6	7599	23 19.3	7671	23 27.3	7743	23 44.4	7815	0 03.4
7528	23 14.3	7600	23 18.9	7672	23 27.5	7744	23 45.0	7816	0 03.8
7529	23 14.1	7601	23 18.8	7673	23 27.7	7745	23 44.8	7817	0 04.0
7530	23 14.3	7602	23 18.8	7674	23 27.9	7746	23 45.4	7818	0 04.2
7531	23 14.8	7603	23 19.0	7675	23 28.0	7747	23 45.6	7819	0 04.4
7532	23 14.4	7604	23 17.9	7676	23 28.9	7748	23 45.0	7820	0 04.6
7533	23 14.4	7605	23 18.9	7677	23 28.1	7749	23 45.9	7821	0 05.3
7534	23 14.5	7606	23 19.1	7678	23 28.5	7750	23 46.7	7822	0 04.8
7535	23 14.3	7607	23 19.0	7679	23 28.8	7751	23 47.0	7823	0 04.8
7536	23 14.3	7608	23 19.3	7680	23 28.5	7752	23 47.0	7824	0 05.2
7537	23 14.6	7609	23 19.5	7681	23 28.6	7753	23 47.1	7825	0 05.2
7538	23 13.5	7610	23 19.6	7682	23 29.1	7754	23 49.2	7826	0 05.2
7539	23 14.4	7611	23 19.6	7683	23 29.1	7755	23 47.9	7827	0 05.5
7540	23 14.5	7612	23 19.8	7684	23 30.5	7756	23 48.5	7828	0 06.4
7541	23 14.7	7613	23 19.9	7685	23 30.6	7757	23 48.8	7829	0 06.4
7542	23 14.8	7614	23 20.0	7686	23 30.2	7758	23 48.9	7830	0 06.2
7543	23 14.6	7615	23 19.9	7687	23 30.9	7759	23 48.9	7831	0 07.3
7544	23 15.0	7616	23 19.5	7688	23 31.2	7760	23 49.3	7832	0 06.6
7545	23 15.5	7617	23 19.8	7689	23 32.7	7761	23 49.6	7833	0 06.5
7546	23 15.2	7618	23 20.2	7690	23 32.9	7762	23 49.8	7834	0 06.7
7547	23 15.0	7619	23 20.4	7691	23 32.6	7763	23 50.3	7835	0 06.8
7548	23 15.1	7620	23 20.1	7692	23 32.8	7764	23 50.9	7836	0 08.0
7549	23 15.3	7621	23 20.4	7693	23 33.3	7765	23 50.8	7837	0 06.9
7550	23 15.3	7622	23 21.6	7694	23 33.4	7766	23 50.9	7838	0 07.0
7551	23 14.6	7623	23 20.5	7695	23 33.3	7767	23 50.9	7839	0 07.0
7552	23 16.2	7624	23 20.4	7696	23 33.9	7768	23 50.9	7840	0 07.1

Right Ascensions of IC Objects

IC	h	m	IC	h	m	IC	h	m	IC	h	m	IC	h	m
1	0	08.4	89	1	16.1	177	1	57.1	265	2	54.7	353	3	55.0
2	0	11.0	90	1	16.5	178	1	58.9	266	2	55.0	354	3	53.3
3	0	12.1	91	1	18.7	179	2	00.2	267	2	53.8	355	3	53.8
4	0	13.4	92	1	19.9	180	2	00.0	268	2	55.4	356	4	07.8
5	0	17.4	93	1	19.0	181	2	00.0	269	2	55.4	357	4	03.8
6	0	19.0	94	1	20.1	182	1	59.8	270	2	55.7	358	4	03.7
7	0	19.1	95	1	19.3	183	1	59.6	271	2	56.0	359	4	19.0
8	0	19.1	96	1	20.3	184	1	59.9	272	2	56.1	360	4	13.0
9	0	19.7	97	1	20.0	185	2	00.1	273	2	57.1	361	4	19.0
10	0	20.4	98	1	21.0	186	2	00.4	274	3	00.1	362	4	16.7
11	0	20.5	99	1	22.5	187	2	01.9	275	3	00.9	363	4	18.9
12	0	20.3	100	1	22.9	188	2	02.0	276	2	58.7	364	4	19.1
13	0	20.4	101	1	24.1	189	2	01.9	277	2	59.8	365	4	19.2
14	0	22.6	102	1	24.4	190	2	02.1	278	3	01.5	366	4	19.6
15	0	28.0	103	1	24.6	191	2	02.5	279	3	01.2	367	4	20.6
16	0	27.9	104	1	24.6	192	2	02.5	280	3	03.3	368	4	22.7
17	0	28.5	105	1	24.7	193	2	02.7	281	3	04.5	369	4	23.5
18	0	28.6	106	1	24.7	194	2	03.1	282	3	05.2	370	4	24.1
19	0	28.7	107	1	25.2	195	2	03.7	283	3	03.9	371	4	30.2
20	0	28.5	108	1	24.7	196	2	03.9	284	3	06.2	372	4	30.1
21	0	29.2	109	1	25.2	197	2	04.1	285	3	04.1	373	4	30.7
22	0	29.6	110	1	25.9	198	2	06.1	286	3	04.8	374	4	32.5
23	0	30.9	111	1	26.0	199	2	06.3	287	3	05.0	375	4	31.1
24	0	31.2	112	1	26.0	200	2	07.4	288	3	07.5	376	4	31.1
25	0	31.2	113	1	26.4	201	2	07.3	289	3	10.3	377	4	31.3
26	0	31.8	114	1	26.3	202	2	07.5	290	3	09.7	378	4	31.5
27	0	33.1	115	1	26.9	203	2	07.5	291	3	07.4	379	4	31.9
28	0	33.1	116	1	26.8	204	2	07.4	292	3	10.3	380	4	31.7
29	0	34.2	117	1	27.4	205	2	07.4	293	3	10.9	381	4	44.4
30	0	34.3	118	1	27.6	206	2	07.5	294	3	10.9	382	4	37.9
31	0	34.4	119	1	27.9	207	2	07.7	295	3	11.0	383	4	39.0
32	0	35.0	120	1	28.2	208	2	08.4	296	3	11.1	384	4	39.3
33	0	35.1	121	1	28.4	209	2	09.0	297	3	13.3	385	4	39.5
34	0	35.6	122	1	28.2	210	2	09.4	298	3	11.3	386	4	40.0
35	0	37.7	123	1	28.8	211	2	11.1	299	3	11.0	387	4	41.7
36	0	37.8	124	1	29.2	212	2	13.6	300	3	14.3	388	4	42.0
37	0	38.5	125	1	29.3	213	2	14.0	301	3	14.8	389	4	42.0
38	0	38.6	126	1	29.8	214	2	14.0	302	3	12.8	390	4	42.1
39	0	39.1	127	1	29.8	215	2	14.2	303	3	12.7	391	4	57.4
40	0	39.5	128	1	31.3	216	2	15.8	304	3	15.0	392	4	46.4
41	0	39.7	129	1	31.6	217	2	16.2	305	3	15.1	393	4	47.9
42	0	41.1	130	1	31.5	218	2	17.1	306	3	13.0	394	4	48.9
43	0	42.4	131	1	33.2	219	2	18.6	307	3	13.8	395	4	49.6
44	0	42.2	132	1	33.3	220	2	19.2	308	3	16.3	396	4	58.0
45	0	42.7	133	1	33.3	221	2	22.7	309	3	16.1	397	5	01.1
46	0	43.0	134	1	33.4	222	2	22.7	310	3	16.7	398	4	58.2
47	0	42.9	135	1	33.2	223	2	22.0	311	3	16.8	399	5	01.8
48	0	43.6	136	1	33.2	224	2	24.7	312	3	18.1	400	5	03.7
49	0	44.0	137	1	33.6	225	2	26.5	313	3	21.0	401	5	04.3
50	0	46.2	138	1	33.0	226	2	27.7	314	3	18.8	402	5	06.3
51	0	46.4	139	1	33.7	227	2	28.0	315	3	19.1	403	5	15.3
52	0	48.4	140	1	33.7	228	2	26.7	316	3	21.4	404	5	13.3
53	0	50.5	141	1	32.8	229	2	27.4	317	3	19.0	405	5	16.2
54	0	50.8	142	1	33.9	230	2	28.8	318	3	20.8	406	5	17.8
55	0	51.7	143	1	34.1	231	2	30.0	319	3	23.4	407	5	17.7
56	0	51.5	144	1	37.7	232	2	31.2	320	3	26.0	408	5	17.9
57	0	54.8	145	1	38.7	233	2	31.6	321	3	24.5	409	5	19.6
58	0	55.1	146	1	38.7	234	2	31.7	322	3	25.9	410	5	22.6
59	0	56.7	147	1	40.0	235	2	32.8	323	3	29.5	411	5	20.3
60	0	56.1	148	1	42.4	236	2	32.9	324	3	26.5	412	5	21.9
61	0	57.1	149	1	42.4	237	2	33.5	325	3	30.8	413	5	22.0
62	0	58.7	150	1	43.0	238	2	35.3	326	3	30.7	414	5	21.9
63	0	59.5	151	1	44.0	239	2	36.5	327	3	31.1	415	5	21.3
64	0	59.4	152	1	44.1	240	2	39.1	328	3	31.2	416	5	23.9
65	1	00.9	153	1	44.6	241	2	37.9	329	3	32.1	417	5	28.1
66	1	00.5	154	1	45.3	242	2	38.5	330	3	32.2	418	5	27.5
67	1	00.3	155	1	47.5	243	2	38.5	331	3	32.4	419	5	31.0
68	1	00.4	156	1	45.5	244	2	39.4	332	3	32.7	420	5	32.3
69	1	01.4	157	1	45.7	245	2	38.9	333	3	34.0	421	5	32.2
70	1	01.1	158	1	45.9	246	2	40.5	334	3	45.2	422	5	32.3
71	1	01.3	159	1	46.5	247	2	40.1	335	3	35.5	423	5	33.4
72	1	01.5	160	1	46.4	248	2	41.4	336	3	38.2	424	5	33.7
73	1	04.9	161	1	48.7	249	2	41.1	337	3	37.1	425	5	37.1
74	1	05.9	162	1	48.9	250	2	40.9	338	3	37.6	426	5	36.8
75	1	07.2	163	1	49.3	251	2	41.2	339	3	38.1	427	5	36.6
76	1	08.2	164	1	49.1	252	2	41.7	340	3	39.5	428	5	36.6
77	1	08.7	165	1	50.2	253	2	42.1	341	3	41.2	429	5	38.3
78	1	08.8	166	1	52.5	254	2	42.1	342	3	46.8	430	5	38.5
79	1	08.8	167	1	51.1	255	2	47.1	343	3	40.1	431	5	40.3
80	1	08.9	168	1	50.5	256	2	49.8	344	3	41.5	432	5	40.9
81	1	09.2	169	1	50.6	257	2	49.9	345	3	41.2	433	5	40.5
82	1	09.1	170	1	52.0	258	2	49.8	346	3	41.7	434	5	41.0
83	1	10.5	171	1	55.2	259	2	50.1	347	3	42.5	435	5	43.0
84	1	11.5	172	1	54.9	260	2	51.1	348	3	44.5	436	5	53.7
85	1	11.8	173	1	56.0	261	2	49.1	349	3	46.3	437	5	51.6
86	1	13.5	174	1	56.3	262	2	51.7	350	3	44.7	438	5	53.0
87	1	14.3	175	1	56.3	263	2	50.6	351	3	47.5	439	5	56.6
88	1	14.5	176	1	56.9	264	2	50.9	352	3	47.6	440	6	18.9

Right Ascensions of IC Objects

IC	α_{2000}	IC	α_{2000}	IC	α_{2000}	IC	α_{2000}	IC	α_{2000}
	h m		h m		h m		h m		h m
441	6 02.7	529	9 18.5	617	10 32.8	705	11 32.9	793	12 28.0
442	6 36.5	530	9 15.3	618	10 32.8	706	11 33.1	794	12 28.1
443	6 16.9	531	9 17.9	619	10 33.5	707	11 33.6	795	12 28.5
444	6 20.4	532	9 19.0	620	10 33.5	708	11 33.9	796	12 29.4
445	6 37.3	533	9 20.4	621	10 33.3	709	11 34.2	797	12 31.9
446	6 31.0	534	9 21.2	622	10 34.6	710	11 34.4	798	12 32.5
447	6 31.2	535	9 22.2	623	10 35.4	711	11 34.7	799	12 33.7
448	6 32.7	536	9 24.6	624	10 36.3	712	11 34.8	800	12 33.9
449	6 45.7	537	9 25.4	625	10 36.5	713	11 34.8	801	12 33.8
450	6 52.2	538	9 27.4	626	10 37.0	714	11 36.5	802	12 35.8
451	6 52.9	539	9 29.1	627	10 37.3	715	11 36.9	803	12 39.6
452	6 48.6	540	9 30.2	628	10 37.6	716	11 39.1	804	12 41.3
453	6 49.1	541	9 30.5	629	10 37.0	717	11 39.4	805	12 41.3
454	6 51.1	542	9 31.2	630	10 38.5	718	11 39.9	806	12 42.2
455	7 35.	543	9 30.9	631	10 39.0	719	11 40.3	807	12 42.3
456	7 00.3	544	9 35.9	632	10 39.2	720	11 42.3	808	12 41.9
457	7 09.4	545	9 36.1	633	10 39.4	721	11 42.5	809	12 42.1
458	7 10.5	546	9 34.9	634	10 40.9	722	11 42.6	810	12 42.1
459	7 10.6	547	9 36.2	635	10 41.7	723	11 43.0	811	12 44.8
460	7 10.7	548	9 38.3	636	10 41.9	724	11 43.4	812	12 44.9
461	7 10.7	549	9 40.7	637	10 42.4	725	11 43.5	813	12 45.2
462	7 11.0	550	9 40.5	638	10 43.8	726	11 43.8	814	12 45.6
463	7 10.9	551	9 40.9	639	10 45.9	727	11 44.5	815	12 46.4
464	7 11.0	552	9 41.3	640	10 46.8	728	11 44.9	816	12 46.7
465	7 11.5	553	9 40.7	641	10 47.8	729	11 45.2	817	12 46.9
466	7 08.6	554	9 41.8	642	10 48.1	730	11 45.6	818	12 46.6
467	7 30.0	555	9 41.9	643	10 49.4	731	11 46.0	819	12 47.2
468	7 17.5	556	9 43.7	644	10 51.5	732	11 46.0	820	12 47.2
469	7 56.	557	9 44.1	645	10 50.2	733	11 46.0	821	12 47.4
470	7 23.5	558	9 45.0	646	10 51.6	734	11 46.2	822	12 47.8
471	7 43.6	559	9 44.7	647	10 50.6	735	11 48.2	823	12 47.8
472	7 43.8	560	9 45.9	648	10 51.0	736	11 48.4	824	12 49.7
473	7 42.4	561	9 46.0	649	10 50.9	737	11 48.5	825	12 50.3
474	7 46.1	562	9 46.1	650	10 50.7	738	11 48.9	826	12 51.3
475	7 47.2	563	9 46.3	651	10 51.0	739	11 50.4	827	12 52.0
476	7 47.3	564	9 46.4	652	10 51.0	740	11 50.6	828	12 52.3
477	7 52.1	565	9 47.8	653	10 52.2	741	11 50.5	829	12 52.4
478	7 53.7	566	9 50.0	654	10 53.9	742	11 51.0	830	12 51.2
479	7 54.4	567	9 50.5	655	10 54.4	743	11 53.4	831	12 52.7
480	7 55.3	568	9 51.1	656	10 55.1	744	11 54.1	832	12 53.8
481	7 59.0	569	9 51.5	657	10 57.9	745	11 54.3	833	12 56.7
482	7 59.8	570	9 51.8	658	10 58.3	746	11 55.6	834	12 56.5
483	7 59.9	571	9 52.5	659	10 58.1	747	11 57.1	835	12 56.9
484	7 59.9	572	9 52.5	660	10 58.5	748	11 57.5	836	12 56.0
485	8 00.3	573	9 53.6	661	10 58.9	749	11 58.6	837	12 57.5
486	8 00.3	574	9 54.4	662	10 59.4	750	11 58.8	838	12 58.2
487	7 59.2	575	9 54.6	663	11 00.0	751	11 58.9	839	12 58.4
488	8 00.8	576	9 55.1	664	11 00.7	752	11 59.3	840	12 58.7
489	8 01.6	577	9 56.1	665	11 00.5	753	11 59.2	841	12 59.8
490	8 03.3	578	9 56.3	666	11 01.3	754	11 59.4	842	13 00.6
491	8 03.8	579	9 56.6	667	11 06.5	755	12 01.2	843	13 01.6
492	8 05.7	580	9 58.0	668	11 06.6	756	12 03.0	844	13 03.3
493	8 07.4	581	9 58.2	669	11 07.3	757	12 03.4	845	13 05.3
494	8 06.4	582	9 59.0	670	11 07.4	758	12 04.2	846	13 05.3
495	8 08.3	583	9 59.1	671	11 07.6	759	12 05.2	847	13 06.0
496	8 09.7	584	9 59.1	672	11 08.0	760	12 05.9	848	13 07.0
497	8 10.1	585	9 59.7	673	11 09.5	761	12 06.0	849	13 07.6
498	8 09.4	586	9 59.9	674	11 11.1	762	12 08.1	850	13 07.8
499	8 46.	587	10 03.0	675	11 10.7	763	12 08.2	851	13 08.5
500	8 12.6	588	10 02.2	676	11 12.7	764	12 10.2	852	13 07.6
501	8 18.8	589	10 04.4	677	11 13.9	765	12 10.5	853	13 08.6
502	8 22.0	590	10 05.9	678	11 14.1	766	12 10.9	854	13 09.8
503	8 22.2	591	10 07.5	679	11 16.6	767	12 11.1	855	13 10.6
504	8 22.6	592	10 07.9	680	11 18.0	768	12 11.9	856	13 10.7
505	8 23.3	593	10 08.3	681	11 18.6	769	12 12.5	857	13 13.8
506	8 23.4	594	10 08.6	682	11 21.2	770	12 13.0	858	13 14.9
507	8 25.6	595	10 09.7	683	11 21.4	771	12 15.2	859	13 15.0
508	8 28.4	596	10 10.6	684	11 21.6	772	12 15.2	860	13 15.1
509	8 32.0	597	10 10.2	685	11 22.1	773	12 18.1	861	13 15.1
510	8 32.1	598	10 13.1	686	11 23.1	774	12 18.8	862	13 16.2
511	8 40.8	599	10 13.3	687	11 24.3	775	12 18.9	863	13 17.2
512	9 04.	600	10 17.2	688	11 23.7	776	12 19.0	864	13 17.2
513	8 33.0	601	10 18.2	689	11 23.6	777	12 19.4	865	13 17.6
514	8 35.4	602	10 18.3	690	11 24.3	778	12 19.4	866	13 17.2
515	8 35.5	603	10 19.4	691	11 26.7	779	12 19.8	867	13 17.2
516	8 35.8	604	10 23.8	692	11 25.9	780	12 19.9	868	13 17.4
517	8 36.3	605	10 22.4	693	11 26.8	781	12 20.1	869	13 17.5
518	8 37.1	606	10 23.5	694	11 28.5	782	12 21.6	870	13 17.5
519	8 40.6	607	10 24.2	695	11 28.0	783	12 21.6	871	13 17.9
520	8 53.7	608	10 24.3	696	11 28.6	784	12 22.6	872	13 18.2
521	8 46.8	609	10 25.5	697	11 28.6	785	12 23.0	873	13 18.3
522	8 54.5	610	10 26.5	698	11 29.0	786	12 23.2	874	13 19.0
523	8 53.2	611	10 26.5	699	11 29.1	787	12 25.5	875	13 17.1
524	8 58.2	612	10 27.1	700	11 29.3	788	12 26.1	876	13 18.5
525	9 01.3	613	10 27.1	701	11 30.8	789	12 26.3	877	13 19.0
526	9 02.6	614	10 26.9	702	11 30.9	790	12 26.5	878	13 19.0
527	9 09.6	615	10 27.3	703	11 31.8	791	12 27.0	879	13 19.7
528	9 09.4	616	10 32.8	704	11 31.9	792	12 27.1	880	13 19.1

IC	α_{2000}	IC	α_{2000}	IC	α_{2000}	IC	α_{2000}	IC	α_{2000}
	h m		h m		h m		h m		h m
881	13 20.0	969	14 01.8	1057	14 46.0	1145	15 46.2	1233	16 48.4
882	13 20.2	970	14 02.5	1058	14 49.1	1146	15 48.5	1234	16 52.9
883	13 20.6	971	14 03.8	1059	14 50.7	1147	15 50.1	1235	16 52.1
884	13 22.9	972	14 04.4	1060	14 51.9	1148	15 56.9	1236	16 58.5
885	13 22.6	973	14 06.5	1061	14 51.2	1149	15 58.0	1237	16 56.3
886	13 23.9	974	14 06.6	1062	14 51.3	1150	15 58.3	1238	17 00.6
887	13 24.2	975	14 07.2	1063	14 52.2	1151	15 58.5	1239	17 00.8
888	13 25.8	976	14 08.7	1064	14 52.2	1152	15 56.7	1240	17 01.0
889	13 26.6	977	14 08.7	1065	14 49.3	1153	15 56.8	1241	17 01.4
890	13 28.4	978	14 09.0	1066	14 53.0	1154	15 52.5	1242	17 08.7
891	13 30.0	979	14 09.3	1067	14 53.1	1155	16 00.6	1243	17 10.6
892	13 31.8	980	14 10.4	1068	14 53.5	1156	16 00.6	1244	17 10.6
893	13 31.8	981	14 10.5	1069	14 51.0	1157	16 01.0	1245	17 12.6
894	13 32.1	982	14 10.0	1070	14 53.9	1158	16 01.5	1246	17 14.3
895	13 32.3	983	14 10.1	1071	14 54.2	1159	16 01.0	1247	17 16.4
896	13 34.1	984	14 10.1	1072	14 54.2	1160	16 01.1	1248	17 11.8
897	13 33.9	985	14 11.5	1073	14 54.2	1161	16 01.3	1249	17 14.9
898	13 34.2	986	14 11.4	1074	14 52.0	1162	16 01.3	1250	17 14.4
899	13 34.9	987	14 11.5	1075	14 54.8	1163	16 01.5	1251	17 10.1
900	13 34.7	988	14 14.5	1076	14 55.0	1164	15 55.1	1252	17 15.8
901	13 35.7	989	14 14.8	1077	14 57.4	1165	16 02.1	1253	17 19.8
902	13 36.0	990	14 15.7	1078	14 56.5	1166	16 02.1	1254	17 11.5
903	13 38.4	991	14 17.7	1079	14 56.6	1167	16 03.9	1255	17 23.1
904	13 38.6	992	14 18.3	1080	14 58.1	1168	16 04.0	1256	17 23.8
905	13 40.1	993	14 18.1	1081	14 58.9	1169	16 04.2	1257	17 27.1
906	13 40.1	994	14 18.3	1082	14 58.9	1170	16 04.5	1258	17 27.3
907	13 39.5	995	14 16.6	1083	14 55.6	1171	16 04.9	1259	17 27.4
908	13 41.2	996	14 17.0	1084	15 01.3	1172	16 04.9	1260	17 27.4
909	13 40.8	997	14 19.9	1085	15 02.7	1173	16 05.2	1261	17 23.5
910	13 41.1	998	14 20.2	1086	15 03.4	1174	16 05.4	1262	17 33.0
911	13 41.4	999	14 19.6	1087	15 06.7	1175	16 05.3	1263	17 33.1
912	13 41.4	1000	14 19.7	1088	15 06.7	1176	16 05.4	1264	17 33.3
913	13 41.5	1001	14 20.7	1089	15 07.4	1177	16 05.3	1265	17 36.7
914	13 41.7	1002	14 20.7	1090	15 03.7	1178	16 05.5	1266	17 45.6
915	13 43.5	1003	14 20.9	1091	15 08.2	1179	16 05.4	1267	17 38.7
916	13 42.6	1004	14 20.9	1092	15 07.5	1180	16 05.4	1268	17 50.7
917	13 42.7	1005	14 18.3	1093	15 07.7	1181	16 05.6	1269	17 52.1
918	13 42.8	1006	14 23.0	1094	15 07.7	1182	16 05.6	1270	17 47.8
919	13 42.9	1007	14 24.6	1095	15 08.5	1183	16 05.6	1271	18 05.5
920	13 45.5	1008	14 25.0	1096	15 08.5	1184	16 05.7	1272	18 04.9
921	13 43.2	1009	14 26.3	1097	15 08.5	1185	16 05.7	1273	18 05.0
922	13 43.3	1010	14 27.3	1098	15 06.4	1186	16 05.7	1274	18 09.5
923	13 43.3	1011	14 28.1	1099	15 06.9	1187	15 59.3	1275	18 10.0
924	13 45.6	1012	14 27.2	1100	15 06.3	1188	16 06.1	1276	18 10.7
925	13 43.4	1013	14 27.8	1101	15 10.9	1189	16 06.2	1277	18 10.2
926	13 43.5	1014	14 28.3	1102	15 11.1	1190	16 06.3	1278	18 10.5
927	13 45.9	1015	14 28.3	1103	15 11.6	1191	16 06.5	1279	18 11.1
928	13 43.7	1016	14 28.8	1104	15 12.8	1192	16 06.6	1280	18 12.2
929	13 43.7	1017	14 28.1	1105	15 13.3	1193	16 06.5	1281	18 11.6
930	13 43.8	1018	14 28.3	1106	15 14.0	1194	16 06.7	1282	18 14.1
931	13 43.8	1019	14 28.1	1107	15 14.2	1195	16 06.7	1283	18 17.3
932	13 43.8	1020	14 28.8	1108	15 16.8	1196	16 08.0	1284	18 17.7
933	13 45.3	1021	14 29.2	1109	15 17.1	1197	16 08.3	1285	18 16.1
934	13 44.0	1022	14 30.0	1110	15 12.1	1198	16 08.6	1286	18 16.2
935	13 44.0	1023	14 32.4	1111	15 14.4	1199	16 10.6	1287	18 31.3
936	13 44.0	1024	14 31.4	1112	15 17.9	1200	16 04.5	1288	18 29.4
937	13 44.5	1025	14 31.5	1113	15 18.3	1201	16 05.8	1289	18 29.8
938	13 44.6	1026	14 31.2	1114	15 11.3	1202	16 13.0	1290	18 38.5
939	13 47.7	1027	14 29.8	1115	15 22.4	1203	16 15.3	1291	18 33.9
940	13 47.9	1028	14 32.5	1116	15 21.9	1204	16 07.1	1292	18 44.8
941	13 48.5	1029	14 32.5	1117	15 24.4	1205	16 14.3	1293	18 41.7
942	13 47.6	1030	14 33.7	1118	15 25.1	1206	16 15.3	1294	18 49.9
943	13 50.5	1031	14 34.6	1119	15 25.7	1207	16 19.4	1295	18 54.6
944	13 51.5	1032	14 34.7	1120	15 26.2	1208	16 15.7	1296	18 53.3
945	13 48.0	1033	14 34.8	1121	15 27.8	1209	16 18.7	1297	19 17.4
946	13 52.1	1034	14 37.2	1122	15 29.5	1210	16 14.5	1298	19 18.5
947	13 52.7	1035	14 38.1	1123	15 28.9	1211	16 16.8	1299	19 22.6
948	13 52.4	1036	14 38.3	1124	15 30.0	1212	16 15.5	1300	19 24.1
949	13 52.2	1037	14 38.4	1125	15 33.1	1213	16 22.0	1301	19 26.6
950	13 52.4	1038	14 39.4	1126	15 35.0	1214	16 16.2	1302	19 30.9
951	13 51.7	1039	14 40.5	1127	15 35.9	1215	16 15.6	1303	19 31.5
952	13 53.7	1040	14 40.3	1128	15 37.9	1216	16 16.0	1304	19 35.5
953	13 55.0	1041	14 40.6	1129	15 32.0	1217	16 16.1	1305	19 39.3
954	13 50.0	1042	14 40.6	1130	15 37.8	1218	16 16.8	1306	19 41.7
955	13 55.7	1043	14 40.7	1131	15 38.9	1219	16 24.4	1307	19 42.8
956	13 54.7	1044	14 41.5	1132	15 40.0	1220	16 29.2	1308	19 45.1
957	13 56.1	1045	14 40.7	1133	15 41.2	1221	16 34.7	1309	20 03.1
958	13 56.5	1046	14 37.8	1134	15 44.9	1222	16 35.1	1310	20 10.0
959	13 56.0	1047	14 42.4	1135	15 45.6	1223	16 35.4	1311	20 10.3
960	13 56.0	1048	14 42.9	1136	15 47.6	1224	16 42.9	1312	20 16.8
961	13 55.8	1049	14 39.6	1137	15 48.9	1225	16 36.9	1313	20 18.7
962	13 57.3	1050	14 44.1	1138	15 48.2	1226	16 41.1	1314	20 17.7
963	13 57.0	1051	14 44.2	1139	15 29.6	1227	16 40.1	1315	20 17.4
964	13 57.7	1052	14 44.2	1140	15 49.1	1228	16 42.0	1316	20 22.4
965	13 57.5	1053	14 45.6	1141	15 49.6	1229	16 45.0	1317	20 23.3
966	13 58.2	1054	14 46.5	1142	15 49.4	1230	16 45.3	1318	20 22.2
967	13 58.4	1055	14 47.4	1143	15 30.7	1231	16 46.9	1319	20 26.0
968	14 00.6	1056	14 45.8	1144	15 51.3	1232	16 49.1	1320	20 26.4

Right Ascensions of IC Objects

IC	α2000 (h m)	IC	α2000 (h m)	IC	α2000 (h m)	IC	α2000 (h m)	IC	α2000 (h m)
1321	20 28.2	1409	21 53.3	1497	23 28.8	1585	0 47.3	1673	1 20.8
1322	20 30.1	1410	21 56.0	1498	23 32.0	1586	0 47.9	1674	1 19.0
1323	20 30.5	1411	21 56.1	1499	23 32.0	1587	0 48.8	1675	1 21.0
1324	20 32.2	1412	21 58.3	1500	23 33.3	1588	0 51.0	1676	1 21.0
1325	20 32.8	1413	21 58.5	1501	23 34.8	1589	0 51.5	1677	1 21.2
1326	20 33.0	1414	21 58.3	1502	23 36.2	1590	0 53.1	1678	1 21.0
1327	20 35.7	1415	21 58.7	1503	23 38.5	1591	0 52.1	1679	1 21.8
1328	20 42.0	1416	21 58.8	1504	23 41.3	1592	0 53.5	1680	1 21.9
1329	20 43.7	1417	22 00.4	1505	23 41.6	1593	0 54.7	1681	1 21.4
1330	20 46.3	1418	22 02.0	1506	23 44.8	1594	0 53.7	1682	1 22.2
1331	20 47.9	1419	22 03.0	1507	23 45.6	1595	0 53.8	1683	1 22.6
1332	20 51.9	1420	22 02.6	1508	23 45.9	1596	0 54.7	1684	1 22.9
1333	20 52.3	1421	22 03.1	1509	23 47.2	1597	0 53.5	1685	1 23.0
1334	20 52.2	1422	22 03.0	1510	23 50.7	1598	0 54.7	1686	1 23.2
1335	20 53.1	1423	22 03.2	1511	23 51.0	1599	0 54.5	1687	1 23.4
1336	20 55.1	1424	22 03.2	1512	23 51.0	1600	0 55.0	1688	1 23.4
1337	20 56.9	1425	22 03.4	1513	23 53.5	1601	0 55.6	1689	1 23.8
1338	20 57.0	1426	22 03.9	1514	23 54.2	1602	0 55.9	1690	1 23.8
1339	20 57.9	1427	22 03.3	1515	23 56.2	1603	0 57.0	1691	1 24.5
1340	20 56.2	1428	22 04.4	1516	23 56.3	1604	0 58.0	1692	1 24.6
1341	21 00.4	1429	22 06.9	1517	23 56.4	1605	0 57.6	1693	1 24.0
1342	21 00.4	1430	22 08.5	1518	23 57.1	1606	0 58.4	1694	1 24.8
1343	21 01.2	1431	22 07.7	1519	23 57.1	1607	0 58.9	1695	1 25.0
1344	21 01.3	1432	22 10.1	1520	23 58.0	1608	0 59.4	1696	1 24.9
1345	21 01.4	1433	22 12.2	1521	23 59.0	1609	0 59.8	1697	1 25.1
1346	21 01.7	1434	22 10.5	1522	23 59.1	1610	1 01.7	1698	1 25.4
1347	21 01.7	1435	22 13.5	1523	23 59.1	1611	0 59.7	1699	1 25.4
1348	21 01.7	1436	22 13.9	1524	23 59.3	1612	1 00.0	1700	1 25.5
1349	21 01.8	1437	22 15.7	1525	23 59.4	1613	1 04.8	1701	1 25.8
1350	21 02.0	1438	22 16.5	1526	0 01.6	1614	1 05.1	1702	1 25.9
1351	21 01.9	1439	22 16.7	1527	0 02.4	1615	1 04.1	1703	1 26.4
1352	21 01.9	1440	22 16.5	1528	0 05.1	1616	1 04.9	1704	1 26.9
1353	21 01.9	1441	22 15.3	1529	0 05.2	1617	1 04.3	1705	1 26.7
1354	21 02.0	1442	22 16.5	1530	0 07.3	1618	1 06.0	1706	1 27.2
1355	21 02.0	1443	22 19.1	1531	0 09.6	1619	1 07.4	1707	1 28.8
1356	21 02.9	1444	22 22.3	1532	0 09.9	1620	1 07.1	1708	1 24.9
1357	21 05.9	1445	22 25.5	1533	0 10.6	1621	1 06.4	1709	1 27.9
1358	21 06.5	1446	22 29.1	1534	0 13.8	1622	1 07.5	1710	1 30.8
1359	21 08.7	1447	22 30.0	1535	0 14.0	1623	1 07.7	1711	1 30.9
1360	21 10.8	1448	22 34.6	1536	0 14.2	1624	1 05.3	1712	1 31.4
1361	21 11.5	1449	22 35.1	1537	0 16.0	1625	1 07.7	1713	1 32.7
1362	21 11.8	1450	22 38.0	1538	0 18.0	1626	1 06.1	1714	1 32.9
1363	21 10.6	1451	22 46.2	1539	0 18.4	1627	1 08.2	1715	1 33.6
1364	21 13.3	1452	22 45.9	1540	0 19.8	1628	1 08.8	1716	1 33.5
1365	21 13.9	1453	22 46.8	1541	0 20.0	1629	1 09.4	1717	1 32.5
1366	21 14.1	1454	22 42.6	1542	0 20.6	1630	1 08.3	1718	1 38.4
1367	21 14.2	1455	22 53.9	1543	0 20.9	1631	1 08.8	1719	1 37.6
1368	21 14.3	1456	22 55.3	1544	0 21.3	1632	1 10.7	1720	1 40.4
1369	21 12.1	1457	22 55.4	1545	0 21.3	1633	1 09.9	1721	1 41.4
1370	21 15.2	1458	22 56.8	1546	0 21.5	1634	1 11.1	1722	1 43.0
1371	21 20.3	1459	22 57.2	1547	0 21.6	1635	1 11.1	1723	1 43.2
1372	21 20.3	1460	22 57.1	1548	0 21.9	1636	1 11.6	1724	1 43.2
1373	21 20.6	1461	22 58.6	1549	0 23.2	1637	1 11.0	1725	1 45.2
1374	21 21.0	1462	22 58.6	1550	0 24.4	1638	1 12.3	1726	1 45.3
1375	21 21.0	1463	22 59.3	1551	0 27.6	1639	1 11.8	1727	1 47.5
1376	21 24.7	1464	23 03.2	1552	0 29.6	1640	1 11.9	1728	1 47.7
1377	21 25.4	1465	23 02.9	1553	0 32.7	1641	1 09.3	1729	1 47.9
1378	21 23.0	1466	23 03.7	1554	0 33.1	1642	1 12.4	1730	1 50.0
1379	21 26.0	1467	23 04.9	1555	0 34.6	1643	1 12.2	1731	1 50.2
1380	21 27.1	1468	23 05.2	1556	0 35.1	1644	1 09.2	1732	1 50.8
1381	21 27.6	1469	23 06.5	1557	0 35.5	1645	1 12.5	1733	1 50.7
1382	21 26.9	1470	23 05.2	1558	0 35.8	1646	1 12.7	1734	1 49.3
1383	21 27.7	1471	23 08.7	1559	0 36.9	1647	1 13.2	1735	1 50.9
1384	21 27.8	1472	23 09.2	1560	0 37.7	1648	1 13.7	1736	1 50.9
1385	21 28.9	1473	23 11.1	1561	0 38.5	1649	1 11.8	1737	1 51.7
1386	21 29.6	1474	23 12.8	1562	0 38.6	1650	1 12.3	1738	1 51.1
1387	21 29.6	1475	23 14.0	1563	0 39.0	1651	1 13.5	1739	1 50.4
1388	21 29.9	1476	23 15.3	1564	0 39.2	1652	1 15.0	1740	1 51.3
1389	21 32.1	1477	23 17.2	1565	0 39.4	1653	1 15.1	1741	1 51.9
1390	21 32.5	1478	23 18.2	1566	0 39.4	1654	1 15.2	1742	1 53.2
1391	21 35.1	1479	23 18.7	1567	0 39.6	1655	1 11.9	1743	1 52.9
1392	21 35.6	1480	23 19.0	1568	0 39.9	1656	1 15.6	1744	1 53.6
1393	21 40.2	1481	23 19.4	1569	0 40.4	1657	1 14.1	1745	1 53.0
1394	21 40.2	1482	23 20.8	1570	0 40.6	1658	1 15.8	1746	1 54.3
1395	21 41.7	1483	23 22.4	1571	0 40.7	1659	1 16.1	1747	1 57.6
1396	21 39.1	1484	23 22.7	1572	0 41.2	1660	1 12.6	1748	1 56.1
1397	21 44.0	1485	23 22.7	1573	0 42.2	1661	1 16.2	1749	1 56.2
1398	21 45.9	1486	23 23.8	1574	0 43.1	1662	1 12.6	1750	1 56.4
1399	21 46.1	1487	23 24.6	1575	0 43.6	1663	1 14.1	1751	1 56.4
1400	21 46.2	1488	23 24.8	1576	0 44.2	1664	1 14.3	1752	1 57.3
1401	21 46.9	1489	23 26.5	1577	0 44.6	1665	1 17.7	1753	1 57.3
1402	21 44.8	1490	23 29.0	1578	0 44.5	1666	1 18.5	1754	1 56.9
1403	21 50.5	1491	23 29.4	1579	0 45.6	1667	1 17.6	1755	1 57.2
1404	21 50.9	1492	23 30.7	1580	0 46.3	1668	1 18.8	1756	1 57.0
1405	21 50.8	1493	23 30.5	1581	0 46.1	1669	1 20.1	1757	1 57.1
1406	21 51.0	1494	23 30.8	1582	0 46.3	1670	1 19.2	1758	1 56.9
1407	21 52.3	1495	23 30.8	1583	0 47.2	1671	1 19.6	1759	1 57.9
1408	21 53.2	1496	23 30.7	1584	0 47.4	1672	1 20.7	1760	1 57.5

Right Ascensions of IC Objects

IC	α_{2000}	IC	α_{2000}	IC	α_{2000}	IC	α_{2000}	IC	α_{2000}
	h m		h m		h m		h m		h m
1761	1 58.9	1849	2 48.2	1937	3 26.8	2025	4 00.4	2113	4 59.6
1762	1 57.8	1850	2 48.7	1938	3 27.2	2026	4 03.9	2114	4 54.6
1763	1 58.8	1851	2 51.8	1939	3 27.8	2027	4 06.7	2115	4 57.1
1764	2 00.4	1852	2 49.0	1940	3 27.7	2028	4 01.3	2116	4 57.4
1765	2 00.6	1853	2 48.0	1941	3 32.2	2029	4 01.3	2117	4 57.2
1766	2 01.2	1854	2 49.3	1942	3 28.0	2030	4 04.9	2118	5 06.9
1767	2 00.0	1855	2 49.3	1943	3 38.7	2031	4 05.9	2119	5 07.2
1768	2 00.8	1856	2 48.9	1944	3 29.7	2032	4 07.1	2120	5 18.2
1769	2 00.9	1857	2 49.7	1945	3 29.3	2033	4 07.2	2121	5 19.7
1770	2 02.2	1858	2 49.1	1946	3 29.4	2034	4 06.6	2122	5 19.0
1771	2 02.3	1859	2 49.6	1947	3 30.6	2035	4 09.0	2123	5 21.9
1772	2 02.6	1860	2 49.6	1948	3 30.9	2036	4 10.0	2124	5 21.9
1773	2 04.0	1861	2 53.3	1949	3 31.0	2037	4 08.3	2125	5 24.4
1774	2 03.9	1862	2 52.0	1950	3 31.1	2038	4 08.9	2126	5 21.9
1775	2 05.3	1863	2 54.9	1951	3 31.1	2039	4 09.0	2127	5 21.9
1776	2 05.2	1864	2 53.2	1952	3 33.4	2040	4 13.0	2128	5 22.8
1777	2 06.1	1865	2 55.4	1953	3 33.7	2041	4 12.6	2129	5 31.3
1778	2 06.3	1866	2 54.9	1954	3 31.6	2042	4 11.7	2130	5 31.8
1779	2 06.5	1867	2 55.9	1955	3 31.4	2043	4 11.2	2131	5 32.3
1780	2 07.0	1868	2 56.1	1956	3 35.6	2044	4 11.2	2132	5 32.5
1781	2 06.9	1869	2 58.1	1957	3 32.2	2045	4 14.6	2133	5 42.2
1782	2 07.3	1870	2 57.9	1958	3 32.8	2046	4 11.4	2134	5 23.0
1783	2 10.1	1871	3 06.4	1959	3 33.2	2047	4 14.9	2135	5 33.2
1784	2 16.2	1872	3 04.6	1960	3 32.6	2048	4 14.3	2136	5 33.2
1785	2 16.4	1873	3 03.8	1961	3 33.6	2049	4 12.1	2137	5 34.3
1786	2 16.0	1874	3 06.4	1962	3 35.6	2050	4 13.9	2138	5 34.3
1787	2 16.2	1875	3 03.9	1963	3 35.5	2051	3 52.0	2139	5 35.3
1788	2 15.8	1876	3 04.5	1964	3 33.6	2052	4 15.0	2140	5 33.2
1789	2 17.1	1877	3 03.2	1965	3 33.2	2053	4 15.8	2141	5 42.3
1790	2 17.6	1878	3 03.7	1966	3 34.1	2054	4 07.2	2142	5 33.1
1791	2 17.7	1879	3 03.9	1967	3 37.7	2055	4 17.8	2143	5 46.9
1792	2 19.0	1880	3 06.5	1968	3 34.7	2056	4 16.5	2144	5 50.2
1793	2 21.6	1881	3 09.2	1969	3 36.2	2057	4 21.9	2145	5 40.4
1794	2 21.5	1882	3 07.8	1970	3 36.5	2058	4 17.9	2146	5 37.8
1795	2 26.5	1883	3 09.7	1971	3 36.0	2059	4 20.4	2147	5 47.8
1796	2 22.8	1884	3 09.7	1972	3 36.4	2060	4 17.9	2148	5 39.2
1797	2 25.5	1885	3 06.7	1973	3 36.4	2061	4 24.0	2149	5 56.3
1798	2 26.3	1886	3 08.0	1974	3 36.7	2062	4 32.8	2150	5 51.3
1799	2 28.7	1887	3 10.2	1975	3 39.1	2063	4 22.9	2151	5 52.6
1800	2 28.6	1888	3 11.0	1976	3 37.2	2064	4 23.5	2152	5 57.9
1801	2 28.2	1889	3 11.0	1977	3 40.8	2065	4 21.5	2153	6 00.1
1802	2 28.7	1890	3 10.0	1978	3 37.1	2066	4 23.5	2154	6 01.1
1803	2 29.3	1891	3 10.2	1979	3 36.7	2067	4 30.8	2155	6 00.8
1804	2 29.4	1892	3 08.4	1980	3 37.0	2068	4 26.6	2156	6 04.8
1805	2 32.7	1893	3 10.3	1981	3 40.5	2069	4 25.9	2157	6 05.0
1806	2 29.6	1894	3 10.5	1982	3 37.7	2070	4 24.6	2158	6 05.3
1807	2 30.4	1895	3 09.6	1983	3 40.9	2071	4 26.2	2159	6 09.9
1808	2 30.5	1896	3 08.0	1984	3 39.9	2072	4 26.9	2160	5 55.5
1809	2 31.6	1897	3 10.8	1985	3 44.6	2073	4 26.6	2161	5 57.2
1810	2 29.4	1898	3 .0.3	1986	3 40.6	2074	4 31.3	2162	6 12.9
1811	2 30.6	1899	3 11.8	1987	3 40.2	2075	4 31.0	2163	6 16.5
1812	2 29.5	1900	3 16.0	1988	3 42.8	2076	4 28.1	2164	6 06.9
1813	2 30.8	1901	3 16.1	1989	3 41.9	2077	4 32.1	2165	6 21.7
1814	2 31.1	1902	3 16.2	1990	3 47.5	2078	4 31.9	2166	6 27.0
1815	2 34.3	1903	3 13.1	1991	3 44.7	2079	4 28.5	2167	6 31.3
1816	2 31.9	1904	3 15.0	1992	3 45.1	2080	4 32.3	2168	6 33.8
1817	2 33.8	1905	3 18.8	1993	3 47.1	2081	4 29.0	2169	6 31.2
1818	2 34.1	1906	3 16.1	1994	3 45.8	2082	4 29.1	2170	6 34.1
1819	2 35.7	1907	3 19.9	1995	3 50.3	2083	4 30.7	2171	6 44.4
1820	2 35.8	1908	3 15.1	1996	3 45.0	2084	4 32.1	2172	6 46.9
1821	2 36.4	1909	3 17.3	1997	3 44.9	2085	4 31.4	2173	6 50.8
1822	2 35.7	1910	3 18.0	1998	3 51.5	2086	4 31.6	2174	7 09.1
1823	2 38.6	1911	3 20.8	1999	3 47.7	2087	4 40.0	2175	6 59.7
1824	2 41.3	1912	3 16.8	2000	3 49.1	2088	4 43.7	2176	7 07.5
1825	2 38.9	1913	3 19.6	2001	3 50.9	2089	4 32.6	2177	7 05.1
1826	2 39.1	1914	3 19.4	2002	3 54.4	2090	4 44.7	2178	7 07.6
1827	2 39.7	1915	3 19.7	2003	3 56.4	2091	4 46.6	2179	7 15.5
1828	2 40.4	1916	3 20.3	2004	3 51.8	2092	4 46.8	2180	7 11.3
1829	2 40.7	1917	3 22.2	2005	3 57.6	2093	4 47.6	2181	7 13.2
1830	2 39.1	1918	3 26.2	2006	3 54.1	2094	4 48.4	2182	7 14.2
1831	2 44.1	1919	3 26.0	2007	3 55.4	2095	4 48.7	2183	7 16.9
1832	2 41.9	1920	3 24.2	2008	3 55.4	2096	4 49.6	2184	7 29.4
1833	2 41.6	1921	3 24.7	2009	3 53.6	2097	4 50.3	2185	7 23.2
1834	2 42.8	1922	3 24.7	2010	3 52.0	2098	4 50.7	2186	7 22.7
1835	2 43.8	1923	3 24.8	2011	3 52.5	2099	4 50.8	2187	7 22.7
1836	2 43.3	1924	3 25.0	2012	3 52.8	2100	4 51.2	2188	7 22.7
1837	2 43.5	1925	3 25.3	2013	3 56.7	2101	4 51.6	2189	7 25.0
1838	2 44.7	1926	3 25.2	2014	3 55.4	2102	4 51.9	2190	7 29.9
1839	2 44.8	1927	3 25.2	2015	3 58.0	2103	4 39.8	2191	7 30.3
1840	2 43.8	1928	3 27.5	2016	4 01.9	2104	4 56.5	2192	7 33.3
1841	2 45.6	1929	3 25.5	2017	3 56.7	2105	4 49.4	2193	7 33.3
1842	2 45.4	1930	3 28.8	2018	3 57.9	2106	4 56.6	2194	7 33.7
1843	2 45.4	1931	3 28.8	2019	4 02.0	2107	4 58.3	2195	7 28.4
1844	2 45.8	1932	3 25.9	2020	3 59.0	2108	4 57.3	2196	7 34.1
1845	2 44.9	1933	3 25.7	2021	3 59.4	2109	4 59.0	2197	7 34.3
1846	2 47.7	1934	3 31.4	2022	3 58.7	2110	4 59.0	2198	7 34.1
1847	2 47.9	1935	3 26.2	2023	3 59.7	2111	4 51.9	2199	7 34.9
1848	2 51.2	1936	3 26.4	2024	4 00.1	2112	5 00.5	2200	7 28.3

Right Ascensions of IC Objects

IC	α_{2000}	IC	α_{2000}	IC	α_{2000}	IC	α_{2000}	IC	α_{2000}
	h m		h m		h m		h m		h m
2201	7 36.2	2289	8 19.1	2377	8 26.4	2465	9 23.6	2553	10 09.3
2202	7 27.9	2290	8 19.3	2378	8 28.5	2466	9 23.7	2554	10 08.9
2203	7 40.6	2291	8 19.3	2379	8 26.4	2467	9 24.9	2555	10 11.7
2204	7 41.2	2292	8 19.4	2380	8 28.6	2468	9 25.0	2556	10 12.6
2205	7 46.9	2293	8 19.6	2381	8 28.4	2469	9 23.0	2557	10 16.1
2206	7 45.8	2294	8 19.4	2382	8 28.7	2470	9 25.0	2558	10 14.7
2207	7 49.8	2295	8 19.4	2383	8 29.6	2471	9 25.2	2559	10 14.8
2208	7 52.5	2296	8 19.5	2384	8 34.5	2472	9 26.5	2560	10 16.3
2209	7 56.2	2297	8 20.1	2385	8 35.1	2473	9 27.4	2561	10 19.1
2210	7 57.1	2298	8 20.1	2386	8 34.8	2474	9 27.2	2562	10 18.8
2211	7 57.7	2299	8 20.2	2387	8 38.6	2475	9 27.9	2563	10 18.9
2212	7 59.0	2300	8 20.2	2388	8 40.0	2476	9 27.9	2564	10 21.4
2213	7 59.0	2301	8 20.2	2389	8 48.0	2477	9 27.9	2565	10 21.3
2214	7 59.9	2302	8 20.3	2390	8 41.8	2478	9 27.9	2566	10 22.4
2215	7 59.6	2303	8 20.3	2391	8 40.2	2479	9 28.1	2567	10 22.0
2216	7 59.5	2304	8 20.6	2392	8 44.5	2480	9 28.2	2568	10 22.5
2217	8 00.8	2305	8 20.7	2393	8 46.8	2481	9 27.4	2569	10 22.9
2218	8 01.6	2306	8 20.7	2394	8 47.1	2482	9 27.0	2570	10 21.6
2219	8 02.6	2307	8 20.7	2395	8 41.1	2483	9 29.5	2571	10 21.6
2220	7 56.8	2308	8 20.9	2396	8 46.7	2484	9 26.8	2572	10 25.0
2221	8 05.1	2309	8 20.8	2397	8 46.7	2485	9 27.2	2573	10 23.5
2222	8 05.2	2310	8 20.8	2398	8 46.7	2486	9 30.3	2574	10 28.4
2223	8 05.8	2311	8 18.8	2399	8 47.8	2487	9 30.2	2575	10 25.4
2224	8 05.8	2312	8 20.9	2400	8 48.0	2488	9 27.6	2576	10 26.0
2225	8 06.4	2313	8 20.9	2401	8 48.1	2489	9 31.2	2577	10 28.0
2226	8 06.2	2314	8 21.1	2402	8 48.1	2490	9 33.1	2578	10 27.4
2227	8 07.3	2315	8 21.2	2403	8 46.2	2491	9 35.2	2579	10 29.3
2228	8 07.1	2316	8 21.3	2404	8 48.1	2492	9 33.2	2580	10 28.3
2229	8 09.7	2317	8 21.4	2405	8 48.7	2493	9 36.3	2581	10 27.4
2230	8 10.9	2318	8 21.5	2406	8 48.1	2494	9 36.1	2582	10 29.2
2231	8 11.0	2319	8 21.6	2407	8 48.1	2495	9 38.2	2583	10 31.2
2232	8 12.9	2320	8 21.6	2408	8 48.3	2496	9 38.7	2584	10 29.9
2233	8 14.0	2321	8 21.7	2409	8 48.4	2497	9 41.1	2585	10 30.4
2234	8 13.9	2322	8 21.7	2410	8 48.5	2498	9 41.3	2586	10 31.0
2235	8 13.6	2323	8 21.7	2411	8 48.5	2499	9 41.4	2587	10 31.0
2236	8 13.6	2324	8 22.0	2412	8 49.4	2500	9 42.3	2588	10 31.8
2237	8 14.1	2325	8 22.1	2413	8 49.5	2501	9 38.8	2589	10 32.1
2238	8 14.1	2326	8 22.2	2414	8 49.8	2502	9 43.2	2590	10 36.3
2239	8 14.1	2327	8 21.4	2415	8 50.0	2503	9 43.2	2591	10 36.6
2240	8 14.8	2328	8 22.3	2416	8 50.5	2504	9 38.6	2592	10 35.1
2241	8 15.1	2329	8 22.4	2417	8 51.2	2505	9 45.1	2593	10 36.3
2242	8 15.2	2330	8 22.4	2418	8 51.4	2506	9 45.2	2594	10 36.1
2243	8 15.3	2331	8 22.6	2419	8 52.2	2507	9 44.6	2595	10 37.6
2244	8 15.4	2332	8 22.7	2420	8 51.5	2508	9 47.1	2596	10 34.2
2245	8 15.5	2333	8 23.0	2421	8 54.4	2509	9 46.9	2597	10 37.8
2246	8 16.0	2334	8 23.0	2422	8 54.4	2510	9 47.7	2598	10 39.7
2247	8 16.1	2335	8 23.1	2423	8 54.8	2511	9 49.4	2599	10 37.4
2248	8 16.1	2336	8 23.3	2424	8 56.8	2512	9 49.4	2600	10 46.7
2249	8 16.6	2337	8 23.3	2425	8 55.8	2513	9 50.0	2601	10 47.1
2250	8 16.5	2338	8 23.6	2426	8 58.5	2514	9 50.0	2602	10 43.2
2251	8 16.7	2339	8 23.6	2427	9 01.0	2515	9 54.6	2603	10 48.4
2252	8 16.7	2340	8 23.6	2428	9 03.2	2516	9 54.8	2604	10 49.4
2253	8 16.5	2341	8 23.7	2429	9 03.8	2517	9 52.7	2605	10 49.8
2254	8 16.7	2342	8 23.5	2430	9 04.5	2518	9 56.0	2606	10 50.3
2255	8 16.7	2343	8 23.9	2431	9 04.5	2519	9 56.0	2607	10 50.3
2256	8 16.8	2344	8 23.9	2432	9 04.6	2520	9 56.4	2608	10 50.3
2257	8 17.2	2345	8 24.1	2433	9 05.5	2521	9 57.3	2609	10 50.3
2258	8 17.3	2346	8 24.2	2434	9 07.2	2522	9 55.2	2610	10 52.2
2259	8 17.3	2347	8 24.2	2435	9 06.8	2523	9 55.2	2611	10 52.7
2260	8 17.5	2348	8 24.4	2436	9 05.4	2524	9 57.5	2612	10 53.6
2261	8 17.6	2349	8 24.3	2437	9 05.5	2525	9 58.4	2613	10 54.3
2262	8 17.4	2350	8 24.5	2438	9 14.0	2526	9 57.1	2614	11 01.6
2263	8 17.7	2351	8 24.6	2439	9 08.6	2527	10 00.1	2615	11 02.0
2264	8 17.8	2352	8 24.7	2440	9 15.5	2528	9 59.1	2616	11 02.2
2265	8 17.8	2353	8 24.6	2441	9 10.0	2529	9 59.5	2617	11 02.2
2266	8 17.7	2354	8 24.7	2442	9 10.1	2530	10 01.5	2618	11 02.0
2267	8 18.0	2355	8 24.9	2443	9 11.5	2531	9 59.9	2619	11 02.2
2268	8 18.1	2356	8 25.0	2444	9 12.8	2532	10 00.1	2620	11 02.3
2269	8 18.2	2357	8 25.1	2445	9 13.2	2533	10 00.5	2621	11 00.3
2270	8 18.0	2358	8 25.1	2446	9 13.5	2534	10 01.5	2622	11 03.5
2271	8 18.4	2359	8 25.3	2447	9 13.5	2535	10 04.5	2623	11 03.8
2272	8 18.1	2360	8 25.2	2448	9 07.1	2536	10 03.5	2624	11 07.3
2273	8 18.2	2361	8 25.7	2449	9 15.2	2537	10 03.9	2625	11 07.3
2274	8 18.2	2362	8 25.7	2450	9 15.7	2538	10 03.9	2626	11 09.0
2275	8 18.2	2363	8 25.8	2451	9 15.7	2539	10 04.3	2627	11 09.9
2276	8 18.5	2364	8 25.9	2452	9 15.9	2540	10 06.9	2628	11 11.6
2277	8 18.5	2365	8 26.3	2453	9 15.8	2541	10 05.8	2629	11 12.6
2278	8 18.6	2366	8 26.3	2454	9 16.0	2542	10 07.9	2630	11 12.7
2279	8 18.6	2367	8 24.2	2455	9 16.8	2543	10 08.4	2631	11 09.8
2280	8 18.7	2368	8 26.0	2456	9 17.5	2544	10 08.4	2632	11 13.1
2281	8 18.9	2369	8 26.3	2457	9 17.1	2545	10 06.6	2633	11 13.2
2282	8 19.3	2370	8 26.4	2458	9 21.6	2546	10 07.1	2634	11 13.5
2283	8 19.3	2371	8 26.6	2459	9 19.1	2547	10 10.1	2635	11 13.5
2284	8 19.0	2372	8 26.7	2460	9 19.3	2548	10 07.9	2636	11 13.6
2285	8 19.1	2373	8 26.9	2461	9 19.9	2549	10 10.2	2637	11 13.8
2286	8 19.1	2374	8 28.3	2462	9 22.9	2550	10 10.4	2638	11 13.9
2287	8 19.1	2375	8 26.3	2463	9 23.0	2551	10 10.7	2639	11 13.9
2288	8 19.3	2376	8 28.4	2464	9 23.4	2552	10 10.8	2640	11 14.1

IC	α_{2000}	IC	α_{2000}	IC	α_{2000}	IC	α_{2000}	IC	α_{2000}
	h m		h m		h m		h m		h m
2641	11 14.2	2729	11 20.1	2817	11 26.3	2905	11 31.8	2993	12 05.2
2642	11 14.2	2730	11 20.1	2818	11 26.5	2906	11 31.8	2994	12 05.5
2643	11 14.5	2731	11 20.2	2819	11 26.5	2907	11 31.8	2995	12 05.8
2644	11 14.5	2732	11 20.2	2820	11 26.4	2908	11 31.8	2996	12 05.9
2645	11 14.5	2733	11 20.4	2821	11 26.6	2909	11 31.8	2997	12 05.8
2646	11 14.6	2734	11 20.4	2822	11 26.6	2910	11 31.9	2998	12 05.9
2647	11 14.7	2735	11 21.0	2823	11 26.7	2911	11 32.1	2999	12 05.9
2648	11 14.7	2736	11 20.9	2824	11 27.1	2912	11 32.1	3000	12 06.1
2649	11 14.8	2737	11 21.1	2825	11 27.0	2913	11 31.8	3001	12 06.2
2650	11 14.9	2738	11 21.3	2826	11 27.1	2914	11 32.2	3002	12 07.1
2651	11 14.9	2739	11 21.2	2827	11 27.2	2915	11 32.3	3003	12 07.1
2652	11 14.9	2740	11 21.3	2828	11 27.2	2916	11 32.3	3004	12 07.2
2653	11 14.9	2741	11 21.3	2829	11 27.2	2917	11 32.3	3005	12 07.2
2654	11 15.1	2742	11 21.3	2830	11 27.4	2918	11 32.4	3006	12 07.4
2655	11 15.1	2743	11 21.4	2831	11 27.4	2919	11 32.6	3007	12 07.4
2656	11 15.1	2744	11 21.7	2832	11 27.4	2920	11 32.8	3008	12 08.0
2657	11 15.2	2745	11 21.5	2833	11 27.4	2921	11 32.8	3009	12 08.0
2658	11 15.2	2746	11 21.6	2834	11 27.5	2922	11 32.9	3010	12 07.9
2659	11 15.5	2747	11 21.7	2835	11 27.5	2923	11 32.9	3011	12 08.2
2660	11 15.5	2748	11 21.7	2836	11 27.6	2924	11 32.9	3012	12 08.5
2661	11 15.5	2749	11 21.7	2837	11 27.7	2925	11 33.2	3013	12 08.5
2662	11 15.5	2750	11 21.9	2838	11 27.8	2926	11 33.1	3014	12 08.5
2663	11 15.6	2751	11 22.1	2839	11 27.8	2927	11 33.1	3015	12 09.0
2664	11 15.6	2752	11 22.0	2840	11 27.8	2928	11 33.5	3016	12 09.4
2665	11 15.7	2753	11 22.0	2841	11 27.8	2929	11 33.5	3017	12 09.4
2666	11 15.7	2754	11 22.0	2842	11 27.8	2930	11 33.7	3018	12 09.5
2667	11 15.7	2755	11 22.0	2843	11 28.0	2931	11 33.8	3019	12 09.4
2668	11 15.5	2756	11 22.0	2844	11 28.0	2932	11 33.9	3020	12 09.6
2669	11 15.9	2757	11 22.0	2845	11 28.0	2933	11 34.2	3021	12 10.0
2670	11 16.0	2758	11 22.0	2846	11 28.0	2934	11 34.3	3022	12 09.9
2671	11 16.1	2759	11 22.2	2847	11 28.1	2935	11 34.8	3023	12 10.1
2672	11 16.1	2760	11 22.2	2848	11 28.2	2936	11 34.9	3024	12 10.3
2673	11 16.1	2761	11 22.3	2849	11 28.2	2937	11 35.1	3025	12 10.4
2674	11 16.2	2762	11 22.3	2850	11 28.2	2938	11 35.6	3026	12 10.6
2675	11 16.2	2763	11 22.3	2851	11 28.3	2939	11 35.6	3027	12 10.5
2676	11 16.3	2764	11 27.1	2852	11 28.2	2940	11 36.0	3028	12 10.5
2677	11 16.3	2765	11 22.4	2853	11 28.3	2941	11 36.2	3029	12 10.8
2678	11 16.4	2766	11 22.4	2854	11 28.3	2942	11 36.2	3030	12 11.1
2679	11 16.4	2767	11 22.4	2855	11 28.4	2943	11 36.7	3031	12 11.1
2680	11 16.4	2768	11 22.4	2856	11 28.2	2944	11 36.6	3032	12 11.1
2681	11 16.6	2769	11 22.4	2857	11 28.5	2945	11 37.1	3033	12 11.1
2682	11 16.6	2770	11 22.4	2858	11 28.6	2946	11 37.5	3034	12 11.9
2683	11 16.9	2771	11 22.5	2859	11 28.7	2947	11 37.5	3035	12 12.2
2684	11 17.0	2772	11 22.5	2860	11 28.7	2948	11 38.8	3036	12 12.2
2685	11 17.0	2773	11 22.6	2861	11 29.0	2949	11 40.9	3037	12 12.4
2686	11 17.1	2774	11 22.6	2862	11 28.7	2950	11 41.6	3038	12 12.6
2687	11 17.3	2775	11 22.7	2863	11 28.9	2951	11 43.4	3039	12 12.5
2688	11 17.3	2776	11 22.7	2864	11 29.0	2952	11 44.3	3040	12 12.7
2689	11 17.3	2777	11 22.7	2865	11 29.0	2953	11 44.4	3041	12 12.7
2690	11 17.4	2778	11 22.7	2866	11 29.0	2954	11 45.2	3042	12 12.8
2691	11 17.4	2779	11 22.8	2867	11 29.0	2955	11 45.1	3043	12 12.8
2692	11 17.6	2780	11 22.8	2868	11 29.1	2956	11 45.2	3044	12 12.8
2693	11 17.6	2781	11 22.8	2869	11 29.1	2957	11 45.6	3045	12 13.0
2694	11 17.6	2782	11 22.9	2870	11 29.1	2958	11 45.7	3046	12 13.1
2695	11 17.8	2783	11 22.9	2871	11 29.3	2959	11 46.1	3047	12 13.3
2696	11 17.8	2784	11 23.2	2872	11 29.0	2960	11 46.3	3048	12 13.4
2697	11 17.9	2785	11 23.3	2873	11 29.5	2961	11 47.8	3049	12 13.5
2698	11 17.9	2786	11 23.3	2874	11 29.5	2962	11 49.1	3050	12 13.7
2699	11 17.9	2787	11 23.3	2875	11 29.6	2963	11 49.4	3051	12 13.9
2700	11 18.0	2788	11 23.4	2876	11 29.6	2964	11 49.8	3052	12 13.9
2701	11 18.0	2789	11 23.5	2877	11 29.6	2965	11 54.0	3053	12 14.0
2702	11 18.0	2790	11 23.6	2878	11 29.6	2966	11 50.4	3054	12 14.3
2703	11 18.1	2791	11 23.6	2879	11 29.7	2967	11 50.8	3055	12 14.4
2704	11 18.1	2792	11 23.7	2880	11 29.9	2968	11 52.6	3056	12 14.6
2705	11 18.1	2793	11 23.8	2881	11 29.9	2969	11 52.6	3057	12 15.0
2706	11 18.5	2794	11 24.1	2882	11 30.2	2970	11 53.2	3058	12 14.9
2707	11 18.5	2795	11 24.1	2883	11 30.3	2971	11 53.5	3059	12 14.9
2708	11 18.6	2796	11 24.1	2884	11 27.7	2972	11 53.7	3060	12 15.0
2709	11 18.8	2797	11 24.4	2885	11 30.4	2973	11 53.8	3061	12 15.1
2710	11 18.8	2798	11 24.4	2886	11 30.4	2974	11 53.9	3062	12 15.1
2711	11 18.8	2799	11 24.4	2887	11 30.5	2975	11 54.2	3063	12 15.1
2712	11 18.9	2800	11 24.5	2888	11 30.6	2976	11 54.5	3064	12 15.2
2713	11 19.2	2801	11 24.5	2889	11 30.6	2977	11 55.2	3065	12 15.2
2714	11 17.9	2802	11 24.5	2890	11 30.8	2978	11 56.4	3066	12 15.3
2715	11 19.2	2803	11 24.6	2891	11 30.8	2979	11 56.9	3067	12 15.2
2716	11 19.3	2804	11 24.9	2892	11 30.8	2980	11 57.5	3068	12 15.4
2717	11 19.3	2805	11 25.0	2893	11 30.9	2981	11 57.8	3069	12 15.4
2718	11 19.4	2806	11 25.3	2894	11 31.0	2982	11 57.8	3070	12 15.4
2719	11 19.5	2807	11 25.3	2895	11 31.0	2983	11 58.3	3071	12 15.5
2720	11 19.6	2808	11 25.5	2896	11 31.2	2984	11 59.1	3072	12 15.6
2721	11 19.7	2809	11 25.6	2897	11 31.3	2985	11 59.2	3073	12 15.6
2722	11 19.7	2810	11 25.8	2898	11 31.3	2986	11 59.8	3074	12 15.7
2723	11 19.8	2811	11 25.8	2899	11 31.3	2987	12 03.4	3075	12 15.8
2724	11 19.8	2812	11 25.9	2900	11 31.5	2988	12 03.7	3076	12 16.1
2725	11 20.0	2813	11 26.1	2901	11 31.5	2989	12 04.7	3077	12 16.1
2726	11 20.0	2814	11 26.1	2902	11 31.6	2990	12 04.7	3078	12 16.1
2727	11 20.0	2815	11 26.3	2903	11 31.7	2991	12 05.1	3079	12 16.1
2728	11 20.1	2816	11 26.3	2904	11 31.7	2992	12 05.2	3080	12 16.2

Right Ascensions of IC Objects

IC	α_{2000}	IC	α_{2000}	IC	α_{2000}	IC	α_{2000}	IC	α_{2000}
	h m		h m		h m		h m		h m
3081	12 16.2	3169	12 20.4	3257	12 23.7	3345	12 26.5	3433	12 30.4
3082	12 16.2	3170	12 20.4	3258	12 23.7	3346	12 26.7	3434	12 30.5
3083	12 16.4	3171	12 20.3	3259	12 23.8	3347	12 26.7	3435	12 30.6
3084	12 16.3	3172	12 20.4	3260	12 23.9	3348	12 26.6	3436	12 30.5
3085	12 16.4	3173	12 20.5	3261	12 23.9	3349	12 26.7	3437	12 30.8
3086	12 16.5	3174	12 20.4	3262	12 23.8	3350	12 26.8	3438	12 31.0
3087	12 16.5	3175	12 20.4	3263	12 23.8	3351	12 26.7	3439	12 31.0
3088	12 16.5	3176	12 20.5	3264	12 23.9	3352	12 26.8	3440	12 31.1
3089	12 16.4	3177	12 20.6	3265	12 24.0	3353	12 26.7	3441	12 31.2
3090	12 16.5	3178	12 20.6	3266	12 24.0	3354	12 26.9	3442	12 31.3
3091	12 16.6	3179	12 20.6	3267	12 24.1	3355	12 26.8	3443	12 31.3
3092	12 16.6	3180	12 20.4	3268	12 24.1	3356	12 26.8	3444	12 31.2
3093	12 16.7	3181	12 20.7	3269	12 24.1	3357	12 26.8	3445	12 31.3
3094	12 16.9	3182	12 20.8	3270	12 24.1	3358	12 26.9	3446	12 31.3
3095	12 16.9	3183	12 20.8	3271	12 24.2	3359	12 26.9	3447	12 31.4
3096	12 16.9	3184	12 20.7	3272	12 24.2	3360	12 26.8	3448	12 31.4
3097	12 17.0	3185	12 20.9	3273	12 24.3	3361	12 27.0	3449	12 31.4
3098	12 17.2	3186	12 20.9	3274	12 24.3	3362	12 26.9	3450	12 31.4
3099	12 17.1	3187	12 20.9	3275	12 24.3	3363	12 27.0	3451	12 31.4
3100	12 17.2	3188	12 20.9	3276	12 24.2	3364	12 27.1	3452	12 31.5
3101	12 17.3	3189	12 20.9	3277	12 24.3	3365	12 27.1	3453	12 31.5
3102	12 17.4	3190	12 21.0	3278	12 24.3	3366	12 27.3	3454	12 31.6
3103	12 17.5	3191	12 21.1	3279	12 24.4	3367	12 27.2	3455	12 31.7
3104	12 18.8	3192	12 21.1	3280	12 24.4	3368	12 27.3	3456	12 31.7
3105	12 17.6	3193	12 20.9	3281	12 24.5	3369	12 27.3	3457	12 31.9
3106	12 17.8	3194	12 21.2	3282	12 24.5	3370	12 27.6	3458	12 31.7
3107	12 17.8	3195	12 21.3	3283	12 24.5	3371	12 27.3	3459	12 31.9
3108	12 17.8	3196	12 21.5	3284	12 24.6	3372	12 27.4	3460	12 31.8
3109	12 17.8	3197	12 21.4	3285	12 24.6	3373	12 27.5	3461	12 32.0
3110	12 17.7	3198	12 21.5	3286	12 24.6	3374	12 27.5	3462	12 32.0
3111	12 17.8	3199	12 21.7	3287	12 24.6	3375	12 27.7	3463	12 32.1
3112	12 17.8	3200	12 21.6	3288	12 24.7	3376	12 27.8	3464	12 32.0
3113	12 18.0	3201	12 21.7	3289	12 25.0	3377	12 27.9	3465	12 32.2
3114	12 17.9	3202	12 21.7	3290	12 25.2	3378	12 28.1	3466	12 32.2
3115	12 18.0	3203	12 21.7	3291	12 24.9	3379	12 28.1	3467	12 32.3
3116	12 18.0	3204	12 21.8	3292	12 24.8	3380	12 28.1	3468	12 32.3
3117	12 18.1	3205	12 21.8	3293	12 24.9	3381	12 28.3	3469	12 32.2
3118	12 18.2	3206	12 21.8	3294	12 24.8	3382	12 28.2	3470	12 32.4
3119	12 18.1	3207	12 21.9	3295	12 24.8	3383	12 28.2	3471	12 32.3
3120	12 18.4	3208	12 22.0	3296	12 25.0	3384	12 28.2	3472	12 32.3
3121	12 18.4	3209	12 22.1	3297	12 25.0	3385	12 28.2	3473	12 32.3
3122	12 18.3	3210	12 22.0	3298	12 25.0	3386	12 28.4	3474	12 32.6
3123	12 18.4	3211	12 22.1	3299	12 25.1	3387	12 28.3	3475	12 32.7
3124	12 18.5	3212	12 22.1	3300	12 25.0	3388	12 28.4	3476	12 32.7
3125	12 18.4	3213	12 22.1	3301	12 25.2	3389	12 28.4	3477	12 32.6
3126	12 18.6	3214	12 22.2	3302	12 25.2	3390	12 28.5	3478	12 32.7
3127	12 18.5	3215	12 22.1	3303	12 25.2	3391	12 28.4	3479	12 32.7
3128	12 18.7	3216	12 22.2	3304	12 25.2	3392	12 28.7	3480	12 32.7
3129	12 18.7	3217	12 22.2	3305	12 25.2	3393	12 28.7	3481	12 32.9
3130	12 18.8	3218	12 22.2	3306	12 25.2	3394	12 28.8	3482	12 33.0
3131	12 18.8	3219	12 22.3	3307	12 25.4	3395	12 28.7	3483	12 33.2
3132	12 18.8	3220	12 22.4	3308	12 25.3	3396	12 28.7	3484	12 33.1
3133	12 18.9	3221	12 22.3	3309	12 25.4	3397	12 28.8	3485	12 33.2
3134	12 18.9	3222	12 22.3	3310	12 25.5	3398	12 29.0	3486	12 33.2
3135	12 18.9	3223	12 22.5	3311	12 25.5	3399	12 28.9	3487	12 33.2
3136	12 19.0	3224	12 22.6	3312	12 25.5	3400	12 29.0	3488	12 33.1
3137	12 19.0	3225	12 22.6	3313	12 25.5	3401	12 29.0	3489	12 33.2
3138	12 19.0	3226	12 22.6	3314	12 25.5	3402	12 29.0	3490	12 33.2
3139	12 19.0	3227	12 22.6	3315	12 25.7	3403	12 29.0	3491	12 33.2
3140	12 19.0	3228	12 22.7	3316	12 25.6	3404	12 29.2	3492	12 33.2
3141	12 18.9	3229	12 22.7	3317	12 25.6	3405	12 29.0	3493	12 33.4
3142	12 19.1	3230	12 22.7	3318	12 25.8	3406	12 29.1	3494	12 33.2
3143	12 19.1	3231	12 22.7	3319	12 25.8	3407	12 29.0	3495	12 33.5
3144	12 19.2	3232	12 22.8	3320	12 25.8	3408	12 29.3	3496	12 33.5
3145	12 19.2	3233	12 22.9	3321	12 25.8	3409	12 29.4	3497	12 33.5
3146	12 19.2	3234	12 22.9	3322	12 25.9	3410	12 29.1	3498	12 33.5
3147	12 19.3	3235	12 23.0	3323	12 25.8	3411	12 29.2	3499	12 33.7
3148	12 19.3	3236	12 23.0	3324	12 25.8	3412	12 29.3	3500	12 33.8
3149	12 19.3	3237	12 23.0	3325	12 25.8	3413	12 29.4	3501	12 33.8
3150	12 19.5	3238	12 23.1	3326	12 25.9	3414	12 29.4	3502	12 33.7
3151	12 19.5	3239	12 23.1	3327	12 26.0	3415	12 29.4	3503	12 33.8
3152	12 19.6	3240	12 23.2	3328	12 25.9	3416	12 29.6	3504	12 34.1
3153	12 19.6	3241	12 23.1	3329	12 25.9	3417	12 29.7	3505	12 34.1
3154	12 19.6	3242	12 23.2	3330	12 25.9	3418	12 29.7	3506	12 34.2
3155	12 19.8	3243	12 23.2	3331	12 26.0	3419	12 29.7	3507	12 34.1
3156	12 19.7	3244	12 23.2	3332	12 26.1	3420	12 29.7	3508	12 34.1
3157	12 19.7	3245	12 23.3	3333	12 26.2	3421	12 29.6	3509	12 34.3
3158	12 19.8	3246	12 23.3	3334	12 26.2	3422	12 29.7	3510	12 34.3
3159	12 19.9	3247	12 23.3	3335	12 26.3	3423	12 29.8	3511	12 34.2
3160	12 20.0	3248	12 23.3	3336	12 26.3	3424	12 29.7	3512	12 34.2
3161	12 20.0	3249	12 23.3	3337	12 26.3	3425	12 29.9	3513	12 34.2
3162	12 20.0	3250	12 23.3	3338	12 26.4	3426	12 30.0	3514	12 34.3
3163	12 20.0	3251	12 23.3	3339	12 26.5	3427	12 30.1	3515	12 34.3
3164	12 20.1	3252	12 23.4	3340	12 26.5	3428	12 30.1	3516	12 34.3
3165	12 20.0	3253	12 23.7	3341	12 26.4	3429	12 30.1	3517	12 34.5
3166	12 19.9	3254	12 23.5	3342	12 26.5	3430	12 30.2	3518	12 34.5
3167	12 20.2	3255	12 23.6	3343	12 26.6	3431	12 30.4	3519	12 34.5
3168	12 20.3	3256	12 23.7	3344	12 26.5	3432	12 30.4	3520	12 34.5

IC	α_{2000}	IC	α_{2000}	IC	α_{2000}	IC	α_{2000}	IC	α_{2000}
	h m		h m		h m		h m		h m
3521	12 34.6	3609	12 38.5	3697	12 43.0	3785	12 47.9	3873	12 54.5
3522	12 34.8	3610	12 38.8	3698	12 43.3	3786	12 47.6	3874	12 54.6
3523	12 34.7	3611	12 39.1	3699	12 43.3	3787	12 47.7	3875	12 54.6
3524	12 34.7	3612	12 39.1	3700	12 43.3	3788	12 48.1	3876	12 54.8
3525	12 34.8	3613	12 39.1	3701	12 43.5	3789	12 48.1	3877	12 54.8
3526	12 34.7	3614	12 39.0	3702	12 43.5	3790	12 48.2	3878	12 54.5
3527	12 34.7	3615	12 39.0	3703	12 43.4	3791	12 47.5	3879	12 54.5
3528	12 34.9	3616	12 39.2	3704	12 43.7	3792	12 48.3	3880	12 54.8
3529	12 34.8	3617	12 39.4	3705	12 43.7	3793	12 48.2	3881	12 54.8
3530	12 34.8	3618	12 39.2	3706	12 43.8	3794	12 48.4	3882	12 54.9
3531	12 34.9	3619	12 39.3	3707	12 43.5	3795	12 48.1	3883	12 55.3
3532	12 35.0	3620	12 39.3	3708	12 43.9	3796	12 48.5	3884	12 55.0
3533	12 35.0	3621	12 39.5	3709	12 44.0	3797	12 48.6	3885	12 54.7
3534	12 35.2	3622	12 39.5	3710	12 44.1	3798	12 48.7	3886	12 55.0
3535	12 35.2	3623	12 39.4	3711	12 44.2	3799	12 49.0	3887	12 54.7
3536	12 35.2	3624	12 39.6	3712	12 44.3	3800	12 48.5	3888	12 54.7
3537	12 35.4	3625	12 39.7	3713	12 44.1	3801	12 49.0	3889	12 54.9
3538	12 35.2	3626	12 39.5	3714	12 44.4	3802	12 48.7	3890	12 54.8
3539	12 35.3	3627	12 39.5	3715	12 44.4	3803	12 49.1	3891	12 55.0
3540	12 35.4	3628	12 39.7	3716	12 44.8	3804	12 48.8	3892	12 55.1
3541	12 35.4	3629	12 39.8	3717	12 44.4	3805	12 48.7	3893	12 55.1
3542	12 35.8	3630	12 39.8	3718	12 44.8	3806	12 48.9	3894	12 55.5
3543	12 35.7	3631	12 39.8	3719	12 44.8	3807	12 49.5	3895	12 55.2
3544	12 35.8	3632	12 40.0	3720	12 44.8	3808	12 49.0	3896	12 56.6
3545	12 35.7	3633	12 40.2	3721	12 44.8	3809	12 49.1	3897	12 55.3
3546	12 35.7	3634	12 40.2	3722	12 44.9	3810	12 49.1	3898	12 55.4
3547	12 35.8	3635	12 40.2	3723	12 44.5	3811	12 49.4	3899	12 55.7
3548	12 35.9	3636	12 40.2	3724	12 44.9	3812	12 49.9	3900	12 55.7
3549	12 35.8	3637	12 40.3	3725	12 44.9	3813	12 50.0	3901	12 55.9
3550	12 35.9	3638	12 40.3	3726	12 44.7	3814	12 49.5	3902	12 55.6
3551	12 35.9	3639	12 40.9	3727	12 45.1	3815	12 49.6	3903	12 55.6
3552	12 35.9	3640	12 40.4	3728	12 45.1	3816	12 49.6	3904	12 55.9
3553	12 35.9	3641	12 40.4	3729	12 44.9	3817	12 49.7	3905	12 56.1
3554	12 35.9	3642	12 40.4	3730	12 45.1	3818	12 49.8	3906	12 55.8
3555	12 35.9	3643	12 40.7	3731	12 45.2	3819	12 50.3	3907	12 56.3
3556	12 36.0	3644	12 40.6	3732	12 45.2	3820	12 49.7	3908	12 56.7
3557	12 36.1	3645	12 40.5	3733	12 45.3	3821	12 50.0	3909	12 56.0
3558	12 36.2	3646	12 40.5	3734	12 45.2	3822	12 50.4	3910	12 56.1
3559	12 36.1	3647	12 40.9	3735	12 45.3	3823	12 49.7	3911	12 56.2
3560	12 36.1	3648	12 40.9	3736	12 45.3	3824	12 50.5	3912	12 56.1
3561	12 36.1	3649	12 40.8	3737	12 45.3	3825	12 50.6	3913	12 56.5
3562	12 36.2	3650	12 40.7	3738	12 45.4	3826	12 50.7	3914	12 56.4
3563	12 36.1	3651	12 40.8	3739	12 45.4	3827	12 50.8	3915	12 56.7
3564	12 36.2	3652	12 41.0	3740	12 45.5	3828	12 50.4	3916	12 56.5
3565	12 36.2	3653	12 41.2	3741	12 45.6	3829	12 52.2	3917	12 56.9
3566	12 36.3	3654	12 41.2	3742	12 45.5	3830	12 50.9	3918	12 56.9
3567	12 36.4	3655	12 41.2	3743	12 45.7	3831	12 51.3	3919	12 56.8
3568	12 32.9	3656	12 41.2	3744	12 45.7	3832	12 50.8	3920	12 56.8
3569	12 36.1	3657	12 41.3	3745	12 45.6	3833	12 51.5	3921	12 57.0
3570	12 36.3	3658	12 41.3	3746	12 45.6	3834	12 51.5	3922	12 57.0
3571	12 36.3	3659	12 41.5	3747	12 45.6	3835	12 50.9	3923	12 57.0
3572	12 36.5	3660	12 41.6	3748	12 45.8	3836	12 51.1	3924	12 57.4
3573	12 36.5	3661	12 41.6	3749	12 45.9	3837	12 51.5	3925	12 57.3
3574	12 36.5	3662	12 41.6	3750	12 46.0	3838	12 52.0	3926	12 57.5
3575	12 36.5	3663	12 41.7	3751	12 45.6	3839	12 51.8	3927	12 58.2
3576	12 36.6	3664	12 41.7	3752	12 46.1	3840	12 51.8	3928	12 57.3
3577	12 36.6	3665	12 41.8	3753	12 46.1	3841	12 51.8	3929	12 57.7
3578	12 36.6	3666	12 41.8	3754	12 46.2	3842	12 51.6	3930	12 57.4
3579	12 36.5	3667	12 41.5	3755	12 46.1	3843	12 51.7	3931	12 58.0
3580	12 36.6	3668	12 41.5	3756	12 46.3	3844	12 52.1	3932	12 58.1
3581	12 36.6	3669	12 41.6	3757	12 46.0	3845	12 52.2	3933	12 57.9
3582	12 36.5	3670	12 41.9	3758	12 45.9	3846	12 52.7	3934	12 58.3
3583	12 36.7	3671	12 41.8	3759	12 46.3	3847	12 52.6	3935	12 58.2
3584	12 36.8	3672	12 42.1	3760	12 46.4	3848	12 52.7	3936	12 58.3
3585	12 36.7	3673	12 42.1	3761	12 46.5	3849	12 52.6	3937	12 58.4
3586	12 36.9	3674	12 42.1	3762	12 46.6	3850	12 52.7	3938	12 58.4
3587	12 36.8	3675	12 42.1	3763	12 46.8	3851	12 53.1	3939	12 58.5
3588	12 36.9	3676	12 42.2	3764	12 47.0	3852	12 53.1	3940	12 58.3
3589	12 37.0	3677	12 42.2	3765	12 46.6	3853	12 53.2	3941	12 58.3
3590	12 36.9	3678	12 42.2	3766	12 47.0	3854	12 53.2	3942	12 58.3
3591	12 37.0	3679	12 42.2	3767	12 47.0	3855	12 53.4	3943	12 58.6
3592	12 36.9	3680	12 42.0	3768	12 46.7	3856	12 53.8	3944	12 58.7
3593	12 37.0	3681	12 42.0	3769	12 46.8	3857	12 53.9	3945	12 58.5
3594	12 36.9	3682	12 42.3	3770	12 47.3	3858	12 53.9	3946	12 58.8
3595	12 37.1	3683	12 42.3	3771	12 46.9	3859	12 54.4	3947	12 58.9
3596	12 37.3	3684	12 42.4	3772	12 47.1	3860	12 54.1	3948	12 59.0
3597	12 37.4	3685	12 42.5	3773	12 47.2	3861	12 53.9	3949	12 58.9
3598	12 37.4	3686	12 42.6	3774	12 46.9	3862	12 53.8	3950	12 59.1
3599	12 37.7	3687	12 42.6	3775	12 47.2	3863	12 53.9	3951	12 59.2
3600	12 37.6	3688	12 42.6	3776	12 47.2	3864	12 54.2	3952	12 58.9
3601	12 37.8	3689	12 42.6	3777	12 47.4	3865	12 54.2	3953	12 59.2
3602	12 38.1	3690	12 42.8	3778	12 47.0	3866	12 54.3	3954	12 59.2
3603	12 38.2	3691	12 42.8	3779	12 47.3	3867	12 54.3	3955	12 59.1
3604	12 38.4	3692	12 42.9	3780	12 47.1	3868	12 54.3	3956	12 58.9
3605	12 38.3	3693	12 43.0	3781	12 47.4	3869	12 54.4	3957	12 59.1
3606	12 38.4	3694	12 43.1	3782	12 47.3	3870	12 54.4	3958	12 59.2
3607	12 38.5	3695	12 43.1	3783	12 47.4	3871	12 54.4	3959	12 59.1
3608	12 38.6	3696	12 43.2	3784	12 47.9	3872	12 54.5	3960	12 59.1

Right Ascensions of IC Objects

IC	α_{2000}	IC	α_{2000}	IC	α_{2000}	IC	α_{2000}	IC	α_{2000}
	h m		h m		h m		h m		h m
3961	12 59.1	4049	13 00.7	4137	13 04.0	4225	13 20.0	4313	13 38.4
3962	12 59.3	4050	13 00.7	4138	13 04.0	4226	13 20.5	4314	13 38.4
3963	12 59.2	4051	13 00.9	4139	13 04.1	4227	13 20.9	4315	13 40.0
3964	12 59.2	4052	13 00.7	4140	13 04.1	4228	13 21.6	4316	13 40.3
3965	12 59.4	4053	13 01.0	4141	13 04.1	4229	13 22.6	4317	13 41.8
3966	12 59.3	4054	13 01.0	4142	13 03.8	4230	13 22.1	4318	13 43.3
3967	12 59.2	4055	13 01.0	4143	13 03.8	4231	13 23.2	4319	13 43.4
3968	12 59.4	4056	13 00.7	4144	13 03.9	4232	13 23.4	4320	13 44.1
3969	12 59.5	4057	13 01.1	4145	13 03.8	4233	13 24.0	4321	13 44.4
3970	12 59.2	4058	13 01.2	4146	13 04.2	4234	13 23.1	4322	13 43.7
3971	12 59.5	4059	13 01.3	4147	13 04.2	4235	13 23.9	4323	13 45.1
3972	12 59.3	4060	13 00.8	4148	13 04.2	4236	13 23.6	4324	13 45.4
3973	12 59.5	4061	13 01.0	4149	13 04.0	4237	13 24.5	4325	13 47.6
3974	13 05.3	4062	13 01.0	4150	13 04.2	4238	13 24.0	4326	13 48.4
3975	12 59.2	4063	13 01.1	4151	13 04.0	4239	13 24.4	4327	13 48.7
3976	12 59.5	4064	13 01.1	4152	13 04.0	4240	13 24.5	4328	13 49.1
3977	12 59.3	4065	13 01.2	4153	13 04.4	4241	13 24.8	4329	13 49.1
3978	12 59.6	4066	13 01.7	4154	13 04.5	4242	13 24.7	4330	13 47.2
3979	12 59.4	4067	13 01.3	4155	13 04.2	4243	13 25.9	4331	13 49.4
3980	12 59.5	4068	13 01.3	4156	13 05.0	4244	13 25.0	4332	13 49.9
3981	12 59.4	4069	13 01.4	4157	13 04.3	4245	13 26.1	4333	14 05.
3982	12 59.3	4070	13 01.7	4158	13 04.4	4246	13 26.1	4334	13 49.8
3983	12 59.3	4071	13 02.0	4159	13 04.8	4247	13 26.7	4335	13 49.7
3984	12 59.7	4072	13 01.4	4160	13 04.8	4248	13 26.8	4336	13 50.7
3985	12 59.7	4073	13 01.4	4161	13 04.6	4249	13 27.2	4337	13 52.2
3986	13 01.5	4074	13 01.8	4162	13 05.1	4250	13 26.3	4338	13 52.7
3987	12 59.4	4075	13 01.8	4163	13 05.1	4251	13 27.4	4339	13 53.5
3988	12 59.5	4076	13 01.8	4164	13 05.2	4252	13 27.5	4340	13 53.6
3989	12 59.5	4077	13 01.6	4165	13 05.0	4253	13 27.5	4341	13 53.6
3990	12 59.6	4078	13 01.7	4166	13 05.4	4254	13 27.8	4342	13 54.4
3991	12 59.6	4079	13 01.9	4167	13 05.5	4255	13 28.0	4343	13 55.0
3992	12 59.5	4080	13 02.0	4168	13 05.2	4256	13 27.0	4344	13 55.2
3993	12 59.5	4081	13 01.9	4169	13 05.2	4257	13 27.3	4345	13 55.2
3994	12 59.8	4082	13 01.6	4170	13 05.6	4258	13 27.9	4346	13 55.7
3995	12 59.6	4083	13 01.6	4171	13 05.4	4259	13 29.5	4347	13 57.6
3996	12 59.5	4084	13 01.7	4172	13 05.6	4260	13 29.5	4348	13 55.7
3997	12 59.6	4085	13 01.6	4173	13 06.2	4261	13 29.9	4349	13 55.8
3998	12 59.8	4086	13 01.7	4174	13 05.5	4262	13 30.3	4350	13 57.2
3999	13 00.5	4087	13 02.0	4175	13 05.8	4263	13 28.6	4351	13 57.9
4000	12 59.6	4088	13 01.8	4176	13 06.3	4264	13 30.3	4352	13 58.4
4001	12 59.6	4089	13 02.1	4177	13 06.3	4265	13 30.4	4353	13 57.1
4002	12 59.7	4090	13 01.8	4178	13 05.7	4266	13 29.1	4354	13 58.6
4003	12 59.7	4091	13 02.2	4179	13 05.8	4267	13 30.6	4355	13 58.1
4004	12 59.7	4092	13 02.2	4180	13 06.0	4268	13 29.2	4356	13 58.7
4005	13 00.0	4093	13 02.1	4181	13 06.1	4269	13 29.4	4357	14 00.7
4006	12 59.8	4094	13 02.0	4182	13 05.8	4270	13 30.8	4358	14 03.5
4007	13 00.1	4095	13 02.3	4183	13 06.0	4271	13 29.4	4359	14 05.4
4008	13 00.1	4096	13 02.3	4184	13 05.9	4272	13 31.2	4360	14 04.1
4009	12 59.9	4097	13 02.1	4185	13 06.2	4273	13 31.4	4361	14 04.1
4010	12 59.9	4098	13 02.1	4186	13 06.0	4274	13 31.4	4362	14 05.4
4011	13 00.1	4099	13 02.4	4187	13 06.0	4275	13 31.7	4363	14 04.2
4012	13 00.1	4100	13 02.0	4188	13 06.0	4276	13 32.2	4364	14 04.3
4013	13 00.0	4101	13 02.2	4189	13 06.0	4277	13 30.3	4365	14 03.8
4014	13 00.2	4102	13 02.3	4190	13 05.9	4278	13 30.4	4366	14 05.2
4015	13 00.0	4103	13 02.4	4191	13 08.8	4279	13 32.5	4367	14 05.6
4016	13 00.0	4104	13 02.3	4192	13 06.1	4280	13 32.5	4368	14 04.7
4017	13 00.3	4105	13 02.3	4193	13 06.1	4281	13 32.6	4369	14 04.1
4018	13 00.0	4106	13 02.6	4194	13 06.1	4282	13 31.3	4370	14 04.2
4019	13 00.3	4107	13 02.7	4195	13 06.3	4283	13 32.2	4371	14 04.2
4020	13 00.0	4108	13 02.5	4196	13 07.6	4284	13 31.5	4372	14 05.7
4021	13 00.2	4109	13 03.0	4197	13 08.1	4285	13 31.8	4373	14 05.7
4022	13 00.1	4110	13 03.0	4198	13 07.7	4286	13 33.7	4374	14 07.5
4023	13 00.4	4111	13 02.9	4199	13 07.5	4287	13 32.7	4375	14 08.1
4024	13 00.1	4112	13 02.7	4200	13 09.6	4288	13 34.6	4376	14 10.8
4025	13 00.5	4113	13 03.1	4201	13 07.8	4289	13 34.9	4377	14 17.0
4026	13 00.4	4114	13 02.7	4202	13 08.4	4290	13 35.3	4378	14 12.1
4027	13 00.2	4115	13 02.8	4203	13 08.3	4291	13 37.0	4379	14 12.1
4028	13 00.3	4116	13 03.2	4204	13 08.4	4292	13 35.8	4380	14 10.0
4029	13 00.2	4117	13 02.8	4205	13 08.7	4293	13 36.0	4381	14 11.0
4030	13 00.5	4118	13 02.9	4206	13 09.4	4294	13 36.5	4382	14 11.1
4031	13 00.3	4119	13 03.3	4207	13 09.5	4295	13 36.5	4383	14 12.2
4032	13 00.4	4120	13 03.0	4208	13 09.6	4296	13 36.6	4384	14 11.9
4033	13 00.5	4121	13 03.4	4209	13 10.4	4297	13 35.3	4385	14 14.7
4034	13 00.3	4122	13 03.4	4210	13 10.8	4298	13 36.7	4386	14 15.0
4035	13 00.3	4123	13 03.1	4211	13 10.9	4299	13 36.8	4387	14 15.0
4036	13 00.4	4124	13 03.5	4212	13 12.1	4300	13 35.4	4388	14 16.0
4037	13 00.3	4125	13 03.6	4213	13 12.1	4301	13 35.6	4389	14 16.8
4038	13 00.4	4126	13 03.6	4214	13 17.7	4302	13 35.6	4390	14 17.0
4039	13 00.7	4127	13 03.3	4215	13 16.2	4303	13 37.3	4391	14 16.3
4040	13 00.6	4128	13 03.7	4216	13 17.0	4304	13 36.0	4392	14 15.9
4041	13 00.7	4129	13 03.7	4217	13 17.2	4305	13 36.0	4393	14 17.8
4042	13 00.7	4130	13 03.8	4218	13 17.1	4306	13 36.3	4394	14 16.5
4043	13 00.7	4131	13 03.4	4219	13 18.5	4307	13 36.5	4395	14 17.2
4044	13 00.8	4132	13 03.6	4220	13 17.9	4308	13 36.8	4396	14 17.5
4045	13 00.8	4133	13 03.8	4221	13 18.5	4309	13 38.7	4397	14 17.9
4046	13 00.7	4134	13 04.4	4222	13 19.5	4310	13 38.9	4398	14 18.2
4047	13 01.0	4135	13 03.6	4223	13 18.9	4311	13 40.1	4399	14 18.3
4048	13 00.6	4136	13 04.4	4224	13 19.1	4312	13 40.5	4400	14 22.3

Right Ascensions of IC Objects

IC	α_{2000}	IC	α_{2000}	IC	α_{2000}	IC	α_{2000}	IC	α_{2000}
	h m		h m		h m		h m		h m
4401	14 19.4	4489	14 43.2	4577	15 42.7	4665	17 46.3	4753	18 43.5
4402	14 21.2	4490	14 45.4	4578	15 53.2	4666	17 45.8	4754	18 44.0
4403	14 18.3	4491	14 44.5	4579	15 42.8	4667	17 46.3	4755	18 45.0
4404	14 10.8	4492	14 42.6	4580	15 43.2	4668	17 46.9	4756	18 39.0
4405	14 19.4	4493	14 44.4	4581	15 44.0	4669	17 47.2	4757	18 43.9
4406	14 22.4	4494	14 44.5	4582	15 45.7	4670	17 55.1	4758	18 46.4
4407	14 23.6	4495	14 44.2	4583	15 46.4	4671	17 55.1	4759	18 45.7
4408	14 21.2	4496	14 43.9	4584	16 00.2	4672	18 02.4	4760	18 45.7
4409	14 21.5	4497	14 44.3	4585	16 00.3	4673	18 03.3	4761	18 43.9
4410	14 22.3	4498	14 45.0	4586	15 54.9	4674	18 08.2	4762	18 32.5
4411	14 25.0	4499	15 00.1	4587	15 59.9	4675	18 03.2	4763	18 33.5
4412	14 23.2	4500	14 44.6	4588	16 04.9	4676	18 02.8	4764	18 47.0
4413	14 23.0	4501	14 47.5	4589	16 07.4	4677	17 58.3	4765	18 47.3
4414	14 23.8	4502	14 45.3	4590	16 08.3	4678	18 08.0	4766	18 47.5
4415	14 24.4	4503	14 46.4	4591	16 12.3	4679	18 11.4	4767	18 47.7
4416	14 24.4	4504	14 46.5	4592	16 12.0	4680	18 13.5	4768	18 41.8
4417	14 24.9	4505	14 46.6	4593	16 11.7	4681	18 08.3	4769	18 47.7
4418	14 25.3	4506	14 46.7	4594	16 11.3	4682	18 16.4	4770	18 48.1
4419	14 25.8	4507	14 47.7	4595	16 20.7	4683	18 08.7	4771	18 48.3
4420	14 25.6	4508	14 47.8	4596	16 16.1	4684	18 09.1	4772	18 39.9
4421	14 28.1	4509	14 48.4	4597	16 17.8	4685	18 09.3	4773	18 51.3
4422	14 26.0	4510	14 50.7	4598	16 18.2	4686	18 13.6	4774	18 48.2
4423	14 26.3	4511	14 52.1	4599	16 19.3	4687	18 13.7	4775	18 48.4
4424	14 27.5	4512	14 49.9	4600	16 18.3	4688	18 08.1	4776	18 45.8
4425	14 26.7	4513	14 52.3	4601	16 20.0	4689	18 13.7	4777	18 48.1
4426	14 27.3	4514	14 50.9	4602	16 23.4	4690	18 10.5	4778	18 50.0
4427	14 27.0	4515	14 51.1	4603	16 25.6	4691	18 08.7	4779	18 50.5
4428	14 27.4	4516	14 53.9	4604	16 25.6	4692	18 14.8	4780	18 50.0
4429	14 27.7	4517	14 54.5	4605	16 30.2	4693	18 09.2	4781	18 51.7
4430	14 29.4	4518	14 57.7	4606	16 31.6	4694	18 15.4	4782	18 50.9
4431	14 27.1	4519	14 54.8	4607	16 30.3	4695	18 17.4	4783	18 51.5
4432	14 29.8	4520	14 55.1	4608	16 46.9	4696	18 20.3	4784	18 52.9
4433	14 27.8	4521	14 59.6	4609	16 33.0	4697	18 12.5	4785	18 52.9
4434	14 27.9	4522	15 11.5	4610	16 33.6	4698	18 21.0	4786	18 52.7
4435	14 27.5	4523	15 05.2	4611	16 33.7	4699	18 18.5	4787	18 56.1
4436	14 27.9	4524	15 02.1	4612	16 33.8	4700	18 17.1	4788	18 54.7
4437	14 27.4	4525	15 02.4	4613	16 37.3	4701	18 16.5	4789	18 56.3
4438	14 28.6	4526	15 02.6	4614	16 37.8	4702	18 23.1	4790	18 56.6
4439	14 28.7	4527	15 05.7	4615	16 37.9	4703	18 18.9	4791	18 49.0
4440	14 29.0	4528	15 01.4	4616	16 38.0	4704	18 27.9	4792	18 55.7
4441	14 31.4	4529	15 06.4	4617	16 42.1	4705	18 28.2	4793	18 56.9
4442	14 28.8	4530	15 03.8	4618	16 57.9	4706	18 19.6	4794	18 57.1
4443	14 29.3	4531	15 04.4	4619	16 44.2	4707	18 20.1	4795	18 57.2
4444	14 31.7	4532	15 04.5	4620	16 48.5	4708	18 13.7	4796	18 56.5
4445	14 31.9	4533	15 04.4	4621	16 50.8	4709	18 24.3	4797	18 56.5
4446	14 29.0	4534	15 08.2	4622	16 52.1	4710	18 28.7	4798	18 58.3
4447	14 29.6	4535	15 08.7	4623	16 51.2	4711	18 28.1	4799	18 58.9
4448	14 40.5	4536	15 13.2	4624	16 51.5	4712	18 31.1	4800	18 58.7
4449	14 31.3	4537	15 17.5	4625	16 52.9	4713	18 30.0	4801	18 59.6
4450	14 32.1	4538	15 21.2	4626	16 53.4	4714	18 30.9	4802	18 55.1
4451	14 34.6	4539	15 18.5	4627	16 54.1	4715	18 26.2	4803	19 00.6
4452	14 32.4	4540	15 20.1	4628	16 57.0	4716	18 32.7	4804	19 01.1
4453	14 34.5	4541	15 29.9	4629	16 56.2	4717	18 33.3	4805	19 02.0
4454	14 33.3	4542	15 22.1	4630	16 55.1	4718	18 33.8	4806	19 01.5
4455	14 34.5	4543	15 24.6	4631	17 11.0	4719	18 33.2	4807	19 02.3
4456	14 34.1	4544	15 29.4	4632	16 58.5	4720	18 33.5	4808	19 01.1
4457	14 34.5	4545	15 41.5	4633	17 13.8	4721	18 34.5	4809	19 04.0
4458	14 37.2	4546	15 27.0	4634	17 01.6	4722	18 34.5	4810	19 03.0
4459	14 34.5	4547	15 27.3	4635	17 15.7	4723	18 35.8	4811	19 05.8
4460	14 34.6	4548	15 27.4	4636	16 59.0	4724	18 38.6	4812	19 01.1
4461	14 35.0	4549	15 29.2	4637	17 05.2	4725	18 31.6	4813	19 05.8
4462	14 35.0	4550	15 34.8	4638	17 01.2	4726	18 36.9	4814	19 05.0
4463	14 35.8	4551	15 33.9	4639	17 02.9	4727	18 37.9	4815	19 06.7
4464	14 37.8	4552	15 35.0	4640	17 23.9	4728	18 37.9	4816	19 01.8
4465	14 35.9	4553	15 35.0	4641	17 24.2	4729	18 40.0	4817	19 06.2
4466	14 36.7	4554	15 35.1	4642	17 11.8	4730	18 38.8	4818	19 06.0
4467	14 36.8	4555	15 48.3	4643	17 08.5	4731	18 38.7	4819	19 07.1
4468	14 38.4	4556	15 35.5	4644	17 24.6	4732	18 33.9	4820	19 09.2
4469	14 37.3	4557	15 34.6	4645	17 14.6	4733	18 26.5	4821	19 09.5
4470	14 28.1	4558	15 35.8	4646	17 23.9	4734	18 38.4	4822	19 14.9
4471	14 36.4	4559	15 35.9	4647	17 26.0	4735	18 39.7	4823	19 12.2
4472	14 40.2	4560	15 35.8	4648	17 16.0	4736	18 38.6	4824	19 13.2
4473	14 37.9	4561	15 36.9	4649	17 15.8	4737	18 39.9	4825	19 17.3
4474	14 38.4	4562	15 36.0	4650	17 15.9	4738	18 40.4	4826	19 12.3
4475	14 38.4	4563	15 36.0	4651	17 24.7	4739	18 40.8	4827	19 13.3
4476	14 39.9	4564	15 36.6	4652	17 26.4	4740	18 43.0	4828	19 13.6
4477	14 38.5	4565	15 36.6	4653	17 27.1	4741	18 41.6	4829	19 12.6
4478	14 39.2	4566	15 36.7	4654	17 37.1	4742	18 41.9	4830	19 13.8
4479	14 38.7	4567	15 37.5	4655	17 34.6	4743	18 41.3	4831	19 14.7
4480	14 39.8	4568	15 40.1	4656	17 37.7	4744	18 41.8	4832	19 14.1
4481	14 40.1	4569	15 40.8	4657	17 32.7	4745	18 42.6	4833	19 15.6
4482	14 40.1	4570	15 41.3	4658	17 37.2	4746	18 45.9	4834	19 16.5
4483	14 40.3	4571	15 41.9	4659	17 34.2	4747	18 45.9	4835	19 15.5
4484	14 47.7	4572	15 41.9	4660	17 21.6	4748	18 42.7	4836	19 16.3
4485	14 40.5	4573	15 42.0	4661	17 51.0	4749	18 42.9	4837	19 15.3
4486	14 41.9	4574	15 42.0	4662	17 47.1	4750	18 43.0	4838	19 16.8
4487	14 42.0	4575	15 42.3	4663	17 45.5	4751	18 43.2	4839	19 15.6
4488	14 42.8	4576	15 42.6	4664	17 49.0	4752	18 43.8	4840	19 15.9

IC	α_{2000}	IC	α_{2000}	IC	α_{2000}	IC	α_{2000}	IC	α_{2000}
	h m		h m		h m		h m		h m
4841	19 20.8	4929	20 06.7	5017	20 32.1	5105	21 24.4	5193	22 15.7
4842	19 19.5	4930	20 02.4	5018	20 22.2	5106	21 28.6	5194	22 17.1
4843	19 19.3	4931	20 00.8	5019	20 30.8	5107	21 28.3	5195	22 15.7
4844	19 19.0	4932	20 02.3	5020	20 30.6	5108	21 32.9	5196	22 20.2
4845	19 20.4	4933	20 03.5	5021	20 33.5	5109	21 33.9	5197	22 19.8
4846	19 16.5	4934	20 07.2	5022	20 41.1	5110	21 30.6	5198	22 17.7
4847	19 23.5	4935	20 04.6	5023	20 38.1	5111	21 28.2	5199	22 19.5
4848	19 22.8	4936	20 05.9	5024	20 40.1	5112	21 29.5	5200	22 22.3
4849	19 25.4	4937	20 05.3	5025	20 45.0	5113	21 29.7	5201	22 21.4
4850	19 20.4	4938	20 06.2	5026	20 48.5	5114	21 34.1	5202	22 22.9
4851	19 25.5	4939	20 07.2	5027	20 41.1	5115	21 30.5	5203	22 22.6
4852	19 26.4	4940	20 05.7	5028	20 43.4	5116	21 37.1	5204	22 20.7
4853	19 30.9	4941	20 07.0	5029	20 40.3	5117	21 32.5	5205	22 22.8
4854	19 27.4	4942	20 06.8	5030	20 40.6	5118	21 40.3	5206	22 24.1
4855	19 27.5	4943	20 06.5	5031	20 45.3	5119	21 34.0	5207	22 23.5
4856	19 27.5	4944	20 07.1	5032	20 45.4	5120	21 38.8	5208	22 24.6
4857	19 28.6	4945	20 11.3	5033	20 43.8	5121	21 41.3	5209	22 23.1
4858	19 28.6	4946	20 06.0	5034	20 43.7	5122	21 39.8	5210	22 22.5
4859	19 30.8	4947	20 07.5	5035	20 44.3	5123	21 44.8	5211	22 22.7
4860	19 31.5	4948	20 06.5	5036	20 44.7	5124	21 39.9	5212	22 23.5
4861	19 29.2	4949	20 07.3	5037	20 45.6	5125	21 41.8	5213	22 25.0
4862	19 31.7	4950	20 08.4	5038	20 46.9	5126	21 40.1	5214	22 23.7
4863	19 28.3	4951	20 09.5	5039	20 43.2	5127	21 39.8	5215	22 27.0
4864	19 40.1	4952	20 08.6	5040	20 52.3	5128	21 42.7	5216	22 24.7
4865	19 30.9	4953	20 10.1	5041	20 43.6	5129	21 47.8	5217	22 23.9
4866	19 34.6	4954	20 04.8	5042	20 47.8	5130	21 50.4	5218	22 28.1
4867	19 26.5	4955	20 04.9	5043	20 46.7	5131	21 47.4	5219	22 28.7
4868	19 33.5	4956	20 11.5	5044	20 50.6	5132	21 42.3	5220	22 28.2
4869	19 36.0	4957	20 09.6	5045	20 50.7	5133	21 42.4	5221	22 28.9
4870	19 37.6	4958	20 15.5	5046	20 43.2	5134	21 43.0	5222	22 29.9
4871	19 35.7	4959	20 11.0	5047	20 43.8	5135	21 48.3	5223	22 29.8
4872	19 35.7	4960	20 15.4	5048	20 51.6	5136	21 48.8	5224	22 30.5
4873	19 34.9	4961	20 11.5	5049	20 47.4	5137	21 51.6	5225	22 31.5
4874	19 36.4	4962	20 15.9	5050	20 45.3	5138	21 53.5	5226	22 31.7
4875	19 37.7	4963	20 12.1	5051	20 52.3	5139	21 50.4	5227	22 34.1
4876	19 37.7	4964	20 17.4	5052	20 52.1	5140	21 54.3	5228	22 32.4
4877	19 37.9	4965	20 12.5	5053	20 53.6	5141	21 53.3	5229	22 34.8
4878	19 38.8	4966	20 12.3	5054	20 53.7	5142	21 55.3	5230	22 35.6
4879	19 39.7	4967	20 16.4	5055	20 52.9	5143	21 56.3	5231	22 34.0
4880	19 40.5	4968	20 14.6	5056	20 49.0	5144	21 53.9	5232	22 37.8
4881	19 40.4	4969	20 12.9	5057	20 47.2	5145	21 54.2	5233	22 36.6
4882	19 40.4	4970	20 16.9	5058	20 47.4	5146	21 53.4	5234	22 40.2
4883	19 42.0	4971	20 17.0	5059	20 51.3	5147	21 59.4	5235	22 41.4
4884	19 42.7	4972	20 17.7	5060	20 54.6	5148	21 59.5	5236	22 41.5
4885	19 43.9	4973	20 14.6	5061	20 47.6	5149	21 58.7	5237	22 42.3
4886	19 43.1	4974	20 15.3	5062	20 48.2	5150	21 59.2	5238	22 41.5
4887	19 48.3	4975	20 14.0	5063	20 52.0	5151	21 58.9	5239	22 31.1
4888	19 44.9	4976	20 15.5	5064	20 52.6	5152	22 02.9	5240	22 41.9
4889	19 45.3	4977	20 11.9	5065	20 51.8	5153	22 00.4	5241	22 41.5
4890	19 45.6	4978	20 14.6	5066	20 57.1	5154	22 04.6	5242	22 41.2
4891	19 45.3	4979	20 14.7	5067	20 47.8	5155	22 02.1	5243	22 41.4
4892	19 49.5	4980	20 15.5	5068	20 50.8	5156	22 03.3	5244	22 44.2
4893	19 50.6	4981	20 19.7	5069	21 00.0	5157	22 03.4	5245	22 45.1
4894	19 47.0	4982	20 20.4	5070	20 50.8	5158	22 06.4	5246	22 46.6
4895	19 45.0	4983	20 16.1	5071	21 01.3	5159	22 02.7	5247	22 46.9
4896	19 49.1	4984	20 16.3	5072	21 02.0	5160	22 03.2	5248	22 44.7
4897	19 49.3	4985	20 20.7	5073	21 03.3	5161	22 05.6	5249	22 47.1
4898	19 47.8	4986	20 17.2	5074	21 00.9	5162	22 08.1	5250	22 47.3
4899	19 54.4	4987	20 17.3	5075	21 04.5	5163	22 05.8	5251	22 45.1
4900	19 50.3	4988	20 21.8	5076	20 55.9	5164	22 06.0	5252	22 48.1
4901	19 54.4	4989	20 19.5	5077	21 09.0	5165	22 10.1	5253	22 45.4
4902	19 54.4	4990	20 21.5	5078	21 02.6	5166	22 06.1	5254	22 46.0
4903	19 58.2	4991	20 18.4	5079	21 05.5	5167	22 07.5	5255	22 45.8
4904	19 58.5	4992	20 23.5	5080	21 02.5	5168	22 08.8	5256	22 49.8
4905	19 56.1	4993	20 22.0	5081	21 03.0	5169	22 10.2	5257	22 52.3
4906	19 56.8	4994	20 19.7	5082	21 04.7	5170	22 12.5	5258	22 51.5
4907	19 56.2	4995	20 20.0	5083	21 03.8	5171	22 10.9	5259	22 52.8
4908	19 56.9	4996	20 16.5	5084	21 09.2	5172	22 09.9	5260	22 54.3
4909	19 56.7	4997	20 20.2	5085	21 13.4	5173	22 14.8	5261	22 54.4
4910	19 57.8	4998	20 22.2	5086	21 08.5	5174	22 12.7	5262	22 55.2
4911	19 57.7	4999	20 23.9	5087	21 14.3	5175	22 12.7	5263	22 58.2
4912	20 06.8	5000	20 22.4	5088	21 09.4	5176	22 14.9	5264	22 56.9
4913	19 56.8	5001	20 26.3	5089	21 11.0	5177	22 11.6	5265	22 57.2
4914	19 58.1	5002	20 26.7	5090	21 11.6	5178	22 12.5	5266	22 58.3
4915	19 58.5	5003	20 25.2	5091	21 17.7	5179	22 16.1	5267	22 57.2
4916	19 58.3	5004	20 25.4	5092	21 16.2	5180	22 11.1	5268	22 56.2
4917	19 58.9	5005	20 25.3	5093	21 18.8	5181	22 13.4	5269	22 57.7
4918	19 59.3	5006	20 23.7	5094	21 17.8	5182	22 16.1	5270	22 57.9
4919	20 00.2	5007	20 25.6	5095	21 17.3	5183	22 15.4	5271	22 58.0
4920	20 00.1	5008	20 32.7	5096	21 18.4	5184	22 16.1	5272	22 59.6
4921	20 03.3	5009	20 32.6	5097	21 15.0	5185	22 17.8	5273	22 59.5
4922	19 59.5	5010	20 31.0	5098	21 15.0	5186	22 18.8	5274	22 58.5
4923	20 01.0	5011	20 28.6	5099	21 15.0	5187	22 18.3	5275	22 58.6
4924	19 59.9	5012	20 29.5	5100	21 21.7	5188	22 18.4	5276	22 58.7
4925	20 01.2	5013	20 28.6	5101	21 21.9	5189	22 16.2	5277	23 01.9
4926	20 00.2	5014	20 35.3	5102	21 26.3	5190	22 19.0	5278	23 00.6
4927	20 01.8	5015	20 28.6	5103	21 29.2	5191	22 15.0	5279	23 03.0
4928	20 10.2	5016	20 35.6	5104	21 21.5	5192	22 15.2	5280	23 03.8

Right Ascensions of IC Objects

IC	α_{2000}	IC	α_{2000}	IC	α_{2000}	IC	α_{2000}	IC	α_{2000}
	h m		h m		h m		h m		h m
5281	23 02.4	5303	23 17.9	5325	23 28.7	5347	23 41.5	5369	23 59.8
5282	23 02.7	5304	23 18.2	5326	23 29.5	5348	23 45.0	5370	0 00.1
5283	23 03.3	5305	23 18.0	5327	23 30.3	5349	23 46.3	5371	0 00.2
5284	23 06.8	5306	23 18.1	5328	23 33.2	5350	23 47.2	5372	0 00.4
5285	23 06.9	5307	23 18.2	5329	23 33.3	5351	23 47.3	5373	0 00.4
5286	23 09.8	5308	23 19.3	5330	23 33.5	5352	23 47.4	5374	0 01.1
5287	23 09.4	5309	23 19.2	5331	23 33.5	5353	23 47.5	5375	0 01.1
5288	23 11.7	5310	23 20.8	5332	23 34.5	5354	23 47.5	5376	0 01.4
5289	23 10.9	5311	23 20.6	5333	23 34.9	5355	23 47.2	5377	0 02.1
5290	23 12.9	5312	23 21.0	5334	23 34.7	5356	23 47.5	5378	0 02.6
5291	23 13.7	5313	23 22.0	5335	23 35.8	5357	23 47.4	5379	0 02.7
5292	23 13.8	5314	23 21.1	5336	23 36.3	5358	23 47.7	5380	0 02.7
5293	23 14.7	5315	23 21.3	5337	23 36.4	5359	23 47.7	5381	0 03.2
5294	23 16.2	5316	23 21.9	5338	23 36.5	5360	23 47.9	5382	0 03.4
5295	23 15.5	5317	23 23.4	5339	23 38.1	5361	23 51.4	5383	0 03.8
5296	23 15.7	5318	23 24.0	5340	23 38.6	5362	23 51.6	5384	0 04.2
5297	23 16.0	5319	23 24.8	5341	23 38.4	5363	23 52.2	5385	0 06.4
5298	23 16.1	5320	23 27.4	5342	23 38.6	5364	23 56.2	5386	0 06.5
5299	23 16.3	5321	23 26.3	5343	23 39.4	5365	23 57.6		
5300	23 16.6	5322	23 27.5	5344	23 39.3	5366	23 57.7		
5301	23 18.8	5323	23 27.6	5345	23 39.6	5367	23 58.7		
5302	23 19.6	5324	23 28.3	5346	23 41.0	5368	23 59.3		

COMPUTER VERSION

For the convenience of readers who wish to use the information in *NGC 2000.0* on a computer, Sky Publishing Corporation has prepared an IBM PC format diskette version (360K). It includes the NGC or IC number, type code, right ascension and declination for 2000.0, size, and magnitude for all 13,226 objects in the catalogue. The constellations and descriptions are omitted.

The data can be used for computerized searches for specific objects, classes of objects, and by position. The diskette includes a demonstration program (in GW-BASIC) for accessing the data, or you can write your own using the format of the data presented in the remarks section of the program. All the material on the diskette is protected under United States Copyright Law, but the diskette is not copy protected (so you can make backup copies).

Prices and specifications subject to change. This order blank may be photocopied.

Price: $19.95 postpaid in the United States. Outside the U. S. add $4 for postage.

Payment must be in United States funds by check or bank draft on a U. S. bank, by International Money Order, or by Visa or MasterCard.

Enclosed is $_____ for _____ copies of the diskette version of **NGC 2000.0**. If payment is by Visa or MasterCard fill in the blanks below.

Name _____

Address _____

_____

☐ **Visa**   ☐ **MasterCard**   Expiration date _____

Card No. _____

Signature _____

Sky Publishing Corporation
P. O. Box 9111
Belmont, Mass. 02178-9111, U.S.A.
Phone: 617-864-7360   FAX: 617-864-6117

COMPUTER VERSION

For the convenience of readers who wish to use the information in *NGC 2000.0* on a computer, Sky Publishing Corporation has prepared an IBM PC format diskette version (360K). It includes the NGC or IC number, type code, right ascension and declination for 2000.0, size, and magnitude for all 13,226 objects in the catalogue. The constellations and descriptions are omitted.

The data can be used for computerized searches for specific objects, classes of objects, and by position. The diskette includes a demonstration program (in GW-BASIC) for accessing the data, or you can write your own using the format of the data presented in the remarks section of the program. All the material on the diskette is protected under United States Copyright Law, but the diskette is not copy protected (so you can make backup copies).

Prices and specifications subject to change. This order blank may be photocopied.

Price: $19.95 postpaid in the United States. Outside the U. S. add $4 for postage.

Payment must be in United States funds by check or bank draft on a U. S. bank, by International Money Order, or by Visa or MasterCard.

Enclosed is $_____ for _____ copies of the diskette version of **NGC 2000.0**. If payment is by Visa or MasterCard fill in the blanks below.

Name _____

Address _____

_____

☐ **Visa**   ☐ **MasterCard**   Expiration date _____

Card No. _____

Signature _____

Sky Publishing Corporation
P. O. Box 9111
Belmont, Mass. 02178-9111, U.S.A.
Phone: 617-864-7360   FAX: 617-864-6117

COMPUTER VERSION

For the convenience of readers who wish to use the information in *NGC 2000.0* on a computer, Sky Publishing Corporation has prepared an IBM PC format diskette version (360K). It includes the NGC or IC number, type code, right ascension and declination for 2000.0, size, and magnitude for all 13,226 objects in the catalogue. The constellations and descriptions are omitted.

The data can be used for computerized searches for specific objects, classes of objects, and by position. The diskette includes a demonstration program (in GW-BASIC) for accessing the data, or you can write your own using the format of the data presented in the remarks section of the program. All the material on the diskette is protected under United States Copyright Law, but the diskette is not copy protected (so you can make backup copies).

Prices and specifications subject to change. This order blank may be photocopied.

Price: $19.95 postpaid in the United States. Outside the U. S. add $4 for postage.

Payment must be in United States funds by check or bank draft on a U. S. bank, by International Money Order, or by Visa or MasterCard.

Enclosed is $_____ for _____ copies of the diskette version of **NGC 2000.0**. If payment is by Visa or MasterCard fill in the blanks below.

Name _____

Address _____

_____

□ **Visa**　□ **MasterCard**　Expiration date _____

Card No. _____

Signature _____

Sky Publishing Corporation
P. O. Box 9111
Belmont, Mass. 02178-9111, U.S.A.
Phone: 617-864-7360　FAX: 617-864-6117